BIOLOGY

SCIENCE SHEPHERD
BIOLOGY TEXTBOOK

Published by:
Ohana Life Press, LLC
1405 Capitol Dr.
Suite C-202
Pewaukee, WI 53072
www.ScienceShepherd.com

Written by Scott Hardin, MD

ACKNOWLEDGEMENTS

Photo Credits
Photos.com
iStock.com
Indigo Instruments (www.indigo.com)
Bill Hardin

Graphic Illustration Credits
Alex Hardin
Katie Hardin
Scott Hardin

Graphic Design
Jason Brown

Some images in Chapters 17 - 19 are licensed through the following Creative Commons licenses. Use of an image does not imply approval of or endorsement by the copyright holder.

3.0 unported: This work is licensed under the Creative Commons Attribution-ShareAlike 3.0 Unported License. To view a copy of this license, visit http://creativecommons.org/licenses/by-sa/3.0/ or send a letter to Creative Commons, 444 Castro Street, Suite 900, Mountain View, California, 94041, USA.

2.5 generic: This work is licensed under the Creative Commons Attribution-ShareAlike 2.5 Generic License. To view a copy of this license, visit http://creativecommons.org/licenses/by-sa/2.5/ or send a letter to Creative Commons, 444 Castro Street, Suite 900, Mountain View, California, 94041, USA.

2.0 generic: This work is licensed under the Creative Commons Attribution-ShareAlike 2.0 Generic License. To view a copy of this license, visit http://creativecommons.org/licenses/by-sa/2.0/ or send a letter to Creative Commons, 444 Castro Street, Suite 900, Mountain View, California, 94041, USA.

1.0 generic: This work is licensed under the Creative Commons Attribution-ShareAlike 1.0 Generic License. To view a copy of this license, visit http://creativecommons.org/licenses/by-sa/1.0/ or send a letter to Creative Commons, 444 Castro Street, Suite 900, Mountain View, California, 94041, USA.

ISBN: 978-0-9828568-4-0

Printed in the United States of America

Table of Contents

Author's Note

Psalms 33:9: For he spoke, and it came to be; he commanded, and it stood firm.

We have been homeschooling our six children since 1998. As our oldest child got nearer and nearer to first junior and then senior high school, we began to have conversations with other parents about continuing homeschooling as our children proceeded through the higher grade levels. Unfortunately, some parents made the decision not to continue homeschooling their children through the higher grades, and one of the most common reasons was because of concern about not being able to provide excellent higher level science education. We have developed the Science Shepherd Life Science and Biology programs so that parents can feel confident their children's higher level science needs will be more than adequately met, thus helping to allow the continuance of homeschooling through the higher grade levels. These two courses provide meaningful learning through focused self-directed study, alleviating the need for parents to have "advanced knowledge" in the biological sciences. The intent behind Life Sciences and Biology is that they will serve as a complete teaching program so that parents do not need to have any science related training or knowledge.

Both courses are designed similarly, with the entire courses presented in complementary textbook format and DVD audio/video format. The information in the texts and DVDs are parallel to one another, such that the textbook format provides 100% of the material that is presented in the DVD, and vice-versa. This allows you to utilize whichever format suits your student best. Most students find, though, that learning the material in combination form is the most effective in retaining the information. For example, your students may find it the most useful to first read the textbook material, and then watch the DVD video that covers the same exact information as they follow along in the book. They should feel free to write notes in the book. This method allows students to have rapid reinforcement of information presented in different forms so that it sticks.

Life Science is directed to students in the 7th – 9th grade levels, while Biology is most appropriate for students in the 10th-12th grade levels. The Biology material also contains many advanced concepts that are commonly found in introductory college level courses, presented in a clear and concise manner. In order to help you and your student assess mastery of the information, there are multiple questions to be answered at the end of every chapter. These questions are mainly in the form of fill-in-the-blank, short essay type questions, and "True/False" format. Comprehensive answers and explanations to every question are included in the DVD for each and every question. Although Life Science and Biology can be learned totally independently by your child, each course includes a complete Parent Guide with detailed information relating to the answers to all of the questions. Between the answers to the questions in the DVD and the information in the Parent Guide, there should be no confusion as to why a question was answered the way it was.

One of the biggest science-related homeschool parental concerns is that of the dreaded "science lab." We all want to be sure that our kids get laboratory exposure during their education, and so I have integrated a complete biology science lab experience into the Biology curriculum. There is a comprehensive lab book that describes the materials and methods of each lab, and every lab is presented step by step on the DVD with specific demonstration using the exact same materials as your student will use (the needed materials for the labs, including the microscope, are available in our comprehensive lab kit). During the DVD lab presentation, I provide many helpful hints to make the lab "work" better. Most importantly, since students often don't know exactly what they are looking for (especially labs that use the microscope), all expected results are demonstrated in the video for each lab, using pictures taken through the same microscope used by the students or of the actual lab results that I got doing the lab myself.

Since these are science courses that were written by a Christian, probably the most common question I am asked is, "What about evolution and creation?" There are several facets to the answer of this critically important question. I took great care to try to present the information in Life Science and Biology in an objective way. As a physician, I have learned that there should not be any bias to the presentation of objective facts. Science is the systematized method to collect and analyze objective information to help explain the natural world around us. Science does not deserve to be presented in a biased fashion. Scientific facts are scientific facts, regardless of whether you look at them through a creation or evolution filter. Animals can be classified into Kingdoms and phyla and orders, etc. regardless of their supposed evolutionary relationships to one another. A lobster's anatomy and a human's anatomy is exactly as it is whether or not you believe in creation or evolution. The biochemical reactions of photosynthesis and the Krebs cycle occur exactly as they do without regard to evolution or creation. Science is the study and explanation of what we observe in nature and, when you get right down to it, what we observe scientifically is what we observe scientifically irrespective of the creation/evolution debate. In that sense, I try to present the information in a straightforward and easily understandable way that is often lost when the attempt is made to relate the observable science as having a creation or evolution basis.

As I wrote these two courses, I read many other Biology, Life Science, Physical Science, etc. textbooks and was constantly struck at how confusing the facts (in other words, the information that the student was supposed to be learning) became when the authors went out of their way to try to use the scientific data to "prove" that evolution or creation is true. The bottom line is that there is absolutely no "scientific" way to prove that either creation or evolution is true because neither one of those concepts is "science;" rather, they are philosophies that relate – in general terms – to the origin of everything in the universe and – specifically – to the presence of life on earth. If a person's philosophy is that the Bible is the unerringly accurate word of God and that the earth and stars were created, as was life on this planet, through the act of God speaking, then you believe in creation. However, if a person is an atheist or agnostic, then creation can't possibly explain the presence of life, and so another explanation is needed – evolution. That creation and evolution are diametrically opposed viewpoints is obvious, as is the fact that neither one of those viewpoints has anything to do with the actual observable scientific facts as collected using the scientific method. I try very hard to present these courses in a straight forward way so they are easy to learn. The only time that science is "hard" is when the teacher gets too fancy trying to teach it.

However, the treatment of creation and evolution is very thorough. Ignoring these two critical philosophies in the development of a science course would be irresponsible. My point in the chapters in both Biology and Life Science is to discuss the information in much the same way that your child will encounter it in the real, secular world. However, I take a turn and look at much of the actual scientific "evidence" that evolutionists use to "prove" their case and see if it actually holds up to objective scrutiny.

In Biology, I present creation and evolution in three chapters, The Origin of Life, Evolution and Creation: Principles and Evidence, and Speciation and Adaptation. These chapters critically evaluate the observed, objective scientific information as it relates both to evolution and creation. This allows students to review the merits of both ways of interpreting the pertinent science relating to the ultimate question of where we came from. However, as they read through these three chapters (and watch them on DVD) and dissect the scientific data, it is obvious that there is very little, if any, truly scientific merit to the philosophy of evolution. It also becomes obvious that the creation viewpoint is very well supported by observed scientific information. Students clearly see the data just does not support "molecules to man" evolution and will come away with the ultimate understanding that evolution is really only the biased opinions (primarily of atheists), and not objective interpretation of scientific data, that has shaped the evolutionary thesis. Students will come to understand that, as a hypothesis to explain the origin of life, evolution makes many predictions about what type of scientific data should be uncovered, but the data that has been found is absolutely contrary to what evolution predicts. As well, students will learn that, as an explanation for the origin of life, creation also makes predictions about what type of scientific data should be found, and creation holds up quite well. Students will learn that most of the scientific data that has been found to date support not only the Biblical account of creation but also the Genesis account of the Flood. After this objective presentation of the evolutionist and creationist viewpoints, it is clear creation is the best explanation for earth's wonderful biodiversity.

In Life Science, the philosophies of evolution and creation are explored as explanations for the origin of life in one chapter. Evolution is first exposed not as a scientific fact (as we are all constantly told it is), but rather as a philosophy that attempts to explain the origin of life and the presence of biodiversity without God being involved. Creation is explained as a philosophy that explains the origin of life and all species through the miraculous creation process described in Genesis. Several common evolutionary "truths" are also looked at by dissecting the actual scientific data. It is obvious by the end of the chapter that evolution does not hold up to true scientific scrutiny and that creation is a much more reasonable, and scientifically sound, explanation for the origin of life. We appreciate the confidence you have in our curriculum to provide your most precious children with their science-related education. If you should have any questions or concerns regarding these materials, please contact us at the email address listed below.

God Bless,

Scott Hardin MD

contact@scienceshepherd.com

Preface to the Second Edition

The first edition has been pretty well received by reviewers and, more importantly, parents and students. It is gratifying to receive thanks and compliments, which really serve as great blessings to me. I am also very grateful to the many parents and students who have asked questions and made suggestions regarding what they might like to see either in the next edition or in an entirely new subject.

Over the past couple of years, I had become increasingly convicted by the Holy Spirit that my first edition treatment of creation and evolution was not what it should be, that God wanted more. In the first edition, the presentation was much softer as related to the correlation of biblical principles to scientific interpretation. One affects the other and I really felt that God was telling me that I needed to incorporate more theologically based and exegetically sounder creation and evolution chapters into the biology curriculum.

To that end, very little in chapters 1–16 and 20–34 has changed. The science remains the science and I didn't feel the need to change that really at all. The material is still presented in the same straightforward way as in the first edition. The creation and evolution chapters, though, 17–19, are completely retooled. If you have used our first edition, you will see that there is very little that is familiar in chapters 17–19.

Of course, I remain very true to fundamental Christianity. That has not changed and will not ever change. However, I felt very clearly that God wanted me to more directly point out the many failures of the evolution model to accurately predict and describe scientific data. At the same time, the creation and evolution chapters are not just about pointing out the scientific blind spots of evolution; they are also about pointing out the strengths of the creation model to predict and describe the scientific data. The three chapters are heavily based in the history of creation and evolution and the present day critical assessment of the scientific data and how it stacks up when measured against the creation and evolution models. There is both more science and fundamental theology in the three chapters.

Why do I think God wanted this? I can only answer that evolution is _the most powerful_ tool in Satan's tool box to wage war against God's people. There is no one position that is as anti-God and all-pervasive as the "how-we-got-here-without-God" evolution story. It is taught with fervor throughout all the world's public schools and universities. It is even taught in a majority of primary and secondary schools and colleges that consider themselves as providers of Christian education. Evolutionary principles are in part or in whole directly responsible for pretty much all of the atrocities that man has committed against man over the past 110 years – Nazism, abortion and Planned Parenthood, the development of Marxism and communism – all have flourished directly because of evolutionary thought. We need to know the enemy in order to stay clear and defeat him.

I got the definite feeling that God wanted me to do my part of Kingdom building with this second edition. I pray that I have.

Introduction

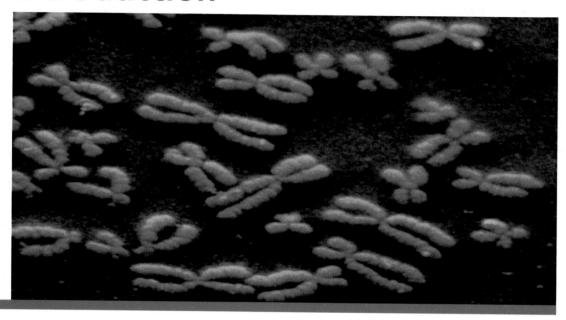

1

1.0 CHAPTER PREVIEW

In this chapter we will:

- Discuss the following properties that all living things have in common:
    - They are made up of one or more cells.
    - They contain DNA.
    - They reproduce.
    - They are complex and organized.
    - They respond to their surroundings.
    - They extract energy from their environment.
    - They maintain homeostasis.
    - They grow.
    - They can be systematically classified.

- Explore the principles and practice of the scientific method.

- Discuss the SI measurement units.

- Discuss properties of light and electron microscopes.

1.1 INTRODUCTION TO BIOLOGY

Biology is the study—or science—of life and how that life interacts with the environment and other life forms. This first chapter will serve as an introduction to all of the concepts we will be exploring during this year. In order to understand more clearly what is meant by "life," we will explore the following properties, which all living things have in common: they are made up of one or more cells; they contain DNA; they reproduce; they are complex and organized; they are responsive to their environment; they extract energy from their surroundings; they maintain homeostasis; they grow; and they can be systematically classified.

Figure 1.1.1

Giardia lamblia
This is a picture of *G. lamblia*, an organism which causes infectious diarrhea. It is a unicellular organism.

1.2 CELLS

All life forms are made up of cells. Therefore, the cell is the basic functional unit of all life. Some life forms—or **organisms**—are made up of only one cell. They are called **unicellular organisms**. Other organisms are made up of many cells and are called **multicellular organisms**.

Figure 1.2.1

DNA
This deer, and all of the plants visible in this picture, are composed of millions, billions, or trillions of cells, depending on the size of the organism. Like all living things, deer grow to look and act like deer because of its DNA. DNA is called the blueprint of life because it contains all of the information a cell, and organism, needs to function properly. DNA instructs the cell, and organism, how it is to look and function. Without DNA, life would not exist.

1.3 DEOXYRIBONUCLEIC ACID (DNA)

All life forms **contain DNA, or deoxyribonucleic acid**. DNA is a very complex molecule which instructs the cells which proteins to produce and when to produce them. It also contains the information the cell needs to duplicate, or **reproduce**. DNA contains all of the information the cell needs to work properly. Proteins are used to communicate and carry out the instructions. These same proteins then take part in almost all of the chemical reactions which the cell performs. Finally, the proteins that are made, as directed by DNA, determine the characteristics of the cell and of the multicellular organism as a whole.

DNA is passed from parents to offspring, and this serves as the basis for heredity, which will be discussed more in the genetics section of this course. In short, DNA is the material inside all living organisms that tells the organism how it is supposed to function, what kind of cell it is, and when to reproduce itself. There will be much, much more about DNA later in our book.

1.4 REPRODUCTION

All life forms make more of themselves, or reproduce, for the purpose of generating more organisms like themselves. This assures the survival of that life form. No non-living things reproduce themselves. There are two kinds of reproduction—**sexual and asexual**. Some organisms reproduce asexually, some reproduce sexually, and some are able to reproduce both sexually and asexually. The way the cell and organism reproduce is controlled by the DNA.

Asexual reproduction is typically performed by single-celled organisms, fungi, and some plant and algae species. It is accomplished by a single cell splitting into one or more cells exactly like it. In usual circumstances, this type of reproduction does not cause a change in the genetic material from the parent to the offspring, so the offspring that result from asexual reproduction are genetically identical to the parent and any other offspring from the same parent. This process is similar to making photocopies in that all of the copies (offspring) are an exact copy of the original (parent).

Sexual reproduction requires a male and a female organism to mate—or to combine their genetic material—resulting in offspring that are genetically different from each parent. The offspring's traits—how the organism looks and acts—are a mixture of the **traits** of the male and female parent. Offspring reproduced asexually always look exactly the same, but offspring produced sexually are rarely identical.

1.5 COMPLEX AND ORGANIZED

All life forms are **highly organized** and **complex** structures. Even what some biologists may call "simple life forms" are actually complex organisms. This is proven by the utter inability of any scientist to create life from only the basic molecules which make up a living organism. Life is both organized and complex as directed by its DNA. This complexity occurs on a multi-level basis. Life forms are organized specifically in regard to their atoms, atoms are specifically arranged into molecules, molecules are organized into cells, cells are organized into tissue, tissue is organised into organs, and organs are specifically arranged into organisms.

But it doesn't stop there. Organisms are grouped into **populations** (a collection of similar organisms), and populations are organized at an **ecosystem** level. An ecosystem is a group of populations interacting in their environment. At all levels, living organisms are highly organized.

1.6 RESPONSIVE

All living things are responsive to their environments. This means that they have various ways to sense changes in their environment and react to those changes. The ability to respond is controlled by varied **receptors**. Receptors are specialized molecules, structures, or chemicals that allow the organism to sense and respond to its environment. These sensing and responsive abilities of an organism help it to locate food, find shelter, and find a mate. Eyes, ears, chemical receptors in a snake's mouth, and the lateral line system of fish are all types of receptors that help organsisms sense and respond to the environment.

1.7 ENERGY EXTRACTION

Staying alive requires energy. Countless chemical reactions occur every minute in all cells and these reactions require energy to occur. All living organisms extract the energy they need from their environment and have specific ways to utilize the extracted energy in order to reproduce, obtain nutrients, etc. **Metabolism** is the process by which an organism extracts energy from its surroundings and uses it to sustain itself.

The majority of the energy on earth which all living organisms use for their sustenance ultimately comes from the sun. Plants, through the metabolic process of **photosynthesis**, are able to capture the energy from the sun and use it to grow and reproduce. Photosynthesis is a series of chemical reactions that plants use to make sugar molecules using energy from the sun. Plants then use the sugar molecules to make energy molecules. The energy molecules are used to run vital chemical reactions. Animals are not able to make their own sugar molecules, though. Animals make their energy molecules from the food they eat. Animals eat plants or other animals to obtain sugar molecules. The sugar molecules are then used to make energy moelcules that fuel the animal's vital chemical reactions. The biological process of an animal or plant using sugar molecules to make energy molecules is called **cellular respiration**.

Animals that are only able to derive their energy from plants and do not eat other animals are called **herbivores**. Some examples of herbivores are giraffes, elephants, and gerbils. Animals that can only derive their energy from other animals are called **carnivores**. Examples of these are tigers, lions, and wolves. Finally, there are organisms that are able to derive energy from either plants or animals; these are called omnivores. Humans and bears, for example, are **omnivores**.

Another way to view the energy extraction situation in nature is through a food chain in which the energy passes from **producers** (plants, by and large) to **consumers** (herbivores, carnivores, and omnivores) and finally to the **decomposers**. Decomposers are organisms like certain bacteria and fungi that break down the remains of other organisms. Decomposers can either be carnivores (who "decompose" by eating the remains of animals), or herbivores (who break down the remains of plants). This transfer of energy from producer to consumer to decomposer is called **the food chain**.

Figure 1.7.1

The Complexity and Flow of Atoms, Molecules, and Organisms in the Circle of Life.
This graphic illustrates the complexity and highly organized structure of living organisms. It also demonstrates the dependence organisms have upon one another. Start the figure by looking at the sub-atomic particles way down in the lower left hand corner. The first series of lines from subatomic particles to "multicelled organism" indicate the increasing complexity of how cells are organized within life forms. A group of organisms makes up a population of the same organisms. Populations of different organisms make up a community, and communities are organized into ecosystems. Then, moving downward from ecosystem, the relationship of energy transfer is indicated. The sun is the ultimate source of energy for almost all organisms on earth. Producers release oxygen (O_2) when they make sugar from the sun's energy. Animals use that oxygen for their survival and release carbon dioxide (CO_2). The carbon dioxide is then taken up by the plants. The remainder of the flow of energy and molecules is as indicated. This is simply to be used as a tool to begin understanding how complex nature is. We will be discussing all of these issues much more in this course.

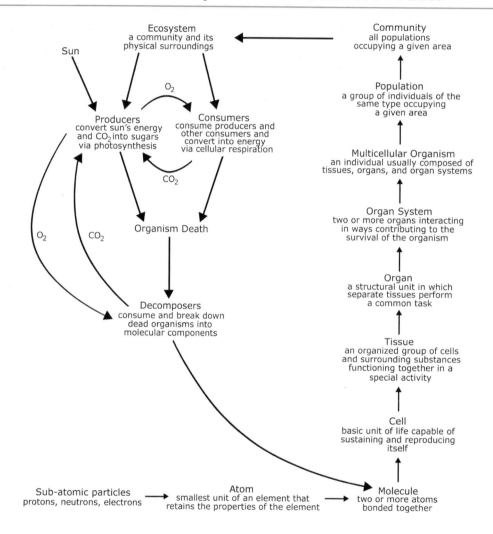

1.8 HOMEOSTASIS

All life forms have the need to maintain a stable internal environment within the single cell or multi-cellular organism to ensure that the metabolic needs of the organism are able to be met.

This means the organism needs a way to ensure its temperature, hydration, acidity, and other physiologic needs are maintained within the strict limits necessary for the organism to carry out its metabolic needs. This is called **homeostasis**. Generally speaking, if homeostasis is not maintained properly within an organism, it becomes quite sick, or even dies.

Maintaining proper body temperature is a good example of homeostasis. Humans, as mammals, are able to maintain a fairly constant internal temperature. When a mammal is too hot, it begins to sweat to cool itself. If a mammal is too cool, it is able to increase its internal temperature. Reptiles, such as snakes, on the other hand, have a different way to maintain a normal body temperature. If a reptile is too cold, it moves into the sun to warm itself up. If it is too hot, it moves into the shade. This is because reptiles are not able to maintain a constant body temperature on their own. Their body temperature is dependent on the outside temperature. They still need to maintain a "normal" body temperature but have a different way of doing it than mammals.

Figure 1.8.1

Homeostasis
Organisms have many different ways of maintaining homeostasis. Dogs maintiain temperature homeostasis by panting. Reptiles maintain homeostasis by changing their environment. If a snake is cold, it moves into the sun. If it is hot, it moves into the shade.

1.9 GROWTH

All living organisms grow. Whether the organism is a one-celled bacterium or a trillion-celled human, all organisms grow at some point in their life cycle. Single-celled organisms grow as the cell gets larger. However, a single-celled organism can only grow so big. Multicellular organisms grow by cell reproduction. Cell reproduction increases the number of cells making up the organism. As the number of cells increases, the organism gets larger.

1.10 CLASSIFICATION

The final common property of life forms is that they have been assigned to groups based on their common properties. It is important to remember that not all life forms have been studied or classified yet. It has been estimated that there are 40 million species on earth and we have only studied about 2 million of them.

Figure 1.10.1

The Six Kingdoms and Representative Examples

Kingdom	Example
Archaebacteria	Methanogens
Eubacteria	*Escherichia coli*
Protista	Protozoa
Fungi	Molds and Fungus
Plantae	Moss, Trees, Flowers, Bushes
Animalia	Mammals, Birds, Reptiles, Amphibians, Insects

We have already discussed two possible ways to classify all life forms on earth: 1) the producers, consumers, and decomposers system, and 2) the herbivores, carnivores, and omnivores system. However, these systems do not allow for a great deal of specificity when classifying life forms. Another system is used that has been in place—though modified from time to time—for almost 300 years, since it was first devised by Linnaeus in the 16th century.

The **taxonomy** (or classification) system in use today is a seven level, six kingdom system. Life forms are first divided into kingdoms based upon common characteristics, then divided further into other groupings as indicated in the next paragraph until the organism has been placed into the appropriate seven levels.

The levels of classification in the binomial six kingdom taxonomy system are (moving top to bottom, from the more general to the more specific):

> **Kingdom**
>   **Phylum (or Division)**
>   **Class**
>   **Order**
>   **Family**
>   **Genus**
>   **Species**

The levels of classification listed above are the same for plants as they are for animals, with the exception of one level. In the kingdoms of Plantae and Fungi, instead of using phylum, the term division is often used. As can be seen in Figure 1.10.1, all of the over two million already classified organisms are grouped into six kingdoms.

As an example of how this system works, the specific classification breakdown for humans is the following:

Kingdom	Animalia
Phylum	Chordata
Class	Mammalia
Order	Primates
Family	Hominidae
Genus	Homo
Species	sapiens
Sub-species	sapiens

As you read down the classification for humans, the kingdom is the least specific. That means there are many organisms classified in the Kingdom Animalia. As you move down the levels, the classes become more specific. That means there are fewer and fewer organisms in each level of classification as the one above it. For example, there are fewer organisms classified in the Order Primates as there are in the Class Mammalia.

Once you reach the genus and species, you have reached the most specific classification level. For example, there are only a few types of bacteria classified in the *Clostridium* genus. However, there is only one organism classified as the species *Clostridium botulinum*. Occasionally, two organisms are so similar that they have the same genus and species name and are further classified as sub-species. For example, there are two organisms classified as *Homo sapiens*—*Homo sapiens sapiens* (modern humans) and *Homo sapiens neanderthalensis* (a now extinct group of humans). Most organisms are not classified as sub-species, but simply as a species.

Per convention, organisms are referred to by scientists using their genus and species name. This is a two-part name called the **binomial name**. Note that binomial names are written either with the genus and the species name underlined or in italics as I have done. The genus is always written starting with a capital and the species is started with a lower case letter. Look at figure 1.1.1 and see the binomial name for the bacteria shown. Organisms are always referred to using their binomial name because this avoids any confusion since there is only one organism on the planet with that name. In the case of species which are classified into a sub-species, then the name is written with all three names. For example, humans are referred to as *Homo sapiens sapiens*, or *H. sapiens sapiens*.

This classification system allows for a great deal of specificity to name any potential life form is encountered on the planet. In addition, there is an infinite number of species that can be classified in this manner due to the seven-level system. Even today, though, as we learn more about particular species, they are sometimes reclassified by scientists into different levels of classification. We will discuss much more about classification systems as the year goes on. Do not get bogged down on this subject now.

1.11 SCIENTIFIC METHOD

All disciplines that are classified as "science" conform to a systematic way of obtaining and methodically analyzing data or observations about a subject called **scientific method**. The scientific method, quite simply, explains how scientists ask questions or answer questions.

The scientific method begins with a question regarding any subject. Then the process of **observation** begins. Observation is the collection of data—or facts—related to the question that needs to be answered. Once some data has been collected, a **hypothesis** is able to be formed. A hypothesis is an educated statement that explains the observations made up to the point the hypothesis statement is formed. A good hypothesis not only explains the data collected, but also predicts what future data will be collected.

Following the formation of the hypothesis statement, the **experimentation** stage of the scientific method begins. During the experimentation period, more and more data is collected and analyzed to test the hypothesis statement.

There are different types of experiments that can be performed. The most simple is the **observation experiment**. Data is collected by using the five senses—taste, touch, vision, smell, and hearing. The observations are written down and assessed after the experiment is completed.

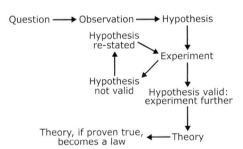

Figure 1.11.1

The Scientific Process.
This is a continually changing process that takes into account the meaning of all information acquired. At times, hypotheses (or even entire theories) have to be re-thought, re-stated, or tested further because of new information obtained in the scientific process.

Most experiments, though, are **controlled experiments**. This type of experiment is designed to test the effects of changing one **factor** on the hypothesis. A variable is anything in an experiment which may affect the outcome. In a controlled experiment, two groups are studied to assess the effects of changing one variable on the outcome of the experiment. This is done to test whether or not the hypothesis is accurate in predicting the outcome of future data.

One group in a controlled experiment is called the **control group**, and the other is the **experimental group**. The control group is exposed to certain factors, and the results are collected. The experimental group is exposed to the exact same factors as the control group, except that one factor is changed. The factor that is changed is called the **variable**. At the end of the experiment, the effects of the variable are evaluated in the experimental group as compared to the control group.

For example, you make the observation that plants almost always grow straight up out of the ground. You hypothesize that the reason they do so is because they grow toward the sun. Since the sun is above the plants, they naturally grow straight up from the earth. The implication in this hypothesis is that if plants are not exposed to the sun, they will not grow straight up. Now you need to devise an experiment to test that hypothesis. The variable that is very easy to control is whether or not the plants are exposed to sun. You devise an experiment in which the control plants are grown in the presence of full sunlight and the experimental plants are grown in the dark. If your hypothesis is correct, then the plants that are grown in the dark should not grow straight up in the air. You plant seeds in pots, water the two groups the same amount, and monitor their growth. You are surprised to find that both sets of plants grow straight upward. That means that your hypothesis is incorrect. You now know that plants grow straight up regardless of their exposure to the sun and you need to revise or restate your hypothesis statement and then design a new experiment to test the new hypothesis.

1.12 THEORY

During the experimental phase, more and more data is collected and evaluated as to whether it is consistent with the experimental hypothesis, or not. If the data is consistent, then there is further experimentation performed in multiple controlled experiments to continue to test the hypothesis. When a large amount of data is collected and remains consistent with the hypothesis statement, then the hypothesis becomes a **theory**. A scientific theory comes as close to a complete explanation of a question as possible. A theory also accurately explains experimental data which is collected. However, if the data collected does not accurately predict the next batch of data which is collected, one of two things needs to occur: either the hypothesis needs to be reformulated, or it needs to be discarded.

1.13 MEASUREMENTS

Finally, there needs to be a way for the scientific experiments to be reported. This is accomplished through scientists discussing their results in scientific journals, at scientific meetings, and on the Internet. By sharing their experimental design and results, other scientists are able to further test the hypothesis and report their findings. This method ensures that strict experimental conditions are maintained, and that results from one scientist are able to be reproduced by other researchers.

In order for the scientific method to be meaningful and universal, scientists have devised a way of expressing results in measurements that any scientist can understand. This is done by using a single standard of measurement called the **International System of Measurement**, or **SI units**, for short. This system is also called the metric system. Figure 1.13.1 lists units that are directly measurable. They serve as the basis for the rest of the SI units' values.

Not all units are measurable units. Some units need to be calculated, such as those for surface area, temperature, volume, and velocity. These are called **derived units** and are the result of mathematical relationships between two base units, or other derived units. These are listed in Figure 1.13.3

Figure 1.13.1

SI Base Units

Base Unit	Name	Abbreviation
Time	second	s
Length	meter	m
Mass	kilogram	kg
Electric current	ampere	A
Amount of substance	mole	mol
Luminous intensity	candela	cd
Thermodynamic temperature	kelvin	K

Figure 1.13.2

SI Modifiers/Prefixes

Prefix	Abbreviation	Factor of base unit	Example
pico-	p	10^{-12}	1 picometer = .000000000001 meters
nano-	n	10^{-9}	1 nanogram = .000000001 grams
micro-	µ	10^{-6}	1 microamp = .000001 amperes
milli-	m	10^{-3}	1 millimole = .001 moles
centi-	c	10^{-2}	1 centimeter = .01 meters
deci-	d	10^{-1}	1 decisecond = .1 seconds
deka-	da	10	1 dekamole = 10 moles
hecto-	h	10^{2}	1 hectogram = 100 grams
kilo-	k	10^{3}	1 kiloamp = 1000 amps
mega-	M	10^{6}	1 megacandela = 1,000,000 candelas
giga-	G	10^{9}	1 gigasecond = 1,000,000,000 seconds

Figure 1.13.3

Derived Units

Unit	Name	Abbreviation
Area	square meter	m^2
Volume	cubic meter	m^3
Mass density	kilogram per cubic meter	kg/m^3
Specific volume	cubic meter per kilogram	m^3/kg
Celsius temperature	degree Celsius	$^{\circ}C$

1.14 MICROSCOPY

One of the most common instruments used in the study of biology is the **microscope**. A microscope is an instrument that produces large images of even incredibly small objects. A **light microscope** is the standard microscope in scientific use. It is a made of a series of lenses through which light is passed to obtain an image of a small object. The light source can be direct light (such as from a light bulb) or reflected light (such as from a mirror) to **illuminate**—or "light up"—the small object so that the enlarged image can be viewed. The image of the object is then viewed through a lens or a television/computer screen. The amount that the image is enlarged is called the **magnification**. Most light microscopes are capable of magnifying an image up to 2000 times (or 2000x) its normal size.

Figure 1.14.1

Microscopic, TEM and SEM Views of Escherichia coli.

This figure demonstrates the different abilities of three different types of microscopes. The image on the left is taken through a regular light microscope. This type of picture is called a light micrograph. This organism is a unicellular animal called an amoeba. This is magnified approximately 400x. The middle picture is taken from a type of electron microscope called a transmission electron microscope (TEM). This type of picture is called an electron micrograph. This is of a bacterium called *E. coli* and it is magnified approximately 5000x. The image on the right is an electron micrograph taken with a scanning electron microscope (SEM). Notice the SEM gives a three dimensional image, whereas the TEM gives a two dimensional image. This is an image of a tick, magnified approximately 500x.

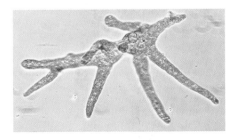
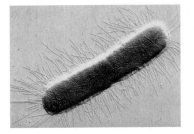

1.15 ADVANCED

The light microscope is limited to magnifying an image to 2000x because magnifying the image any larger makes the image too blurry to see detail. The ability to see detail well under magnification is called **resolution**. The light microscope has a resolution that is limited to magnifying an image 2000 times its normal size (or 2000x).

In order to further our knowledge of biology and other sciences, a way was devised to magnify images much larger without affecting their resolution. This method is called electron microscopy. An **electron microscope** bounces a beam of electrons off of an object instead of light. Instead of the image of the object being collected in a lens to be viewed, the image from an electron microscope is collected in magnetic lenses. The image is then converted into a signal and is usually displayed on a screen like a television or computer monitor. An electron microscope allows for magnification of an object up to 200,000x. This means an electron microscope can enlarge things 200,000 times their original size. Electron microscopes also give excellent resolution. That means that even though it enlarges objects to thousands of times their normal size, the detail of the image is not distorted. Unfortunately, the use of electron microscopes is limited due to their cost (several million dollars each).

There are two main types of electron microscopes. The **transmission electron microscope (TEM)** allows for the study of non-living objects by embedding the object in a frozen block and slicing it into extremely thin pieces. The electron beam is passed through the object in one plane. This method of study of microscopy has been crucial in advancing our knowledge of the interiors of cells. Like light microscopy, the TEM gives a 2D image.

The **scanning electron microscope (SEM)** is an excellent tool for studying living small things. In SEM, the electron beam is swept across an intact, rather than thinly sliced, sample and gives a 3D image of the object. It does not allow for as much magnification as the TEM does, though.

1.16 PEOPLE OF SCIENCE

Anton van Leeuwenhoek (1632-1723) It is a hard call regarding who should be the first person listed in the People of Science section. Mr. van Leeuwenhoek was chosen for several reasons. First of all, he had absolutely no training in biology. He was a janitor and owned his own dry goods store in Holland. Second, he did things no one expected could be done at the time, which raised him to great prominence. In his spare time, he liked to grind lenses used for eye glasses. However, van Leeuwenhoek was able to grind lenses smaller than any else ever had—some as small as a pinhead. He was able to hand grind lenses 300 years ago which are still the envy of microscope makers. It was this hobby that led him to discover the microscope. Due to his perfection of grinding high optic lenses, he was able to see things never before seen. He was the first human to ever see bacteria, yeast, muscle fibers, and blood flowing through blood vessels. The scientific community rapidly adopted his technology, and his observations led to a revolution in biology that lasted several hundred years. His determined approach to a hobby led to one of the most significant contributions to science.

1.17 KEY CHAPTER POINTS

- Every organism which is alive shares the following properties: they are made up of one or more cells; they contain DNA; they reproduce; they are complex and organized; they are responsive to their environment; they extract energy from their surroundings; they maintain homeostasis; and they grow.

- All organisms are classified using the seven level, six kingdom, taxonomic system.

- Biology, as a science, is subject to the scientific method.

- SI units (i.e. the "metric system") are standardized units of measurements used in all scientific studies.

- Many instruments are used to make scientific observations. One of the most important in biology is the microscope.

- Electron microscopes have much better resolution than light microscopes.

1.18 DEFINITIONS

asexual reproduction
The production of a new organism that only requires one parent. This type of reproduction normally does not cause any change in the genetic material from parent to offspring.

binomial
The two-part name of an organism that has been classified using the six kingdom system.

biology
The study—or science—of life.

carnivore
An animal that extracts its energy from other animals. Simply put, a meat eater.

cellular respiration
The process by which producers produce their energy from the sugars they make during photosynthesis or the way that consumers produce their energy from the food they eat.

consumer
An organism that uses a producer or other consumers for its energy source. All animals are examples of consumers.

controlled experiment
A type of experiment in which two sets of groups are studied—a control group and an experimental group—to understand the effect of changing one condition.

control group
The group in a controlled experiment that is not subjected to a changed variable.

decomposers
Organisms that derive their energy from dead organisms.

DNA (deoxyribonucleic acid)
The molecule that contains the genetic material in all life forms.

ecosystem
The relationship between more than one population and the environment in which they live.

electron microscope
A microscope which bounces a beam of electrons off of an object to acquire the image.

environment
The surroundings in which an organism lives. This can refer to an external (outside) environment (such as a rain forest) or an internal environment (such as a human being when discussing a bacteria that is making someone ill).

experiment
A careful method of testing a hypothesis.

experimental group
The group in a controlled experiment that is exposed to a variable.

food chain
The process of the transfer of energy from the sun, to the producers, to the consumers, to the decomposers.

herbivore
An animal that extracts its energy only from plants. Simply put, a plant-eater.

homeostasis
The maintenance of a stable internal environment in order for an organism to live.

hypothesis
An educated statement that explains observations. A hypothesis statement is made early on in the scientific method.

International System of Measurement, or SI Units
A standard set of units that are used by all scientists around the world.

light microscope
A system of connected lenses which acquires an image by reflecting light off of, or shining light through, the object.

magnification
The amount by which an image is enlarged by a microscope.

metabolism
The process by which an organism extracts energy from its surroundings and uses it to sustain itself.

microscope
An instrument that produces enlarged images of very small objects.

offspring
The organism that receives the genetic material and is formed as a result of reproduction.

omnivore
An animal that can extract its energy from either plants or animals.

organism
The resulting structure that is formed when one or more cells are grouped together to carry on the activities of life. Examples range from a one-celled bacterium to a trillion-celled human being or tree.

parent
The organism(s) that supplies the genetic material during reproduction.

photosynthesis
The process by which the energy of the sun is captured and used to make sugar molecules.

population
A group of similar organisms that live in the same area.

producer
An organism that uses photosynthesis to produce its own energy source. All plants are examples of a producer.

receptor
Specialized molecules or organs that all life forms possess that allow them to sense and respond to changes in their environments.

resolution
The ability to see an image's fine detail.

reproduction
The formation of a new organism or cell from already living organisms or cells in order to propagate—or spread—the species or make new cells.

scientific method
The systematic collection and analysis of data.

sexual reproduction
   The production of one or more offspring as a result of a male and female of the species combining their genetic material. This type of reproduction results in changes in genetic material from parent to offspring and requires two parent organisms.

taxonomy
   The orderly classification of plants and animals according to their observed natural relationships to one another as well as similarities in structure and function.

theory
   A hypothesis which has undergone extensive experimentation and has been found to completely explain a question.

STUDY QUESTIONS

1. Describe or list the common properties that all life forms share.

2. What is a food chain?

3. How do plants obtain their sugar molecules?

4. How does an herbivore obtain its daily energy? Where does a carnivore obtain its daily energy?

5. How is an omnivore different from a carnivore?

6. What is the process of a producer, consumer, or decomposer making energy molecules from sugar molecules called?

7. Describe homeostasis and explain why it is important.

8. List three ways that organisms can be scientifically classified.

9. Describe the taxonomy system most commonly used to classify organisms today.

10. What is a hypothesis statement?

11. What is the next step of the scientific method after the hypothesis statement is formulated?

12. Is the experimental group or control group exposed to the variable in a controlled experiment?

13. What must a scientist do if the data collected during hypothesis testing does not support the hypothesis statement?

14. What is important about the units used in the SI system?

15. Define magnification and resolution.

16. Which type of electron microscope provides a three dimensional image of an object?

The Composition and Chemistry of Life

2

2.0 CHAPTER PREVIEW

In this chapter we will:

- Understand how organisms obtain the energy they need to live and the relationship between photosynthesis and cellular respiration.

- Investigate the properties of the building blocks of all matter—atoms and molecules.

- Define isotopes and their properties.

- Investigate how covalent and ionic chemical bonds form by following the Law of Conservation of Mass.

- Discuss the unique properties of water that make it the best substance to surround and fill cells.

- Introduce basic concepts of solutes, solvents, acids, and bases.

2.1 BASIC ENERGY CONCEPTS

Energy concepts will be discussed much more in future chapters. However, a basic understanding of this concept is needed to keep the big picture in mind.

All life forms require energy to live. This energy comes from sugars and is used by the organism to fuel chemical reactions. The chemical reactions are required for the organism to live. Where do the sugars come from? As discussed in Chapter 1, all life forms must extract energy from the environment in order to live. The energy which is extracted is then converted by the organism into sugar molecules. **Sugars** are the universal fuel which all organisms use for their metabolism.

Figure 2.1.1

The Cycle of Energy Flow in Nature
Note the circle created in the flow of various components of the cycle. For example, during photosynthesis, not only do plants make sugars which ultimately provide all of the available energy to other organisms on earth, but they also give off oxygen. Oxygen is required by all organisms for cellular respiration. During cellular respiration, carbon dioxide gas is given off and this is used by the producers during photosynthesis. Plants release oxygen into the air, which is necessary for non-plant life to survive. The substances that all life forms need are constantly recycled in the food/energy cycle.

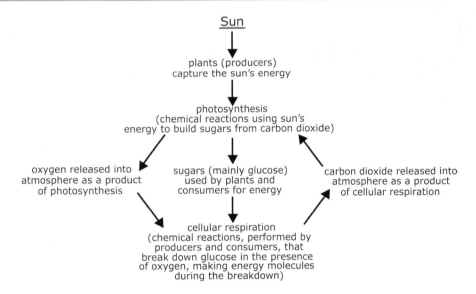

The starting point for the production of all sugars which life forms use to survive is the sun. Producers make their sugars from the energy of the sun through the process of **photosynthesis**. During photosynthesis, the energy from the sun's rays is trapped by cells of the plant. Once trapped, this energy is then used by the plant to make sugar molecules. Once sugars are made, producers use them to make molecules of ATP (adenosine triphosphate). ATP then provides the energy the producers need to drive their metabolism. The process of making molecules of ATP from sugars is called **cellular respiration**. Also, when consumers eat the producers or other consumers, they extract the energy and convert it into their own molecules of ATP. This is also done through cellular respiration. (See Figure 2.1.1 for details.) Both photosynthesis and cellular respiration are going to be covered in much more detail in upcoming chapters. For now, you simply need to know that all of these processes are dependent on one another.

2.2 MATTER

Matter is anything that takes up space and has mass. **Mass** is defined as the quantity of matter an object has. Mass is **not** technically the weight of an object, because the weight of an object depends on the forces of gravity that an object is subject to. For example, this book will have the same quantity of matter—or mass—regardless of where the book is located. Its mass is the same on the earth as it is on the moon. But if the book were taken to the moon, it would have less weight than it has on the earth since the moon has less gravitational pull than the earth.

It is also important to remember that matter exists even if you cannot see it. Matter exists in every solid, liquid, and gas object. The air we breathe is made up of matter, just like a rock or the water in the ocean. The molecules of a rock are more densely packed together and maintain their shape more than the molecules of a liquid. The molecules of a gas have little attraction to one another, so they move around more freely and do not maintain a definite shape.

2.3 CHANGES IN MATTER

Matter can be changed in two different ways. It can undergo a **physical change** (in which the appearance is changed, but not the chemical makeup of the matter), or it can undergo a **chemical change**, in which the molecules of the matter are altered.

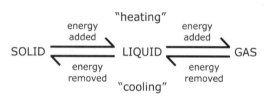

Figure 2.3.1

Forms of Matter
All matter exists in three forms. Gasses can be transformed into liquids by removing heat. This is called cooling. Removing energy from a liquid—or cooling—will form a solid. Adding energy to a solid will transform the solid into a liquid. Further heating of a liquid will turn it into a gas.

For example, to change a gas to a liquid, energy must be removed from the gas (i.e. the gas is cooled). Further cooling of the liquid will change it to a solid. The reverse is true to change a solid to a liquid and then to a gas: energy (i.e. heat) is added, which will cause the solid to change to a liquid. More energy (heat) will then cause the liquid to change to a gas. The matter you have heated is still made of the same molecules. It is simply in a different form.

For example, let's say you take a piece of ice and place it in a pot on the stove. The ice is made of water molecules (H_2O) which have low energy because the water is frozen. As the ice is heated, energy is added. The frozen molecules of the H_2O begin to move faster and faster because of the added energy (heat). When enough heat has been added to the ice, it melts into a liquid. The liquid is still made of molecules of H_2O, but now it is a liquid because energy has been added in the form of heat. As the liquid water is heated further, the water molecules gain more energy. Once enough energy has been added, the liquid water turns into gaseous water. Water in gas form is called steam. Even though the water has changed from ice to water to steam, it was always still physically made up of molecules of H_2O.   When you trim your fingernails, there has been a physical change to the nails—they have been cut—but they are still nails. These are all examples of physical changes of matter.

Chemical changes occur when there is a chemical reaction that takes place. This results in changes in the actual molecules which make up the matter undergoing a chemical reaction. For example, when propane gas is burned in a propane torch, the molecules of the propane interact with molecules of oxygen to make water vapor (steam) and carbon dioxide gas. Following a chemical change to matter, the molecules you start with are different than the molecules you end up with. Anytime a chemical reaction has taken place, you automatically know there has been a chemical change to the matter involved.

2.4 BASIC BUILDING BLOCKS OF MATTER

All matter is made up of basic building blocks. The smallest building block of matter is called the **atom**. Each atom is made up of protons, neutrons, and electrons (except hydrogen, which only has one proton, one electron, and no neutron). Groups of atoms connected together are **molecules**. If the atoms of a molecule are all the same type of atom, then we call that molecule an **element.** Please realize that even if there are only two atoms linked together, it is still a molecule. By far, the great majority of atoms in all organisms are in the form of molecules.

2.5 ATOMS AND ELEMENTS

As stated, atoms are the smallest complete structures that make up all matter. Another definition for **element** is "matter composed of only one type of atom." For example, pure oxygen contains only oxygen atoms. While there are over one hundred known elements, *more than 90% of all life mass is composed of the elements carbon, oxygen, hydrogen, and nitrogen.*

The atom is divided into two "parts." The center part is called the **nucleus** and the area outside of the nucleus is called the **electron shell**. Inside the electron shell and the nucleus are the **subatomic particles**. The subatomic particles are simply particles that are smaller than an atom. The subatomic particles we are going to learn about in this course are called **electrons, protons, and neutrons**. There are also other forms of subatomic particles, but for this course, we are only learning about the proton, neutron, and electron.

Figure 2.5.1

Subatomic Particles and Properties

Particle	Charge	Location
neutron	none	nucleus
proton	positive	nucleus
electron	negative	electron shell

Figure 2.5.2

Atomic Structure
Atoms contain protons, neutrons and electrons. The nucleus holds protons and neutrons while electrons orbit the nucleus.

P = proton   N = neutron   e = electron

Ionic –

Covalent –

2.6 BOHR MODEL

Figure 2.6.1 is a model of what an atom looks like, called the **Bohr Model**. Although we will be covering other models that predict what atoms may look like and how they interact as well, this is the model we will use most of the time.

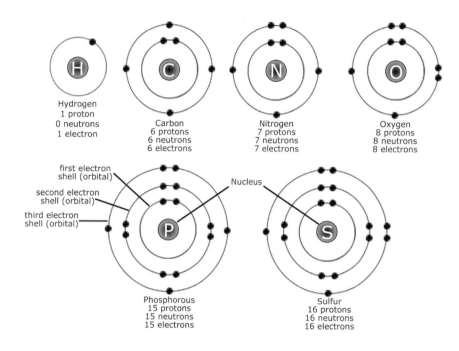

Hydrogen
1 proton
0 neutrons
1 electron

Carbon
6 protons
6 neutrons
6 electrons

Nitrogen
7 protons
7 neutrons
7 electrons

Oxygen
8 protons
8 neutrons
8 electrons

first electron
shell (orbital)

second electron
shell (orbital)

third electron
shell (orbital)

Nucleus

Phosphorous
15 protons
15 neutrons
15 electrons

Sulfur
16 protons
16 neutrons
16 electrons

Figure 2.6.1

Bohr Models of the Most Prevalent Atoms of Life

In a Bohr model, the protons and neutrons are collectively shown as a circle in the center of the atom. The "H," "C," "N," etc., correspond to the nucleus. It is accepted as standard that the protons and neutrons are contained in the circle and not drawn individually. Electrons, though, are shown individually. As you can see, every Bohr model has a different number of electrons surrounding it. That is because every atom has a different number of electrons. Each electron "ring," also called an "orbital" or "shell," can hold a specific number of electrons. As you see, the first electron shell can only hold two electrons. Once the first shell is filled with 2 electrons, electrons are placed in the next shell until that one is full. The second electron shell can hold 8 electrons. As we move through this chapter, you will learn how to draw a Bohr diagram correctly and how to know how many protons, neutrons, and electrons each element has. For example, you will learn why oxygen—"O"—has 8 electrons in 2 shells while sulfur has 16 electrons in 3 shells.

2.7 PROTONS AND NEUTRONS

The nucleus contains two separate subatomic particles called **protons** and **neutrons**. Protons and neutrons are much, much larger and have more mass than electrons. More than 95% of the mass of an atom is contained in the nucleus. If we could enlarge an atom so that the nucleus was as large as an acorn and put it in the center of a large sports stadium, the electrons would be orbiting the nucleus way out at the last set of seats. Most of the space in any given atom is empty, with only a small part being taken up by the protons, neutrons, and electrons.

2.8 CHARGE OF SUBATOMIC PARTICLES

Protons are said to be positively charged, and electrons are said to be negatively charged. Even though protons are physically larger than electrons, they each have the same equality of charge. That means the positive charge of one proton is equal to the negative charge of one electron. Electrons have a much higher energy content than protons, which is why the larger proton has an equal positive charge as the smaller, negatively-charged electron. Neutrons have no charge, or are said to be neutral.

Since protons are in the nucleus, the nucleus is positively charged. The negatively charged electrons orbit around the positively charged nucleus. It is the attraction of the positive nucleus to the negative electrons which holds atoms together. Normally, the overall charge of an atom is neutral. That means a normal atom has no overall charge, because the number of protons and electrons are equal. However, there are atoms in which the number of protons does not equal the number of electrons. These types of atoms are called **ions**.

2.9 SUBATOMIC PARTICLES ARE ALL THE SAME

Any given proton, neutron, or electron is the same no matter which atom it comes from. That is to say that a proton from a helium atom is exactly the same as a proton from a carbon atom, and these are both exactly the same as a proton from a uranium atom. The same relationship holds true for electrons and neutrons. What makes atoms different is the *number* of protons, neutrons, and electrons that an atom contains.

A carbon atom, for instance, contains 6 protons, 6 neutrons, and 6 electrons. But while a nitrogen atom contains the same *type* of protons, neutrons, and electrons as a carbon atom, the nitrogen atom contains 7 protons, 7 neutrons, and 7 electrons. It is the number of protons, neutrons, and electrons that an atom of one type contains that makes it different from an atom of another type.

2.10 ATOMIC NUMBER AND ATOMIC SYMBOL

In biology, we have classified the elements in the periodic table of the elements. Please see the periodic table of elements (which is inside the back cover of the book) for a complete listing of all elements known at the time of printing. Each element has a unique one or two letter abbreviation to identify it; this is called the **atomic symbol**. The number of protons that an atom contains is called the **atomic number**. Each element has a unique atomic number that identifies it.

Figure 2.10.1

How do you read the periodic table of the elements?
The atomic number indicates the number of protons the element contains. The atomic number is also equal to the number of electrons since the number of protons and electrons are equal in a neutral element. The atomic symbol (sometimes called the chemical symbol) is the one or two letter abbreviation for the element. The atomic mass is the "weight" of the atom in atomic mass units and generally equals the number of protons plus the number of neutrons. The reason the atomic mass does not exactly equal the number of protons plus the number of neutrons is because even though they are small, electrons do have a small amount of mass. Hydrogen has one proton and one electron. It has no neutrons. We know that the mass of a proton is one. The atomic mass of hydrogen is 1.0079. That means we can estimate the mass of one electron as 0.0079 atomic mass units. An atomic mass unit is a unit of measurement of the relative mass of subatomic particles. In carbon, there are 6 protons and 6 neutrons. We can estimate the atomic mass by adding the number of protons with the number of neutrons, or 6 + 6. This results in an atomic mass of 12, close to the actual value of 12.011.

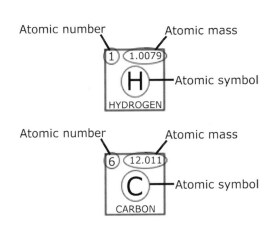

2.11 ATOMIC MASS

Even though they are unbelievably small, protons, electrons, and neutrons have their own mass. The mass of a proton and a neutron are almost exactly the same. The amount of mass of a proton is equal to 1 atomic mass unit. The amount of mass for a neutron is slightly more than 1 atomic mass unit. Although electrons are very, very small, they do have a slight mass associated with them. This is why the atomic mass of hydrogen is slightly more than one. **(Do not get bogged down with this concept right now, you will learn much more about it in chemistry).**

Therefore, the **atomic mass** of an atom—or element—can be nearly arrived at by adding the number of protons with the number of neutrons in the nucleus. As stated before, the number of protons always equals the number of electrons in a neutrally charged atom. **HOWEVER, be aware that the number of protons does not always equal the number of neutrons.** For example, we know that carbon has the same number of protons and neutrons in its nucleus (6 of each), as does nitrogen (7 protons and 7 neutrons). But if we look at the graphic of the element argon, we see the atomic number is 18. That means there are 18 protons in the nucleus of argon. If you assumed that there were equal numbers of neutrons as protons in the nucleus of argon, you would conclude that the atomic weight is 36—but it is not! The atomic weight is 39.95. Therefore, by subtracting the atomic number (18) from the atomic weight (39.95, which is almost 40), you arrive at the conclusion that there are 22 neutrons in the element argon, which is correct.

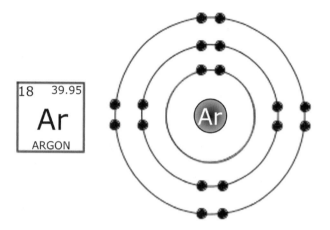

Figure 2.11.1

Argon
This element, like all of the elements in row VIIIA of the periodic table, has a full outer electron shell. This means they are stable, non-reactive atoms (**inert**) and do not easily form molecules with other elements. All of the elements in row VIIIA are called Noble gasses. The left figure shows argon as it appears in the periodic table of the elements. The figure on the right is a Bohr model of argon. Argon has an atomic number of 18, which means it has 18 protons and 18 electrons.

2.12 ELECTRON SHELLS

The other subatomic particle is the electron. The electron is a high-energy particle. This is why even though it is a lot smaller than a proton, it has an equal negative charge as compared to the proton's positive charge.

Electrons **orbit** the nucleus much like the planets orbit the sun. The electrons are arranged in **shells**—or energy levels—as indicated by the Bohr model we have already looked at. Each shell can hold a certain number of electrons, and the electrons orbit in **pairs within each shell**. Electron shells are also called **orbitals** or **clouds**.

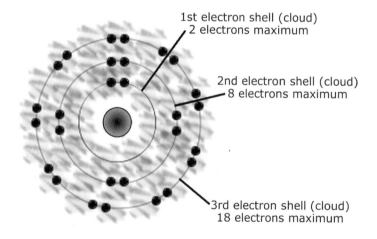

1st electron shell (cloud)
2 electrons maximum

2nd electron shell (cloud)
8 electrons maximum

3rd electron shell (cloud)
18 electrons maximum

Figure 2.12.1

Schematic of the first three electron shells, or clouds.
Remember the atom is a three dimensional structure, so electrons do not orbit in a consistent circular pathway around the nucleus. They orbit in pairs and are contained in specific areas outside of the nucleus. For example, the two electrons closest to the nucleus do not orbit the nucleus in a pathway further from the nucleus than the electrons that are in the second energy level. Thus, the "electron cloud theory" is an attempt to predict where the electrons would be expected to be found in any given atom. The two electrons in the first energy level are expected to be closer to the nucleus than the eight electrons in the second energy level, and those eight electrons in the second energy level are expected to be closer to the nucleus than the third level of electrons, and so forth.

The first energy shell (or level) can hold a maximum of 2 electrons (orbiting as one pair), the second energy shell can hold a maximum of 8 electrons (orbiting as four pairs), the third energy shell can hold a maximum of 18 electrons (orbiting as nine pairs), and so forth. You do not need to know how many electrons the levels outside of the third level can hold for this course.

Hydrogen has an atomic number of 1. That means there is one proton in hydrogen. Since the number of electrons always equals the number of protons, there is only one electron in hydrogen. This is another way of saying that there is one open "slot" for another electron to fill the first energy level. Because energy levels closest to the nucleus completely fill before the others start to fill, there is one open slot—or unfilled electron position—in hydrogen. In most elements, the electron shells are not completely filled.

When you draw a Bohr model, you place the electrons in the proper shell according to what you know. If the atom has four electrons, when you make the Bohr model, the two electrons are placed in the first electron shell, and the next two are placed in the second energy shell. You are also expected to know how many electrons the first three orbitals can hold—2 in the first, 8 in the second, and 18 in the third.

2.13 ATOMIC PROPERTIES

The **properties of an atom**—or how an atom behaves when exposed to other atoms and molecules—are determined mainly by the number of electrons the atom contains. This is because it has been found that atoms with unfilled electron shells are more reactive than those with filled shells. If the atom has unfilled electron energy levels, it is more likely to combine—or react with other atoms that have unfilled electron energy levels. Conversely, if an atom has filled outer electron shells, it is not likely to react with other atoms. These types of atoms with filled outer shells are called **inert**. Note that the four atoms—oxygen, nitrogen, carbon, and hydrogen—make up more than 90% of all living matter. These four atoms all have unfilled electron shells and are reactive with other atoms that have unfilled electron shells. On the other hand, atoms with filled electron shells—the **Noble gasses**—react with few other atoms naturally.

Figure 2.13.1

Filled versus unfilled electron energy levels and reactivity

Compare the outer electron structures of carbon and neon. Notice that carbon has four electrons in the second electron shell (which can hold a total of eight). The four open electron "slots" of carbon in its outer shell make it very reactive because the carbon "looks" for electrons to fill its shell. Neon has eight electrons in the outer shell. That means that neon has a filled outer electron shell. Having a full electron shell makes an atom more stable and so atoms with filled outer shells do not react with other atoms. Note that, like argon, neon is in Row VIIIA and is a Noble gas.

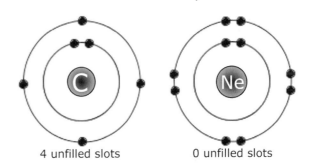

4 unfilled slots   0 unfilled slots

All of this information regarding atoms is not hard if you take the time to understand the relationships of protons (atomic number), neutrons (neutrons plus protons equals the atomic mass), and electrons (equal to the number of protons) to one another. Once you understand that, the rest is a simple manipulation of numbers.

2.14 ISOTOPES

An element (or atom) is defined by the number of protons and electrons it contains. For example, an atom which contains 6 protons and 6 electrons is carbon. There is only one atom which contains 6 protons and 6 electrons. Likewise, there is only one atom which contains 78 protons and 78 electrons. That is platinum. All elements (atoms) are defined by the number of protons and electrons the atom contains.

However, some atoms can contain different numbers of neutrons and still be the same element. Remember, an element is defined by the number of protons and electrons it contains. There are some forms of the same element that can differ in the number of neutrons they contain. This is called an **isotope**.

For example, there are three isotopes of carbon—carbon 12, carbon 13, and carbon 14. All carbon atoms contain 6 protons and 6 electrons. The carbon 12 isotope has 6 neutrons along with 6 protons in the nucleus, for an atomic mass of 12. Carbon 13 has 7 neutrons and 6 protons for an atomic mass of 13. Carbon 14 has 8 neutrons and 6 protons for an atomic mass of 14. However, these three isotopes chemically behave in the same way because they all contain 6 electrons.

Figure 2.14.1

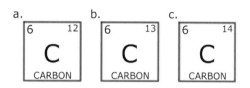

a.   b.   c.

The Isotopes of Carbon
Here are the three forms of carbon as they would appear in the periodic table of the elements. Note that since they are the same element, the atomic number (the number of protons) is the same for all three isotopes. All three forms of carbon also have the same number of electrons: 6. However, the atomic mass is different because carbon 12 has 6 neutrons, carbon 13 has 7 neutrons, and carbon 14 has 8 neutrons. You can see in the upper right corner of the element box that the atomic mass changes from 12 to 13 to 14 for the three isotopes of carbon.

2.15 MOLECULES

We have already noted that molecules are two or more atoms joined together. The reason that atoms combine to form molecules is that atoms are usually more stable when they are bonded together than when they are separate. They are more stable when bonded together because most times when atoms combine they fill the outer electron levels with eight electrons. This is called the **octet rule**. Hydrogen and helium are special cases regarding the octet rule. Hydrogen and helium are special because their outer shells can only hold two electrons. Therefore, the bonding rule is called the **duet rule**.

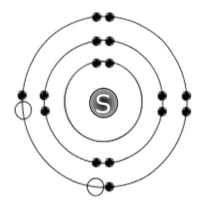

Figure 2.15.1

The Octet Rule and the Element Sulfur.
Sulfur has the atomic number of 16, which means it has 16 protons and 16 electrons. Its atomic mass is 32, which means that it also has 16 neutrons. Notice that sulfur has 8 electrons in the second shell, and 6 electrons in the outer shell. The octet rule states that an element with 8 electrons (or 4 pairs) in its outer shell has more stability than an element that does not have 4 pairs of electrons. Therefore, elements will bond with one another in a way that the outer electron shell has 8 electrons. The open circles in the outer shell indicate sulfur will combine with 2 other electrons to fulfill the octet rule.

Let's take an element with more subatomic particles as an example. Sulfur has an atomic number of 16, so there are 16 protons and 16 electrons in this element. The electron shells are filled as follows: there are 2 electrons completely filling the first energy level, and 8 electrons completely filling the second energy level. That means there are 6 electrons left over, and they go into the third energy level. Remember that the third energy level can hold a total of 18 electrons, so the remaining electrons of sulfur only take up 6 of those slots. The octet rule would lead to the conclusion that sulfur would ideally combine with other atom(s) such that it acquires two more electrons in its outer shell. This will satisfy the octet rule and give sulfur 8 electrons in its outer shell.

2.16 CHEMICAL BONDS ARE FORMED BY CHEMICAL REACTIONS

The reason we are taking so much time to understand atoms and their electron properties is that the electrons are what participate in **chemical bonds**. Chemical bonds form when electrons in one atom interact with electrons in another atom causing the two atoms to "stick" together.

A type of shorthand is used when showing what happens in a chemical reaction, or bond. Chemically, the hydrogen reaction described above is written as:

$$H + H \longrightarrow H_2$$

"H" stands for hydrogen and the plus sign indicates that the two bond together to form a molecule of hydrogen, H_2. Realize that when this happens, the single electron from each of the hydrogen atoms combines with another to fill the first electron shell. This forms a stable bond since the outer shell is completely filled.

A slightly more complicated example occurs when a carbon atom (C) combines with four chlorine (Cl) atoms to form carbon tetrachloride (CCl_4). This is another example of a chemical change which occurs in matter as the carbon atom combines with the chlorine atoms and the product has completely different properties than either the carbon or the chlorine alone.

The reaction to form carbon tetrachloride is chemically written as:

$$C + 4Cl \longrightarrow CCl_4$$

Here, the "4" indicates that four molecules of chlorine are needed to combine with one molecule of carbon. Also note in both the hydrogen and carbon tetrachloride reactions that there is a subscript on the end product indicating how many molecules of each element are contained in the end product. In the hydrogen case, there are 2 atoms of hydrogen, and in the carbon tetrachloride example the end product contains 1 molecule of carbon and 4 molecules of chlorine.

Figure 2.16.1

Covalently Bonded Carbon Tetrachloride Molecule
The Bohr model for carbon tetrachloride. Notice that the octet rule is satisfied for all bonded elements. Also note that there is no overall charge as the electrons are shared equally between the carbon and each of the four chloride atoms carbon bonds to.

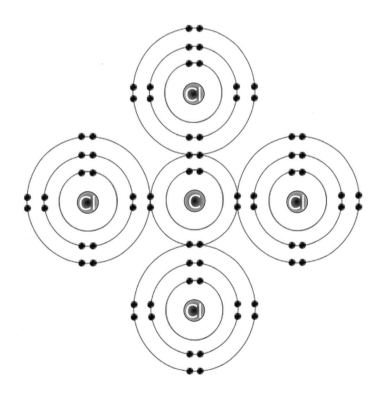

There are two types of chemical bonds– ionic and covalent. This means there are two slightly different ways in which the electrons can be shared by atoms in a chemical bond. Either way a bond forms, this results in a chemical change in the matter involved in the bond.

2.17 COVALENT CHEMICAL BONDS

Covalent bonds are formed when electrons are equally shared in the bond. Covalent bonds are stable bonds and much stronger than ionic bonds. This means that it requires more energy to break a covalent bond apart than to break an ionic bond. Also, there is no overall charge that results from a covalent bond—it is neutral. The ionic bond, however, results in a positive charge on one atom and a negative charge on the other.

Rarely is any bond a "perfect" covalent or a "perfect" ionic bond. Most bonds have characteristics of both. The bonds are classified as one or the other based on which one they most closely resemble.

The simplest type of covalent bond forms when two hydrogen atoms bond. The single electron of one hydrogen and the single electron of another hydrogen are shared, filling the outer electron shell of each hydrogen. This completes the duet rule.

2.18 POLAR AND NON-POLAR COVALENT BONDS

Within the category of covalent bonds there exist two separate types—polar and non-polar covalent bonds. **Polar** covalent bonds occur when the electrons of a covalent bond are slightly more attracted to one atom of the bond than another (please see water discussion below). **Non-polar** covalent bonds are formed when there is no unequal sharing of electrons.

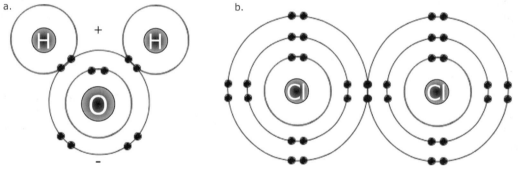

Figure 2.18.1

Polar and non-polar covalent bonds.
Figure (a) shows a polar covalent bond that is formed when 2 atoms of H bond to 1 atom of O to form water, H_2O. Note that the nucleus of oxygen is larger than that of hydrogen due to oxygen having 8 protons and 8 neutrons in the nucleus, while hydrogen only has 1 proton. Because the oxygen has more protons—or positive charges—than the hydrogen, it "pulls" the electrons towards it more than the hydrogen atoms can. This results in the electrons being closer to the oxygen and giving the oxygen end of the molecule a slightly negative charge. Since the electrons are farther from the hydrogen, a slightly positive charge results on the hydrogen end of the molecule, as shown. Figure (b) demonstrates a non-polar covalent bond between two chlorine molecules. The nucleus of one chlorine has the exact same number of protons as the other nucleus of chlorine, therefore the electrons are shared equally and there is no "pulling" of electrons toward one end of the molecule or the other. Also note that the CCl_4 molecule in Figure 2.16.1 forms non-polar covalent bonds.

2.19 IONIC BONDS

An **ion** is an atom that has a charge. This occurs when the number of protons does not equal the number of electrons. If there are more electrons (negative charge) than protons (positive charge), then the atom will be a **negative ion**. If there are more protons than electrons, the atom will be a **positive ion**. Atoms do NOT lose or gain protons to cause them to be charged. In order for an atom or molecule to become charged, it must lose or gain an electron. When an electron is gained, the molecule or atom becomes negatively charged. When an electron is lost, a molecule or an atom becomes positively charged.

Since a negative ion and a positive ion have opposite charges, they attract one another. In fact they are attracted to one another so strongly that they form a bond based purely on their charges (rather than by sharing electrons as occurs in covalent bonds). This forms an ionic bond. Therefore, **ionic bonds** occur when there is a bond formed due to the attraction of a negatively charged ion with a positively charged ion. Ionic bonds are weaker than covalent bonds.

Why do ions form? Because forming an ion actually makes an atom more stable, and here is how that works: we will use the ion bond that forms between table salt—sodium chloride. The sodium (atomic number 11) has 2 electrons in the first energy level, 8 electrons in the second energy level, and only 1 in the third level. The chlorine (atomic number 17) has filled first and second energy levels, but has an opening in the third energy level for one electron. Following the octet rule, the electron from the sodium atom's third energy level "leaves"—or is **donated** –and becomes part of the chlorine atom. The sodium is referred to as an **electron donor**. This results in a full second energy level for the chlorine atom with 8 electrons. The chlorine is called an **electron acceptor**. In addition, even though the sodium has donated 1 electron, in doing so it is left with a filled outer shell. Both the chlorine atom with the extra electron and the sodium minus 1 electron are more stable because their outer shells are filled. This results in the sodium atom having 1 more proton than electron, so the sodium is positively charged and is called a **sodium ion**. Forming ions, then, helps the atoms to fulfill the octet rule, which makes them more stable.

As for the chlorine atom in this situation, remembering that electrons like to 1) hang out in pairs and 2) follow the octet rule, we see that chlorine has 7 electrons in its outer electron shell. Therefore, the chlorine will accept the electron donated by the sodium. This gives the chlorine atom 8 electrons in its outer shell, and one more electron than proton. Therefore, the chlorine atom is charged negatively and is called a **chloride ion**. Again do not get overly bogged down in the details as you will learn this completely in chemistry.

Since the sodium is now charged positively, and the chlorine is now charged negatively, these opposite charges attract each other, forming an ionic bond. Ionic bonds are not as strong as covalent bonds.

We have seen thus far that in most cases, the charge of an atom is neutral. But, in certain circumstances, there are atoms that do have a charge.

As an example of an ionic bond, let us take what happens when salt—NaCl (or sodium chloride)—is dissolved in water—H_2O. The NaCl dissolves in the H_2O and the sodium (Na^+) and chloride (Cl^-) break apart—or **dissociate**—into individual Na and Cl atoms. Chemically, this is written:

$$NaCl \xrightarrow{H_2O} Na^+ + Cl^-$$

Figure 2.19.1

The Model for the Ion Formation and Ionic Bonding Process in Sodium Chloride

The top of the figure shows the two atoms as they naturally exist, with the sodium having 1 electron in its outer shell, and the chlorine having 7 electrons in its outer shell. The arrow indicates the "donation" of 1 electron from the sodium to the chlorine, which fulfills the octet rule for each atom. This also results in a positive charge for the sodium and a negative charge for the chlorine. These opposite charges attract each other, forming an ionic bond.

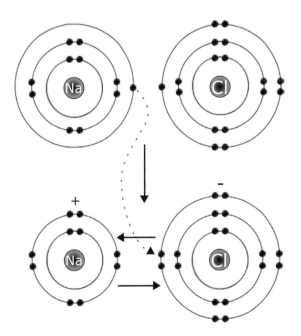

2.20 REACTANTS AND PRODUCTS

The atoms or molecules that are on the left side of the chemical equation (in the example above, the NaCl) are called the **reactants**. The molecules or elements that are on the right side of a chemical equation (in our examples, the H_2 and CCl_4) are called **end products**, or simply **products**.

2.21 LAW OF CONSERVATION OF MASS

Notice that in a chemical equation, the number of reactant atoms equals the number of end product atoms. In our example above, there is one Na atom on the left and one Na atom on the right. There is one Cl atom on the left and one on the right. Each side of the equation is balanced. This "balance" of molecules that takes place in chemical reactions is necessary and is called the **Law of Conservation of Mass**. When we look at different elements that can take part in a reaction, we can predict how many molecules of each will be needed to complete the reaction by remembering the Law of Conservation of Mass. As it pertains to chemistry, this law states that the number of reactant atoms must equal the number of end-product atoms. That means that the number of individual atoms on the left side of an equation must equal the number of the same individual atom on the right side of the equation. The reactant atoms must equal the product atoms.

Another way of stating this law is that atoms (matter) can neither be created nor destroyed in a chemical reaction. This makes sense if you think about it. Based on our scientific observations of the past 500 years, where will the atoms go, or where will they come from, if this law is not true? All of the matter present on earth is here to stay—rarely does any matter leave the earth or enter the earth. The earth is considered a **closed system**. A closed system is one in which matter can neither enter nor leave.

Let's use a more complicated example to demonstrate this law and be certain we understand it. We will look at the chemical reaction between iron and oxygen to create iron oxide (rust). The reactants are iron—Fe—and oxygen—O_2. The end product is iron oxide—Fe_2O_3. If we write that chemically, it looks like this:

$$Fe + O_2 \rightarrow Fe_2O_3$$

However, the Law of Conservation of Mass is not satisfied because on the left side of the equation there is 1 atom of iron, and on the right there are 2. Also, the oxygen reactant has 2 atoms while the oxygen product has 3.

In order to satisfy the Law, the number of oxygen atoms on the reactant side must equal the number of oxygen atoms on the product side. And the number of iron atoms on the reactant side must equal the number of iron atoms on the reactant side. So we balance the equation like this:

$$4Fe + 3O_2 \rightarrow 2Fe_2O_3$$

Now, the conservation law is satisfied since there are 4 atoms of iron on both the reactant and product sides, and 6 atoms of oxygen on both the reactant and product sides. The Law of Conservation of Mass needs to be followed in all chemical reactions. A common way that biologists state that is that the reaction must be balanced.

2.22 WATER

Water is an important molecule for organisms to be able to maintain life. Seventy to eighty percent of the matter of any given organism is water. The reason that it is so useful is due to its chemical structure which gives it many unique properties.

Water forms via covalent polar bonds. This occurs because in the chemical structure of H_2O, the oxygen nucleus contains 8 protons, and the hydrogen nucleus only contains 1 proton. Therefore, there is a relatively stronger positive charge for the nucleus of the oxygen when compared to the hydrogen. This stronger positive charge results in the electrons of the covalent bond "shading" more toward the oxygen atom than the hydrogen atom. Although this does result in a slightly unequal charge distribution in the water molecule, this is *not* an ionic bond. The polar nature of the hydrogen and oxygen bond in water makes it effective at dissolving a wide range of substances, including salts, sugars, and proteins. This means that water is an excellent solvent.

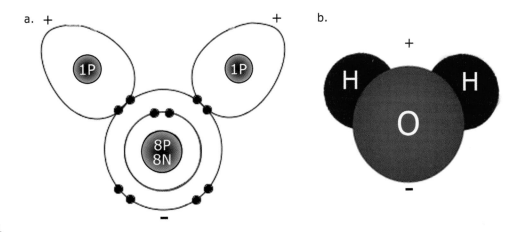

Figure 2.22.1

The Polar Nature of the Water Molecule
Figure (a) indicates the unequal sharing of the electrons in the water molecule. Again note the slight positive charge of the water molecule on the hydrogen end, and the slight negative charge of the water molecule on the oxygen end. The orbits of the electrons for hydrogen are egg shaped because the more positive charge of the oxygen atom slightly distorts the usual orbital pathway. The 8 protons of the oxygen atom exert a greater pull of the electrons than the single proton of either hydrogen atom. As a result, the electrons orbit closer to the oxygen than the hydrogen. This results in the slightly unequal, overall charge of water with one end being more negative than the other. Figure (b) is a different model to represent molecules. This is called the **space filling model**. This is a somewhat easier way to visualize the polar nature of the water molecule.

In addition, the polarity of water allows another type of bond to form within the water called a **hydrogen bond**. Because the electrons shade toward the oxygen molecule, this causes the oxygen to be charged slightly negative. This slight negativity then attracts other slightly positive hydrogen atoms from other water molecules, forming a weak bond.

Figure 2.22.2

Model for Hydrogen Bonding Which Occurs Between Water Molecules
The space-filling model is used to visualize the process of hydrogen bonding in the water molecule. The hydrogen-bonding process occurs due to the slightly negative parts of the water molecule being attracted to the slightly positive parts of other water molecules (indicated by the dotted lines). Although this is a weak interaction, it is important in nature, and is the property of water that allows certain animals or bugs to walk on top of water. Also, if a small pin is carefully placed on top of water, it will not sink. This is called surface tension. Surface tension occurs because the polar nature of the water molecule causes hydrogen bonding.

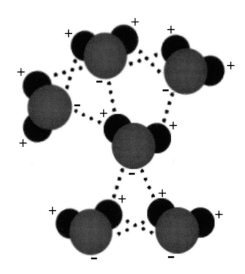

Another property of water that allows for hydrogen bonding is the actual structure of the molecule itself. Notice the space filling model of water is not "straight," but looks more like a Mickey Mouse hat. This allows other water molecules to fit in the open spaces and pack tightly together, resulting in stronger hydrogen bonds.

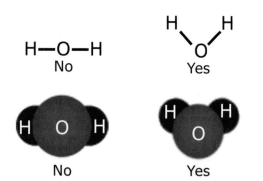

Figure 2.22.3

Non-linear Nature of the Water Molecule
Water is not a linear, or straight, molecule. Rather, it looks like a Mickey Mouse hat.

The final property of water which makes it specially suited for use by organisms is that the temperature of water rises and falls very slowly. This allows organisms to be able to regulate their temperatures effectively (i.e. maintain homeostasis).

2.23 SOLUTIONS, SOLVENTS, AND SOLUTES

A **solution** is a homogeneous ("same throughout") combination of atoms in a liquid, solid, or gas. For example, the water in the ocean is a homogeneous solution of NaCl and H_2O molecules. The **solvent** is that part of the solution that is in greater quantities, and the **solute** is that part of the solution that is in lesser quantities. Typically, the amount of a solution and the amount of a solute are compared to one another based on the number of molecules of each present in the solution. For example, in the case of ocean water, the solvent is H_2O and the solute is NaCl. Why? Because there are many, many more molecules of H_2O in ocean water than there are Na^+ or Cl^- ions.

Here is what is really important about solutions: metabolic reactions of all organisms occur within solution environments. In almost every biological organism which exists, the solvent of the solution is water. This is important to understand.

It is true that all solutions are homogeneous, but not all solutions are of equal concentration. A solution of 1 tablespoon of salt dissolved in a cup of water would be of much weaker concentration than 5 tablespoons of salt dissolved in one cup of water.

2.24 ACIDS AND BASES

A hydrogen atom will rarely break away from the remaining hydroxide molecule in pure water. However, there are always a few **hydrogen ions**, H^+, and a few **hydroxide** ions, OH^- floating around even in pure water H_2O. The pH of a solution depends upon the amount of hydrogen ions and hydroxide ions present in the solution. Since pure water has few of these free ions floating around in it (and when there are ions floating around there is an equal number of H^+ and OH^-), the pH of pure water is 7. A solution whose pH is 7 is said to be neutral. Therefore, in pure water, there are few hydrogen or hydroxide ions. The measurement of whether or not a solution is an acid or a base depends on the concentration of H^+ ions that are contained in the solution relative to the concentration of OH^- ions. An **acid** contains more H^+ ions than OH^- ions. The more H^+ ions there are, the stronger an acid it will be. A **base** is a solution with more OH^- ions than H^+ ions. The more OH^- ions there are the stronger a base it will be.

2.25 pH Scale

In order to measure the acidity of a solution, a scale has been formulated called the **pH scale**. It is organized as follows:

- A solution with a higher concentration of H^+ ions and lower concentrations of OH^- ions has a pH lower than 7 and is said to be **acidic**.

- A solutions with an equal concentration of OH^- and H^+ ions has a pH of 7 and is said to be neutral.

- A solution with lower concentrations of H^+ ions and higher concentrations of OH^- ions has a pH higher than 7 and is said to be **basic**. (You should be aware that sometimes basic solutions are also called **alkaline solutions**.)

Figure 2.25.1

The pH Scale

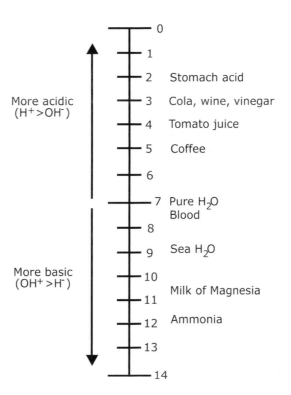

2.26 INDICATORS

There are various liquids that can be added to a solution to determine if the solution is an acid or a base. These liquids are called **indicators**. Indicators are usually chemicals which change colors depending on the pH of a solution. When an indicator is added to a solution, it changes color to indicate whether that solution is an acid or a base. A common indicator is bromthymol blue. When bromthymol blue is in a solution with a neutral pH, it is green. When it is in an acidic solution, it is yellow. When it is in an alkaline solution it is blue. There are also electrical meters which can be used to measure pH. We will learn more about this in the lab for this week.

2.27 PEOPLE OF SCIENCE

John Dalton (1766–1844) was a great scientific mind from England. He was the first to propose that elements were made up of tiny particles that today we call atoms. He also deduced that only one type of atom was contained in each element. He produced a multitude of other original scientific research, including the scientific basis of color blindness. He was such an ardent follower of the scientific method, in fact, that he was a lecturer for six years in chemistry at an English university despite the fact that he had no formal training in chemistry.

Neils Bohr (1885-1962) was born in Denmark. He was a great physicist and won the 1922 Nobel Prize for his work on the structure of the atom. He was Professor of Physics at the University of Copenhagen for most of his career, although he did leave the country for a time when the Nazis invaded during World War II. He was an advisor at Los Alamos during the development of the atomic bomb. Following his return to Denmark after the war ended, he was an advocate for the peaceful use of atomic energy and continued to advance theories in quantum physics.

2.28 KEY CHAPTER POINTS

- All life forms require energy to live.

- Everything that exists—living and non-living—is composed of matter. This matter can undergo physical and chemical changes.

- Atoms are the smallest units of matter. They are composed of protons, neutrons, and electrons.

- Protons and neutrons make up the nucleus of the atom. Electrons orbit the nucleus in shells (also called clouds and orbitals).

- Atoms can link to one another by covalent or ionic bonds to form larger molecules. This occurs through chemical reactions which follow the Law of Conservation of Mass.

- Water is special because it is a polar molecule which is non-linear and hydrogen bonds with other water molecules. This gives water unique properties which make it critical in the maintenance of life.

- The pH scale measures acidity of solutions.

2.29 DEFINITIONS

acid
A solution that has a higher concentration of hydrogen ions than hydroxide ions.

atom
The smallest, indivisible building block of matter. Each atom is made up of a nucleus and an electron shell.

atomic mass
The "weight" of an element determined by the addition of the protons and the neutrons. The result is expressed in "atomic mass units."

atomic number
A number assigned to every element that corresponds to the number of protons in the nucleus of the most common form of the element.

atomic symbol
A one or two letter abbreviation to identify an element.

base
A solution that has a higher concentration of hydroxide ions than hydrogen ions.

Bohr Model
A commonly used model to describe how atoms look and interact with one another.

chemical bond
Electrons combining together from different atoms resulting in the formation of a molecule.

covalent bond
Equal sharing of electrons between atoms involved in a chemical bond.

dissociate
The "falling apart" (or dissolving) of ions in a solution.

electron
Negatively charged subatomic particles that orbit the nucleus of an atom.

electron shell (energy level)
The area outside of the nucleus where electrons are found orbiting the nucleus.

element
A group of the same atoms bonded together. An element is matter composed only of the same type of atom.

hydrogen bond
Bonds that form between hydrogen and a polar molecule in a solution containing polar chemical bonds.

ion
An atom that has a positive or negative charge.

ionic bond
A chemical bond that forms due to the attraction of a positive ion to a negative ion.

isotope
Different forms of the same element that differ only in the number of neutrons.

Law of Conservation of Mass
The law that no mass can be lost or destroyed in a chemical reaction; the number of molecules on the reactant side must equal the number of molecules on the product side.

mass
The quantity of matter an object has.

matter
Anything that takes up space and has mass. Matter can exist in solid, liquid, or gas forms.

molecule
A group of two or more atoms bonded together.

neutron
A neutrally charged subatomic particle located in the nucleus of an atom.

non-polar bond
A covalent bond resulting in the electrons being equally shared by the atoms of the bond.

nucleus
The center part of the atom that contains protons and neutrons.

octet rule
The property of chemical bonding that results in eight electrons filling the outer shell.

pH
The measurement of the acidity or basicity of a solution.

polar bond
A covalent bond resulting in electrons being slightly more attracted to one atom of the bond than the other.

product
>The resulting molecule(s) from a chemical reaction.

proton
>A positively charged subatomic particle that is located in the nucleus of an atom. It has a mass of 1 atomic unit.

reactants
>Elements or atoms that take place in a chemical reaction or bond.

solute
>The molecules of a solution that are in lower quantities.

solution
>A homogeneous combination of atoms in a liquid, solid, or gas.

solvent
>The molecules of a solution that are in greater quantities.

subatomic particles
>Particles that are smaller than an atom. Although there are more than three, the ones we learned about are the proton, neutron, and electron.

STUDY QUESTIONS

1. Which of these is the universal fuel source? Sugars, proteins, or fats?

2. Plants make _____ by capturing and using the sun's energy.

3. What is the process in question #2 called?

4. What is the process called that consumers use to obtain their energy from the foods they ingest?

5. Define matter. How is it different from mass?

6. What are the three subatomic particles?

7. Define an element. List the four most common elements that make up more than 90% of all life mass.

8. Draw and label a Helium atom as it would appear in a Bohr model of the atom.

9. In what part of the atom is the majority of its mass located?

10. True or False? The actual neutron of a technetium atom is physically different than a neutron of a helium atom.

11. Use the periodic table of the elements to give the atomic symbol and the number of protons, neutrons and electrons for the following elements: hydrogen, neon, nickel, bismuth, potassium, gadolinium, and magnesium.

12. The number of protons in a neutral atom always equals the number of _____?

13. True or False? Electrons are much larger than protons.

14. How many electron shells are there in hydrogen? Carbon? Sodium? Silicon? Chlorine? Oxygen?

15. Electrons orbit the nucleus in _____?

16. What is an isotope?

17. When atoms bond together, how many electrons do they prefer to have in their outermost energy shell? What is this called?

18. What is a covalent bond? An ionic bond?

19. Write a chemical reaction for the bonding of carbon (C) with oxygen (O_2) to form CO_2. Please be sure to follow the Law of the Conservation of Mass.

20. In question #19, which substances are the reactants and which are the product(s)?

21. What is an atom called that has a charge (i.e. is not neutral)?

22. True or False? An ionic bond can form between an atom with a positive charge and an atom with a negative charge.

23. If we mixed sodium chloride in water, what would happen to the NaCl? Write the chemical equation for this reaction.

24. List the three important properties of water that we discussed in this chapter.

25. In a solution, what is the part of the solution that is greater in concentration called? What is the part of the solution that is lesser in concentration called?

26. What is the main property of a solution that has a low pH?

Basic Biochemistry of the Molecules of Life

3

3.0 CHAPTER PREVIEW

In this chapter we will:

- Define what organic molecules are and why they are important to life.

- Understand the difference between organic and inorganic molecules.

- Learn about isomers and why they require the use of structural formulae.

- Investigate how the four classes of organic molecules—carbohydrates, proteins, lipids, and nucleic acids—are made and broken down by chemical reactions in the cell.

3.1 OVERVIEW

Depending on the organism, between 70% and 90% of cells are composed of water. The rest of the cell is made up of **organic molecules**. The term **organic** refers to complex molecules that are **synthesized**—or made—by all life forms. They are essential to life. Although the term "organic" was initially used to indicate that these molecules were only able to be made by living organisms, there are some organic molecules that can be synthesized in a laboratory.

3.2 ORGANIC MOLECULES

Because of the structural importance of carbon in organic molecules, the term **"carbon compound"** is also used. For the purposes of this course, **all organic molecules contain carbon and hydrogen.** Some chemists feel that all molecules that contain carbon are organic molecules. There is debate about whether molecules like carbon dioxide (CO_2) and the cyanides like potassium cyanide (KCN) are truly organic molecules or not, even though they do contain carbon. Therefore, we will use the criteria that organic molecules contain carbon and hydrogen. Also, as you will see, many of the organic molecules contain oxygen. We will learn about the molecules of life, or organic molecules, in this chapter. There are four classes of organic molecules: **carbohydrates, proteins, lipids**, and **nucleic acids**. Together, these molecules make up the building blocks of all cells and organisms.

The study of **organic chemistry** deals with the role that carbon, hydrogen, and oxygen molecules play in maintaining the life and energy cycle. Building an organic molecule begins with photosynthesis. Remember that during photosynthesis sugars are made using the energy of the sun. Since sugars are carbohydrates, producers are the entry point for making organic molecules. During photosynthesis, producers link carbon atoms together to oxygen and hydrogen atoms to build carbohydrates. The carbon comes from carbon dioxide in the air. The hydrogen and oxygen molecules come from water. The sugars are then converted by producers and consumers during cellular respiration into energy molecules called **adenosine triphosphate** (ATP). The energy from the molecules of ATP are then used by the organism to drive all of the chemical reactions which the organism uses to make proteins, lipids, carbohydrates, and nucleic acids.

3.3 ORGANIC VS. INORGANIC MOLECULES

To contrast organic and inorganic molecules, organic molecules tend to be large, with a large number of atoms, while inorganic molecules tend to be very small. Organic molecules always bond covalently, while inorganic molecules usually bond ionically. Also, organic molecules contain carbon, while inorganic molecules do not. Most chemists state that all molecules containing bonds between carbon and hydrogen are organic molecules. Molecules which do not contain bonds between carbon and hydrogen are not organic molecules. We depend on inorganic molecules daily. Inorganic molecules make up silicone chips (i.e. computer chips), LCD screens, and fiber optic cables.

3.4 MOLECULAR FORMULAE AND ISOMERS

Because organic molecules are so large and complex, the **molecular** (or **chemical**) **formulas** are not specific enough to describe which molecule we are talking about. A molecular formula is simply an accounting of the number and type of atoms in a molecule. The molecular formula does not tell us anything about how the atoms are linked to one another. For example, both butane and isobutane are molecules that have the simple formula of C_4H_{10}. But as you can see from figure 3.4.1, the form that butane takes is different than the form that isobutane takes. Therefore, simply writing the molecular formula of C_4H_{10} does not allow one to know whether the molecule which is being described by C_4H_{10} is butane or isobutane. Molecules which share the same molecular formula but are different structurally are called **isomers**.

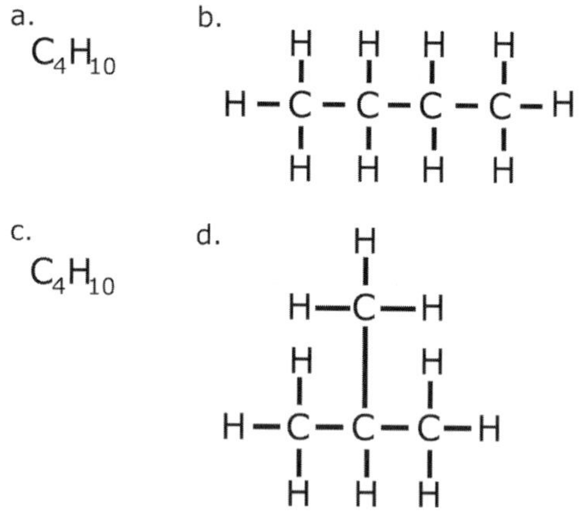

a.

C_4H_{10}

b.

c.

C_4H_{10}

d.

Figure 3.4.1

Isomers Butane and Isobutane

The isomers of butane and isobutane are shown here. Butane is shown in (a) and (b) while isobutane is shown in (c) and (d). They both have the same molecular (chemical) formula, as shown in a and c. However, they have a different structural formula, as shown in b and d. As a result, they have different properties. For example, butane boils at -1° Celsius and isobutane at -12° Celsius.

Since **isomerization** occurs frequently in organic chemistry, we must have a better way to represent molecules which are isomers. Isomerization is the formation of multiple molecules with the same molecular formula but which have different structural appearances from one another. Isomerization is the reason that we use a **structural formula** to describe organic molecules. A structural formula shows the bonding patterns between atoms of a molecule to remove any confusion isomerization may cause. A structural formula is a simple way to show the structure of a molecule.

It should be noted that the structural formula of a molecule can be used for other molecules, too. It is not for organic molecules only (as we showed in the last chapter with the water molecule). Structural formulae give much more information about the molecule than the molecular formula can. While the Bohr diagram would give more information about the molecule and the interactions of the electrons, it is too burdensome to write out for every molecule, especially since the majority of organic molecules contain well over several hundred atoms per molecule. Therefore, the structural formula is used.

3.5 MOLECULES ARE 3-D

An important thing to keep in mind when we write the structural formula for a molecule is that we are writing a two-dimensional representation for a three-dimensional structure. This is the same as realizing that when you draw a flat (two-dimensional) circle on a piece of paper to represent a soccer ball (three-dimensional), you are really representing a structure not only with height and width (two dimensions), but also with depth (the third dimension). It is the same with structural formulae. If we could draw the structural formula for isobutane in three dimensions, some of the atoms would be extending out of the paper toward you, and some would be going away from you. Of course, some of the atoms would remain in the same plane as the paper. This is the nature of a three dimensional structure being written on a piece of paper. The three dimensional structure of organic molecules is important because they are large molecules, and their function is often determined by their three dimensional structures.

3.6 PHYSICAL PROPERTIES OF ISOMERS ARE DIFFERENT

Isomers are important because the properties of a molecule are based not only on the individual atoms that make up the molecule, but also the three-dimensional structure the molecule takes. For example, let's take the isomers butane and isobutane. As seen on the right, they both have the same molecular formula. The boiling point of butane is -1° Celsius, while that of isobutane is -12° Celsius. Since they both have the same number of the same type of atoms in each molecule, it is the three-dimensional structure of the isomers which makes them different. Isomers have different physical and chemical properties because they have different structures. The structural formula gives a much better idea of the bonding relationships than the molecular formula, and so is preferred in organic chemistry.

3.7 BONDING PATTERNS

When writing the structural formula, we use lines drawn between atoms involved in a bond to indicate which atoms are bonded together. Each single line represents a single covalent bond between atoms. This is another way to indicate that the two atoms are sharing one electron pair. When two lines are drawn between two atoms, it is called a **double covalent bond**. A double bond indicates that the two atoms involved in the bond are sharing two pairs of electrons. When three lines are drawn between two atoms in a bond, it is called a **triple covalent bond**. A triple bond indicates that the atoms of a bond are sharing three pairs of electrons.

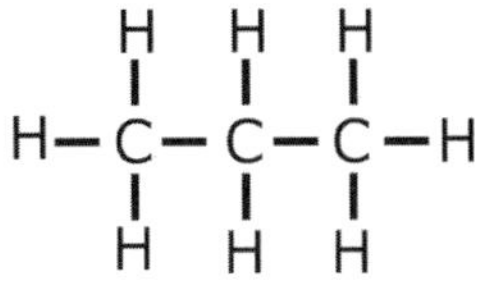

Figure 3.7.1

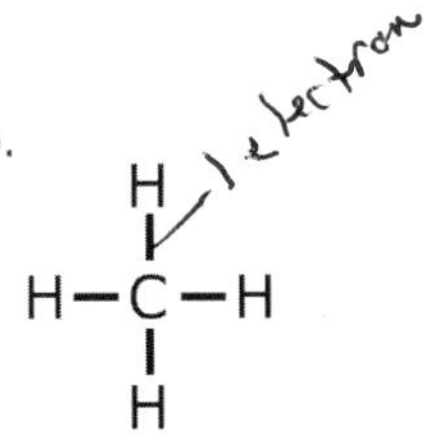

Molecular and Structural Formulae for Single-Bonded Carbon Molecules
Figures (a) and (b) represent the molecular and structural formulae, respectively, for methane. Figures (c) and (d) represent propane.

a. CH_4

b.

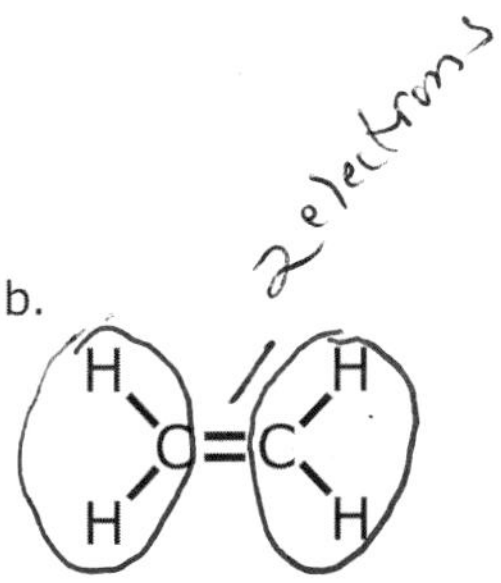

c. C_3H_8

d.

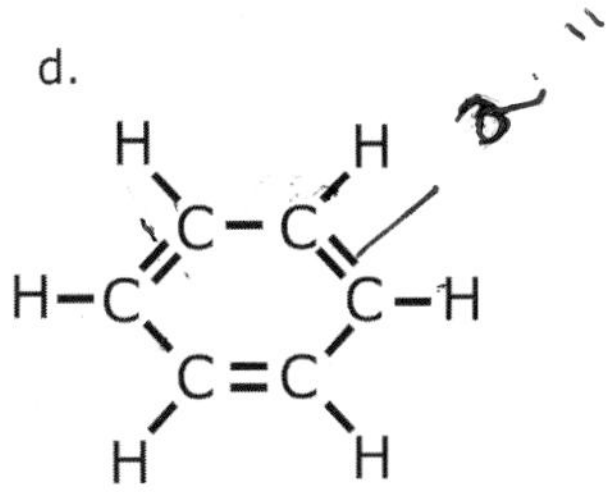

Figure 3.7.2

Molecular and structural formulae for double bonded carbon molecules
Figures (a) and (b) represent the molecular and structural formulae, respectively, for ethene and figures (c) and (d) for the cyclic (ring) molecule of benzene.

a. C_2H_4

b.

c. C_6H_6

d.

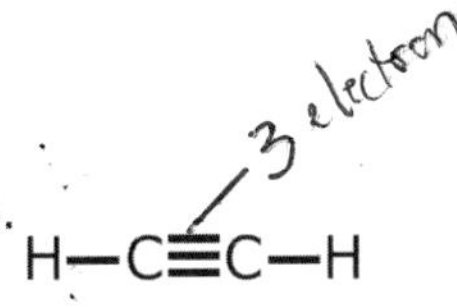

Figure 3.7.3

Molecular and Structural Formulae for Triple-Bonded Molecules
Figures (a) and (b) represent the molecular and structural formulae, respectively, for acetylene. Triple bonds are "stronger" than double bonds, and double bonds are "stronger" than single bonds. That means it is harder to break double bonds than single bonds, and harder yet to break triple bonds than double bonds. This relationship is seen practically when the bonds of propane (single bonds), ethene (double bonds) and acetylene (triple bonds) are broken by igniting the three gasses. Because the bonds of acetylene are harder to break, when they are broken by burning the gas, the flame is much hotter than ethene, and ethene burns hotter than propane.

a. C_2H_2

b.

3.8 CARBON IS THE SPECIAL ATOM

Carbon is uniquely suited for function as the basic atom of life due to its electron orbital structure. Carbon has 6 protons, 6 neutrons, and 6 electrons. There are two electrons in the first orbital and four electrons in the second orbital. That means that carbon can bond to four other atoms to obtain the electrons that it needs to fill its outer shell (remember the octet rule). Since carbon can bond to four other atoms, that allows it to participate in a variety of bonding patterns.

Because of its ability to form four bonds, carbon is highly versatile. It is this versatility that allows isomers to form. For example, because of the properties of carbon, it allows carbon to bond in a straight line, branched, or even in a ring structure. All three of these forms are seen in organic molecules. The large variety of bonding patterns or shapes carbon can accommodate make it specially suited to be the backbone atom of all organic molecules.

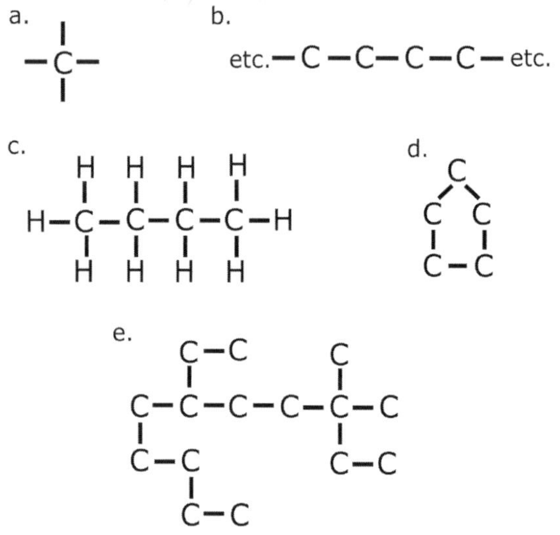

Figure 3.8.1

Summary of the Unique Properties of Carbon
Carbon has the ability to form four covalent bonds with other atoms (a). Carbon can also repeatedly bond to itself (b), forming not only linear molecules (c), but also ring structures (d). Finally, carbon easily forms infinitely branching molecules, allowing it to form the backbone of huge organic macromolecules (e).

3.9 ORGANIC REACTIONS

Organic reactions are the reactions that organisms use to build—**or synthesize**—organic molecules. Any time a protein is built inside of a cell from smaller units, organic reactions are used. Organic reactions which synthesize organic molecules are called **anabolic reactions**.

In addition, there are times when organic reactions are also used to break large molecules down into smaller pieces. Any time our bodies need some energy, and we have not eaten for several hours, our bodies begins to break down a large carbohydrate molecule called glycogen into smaller sugar molecules for our cells to use for energy. Organic reactions which are used to break organic molecules down into smaller pieces are called **catabolic reactions**.

3.10 POLYMERS ARE BUILT FROM MONOMERS

All organic molecules start as tiny molecules, called **monomers**. A monomer is the basic building unit of organic molecules. Each class of organic molecule—protein, carbohydrate, fat, and nucleic acid—has its own special type of monomer. The organism performs special anabolic reactions which link one monomer to another. As the organism links more and more monomers to the molecule, it is called a **polymer**. Of note, monomers can be obtained by breaking down the larger polymer molecules. The organism does this through catabolic reactions.

The **starch** that makes up the potato is an example of a polymer. Starch is a carbohydrate. It is made by repeatedly linking together smaller sugar monomer units. Cooking oil is a polymer of fat molecules. Muscle is a polymer of smaller protein units. Many organic polymer molecules are built much larger than other molecules. Eventually, if the polymer becomes large enough, it is called a **macromolecule**. The nucleic acids **deoxyribonucleic acid** (DNA) and **ribonucleic acid** (RNA) are examples of macromolecules. All proteins, carbohydrates, fats, and nucleic acids are synthesized by anabolic reactions from smaller monomer units. We are going to learn more about this in the next few pages.

Figure 3.10.1

The Biochemical Process of Building a Macromolecule
Macromolecules are very, very large. There are thousands—even millions—of atoms in every macromolecule. They are made by special protein molecules in every cell called enzymes. In fact, most enzymes are macromolecules. Enzymes function to repeatedly link monomers to a growing polymer molecule. As more and more monomers are added to the polymer, it becomes extremely large and is termed a macromolecule. The chemical reactions which the enzyme performs to build polymers and macromolecules are called condensation synthesis or dehydration synthesis reactions, because one of the products of the reaction is water. These reactions require energy, which the cell obtains from ATP. Remember that ATP is made through the process of cellular respiration. We will learn more about cellular respiration in an upcoming chapter.

Monomer unit → Repeated linking of monomer units to growing molecule → Polymer → Further monomer linking → Macromolecule

Figure 3.10.2

Monomer Subunits of Polymers
Polysaccharides (carbohydrates) are made by linking together monosaccharide subunits. Lipids are made by linking fatty acid molecules to a glycerol backbone. Repeatedly linking together amino acids results in the production of a protein. Repeated bonding of nucleotides to one another makes a nucleic acid.

Monomer	Polymer
monosaccharide	polysaccharide
fatty acid and glycerol	lipid (fat)
amino acid	proteins
nucleotide	nucleic acid

3.11 DEHYDRATION SYNTHESIS REACTIONS

Dehydration synthesis reactions are anabolic reactions which make polymers from monomer units. When the cell performs a dehydration synthesis reaction, two monomers are linked together, and water is a product of the reaction. Sometimes dehydration synthesis reactions are also called condensation reactions. Since water is "removed" during the reaction, the name dehydration synthesis reaction is given. In this type of reaction, a hydrogen (H^+) from one monomer is removed and a hydroxide group (OH^-) from the other monomer is removed to form water (H_2O) as a product. The ends of the molecules that had the hydrogen and hydroxide ions removed are then linked together to form a new and larger molecule. This process is repeated tens, hundreds, or even thousands of times on the same molecule, depending on the molecule that the organism needs to synthesize. Each time a dehydration synthesis reaction is performed, a monomer is added to the growing polymer.

Figure 3.11.1

Generalized Condensation (dehydration) Synthesis Reaction
The generalized chemical reaction sequence of a condensation synthesis reaction is shown here. "Monomer" represents monosaccharides in the case of carbohydrates, amino acids in the case of proteins, and fatty acids in the case of lipids. Through the actions of enzymes, an OH^- group from one monomer and an H^+ atom from the other monomer are removed. The site where these molecules are removed from each monomer is where the monomers are linked together. Water is released in the process (a). This reaction is repeated over and over, resulting in the growth of an organic polymer (b). This is the general biochemical reaction used by all cells to manufacture proteins, carbohydrates, nucleic acids, and lipids.

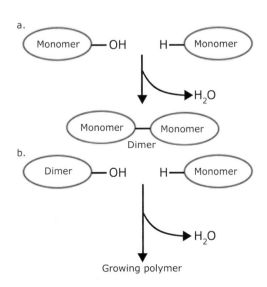

a.
Monomer—OH   H—Monomer
→ H₂O
Monomer—Monomer
Dimer

b.
Dimer—OH   H—Monomer
→ H₂O
Growing polymer

3.12 HYDROLYSIS REACTIONS

Hydrolysis reactions are catabolic reactions which remove monomers from a polymer one at a time. Sometimes the word **hydration reaction** is used instead of hydrolysis reaction. They both mean the same thing. A hydrolysis reaction is performed by adding water to the polymer at a key location. The cell utilizes water and breaks it into the H^+ and OH^- ions. The bond on the polymer is then broken, and the gaps are filled in by the H^+ or OH^- ion as indicated. This process can also occur multiple times in order to break the molecule down as much as the organism needs it to be broken down. Each time a hydrolysis reaction occurs, one monomer is removed from the polymer.

Be aware that these reactions do not occur haphazardly in the cell. Dehydration synthesis and hydration reactions are highly regulated. They require specialized proteins called enzymes to perform the reactions. (We will have much more on this later.)

Figure 3.12.1

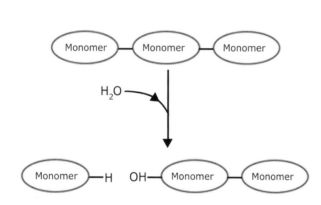

Generalized Hydrolysis Reaction, Breaking the Bonds of the Monomer Units of a Polymer
Also controlled by enzymes, in this type of reaction, a water molecule is added to the bond between two monomers of an organic polymer. This breaks the bond and releases one of the monomer units from the polymer. This process is repeated over and over, removing one monomer from the polymer at a time. This is the reverse of the dehydration synthesis reaction. An H^+ is attached to one end of the monomer, and an OH^- to the other end. Hydrolysis reactions are the chemical reactions which occur in our guts that allow us to digest our food. The large carbohydrate, protein and lipid molecules are broken down in this fashion by enzymes in the gut, and then the individual monomer units are absorbed in the intestine.

3.13 CARBOHYDRATES: THE "SACCHARIDES"

As stated in chapter 2, sugars are the universal fuel for all life forms. While it is true that lipids and proteins can be used for fuel if absolutely needed, the first and best source of energy comes from carbohydrates. A general term used to denote a carbohydrate of any size is **saccharide**.

Carbohydrates are organic compounds that are synthesized by the cell. You can recognize a carbohydrate because their names usually end in –ose. Carbohydrates are made up of only carbon, oxygen, and hydrogen. They generally have two hydrogen atoms for each oxygen atom. (Sometimes the general simple formula CH_2O is used to indicate a carbohydrate.) However, the number and orientation of the carbon atoms determine exactly which sugar each carbohydrate is.

3.14 MONOSACCHARIDES ARE THE MONOMERS FROM WHICH CARBOHYDRATE POLYMERS ARE BUILT

Carbohydrates are diverse, as are all of the organic molecules. The most basic form of a carbohydrate is a **monosaccharide.** A monosaccharide is a sugar that has between three and seven carbon atoms per molecule.

Glucose and fructose are common monosaccharides. **Glucose** is the sugar that animals use for their fuel source, while **fructose** is the plant sugar that makes many fruits sweet. Note that glucose and fructose both have the molecular formula of $C_6H_{12}O_6$, which means that these two molecules are isomers.

Monosaccharides are the monomer units from which carbohydrates are built. Carbohydrates are polymers of monosaccharides.

Figure 3.14.1

Common Monosaccharides

Two of the most common monosaccharides are shown to the right. The molecule depicted in (a) is glucose; the molecule depicted in (b) is fructose. Glucose is the carbohydrate that is metabolized during cellular respiration to produce the energy molecule ATP. Fructose is a common sugar that makes fruit sweet. Note that the molecular formula for both of these monosaccharides is $C_6H_{12}O_6$, but they have distinctly different structures. Since isomers are two or more moleucles with the same chemical formulae but different stuctural formulae, that means that fructose and glucose are isomers. In addition, the arrow indicates that these molecules exist in two different structural forms. Different structural forms of the same molecule are called conformations. One conformation for glucose and fructose is a ring molecule. The other conformation is a linear (or straight) molecule. The arrow between the two conformations indicate the molecule can exist as either/or. Most sugars take on the ring structure because it is more stable. However, if we were to take a blood sample from a person and look at the glucose molecules in the blood, we would see that most of the molecules were in the ring structure, but some would be linear. A final note on the way the ring structures are drawn: notice that at each "point" of the ring, there is no indication of what molecule is there, with the exception of oxygen. Carbon often goes unlabelled in organic chemistry's structural formulae because it is such an important molecule. It is therefore assumed that, unless the molecule is specifically labeled otherwise, the "points" of the ring structures are carbon molecules. This is the case for all molecules in organic chemistry, not just carbohydrates. Any time there are bonding lines that intersect, and the atom at the intersection is not identified, it is assumed the atom is carbon.

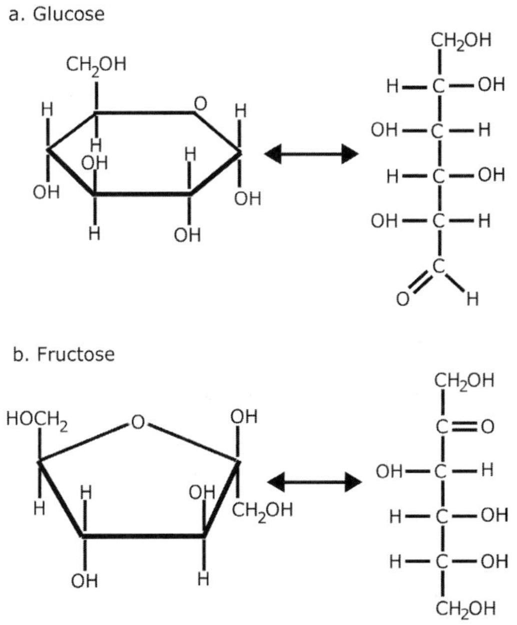

a. Glucose

b. Fructose

3.15 MONOSACCHARIDE ISOMERS AND CONFORMATION

There are two forms in which the monosaccharides can exist—**cyclic** (ring) and **straight chain**. This is possible because, depending on the conditions around the molecule, the nature of the monosaccharide molecules favors different isomers. Notice that the ring structures do not have any specific atom listed at the "corners" of the molecule. Organic chemistry has adopted this notation with ring structures, and it is assumed that the atom at the corners of the ring structures is carbon, unless otherwise noted.

It is not important to remember the actual molecular structures, but it is important to know that the monosaccharides can easily change their **conformation** (or structural appearance) depending on conditions. It is also important to know the isomers of the monosaccharides exist in the straight chain and cyclic form. Usually most monosaccharides exist in the cyclic form. You will learn much more about this in chemistry.

3.16 POLYSACCHARIDE SYNTHESIS AND GLYCOSIDIC BONDS

The reaction that is used by the organism to build bigger sugars from the smaller monomer units is the **dehydration synthesis reaction**. As noted above, this is the same general type of anabolic reaction that is used to build lipids, nucleic acids, and proteins. However, each of the four classes of organic molecules have their own unique reaction which synthesizes the polymer molecules.

Synthesizing carbohydrates involves removing a hydroxide group (OH^-) from one saccharide and one hydrogen atom (H^+) from the other saccharide. This results in the formation of one molecule of water (H_2O) and the new sugar. The new molecule is held together with an oxygen molecule in the middle, linked to a carbon atom on one saccharide unit and another carbon atom on the other saccharide unit. The oxygen atom is a "bridge" between the two saccharide units. This type of bond is called a **glycosidic bond**.

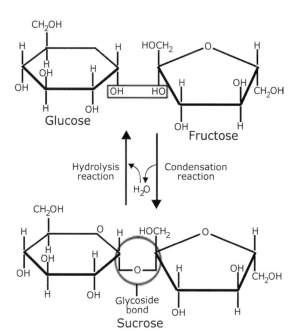

Figure 3.16.1

Glycoside Bond
The formation of a glycoside, or glycosidic, bond is shown for the anabolic condensation synthesis reaction of the monosaccharides glucose and fructose to form the disaccharide sucrose. Sucrose is table sugar. Note that water is a product of the condensation reaction and that the oxygen molecule bonds to a carbon on the glucose and a carbon on the fructose to form the glycoside bond. During the catabolic hydrolysis reaction, water is added to the glycoside bond and the two monomers separate.

Glycosidic bonds can also be "reversed." Reversing a glycosidic bond is called breaking a glycosidic bond. A glycosidic bond is broken by a hydrolysis reaction. When water is added to a glycosidic bond, the molecules held together by the glycosidic bond are broken apart.

3.17 DISACCHARIDES

Monosaccharides are the monomers used by organisms to build bigger sugars. The next biggest size, structurally speaking, in the carbohydrate class is the **disaccharides**. A disaccharide is formed when two monosaccharides are linked together. This occurs via the hydration synthesis reaction, when a hydrogen ion from one monosaccharide is removed and a hydroxide ion from the other monosaccharide is removed to form the new disaccharide plus one molecule of water. The two monosaccharide units of a disaccharide are held together by a glycosidic bond. If the organism needs to, the disaccharide bond can be broken by a hydrolysis reaction. Water is added to the glycosidic bond of the disaccharide. This separates both of the monosaccharides.

There are many disaccharide sugar molecules. A few of the common disaccharides are **sucrose, maltose, and lactose**. Sucrose is also known as table sugar. It is formed from a glucose and a fructose molecule getting linked together. Maltose is a common sugar that is used to make beer. It is formed by linking together two glucose molecules. Lactose is the sugar that is in dairy products such as milk and ice cream. It is formed by linking together a glucose and a galactose molecule. The reason that some people are "lactose intolerant" is because they lack the enzyme in their gut to digest lactose. When this is the case, they get a lot of gas, and sometimes diarrhea, whenever they eat dairy products.

Figure 3.17.1

Saccharide Synthesis and Hydrolysis Reactions
Maltose (a) is formed by linking together two molecules of glucose. Therefore, glucose is the monosaccharide from which the disaccharide maltose is made. This reaction occurs through the action of an enzyme which removes a H^+ from one of the glucose molecules and an OH^- from the other. After the hydrogen and hydroxide groups are removed, the enzyme links the two glucose molecules together with a glycosidic bond. Again, note that water is a product of this reaction. The reverse reaction, a hydrolysis reaction, is also shown. In this reaction, an enzyme adds water to the glycosidic bond, breaking it and forming the two monomers. The dehydration synthesis and hydrolysis reactions are also shown for lactose (b). Notice that in the synthesis reactions shown, glucose and galactose are both isomers of one another. They have the molecular formula of $C_6H_{12}O_6$. The product dimers (maltose and lactose) are also isomers as the molecular formula is $C_{12}H_{22}O_{11}$.

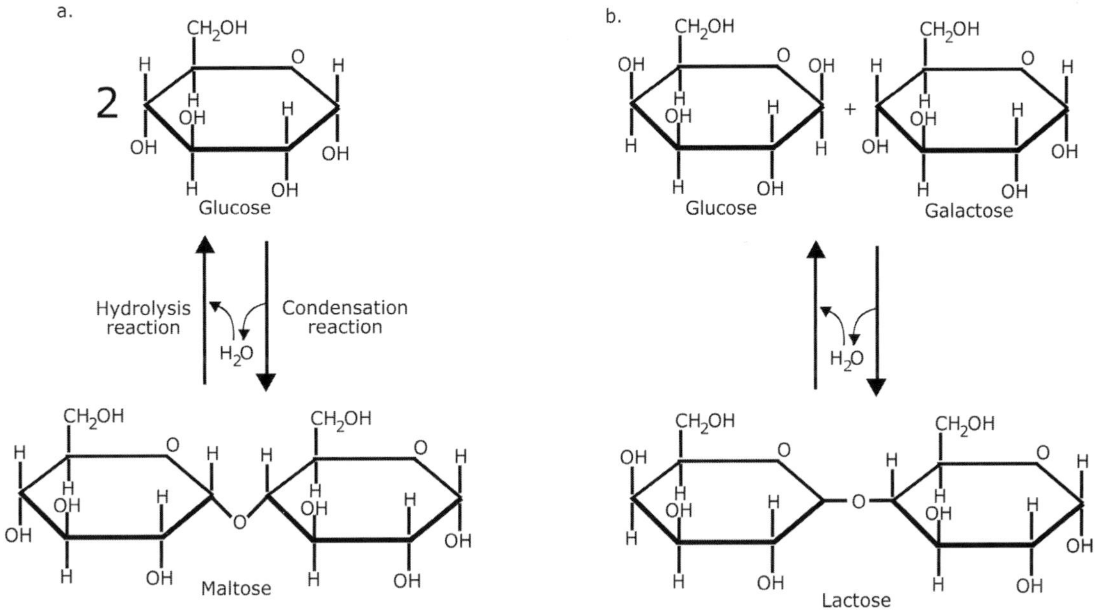

3.18 POLYSACCHARIDES

The next largest class of sugars are the **polysaccharides,** which result from linking together more than two monosaccharides. All polysaccharides are formed by the repeated linking of monosaccharides to the growing polysaccharide chain. Each time a new monosaccharide is added to the chain, it is held there by a glycosidic bond. One of the common polysaccharides is called **amylose.** Amylose (general molecular formula $C_6H_{10}O_5$) is commonly used in plants as a storage form of carbohydrate that the plant can break down and use later for fuel. The general molecular formula means that if there is known to be 60 units of glucose linked together to form the amylose molecule, the molecular formula of that specific molecule would be 60 times $C_6H_{10}O_5$, or $C_{360}H_{600}O_{300}$.

Figure 3.18.1

Synthesis of the Polysaccharide Amylose
Amylose starts as a dimer of glucose molecules linked by a glycosidic bond. Enzymes then continue to link glucose molecules to the growing polymer one by one via glycosidic bonds, until an amylose molecule is formed. Amylose can be up to 150 glucose monomers bonded together. If the organism needs glucose for energy, then it can perform the hydrolysis reaction to remove as many monomers of glucose as are needed.

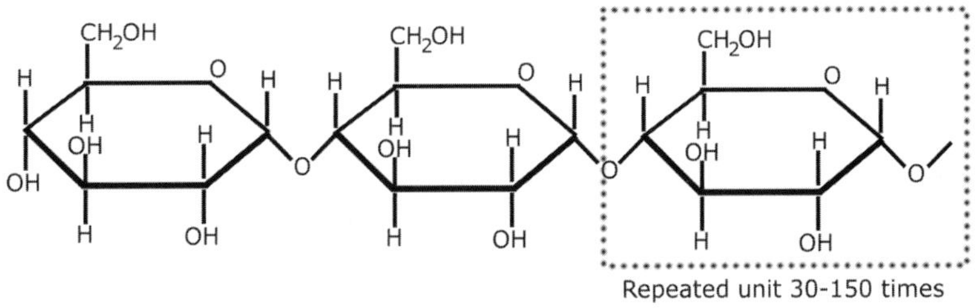

Repeated unit 30-150 times

3.19 CARBOHYDRATE MACROMOLECULES

As polysaccharides grow larger, they become polymers. **Glycogen, cellulose, and starch** are common in all life forms. They are both carbohydrate macromolecules. Glycogen is the main storage form of carbohydrates in animals. It is especially abundant in the liver and skeletal muscles. It is formed from links of hundreds of glucose molecules. If needed, glycogen is broken down by the animal and used for energy.

Starch accounts for about 50% of the carbohydrate calories that are eaten by humans. It is very abundant in plants. It is formed from hundreds of molecules of amylose and amylopectin linking together. Cellulose is a plant structural carbohydrate polymer and is the most abundant organic molecule on the planet.

3.20 LIPIDS (FATS)

Lipids are organic molecules that are also formed from multiple oxygen, carbon, and hydrogen atoms. However, there are many more carbon and hydrogen atoms than oxygen atoms in lipids as compared to the carbohydrates. Lipids are structurally more complex than carbohydrates. Because of this, no general, simple chemical formula can be written to represent them as one can be with carbohydrates.

The lipid class of molecules includes all fats, steroids, waxes, oils, and triglycerides. These molecules are generally used for insulation and as a fuel source. They can also be used for cooking (vegetable oils and lard). Unlike the carbohydrates and proteins, these molecules are not soluble in water.

3.21 FATTY ACIDS

A **fatty acid** is a long carbon chain with a **carboxylic acid group** on one end of the molecule. A carboxylic acid group, also called a carboxyl group, is one carbon atom, two oxygen atoms and one hydrogen atom linked together. It is chemically written as -COOH. See Figure 3.21.1.

Fatty acids occur in two forms—**saturated** and **unsaturated.** The saturation refers to how "saturated" the fatty acid is with hydrogen atoms (or how many there are). Look at Figure 3.21.2 of the fatty acids and pay attention to the carbon and hydrogen atoms. Notice that the saturated fatty acid has a lot of hydrogen atoms and no double bonds between the carbon atoms. The unsaturated fatty acids have fewer hydrogen atoms and many more double bonds between the carbon atoms.

This is important because we now know that fats that are in the form of saturated fatty acids—such as fats from animals—are much more likely to cause clogging of the arteries than unsaturated fats are. You can always tell when a fat is saturated because it is solid at room temperature; whereas an unsaturated fat is liquid at room temperature.

Figure 3.21.1

Typical Fatty Acid Structure
This is the fatty acid molecule, palmitic acid. It is a molecule that has the molecular formula of $C_{16}H_{34}O$. The circled part of the molecule is the carboxylic acid (carboxyl) group and the long carbon chain is referred to as the carbon backbone. The carboxyl end of the molecule is soluble in water—we call it hydrophylic, or water loving—while the long carbon backbone is not—making it hydrophobic, or water afraid. This property of fats and fatty acids will have important implications and will be further discussed when we cover the cell membrane.

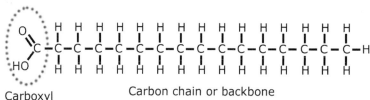

Carboxyl group

Carbon chain or backbone

Figure 3.21.2

Saturated and Unsaturated Fatty Acids
Fatty acids are classified as either saturated or unsaturated, depending on whether or not there are double bonds between the carbon atoms of the carbon backbone. If there are no double bonds between carbon atoms, that allows more hydrogen atoms to bond to the carbon. This means that the carbon backbone is saturated with hydrogen atoms and is called a saturated fatty acid. If there are double bonds between the carbon atoms, this allows for fewer hydrogen atoms to bond to carbon, meaning the fat is not as saturated with hydrogen. These fatty acids are called unsaturated fatty acids.

Saturated   Unsaturated

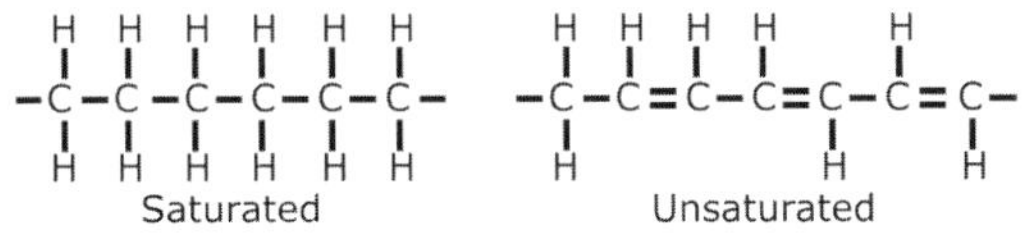

3.22 GLYCEROL BACKBONE AND ESTER BONDS

The backbone of the lipid molecule is called **glycerol**. Glycerol is a three-carbon molecule with one hydroxide group (OH⁻) on each carbon. An individual fat molecule is formed by linking between one and three fatty acid molecules to one glycerol molecule. This occurs via a dehydration synthesis reaction which removes one H^+ ion from one of the carbon atoms on the glycerol molecule, and then removes one OH^- ion from the carboxylic acid group of the fatty acid molecule to form the lipid and a water molecule. This type of bond is called an **ester bond**. Note that the ester bond is similar to the glycosidic bond. It is essentially an oxygen bridge between a carbon of the glycerol and a carbon on the fatty acid chain. Depending on the molecule the organism needs, a fatty acid can be linked to one, two, or all three carbon atoms of the glycerol.

Figure 3.22.1

Synthesis of a Fat Molecule
The making of a fat molecule begins with a glycerol molecule and a fatty acid molecule. Look at Figure 3.21.1 if needed to see the structure of a fatty acid. The "R" corresponds to the rest of the fatty molecule, as in Figure 3.21.2. The R group may be saturated or unsaturated. The condensation synthesis reaction removes the OH group from glycerol and an H from the carboxyl end of the fatty acid. The oxygen from the fatty acid links the carbon from the glycerol to the carbon of the fatty acid. The molecule shown on the right has had one fatty acid linked to the glycerol. This is called a monoglyceride. If another fatty acid is linked to the red carbon by an ester bond, there would be two fatty acids linked to the glycerol. This is called a diglyceride. If a third fatty acid is linked to the blue carbon, it is called a triglyceride.

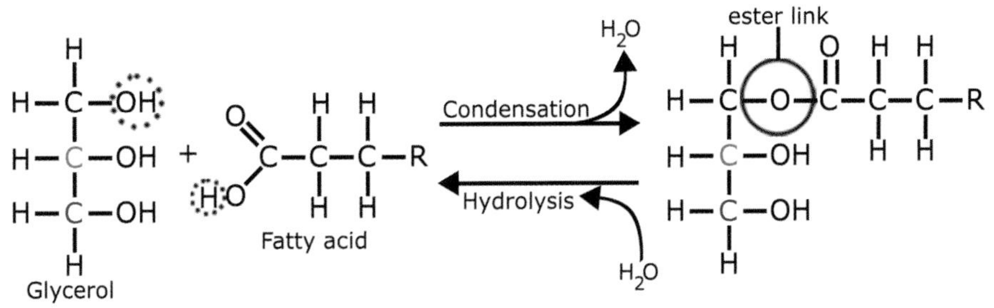

Figure 3.22.2

Triglyceride Structure
This molecule is a triglyceride. Three fatty acids have been linked to the three carbon glycerol molecule through three ester bonds. If there were only one fatty acid attached to the glycerol, the molecule would be a mono-glyceride. If there were two fatty acids attached, the molecule would be a diglyceride. The fat molecule is named depending on the number of fatty acids attached to the glycerol backbone and how long the fatty acid chains are. The fatty acid chains correspond to the "R" on the molecule shown to the right.

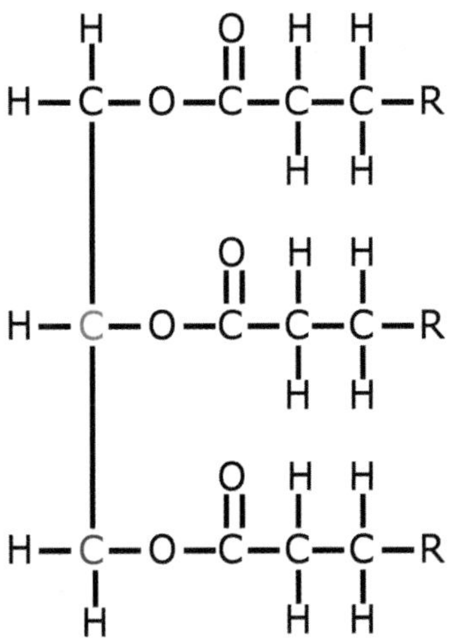

3.23 PROTEINS

Proteins are important structural molecules of all living things. Special types of proteins called **enzymes** are also responsible for running all biochemical reactions in a cell. Proteins are structurally diverse and complex molecules. They contain carbon, oxygen, and hydrogen, of course, but also other molecules such as sulfur and nitrogen. Because of the nature of the protein molecules, they are usually extremely large.

3.24 AMINO ACIDS ARE THE MONOMERIC UNITS OF PROTEINS

Like carbohydrates and lipids, proteins are built one molecule at a time. The monomeric unit of the protein is an **amino acid**. For a long time it was thought that there were 20 amino acids, but recent research has found a 21st amino acid. The basic structure of the amino acid is as depicted in Figure 3.24.1. There is a central carbon atom attached to a COOH⁻ group, a hydrogen atom, an amino group (NH_3^+), and what is called an "R" group (or "rest of the molecule"). Do not misunderstand the R group as unimportant; it is the R group that makes amino acids different from one another.

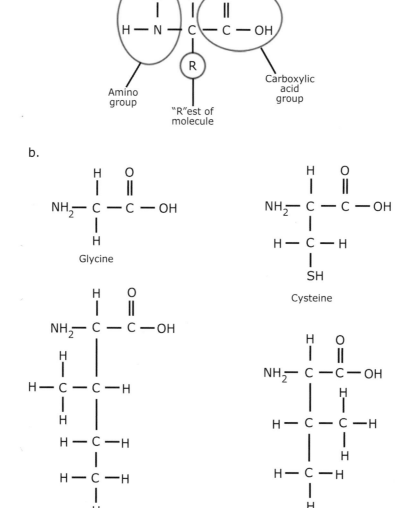

Figure 3.24.1

Amino Acid Structure

The generalized structure of an amino acid is detailed in (a). Since all amino acids contain this same basic structure, it is the "rest" group of the molecule that makes one amino acid different from another. Four different amino acids are shown in (b), with glycine being, molecularly speaking, the simplest. The "R" group is a hydrogen atom. Cysteine contains a sulfur atom bonded to a hydrogen atom as the "R" group. The "R" groups for isoleucine and valine are as indicated.

3.25 PEPTIDE BONDS

When a protein is made, one amino acid is linked to another by—take a guess—a dehydration synthesis. (Make note of the similarities in how the organic molecules are built!) This process involves removing the hydroxide (OH) group from the carboxylic acid of one amino acid and a hydrogen (H) from the nitrogen end of the other amino acid. This results in the formation of water and a new bond between carbon and nitrogen. This new bond is called a **peptide bond**.

3.26 DI– AND POLYPEPTIDES

A protein that has only two amino acids in it is called a **di-peptide**. As the protein undergoes more and more peptide bonding and gets larger and larger, it is called a **polypeptide**. A polypeptide can be as large as several thousand amino acids linked together. Polypeptides are formed by repeated condensation hydration synthesis reactions, adding more and more amino acids to the growing polypeptide.

Figure 3.26.1

Dehydration Synthesis and Hydrolysis Reactions of Proteins
The generalized reactions which are responsible for synthesizing proteins and breaking them down are shown here. The peptide bond is created by an enzyme. The enzyme first removes a H+ from the amino group of one amino acid and an OH- group from the carboxyl group of the other amino acid. These two molecules then combine to form water, H_2O. Then the enzyme links together the C and the N, which forms the peptide bond. As is the case with carbohydrates and lipids, the hydrolysis reaction is the reverse of the condensation synthesis. Notice that the dipeptide has a free nitrogen group on one end and a free carboxyl group on the other end. These ends participate in further peptide bonding to allow the dipeptide to be grown into a polypeptide.

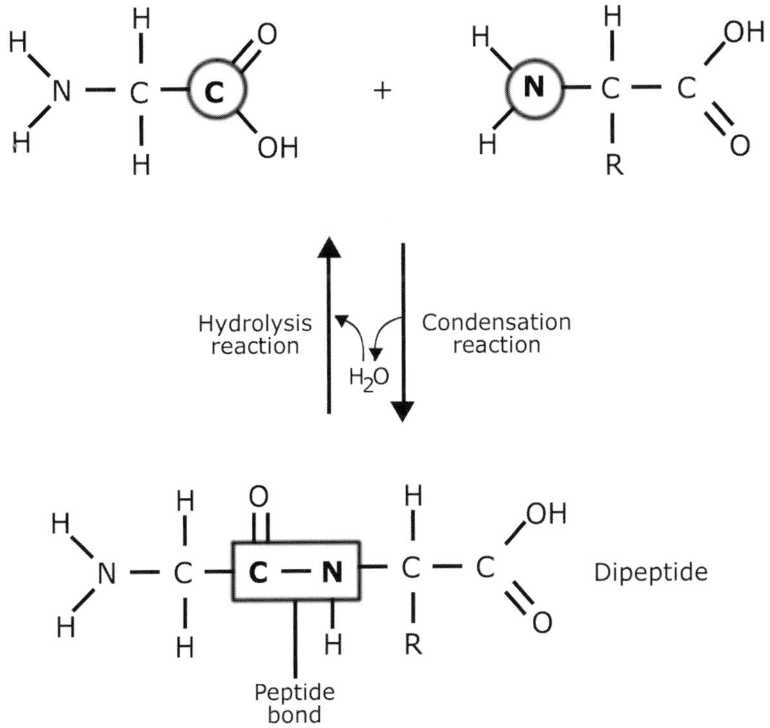

3.27 NUCLEIC ACIDS

These are specialized organic molecules that are also large and complex, but not as complex as some of the larger proteins. They are several thousand monomers long. Some are millions of monomers in size. We will be talking about these much more in the future, so for now all we will need to know is the following information.

Nucleic acids are like the library of the cell. They contain the information which tells the cell how to reproduce itself. Nucleic acids also provide the information the cell needs to make all of the molecules. They also have other functions which we will be exploring in the future.

3.28 NUCLEOTIDES

Nucleic acids are polymers of **nucleotides.** Therefore, nucleotides are the monomeric units of the nucleic acids. A nucleotide is composed of three subunits:

- a central 5-carbon sugar called a pentose

- a phosphate group linked to the pentose

- a nitrogenous base linked to pentose opposite the phosphate group

A nitrogenous base is simply a molecule group which contains nitrogen and has a basic pH. The thing that makes one nucleotide different from another nucleotide is the nitrogenous base.

Common nucleic acids are **deoxyribonucleic acid (DNA), ribonucleic acid (RNA), and adenosine triphosphate (ATP)**.

3.29 DNA, OR DEOXYRIBONUCLEIC ACID

DNA is the nucleic acid macromolecule that contains the genetic information. Therefore, DNA contains all the information the cell and organism require to tell the organism how to function properly. DNA also contains information which tells the organism how to reproduce itself and how to build proteins. There are four different nucleotides from which DNA is built. Like all nucleotides, the nucleotides of DNA all contain a phosphate group. Its pentose is **deoxyribose**. The **nitrogenous bases** that are used in DNA are thymine, cytosine, adenine, and guanine. DNA is made by the repeated linking together of these four nucleotides in different sequences. Although there are only four nucleotides which compose DNA, an individual DNA molecule can be several million nucleotides long.

Adenine (A)
Guanine (G)
Cytosine (C)
Thymine (T)

Figure 3.29.1

Nucleotides of DNA
Even though a single molecule can be more than one million monomer units long, it is composed of only four different nucleotides, linked together to form a nucleic acid macromolecule. Below is the general structure of a DNA nucleotide. The central sugar is deoxyribose. It has a phosphate group on one end and one of four nitrogen bases on the other.

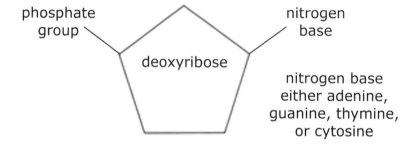

phosphate group — deoxyribose — nitrogen base

nitrogen base
either adenine,
guanine, thymine,
or cytosine

Figure 3.29.2

Double Helical Structure of DNA
We will learn much more about DNA in the genetics chapters. Note for now that DNA is a twisted molecule, a molecular structure referred to as a helix. It is built from the four nucleotides adenine ("A"), thymine ("T"), guanine ("G"), and cytosine ("C"). The two blue "strands" of DNA are held together in the middle by special bonds that form between the nucleotides of opposite strands. DNA is a doublestranded helix. It looks like a spiral staircase.

3.30 RNA, OR RIBONUCLEIC ACID

Ribonucleic acid (RNA) is the nucleic acid molecule that is important in protein synthesis. RNA carries the information from DNA to the protein-making machinery of the cell. The information instructs which protein is to be made and how to make it. Also, during protein synthesis, RNA carries the proper amino acid to the protein-building machinery of the cell. There are four nucleotides from which RNA is built. They each contain a phosphate group. Its pentose is **ribose.** Its nitrogenous bases are uracil (instead of thymine), cytosine, adenine, and guanine.

Figure 3.30.1

Nucleotides of RNA
RNA is not as large as DNA, but it is still a large molecule. It is also made up of only four nucleotides. The nucleotide structure is very similar to DNA except the central five carbon sugar is ribose. Also, RNA uses the nucleotide uracil instead of thymine.

Adenine (A)
Guanine (G)
Cytosine (C)
Uracil (U)

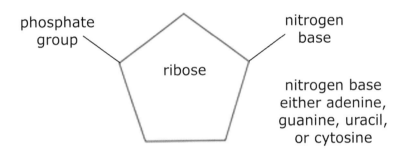

phosphate group — ribose — nitrogen base

nitrogen base either adenine, guanine, uracil, or cytosine

3.31 ATP, OR ADENOSINE TRIPHOSPHATE

Adenosine triphosphate (ATP) is a special nucleotide. We have already discussed it quite a bit in the first three chapters. ATP is called the universal energy source because it is the molecule that supplies almost all of the energy needed for chemical reactions to occur. As you recall, ATP is made through the process of cellular respiration (which we will learn all about in Chapter 8). Since ATP is a nucleotide, it is composed of a central carbon sugar. Its pentose is ribose. Attached to one end of the ribose is the nitrogen base adenine. Attached to the other side of the ribose is not one but three phosphate groups (hence the name "triphosphate"). It is these phosphate groups which make ATP special. We will learn all about their function in Chapter 8. ATP is often called the "fuel" of the cell because it provides the energy the cell needs to live. We will learn the structure and function of ATP in the chapter on cellular respiration.

Realize that this chapter has been a brief overview of the organic molecules. This information will be necessary for the following chapters. We will explore the organic molecules in depth later this year.

3.32 PEOPLE OF SCIENCE

Freidrich Wohler, (1800-1882), was a pioneer in organic chemistry. In his day, it was thought that organic molecules could only be synthesized by living organisms. However, he became the first person to make an organic compound in the laboratory when he made **urea** (an organic compound) from ammonium cyanate (an inorganic compound). This discovery made him famous. He became a professor of chemistry at a university in his home country of Germany where he advanced the study of benzoic acid and metabolism. He was the first to isolate the elements aluminum and beryllium. He also developed a method to prepare phosphorus that is still widely in use today.

3.33 KEY CHAPTER POINTS

- Organic molecules always contain carbon and hydrogen, and often contain oxygen.

- Because of isomers, writing the structural formula for a molecule is preferred over the simple chemical (molecular) formula.

- Carbon has many unique properties which make it specially suited to serve as the main atom in organic molecules.

- Polymers are built from monomers using dehydration (or condensation) synthesis reactions.

- Polymers can be broken into their smaller monomeric units using hydrolysis reactions.

- Carbohydrates are built from monosaccharide monomers through the glycosidic bond.

- Lipids are built by linking up to three fatty acids to a backbone molecule of glycerol using the ester bond.

- Proteins are built from amino acid monomers through the peptide bond.

- Nucleic acids are built from nucleotides.

3.34 DEFINITIONS

amino acid
The basic monomeric unit of proteins. These have a general structure of a central carbon atom bonded to a $COOH^-$ group, an NH_3^+ group, a hydrogen atom, and the R group.

carbohydrate
The organic molecule that contains carbon, hydrogen, and oxygen. It has the relationship of two hydrogen atoms for every oxygen atom. These can be generally represented as CH_2O.

carboxylic acid group
A general description of a group of one carbon atom, two oxygen atoms, and one hydrogen atom bonded together. This is chemically represented $COOH^-$.

dehydration (condensation) synthesis reaction
The reaction used by organisms to build carbohydrates, proteins, nucleic acids, and lipids (among others). One of the products of this reaction is water.

deoxyribose
The pentose that is used in DNA.

dipeptide
A protein that is made up of two amino acids. They are joined by a dehydration reaction synthesis.

disaccharide
A molecule formed by linking together two monosaccharides.

double covalent bond
A bond in which two pairs of electrons are shared between two atoms. This is represented as two lines drawn between atoms in the structural model.

ester bond
The bond that forms between the hydroxyl group (OH^-) of glycerol and the carboxylic acid group of a fatty acid to form a lipid.

fatty acid
A molecule that is formed from a long carbon chain with a carboxylic acid group on one end. This is one of the building blocks of fats.

glycerol
>One of the building blocks of fats, this is a molecule with three carbon atoms bonded together and a hydroxide group (OH^-) attached to each carbon atom. Fats are synthesized by bonding a fatty acid to the carbon atom and removing the OH^- group via a dehydration synthesis reaction.

glycoside bond
>The bond that results from the dehydration synthesis to form polysaccharides. It involves a bond of C-O-C.

hydrolysis or hydration reaction
>The reaction used by organisms to break down organic molecules into monomers. Water is one of the reactants in this reaction.

isomer
>Molecules that have the same simple chemical formula, but different structural formula. (See the previous example of butane and iso-butane.)

lipid
>Organic molecules that are made up of carbon, hydrogen, and oxygen. This is a general term that includes fats, waxes, oils, triglycerides, and steroids. These molecules are formed using glycerol and fatty acids linked together via hydration synthesis reactions.

macromolecule
>A very large polymer. Examples are DNA and RNA.

monomer
>The building blocks of organic molecules. These are linked together to form larger molecules.

monosaccharide
>The monomeric unit of the carbohydrates. They are saccharides that contain between three and seven carbon atoms.

nitrogenous base
>A nitrogen-containing group that is bonded to the pentose of a nucleotide. The four bases in DNA are thymine, cytosine, adenine, and guanine.

nucleotide
>The monomeric units of the macromolecules nucleic acids. These are composed of a pentose sugar, a nitrogenous base, and a phosphate group.

organic chemistry
>The study of the principles of organic compounds.

organic compounds
>Molecules that are made by living organisms that use carbon as their backbone, but also commonly contain hydrogen and oxygen.

peptide bond
>The bond that joins together amino acids in order to synthesize proteins. It is formed by a dehydration synthesis reaction that bonds a carbon atom from one amino acid to a nitrogen atom from the second amino acid.

phosphate group
>A molecule consisting of three oxygen atoms linked to one phosphorous atom.

polymer
>A large molecule that has been formed by repeatedly linking together monomers.

polypeptide
>A protein that is made up of many amino acids bonded together by peptide bonds.

polysaccharide
>A larger carbohydrate molecule formed by repetitive hydration synthesis reactions utilizing monosaccharides.

proteins

These are complex organic molecules that contain not only carbon, hydrogen, and oxygen, but also other atoms such as sulfur and nitrogen. These are synthesized from monomers called amino acids.

ribose

The pentose that is used by RNA and ATP.

saccharide

A general term to describe carbohydrates (or sugars).

saturated fatty acid

A fatty acid that has many hydrogen atoms bonded to the carbon backbone (i.e. the molecule is saturated with hydrogen). This results in a molecule with few to no double bonds between carbon atoms.

single covalent bond

A bond in which one pair of electrons is shared between two atoms. This is represented as one line drawn between atoms in the structural model.

starch

A sugar polymer that is used as a storage molecule.

structural formula

A representation of a molecule that shows the relationships of bonds to the atoms. This provides more detail about the molecule than the simple chemical formula.

synthesize

To build larger molecules (polymers) from smaller molecule precursors (monomers).

triple covalent bond

A bond in which three pairs of electrons are shared between two atoms. This is represented as three lines drawn between atoms in the structural model.

unsaturated fatty acid

A fatty acid that has few hydrogen atoms bonded to the carbon backbone (i.e., the molecule is unsaturated with hydrogen). This results in a molecule with many double bonds between carbon atoms.

STUDY QUESTIONS

1. What does the term organic compound (or molecule) mean?

2. What is another term for an organic molecule, and why might it be a better term to use than "organic"?

3. What do all organic molecules have in common? (There are several potential answers for this.)

4. True or False? Inorganic molecules are much smaller than organic molecules.

5. True or False? The chemical formula C_8H_{18} refers to only one specific molecule type. Please explain your answer.

6. How is the problem described in #5 resolved when writing a formula for an organic compound?

7. What type of covalent bond is C-C? C=C?

8. Write a structural formula for a triple bond between carbon atoms and the single bond between carbon and hydrogen atoms in the molecule C_2H_2.

9. Write the possible structural formula(s) for C_6H_{14} and C_4H_{10}. (There may be more than one for each.)

10. Larger _____ are synthesized from smaller _____ subunits via _____ _____ reactions.

11. What is always one of the products in a dehydration synthesis reaction?

12. What happens when the cell uses a hydrolysis reaction on one of its organic molecules?

13. What does the general chemical formula CH_2O refer to?

14. What holds together two saccharides?

15. What is glycogen?

16. True or False? Lipids are structurally less complex than proteins.

17. True or False? Lipids are structurally more complex than carbohydrates.

18. Write the chemical formula for a carboxylic acid group.

19. What two types molecules are the lipids made of?

20. What is the monomeric unit of a protein?

21. How are proteins made from their monomeric subunits? (This answer is complex.)

22. What is larger, a nucleotide or a nucleic acid?

23. What are the three components of a nucleotide?

PLEASE TAKE TEST #1 IN TEST BOOKLET

Introduction to the Cell and Cell Membrane

4

4.0 CHAPTER PREVIEW

In this chapter we will:

- Review "cell theory."

- Discuss the general features and functions of a cell.

- Define the two basic cell types—prokaryote and eukaryote.

- Review basic cell structure.

- Investigate the structure and function of the outer boundary of the cell—the cell membrane.

- Understand why cells are "so small."

4.1 OVERVIEW

We will be looking at all cells (plant, animal, bacterial, algae, etc.) in this section and exploring what the parts of a cell are. This will serve as the basis of understanding for much more information on cells and cell processes we will be studying in the future.

The idea that the "cell" was the basic unit of life started to be understood in 1655. At that time Robert Hooke first observed cork cells under a crude microscope. He saw things that had never been seen before. The development of cell theory took off from there.

Over the next 200 years, it was found that cells had a covering called a membrane and an object in the middle of the cell called a nucleus. First it was thought that cells were hollow, but in the 1800s it was discovered that cells contained fluid. It was found that all plants and animals were made up of cells, and that all cells arise from other living cells.

4.2 CELL THEORY

From the above observations, we now have a developed **cell theory** to explain what has been observed about cells over the past 350 years. Cell theory states that:

- cells are the basic units of structure and function for all life

- all living things are made up of one or more cells

- all cells are produced from other living cells (meaning that cells do not ever arise on their own)

An extension of cell theory states that in multicellular organisms, cells that have similar functions are grouped together to form tissues and organs. Just as a review, recall that a group of cells which have the same function is called a **tissue**. A group of tissues which perform the same function is called an **organ**.

There has been such a huge increase in knowledge of cells that there is a special branch of biology called **cytology.** Cytology is the study of cells.

4.3 GENERAL FEATURES OF CELLS

Cells are extremely diverse structures. They have many different shapes, and some, like the amoeba, can even change their shape. Generally the shape of a cell is determined by its function. Remember that since cells are three dimensional structures, their shapes are named after three dimensional structures. For example, a cell is not "round" (two dimensional), but is a "sphere" (three dimensional). A cell is not "square," but is a "cube."

Cells across the spectrum of life have diverse sizes. A cell can be minute or visibly large: from a bacteria at 0.2 micrometers in diameter to a 6 ½ foot long nerve cell from the leg of a giraffe (that's 2 meters). Most cells from plants and animals, though, are about 50 micrometers in size.

Figure 4.3.1

Sizes of Commonly Encountered Biological Organisms
The naked eye can see objects a little smaller than 0.1 mm, but objects have to be much larger than that for accurate detail to be observed with the unaided eye. Light microscopes can identify objects as small as 100 nm, but resolution is not good for objects that small. Electron microscopes are used to accurately view objects smaller than 0.1 mm. Some of the newer and more powerful electron microscopes can even begin to identify details of atoms.

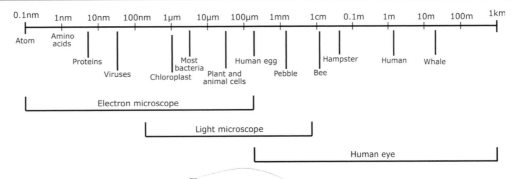

Cells have varying textures, or appearances. The cell surface can be smooth or rough. Some cells, such as sperm or some bacteria, have "tails" called flagella that are used for propulsion.

Figure 4.3.2

Cells Come in Different Shapes and Sizes
As can be seen from the pictures below, cells come in different shapes and sizes. The figure on the left is of a single-celled organism called *Giardia lamblia*. *Giardia* is an organism that commonly infects the intestinal tract and causes diarrhea. As you can see, it has a unique shape. The center picture is pollen from a flower. Pollen is usually spherical and often has small pointy projections extending off the cell surface as seen. The cells on the right are human red blood cells. Some of the red blood cells look round and others look kind of flat. Red blood cells have a "bi-concave" cell shape. That means they look kind of like a donut—they are round, and the edges of the cell are a lot "taller" than the center. The round ones look round because they are oriented with their flat sides facing the camera, like you are looking down on the "hole-side" of a donut. The other red blood cells look flat because they are seen from the side.

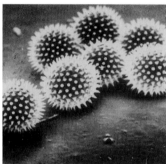
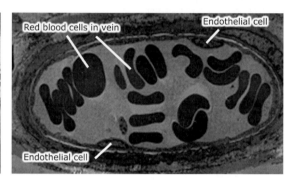

4.4 UNICELLULAR AND MULTICELLULAR ORGANISMS

The very nature of the organism is determined by cells, as well. Some organisms, called **unicellular organisms,** are composed of only one cell. Other organisms are composed of two or more cells. These are called **multicellular organisms**. All bacteria are unicellular. Plants, animals, humans, and insects are all multicellular organisms. According to various estimates, a human being has between 10 and 100 trillion cells. Only in multicellular organisms can cells form tissues and organs.

4.5 COMMON STRUCTURES OF ALL CELLS

All cells, whether from a unicellular or multicellular organism, have structures in common. All cells have a barrier around them which protects them from the outside world. This barrier is called the **cell membrane**. The cell membrane is composed of molecules of fat, protein, and carbohydrates. All cells contain DNA (deoxyribonucleic acid). All cells also contain separate units inside of them which perform certain functions. These units are called **organelles**.

4.6 EUKARYOTIC CELLS

However, there are two types of cells that make up life—prokaryotic cells and eukaryotic cells. **Eukaryotic cells** (or **eukaryotes**) are cells that contain organelles that have their own membrane surrounding them within the cytoplasm. Eukaryotes also have a separate membrane-bound compartment within the cytoplasm called the nucleus, which houses the genetic material DNA. All animal cells, plant cells and fungi are eukaryotic cells. Most plant cells and all fungi cells also have a cell wall. The cell wall of fungi and plants are composed of different carbohydrate molecules than those of prokaryotes. Animal cells do not have cell walls.

4.7 PROKARYOTIC CELLS

Prokaryotic cells (or **prokaryotes**) are cells in which there is no nucleus. The DNA is floating around within the cytoplasm. But the DNA is still highly organized and is kept in an area of the cell called the **nucleoid**. Prokaryotes also contain far fewer organelles than the eukaryotes. In addition, the cell membrane of all prokaryotes is surrounded by the **cell wall**. The cell wall is composed of specialized sugar molecules and serves to further protect prokaryotes from the environment. Organisms classified in the kingdoms of Eubacteria and Archaebacteria make up the prokaryotes.

Figure 4.7.1

The Three Cell Types
Figure (a) represents the general structure of a prokaryotic cell. All prokaryotes are bacteria. The outer purple layer is the cell wall. Inside of that is the cell membrane. Within the cytoplasm are the nucleoid and ribosomes. The nucleoid is the area where the prokaryotic DNA is found. Ribosomes make proteins. Figure (b) represents a typical plant cell. All plants are eukaryotes. Like the prokaryotes, most plants have cell walls. However, the cell wall is made up of different carbohydrate molecules in bacteria and plants. Figure (c) represents a typical animal cell. Animals are also eukaryotes. Animal cells do not have a cell wall. Notice that inside the plant and animal cell there are many more organelles than inside of the prokaryotic cell. All eukaryotic cells have many organelles that are covered with their own membrane. Prokaryotes do not have membrane-bound organelles.

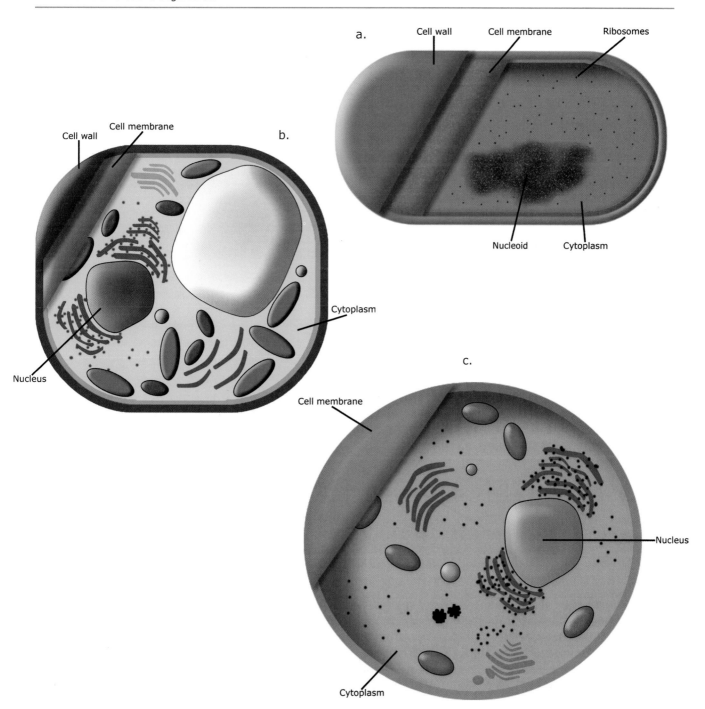

Figure 4.7.2

Summary of the Differences Between Eukaryotic and Prokaryotic Cells

Feature	Prokaryote	Eukaryote
cell (plasma) membrane	yes, all	yes, all
nucleus	no	yes, all
nuclear material	free floating in cell in area called the nucleoid	organized inside of membrane-bound nucleus, usually in the form of chromosomes
organelles	few organelles with no membrane	many complex organelles with membranes
cell wall	yes, some	Animals—no; plants—most
cytoplasm	yes	yes

4.8 FUNCTIONS OF A CELL: REPRODUCTION

In general, the function of a cell should remind you of the properties of life that were discussed in Chapter 1. Since the cell is the basic unit of life, the properties of life are the same as the properties of the cell. As you remember, these properties include:

- having one or more cells
- containing DNA
- having the ability to reproduce
- being complex and organized
- responding to the environment
- being able to extract energy from their surroundings
- maintaining homeostasis
- having the ability to grow

Encoded in every cell's DNA are the instructions for the cell's reproduction. This results in the production of more cells like itself. This is true whether the cell that is reproducing is a bacteria or the cell of a human pancreas.

4.9 FUNCTIONS OF A CELL: ABSORPTION

Absorption is the process that cells use to bring substances into the cell from outside the cell. Typically, the substances brought into the cell are things the cell needs to survive. Substances transported into the cell are needed for the cell to live and perform whatever functions the cell needs to perform.

The structure of the cell that has the most influence on what does and does not get into a cell is the cell membrane. The cell membrane lets in things the cell needs, and keeps out things that are not needed, or are dangerous to the cell. Nutrient molecules (proteins, carbohydrates, and lipids) and vitamins are examples of substances that cells absorb.

4.10 FUNCTIONS OF A CELL: DIGESTION/PROCESSING

Once substances are transported into the cell, they need to be processed. **Digestion** is the way a cell processes substances. Digestion results in the cell breaking down a large molecule into smaller ones. For example, in the last chapter we talked about breaking down carbohydrate polymers into smaller monomer subunits. This process occurs inside the cell after a large carbohydrate is absorbed and needs to be processed further.

Another form of processing is cellular respiration. This occurs continuously in cells and is how consumer cells obtain their energy. For example, in animal cellular respiration, the carbohydrate monomer glucose is broken down in association with absorbed oxygen. This occurs in a series of reactions, the purpose of which is to make energy molecules—ATP, or adenosine triphosphate—which the cell can use. This process will be discussed in much more detail in upcoming weeks.

4.11 FUNCTIONS OF A CELL: BIOSYNTHESIS

All cells make stuff from substances that are absorbed. Proteins, carbohydrates, and lipids are all made from the molecules that cells absorb and digest. The process of making molecules using absorbed molecules is called **biosynthesis**. Some cells make hormones, some cells make proteins, and some cells make antibodies. Other cells make toxins (substances that kill other cells). But all cells synthesize some substance that is of use to the cell/organism. Which substance the cell makes depends on what kind of cell it is, and what the cell is instructed to make by the DNA.

No matter what the substance which is biosynthesized, once a cell makes a substance, there is a need to get the substance out of the cell. If not, the cell would fill with waste products and synthesized molecules and burst. These processes will be described in more detail in the next chapter. However, the basic processes need to be understood in a little detail for now.

4.12 FUNCTIONS OF A CELL: MOVING SUBSTANCES OUT OF THE CELL

Excretion is the process that cells use to rid themselves of waste products. More specifically, excretion involves the removal of waste products that are soluble in the fluids inside the cell. For elimination of substances that are not soluble inside the cell, the process is called **egestion**. Egestion requires more energy than excretion. **Secretion** is the process used by the cell to release biosynthetic substances that are to be used by other cells. This process is not used to transport waste products out of the cell.

4.13 FUNCTIONS OF A CELL: RESPOND TO THE ENVIRONMENT

All cells have the ability to move. This **movement** may be on a small scale, such as when the cell membrane changes its structure from one minute to another, re-arranging proteins. Or, the movement may be on a large scale, such as when muscle cells cause an animal to run.

Irritability does not refer to a cell becoming cranky or crabby. It refers to the property of a cell to sense and respond to the environment. This works hand in hand with homeostasis and movement.

4.14 FUNCTIONS OF A CELL: MAINTAIN HOMEOSTASIS

In order for the cell to be able to perform all of the above functions, conditions that allow a cell or organism to live are closely maintained. This is called homeostasis. If there are wide variances in the cell's temperature, then the cell cannot maintain life. If there are wide variances in the concentration of ions inside of a cell, it will die. It is a property of each individual cell to maintain the optimal conditions needed for the cell to live and function properly.

4.15 FUNCTIONS OF A CELL: PROTECTION

We will be discussing this in further detail in following chapters, but it is important to understand some basic concepts now. All cells have a **cell membrane.** The cell membrane is also called the **plasma membrane**. This is mostly a fatty and protein structure that serves as the boundary of the cell to keep all of the inside stuff in and all of the outside stuff out. Some cells also have a **cell wall**. This is an additional protective layer that surrounds the plasma membrane. The cell wall also helps the plant cell maintain the proper shape. Only plants, fungi, and bacteria have cell walls. Animals do not have cell walls. Much more cell wall structure and function will be covered in the plant chapters.

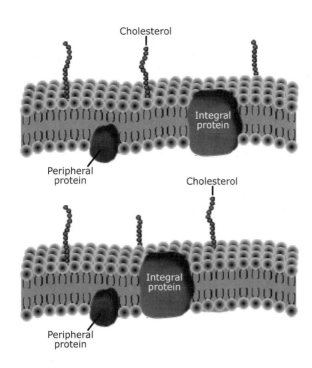

Figure 4.15.1

Cellular movement can be on a large or small scale.
Although we usually think of "movement," as something we can easily see or do, there are many different kinds of movement in biology. Some movement—a dog running or a fish swimming—is obvious. However, there are other types of movements which occur in cells continuously that are more important. The type of movement which occurs within the cell membrane is an example. Notice that from the top panel to the bottom panel, the proteins within the cell membrane have changed positions. This type of movement is in part related to how the cell is able to regulate what comes in and goes out of the cell. This is an example of movement on a very small scale, but it is extremely important nonetheless. We will talk about other types of movement later in the taxonomy chapters.

4.16 INSIDE OF THE CELL

The inside of the cell is filled with a jelly-like fluid called **cytoplasm**. Floating inside of the cell within the cytoplasm are structures called **organelles.** Organelles are structures inside a cell that perform various functions critical to the cell's life. Also inside the cell, and within the cytoplasm, is the **nuclear material** (DNA). If the cell is a eukaryotic cell, the DNA is housed within its own compartment, the nucleus. If the cell is a prokaryotic cell, the DNA is free in the cytoplasm.

4.17 REVIEW OF CELL STRUCTURE

To review, all cells have a plasma membrane, cytoplasm, and nuclear material. In eukaryotes, there are membrane-bound organelles and nucleoli (plural of nucleus) in the cytoplasm. In prokaryotes, the DNA is not housed in its own separate compartment. It is critical to understand that prokaryotic cells and eukaryotic cells are separated from one another on the basis of whether or not the DNA is contained in a nucleus. The Kingdoms Archaebacteria and Eubacteria contain the prokaryotes. The Kingdoms of Protista, Fungi, Plantae, and Animalia are all composed of organisms which are eukaryotic cell types.

4.18 CELL MEMBRANE

In eukaryotes and prokaryotes with no cell wall, the cell membrane is the outermost layer of the cell. In eukaryotes and prokaryotes with a cell wall, the cell membrane is inside the wall. Either way, the cell membrane is a major protective structure for the cell. The cell membrane also regulates which molecules or substances flow in and out of all cells and give the cell its shape. Essential molecules like oxygen are freely allowed into the cell, just as common waste products like carbon dioxide are freely allowed out of the cell.

The majority of the molecules of the cell membrane are made up of lipids and proteins. However, there are also carbohydrates and cholesterol in the cell membrane.

4.19 PHOSPHOLIPID

The lipid of the cell membrane is a special one called a **phospholipid**. A phospholipid is special because of its structure; it contains the glycerol base as all lipids do, with two fatty acid chains and one phosphate group attached to the glycerol. A phosphate group contains phosphorous and forms bonds via polar covalent bonds. (Remember from Chapter 2 that water also forms by polar covalent bonds). Polar molecules easily mix in with water (in other words, they are **hydrophilic**, which means "water loving.") Fatty acids are non-polar, and one of the properties of a non-polar molecule is that it does not mix well with water (making them **hydrophobic**, or "water fearing.") Therefore, we say that one end of the phospholipid is polar (the phosphate end) and one end is non-polar (the fatty acid end). Another way of stating this is to say that the phospholipid molecule has a hydrophilic head and a hydrophobic tail.

Since the space inside and outside of a cell is mainly composed of water, when many phospholipids are placed in this mixture, they orient themselves in a specific way. The hydrophobic ends of the molecules cluster as far from the water as they can, while the hydrophilic ends like to be in the water.

4.20 LIPID BILAYER

The cell membrane is not a single layer of phospholipid molecules. Rather, it is a double layer of phospholipid molecules. One end of the phospholipid has a phosphate group attached to it. This is called the hydrophilic ("water loving") head because the phosphate group can easily enter water. The other end of the phospholipid has two fatty acid chains. These are called hydrophobic ("water fearing") tails because fatty acid chains do not mix into water at all. You can see from Figure 4.20.1 that the hydrophobic tails of both layers cluster together on the inside of the membrane (to get as far from the water surrounding them as possible). The hydrophilic heads protrude into the water matrix surrounding them. This two-layer orientation of the cell membrane is called the **lipid bilayer**.

Figure 4.20.1

Phospholipids and the Lipid Bilayer of the Cell Membrane

Figure (a) represents the basic unit of the lipid bilayer, the phospholipid molecule. "R" represents the rest of the molecule. In the case of the fatty acid, the "R" represents repeated molecules of carbon and hydrogen molecules linked in repeating chains. Figure (b) represents the conceptualization of the appearance of an individual fatty acid molecule, and how the fatty acids fit together in the lipid bilayer model. The end of the molecule with the phosphate group represents the "hydrophilic head," and the fatty acid end represents the "hydrophobic tail." Notice that the hydrophilic heads are lined up to the outside of the membrane, and the hydrophobic tails line up to the interior of the membrane. One outer edge of the membrane (one "row" of hydrophobic heads) is in direct contact with the inside of the cell (the cytoplasm) and the other outer edge is in direct contact with the outside of the cell (the extra-cellular matrix).

a.

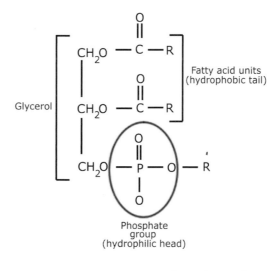

b.

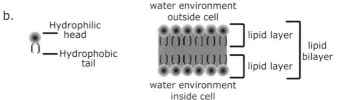

Almost all eukaryotic organelles also have their own membrane enclosing them, including the nucleus. The membrane structure of the cell membrane, organelle membranes, and the nuclear membrane is the same—a lipid bilayer. Realize that this means the structure of prokaryotic cell membrane is a lipid bilayer just as the structure of eukaryotic cell membrane is a lipid bilayer. The basic point is that all biological membranes are lipid bilayers.

4.21 PROPERTIES OF LIPID BILAYER

The next most prominent molecules in a membrane, after lipids, are proteins. The proteins in the membrane have varied functions. Some membrane proteins are used for structural support. Some are functional proteins, such as enzymes that function to break down other molecules or speed up certain reactions. Other proteins function as channels in the membrane that allow only specific substances to move in or out of the cell through the channel. This property of selective transport through the membrane means it is **semi-permeable**; only certain molecules and substances are able to pass through the membrane into and out of the cell. Semi-permeability provides protection for the cell to keep in what the cell needs inside and to keep out what may be harmful to the cell's interior.

4.22 MEMBRANE PROTEINS

Proteins can be associated with the membrane in two different ways. If the protein is attached only to the surface of the membrane, then it is referred to as a **peripheral protein**. If the protein is embedded in the membrane, it is called an **integral protein**.

Integral proteins can either partially or completely span the entire width of the membrane. In order for the integral protein to be embedded in the membrane, it must have a hydrophobic portion of the molecule that will allow it to associate with the hydrophobic portion of the phospholipids. Since the middle of the lipid bilayer is hydrophobic, in order for a membrane protein to pass through the middle of the cell membrane, that portion of the membrane protein in direct contact with the middle of the membrane must also be hydrophobic. If there is no hydrophobic portion on a membrane protein, it will not be able to mix into the hydrophobic part of the membrane.

One of the major functions of integral proteins is to serve as attachment sites. Special proteins, which hold cells to one another in animals, called the extracellular matrix, attach to integral proteins. Also, special proteins on the inside of the cell, which internally hold the cell together, called the cytoskeleton, attach to integral proteins. We will discuss the extracellular matrix and cytoskeleton more in the next chapter.

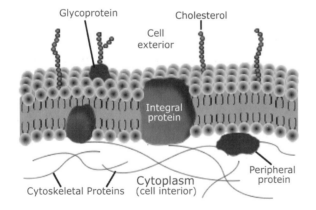

Figure 4.22.1

Structure of the Cell Membrane: Peripheral and Integral Proteins and Other Molecules
Integral proteins are embedded in the lipid bilayer, while peripheral proteins are attached to the surface of the membrane. Cholesterol extends into the extracellular matrix outside the cell, as do other proteins and molecules. On the cytoplasmic side of the cell (the interior of the cell), the structural support of the cell—the cytoskeletal proteins—anchor onto the peripheral proteins. Cytoskeletal proteins help to maintain the shape of the cell.

Another important function of integral proteins regards the semi-permeable nature of the membrane. Semi-permeability is controlled in part by the integral proteins. Integral proteins that span the entire membrane function as channels. When channels created by integral proteins are open, substances can move into or out of the cell. When they are closed, substances stay in or out of the cell. Peripheral proteins often send signals to integral proteins to tell them when to open and close. There are also specific types of peripheral proteins on all cells that indicate what type of cell a cell is. For example, specific kinds of peripheral proteins on muscle cells indicate that a muscle cell is a muscle cell.

4.23 FLUID MOSAIC MODEL

There have been many ways that the structure and function of the cell membrane have been conceptualized over the years. Since the early 1970s, the **fluid mosaic model** has been favored as the best way to describe how the molecules of the cell membrane interact and behave.

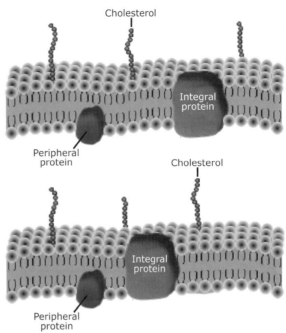

Figure 4.23.1

Fluid Mosaic Model of the Cell Membrane
The fluid mosaic model is conceptualized as the surface of the cell membrane being in a constant state of flux. Surface molecules and peripheral and integral proteins are constantly moving within the lipid bilayer. Rather eloquent research has shown that this is true. From moment to moment, the integral and peripheral proteins and the cholesterol molecules are able to move within the membrane much as people are able to change their positions in a pool by walking or swimming. This movement is likely not random, but highly regulated from the cell's nucleus.

The fluid portion refers to the fact that the lipid bilayer is not rigid like a wall, but is fluid. This means that there can be, and is, movement of the cell membrane itself, as well as movement of molecules within the membrane. Think of the movement of the membrane itself as what happens when you shake a water balloon. The walls of the balloon stretch a bit, but do not break. This type of "stretchiness" is also seen with cell membranes.

The mosaic nature of the membrane could not exist if the membrane were not fluid. This portion of the model was developed following electron microscopic studies showing the proteins continually changing their position within the membrane. Think of this property of the cell membrane as a crowded room. The other people in the room represent the lipid bilayer and other proteins. You are a protein. When you need to move from one area of the crowded room to another, the people (lipid and protein molecules) move slightly out of your way to let you pass. This is exactly what happens in the cell membrane. Proteins and other molecules within the cell membrane are able to move from one area of the lipid bilayer to another. This is the mosaic part of the model. This dynamic nature of proteins is true of integral and peripheral proteins.

4.24 CELLULAR TRANSPORT

As noted, the cell membrane functions as the "gate keeper" for what can and cannot get into or out of the cell. There are a number of processes the cell uses to bring substances into and send substances out of the cell. The processes to take substances out of the cell were briefly discussed earlier in this chapter, and will more completely be covered in the next chapter. We will now deal with the functions of the cell membrane as it relates to transport processes.

4.25 DIFFUSION

The simplest form of transport across the membrane is **diffusion**. Diffusion is the movement of molecules from an area of higher concentration to an area of lower concentration. This occurs as random movement of the molecules across a **concentration gradient** (the difference in the concentration of molecules from the higher concentration to the lower concentration). Although the movement of the molecules is random, it is much more likely that the molecules will move from the area of the higher concentration to that of the lower. Because the cell does not need to use any energy to achieve the process of diffusion, it is a mode of **passive transport**.

Over time, as more molecules move from the higher to lower concentration, the concentrations in the two areas will eventually become equal, existing in a state of **equilibrium**. Once this occurs, since there is no longer a concentration gradient present, there will still be movement of the molecules randomly, but they are as likely to move one way as another.

The cell membrane acts as a barrier between the inside and the outside world for the cell. It does allow some molecules that are tiny, or dissolvable in the cell membrane, to move through it based on a concentration gradient. In other words, the cell membrane is itself a semi-permeable membrane. It allows some molecules into and out of itself by the process of diffusion.

For example, oxygen and carbon dioxide are both small molecules that dissolve in the cell membrane. This means that they are able to pass freely across the cell membrane. Oxygen is generally at a higher concentration outside the cell than inside the cell. That means a concentration gradient exists, and this allows the oxygen to pass through the cell membrane by diffusion. When a molecule moves from an area of high concentration to an area of low concentration, it is said to move "down" its concentration gradient. So to move down a concentration gradient means moving from high to low concentration. This is how cells obtain the oxygen they need to survive. Carbon dioxide, on the other hand, is higher in concentration on the inside of the cell than the outside. The CO_2 moves down the concentration gradient and is eliminated from the cell by moving out of the cell via diffusion.

Figure 4.25.1

Simple Diffusion

(a) Carbon dioxide molecules are contained within a semi-permeable membrane. The membrane is only permeable to the carbon dioxide. That means no matter what else is inside or outside of the membrane, only carbon dioxide molecules can pass through. Since carbon dioxide is a gas, the molecules are in constant motion within the membrane, moving around inside, bumping into the membrane and one another. The concentration of carbon dioxide molecules is much higher inside the membrane than outside. Since the membrane is permeable to the CO_2, diffusion will occur from the inside of the membrane to the outside of the membrane due to the presence of a concentration gradient.

(b) By chance alone (through the random movements of the molecules), some of the molecules have passed through the membrane and into the space outside of the membrane. Note that a concentration gradient still exists, although it is not as strong as in (a), since there are still more carbon dioxide molecules within the membrane than outside of it.

(c) Diffusion has resulted in the fairly equal dispersion of carbon dioxide inside and outside of the semi permeable membrane.

Equilibrium has been established.

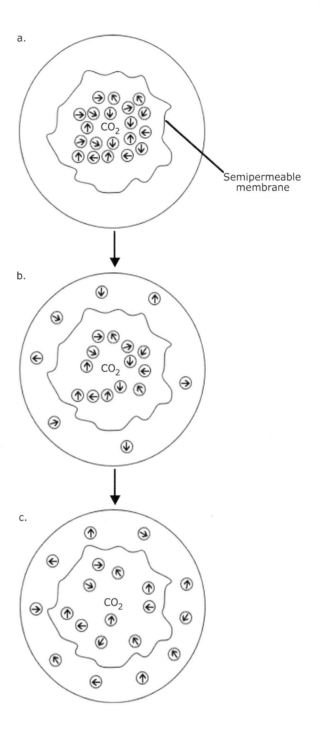

a.

Semipermeable membrane

b.

c.

4.26 GATED CHANNELS

Another form of diffusion occurs to transport ions across the membrane. As already noted, not all molecules are soluble in the cell membrane; therefore they cannot enter the cell via simple diffusion. There are small openings (created by integral proteins) in the cell membrane which allow certain ions to pass through called **gated channels**. Usually, each ion has a specific type of channel through which only it passes. For example, only sodium can pass through a sodium channel, while potassium would not be able to enter through a sodium channel. Some gated channels are always open, while others are closed, waiting for an environmental stimulus to cause them to open. This is considered diffusion because random movements of the ions cause them to come into contact with, then move through, the gated channel. Also, the movement of the ion occurs down its concentration gradient, just as does diffusion. The cell does not need to expend any energy to perform gated channel transport, making this another type of passive transport.

Figure 4.26.1

Gated Channel Transport
The channel within the plasma membrane represents a gated ion channel, which is only permeable to the molecule represented by the circle. When the molecule comes into contact with the gated channel through random movement, the gate "opens" and the molecule passes freely through the channel into, or out of, the cell. The gated channel is not permeable to all molecules. Others are unable to pass because the gate does not "open" for them. As a form of diffusion, this process occurs down the concentration gradient. Often, the gated-channel protein undergoes a change in its shape when the molecule it transports comes in contact with it, causing the protein to "swallow" and move the molecule across the cell membrane.

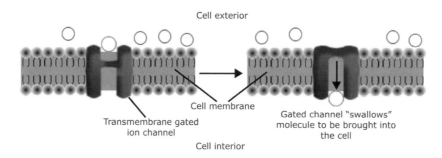

4.27 OSMOSIS

Osmosis is another mode of transportation used by cells. This specifically involves the transport of a solvent across a semi-permeable membrane. Osmosis is also a mode of passive transport. It is the movement of solvent molecules from an area of low solute concentration to an area of high solute concentration. In osmosis, the semi permeable membrane allows the solvent molecules to pass freely, but restricts movements of the solute.

Osmosis is extremely important in biology because it is the primary way that water moves into and out of all cells. Therefore, we will specifically discuss osmosis when water is the solvent, but be aware osmosis can involve other solvent/solute systems.

Life exists as mixtures of liquid environments (solvent) and other molecules (solute), both on the inside and the outside of the cell. In a solvent/solute system, you will recall that the molecules having the higher concentration are the solvent, and those with the lower concentrations are the solute. In general, in most living organisms, the solvent is water (both inside and outside the cell). Usually, the solute is a mixture of ions, proteins, and carbohydrates. To recap, in biological systems:

- the semi permeable membrane is the lipid bilayer (the membrane surrounding the cell, nucleus, and organelles)

- the solvent is water

- the solute is a mixture of proteins, ions, and carbohydrates

In most biological systems, then, water can flow across the cell membrane (another example of the lipid bilayer being semi-permeable). When there is a higher concentration of the solute on one side of the membrane, the flow of the solvent will be away from the lower concentration of solute toward the high solute concentration. A solution whose concentration has a higher concentration of solute is **hypertonic**, and a solution whose concentration of solute is lower is **hypotonic**. When two environments have the same solute concentration, they are said to be **isotonic**.

Figure 4.27.1

Osmosis

The process of osmosis. The semi-permeable membrane divides a beaker which contains water as the solvent. On the right side of the membrane, there is a hypertonic solution (or high-solute concentration); on the left there is a hypotonic solution (or low-solute concentration). The solvent (water) is "pulled" across the membrane by the hypertonic solution and moves from the hypotonic solution across the membrane into the hypertonic solution. Unlike diffusion, osmosis is not random, but specific molecule movement. The solvent (water) will stop moving across the membrane when the concentration on either side of the membrane becomes isotonic. And yes, this can occur even against gravity as is shown!

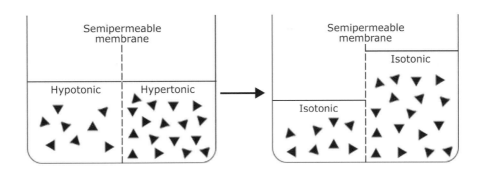

As an example, let's imagine that a cell is in an environment in which it is surrounded by a lot of water (high concentration of solvent) and few other molecules (low concentration of solute). This would be referred to as a hypotonic environment *outside* the cell. At the same time, the inside of the cell has a low concentration of water (solvent) and a higher concentration of other molecules (solute). This would be referred to as a hypertonic environment *inside* the cell. In this situation, the water will flow from the hypotonic solution toward the hypertonic solution. In effect, the high solute concentration "pulls" the solvent across the semi-permeable membrane towards the high solute concentration. Therefore, the flow of the solvent—water—will be into the cell.

Figure 4.27.2

Examples of the Effects of Cells Exposed to Different Solute/Solvent Environments

Cells are happiest in isotonic environments (see (a)) because there is no overall net movement of water into or out of the cell (although water does move, it is an even movement of the water into and out of the cell). In hypertonic environments (b), there is a higher concentration of solutes outside of the cell than inside the cell. This "pulls" the water from the area of low solute concentration to the area of higher solute concentration; in other words, water moves from the inside of the cell, across the cell membrane and out of the cell. This causes the cell to shrivel. In hypotonic environments (c), there is a higher concentration of solutes inside of the cell than outside, and water moves into the cell, causing it to swell and sometimes burst. This relationship of osmosis to the fluid balance in cells is crucial in medicine. A hospital will often give sick people important fluids through their veins, but if we are not careful to give them the correct fluids, our patients could experience some of the problems with hypertonicity or hypotonicity we've discussed.

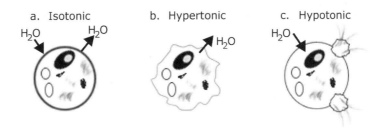

4.28 REVIEW OF PASSIVE TRANSPORT MECHANISMS

To review, osmosis, gated channel transport, and diffusion represent movement of molecules down their concentration gradient. Since these forms of transport do not require the cell to expend energy, they are considered modes of passive transport.

4.29 ACTIVE TRANSPORT

In contrast to passive transport mechanisms, some modes of transport require the cell to expend energy in order to move molecules across the membrane. These processes are called **active transport** and use integral proteins—called **active transport channels**—to run the process of moving molecules across the membrane. Active transport is called active because it requires the cell to use energy to move molecules. Why? We will find out below.

Active transport channels are generally closed and are stimulated to open by an environmental stimulus. When the channel is stimulated to open, it "pumps" a molecule across the cell membrane. Like gated channels, active transport channels only move one specific type of molecule. Often this is referred to as a cell "pump" because, unlike the passive transport modes, active transport pumps molecules from areas of low concentration to areas of high concentration. This is movement of molecules up (or against) a concentration gradient and requires the cell to expend energy to accomplish.

Figure 4.29.1

General Schematic for Active Transport
This is a general schematic for the process of active transport into the cell (left) and out of the cell (right). The cell pump protein is an integral protein which requires energy to pump molecules into and out of the cell. The energy is supplied by a molecule called ATP (we will learn about ATP in a couple of chapters). Energy is required because the movement of molecules in active transport is against their concentration gradient. If there was no active transport mechanism, the molecules would not be able to cross the cell membrane. Depending on the transport channel, sometimes they can only move molecules one way, and sometimes they can move them both into and out of the cell.

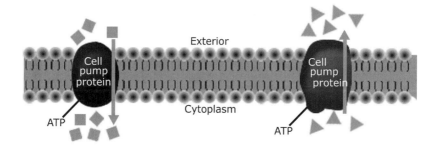

4.30 CYTOSIS

Some molecules that need to enter or exit the cell are too big to be moved across the membrane with either active or passive transport mechanisms. In order to accomplish this, the cell uses the process of "cytosis." Cytosis is when a cell forms a membrane-coated vesicle around the substance to be moved, then moves it into or out of the cell. **Endocytosis** is the process to get substances into the cell. **Exocytosis** is the process to get substances out of the cell. Both of these processes use energy to perform, but are functionally much different than active transport because cell pumps are not used (vesicles are).

Endocytosis involves two separate mechanisms. When large solid substances or entire cells are moved across the membrane, the process is called **phagocytosis**. When the cell moves larger quantities of solute or fluid into the cell, the process is called **pinocytosis**. In either case, the cell forms a pocket around the substance to ingest, then "pinches itself off" to bring the substance into the cell. Once the substance enters the cell, it is contained in the part of the cell membrane that "pinched off" to separate from the cell. This self-contained structure is called a **vesicle**. See the figure for more details on these two processes.

In exocytosis, the cell forms a membraned vesicle around the substance to be eliminated from the cell. The vesicle then moves to the cell membrane and joins with it, and the substances are ejected into the cell exterior.

Figure 4.30.1

General Schematic of the Cytosis Processes

This is the general concept of the processes of "cytosis," with endocytosis (left) and exocytosis (right) being demonstrated. In panel (a), the cell membrane is folding around the material to be engulfed into the cell (endocytosis). The material to be removed from the cell (exocytosis) is contained in a double-membraned vesicle and is moving toward the cell surface. In (b), the material involved in endocytosis has been almost completely surrounded by the cell membrane. The next step is for the cell membrane to pinch a part of itself off, which forms a vesicle around the material and allows it to move into the cytoplasm. The vesicle containing the material involved in exocytosis has fused with the cell membrane. The membrane then opens to the outside of the cell. In panel (c), the vesicle has completely formed around the endocytosed material and will be transported to wherever the cell needs it. The exocytosed material is ejected into the space outside of the cell as the vesicle membrane takes the shape of the cell membrane in general. These processes occur continuously in the cell. If the endocytosed material is a liquid, the process is called pinocytosis. If it is solid material it is called phagocytosis.

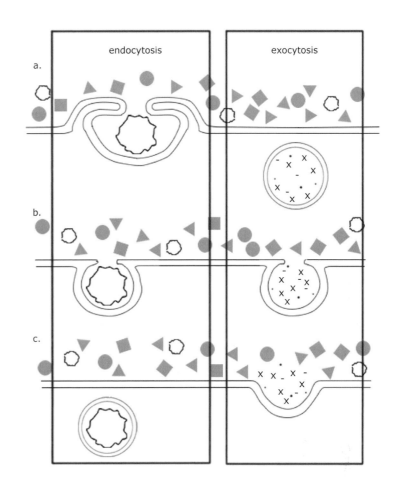

Figure 4.30.2

Summary of Transport Mechanisms

General Mode of Transport	Specific Examples	Energy Required	Movement of Molecules or Material
passive	diffusion, ion channel, osmosis	no	down concentration gradient
active	membrane pump	yes	up concentration gradient
cytosis	phagocytosis, pinocytosis, exocytosis	yes	up or down concentration gradient

4.31 ADVANCED

Why are cells so small? This is because of the surface to volume ratio. The property of this ratio has important implications on how big a cell can be and still live. Since the cell is essentially a sphere, as the cell gets larger, its surface area increases with the square or the diameter, but the volume increases with the cube of the diameter. This means that, proportionally, the volume of a cell increases more rapidly than the surface area of the cell as a cell increases its size. Although we used a spherical cell as an example, the same relationship holds true for a cell of any shape—as a cell gets larger and larger, its volume increases in direct relation to the surface area.

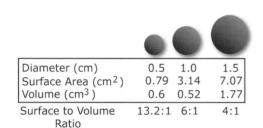

Diameter (cm)	0.5	1.0	1.5
Surface Area (cm^2)	0.79	3.14	7.07
Volume (cm^3)	0.6	0.52	1.77
Surface to Volume Ratio	13.2:1	6:1	4:1

Figure 4.31.1

Surface to Volume Ratio as it Relates to Cell Size
As can be seen from the graphic, as the size of a spherical cell becomes larger, its volume increases more so than the surface area. Since the cell relies on its surface area to absorb nutrients and eliminate wastes, there comes a certain volume of the cell which the surface area cannot support. That means the cell needs more nutrients than the limited surface area of the cell can absorb, and needs to eliminate more wastes than can be passed across the cell membrane outside the cell.

All nutrients need to come into the cell from the outside, and all biosynthesized products and wastes need to be eliminated from inside of the cell. As stated above, all movement processes occur across the cell membrane. That means that cells are dependent upon the membrane surface area to provide for the movement of substances into and out of the cell. However, the metabolic needs of the cell are more determined by the volume of the cell. Therefore, there will be a theoretical size at which the surface area of the cell cannot facilitate the proper passage of substances to and from the cell and the cell dies.

4.32 PEOPLE OF SCIENCE

Robert Hooke (1635-1703) was an English scientist and architect who first termed the word "cell" after looking at some cork using a microscope he devised on his own. He was the inventor of the compound microscope, in which a series of lenses are used to magnify an image; it is still the most common microscope in use today. He also invented several practical items, such as the universal joint (still used in cars and trucks today). He was the first to describe some properties of elasticity and work out a formula that is referred to, 300 years later, as Hooke's Law.

4.33 KEY CHAPTER POINTS

- Cell theory states that cells are the basic functional unit of all life.

- Organisms which contain only one cell are unicellular organisms. Cells which contain more than one cell are multicellular organisms.

- All cells:
    - have DNA
    - have diverse shapes and functions
    - have a cell membrane to protect it and organelles inside
    - reproduce themselves
    - can absorb nutrients from their environments
    - can digest and process nutrients
    - can synthesize organic molecules
    - can move substances into, out of, and throughout the cell
    - can respond to the environment
    - can maintain homeostasis

- There are two basic cell types—prokaryote and eukaryote.

- The cell membrane protects the cell from the environment.

- The cell interior contains the organelles and DNA.

- The cell membrane is a two layer structure composed of phospholipids and proteins.

- The cell membrane transports substances into and out of the cell in a variety of ways.

4.34 DEFINITIONS

absorption
The process of transporting substances into the cell.

active transport
One of several modes of transport that require the cell to expend energy in order to move molecules across the membrane.

active transport channels
Protein channels within membranes that allow molecules to move across the cell membrane.

biosynthesis
The process of making molecules by using absorbed molecules.

cell (plasma) membrane
The barrier around all cells which protects them from the outside world.

cell theory
The theory that cells are the basic units of structure and function for all life.

cell wall
A protective layer that surrounds the cell membrane.

concentration gradient
The difference in the concentration of molecules on one side of a membrane as compared to the other side.

cytology
The study of cells.

cytoplasm
The jelly-like fluid that fills the inside of a cell.

diffusion
The movement of molecules from an area of higher concentration to an area of lower concentration.

digestion
The way a cell (or organism) takes in and processes substances/molecules.

egestion–
The process that cells use to get rid of non-soluble waste products.

endocytosis
The process which uses vesicles to transport substances (which are not soluble in the cell membrane) into a cell.

equilibrium
The state of being equal or even.

eukaryotic cells (Eukaryotes)
Cells that contain a nucleus and membrane-bound organelles.

excretion
The process that cells use to rid themselves of soluble waste products.

exocytosis
The process used to get substances (which are not soluble in the cell membrane) out of a cell using vesicles.

fluid mosaic model
A model that shows how the molecules of the cell membrane interact and behave.

gated channels
Openings in the cell membrane, created by transmembrane proteins, which allow certain ions to pass through.

hydrophobic
Molecules which do not dissolve in water; "water fearing."

hydrophylic
Molecules which dissolve in water; "water loving."

hypertonic
A solution whose concentration has a higher concentration of solute than the cytoplasm.

hypotonic
A solution whose concentration of solute is lower than the cytoplasm.

integral protein
A protein that is embedded in the cell membrane.

irritability
The ability of a cell to sense and respond to the environment.

isotonic
A solution whose concentration of solute is the same as the cytoplasm.

lipid bilayer
The two-layer orientation of the cell membrane made up of lipid molecules.

movement
The ability to move that all cells have, whether on a large or small scale.

multicellular organisms
Organisms that are composed of two or more cells.

nuclear material
Deoxyribonucleic acid; DNA.

nucleoid
The area of a prokaryotic cell where DNA is found.

organelles
Units inside all cells which perform certain functions.

organs
A group of tissues which have a common function.

osmosis
A mode of passive transport that cells use involving the movement of a solvent across a semi-permeable membrane from an area of low solute concentration to an area of high solute concentration.

passive transport
A mode of transport that does not require the cell to use any energy.

peripheral protein
Protein that is attached only to the surface of the cell membrane.

phagocytosis
The process of moving large substances, or entire cells, into a cell using a vesicle system.

phospholipid
The types of lipid which make up the cell membrane.

pinocytosis
The process of moving large quantities of solute or fluid into a cell using a vesicle.

prokaryotic cells (prokaryotes)
Cells in which there is neither a nucleus nor any membrane-bound organelles.

secretion
   The cellular process to release biosynthetic substances that are to be used by other cells.

semi-permeable
   The property of a membrane to only allow certain substances to pass across it.

tissue
   Cells with the same functions which congregate together.

unicellular organisms
   Organisms that are composed of only one cell.

vesicle
   The "pinched off" part of a cell membrane containing a substance that has entered the cell.

STUDY QUESTIONS

1. What is the cell theory? Please describe not only what the cell theory states, but also what it attempts to explain.

2. Why would you not describe a living cell as being "round" or "square"? What would be better descriptors of those two cell shapes?

3. True or False? An organism that is made up of only one cell is not a life form.

4. This is only for fun, but how many cells do you think are in a human being? Thousands, millions, billions, trillions, or quadrillions?

5. List the functions of a cell. Are these pretty much the same or are they different than the properties of life discussed in Chapter 1?

6. True or False? All cells have a cell membrane, a cell wall, and cytoplasm.

7. If you were standing in a cell's cytoplasm and you were looking at a nucleoid, what type of cell would you be in? (prokaryotic or eukaryotic).

8. Onto what membrane structure do the extracellular matrix and cytoskeletal proteins anchor?

9. What are two functions of the cell wall?

10. Draw a cell membrane with a lipid bilayer, integral, and peripheral proteins, carbohydrates and cholesterol; then label each component.

11. What is it about the cell membrane that makes it semi-permeable? (This is more complicated than saying it selectively transports certain items across the membrane.)

12. True or False? Peripheral proteins usually function as membrane channels.

13. In order for an integral protein to be located within the cell membrane *and* come in contact with the watery environment in and around the cell, what type of regions on the molecule does it need to contain?

14. Where would a hydrophilic molecule tend to congregate—on the inside of the lipid bilayer or on the surface? What about a hydrophobic molecule?

15. List three types of passive transport. Which one requires integral proteins to accomplish the task?

16. How are diffusion and osmosis the same? How are they different?

17. What is the main difference that distinguishes passive transport from active transport?

18. Describe what would happen if a human muscle cell were to be placed in a hypertonic, hypotonic, and isotonic solution. Why?

19. What is similar about phagocytosis and pinocytosis? How are they different?

20. What is the self-contained, intra-cytoplasmic (inside the cytoplasm), membrane-bound structure that participates in the "cytosis" process called?

The Cell Interior and Function

5

5.0 CHAPTER PREVIEW

In this chapter we will:

- Investigate and understand the organization and function of the cell interior.

- Define the differences between eukaryotic and prokaryotic cell structure.

- Discuss the structure and function of the following eukaryotic organelles and structures:
    - Protoplasm
    - Cytoplasm
    - Nucleoplasm
    - Cytoskeleton
    - Nucleus
    - Ribosome
    - Endoplasmic reticulum
    - Golgi apparatus
    - Lysosomes and peroxisomes
    - Mitochondria
    - Plastids
    - Vacuoles
    - Middle lamella
    - Extracellular matrix

5.1 OVERVIEW

Once again, the focus of this chapter will be the cell, but now we will learn about the interior structures - organelles - and their functions in eukaryotic cells. We will cover the prokaryotic cells later in the course. Eukaryotes are more complex cell structures than the already complex prokaryotes. Eukaryotic cells contain a membrane-bound nucleus. They also have complicated, membrane-bound organelles. Prokaryotic cells do not have membrane-bound organelles.

The cell's structural plan calls for the interior to be surrounded by the cell membrane. Within the boundaries of the membrane, the cell is filled with a jelly-like substance, called the cytoplasm. Organelles are found in the cytoplasm. The cytoplasm is jelly-like so molecules and organelles can move through it effectively. There are many things transported through the cytoplasm every minute.

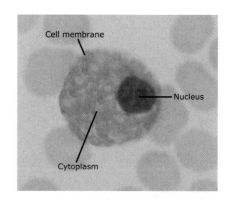

Figure 5.1.1

Basic cell structure
This is a light micrograph of an animal cell. The basic structures of the cell are labeled. All eukaryotic cells have this general structure of a cell nucleus surrounded by cytoplasm. The structure we learned about last chapter—the cell membrane—holds everything inside the cell and protects the cell from the environment.

5.2 ORGANELLES – GENERAL

Organelles are the individual functional units of all cells. Because any given cell has complicated functions that must be performed, the different functions of the cell are divided and spread out among the various structures inside the cell. For example, the protein-making organelle is called a ribosome. Vesicles function as storage and transport organelles. The nucleus is the organelle that houses and protects DNA in eukaryotic cells.

The organelles that are found in all eukaryotic cells are: protoplasm, cytoplasm, nucleoplasm, cytoskeleton, nucleus, nucleolus, ribosome, endoplasmic reticulum, Golgi apparatus, mitochondrion (plural mitochondria), lysosome/peroxisome and vacuoles. Structures that are found only in animal cells are centrioles. Structures that are found only in plant cells are plastids. Prokaryotic cells only contain one true organelle – ribosomes.

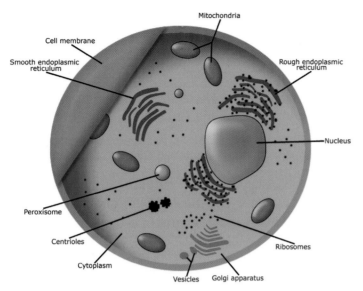
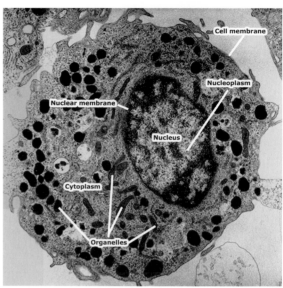

Figure 5.2.1

General structure and organelles of eukaryotic cells
Above is an updated version of the animal cell graphic we saw last chapter. All of the organelles are labeled. The right electron micrograph is a human blood cell. The resolution is not good enough to make out many of the organelles, though. The nucleus is easily visible. It is filled with a jelly-like inside called nucleoplasm. Everything outside of the nucleus is called cytoplasm. Cytoplasm is a mixture of water, organelles, molecules and ions. The larger "sausage-shaped" organelles are mitochondria. Mitochondria manufacture almost all of the energy molecules for the cell. The large circular organelles with the light interior are vesicles. The very small black dots in the cytoplasm are ribosomes. They are all over the cytoplasm of most cells. As we proceed through this chapter, we will learn the function of all of the organelles shown.

5.3 PROTOPLASM

Technically, the **protoplasm** refers to all substances and objects contained inside the cell membrane. The protoplasm, therefore, includes the organelles, nucleus, and fluid inside the cell. The protoplasm is basically all the "stuff" within the boundaries of the cell membrane. The easiest way to remember what the protoplasm includes is that it consists of the cytoplasm and nucleus.

Technically, the breakdown of the protoplasm is as follows:

- The **cytoplasm** refers to all the structures outside the nucleus but inside the cell membrane.

- The cytoplasm contains the **cytosol**, which is the aqueous component of the cytoplasm.

- The cytosol contains about 70% water. The remaining 30% consists of ions and various soluble molecules such as proteins, enzymes, carbohydrates, and lipids.

- The cytoplasm includes all of the organelles except the nucleus. The nucleus is not considered to be part of the cytoplasm; it is part of the protoplasm.

- The cytoplasm also contains the skeletal structure of the cell called the cytoskeleton.

This mixture of the cytosol, the organelles, and the cytoskeleton give the cytoplasm the overall consistency of jelly.

5.4 NUCLEOPLASM

The nucleus is a large, membrane-bound organelle. Like the cell, the nucleus also has a fluid interior. This "plasm" of the nucleus is not called cytoplasm, though. It is called **nucleoplasm**. Like the cytoplasm, the nucleoplasm is mainly composed of water, ions and soluble molecules. In addition, eukaryotic DNA (deoxyribonucleic acid) is stored within the nucleoplasm. Recall that prokaryotic DNA is free within the cytoplasm.

The function of the cytoplasm and nucleoplasm is significant. The aqueous nature allows for molecules, ions, and organelles to be transported within the cell. The various molecules that are dissolved in the cytosol allow the organelles to use them for macromolecule synthesis. Also, the cytoplasm and nucleoplasm contribute to the maintenance of the cell's shape.

5.5 CYTOSKELETON

The cytoplasm and nucleoplasm exert a force directed outward from the inside to the outside. The cell membrane and nuclear membrane are not strong enough to counteract that force, however. If the structural integrity of the cell were left only to the cytoplasm and the nucleoplasm, both the cell and its nucleus would burst from the pressure. Fortunately, a complex network of proteins - called the **cytoskeleton -** is present to strengthen the cell and keep this from happening. The cytoskeletal proteins form an extensive meshwork, anchoring onto the interior of the cell membrane and the exterior of the nuclear membrane. There are also fibers that run between each other. Not only does the cytoskeleton serve to hold the cell together, it also:

- serves as an anchoring site for cell organelles and enzymes

- functions as the roadway for the movement of organelles and molecules within the cytoplasm

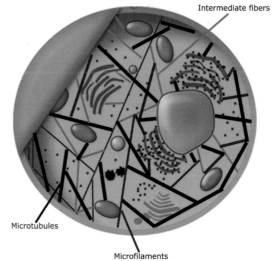

Figure 5.5.1

Cytoskeleton
I have modified the animal cell graphic to represent what the cytoskeleton looks like. It looks kind of messy now, but that is what the cytoskeleton looks like—a very intricate interlacing of microtubules, intermediate fibers and microfilaments. This serves to hold the cell together, anchor organelles and enzymes in place and as a transport pathway within the cell.

5.6 CYTOSKELETAL PROTEINS, CILIA, AND FLAGELLA

The cytoskeleton is made up of three types of proteins: microtubules, intermediate fibers, and microfilaments. **Microtubules** are the largest of the cytoskeletal proteins and are composed of the protein **tubulin**. They are long, thin, and hollow tubes that are found just inside the cell membrane. Microtubules serve to provide structural support for the cell. Microfilaments are the smallest of the cytoskeletal proteins and are made of solid rods of the protein **actin**. Two chains of actin twisted together form a microfilament. Actin filaments are important in skeletal muscle contraction and intracellular transport. **Intermediate fibers** are cleverly named because they are not quite as big as microtubles, nor quite as small as micro-filaments. All three classes of cytoskeletal proteins interlace with one another to hold the cell together and provide a highway system. These are especially important structural cell supports.

Figure 5.6.1

Cytoskeletal Proteins and Their Function

Protein	Function
actin – microfilaments	cell structure; support; intracellular transport
intermediate fibers	cell structure; support
tubulin - microtubules	cell structure; support; intracellular transport; separate cells during cell division, make up eukaryotic flagella, cilia and centrioles

Microtubules also make up the structure of eukaryotic **flagella** and **cilia**. A flagellum is a long, thin projection from the cell surface that propels some eukaryotic cells by whipping back and forth. Cilia are shorter and more numerous cell projections that also move rhythmically back and forth. Some ciliated organisms use the cilia to move their bodies. This is true of many unicellular, ciliated organisms. Multicellular organisms use cilia to move substances past the cells. One example of this is the use of cilia in the respiratory tract (breathing tract) of animals. The cells that line the respiratory tract are covered with cilia. These beat back and forth in order to keep the areas clean from foreign substances such as dust particles and bacteria.

Flagellum

Figure 5.6.2

Flagella

An electron micrograph of an organism with a flagellum is shown here. One cannot usually tell the difference between a eukaryotic and prokaryotic flagellum just by looking at it, though. This picture happens to be of a prokaryotic flagellum from a bacterium. No matter what the species, though, flagella function by whipping back and forth, propelling the organism. The difference between eukaryotic and prokaryotic flagella is great. All eukaryotic flagella are made up of multiple molecules of the protein tubulin. Prokaryotic flagella are made of a single molecule of the protein flagellin. In addition, eukaryotic flagella are actually extensions of the cytoplasm and are covered by the cell membrane. Prokaryotic flagella simply are molecules that extend out from the surface of the cell membrane.

Microtubules are also important in moving genetic material during cell division. Microtubules make up the main structure of **centrioles**. Centrioles are found only in animal cells, and some fungi and algae. There are no centrioles in plants. Centrioles are important in cell division, where they help to pull the chromosomes (DNA) apart. We will discuss this later in the course. Centrioles are formed from nine sets of three microtubules arranged in a circle.

Cilia

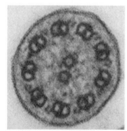

Figure 5.6.3

Cilia

Both of these pictures are from an electron microscope. The picture on the left is of a cell with cilia extending from the surface. Cilia and eukaryotic flagella are both composed of microtubules, as well as other proteins. When cilia and flagella are viewed in cross section with an electron microscope, they have what is called the "**9 + 2 structure.**" This means there are nine pairs of microtubules surrounding a central core of two tubules, as can be seen in the cross section of a cilium on the right. Here, the dark line is the boundary of the cilia. Since cilia and flagella are extensions of the cytoplasm, this corresponds to the cell membrane. On the inside of the dark line, which is within the cytoplasm, are nine outer rings of paired microtubules. In the center are two more microtubules. This is the 9 + 2 structure. Cilia are not found in prokaryotic cells and are shorter than flagella. Also, normally organisms with cilia have more than 10 - sometimes even hundreds - of cilia. Usually eukaryotes with flagella have one or two flagella per cell.

Centrioles

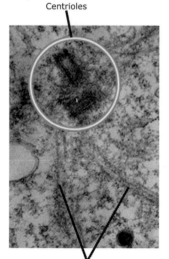

Microtubules

Figure 5.6.4

Centrioles

Here is an electron micrograph of part of the cytoplasm of an animal cell. Centrioles usually are seen paired together. Both centrioles are seen on their sides. Centrioles are made up of microtubules. They are made up of nine triplets of microtubules, rather than the 9 + 2 structure of cilia and flagella.

5.7 EUKARYOTIC ORGANELLES - GENERAL

All eukaryotic cells contain organelles which are more numerous and structurally more complicated than the organelles in prokaryotic cells. Many organelles are common to all eukaryotic cells, while others are found only in plant cells, or only in animal cells.

5.8 NUCLEUS

The **nucleus** is usually the largest organelle in animal cells and is often the largest in plant cells. Eukaryotic cells have a nucleus, but prokaryotic cells do not. The nucleus is surrounded by its own membrane, the **nuclear membrane**. This membrane is not a single lipid bilayer like the cell membrane, but a double lipid bilayer. This means that there is one double lipid bilayer surrounded by another lipid bilayer protecting the nuclear contents. There are holes within the nuclear membrane called **nuclear pores**. Pores allow the passage of materials and molecules into and out of the nucleus. The fluid-like nature of the nucleoplasm allows substances to move through the nucleus.

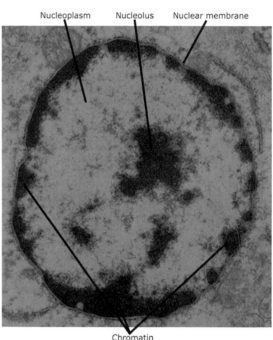

Nucleoplasm   Nucleolus   Nuclear membrane

Chromatin

Figure 5.8.1

Nucleus
This picture is taken from an electron micrograph of an animal cell. The nucleus is the large round structure in the middle of the photo. When cells are not dividing, the DNA is in its unwound state called chromatin. Chromatin usually is found just inside the nuclear membrane. The black material around the edges of the nucleus is DNA in the form of chromatin. The nucleolus is a structure in the nucleus that synthesizes ribosomal parts. Also notice a common feature of eukaryotic cells: the two "wings" coming off the nucleus at about 2 o'clock and 7 o'clock is rough endoplasmic reticulum. It is common for the membrane of rough endoplasmic reticulum to be connected directly to the outer nuclear membrane.

The nucleus has the special function of protecting the DNA from the interior of the cell. The nuclear material - DNA - is stored in the nucleus. It contains the genetic information for the organism and controls basically every function of the cell. The control of the cell, and ultimately the organism, originates in the nucleus. Usually, DNA is kept in the form of **chromatin**. Chromatin is DNA which is loosely coiled around nuclear proteins.

The structure of the nucleus is maintained by a lattice-work of proteins called the **nuclear lamina**. The lamina functions in the nucleus like the cytoskeleton functions in the cytoplasm. The lamina is the skeleton of the nucleus and is made up of intermediate fibers.

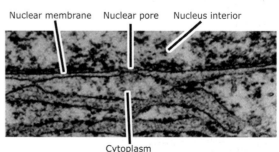

Nuclear membrane   Nuclear pore   Nucleus interior

Cytoplasm

Figure 5.8.2

Nuclear pores
Pores are small holes in the nuclear membrane which allow materials to move into and out of the nucleus. This is a TEM view. Again notice the rough ER attached directly to the nuclear membrane.

Also in the nucleus is a structure called the **nucleolus**. The nucleolus is a spherical structure in the nucleus. It synthesizes ribosome components. Ribosomes are made in smaller pieces by the nucleolus. After the nucleolus manufactures ribosomal components, they are transported out of the nucleus through the nuclear pores and are assembled into complete ribosomes in the cytoplasm.

5.9 RIBOSOMES

Ribosomes are non-membrane bound organelles that manufacture proteins. They have the same basic structure in prokaryotes and eukaryotes. They are made of RNA and proteins and are the small, round, black "dots" in the cytoplasm when viewed with an electron microscope. Ribosomes are the most numerous organelles and are found throughout the cytoplasm. They often cluster together into groups called **polyribosomes** or **polysomes**.

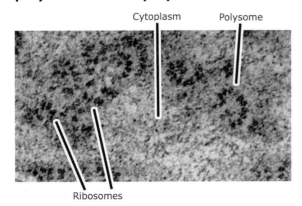

Figure 5.9.1

Ribosomes
These are free ribosomes in the cytoplasm as seen by TEM. They are not attached to endoplasmic reticulum. The groups of ribosomes are called polyribosomes or polysomes.

The way a protein is manufactured is neat. DNA communicates which protein ribosomes are supposed to make by sending a message from the DNA into the cytoplasm. The

message is carried by a molecule called mRNA – **m**essenger **r**ibo**n**ucleic **a**cid. mRNA is a nucleic acid like DNA. mRNA leaves the nucleus through the nuclear pores and delivers the message about which protein to make straight to the ribosomes in the cytoplasm. When the mRNA attaches to a ribosome, the ribosome decodes the message in the mRNA and makes the appropriate protein.

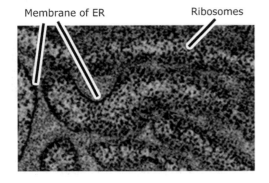

Figure 5.9.2

Rough endoplasmic reticulum
Rough endoplasmic reticulum is shown in the top TEM micrograph. Rough ER has ribosomes attached to its membrane. Ribosomes make the proteins and then pass them directly into the ER for processing and packaging. The bottom micrograph is a TEM shot of smooth ER (with a small section of rough ER at the bottom). (The dark round object in the top of the picture is a vesicle which contains lipid.) Ribosomes are usually found near smooth ER, but do not attach to it.

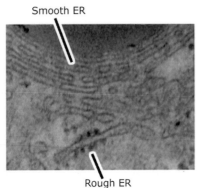

5.10 ENDOPLASMIC RETICULUM (ER)

The endoplasmic reticulum, or ER, is an extensive network of folded membranes and membranous sacs throughout the cytoplasm. ER transports molecules throughout the cell, and also helps the cell maintain its shape. ER connects directly to the nuclear membrane and the cell membrane. When a protein is made by the ribosomes, it passes into the ER, is processed, and then is transported to other areas in the cell. As such, the ER also functions to transport molecules to and from the nucleus through the cytoplasm. In this way, ER is the subway of the cell.

There are two types of ER, **smooth ER** and **rough ER**. Rough ER is named because of the many ribosomes that are attached to it. Once the ribosome makes its protein, it passes directly to the rough ER for packaging and transport. Having the ribosomes attached right to the ER makes this process more efficient. Rough ER is the prominent type of ER found in cells that make a lot of proteins. Rough ER also makes its own membrane and the cellular membrane.

Smooth ER does not have any ribosomes attached to it. This type of ER is prominent in cells that make a lot of lipids and molecules called steroids. Also, smooth ER inactivates harmful breakdown products that build up as a result of cell metabolism.

5.11 GOLGI APPARATUS AND VESICLES

Once the smooth ER or rough ER receives a protein from the ribosome, the ER wraps it into a membrane-bound sac called a **vesicle**. The vesicle then moves from the ER to the **Golgi apparatus**. The Golgi apparatus is a series of stacked and flattened tubes with sacs at the ends of the tubes. The Golgi apparatus functions to store, modify, and further package the products received from the ER. The Golgi manufactures some proteins of its own and makes lysosomes (see below).

The Golgi apparatus attaches small **signal groups** to the molecule that tell the cell where the molecule should be taken. The addition of a signal group to the protein is one of the more important functions of the Golgi. Without the signal group, the cell would not know where a protein was supposed to go. Once the Golgi has modified the molecule, it is again packaged into a transport vesicle and taken wherever it is needed.

Figure 5.11.1

Golgi apparatus and vesicles
This is an electron micrograph of Golgi apparatus. The small round structures coming off the Golgi are vesicles. A number of different chemicals can be contained in the vesicles. Exactly what substances the Golgi packages into a vesicle depends on what type of cell it is in and what the needs of the organism are at the time. There can be many different molecules in the vesicle - from proteins to enzymes which degrade proteins. As a preview for the chapter on protein synthesis, the movement of information to make a protein is: DNA makes an mRNA molecule; mRNA moves into the cytoplasm; ribosomes bind to the mRNA; the ribosome reads the message in the mRNA and makes the protein as directed by the mRNA. The protein moves into the ER and then to the Golgi. The Golgi places a signal sequence on the protein. Signal sequences are like zip codes—they tell the cell where to take the protein. When the Golgi is done with the protein, it packages the protein into a vesicle and it is transported in the cell.

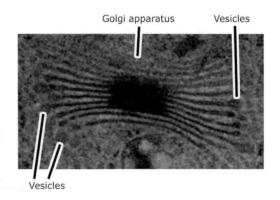

Golgi apparatus   Vesicles

Vesicles

5.12 LYSOSOMES AND PEROXISOMES

Lysosomes are membrane-bound vesicles that contain enzymes to break down proteins, lipids, carbohydrates, and old organelles. They are made in the Golgi apparatus. **Peroxisomes** contain enzymes that break down hydrogen peroxide. Hydrogen peroxide is a toxic substance produced during metabolism. Peroxisomes roam the cell and engulf hydrogen peroxide and then break it down into non-toxic substances. Peroxisomes are assembled independently in the cell. Since lysosomes and peroxisomes contain caustic chemicals, it is important that they do not rupture inside of the cell. If that were to occur (and sometimes it does) the cell would digest itself.

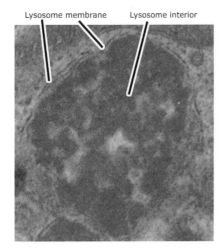

Figure 5.12.1

Lysosomes

Lysosomes are membrane-bound organelles which degrade macromolecules. This is an electron image of a lysosome. Lysosomes are vesicles which contain a strongly acidic interior. They also contain many enzymes to break other molecules down. The enzymes are made in the ER and then passed to the Golgi. The Golgi then forms a lysosome around the enzymes. The lysosome below has substances inside which it will break down with enzymes.

5.13 MITOCHONDRIA

Cells require a lot of energy to perform the countless metabolic processes they perform every minute. **Mitochondria** (singular mitochondrion) are often called the "powerhouse" of the cell because they make almost all of the ATP cells use for their energy source. Mitochondria are a double membrane-bound organelle. The outer membrane forms the boundary of the mitochondrion. The inner membrane folds back on itself throughout the interior of the mitochondrion. These inner folds are called **cristae**. Mitochondria have their own set of DNA, which allows them to replicate themselves inside of the cell without the cell itself dividing. Most cells have hundreds, some thousands, of mitochondria in them.

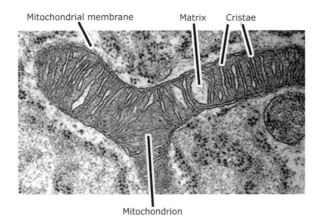

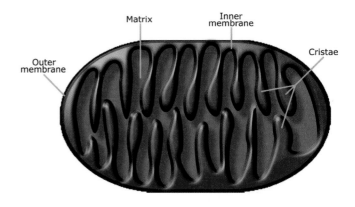

Figure 5.13.1

Mitochondria

Mitochondria are the power plant of the cell. Mitochondria are covered by two membranes, an outer and an inner membrane. The inner membrane folds into the mitochondrion's interior, forming cristae. Mitochondria manufacture almost all of the ATP the cell uses for energy. We will learn much more about this in Chapter 8.

5.14 PLASTIDS

Plastids are double membrane-bound organelles found only in plants and algae. Plastids have two basic functions. They either: 1) perform photosynthesis, or 2) store material such as starch. **Chloroplasts** are plastids that perform photosynthesis. Chloroplasts are double membrane-bound organelles and are where the photosynthetic pigment chlorophyll is contained. We will cover plastids much more thoroughly in the upcoming plant section.

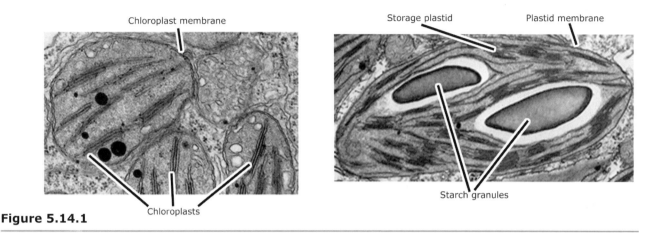

Figure 5.14.1

Plastids

Plastids are not found in animal cells. There are two common types of plastids—chloroplasts and storage plastids. Chloroplasts contain a pigment called chlorophyll. Pigments are molecules that can absorb light. Chlorophyll is the molecule that absorbs the sun's energy for use in making glucose. We will discuss that much more in the photosynthesis chapter. Storage plastids store different molecules. The ones above have starch granules in them. Starch is a polymer of glucose and can be used by the plant—and anything that eats the plant—for energy.

5.15 VACUOLES

Vacuoles are a storage organelle. Vacuoles are membrane-bound sacs specialized to hold specific materials. They may hold food or wastes. Both plant and animal cells have vacuoles. In plant cells, unlike animal cells, the vacuole is often the largest structure visible in the cell.

Figure 5.15.1

Plant cell structure

Here is a graphical representation of a plant cell and its contents. Notice that plant and animal cells contain almost all of the same organelles. However, there are some differences. Plant cells have a cell wall; animal cells do not. A cell wall is an added protection and structural component of plant cells. Animal cells have a pair of centrioles to pull the DNA apart during cell division. Although plant cells also perform cell division, they do not have centrioles. Plant and animal cells both have vacuoles, but the vacuole is often the largest organelle in the plant cell. Usually plant vacuoles are so large they squish all of the other organelles up against the inside of the cell membrane.

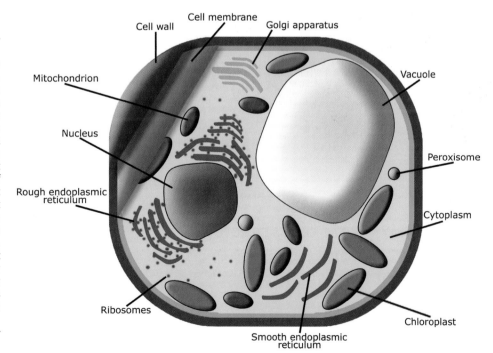

5.16 HOLDING PLANT CELLS TO ONE ANOTHER – THE MIDDLE LAMELLA

As noted, plants have cell walls. But how do all of the cells in a plant stay together? The plant cell secretes a sticky substance that is rich in polysaccharides called the **middle lamella**. These are very sticky molecules. This layer, which is outside the cell wall, literally glues the plant cells together.

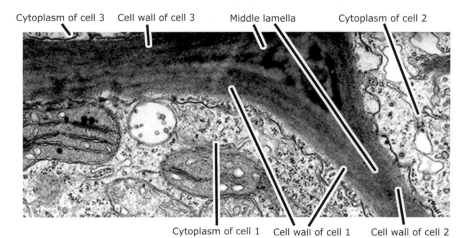

Cytoplasm of cell 3   Cell wall of cell 3   Middle lamella   Cytoplasm of cell 2

Cytoplasm of cell 1   Cell wall of cell 1   Cell wall of cell 2

Figure 5.16.1

Middle Lamella of Plants
The middle lamella is a sticky substance secreted by plant cells which glues the cells together. This is an electron micrograph of three partial plant cells with a clearly defined middle lamella and cell walls.

5.17 HOLDING ANIMAL CELLS TO ONE ANOTHER – THE EXTRACELLULAR MATRIX (ECM)

Animals, though, do not use this same method. Cell walls give the plant structure and rigidity. Since animals do not have cell walls, they have a different way of sticking together and maintaining the organism's shape. Animals have an **extracellular matrix**, which functions not only to glue the cells together, but also as structural support for the tissues.

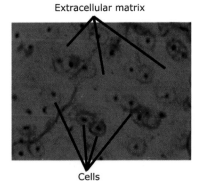

Extracellular matrix

Cells

Figure 5.17.1

Animal ECM
This light micrograph shows the extracellular matrix of cartilage. Cartilage is a tissue which cushions joints. The ECM holds all animal cells together just as the middle lamella holds all plant cells together. Even though they have the same function, they are made of different molecules and have different structures. The ECM is made up of strong molecules that hold cells to one another whereas the middle lamella is made up of sticky molecules.

The extracellular matrix is a complex lattice-work of large molecules called **glycoproteins**. Glycoproteins are carbohydrates linked to proteins. They are interwoven and attached to each other and the surrounding cells. The glycoproteins are secreted by the cells. The three main types of extracellular matrix glycoproteins are **collagen, fibronectin,** and **proteoglycans.**

5.18 PROKARYOTE CELL STRUCTURE

Prokaryotes are all unicellular organisms. All bacteria are prokaryotes and all prokaryotes are bacteria. Almost all prokaryotic cells are several hundred times smaller than the average eukaryote cell. However, a few prokaryotic species are large enough to be seen without a microscope. Ribosomes are the only organelles contained within prokaryote cells. Prokaryotic cells have DNA, but it is not housed in its own membrane-bound compartment; it is found free in the cytoplasm.

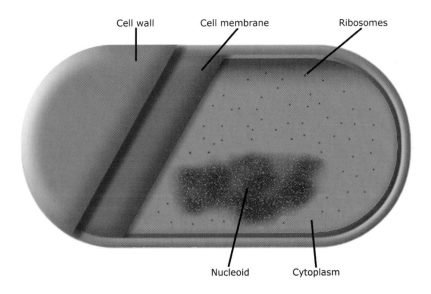

Cell wall Cell membrane Ribosomes

Nucleoid Cytoplasm

Figure 5.18.1

Typical prokaryotic cell

This is the same graphic we saw in Chapter 4. However, now it will help us pull everything together. As mentioned previously, prokaryotes are considered structurally "simple" to many scientists. In a way, this is correct, especially when comparing them to eukaryotes. However, even the simplest prokaryote is extremely complex. No matter how smart scientists think they are, no one has been able to make a fully functional cell in a laboratory. All prokaryotes have a cell wall and a cell membrane. The cell wall is outside the cell membrane and provides an added layer of protection for the organism. As mentioned earlier, the cell wall of bacteria is made up of different carbohydrates than the cell walls of organisms, from Fungi and Plantae. In addition, some prokaryotes have another layer surrounding the cell wall called the capsule. (We will learn much more about bacterial capsules in the future chapter on bacteria.) Inside the cell membrane is the jelly-like substance of the cytoplasm. The cytoplasm contains many ribosomes to make proteins. Also, there is an area within the cytoplasm where the single piece of circular DNA is contained. This area is called the nucleoid.

Figure 5.18.2

Summary of Cell Structures/ Organelles and Their Function

The prokaryotes are the organisms in the Kingdoms Archaebacteria (**A**) and Eubacteria (**E**), and the eukaryotes are the organisms from the Kingdoms Protista (**Pr**), Fungi (**F**), Plantae (**Pl**), and Animalia (**A**).

Structure/Organelle	Type of Cell	Function
cell wall	A, E, F, most Pl	Protection; support
cell membrane	all organisms	boundary/gatekeeper; protection
cytoplasm	all organisms	site of most metabolism; jelly-like environment for substance transport
nucleoplasm	Pr, Pl, F, A	jelly-like environment for transport of substances in/out of nucleus
centriole	Pr, A, F, algae	cell reproduction (mitosis and meiosis)
chloroplast	Pl	photosynthesis
endoplasmic reticulum	all organisms	intracellular transport; molecule packaging
Golgi apparatus	all organisms	Storage; secretion of substances
lysosome	mainly A	intracellular digestion
microfilaments	all organisms	intracellular transport
microtubules	all organisms	intracellular transport
mitochondria	all organisms	energy production/cellular respiration
nucleolus	Pr, Pl, F, A	manufacture ribosome parts
nucleus	Pr, Pl, F, A	houses genetic material
ribosome	all organisms	manufacture proteins
vacuole	Pl, some Pr, F and A	storage of molecules

5.19 PEOPLE OF SCIENCE

Robert Brown (1773-1858) was born in Scotland and studied to be a doctor. He was a surgeon in the army. He became interested mainly in botany and traveled to Australia in 1801. As a result of his observations there, he was known as the leading authority on Australian botany of the early 19th century. While he was viewing preparations of an orchid through a microscope, he saw a large organelle which was the nucleus.

5.20 KEY CHAPTER POINTS

- Organelles are special structures inside of cells that perform specific, specialized functions.
- The inside of a cell is filled with a jelly-like substance called cytoplasm, and the inside of the nucleus contains nucleoplasm.
- The cytoskeleton holds the cell together.
- The nucleus is surrounded by a double lipid bilayer with holes in it, called pores. The nucleus contains the DNA and nucleolus.
- Mitochondria, ribosomes, endoplasmic reticulum, Golgi apparatus, vesicles, vacuoles, peroxisomes, and lysosomes are organelles found in all eukaryotic cells. All of them are bound by a membrane except ribosomes.
- Plants have plastids, a type of organelle not found in animal cells.
- Animal cells have centrioles, a type of organelle not found in plant cells.
- Almost all plant cells are also surrounded by a cell wall. No animal cells have cell walls.
- Animal cells are held to one another by the extracellular matrix.
- Plant cells are held to one another by the middle lamella.
- Prokaryotic cells contain cytoplasm, DNA free in the cytoplasm (not protected by a membrane), and ribosomes.

5.21 DEFINITIONS

9 + 2 Structure
The microtubule structure of cilia and flagella; nine pairs of microtubules surrounding a central core of two tubules.

actin
The protein which makes up microfilaments.

centriole
Microtubules that help pull the DNA apart during cell division. They are composed of 9 triplets of microtubules.

chloroplast
A type of plastid that performs photosynthesis.

chromatin
The collection of DNA and various proteins which are contained in the nucleus.

cilia
Short, numerous cell projections that move rhythmically back and forth.

collagen
One of the glycoproteins that make up the extracellular matrix of animal cells.

cristae
Folds of the inner mitochondrial membrane.

cytoplasm
All of the structures outside the nucleus, but inside of the cell membrane.

cytoskeleton
A complex network of proteins that strengthen the cell and keep it from rupturing.

cytosol
The aqueous component of the cytoplasm.

endoplasmic reticulum (ER)
An extensive network of folded membranes and membranous sacs throughout the cytoplasm.

extracellular matrix
The structure that holds animal cells together.

fibronectin
One of the glycoproteins that make up the extracellular matrix of animal cells.

flagella
A long, thin projection from the cell surface that functions to propel cells by whipping back and forth.

Golgi apparatus
A series of tubes and membranes that store, modify, and package the products received from the ER. The Golgi also manufactures some proteins of its own.

lysosomes
Vesicles that contain enzymes to break down proteins, lipids, carbohydrates, and old organelles.

microtubules
The largest of the cytoskeletal proteins, composed of tubulin.

middle lamella
The sticky layer of polysaccharides that holds plant cells together.

mitochondrion
A cell organelle which manufactures the cells energy molecule, ATP. Plural: mitochondria.

nuclear lamina
The skeleton of the nucleus.

nuclear membrane
The double layer of membrane which surrounds the nucleus.

nuclear pores
Holes in the nuclear membrane which allow mRNA and other molecules to leave the nucleus.

nucleolus
A spherical structure in the nucleus which manufactures ribosomal components.

nucleoplasm
The jelly-like interior of the nucleus.

nucleus
The structure found in the cytoplasm which stores the DNA.

organelles
Units inside all cells which perform specific functions.

peroxisomes
Organelles which contain hydrogen peroxide.

plastids
Organelles that either perform photosynthesis, or store material such as starch. They are found only in plants and algae.

polyribosomes
A grouping of many ribosomes.

polysomes
Same as polyribosome.

proteoglycans
One of the glycoproteins that makes up the extracellular matrix of animal cells.

protoplasm
All of the substances inside the cell membrane.

ribosomes
Organelles that manufacture proteins.

rough ER
ER that has many ribosomes attached to it.

signal group
A short segment of amino acids that are attached onto a protein by the Golgi apparatus, signaling the cell where the protein should be taken.

smooth ER
ER that does not have any ribosomes attached to it.

tubulin
Long, thin, hollow tubes found just inside the cell membrane.

vacuoles
A storage structure in the cytoplasm that may hold food or wastes.

vesicle
A membrane bound organelle which stores substances.

STUDY QUESTIONS

1. Describe the difference between eukaryotic and prokaryotic cells.

2. What is an organelle?

3. What components make up the protoplasm?

4. True or False? The cytosol is mainly made up of soluble molecules and ions.

5. If you are inside the nucleus of a eukaryotic cell and travel from the interior of the nucleus to the interior of the cell, what two jelly-like substances do you travel through?

6. What is the function of the cytoskeleton? What three types of proteins make up the cytoskeleton?

7. Besides the cytoskeleton and nuclear matrix, what three eukaryotic cell structures are composed of microtubules?

8. The nucleus contains one very important molecule and one structure. What are they? What is the function of this structure found in the nucleus?

9. How do substances move in and out of the nucleus?

10. Describe the pathway that a protein takes once it is made by the ribosome.

11. List three double membrane-bound organelles.

12. If you are standing in a cell and you see a membrane bound structure that has starch granules, what type of organelle are you looking at and are you in a plant or animal cell?

13. List at least two ways lysosomes and peroxisomes are similar.

14. What is the middle lamella?

15. How are animal cells held to one another?

16. If you are standing in a cell and you see a nucleoid, in what type of cell are you standing?

PLEASE TAKE TEST #2 IN TEST BOOKLET

Metabolism Overview and Enzymes

6

6.0 CHAPTER PREVIEW

In this chapter we will:

- Define types of metabolism.

- Investigate the properties of potential and kinetic energy and understand that living things convert one form to the other to stay alive.

- Review the First and Second Law of Thermodynamics.

- Investigate the activation energy lowering and energy coupling properties of enzymes.

- Classify types of enzymes based upon the chemical reactions they perform.

- Define cofactors and coenzymes.

6.1 OVERVIEW

The basic concept of this chapter is to understand that all organisms require energy to maintain the order and structure of life. All life forms need a constant supply of energy for growth, reproduction, maintenance, locomotion, and repair. Very few processes which occur in life are able to be completed without an input of energy. Energy used by organisms is derived from the molecule ATP (adenosine triphosphate). The production of ATP will be covered in the next chapter.

6.2 METABOLISM

Energy is the ability to do work. In life, (all energy resides in the covalent bonds of molecules.) We will learn how cells extract this energy in this chapter. The summation of all the energy-requiring and energy-producing reactions in a cell or organism is called **metabolism**. Another way to define metabolism is the totality of chemical processes in a cell or an organism.

6.3 CATABOLIC AND ANABOLIC METABOLISM

Metabolism is an energy-requiring process. There are two basic types of metabolic processes in life—**anabolic** and **catabolic**. Anabolic processes are concerned with the storage of energy (or the building of molecules). Catabolic processes are concerned with the release of energy (or the breaking down of molecules). Generally, the energy produced from catabolic reactions is used by the cell to fuel anabolic processes. Typical anabolic processes are the condensation (dehydration) synthesis reactions to build macromolecules. Typical catabolic processes are the hydrolysis reactions to break molecules down. As you remember, these were discussed in Chapter 3.

6.4 POTENTIAL AND KINETIC ENERGY

There are two types of energy—**potential energy** and **kinetic energy**. Potential energy is the energy of position, or stored energy. It is the ability to do work. Kinetic energy is the energy of motion, or active energy. It is work being done.

Take as an example a rock at rest on the top of a hill. The rock at rest has potential energy in the form of the ability to roll down the hill. However, it is not moving yet, which means it is not doing any work. As soon as someone comes along and pushes the rock, it begins to roll down the hill. As soon as it starts to roll down the hill, the potential energy is converted to kinetic energy. As soon as the rock stops rolling at the bottom of the hill, all of the potential energy has been used up in the form of kinetic energy. Prior to rolling down the hill, the rock is said to have a high potential energy and a low kinetic energy. While the rock is rolling down the hill, it has high kinetic energy and continually loses potential energy. As soon as the rock stops rolling, it has low potential and low kinetic energy. This type of potential energy is called **mechanical energy**. Mechanical potential energy is energy stored in an object. Mechanical kinetic energy is energy which is transferred from one object to another.

Figure 6.4.1

Examples of Kinetic and Potential Energy
The log in figure (a) is not doing any work. It has a low kinetic energy, but high potential energy. This is a type of potential energy called chemical energy. The potential energy is stored in the bonds between the molecules that make up the wood. In figure (b), the wood is now performing work in the form of generating heat and light. The potential energy stored in the molecules of the wood is transformed into kinetic energy as the chemical bonds between the molecules are broken. Burning is a very common way to break chemical bonds and convert potential energy into kinetic energy. The longer the wood burns, the more potential energy is lost and the more kinetic energy is released. In figure (c), the wood has now burned completely and has been reduced to a pile of ash. There is neither potential nor kinetic energy left.

a.

b.

c.

Another example of potential energy is seen in the molecule propane. Propane is a flammable gas and is often used to cook food on an outdoor grill. The potential energy in propane exists in the chemical bonds of the propane. When the bonds are broken by igniting the propane with a match and causing the propane to burn, a great amount of kinetic energy is released in the form of heat and light. In this instance, the propane as a gas has high potential energy. While the propane is burning, it has high kinetic energy. Once the propane is all burned up, there is obviously low potential and low kinetic energy. The type of energy that exists in the bonds of molecules is called **chemical energy**. Chemical potential energy is energy which exists stored within chemical bonds of molecules. Chemical kinetic energy is work which is done as the result of release of energy from a chemical reaction. The energy which is present inside of cells and organisms is chemical energy.

6.5 ENERGY CONVERSION

Note that in the above examples, energy is converted from one form to another. The potential energy is converted into kinetic energy. This is exactly what happens in cells—chemical potential energy in different molecules (mainly glucose and other carbohydrates) is converted into kinetic energy to drive the metabolic needs of the cell. Also, potential energy is stored in chemical bonds to be used later when it is needed. For example, mammals store potential energy from glucose in the form of glycogen. Glycogen is simply a polymer of glucose. It is stored in the liver and muscles. When energy is needed, cells convert glycogen into glucose, then the potential energy of the chemical bonds of the glucose is released by breaking the bonds of the glucose.

6.6 BASIC THERMODYNAMICS

Thermodynamics is the study of energy transformation (or energy conversion) within "systems." A **system** is simply a set of connected components that function to transfer energy. Another way of looking at it is that a system consists of all matter in a specific area. A system may be an individual cell, an individual organism, or the entire planet. There exists in all systems a certain amount of energy. It is critical to understand that the total amount of energy in a system is constant—energy is neither created nor destroyed, it is only converted from one form to another. We see this in the examples of potential and kinetic energy above. The example of the system we were studying above consisted only of a log. Some systems are quite simple, and some are more complex, but all systems follow the rule that energy is neither created nor destroyed within the system; it is converted from one form to another.

In our log example, the "system" is the log, the air around it, and the flame. The energy stored in the chemical bonds of the wood is the potential energy of this system. The potential energy of this system is equal to the kinetic energy which is given off by the system when the log is burned. The kinetic energy of the system is the light and heat energy released from the log when it is burned.

6.7 FIRST LAW OF THERMODYNAMICS

The concept that energy is neither created nor destroyed is called the **First Law of Thermodynamics**. We earlier learned The Law of the Conservation of Mass (which states that matter can neither be created nor destroyed during a chemical reaction). The Law of the Conservation of Mass is actually an extension of the First Law of Thermodynamics. Notice the similarity between the two laws: they both govern our knowledge of chemical reactions and energy conversion.

Figure 6.7.1

Examples of Energy Conversion
There are many different types of energy conversion in nature. On the left is an example of the conversion of the potential energy stored in the bonds of pure oxygen and hydrogen. Both of these molecules are flammable and release huge amounts of energy when burned. They burn and give off both heat and light, in the process increasing entropy of the system. The organized chemical bonds of the hydrogen and oxygen are broken to release heat. Also, kinetic energy is very high during the rocket burn because work is being done lifting the shuttle into space. Plants use the kinetic energy of sunlight to do work. They transform the kinetic energy of the sun into potential energy stored in starch. Starch is a type of carbohydrate macromolecule. Through photosynthesis, plants use the sun's energy to make carbohydrates using the carbon, hydrogen, and oxygen in carbon dioxide and water. Humans and other warm-blooded animals add to the entropy of the earth by generating body heat as a result of the metabolic processes of the organism.

The metabolism of life depends on converting energy from one form to another. Plants convert the kinetic energy of the sun's rays into potential energy in the form of carbohydrate molecules through the process of photosynthesis. Plants then convert this potential energy into kinetic energy to fuel their metabolism. Mammals convert the potential energy from the food they eat—both plant foods and animal foods—into kinetic energy to run their metabolic processes. Also, as noted above, some of the potential energy is stored in the form of carbohydrate polymers (glycogen) to be used at a later time.

It is interesting to note that in living systems, the conversion of potential chemical energy into kinetic chemical energy is not efficient. Only a small percentage of the potential energy is able to be used by the cell to complete chemical reactions. If the First Law is true and energy is neither created nor destroyed, where does the rest of the potential energy go? Is it lost? The answer is, no. The potential chemical energy which is not converted to perform the work of a chemical reaction is lost as heat. If the energy used to perform the work of the chemical reaction is added to the energy lost as heat, it would equal the energy in the form of potential energy at the start of the reaction.

6.8 SECOND LAW OF THERMODYNAMICS

The Second Law of Thermodynamics states that both chemical reactions and systems favor the creation of more disorder, or randomness. The measure of disorder is called **entropy**. Therefore, chemical reactions increase the entropy of the universe. What does that mean? Simply put, it means that almost all chemical reactions release heat! Heat is a non-specific, random form of energy. It is the random movement of molecules. Almost all of the chemical reactions in living systems release heat. By doing this, they increase the entropy of the system.

One of the easiest ways to understand this is to consider what happens in a clean house. A clean house has a high degree of order—everything is in its place. Therefore, there is a low amount of entropy in a clean house. We all know that a clean house has a tendency to get messy; that is, it has a tendency toward increasing entropy. If the house is not cleaned—i.e., if someone does not expend energy to clean it—the house will become messier and messier. That is another way of saying the entropy of the house increases. Finally, after the house has reached the maximal amount of entropy allowed by your parents, the house is cleaned, and the entropy is again lowered. Note that it takes energy (i.e., you cleaning the house) to counteract the entropy (disorder or randomness) of the house.

This is the same as it is with metabolic processes. Although entropy increases with each chemical reaction that occurs in an organism, all organisms expend a lot of energy to counteract this increasing entropy. An organism expending energy to counteract entropy is the same as you expending energy (by cleaning the house) to counteract entropy (the messy house). Fortunately, it requires less energy to counteract increasing entropy of a biological organism than is lost in the process of entropy increasing. If it required more energy to counteract the entropy than was gained by the positive effects of the chemical reactions that created the entropy in the first place, then life would cease to exist. There would simply not be enough energy to counteract the energy lost due to entropy.

6.9 ENZYMES

During energy transfers in living systems, energy is released from the chemical bonds of molecules. Some of that energy is transferred to complete a specific chemical reaction. The rest of the energy is lost as heat. In fact, most of the energy of a chemical reaction is lost as heat. You may imagine that if most of the energy is lost as heat, one would want strict control over the energy transfer process so that too much energy is not needlessly lost. This is in fact what happens.

Recall that the cell is highly ordered. We have learned about the order in terms of the structure of the cell. Now we are going to learn about the highly-ordered chemical reactions of the cell. This high degree of order comes in the form of **enzymes**. Enzymes are large protein molecules in all cells which participate in virtually all chemical reactions of the cell. There are millions of different enzymes in biological systems. However, all enzymes do essentially the same thing—exert strict control over which chemical reactions occur and when. Also, how long any given reaction will occur is highly controlled by enzymes. Another degree of order occurs as the cell constantly works to counteract entropy. We will see below how enzymes function to regulate the chemical reactions of the cell.

6.10 FREE ENERGY AND REACTION TYPES

There are two types of chemical reactions. They are classified based on whether or not the reaction is spontaneous. **Spontaneous reactions** do not require an input of energy to start; they just happen. Other reactions, called **endergonic reactions**, require the input of energy into the reaction before the reaction will start. Once the energy required to start the reaction is put into the reaction, that reaction will proceed until it is completed. The chemical reactions of cells and organisms are endergonic reactions.

Another way of stating this is to consider the concept of **free energy**. Free energy is the amount of energy available to perform work in a system. Free energy is not the total energy in a system, or in a chemical reaction. It is the amount of energy left after the energy required to start the reaction (if any is required) is subtracted from the energy produced by the reaction. Written another way:

energy produced by reaction - energy required to start reaction = free energy

Endergonic reactions require more energy to start the reaction than is given off by the reaction. This means more energy is absorbed by the system than is given off by the system. **Exergonic reactions** release more energy than is required to start the reaction. This means more energy is released by the system than is absorbed. Free energy tells us whether or not a reaction will occur spontaneously, or whether it will require an input of energy to get started.

6.11 EXERGONIC REACTIONS

Chemical reactions that release more energy than they consume are called exergonic reactions. Another way of stating this is to say that exergonic reactions have a net flow of free energy out of the reaction. When an exergonic reaction is completed, the products of the reaction have lower energy than the reactants. Exergonic reactions either occur spontaneously or require little input of energy to get them going. As such, they are difficult to regulate. Because life requires a high degree of order (or control), exergonic reactions generally are not used by living organisms.

One example of an exergonic reaction regards phosphorous. When pure phosphorous comes into contact with the air—more specifically the oxygen in the air—it ignites and glows. This gives off energy in the form of heat and light. As you can imagine, if metabolic processes of organisms were exergonic reactions—occurring spontaneously—the chemical reactions would occur all of the time without any regulation by the organism. This would consume nutrients when they did not need to be consumed and would lead to the death of the organism due to the unregulated consumption of resources.

6.12 ENDERGONIC REACTIONS

Free energy is a measure of whether or not energy flows into a reaction (i.e., energy is required to jump start the reaction) or out of a reaction (i.e., a reaction that occurs spontaneously). If the overall flow of energy is into the reaction, that means it requires energy—usually in the form of heat—to start the reaction. These are called endergonic reactions. Endergonic reactions require an input of energy before they will occur. Another way to view endergonic reactions is that the products of an endergonic reaction possess more energy than the reactants. Endergonic reactions are the reactions which occur in organisms. Since they require the input of energy, these reactions do not occur spontaneously, and the cell is able to highly regulate this kind of reaction.

6.13 ACTIVATION ENERGY

If the cell were to simply rely on endergonic reactions to occur, most of them would not occur, and life would cease to exist. This is because the energy required to initiate the endergonic reactions of life—called the **activation energy—**is so high that organisms cannot generate it. Recall that all endergonic reactions require an input of energy in order to get started. This is the activation energy. All endergonic reactions have a particular activation energy that is constant for that particular reaction. Most of the activation energy needed for endergonic reactions is supplied by the cell in the form of heat. However, the heat required to generate the needed activation for almost all endergonic reactions is so high that it would damage or kill the cell/organism.

Figure 6.13.1

Activation Energy and Enzymes
Through a number of different mechanisms, enzymes significantly lower the activation energy—the energy required to start a reaction. The reaction will still occur without the enzyme, but a significantly higher amount of energy, usually in the form of heat, will be required. The amount of heat required to start a reaction without the enzyme is usually too high to be generated by the organism. In fact, it is often high enough to kill the organism.

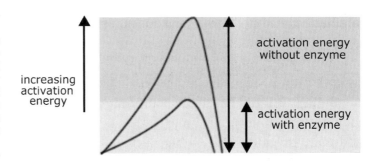

6.14 ENZYMES SOLVE THE ACTIVATION ENERGY PROBLEM

How, then, can life exist if the energy required to start the reactions of life is too high for the cell to generate it? Because of the presence of **enzymes** in all living systems. Enzymes are large catalytic proteins that lower the activation energy of endergonic reactions enough that they can occur safely in an organism. **Catalytic** means that the enzymes accelerate chemical reactions.

Figure 6.14.1

General Reaction Description of Enzyme-Catalyzed Reactions
Figure (a) represents the general reaction of substrate, enzyme, and product. There are thousands of enzymatically driven reactions in nature; therefore there are thousands of enzymes in nature. Each enzyme catalyzes only one specific reaction. In figure (b), the enzymatically driven catabolic reaction of breaking lactose into glucose and galactose is shown. Since it is a hydrolysis reaction, water is added to the glycosidic bond by the enzyme lactase, cleaving the lactose into two monosaccharide units. An important concept to understand about enzymes is they are not changed in the reaction. Enzymes simply create an environment around the molecules involved in the reaction so that less energy is required for the reaction to occur. Once the reaction is completed, the enzyme remains chemically unchanged and is then able to catalyze more reactions. Enzymes emerge from the reactions they catalyze the same after the reaction as they were before it.

a.
$$\text{Substrate} \xrightarrow{\text{Enzyme}} \text{Product}$$

b.
$$\text{Lactose} + H_2O \xrightarrow{\text{Lactase}} \text{Glucose} + \text{Galactose}$$

Generally, any endergonic reaction will occur if there is enough external heat applied to the system. However, high temperatures are dangerous to living systems, so simply elevating the temperature will not work. The need to maintain homeostasis will not allow the organism to drastically elevate its temperature to cause endergonic reactions to occur. Enzymes are the answer to that problem. Since enzymes lower the activation energy for endergonic reactions, the endergonic reactions are able to proceed without injuring the cell or the organism.

6.15 MODELS OF ENZYME FUNCTION: LOCK AND KEY; INDUCED FIT

In all of the figures on the next couple pages representing the interactions between enzyme and substrate, all of the molecules "fit" together. This is because as scientists began to understand more about the function of enzymes, it was noted that any given enzyme only catalyzed one specific reaction. This relationship was correctly likened to a **lock and key**. The molecule which an enzyme binds to is called the **substrate**. The enzyme, due to the three dimensional structure, has only one area where the substrate will "fit". This area where the substrate binds to the enzyme is called the **active site**. The "key" is the substrate, and the "lock" is the active site on the enzyme. The precise fit is the reason that only one enzyme catalyzes one particular reaction; the specificity of the binding site between the enzyme and substrate does not allow for more than one enzyme to catalyze the reaction.

The lock and key hypothesis explained the data obtained during enzyme research for a number of years. However, it was later noted that although the substrate does fit into the enzyme like a key fits into a lock, the enzyme undergoes subtle changes in its three-dimensional shape as the substrate binds to the enzyme. The shape change was not explained by the lock and key model, so it was modified to include the structural change the enzyme undergoes. The model which takes the change in the enzyme shape into account is called the **induced fit theory.**

One of the implications of the induced fit theory is that, as the enzyme structure changes, this allows for chemical groups of the enzyme and substrate to come closer to the substrate. The chemical groups of the enzyme interact with chemical groups of the substrate in order to catalyze the reaction. The closer the chemical groups are, the more efficient the enzyme is at catalyzing the reaction.

6.16 ENZYME TYPES

As stated, enzymes are large and complex proteins that have only one function—to catalyze reactions. The large size and intricate shapes of enzymes causes them to take on complicated three-dimensional structures. Some enzymes function only to speed reactions which break down molecules; these are called **catabolic enzymes**. Others catalyze reactions to synthesize molecules; these are called **anabolic enzymes**. Some enzymes are what are both anabolic and catabolic for the same reaction; these are termed **bidirectional enzymes**. Bidirectional enzymes can function at one time in the breakdown reaction and at other times in the synthesis reaction, depending on the needs of the cell and other factors.

Enzymes have many properties that make them a strict regulation point for the chemical reactions of life. Due to their complex, three-dimensional structures, enzymes are highly specific. A given enzyme does not ever catalyze more than one specific reaction. During the reaction, the enzyme is not changed by the reaction; it simply lowers the activation energy and speeds the reaction up. Unlike the reactants and products, once the reaction is completed, the enzyme emerges unchanged.

Figure 6.16.1

Catabolic Enzymes

This is the conceptual picture of how catabolic enzymes function to catalyze the reactions that break molecules down. In this example, the enzyme is maltase, which catalyzes the reaction to break the disaccharide maltose into two molecules of glucose. In an enzymatic reaction, the molecule upon which the enzyme acts is called the **substrate**. The location on the enzyme where the substrate binds is called the **active site**. Only one specific substrate can fit into – or bind – the active site. Therefore, a given enzyme can catalyze only one particular reaction. In our example, only the substrate maltose can bind the active site of maltase. The property of the active site and substrate being specific for one another and fitting perfectly together is the "lock and key" concept of the induced fit theory. Once maltose binds at the active site, maltase adds water to the glycosidic bond of the maltose via a hydrolysis reaction. Recall that enzymes lower the activation energy of the reaction, which brings us to the next concept of the induced fit theory. Enzymes lower the activation energy because once the substrate binds the active site, slight structural changes to the enzyme occur (the "fit" of the two together "induces" a change in the shape of the enzyme). This structural change brings specific chemical groups on the enzyme closer to chemical groups on the substrate and causes the enzyme and substrate molecules involved in the reaction to be as close to one another as possible (lowering the activation energy). The enzyme emerges from the reaction unchanged, while the substrate is chemically broken into smaller molecules. **All enzymes, whether catabolic or anabolic, emerge from the reaction without undergoing any chemical changes.** In our example, the maltase emerges from the reaction exactly the same as it was before the reaction, while the maltose has been cleaved into two molecules of glucose.

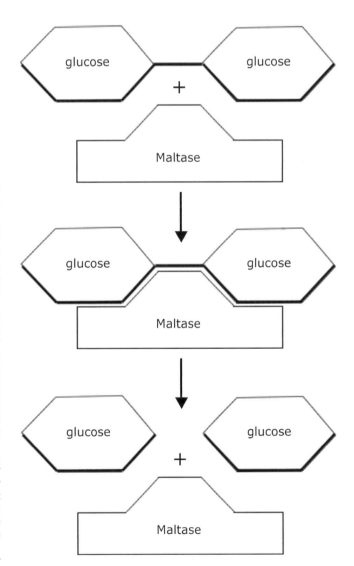

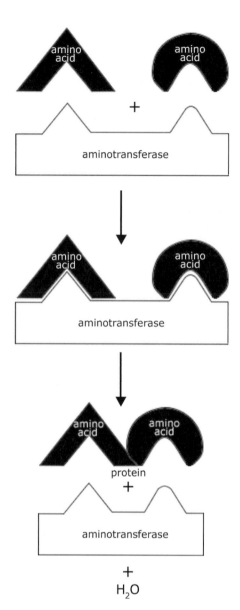

Figure 6.16.2

Anabolic Enzymes

The anabolic function of enzymes is graphically demonstrated in this hydration synthesis reaction of two amino acids linked to form a dipeptide. In an anabolic reaction, the enzyme has two active sites for each substrate molecule to bind to, as can be seen. Once the reaction is completed, the enzyme emerges unchanged; only the reactants and products have changed. Anabolic enzymes catalyze all the molecule building reactions we discussed in Chapter 3. Remember these reactions are called dehydration or condensation synthesis reactions because water is a product of the reaction.

You can often tell that a certain molecule is an enzyme because the enzyme names often end in *–ase* (such as lactase which catalyzes the breakdown of lactose into galactose and glucose). Enzymes are often named for their function. Lactase catalyzes the breakdown of lactose, as noted above. Sucrase catalyzes the breakdown of sucrose into glucose and fructose. Amino transferases (there are many of them, each with specific names) catalyze the reaction of transferring amino acids in protein synthesis.

Figure 6.16.3

Bidirectional Enzymes
Bidirectional enzymes have the ability to catalyze both the anabolic and the catabolic portion of a chemical reaction. Not all enzymes are able to do this. If the cell needs more of the larger molecule—in this example, a protein—the anabolic function of the enzyme is "turned on." The enzyme will begin to bind to the proper amino acids' active sites and catalyze the condensation synthesis reaction. This will link the two amino acids together. If the cell needs the smaller subunits, the catabolic function of the enzyme is turned on, and the protein is broken down into the amino acids. No change occurs to the enzyme in either reaction. It is important to remember that anabolic enzymes and anabolic bidirectional enzymes are not able to link together any two monomer units they want. They are specific and can only link together two equally specific monomers. For example, let's say an enzyme had the ability to link together the monomer units of glucose and galactose. That enzyme can only catalyze the linking of glucose to galactose. It cannot link a glucose to another glucose or a fructose to galactose. Enzymes are so specific they only catalyze one specific reaction and no other. Likewise, catabolic enzymes can only perform one specific hydrolysis reaction to remove monomers from a polymer. For example, the enzyme which splits apart the amino acids phenylalanine and threonine can only split those two amino acids apart.

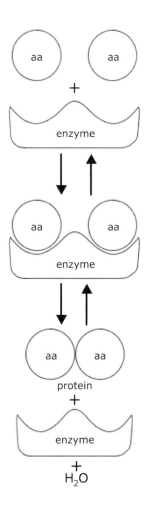

You may think that because enzymes are large molecules, they may be slow-moving. Nothing is farther from the truth. Although enzymes work at different rates, it is not unusual for one enzyme to be able to catalyze 1000 reactions per second! Some enzymes are capable of reacting with 500,000 molecules per second. Remember that enzymes are not molecularly altered during the reaction, so once the reaction is completed, the same enzyme is ready to catalyze an entirely new reaction.

6.17 COENZYMES AND COFACTORS

Some enzymes require "helpers" to become active. These helpers are referred to as **coenzymes** and **cofactors**. Coenzymes and cofactors are not enzymes themselves, but are necessary for the enzyme to function properly. Coenzymes are organic molecules. Cofactors are inorganic molecules. Examples of coenzymes are most vitamins (A, B, D, etc.). Examples of cofactors are iron, copper, and zinc. It is important to remember that while not all enzymes require coenzymes or cofactors, those that do will not work properly if the helpers are not present.

6.18 ATP (ADENOSINE TRIPHOSPHATE)

Hopefully it's apparent that there are numerous energy requirements for life to occur and be maintained. In general, the work the cell needs to perform can be characterized as **mechanical work** (muscle contraction, beating of cilia, etc.), **transport work** (active transport across the cell membrane, movement of nutrients along a nerve cell, etc.) and **chemical work** (the activation energy needed to start endergonic reactions, for example). All three types of work require energy, which is provided by the molecule **ATP**. Almost every single organism on earth uses the molecule ATP to provide the energy needed to fuel their chemical reactions.

Figure 6.18.1

Structure of ATP

This is the molecule ATP, the molecule which supplies almost all of the energy to drive the endergonic reactions of most organisms on earth. It is made up of three groups, as shown. We briefly discussed the structure of this molecule last chapter and will continue to learn about it as we move through the course. Since it is a nucleic acid, it has a central 5 carbon sugar, or pentose. This is called ribose. Covalent bonds link the phosphate group on the left to the ribose. Also, covalent bonds hold the middle and rightward phosphate groups to one another. Biochemists refer to the phosphate group on the right, below, as the "first" phosphate group. The middle phosphate group is referred to as the "second" phosphate group. The phosphate attached directly to the ribose is the "third" phosphate group. The bond that holds the phosphate group to the ribose is not as strong as the bonds which hold the phosphate groups to one another. Recall that when stronger bonds are broken they release more energy than weaker bonds. When the cell needs energy, an enzyme adds water to the bond that is holding the first and second phosphate groups together. This releases energy which the enzyme can then use to complete the reaction it catalyzes. Sometimes, if the cell or enzyme needs more energy quickly, the bond between the second and third phosphate groups is also broken. This releases as much energy as breaking the first phosphate bond. Under certain conditions, the remaining phosphate group bond can be broken between the phosphate and the ribose. This removes the remaining phosphate group from the ribose. This reaction releases only about half of the energy that the first two phosphate bond-breaking reactions released.

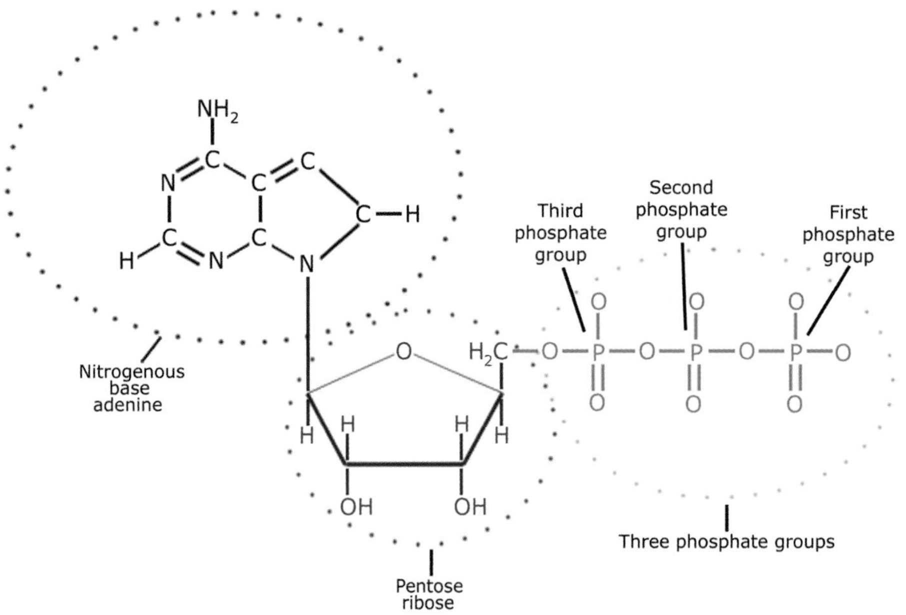

ATP, or adenosine triphosphate, is an extremely important molecule in life. It is made of the nucleotide adenosine with three phosphate groups attached to the ribose. The phosphate bonds are often called "high energy" bonds, not because they are stable (they are actually very unstable bonds) but because a great amount of energy is released when the bond is hydrolyzed, or broken by adding water.

6.19 ENZYMES ARE ENERGY COUPLERS

Not only do enzymes lower the activation energy, but they also use ATP. How? Enzymes are able to harness the energy released when the phosphate bonds of ATP are broken. The enzyme then uses this energy to fuel the endergonic reactions of life. This process is called **energy coupling**. Enzymes are capable of hydrolyzing the phosphate bonds of ATP by adding water to them. When the bonds holding the phosphate groups are hydrolyzed, the released energy is captured by the enzyme and used to start the chemical reaction. We will learn in the next chapter how ATP is made.

Figure 6.19.1

The Hydrolysis of the Phosphate Bonds of ATP Release Energy to Drive the Chemical Reactions of Life

This schematic represents the energy released by breaking the phosphate bonds of ATP. Remember the bonds are broken by adding water to the bond, or hydrolyzing it. The phosphate groups are represented by "P," and the rest of the ATP molecule by "A." The first and second phosphate bonds that are broken by enzymes to obtain the energy from ATP are squiggled because they represent "high energy" bonds. These two bonds represent the bonds between the first and second and the second and third phosphate groups on the previous diagram of ATP. The third bond, which is broken, is not squiggled. This is the bond which holds the third phosphate group directly to the ribose. This is because when the first two phosphate bonds are broken, they release twice as much energy, each, as the third and final bond of ATP that can be broken to obtain energy. The hydrolysis of the first phosphate bond results in the formation of a molecule of adenosine diphosphate (ADP) and a molecule of inorganic phosphate. Energy is also released. Then the enzyme performs its function as an energy coupler to catalyze an endergonic reaction. Normally, the ATP molecule is quickly recycled in the cell. It does this by the addition of a phosphate group back onto the ADP, re-forming ATP. However, under certain conditions, the next phosphate bond of the ADP may be broken. This releases as much energy, in the form of heat, as hydrolyzing the first phosphate bond does. A molecule of adenosine monophosphate (AMP) and an inorganic phosphate molecule are the products of that reaction. The AMP can then be recycled back to ATP by the addition of two phosphate groups. Or, the remaining phosphate bond can be hydrolyzed, releasing energy. Again, hydrolysis of the third phosphate bond releases about half the energy as the first two phosphate bond hydrolysis reactions do. If the enzyme does this, a molecule containing adenosine and another inorganic phosphate molecule are made. The adenosine is then recycled back into ATP by adding three phosphate molecules to it. This recycling mechanism is how the cell is able to continually create its own energy supply. The hydrolysis of the phosphate bonds is performed by the enzymes that need the released energy to drive the chemical reaction which the enzyme catalyzes.

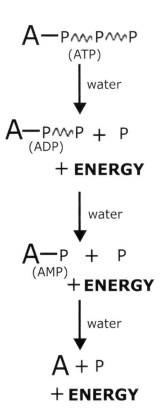

6.20 ADVANCED

Enzymes appear to work by creating "microenvironments" within the active site. The structural change induced by the substrate binding, in the case of enzymes that breakdown large molecules, appears to cause the enzyme to bend the substrate. This causes stress on the bond to be broken, making it easier for the enzyme to cleave the substrate. In the case of synthetic enzymes, the enzyme changes shape so the portions of the enzyme and substrate that directly participate in the reaction are brought closer together to facilitate the bonding reaction.

Another common type of environment created within the active site has to do with pH. Certain reactions are much easier to perform in an acidic or basic environment. When a low pH is needed (i.e., an acidic environment), the active site will contain amino acids that have acidic side chains to create the acidic environment. When a high pH serves to lower the activation energy, the active site will contain amino acids with basic side chains.

How do enzymes know when to start and stop working? There are several methods that researchers have identified, and probably some that have yet to be discovered. One of the most common forms of regulation is called **feedback inhibition**. As the reaction occurs, the products build up and accumulate around the enzyme. When there has been enough product made, the product binds directly to the enzyme, not at the active site but somewhere else on the enzyme molecule. When the product binds to the enzyme, it causes the enzyme to change shape. This alters the structure of the enzyme's active site so it is no longer able to bond to the substrate, and the reaction ceases. The enzyme is then said to be inactive. When the concentration of the product begins to fall, the product molecule comes off the enzyme. This allows the active site to change its shape again so that it can bind to the substrate. The enzyme then becomes active again.

6.21 PEOPLE OF SCIENCE

Daniel Koshland, Jr (1920-2007) is a biochemist that has been active in the research of enzyme systems. He has published extensively on this subject and developed the induced fit theory. He was also the editor of the journal *Science* from 1985-1995.

6.22 KEY CHAPTER POINTS

- Metabolism is the process of breaking down or building up organic molecules.

- All organisms convert potential energy stored in molecules into kinetic energy. This is done following the Laws of Thermodynamics.

- Exergonic reactions result in a net output of energy for the chemical reaction.

- Endergonic reactions result in a net input of energy for the chemical reaction. The energy required to get endergonic reactions going is called activation energy.

- The reactions of life are endergonic reactions and require a high activation energy. Enzymes are special proteins which lower the activation energy such that endergonic reactions can occur safely in all cells.

- Only one enzyme can catalyze one reaction. Enzymes and the molecules they act upon, called substrates, fit together like a lock and key.

- Enzymes which catalyze reactions to build molecules are called anabolic enzymes. Enzymes which catalyze reactions to break molecules down are called catabolic enzymes. Some enzymes can catalyze the anabolic and catabolic reaction and are called bidirectional enzymes.

- Enzymes are able to release the energy stored in ATP and couple that energy to lower the activation energy to fuel endergonic reactions.

- Enzymes know when to start and stop by feedback inhibition.

6.23 DEFINITIONS

activation energy
   The energy required to initiate an endergonic reaction.

active site
   The area where an enzyme binds to the substrate.

anabolic
   A metabolic process concerned with the storage of energy or synthesizing molecules.

anabolic enzymes
   Enzymes that catalyze anabolic reactions.

ATP (adenosine triphosphate)
   The molecule that provides energy for the cell. ATP is used to fuel the endergonic reactions of life.

bidirectional enzymes
   Enzymes that are both anabolic and catabolic for the same reaction.

catabolic
   A metabolic process concerned with the release of energy, or breaking molecules apart.

catabolic enzymes
   Enzymes that catalyze catabolic reactions.

catalytic
   An enzyme's property of "speeding up" an endergonic reaction. This is possible because enzymes lower the activation energy

chemical energy

The potential energy that exists in the bonds of molecules.

chemical work

Work performed by chemical reactions.

coenzymes

Organic molecules that enzymes need to function properly. Coenzymes are not part of the enzyme.

cofactors

Inorganic molecules that enzymes need to function properly. Cofactors are not part of the enzyme.

endergonic reaction

A chemical reaction which absorbs more energy than it releases. An endergonic reaction has a net flow of free energy into the reaction.

energy coupling

The ability of an enzyme to capture the energy released from ATP and use it to fuel the endergonic reaction, which the enzyme catalyzes.

entropy

A measure of disorder or randomness in a system.

enzymes

Large, energy coupling proteins that lower the activation energy of endergonic reactions enough to allow them to occur safely in biological systems.

exergonic reaction

A chemical reaction which releases more energy than it absorbs. An exergonic reaction has a net flow of free energy out of the reaction.

feedback inhibition

The way in which reactions catalyzed by enzymes are regulated. When a product of an enzymatically catalyzed reaction builds up, the high level of the product causes the enzyme to inactivate and the reaction stops. When the level of the product gets lower, the enzyme activates and the reaction starts again.

First Law of Thermodynamics

The concept that energy is neither created nor destroyed in a closed system.

free energy

The amount of energy available to perform work in a system.

induced fit theory

The theory of how enzymes function. The first part of the theory states that the enzyme and substrate fit together like a lock and key. The second part of the theory states that once the enzyme fits into the substrate, the substrate undergoes a change in shape to further enhance the catalytic property of the enzyme.

kinetic energy

The energy of motion, or active energy; work being done.

lock and key

The hypothesis stating that any given enzyme can only catalyzes one specific reaction. As such, an enzyme fits into a substrate like a key fits into a lock.

mechanical energy

Energy which is transferred from one object to another.

mechanical work

Work that is done when energy is transferred from one object to another.

potential energy

Stored energy; the ability to do work.

Second Law of Thermodynamics
The concept that both chemical reactions and systems favor the creation of more disorder or randomness.

substrate
The molecule which an enzyme binds to.

system
A set of connected components that function to transfer energy.

thermodynamics
The study of energy transformation (or transfer) in nature.

transport work
The work a cell performs when moving substances and molecules within the cell.

STUDY QUESTIONS

1. What is energy?

2. In general, the summation of all of an organism's anabolic and catabolic processes is called _____.

3. Describe the difference between potential and kinetic energy.

4. Mechanical and chemical energy are types of what? In which one of these does most of the energy in living organisms exist?

5. What is the study of energy transfer called?

6. Describe how the First Law of Thermodynamics applies to cells using energy in endergonic reactions.

7. Describe the practical application of the Second Law of Thermodynamics as it applies to homeostasis in a human being.

8. What type of reactions are those found in living organisms? Why?

9. If I gave you a powdery substance and asked you to place it in some water, what kind of reaction would have taken place if the powder dissolved in the water? What if the powder did not dissolve at all, even after one week, and then you heated the water and the powder dissolved? What type of reaction would that be?

10. What is the basic function of an enzyme? (Do not answer "to catalyze reactions.")

11. What is the active site of an enzyme? How does it work to catalyze reactions?

12. Why was the "lock and key" hypothesis replaced by the "induced fit" hypothesis?

13. True or False? A cofactor is an inorganic "enzyme helper" or "enzyme activator."

14. How many phosphate bonds of ATP can be broken to release energy?

15. True or False? The cell can only use ATP as an energy source to perform mechanical and chemical work, not transport work.

16. Describe the process of energy coupling.

17. How do enzymes know when to stop catalyzing reactions?

Photosynthesis

7

7.0 CHAPTER PREVIEW

In this chapter we will:

- Describe the ways in which organisms obtain their energy and make their cell mass.

- Investigate the components and properties of the electromagnetic spectrum, including the visible light spectrum.

- Discuss the absorption spectrum of plant leaves and how that relates to photosynthesis.

- Study the plant structures and molecules that perform photosynthesis.

- Learn that, although photosynthesis occurs in many linked biochemical reactions, it is really a two part process—a light absorbing/energy transforming event and a carbon fixation event.

7.1 OVERVIEW

Remember from earlier chapters (mainly 3 and 4), that all life is built upon carbon-containing molecules, the organic molecules. These include carbohydrates, lipids, nucleic acids, and proteins. Where does the carbon come from to synthesize these important compounds? The entry point for carbon into the life cycle is **photosynthesis**. This is an energy-transforming, biochemical process that begins the incorporation of carbon into organic molecules. The process of incorporating carbon into organic molecules is called **carbon fixation**. Therefore, life is literally made possible by the process of photosynthesis. Without it, very few organisms would be able to synthesize organic molecules. Without photosynthesis, producers would not be able to manufacture energy for themselves and the consumers would have nothing to consume to provide their energy. Photosynthesis, therefore, is necessary for the existence of almost every life form on this planet with the exception of a few types of bacteria.

Photosynthesis is the biochemical process in which the sun's energy is transformed into chemical energy. Photosynthesis occurs in all plants, blue-green algae, and some bacteria (remember, organisms that perform photosynthesis are called producers). Once the energy from sunlight is converted to chemical energy, it is available to fuel the metabolic processes of producers and is also available as energy to consumers.

7.2 AUTOTROPHS

Another word to describe producers is "autotroph." An **autotroph** is an organism that is able to manufacture its own cell mass and organic compounds from CO_2 using sunlight or chemical compounds as their source of energy. If the organism uses the sun's energy to make their organic molecules, they do so through the process of photosynthesis. During photosynthesis, the sun's energy is converted into chemical energy by taking the carbon from CO_2 and making it into carbohydrate molecules. Autotrophs that transform energy in this fashion are called **photolithoautotrophs**, or more simply **photoautotrophs**. All plants and photosynthetic bacteria are photoautotrophs. Rather than use the sun's energy, some bacteria convert energy from inorganic molecules, such as sulfur, hydrogen, or ammonia, to make their organic molecules. This type of autotroph is called a **chemolithoautotroph** or more simply **chemoautotroph**. We will be focusing on the processes of the photoautotrophs in this chapter. Also realize there is a large mass of underwater photolithoautotrophs (seaweed, algae, etc.). In fact, there are more photosynthetic organisms underwater than on land.

Figure 7.2.1

Modes of Energy Conversion

The organisms in the top left micrograph are a photosynthetic algae called *Spirogyra*. They are photoautotrophs. The organisms on the top right are a parasitic organism called *Trichinella*. They are heterotrophs and feed off the living flesh of a host. *Trichinella* causes the disease trichinosis, a disease contracted by eating undercooked pork. These parasites infect and live in various tissues, including muscles. The lower left photo shows many green plants, which are photoautotrophs. Standing among them are deer, which are heterotrophs. Deer are herbivores. Herbivores only eat plants. Lions are also heterotrophs. They only eat other consumers, though, and are called carnivores. They eat herbivores and occasionally other carnivores. Humans are also heterotrophs, but are called omnivores because we eat producers and consumers.

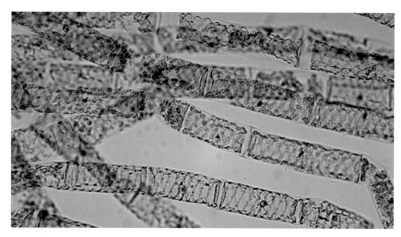
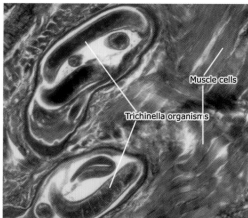

7.3 HETEROTROPHS

In contrast to the autotroph is the **heterotroph**. Heterotrophs are not able to manufacture their own cell mass or organic molecules using inorganic molecules. Heterotrophs ingest organic molecules by eating autotrophs or other heterotrophs. They then make their organic molecules from the organic molecules they ingest. In Chapter 1, heterotrophs were referred to as consumers or decomposers. Any of the names are valid as long as the relationship of where the organic molecules come from is understood. Photoautotrophs (producers) can make their own organic matter from the sun's energy and CO_2. Heterotrophs (consumers and decomposers) must obtain their energy and molecules for their organic matter by ingesting autotrophs or other heterotrophs.

7.4 ELECTROMAGNETIC SPECTRUM

In order to fully understand the process of photosynthesis, it is first important to understand the properties of the light that make the chemical reactions of photosynthesis possible. The sun emits energy in two forms—heat and **radiant energy**. Radiant energy is also called the **electromagnetic spectrum** and is made up of several different components: **radio waves**, **microwaves**, **ultraviolet (UV) rays**, **light**, **infrared (IR) rays**, **x-rays**, and **gamma rays**. As the sun burns, all of these different forms of energy are constantly given off and travel roughly ninety-three million miles to earth. Although you cannot see them, radiant energy travels in **waves**, in discreet units called **photons**.

Some may be having a hard time with this concept. Let's think of it like this. You are familiar with waves in the ocean. "Waves," though, are made up of countless numbers of water molecules. Therefore, an ocean wave is built from many smaller units—the water molecule. You cannot see the individual water molecule, but you can see their added mass as a wave when they travel. Electromagnetic radiation is the same. The "light" which you can see is similar to the wave on the ocean. Light is made up of countless smaller units—photons—just as the ocean waves are made up of countless smaller units—water molecules. However, like the ocean wave, you cannot see the individual units, but you can see their additive effects. The additive effect of the water molecules all traveling together in the ocean wave creates the "wave." The additive effect of the photons all traveling together in light creates "light." Just as ocean waves are built from smaller units, namely water molecules, so are electromagnetic energy waves built from photons.

Figure 7.4.1

The Electromagnetic Spectrum

The electromagnetic spectrum emitted by the sun includes radiation of many wavelengths. This includes energy that is both visible (called visible light) and invisible (all other forms of radiation). As can be seen in figure (a), the shortest of the wavelengths are gamma rays, and the longest are radio waves. The shorter wavelengths contain more energy than the longer wavelengths. The spectrum of radiation which can be seen is a small percentage of the total radiation from the sun. In figure (b), the general photosynthetic reaction is depicted. Only the visible light portion of the electromagnetic spectrum is captured by autotrophs and used for photosynthesis. As can be seen, using the energy of the sun, carbon from CO_2 in the atmosphere is incorporated into carbohydrate molecules, releasing oxygen into the atmosphere.

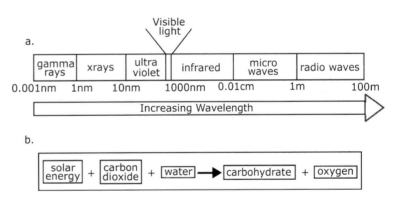

7.5 WAVELENGTH

Like waves in the ocean, waves of radiant energy have peaks and troughs. The distance between the peaks can also be measured. The distance from one peak of a radiant energy wave to the next peak is called the **wavelength**. Wavelength is measured in meters. Wavelengths can be short in the case of gamma rays (as small as 0.001 nanometers, or one-trillionth of a meter), or very long in the case of radio waves (up to 100 meters). Radiant energy that has shorter wavelengths is higher in energy, and radiant energy that has longer wavelengths is lower in energy. That is why x-rays, which have a very short wavelength, can pass right through your body (as do gamma rays), but sunlight cannot (although sunlight does have enough energy to burn your unprotected skin).

7.6 VISIBLE SPECTRUM

Notice that only a small portion of the sun's radiant energy is able to be seen by the human eye. It is called, creatively enough, **visible (or white) light**. It is the visible light portion of the sun's radiant energy that is utilized in photosynthesis. However, even the visible light portion of the sun's radiant energy is made up of radiant energy that has different wavelengths.

What we perceive as "white light" is actually a composite of many colors. However, our eyes cannot perceive all of the individual colors because their wavelengths are mixed together. The light only looks white because all the colors are seen at once. If we take white light and pass it through a prism, the **spectrum—**or color make-up—becomes visible.

7.7 REFRACTION

The **visible spectrum** of white light therefore consists of all the separate colors of light as visualized after white light is passed through a prism. This is possible because a prism has the ability to bend light at different angles—called **refraction**. Light is refracted based upon the differing wavelengths of visible light. Visible light that has shorter wavelengths (for example, light toward the violet end of the spectrum) is bent more than light of longer wavelengths (light at the red end of the spectrum) when it passes through a prism. As the white light passes through the prism, all of the individual wavelengths are bent at slightly different angles and emerge appearing as a rainbow. The primary colors of the white light spectrum are, from longest to shortest wavelengths, R̲ed, O̲range, Y̲ellow, G̲reen, B̲lue, I̲ndigo, and V̲iolet. Notice that if you take the first letters of the colors and put them together, you get the name "ROY G. BIV." This fellow's name has always helped me remember the colors of the spectrum—and keep them in order from longest to shortest wavelengths. The visible light spectrum includes the wavelengths 380 nm (violet) through 750 nm (red).

Figure 7.7.1

The Visible Spectrum
Although light from the sun appears to be "white" in color, it is actually composed of many different colors of light. This can be seen when white light is passed through a prism, resulting in the rainbow appearance—the visible spectrum—as shown below. After passing through a prism, if the light is then passed through a vial containing ground up plant leaves, mostly green with some yellow light emerges. That is because the molecules in the leaves that are responsible for absorbing the light for photosynthesis are best at absorbing indigo, blue, orange, and red light. The molecules that absorb light are called pigments. Since these pigments are responsible for photosynthesis, they are called photosynthetic pigments. When white light is passed through the solution containing photosynthetic pigments, the indigo, blue, orange, and red light is absorbed by the pigments, and the green and yellow light emerges unabsorbed. This is also the reason leaves look green in the summer; photosynthetic pigments absorb the light which hits the leaf and reflect mainly green back to the eyes. That makes the leaves look green. Only light which is absorbed can be used for photosynthesis. Therefore, the energy to drive the chemical reactions of photosynthesis are driven by the energy provided mainly by the absorbed indigo, violet, orange, and red light wavelengths.

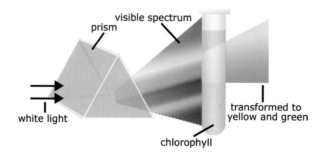

7.8 REFLECTION

As we all know, in the summertime the leaves of plants and flowers look green, and the color yellow looks yellow, and blue looks blue. But why is that? Things look the color they are based on the wavelength of light they reflect. All objects absorb and reflect light differently. A red ball looks red because it absorbs all wavelengths of light in the visible spectrum except for red. The wavelength of red light is 750 nm. When that wavelength enters our eyes, whatever object is reflecting that wavelength looks red. The red ball reflects light that has a wavelength of 750 nm and when light with that wavelength enters our eyes, we see the ball as red. Blue jeans look blue because the fabric absorbs all of the other visible light except blue. Light with a wavelength in the blue light range reflects off the blue jeans and enters our eyes and the blue jeans are seen as blue.

As stated above, photosynthesis utilizes the radiant energy from the spectrum of visible light. Since leaves reflect mainly green light, that light cannot be used to provide energy for photosynthesis; only energy from absorbed light can be used. Light that is absorbed is called the **absorption spectrum**. The energy in the absorption spectrum of plant leaves that is used for photosynthesis is all colors of the visible spectrum except green and some yellow. Therefore, it is the light in the red, orange, indigo, violet and blue wavelengths that provides the energy for photosynthesis to occur.

It is interesting to note that about 58% of the incoming radiant energy from the sun is absorbed by the atmosphere surrounding the earth, so it does not even make it to the earth's surface. Of the 42% of the energy that does make it to the earth's surface, only 0.1%-1.6% is used by autotrophs to fixate carbon.

Figure 7.8.1

Reflection

Every color that we can see is due to the wavelengths of light the object absorbs and reflects. Wavelengths of light which are absorbed by an object are not able to be seen. Wavelengths of light which are reflected are able to be seen. In this picture of an orchid, the leaves appear green because the cells of the leaf absorb a large amount of all other wavelengths of light except for green. Therefore, light which is in the green wavelength is reflected from the object and into our eyes. We perceive the leaves as green because that is the wavelength of light which the leaves do not absorb. Likewise, the center of the flower appears magenta because those cells reflect light which is in the magenta wavelength. This light enters our eyes and we see the flower as having a magenta-colored center. Another way of stating this is that magenta is not in the absorption spectrum of that part of the flower.

7.9 PHOTOSYNTHESIS: TWO SEPARATE, BUT LINKED, REACTIONS

Photosynthesis occurs in a series of two separate, but connected, series of chemical reactions. The two sets of reactions are called the light-dependent reactions and the Calvin cycle (sometimes the Calvin cycle is called the "light-independent reactions"). The light-dependent reactions transform the energy from sunlight into chemical energy. The Calvin cycle uses this transformed energy to remove the carbon from carbon dioxide and make it into carbohydrate molecules.

In order to understand these two steps of photosynthesis, we must first understand the structure of the chloroplast. The chloroplast is where photosynthesis takes place in plants. Although chloroplasts are located throughout plants, they are in highest concentration in the leaves and green stems. Anywhere on a plant that you see green there will be large numbers of chloroplasts carrying out photosynthesis.

Figure 7.9.1

Overview of Photosynthesis

Photosynthesis occurs as two separate, but linked, series of chemical reactions. The overall purpose of photosynthesis is to obtain carbon from carbon dioxide and incorporate it into organic molecules. The organic molecuels made during photosynthesis are carbohydrates (sugars). The figure below starts with the sun hitting the chloroplast. Recall that chloroplasts are a type of organelle called plastids found only in plants. The sun's energy activates the first set of reactions. These are called the light-dependent reactions, or just light reactions. During the light reactions, the energy in sunlight is absorbed by the molecules in the chloroplast—mainly chlorophyll a and b and the carotenoids. The overall purpose of the light reactions is to convert sunlight energy into chemical energy. The chemical energy is stored in molecules that we will learn about in the upcoming sections. The Calvin cycle uses these energy molecules to fuel another series of chemical reactions. During the Calvin cycle, carbon is removed from atmospheric carbon dioxide. Then the carbon is incorporated into a three-carbon sugar molecule called glyceraldehyde-3-phosphate, or G-3-P. Although G-3-P can be converted by the plant into a number of different molecules, it is most often converted to glucose immediately after it is synthesized. The overall reaction of photosynthesis is written at the bottom of the diagram. It takes a total of 12 water molecules and 6 carbon dioxide molecules to make 6 oxygen molecules, 6 water molecules and one six carbon sugar molecule (usually glucose).

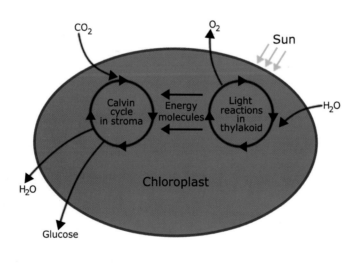

$$12H_2O + 6CO_2 \xrightarrow{\text{Light}} 6O_2 + C_6H_{12}O_6 + 6H_2O$$

7.10 THYLAKOID

Chloroplasts are a type of plastid. Recall that plastids are organelles found only in plants and have a variety of functions. Some plastids store substances while other plastids are chloroplasts. Chloroplasts are surrounded by a double membrane system. The internal membrane system of a chloroplast is called the **thylakoid**. The thylakoid is composed of multiple series of flattened membranous discs, called **grana**. Realize that when we say grana, all that is being referred to is a specific area of the thylakoid. The internal spaces of the discs are all connected to one another. Surrounding the thylakoid is an enzyme-rich solution called the **stroma**. The light dependent reactions occur in the thylakoid and the light independent reactions occur in the stroma.

Figure 7.10.1

Chloroplast and Thylakoid Structure

A tissue called the mesophyll forms the bulk of the leaf structure. When you hold a leaf, the tissue you are touching is essentially all mesophyll. Inside of the mesophyll, there are many different types of tissues, such as structural support tissue and vascular tissue. Also, the mesophyll contains numerous chloroplasts. In figure (a), each chloroplast is surrounded by a double membrane. The internal membrane is called the thylakoid. The thylakoid forms into many series of hollow, flattened discs, called grana. Between the outer membrane and the grana is a fluid filled space called the stroma. The photosynthetic pigments chlorophyll and carotenoids are contained in the membranes of the thylakoid. The thylakoid grana are hollow, and their hollow interiors all are connected such that there is one thylakoid space that snakes around the entire thylakoid system of each chloroplast. The light-dependent reactions occur in the grana. The molecules which partake in the light reactions are actually contained within the thylakoid membrane. The light-independent reactions (also called the Calvin cycle, which use the energy from the light-dependent reactions to fixate carbon) occur in the stroma.

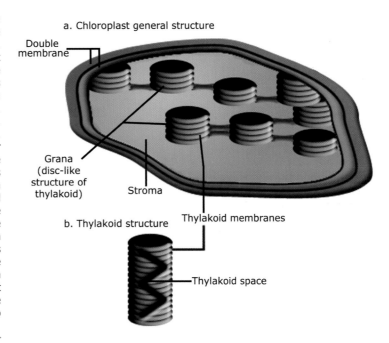

a. Chloroplast general structure

Double membrane

Grana (disc-like structure of thylakoid)

Stroma

b. Thylakoid structure

Thylakoid membranes

Thylakoid space

7.11 CHLOROPHYLL

Chlorophyll is a molecule called a pigment. Pigments are capable of absorbing light. Since the pigments in plants absorb light energy to be used in photosynthesis, they are called photosynthetic pigments. There are several photosynthetic pigments contained in the thylakoid membrane; chlorophyll is one of them and the most numerous kind.

Each grana contains thousands and thousands of chlorophyll pigments. There are two types of chlorophyll, **a** and **b**. Chlorophyll a and b are both green-colored pigments. Since they are green, we know that means they do not absorb light in the green wavelength. Therefore they reflect green light, which is why they look green. We also know if they reflect green, they likely absorb most other wavelengths, which they do (except for some yellow). Chlorophyll is the reason that green parts of plants appear green. Since leaf mesophyll contains large amounts of chlorophyll-containing chloroplasts, the main color which is reflected to our eyes is green. Sunlight energy absorbed by chlorophyll is transformed into energy-containing molecules used to fuel the endergonic reactions of the Calvin cycle.

As a note, photosynthetic bacteria do not have chloroplasts. However, they do have chlorophyll and some other photosynthetic pigments. The chlorophyll is instead attached to membranes within the bacterial cytoplasm.

7.12 CAROTENOIDS

Carotenoids are another class of energy absorbing pigments that are contained within the thylakoid membrane. Carotenoids are pigments of red, yellow, and orange color (which means they reflect those wavelengths of light). Therefore, since they reflect red, yellow, and orange, they absorb blue and some green wavelengths. The carotenoids function to enhance the absorption spectrum of the plant. The more light that can be absorbed, the more radiant energy will be available to the plant to carry out photosynthesis. While the carotenoids do not directly participate in photosynthesis, they "pass along" the energy they absorb to the chlorophyll. Even though the carotenoids do absorb light in the green spectrum, they do not absorb nearly as much as the chlorophyll reflects, so leaves are green.

7.13 FALL COLORS

The reason tree leaves change color in the fall makes an interesting side note. As the fall progresses, tree leaves stop producing chlorophyll, but carotenoids remain. As the chlorophyll pigment is lost, the leaves do not appear green any more. Instead, they will take on whatever color is reflected by the carotenoids remaining in the leaf. The exact color depends on the amounts and types of carotenoids present. That is why tree leaves turn various shades of red, orange, yellow, and brown in the fall. For example, if a particular tree species makes a lot of red-colored pigments, like the fire maple tree, when the green chlorophyll is lost, the main remaining pigment is colored red and the leaves reflect the red wavelengths. This makes a fire maple tree look bright red in the fall.

7.14 PHOTOSYNTHESIS

Photosynthesis is an extremely complicated process, one that is not completely understood even today. We will cover enough basics to comprehend completely what is occurring, without bogging down in vivid or confusing detail. The basic process of photosynthesis is one of energy transformation. During photosynthesis, the sun's energy is absorbed by the photosynthetic pigments and then transformed into usable energy for the plant. Photosynthesis occurs as a two-step process. Each step consists of several complex chemical reactions. The first series of reactions are called the **light-dependent reactions**. During the light-dependent reactions, energy from the sun is absorbed by photosynthetic pigments and transferred to energy containing molecules. These molecules then transfer their energy to the chemical reactions of the second set of reactions, called the **light-independent reactions**, or the **Calvin cycle**. During the Calvin cycle, the energy from the molecules made in the light reactions is used to fuel the endergonic reactions which make glucose from water and carbon dioxide. Basically, the purpose of the light dependent reactions is to make the energy required for the Calvin cycle to make carbohydrates.

The sun's energy, then, is used to drive the endergonic reactions that ultimately end up making carbohydrates. The energy stored in the bonds of carbohydrates is then available to make other organic molecules and keep the cell, and the organism, alive. I hope you recall that carbohydrates are made of carbon, hydrogen and oxygen. Remember the general formula CH_2O. The source of the carbon for the carbohydrates is CO_2 which plants absorb from the air around them. The hydrogen and oxygen for the carbohydrates comes from water.

Figure 7.14.1

Photosynthesis, Chemically Speaking
Figure (a) represents the actual balance of molecules in photosynthesis, calculated for the production of one molecule of glucose. During a complicated set of chemical reactions which utilize a number of enzymes, carbon from carbon dioxide becomes fixated into organic molecules, releasing oxygen in the process. In figure (b), the six water molecules have been subtracted from each side of the equation to illustrate the similarity of life processes as follows: if the reaction in figure (b) is read backwards from right to left, it is exactly the reaction which occurs during the "burning" of glucose to produce the energy molecules of ATP. This is the basic chemical reaction all cells use to obtain energy from the food they eat. This process is called cellular respiration and will be the topic of chapter 8.

a.
$$12\ H_2O + 6\ CO_2 + \text{Light Energy} \longrightarrow C_6H_{12}O_6 + 6\ O_2 + 6\ H_2O$$
$$\text{(glucose)}$$

b.
$$6\ H_2O + 6\ CO_2 + \text{Light Energy} \longrightarrow C_6H_{12}O_6 + 6\ O_2$$

7.15 LIGHT-DEPENDENT REACTIONS

First, we will discuss the overview process of the light-dependent reactions. The first step in photosynthesis is the light-dependent reactions, sometimes called **light reactions**. This set of chemical reactions is called the light reactions because without light these reactions could not occur. Therefore, the light reactions only occur when it is sunny. The whole purpose of the light reactions is for the sun's energy to generate activated electrons. Activated electrons have a lot of energy. This energy is freed and re-captured during the light reactions.

When sunlight is absorbed by chlorophyll, electrons in the chlorophyll molecules are excited. They become so excited that they actually leave the chlorophyll molecules. These are referred to as **excited**, **high energy**, or **activated electrons**. The energy in these activated electrons is harnessed and transferred from the light reactions to the Calvin cycle. The energy needed to drive the endergonic reactions of the Calvin cycle is provided by the light reactions.

7.16 PHOTOSYSTEMS I AND II

There are actually three different parts to the light reactions. These are **photosystem II** (**PS II**, pronounced "P.S. two"), **photosystem I** (**PS I**, pronounced "P.S. one"), and the **electron transport chain**. We will discuss the photosystems and their functions first and then the electron transport chain. A "photosystem" is simply a series of linked enzymes that perform chemical reactions during photosynthesis.

The enzymes of PS I and PS II are contained within the thylakoid membrane. When light strikes the chlorophyll inside the chloroplast, it initiates photosynthesis. Photosystem II is activated first. There are two simultaneous reactions that occur in PS II when chlorophyll absorbs the sun's energy: electrons in the chlorophyll are excited and water molecules are split. The chlorophyll electrons absorb energy from the sunlight and leave the chlorophyll, becoming activated electrons. They are replaced by the electrons released from the splitting of the water molecule.

After leaving the chlorophyll in PS II, the electrons enter an electron transport chain. There are many different electron transport chains in living organisms. Their function is to transfer the energy contained in high-energy electrons from one electron acceptor molecule to another. As the high-energy electron is passed from one electron acceptor to another, it loses some energy. At key points in all electron transport chains, the energy being lost by the electron is trapped by enzymes. The enzymes use this energy to fuel an endergonic reaction that makes some useful molecule from the electron's lost energy.

The activated electrons from PS II enter an electron transport chain, and are passed from one molecule to another. As they are passed they lose energy. Then the electrons are transferred from the electron transport chain to PS I. In PS I, the electrons are again excited by the sun and become activated electrons again. They enter another electron transport chain and are passed from one molecule to another in the chain until they reach the end. Now, let's find out what the "useful molecules" are that are made in the electron transport chains.

Figure 7.16.1

Photosystem I and II

A photosystem is a group of photosynthetic pigments and enzymes. The photosynthetic pigments of PS II absorb energy from the sun and electrons in chlorophyll become activated. These high-energy electrons leave the chlorophyll molecules and then enter the electron transport chain. Enzymes in PS II split water molecules, releasing electrons and oxygen atoms. The electrons replace those lost by chlorophyll and the water is released into the atmosphere. The electrons that entered the electron transport chain are passed from one protein to another in the chain, eventually ending up in PS I. In PS I, the electrons are again excited by the sun.

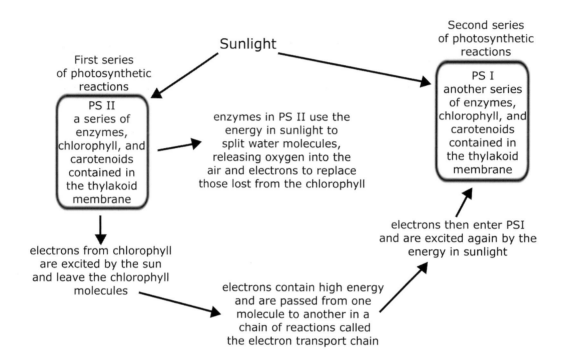

7.17 LIGHT REACTIONS MAKE ATP (ADENOSINE TRIPHOSPHATE) FOR USE IN THE CALVIN CYCLE

As we said, the purpose of electron transport chains is to harness the energy released by the electrons as they are passed from one molecule to another in the chain. There are two electron transport chains in photosynthesis—one after PS II and another after PS I. We will discuss the chain after PS II first.

In the electron transport chain after PS II, the energy released by the falling electrons is captured by enzymes to make molecules of **ATP (adenosine triphosphate)**. The reaction which makes ATP from ADP requires energy, and the energy is transferred from the passed electron to the ATP-making reaction by the energy-coupling effect of an enzyme. This ATP then moves from the thylakoid membrane into the stroma. Once in the stroma, it is used as an energy source by the enzymes of the Calvin cycle.

Figure 7.17.1

The Electron Transport Chain Between PS II and PS I

The structure of the electron transport chain is depicted below. The photosystem molecules and the proteins of the electron transport chain are contained within the thylakoid membranes. Chlorophyll electrons are excited by the energy contained in sunlight waves. The high-energy electrons leave the chlorophyll molecules and enter the electron transport chain. In this chain, the high energy electrons are passed from one protein to another, losing energy as they are passed. At a key point, this energy is captured and used to make ATP. The high energy electrons have lost energy, but are passed to PS I, where they are again excited.

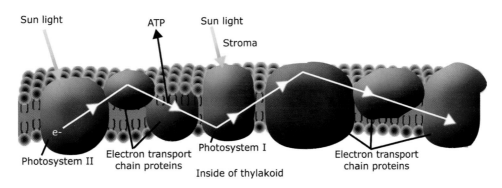

7.18 LIGHT REACTIONS MAKE NADPH FOR USE IN THE CALVIN CYCLE

After the electron's energy is used to make ATP in the electron transport chain, the electrons enter the PS I system and are again excited. This time they enter a different electron transport chain after being excited. At the end of this electron transport chain, the high-energy electrons are transferred to a co-enzyme molecule called **NADP (nicotinamide adenine dinucleotide phosphate)**. Recall a coenzyme is an organic non-enzyme molecule that is required by the enzyme in order for the enzyme to be active. When an electron is transferred to NADP, it is carried on a hydrogen atom. NADP is converted to **NADPH** when it accepts the high energy electron. NADPH is the hydrogenated and "high-energy-carrying" form of NADP. NADPH carries the energy contained in the activated electrons from the light reactions so it can be used in the Calvin cycle. Like ATP, NADPH travels from where it is made in the thylakoid membrane into the stroma where the Calvin cycle takes place.

Figure 7.18.1

The Electron Transport Chain After PS I

Electrons are again excited by the sun's energy and transformed to high-energy electrons. They enter another transport chain, where they ultimately are accepted by NADP. The electrons are carried as a hydrogen atom, and when the electron is transferred from the transport chain to NADP, the molecule NADPH is formed. NADPH is able to carry the energy in the high-energy electron. Both ATP and NADPH move into the stroma, where the energy they contain can be used in the second step of photosynthesis, the Calvin cycle.

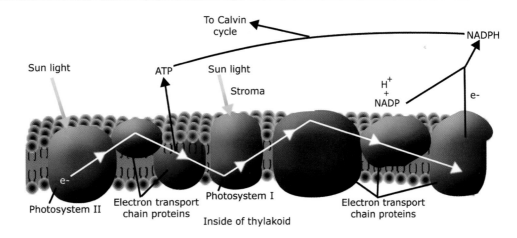

Figure 7.18.2

Summary of the Light Reactions

The light-dependent reactions occur as two separate light-absorbing events occurring in the chlorophyll. The first light-absorbing event occurs in the photosynthetic pigments of photosystem II. Water is split, releasing oxygen and electrons in the process. Also, electrons from the chlorophyll molecules are excited, called high-energy electrons. High-energy electrons enter the electron transport chain. The electrons lost from the chlorophyll are replaced by electrons from the splitting of water. Through a series of chemical reactions, this energy from the activated electrons is passed from one electron acceptor molecule of the chain to another, releasing energy. This energy is captured by enzymes in the electron transport chain and used to make ATP. The electrons pass into PS I and before they lose all of their energy, they are again excited by energy from the sun. This initiates another series of reactions to harness the energy from the re-activated electrons. This time, the actual high-energy electrons are captured by the molecule NADP, forming NADPH in the process. The energy from the ATP and NADPH generated in the light-dependent reactions is then used in the light-independent reactions (also called the Calvin cycle) to make sugars. Why do plants need to go through such a complicated series of reactions to make ATP and NADPH? The chemical reactions of the Calvin cycle that make sugar using carbon, hydrogen and oxygen are endergonic. The energy needed for these endergonic reactions is supplied by ATP and NADPH generated in the light-dependent reactions.

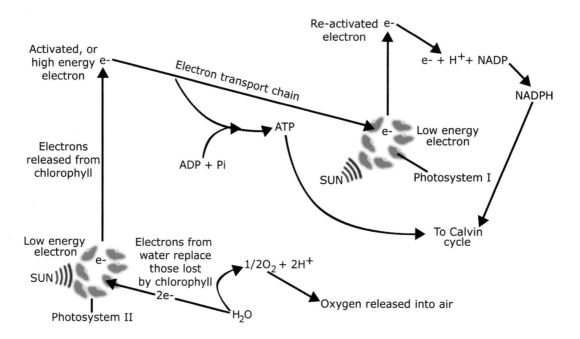

7.19 THE CALVIN CYCLE

NADPH and ATP made in the light-dependent reactions moves from the thylakoid membrane into the stroma. In the stroma, ATP and NADPH are used to fuel the endergonic reactions of the **light-independent** reactions, also called the **Calvin cycle** (so named for its discoverer Melvin Calvin). The Calvin cycle is also called the light-independent reactions because they can occur in the absence of light. The purpose of the Calvin cycle is to make a three carbon carbohydrate from CO_2 and H_2O. This three carbon sugar is called **glyceraldehydes-3-phosphate**, or G-3-P. Once made, G-3-P is usually converted into glucose.

Once the ATP and NADPH enter the stroma, they provide energy for the Calvin cycle. The Calvin cycle is a series of endergonic biochemical reactions during photosynthesis where carbon atoms are taken from CO_2 and hydrogen and oxygen atoms taken from H_2O are combined to form glucose. Calvin cycle enzymes break the phosphate bonds of ATP, releasing energy. Also, energy from the activated electrons carried by the NADPH is captured and used by the Calvin cycle enzymes. The energy is used to drive the endergonic reactions that incorporate carbon into glucose molecules. The summation of these reactions is to split apart CO_2 to obtain the carbon, releasing water in the process, and build a G-3-P molecule.

Figure 7.19.1

The Calvin Cycle
Here is the graphical representation of the Calvin cycle. Remember the purpose of the Calvin cycle is to make new sugar molecules from carbon obtained from carbon dioxide. To review, the process of incorporating inorganic carbon into an organic molecule is called carbon fixation. Step one of the Calvin cycle begins with removing the carbon from carbon dioxide. This process requires energy, and you can see that during the cycle energy is used in the form of ATP and NADPH at various points. After step two of the cycle is completed, one molecule of G-3-P is released. This is a cycle because not all of the molecules leave the cycle once the G-3-P is made. Some molecules remain in the cycle and start the whole set of reactions over again. By the end of step 3, the molecules which are recycled, using some energy from ATP, are ready to start the cycle over again. Each time the cycle turns twice, there have been two molecules of G-3-P made. G-3-P is a three-carbon sugar. Once two molecules of the three-carbon sugar are made, they are linked together to form one six- molecule carbohydrate, usually glucose. This glucose is then available for the plant to be used for cellular respiration (which we will learn about next chapter). Also, this glucose is available to be used for energy by anything that eats the plant.

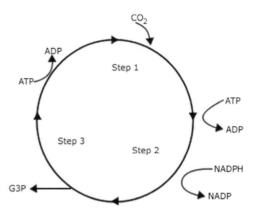

7.20 PRODUCTION OF G-3-P

Strictly speaking, the product of the Calvin cycle is not glucose, but a three-carbon sugar called glyceraldehyde-3-phosphate (G-3-P). Usually, right after it is made, two three-carbon G-3-P molecules are linked together to make the six-carbon sugar glucose. Glucose is then used by the plant in cellular respiration to make many ATP molecules. (We will talk about this in the next chapter.) Often, the glucose is converted into the carbohydrate macromolecules starch and cellulose. Plants store their excess energy molecules as starch. Potatoes and carrots are basically huge collections of starch molecules. When you eat a potato or a carrot, you are eating the excess stored energy of a plant. Cellulose is the major structural molecule of plants.

Let's summarize the light-independent reactions, or Calvin cycle. They occur in the stroma of the chloroplast and are responsible for the manufacture of the three-carbon sugar G-3-P. G-3-P is made from carbon obtained by splitting apart CO2 molecules. The set of biochemical reactions which make up the Calvin cycle are endergonic. The needed energy is supplied by ATP and NADPH produced during the light dependent reactions.

Figure 7.20.1

Complete Photosynthesis
This is a graphical representation of the processes occurring during photosynthesis. It may seem confusing, but you will understand if you simply follow the steps carefully. Start at the top left with the sun. The sun provides the energy needed to run the endergonic reaction that splits water and dislodges two electrons from chlorophyll in PS II. These electrons are the excited electrons that enter the electron transport chain. When the water molecule is split, oxygen and electrons are released. The oxygen exits the leaf into the atmosphere, and the electrons released from the water replace the electrons lost by chlorophyll. While the electron is passed along the transport chain, the energy it loses is harnessed by enzymes and used to make ATP. The electron is then excited again in PS I and re-enters another electron transport chain. This time, the energy lost by the electron is used to make NADPH from NADPH. ATP and NADPH proceed to fuel the endergonic reactions of the Calvin cycle to make G-3-P. The key concepts are: water being split and releasing oxygen gas into the air; excited electrons from chlorophyll entering the electron transport chain; energy (to be used in the Calvin cycle) in the form of ATP and NADPH being generated during the electron transport chain; G-3-P being produced in the Calvin cycle; the cyclical nature of using and generating ADP/ATP and NADP/NADPH.

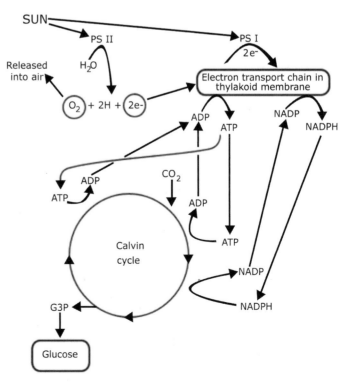

7.21 ADVANCED

There are actually two pathways that the sun's energy can excite to start photosynthesis. They are called the **cyclic** and **non-cyclic pathways**. The "cyclic" and "non-cyclic" refer to the pathway that the excited electrons take. In the cyclic pathway, the excited electrons leave the chlorophyll molecules and then return back to them after they are passed through the electron transport chain and lose their energy. In the non-cyclic pathway, the electrons do not return to the chlorophyll so they need to be replenished. The "renewal" of the electron supply in the non-cyclical pathway comes from the splitting of the water molecule. Usually, the plant uses the non-cyclical pathway. The photosynthetic pathway we just learned about above is the non-cyclical pathway.

The cyclic pathway begins when the PS I system is activated by sunlight. This causes high energy electrons to be liberated directly from the chlorophyll a and then enter the electron transport system. As the electrons pass from one acceptor molecule to the next in the electron transport system, their energy is captured by **ATP synthase**. This enzyme makes ATP from ADP and a phosphate group. This is an endergonic reaction which is fueled by the energy from the activated electrons. Once the electron completes the cycle, it returns to the chlorophyll a. The cyclic pathway results only in the production of ATP.

The non-cyclic pathway is the pathway we have already learned about in this chapter. It begins the same way, from absorbing energy from sunlight. This pathway starts with the PS II system first being activated by the sun, cleaving water, and releasing oxygen gas. At the same time, electrons from chlorophyll are excited and leave the chlorophyll molecule. These electrons are replaced by electrons from splitting water. The activated electrons then pass through the PS II electron transport system, generating ATP via ATP synthase. As the electrons complete the PS II electron transport system, they then enter the PS I system. The electrons are excited again in the PS I system, as we have already learned. However, they do not enter the cyclical system. Instead these activated electrons are diverted to a different electron transport system than is used in the cyclical pathway. This is called the non-cyclical system because the electrons do not return to the chlorophyll from which they came. Instead, the electron is transferred to NADPH. The electron then leaves the PS I system and is carried by the NADPH into the stroma and the Calvin cycle. Again, the electrons which are lost by PS II are replenished by electrons from water.

What happens to that electron which is carried by the NADPH? Recall the electron is in the form of a hydrogen ion. The hydrogen ion is taken from the NADPH and used during the production of G-3-P. For one "turn" of the Calvin cycle, three molecules of CO_2, nine molecules of ATP, and the activated electrons from six molecules of NADPH are needed to make one three-carbon sugar of G-3-P.

Figure 7.21.1

Cyclic and Non-Cyclic Pathways

Below is the graphic representation of the cyclic and non-cyclic pathways of photosynthesis. Figure (a) shows the cyclic pathway. It starts when PS I is excited by the sun. Electrons are excited from chlorophyll a. These activated electrons then enter an electron transport chain. As they pass through the chain, their energy drives the enzyme ATP synthase. ADP is phosphorylated to ATP as a result. The electrons then return to the chlorophyll when they have passed through the electron transport chain and lose all of their energy. The cyclic pathway results only in the production of ATP. It is called the cyclic pathway because the electrons return back to where they started. Figure (b) should look familiar as this is the pathway we have learned about earlier in the chapter. This is the non-cyclic pathway because the electrons do not end up on the same place they started. In the non-cyclic pathway, electrons are excited in chlorophyll and enter the electron transport chain. The excited electrons are replaced by electrons from water. As the electrons are passed down the chain, they lose energy, but are re-excited in PS I. The non-cyclical pathway electrons leave the PS I and PS II systems when they are taken into the NADPH molecule.

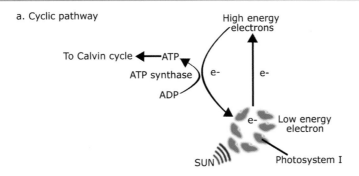

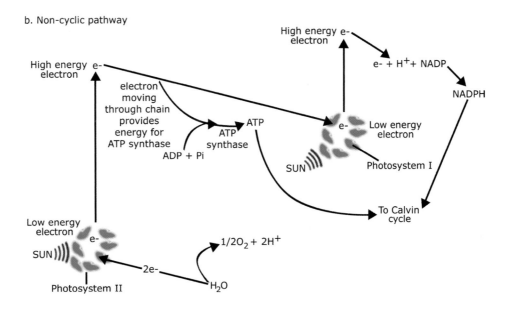

7.22 PEOPLE OF SCIENCE

Melvin Calvin (1911-1997) was born in Minnesota and trained in the United States. He received his PhD in chemistry from the University of Minnesota in 1935. He was a full professor of chemistry at University of California-Berkeley from 1947 until his death. He had many contributions to biology and chemistry, but received the 1961 Nobel Prize in Chemistry for his work in identifying the process of carbon fixation of plants, that is known today as the Calvin cycle.

7.23 KEY CHAPTER POINTS

- Photosynthesis is a set of chemical reactions which photoautotrophs use to convert the sun's energy into carbohydrate molecules.

- Autotrophs are the initial source of all carbon containing molecules on earth.

- The process of bringing carbon into organic molecules is called carbon fixation.

- The sun emits energy in many different forms; this is called the electromagnetic spectrum.

- Plants use energy from the visible light portion of the electromagnetic spectrum for photosynthesis. Only the light which plants absorb can be used for photosynthesis.

- Photosynthesis occurs in the specialized structures called chloroplasts, which contain the light-absorbing pigments chlorophyll and carotenoids.

- Photosynthesis is two separate—but linked—sets of chemical reactions. The light-dependent reactions absorb the sun's energy and the Calvin cycle uses that energy to synthesize glucose.

- Glucose is then made available to the plant, and to heterotrophs, for use in generating molecules of ATP and for synthesizing other organic molecules.

- There are two photosystems in plants which act together to excite and pass on high energy electrons.

- The non-cyclical pathway utilizes PS I and II to generate activated electrons and make ATP and NADPH for use in the Calvin cycle. Electrons do not return to the same molecules from which they came.

- The cyclical pathway utilizes PS I only to make ATP for use in the Calvin cycle. Electrons return to the chlorophyll from which they came.

7.24 DEFINITIONS

absorption spectrum
The wavelength of light that is absorbed by a plant and used for photosynthesis.

ATP
The molecule that provides the energy for a cell to use to fuel endergonic reactions.

ATP synthase
An enzyme that makes ATP from ADP and a phosphate group.

autotroph
An organism that is able to manufacture its own cell mass and organic compounds from CO_2, using the sun's light or chemical compounds as their source of energy.

Calvin cycle
The set of chemical reactions in a plant which creates the three carbon molecule glucose-3-phosphate.

carbon fixation
The process of taking carbon from CO_2 and incorporating it into organic molecules.

carotenoids
Energy-absorbing pigments that are contained within the thylakoid membrane.

chemolithoautotroph (chemoautotroph)
An organism which can make its own cell mass and organic molecules using energy provided by chemical compounds.

chlorophyll
Energy-absorbing pigments that are contained within the thylakoid membrane.

cyclic pathways
The photosynthetic pathway using only PS I in which ATP is generated using activated electrons which are derived and return to chlorophyll.

electromagnetic spectrum
The total amount of radiation energy emitted by the sun.

electron transport chain
A coordinated system of molecules which can pass activated electrons from one to another in order to capture the energy lost by the electron and convert that energy into some useful molecule.

gamma rays
That portion of the electromagnetic spectrum with a wavelength of 0.001 nm to 1 nm.

glyceraldehyde-3-phosphate (G-3-P)
The three carbon sugar produced by the Calvin cycle.

grana
Flattened membranous discs contained in the thylakoid.

heat
A type of energy emitted by the sun.

heterotroph
Organisms that are not able to manufacture their own cell mass or organic molecules and must obtain the needed molecules by ingesting autotrophs or other heterotrophs.

high energy electrons (or activated electrons)
Free electrons that carry a lot of energy. Typically, activated electrons enter into electron transport chains.

infrared (IR) rays
That portion of the electromagnetic spectrum with a wavelength between 1000 nm and 0.01 cm

light-dependent reactions
The photosynthetic reactions which cannot occur without light.

light-independent reactions
The photosynthetic reactions which can occur without light; also called the Calvin cycle.

light reactions
See light-independent reactions.

microwaves
That portion of the electromagnetic spectrum with a wavelength of 0.01 cm to 1 m.

NADPH
A co-enzyme molecule. The hydrogenated form of nicotinamide adenine dinucleotide phosphate (NADP), NADPH functions as a carrier of high-energy electrons.

nicotinamide adenine dinucleotide phosphate (NADP)
A co-enzyme that carries activated electrons.

non-cyclic pathways
The photosynthetic pathway that uses both PS I and PS II. Activated electrons do not return to the molecule from which they originated.

photolithoautotrophs (or photoautotrophs)
Autotrophs that transform energy through photosynthesis to manufacture their own cell mass and organic molecules.

photons
The units in which radiant energy travels.

photosystem I (PS I)
One of the photosynthetic systems which activates electrons.

photosystem II (PS II)
One of the photosynthetic systems which activates electrons.

radiant energy
 See electromagnetic spectrum.

radio waves
 That portion of the electromagnetic spectrum with a wavelength of 1 m to 100 m.

refraction
 The bending of light at different angles.

spectrum
 The color make-up of white light; the colors which a particular object contains.

stroma
 Enzyme-rich solution surrounding the thylakoid.

thylakoid
 The membrane system contained in the chloroplast.

ultraviolet (UV) rays
 That portion of the electromagnetic spectrum with a wavelength of 10 nm to 380 nm.

visible light
 The small portion of the sun's radiant energy that is able to be seen by the human eye; visible light encompasses a spectrum of wavelengths of 380 nm to 780 nm.

visible spectrum
 All of the separate colors of light as visualized after the white light is passed through a prism.

wavelength
 The distance from one peak of a radiant energy wave to the next peak.

waves
 The way in which radiant energy travels.

x-rays
 That portion of the electromagnetic spectrum with a wavelength of 1 nm to 10 nm.

STUDY QUESTIONS

1. Why is photosynthesis important to life on earth? (There are three main reasons, please list them all.)

2. What is carbon fixation?

3. What is the biological term for "producer"? List the two basic types of "producers" and the way in which they produce their cell mass and organic molecules.

4. List the components of the electromagnetic spectrum starting from longest wavelength and moving to shortest. Which of the components has the highest energy? Which has the lowest energy?

5. What is a photon? How does it travel?

6. True or False? Since all electromagnetic radiation travels in photons, the wavelength of x-rays is the same as the wavelength of radio waves.

7. True or False? Visible light, also called white light, makes up a large portion of the radiant energy from the sun.

8. What is the visible spectrum?

9. True or False? The absorption spectrum of plant leaves is mainly green. Why did you answer the way you did?

10. True or False? Plants use the light they reflect to drive photosynthesis. Why did you answer the way you did?

11. Where does photosynthesis occur? Draw and label the structure of the organelle.

12. Write the balanced chemical equation for photosynthesis, and then write in words what the equation says.

13. What are the two groups of photosynthetic reactions called? List the products of each of group of reactions.

14. How are carotenoids and chlorophyll similar? How are they different?

15. What is an electron transport chain? What does it do?

16. What is the purpose of the Calvin cycle? Where does the energy come from for the Calvin cycle to function?

Cellular Respiration

8

8.0 CHAPTER PREVIEW

In this chapter we will:

- Investigate the structure and function of ATP.

- Learn how ATP is utilized by enzymes to fuel endergonic reactions they catalyze.

- Investigate the biological processes of aerobic and anaerobic respiration.

- Study the internal structure of mitochondria and how it relates to aerobic respiration.

8.1 OVERVIEW

No matter what the organism is, it needs energy to drive its metabolic reactions. Plants convert the sun's energy into carbohydrate molecules, mainly glucose. That is photosynthesis. What happens to the glucose once it is made in plants? The glucose is consumed by plants, animals, insects, bacteria, etc, to make molecules of adenosine triphosphate (ATP). Why? Glucose cannot be used directly by the cell for energy. Instead, the energy contained in the chemical bonds of glucose is used to make ATP. ATP is the direct energy source that organisms use to fuel almost all of the endergonic reactions that keep them alive. Almost all living organisms capture energy released during the metabolism of glucose and use it to fuel the endergonic reactions they catalyze.

Figure 8.1.1

The Structure of ATP (adenosine triphosphate)
ATP, adenosine triphosphate, is the universal energy source for living organisms. It is a nucleotide, but a special type. Like other nucleotides, it is made up of three components. The central molecule is the five-carbon sugar ribose. Attached to one end of ribose is the nitrogen base adenine. However, rather than having only one phosphate group attached to the sugar, it has three. The energy generated from ATP comes from breaking the bonds between the phosphate groups. When the bonds are broken through the actions of special enzymes, a lot of energy is released. This energy is then used to drive the endergonic reactions of life.

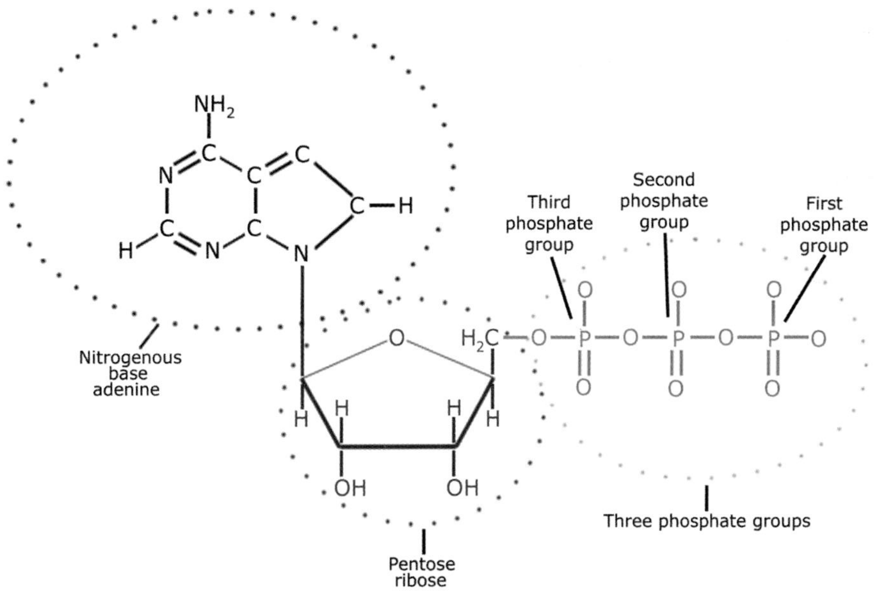

8.2 THE LINK BETWEEN GLUCOSE, ATP, AND CELLULAR RESPIRATION

What is the relationship between glucose and ATP? Both glucose and ATP are used by organisms for energy. However, glucose cannot be used by organisms as a "direct energy" source. That is to say that the energy in glucose cannot be coupled by enzymes to fuel the endergonic reactions they catalyze. Instead, glucose is used as a source of "indirect energy." By that I mean that when glucose is broken down by the cell, energy is released. That energy is captured by enzymes in the cell to make ATP. ATP is then used as the universal fuel source that all enzymes can use to couple to the reactions they catalyze.

Cellular respiration is the set of biochemical reactions used by the cell to make ATP by breaking the chemical bonds of glucose. When glucose is "burned", or catabolized (remember a catabolic reaction breaks a molecule into smaller pieces), the bonds holding the carbon atoms to one another in the glucose molecule are broken. This occurs under the strict regulation of many enzymes in the cell. When the glucose bonds are broken, energy is released. This energy is then coupled by enzymes to the endergonic reactions which make ATP.

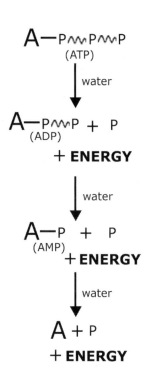

Figure 8.2.1

ATP as the Energy Source of Life: a Review

Recall from Chapter 6 that the energy derived from ATP comes from the highly regulated and enzyme-performed breaking of bonds between phosphate groups. The bonds are broken by a hydrolysis reaction—water is added to the bond, removing one of the phosphate groups and releasing energy (heat). The first hydrolysis reaction of ATP results in the formation of ADP and an inorganic phosphate group (labeled here as "P" but also commonly labeled "Pi"). The energy released from hydrolyzing the bond is coupled by enzymes to create the energy needed to catalyze endergonic reactions. Sometimes, the inorganic phosphate group is linked by the enzyme to another molecule. This forms a new phosphate bond that holds the potential energy of the original phosphate bond of the ATP. Then that phosphate bond can be hydrolyzed to release energy.

Recall that autotrophs make the cell mass and organic molecules they need to live from the sun (photoautotrophs) or from chemicals like ammonia or sulfur (chemoautotrophs). Autotrophs catabolize this glucose during cellular respiration to make ATP molecules. Heterotrophs cannot make their own glucose, though, and must obtain it from eating producers or other consumers. Then heterotrophs catabolize the glucose they ingest to make molecules of ATP during cellular respiration. ATP is then used by all organisms to drive the countless endergonic reactions they perform every minute. This is the purpose of cellular respiration—to break down glucose molecules and capture the energy released to make ATP. In this chapter, we will study the formation of ATP through the reactions involved in the catabolism (or breaking down) of the carbohydrate glucose. This is the most common form of cellular respiration.

8.3 ATP IS USED TO FUEL THE ENDERGONIC REACTIONS OF LIFE

Remember that almost all of the processes a cell or organism performs are endergonic. Cellular respiration provides the energy source needed for cells to drive their endergonic biochemical reactions. Activities such as macromolecule synthesis, muscle contraction, thinking, and digesting food all utilize energy—in the form of ATP—obtained during cellular respiration.

The ATP-derived energy is extracted by two basic reactions. First, water can be added to the phosphate bond, breaking the bond. This is called a hydrolysis reaction. It releases a great deal of energy and forms one inorganic phosphate molecule ("P" or "Pi" for short), one **ADP** (**adenosine diphosphate**) molecule. Secondly, the ATP bond can be hydrolyzed and the Pi group can be added to another molecule, then that phosphate bond can be hydrolyzed, releasing energy. These reactions are highly regulated by the cell and are performed whenever energy is needed to start endergonic reactions. The reaction to directly hydrolyze ATP or to transfer the phosphate group is carried out by the cells of enzymes called **ATPases**.

When an enzyme needs activation energy for the reaction it catalyzes, it gets it from ATP. Usually the enzyme carries out a hydrolysis reaction of ATP. In the process, energy—in the form of heat—is released. The enzyme couples the released heat to the reaction it catalyzes. When its bond is hydrolyzed, ATP is converted into ADP and an inorganic phosphate group. Both the phosphate group and the ADP are recycled by the cell. The ADP is again linked to the phosphate group, making ATP. The process of cellular respiration is all about making ATP from ADP.

Figure 8.3.1

The Use of ATP and an Energy Source
The chemical reaction in figure (a) describes the hydrolysis of the first phosphate bond of ATP. This is an exergonic reaction and is performed by the enzyme which needs the released heat to fuel the reaction the enzyme catalyzes. The hydrolysis of the first bond results in the production of ADP and an inorganic phosphate molecule. Recall that enzymes are energy couplers. They couple the energy released from hydrolyzing the phosphate bond of ATP to the endergonic reaction which the enzyme catalyzes. There are thousands of enzymes in organisms which can hydrolyze ATP and couple the energy to an endergonic reaction. ATP is quickly regenerated in cellular respiration. The ADP enters the mitochondria. Inside the mitochondria, an inorganic phosphate group is re-added to the ADP by the enzyme ATP-ase. Converting ADP into ATP is the last step of cellular respiration. In figure (b), the synthesis of sucrose from a molecule of fructose and glucose is demonstrated as an example of the metabolic reaction in which an inorganic phosphate group from ATP is transferred to another molecule; in our example the phosphate is transferred from ATP to glucose. The bond holding the inorganic phosphate group to glucose holds energy in it. In the next step of the reaction, in the middle panel of figure (b), an enzyme hydrolyzes the phosphate bond on the glucose-P molecule and couples the energy released to bond the glucose and fructose together in a glycosidic bond. The bottom line of figure (b) shows the net reaction. One molecule of ATP provides the energy which allows glucose and fructose to be linked together to form sucrose. But we know it is actually a two-step set of reactions to accomplish this.

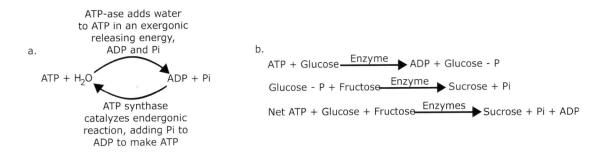

8.4 AEROBIC AND ANAEROBIC RESPIRATION

Cellular respiration can be performed by the cell using oxygen or not using oxygen during glucose metabolism. This means the cell can produce ATP from glucose using oxygen or not using oxygen. When oxygen is used, this is called **aerobic respiration**. When oxygen is not used, it is called **anaerobic respiration**. Aerobic respiration produces much more ATP per molecule of glucose than anaerobic respiration. However, anaerobic respiration is able to provide ATP more quickly than aerobic respiration and so is the preferred source of ATP production when energy is needed in short bursts, such as when sprinting. We will discuss both of these processes in this chapter, although the focus will be on aerobic cellular respiration.

8.5 THE CHEMICAL EQUATION FOR CELLULAR RESPIRATION

Although considered a single process, aerobic cellular respiration involves many metabolic pathways. These pathways are a series of chemical reactions which are linked. The reactions all exist to trap the energy from the breakdown of glucose to make molecules of ATP. The general equation used to describe cellular respiration is:

$$Glucose + O_2 \longrightarrow CO_2 + H_2O + ATP$$

This reaction states that glucose is metabolized using oxygen. The products of metabolizing the glucose with oxygen are carbon dioxide, water, and ATP. The carbon dioxide is exhaled when we breathe. The water can be used for various processes in the body. The ATP is used to fuel the endergonic reactions of life.

It should be noted that many organisms can use molecules other than glucose to make ATP. However it is most common for glucose to be used as the reactant for cellular respiration, and the reactions are most efficient when glucose is used. Therefore, the summation of cellular respiration can be written using glucose as the reactant:

$$C_6H_{12}O_6 + 6O_2 \longrightarrow 6CO_2 + 6H_2O + ATP \text{ (plus heat)}$$

Note that, as pointed out in the last chapter, when written this way, cellular respiration represents the exact opposite chemical process as compared to photosynthesis. This makes sense since photosynthesis is the biological process that makes glucose and cellular respiration is the process that breaks it down.

8.6 FOUR STEPS OF AEROBIC CELLULAR RESPIRATION

Like photosynthesis, aerobic cellular respiration is a multi-step process. It also requires separate, but linked, chemical reactions to be complete. Cellular respiration describes four different sets of reactions which combine to make ATP through the catabolism of glucose. The first step of cellular respiration is **glycolysis**, which occurs in the cytoplasm. Technically speaking, glycolysis is really not a part of cellular respiration; however, cellular respiration uses the products of glycolysis and so cellular respiration cannot occur without glycolysis. The products of glycolysis are then transported into the mitochondria for further processing. Once in the mitochondria, the next step is the **transition reaction**. The transition reaction gets the glycolysis products ready for the next step of aerobic cellular respiration—the **Krebs cycle**. During the Krebs cycle, glucose is broken down, releasing energy. The energy is captured at various points and used to make ATP and some electron-carrying molecules. The final step of aerobic respiration is the passage of these activated electrons to and through the **electron transport chain**. As we review the processes of cellular respiration, you will note many general similarities between it and photosynthesis as it relates to the passage of electrons through an electron transport chain.

8.7 MITOCHONDRIA: STRUCTURE AND FUNCTION

Since the reactions which make up aerobic cellular respiration occur in the mitochondria, we need to understand this organelle better. Mitochondria have long been called the "powerhouse" of the cell because they produce almost all of the ATP the cell uses. Every eukaryotic cell contains mitochondria, but in different numbers. Cells that require a lot of energy, such as muscle cells and brain cells, may have hundreds of mitochondria. Cells that are fairly metabolically quiet, like fat cells, may have only a few. Also note that prokaryotic cells, which have no mitochondria, perform cellular respiration in the cytoplasm.

Figure 8.7.1

Structure of the Mitochondrion

An electron micrograph of several mitochondria is shown left, and the corresponding structures are labeled on the right graphic. Notice that mitochondria can take on different forms—some are sausage shaped and others are plump and spherical. Mitochondria have a double membrane—the outer protects it from the cytoplasm and the inner folds back and forth on itself extensively. There is a space between the inner and outer membranes called the intermembrane space, or also called the outer compartment. The folded inner membranes on the interior of mitochondria are called cristae. They are surrounded by a jelly-like fluid called the matrix. The product of glycolysis enters mitochondria across the outer membrane and is taken to the cristae. Cristae contain the enzymes where the first series of reactions of aerobic cellular respiration take place.

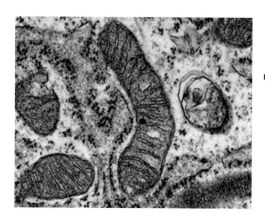
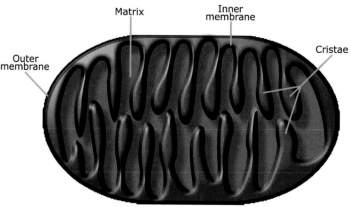

A review of the structure of mitochondria is necessary to understand their function. Mitochondria have a double membrane system. The **outer membrane** protects the inside of the mitochondrion from the contents of the cytoplasm (and vice-versa). The **inner membrane** system holds the molecules which produce most of the ATP in the mitochondrion. Recall, also, that mitochondria possess their own DNA and as such can replicate independent of the cell.

The space between the inner membrane system and the outer membrane is called the **intermembrane space**, also called the **outer compartment**. Hydrogen ions accumulate in the outer compartment, and enzymes and various proteins are found there. The inner membrane system forms into extensive folds, called cristae. The space on the inside of mitochondria, between the cristae, is called the **matrix**.

8.8 GLYCOLYSIS

The initial step in the metabolism of glucose is called glycolysis. Glycolysis is simply the metabolic steps which convert the six-carbon sugar glucose into two three-carbon molecules of **pyruvate**. Basically, glucose is broken in half during glycolysis. This takes place in the cytoplasm and occurs by the action of several different enzymes. Although glycolysis does require the input of two ATP molecules per molecule of glucose metabolized, it results in an output of four ATP molecules per molecule of glucose. That means there is a *net* production of two molecules of ATP per molecule of glucose that undergoes glycolysis. Like anaerobic respiration, glycolysis does not require oxygen. Once the pyruvate is produced, it is then used in either the anaerobic or the aerobic pathway. Therefore, glycolysis is the common starting point in cellular respiration and is not, strictly speaking, solely a part of aerobic respiration or anaerobic respiration.

Figure 8.8.1

Glycolysis

Glycolysis occurs in the cytoplasm outside of the mitochondria. During glycolysis, the six-carbon molecule of glucose is broken in half to form two three-carbon pyruvate molecules. Although this reaction uses two molecules of ATP, it produces four. And so, there is a net production of two molecules of ATP in this first step of cellular respiration. Also, there are two molecules of NADH produced. NADH serves as a carrier of activated electrons. NADH and pyruvate are both transported into the mitochondrion. Pyruvate enters into the first step of cellular respiration—the Krebs cycle. NADH is transported into the mitochondrion, to the electron transport chain.

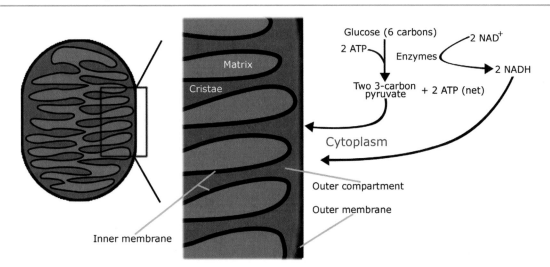

In addition to the two net ATP molecules from the splitting of glucose, two molecules of **NADH** (the **hydrogenated form of nicotinamide adenine dinucleotide**) are formed. As in the case of NADP, which we learned about in the last chapter, **NAD (nicotinamide adenine dinucleotide)** is a type of co-factor and is an electron carrier. It serves to carry the activated electrons to the electron transport chain. NADH is formed at several steps during the metabolism of glucose. NADH brings activated electrons, which are liberated at various points during glucose metabolism, to the electron transport chain. As the electrons are carried through the electron transport chain, the released energy is used to make ATP.

Glycolysis does not require oxygen and it is performed by nearly all living organisms on earth, both eukaryote and prokaryote. However, the next steps of metabolism following the formation of pyruvate differ greatly among various organisms and also depend on the conditions of the cell. We are going to discuss the most common pathways following glycolysis—aerobic and anaerobic respiration—both of which are performed by mammals, including humans. Usually, when oxygen is plentiful in the cells, the pyruvate undergoes aerobic metabolism in a series of the Krebs cycle. If oxygen is not plentiful, as occurs in muscles after prolonged usage, pyruvate will undergo anaerobic metabolism. Remember both aerobic and anaerobic metabolism of glucose (or pyruvate, if you like) are performed to generate energy for the cell in the form of ATP molecules. Aerobic respiration is more efficient than anaerobic, however, meaning that more ATP is made from the aerobic metabolism of glucose than is made from the anaerobic metabolism.

Aerobic respiration occurs entirely inside the mitochondria (remember that glycolysis is not a part of anaerobic respiration, but glycolysis does provide the needed pyruvate for aerobic respiration to occur). It is called "aerobic" because oxygen is needed during the final stages. If oxygen is plentiful, once the pyruvate is formed through glycolysis in the cytoplasm, it moves into the mitochondria.

8.9 TRANSITION REACTION

The first actual step of aerobic respiration occurs once pyruvate enters mitochondria. After pyruvate enters the mitochondria, it undergoes a **transition reaction**, so named because it is the reaction that links glycolysis to aerobic respiration. The transition reaction is also referred to as **pyruvic acid oxidation**. This occurs in the outer compartment of the mitochondria. During the transition reaction, an enzyme converts pyruvate into a two-carbon molecule, called an **acetyl group**. In the process, two hydrogen atoms are removed from the pyruvate, along with their electrons. Removing a hydrogen atom with its electron from a molecule is called an **oxidation reaction**; hence the name pyruvic acid oxidation. The hydrogen atoms with their activated electrons are transferred to another carrier molecule, NADH. The NADH will then take the electrons to the electron transport chain so their energy can be used to make ATP. The cellular respiration electron transport chain works the same way as the ones for photosynthesis do—the activated electrons are passed from one acceptor molecule to another, releasing energy as they are passed. At key points in the chain, enzymes harness the released energy and use it to make ATP.

After the pyruvate is oxidized (in other words, after the two hydrogen atoms are removed) the acetyl group is then attached to a coenzyme called **co-enzyme A**. This new molecule is called **acetyl Co-A**. Co-enzyme A simply carries the carbon atoms of the pyruvate through a series of upcoming chemical reactions. These upcoming chemical reactions break the bonds between the remaining carbon atoms of the pyruvate. These reactions are called the **Krebs cycle**. Co-A itself is not physically altered during the Krebs cycle.

Figure 8.9.1

Transition Reaction

After pyruvate is formed following glycolysis, it moves into the matrix of the mitochondria. In the matrix, the three-carbon pyruvate undergoes the transition reaction. The transition reaction gets the pyruvate molecule ready for the next step of its metabolism, the Krebs cycle. Pyruvate is linked to a molecule of Co-enzyme A (Co-A). Co-A serves as a "carrier." It carries the carbon molecules of pyruvate through the Krebs cycle so they can be metabolized further. During the transition reaction, one carbon atom is removed from the pyruvate and combined with O_2, forming CO_2. The other two carbon atoms are linked to the Co-A, forming the molecule acetyl Co-enzyme A, or Acetyl Co-A. Also during the transition reaction, another two molecules of NADH are formed and are transported to the electron transport chain. Please note that the diagram below shows what happens in regard to NADH for BOTH molecules of pyruvate. When each molecule of pyruvate undergoes the transition reaction, one molecule of NADH is produced. Therefore, there are two molecules of NADH produced for each molecule of glucose which enters the mitochondrion. Since there are two molecules of pyruvate produced per molecule of glucose, and each molecule of pyruvate which enters the mitochondrion produces one molecule of NADH when it undergoes the transition reaction, two molecules of NADH are produced per molecule of glucose.

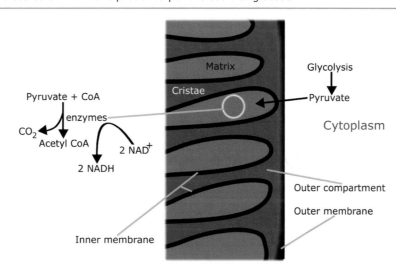

8.10 MOLECULAR ACCOUNTING THROUGH THE TRANSITION REACTION

At this point, I would like to review exactly what has happened to the six original carbon atoms in the glucose molecule that started this whole process of aerobic cellular respiration. Also, we will take an accounting of how many energy molecules have been made up to this point.

Each six-carbon glucose molecule is converted into two three-carbon pyruvate molecules during glycolysis. For each molecule of pyruvate that undergoes the transition reaction, one molecule of carbon is removed from the pyruvate. This molecule of carbon from the pyruvate is linked to two molecules of oxygen, forming carbon dioxide. This leaves the two carbon acetyl group, which is linked to co-enzyme-A. In addition, one molecule of NADH is made per pyruvate molecule which undergoes the transition reaction. This means that after the transition reaction is completed, one molecule of carbon has been removed from the glucose molecule and combined with two molecules of oxygen for each molecule of pyruvate that undergoes the transition reaction. This produces two molecules of CO_2 during the transition reaction for every glucose molecule which originally underwent glycolysis (because there are two pyruvate molecules produced for every molecule of glucose and each pyruvate molecule produces one molecule of carbon dioxide in the transition reaction). Also during the transition reaction, one molecule of ATP and NADH are made per molecule of pyruvate. That is a total of two molecules of ATP and two molecules of NADH produced in the transition reaction per molecule of glucose. Added to the two net molecules of ATP from glycolysis and the two molecules of NADH from glycolysis, for each molecule of glucose that has undergone glycolysis, four molecules of ATP and four molecules of NADH have been generated following completion of the transition reaction.

8.11 THE KREBS CYCLE

The reactions of the **Krebs cycle** take place in the mitochondrial matrix. The **matrix** is the space between the cristae (the matrix is also sometimes called the inner compartment). The cycle is named for the man that first described it, Sir Hans Krebs. The Krebs cycle is also called the **citric acid cycle** or the **tricarboxylic acid cycle** because these molecules are key components of the cycle; however, we will use the name Krebs cycle.

The Krebs cycle is a series of biochemical reactions that start with the acetyl Co-A generated by the transition reaction. There are many steps in the Krebs cycle, but what we need to know is the outcome of the series of reactions, not the detail of each reaction. During the Krebs cycle, the remaining carbon molecules from glucose are catabolized. The bonds between the carbon molecules are broken, which releases energy. Krebs cycle enzymes capture the released energy and make three molecules— some ATP (not much), NADH and **FADH$_2$**. **FAD** is a coenzyme called **flavin adenine dinucleotide**. Like NAD and NADP, it is able to accept activated electrons and carry them to an electron transport chain. FADH$_2$ is the hydrogenated form of FAD and is the form of FAD that is actively carrying activated electrons.

8.12 TURNS OF THE KREBS CYCLE AND ENERGY

Just to be clear at this point, it is important to realize that for every molecule of glucose that is cleaved in the initial step of glycolysis, the Krebs cycle "turns" twice. The glucose was converted into two molecules of pyruvate. The pyruvate is then converted into 2 two-molecule acetyl groups. Each acetyl group is then attached to Co-A; this molecule is called acetyl Co-A. Each time a molecule of acetyl Co-A enters the Krebs cycle, that is considered a "turn." Each molecule of acetyl Co-A causes the Krebs cycle to turn once. As the co-A carries the acetyl group through the Krebs cycle and the remaining carbon molecules are metabolized, there is a net production of one molecule of ATP, three molecules of NADH, and one molecule of FADH$_2$. Since the cycle turns twice for every glucose molecule, there is a net production of two ATP, six NADH, and two FADH$_2$ for each glucose molecule that starts the cycle. These molecules are formed by the energy given off when the bonds between the carbon atoms of the acetyl group are broken during the Krebs cycle.

8.13 TURNS OF THE KREBS CYCLE AND CO$_2$

Another product of the Krebs cycle is CO$_2$. In fact, each one of the six-carbon atoms from the starting glucose molecule is converted into a molecule of CO$_2$ during cellular respiration. That means that a total of six molecules of CO$_2$ are generated per glucose. Where does this come from?

Recall that two of the carbon molecules from the glucose were turned into CO$_2$ during the transition reaction. During the Krebs cycle, each one of the carbon atoms is removed from the acetyl Co-A and reduced to CO$_2$. Each time a bond between carbon molecules is broken, the carbon atom is combined with two atoms of oxygen to form carbon dioxide. There are two carbon atoms left on the acetyl group from each original pyruvate molecule that underwent the transition reaction. As the Co-A carries the acetyl group through the Krebs cycle, each of the two carbon atoms of the acetyl group are removed and combined with oxygen, forming two molecules of carbon dioxide for each molecule of acetyl Co-A which enters the Krebs cycle. Since there are two molecules of acetyl Co-A for every glucose molecule that began the Krebs cycle, there is a total of four molecules of carbon dioxide generated during the Krebs cycle per molecule of glucose that originally started the cycle. Combine these four molecules of carbon dioxide with the two total molecules of carbon dioxide which were formed during the transition reaction, and that equals six molecules of carbon dioxide produced per molecule of glucose that undergoes aerobic respiration. The original six-carbon atoms of glucose are now all accounted for in the form of six molecules of carbon dioxide.

Once the ATP is produced, one of two things happens to it. One, it can stay in the mitochondria to be used for energy for the mitochondria. Two, it is released from the mitochondria into the cytoplasm to be used for endergonic reactions in the cell. What about all of the energy being carried in the form of activated electrons on the NADH and FADH$_2$? It moves from the matrix to the cristae, where it enters the electron transport chain.

Figure 8.13.1

Krebs cycle
After the transition reaction, the Acetyl Co-A enters into the Krebs cycle. The Krebs cycle occurs in the mitochondrial matrix. Remember the two carbon atoms of the pyruvate are linked to the Acetyl Co-A. As the Acetyl Co-A moves through the Krebs cycle, the two remaining carbon atoms are catabolized from the acetyl Co-A. When a carbon from the acetyl group is catabolized, the carbon atom is combined with two oxygen atoms and a molecule of carbon dioxide is formed. Follow the Krebs cycle and you will see there are two molecules of carbon dioxide which are formed for every molecule of pyruvate that enters the Krebs cycle. Since the glucose was broken into two molecules of pyruvate during glycolysis, the Krebs cycle "turns" twice for every molecule of glucose metabolized. Shown here is the output of the Krebs cycle for each molecule of pyruvate. There is an output of one molecule of ATP, three molecules of NADH and one molecule of FADH$_2$ for each molecule of pyruvate that enters the Krebs cycle. To find the output per molecule of glucose, simply double that number—there is an output of two molecules of ATP, six molecules of NADH and two molecules of FADH$_2$. ATP is used directly by the cell for energy. NADH and FADH$_2$ enter the electron transport chain.

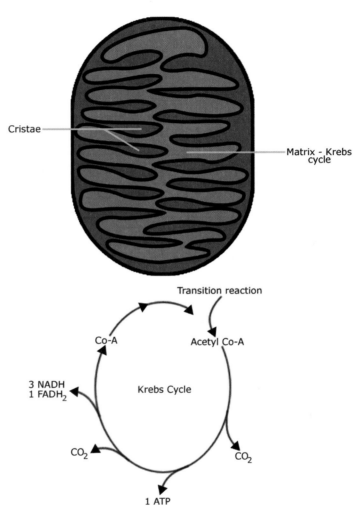

8.14 The Electron Transport Chain

The cristae contain the enzymes that form the **electron transport chain.** Recall from the last chapter that an electron transport chain is a series of molecules that pass high-energy electrons from one molecule to another. As the electron "falls" down the chain, it releases energy. The energy is captured by molecules called coenzymes. The coenzymes use this energy to fuel endergonic reactions which produce ATP. A LOT more ATP is produced in the electron transport chain then is produced directly from the Krebs cycle. The purpose of the Krebs cycle is really not to make ATP. The purpose of the Krebs cycle is to generate molecules of NADH and FADH$_2$ to be used in the electron transport chain where the majority of ATP is made during cellular respiration.

Figure 8.14.1

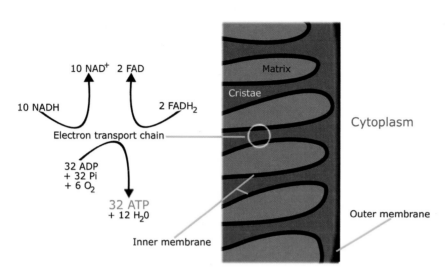

Electron Transport Chain
The electron transport chain occurs in the cristae of the mitochondria. The electron transport chain is where the majority of the ATP is produced. The molecules and enzymes of the cellular respiration electron transport chain are housed within the membranes of the cristae. As the activated electrons are passed through the chain, their energy is captured by enzymes at critical places. The trapped energy is used by the enzymes of the electron transport chain to synthesize ATP from ADP and inorganic phosphate (Pi). The electron carriers NAD^+ and FAD are regenerated. Note that the electron transport chain is when oxygen is used. When the electrons get to the end of the chain, they need somewhere to go. Oxygen serves as the final "acceptor" of the electrons that pass through the chain. When oxygen accepts the electrons, it is converted into molecules of water (H_2O).

During the transformation of the energy carried by NADH and $FADH_2$ in the electron transport chain, thirty-two molecules of ATP are formed for every molecule of glucose. This means that, **in total**, for every molecule of glucose that enters aerobic respiration, about thirty-six ATP molecules are formed—two during glycolysis, two during the Krebs cycle and thirty-two in the electron transport chain. Finally, there are six molecules of water formed per molecule of glucose during the electron transport chain. The water comes from combining the electrons of the hydrogen molecules from the NADH and $FADH_2$ with oxygen. In this way, oxygen serves as the final electron acceptor in aerobic cellular respiration. Thus, this last step, the combining of hydrogen's electrons with oxygen, is why all aerobic creatures need oxygen for aerobic metabolism.

8.15 ENERGY CONVERSION AND AEROBIC RESPIRATION

It seems as though this energy transformation is fairly efficient. However, only about 40% of the energy available in the bonds of the glucose molecule is captured as ATP energy. The rest is lost as heat (recall the entropy discussion in Chapter 6).

Once ATP is made, it is used to fuel endergonic reactions in the cell. When ATP is used, it is hydrolyzed into ADP and Pi. The ADP and the Pi are then transported by the cell back into the mitochondria, where it is then converted back to ATP.

All aerobic organisms—bacteria, yeast, plants, mammals, fish, sponges, reptiles, amphibians, etc.—generate their ATP via the Krebs cycle. Aerobic prokaryotes do not have mitochondria, so their aerobic metabolism takes place in the cytoplasm.

Figure 8.15.1

Summary of Glycolysis and Aerobic Respiration

Below is a summary of glycolysis and aerobic respiration. Although there are a lot of arrows, this is not that complex. All of the arrows for the NAD/NADH and the FAD/FADH$_2$, for example, simply illustrate the circular flow of these molecules. This diagram shows the overall production of molecules for every molecule of glucose. Note, for example, that the ATP production in the Krebs cycle shown below is two molecules of ATP (one molecule of ATP for every turn of the cycle). Note the overall net production is thirty-six molecules of ATP per molecule of glucose.

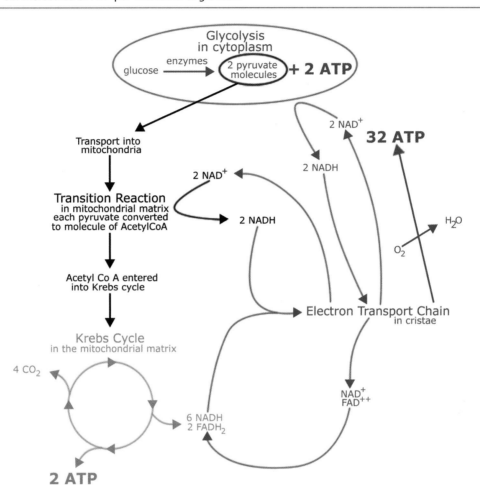

Figure 8.15.2

Net Equation of Aerobic Respiration

This is a slightly different picture of cellular respiration. Either way you look at it, the net production of ATP is thirty-six molecules per molecule of glucose metabolized.

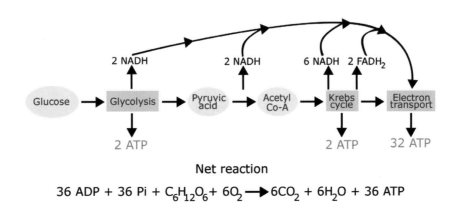

Net reaction

$$36 \text{ ADP} + 36 \text{ Pi} + C_6H_{12}O_6 + 6O_2 \longrightarrow 6CO_2 + 6H_2O + 36 \text{ ATP}$$

8.16 ANAEROBIC RESPIRATION

Aerobic respiration can only occur if oxygen is plentiful in the cell. If it is not, then ATP is generated by anaerobic respiration. Anaerobic respiration is also called **fermentation**. No matter what the name, it describes the process of converting glucose into energy (ATP) without using oxygen. Like aerobic respiration, the first step of anaerobic respiration is glycolysis. Instead of entering mitochondria, pyruvate is diverted to the anaerobic pathway when the cell senses there is not enough oxygen present.

Fermentation is a fairly common form of respiration. Many micro-organisms—such as some bacteria and yeast—use it as their sole source of energy production. Also, animal cells use fermentation when short and quick bursts of energy are needed—such as sprinting—since it produces ATP more quickly than aerobic respiration.

Humans have learned to use the fermentation process in the area of food preparation. It is fermentation that is responsible for producing the holes in Swiss cheese and the rising action of yeast. This is because CO_2 gas is released, causing the gas to form spaces, or holes, in the cheese and take up room in the bread dough. Also, fermentation has been used for thousands of years to make wine and beer, since one of the products of yeast fermentation is ethanol (alcohol).

Although fermentation does lead to an overall net production of ATP, it does not produce nearly as much ATP per molecule of glucose as aerobic respiration does. This means that fermentation is a much less efficient process than aerobic respiration. Typically, while aerobic respiration produces thirty-six ATP molecules per molecule of glucose, fermentation produces a net of two ATP molecules.

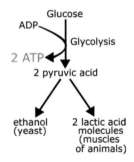

Figure 8.16.1

Anaerobic Respiration
Anaerobic respiration is also called fermentation. Under certain conditions, ATP is made through anaerobic respiration. This process does not use oxygen. In organisms like yeast, fermentation leads to the production of alcohol. In animals, anaerobic respiration commonly occurs in muscles when energy is needed quickly. It results in much less ATP produced per molecule of glucose, but fermentation is able to produce ATP more quickly.

8.17 ADVANCED

We will now discuss the production of ATP in the electron transport chain in more detail. The production of ATP in the Krebs cycle is straight-forward, but exactly how ATP is produced through the electron transport chain is much more complicated, and is not entirely understood, even today.

Hydrogen ions accumulate in high concentrations on one side of the cristae membrane. Hydrogen ions are also called **protons**. This is possible because protein pumps embedded in the cristae, called **proton pumps**, actively pump protons to one side of the membrane (out of the matrix and into the outer compartment). This is done against the hydrogen ion gradient. Since the cell is doing work to actively pump the hydrogen ions against their gradient, this process does require energy—but it uses energy derived from the activated electrons carried by NADH and $FADH_2$, not from ATP. As hydrogen accumulates on one side of the membrane, it flows down its concentration gradient back into the matrix through a gated channel. This gated channel is an enzyme called **ATP synthase**. ATP synthase, also called **ATP-ase**, makes ATP from ADP and Pi. As the protons pass through the ATP synthase, the energy from their movement provides enough heat so that ATP synthase can make ATP from ADP. This is an endergonic reaction which gets the activation energy from the protons flowing through the ATP synthase. This ability of the hydrogen ion gradient to perform work (i.e., to make ATP molecules) is called the **proton motive force**. The process of the hydrogen flowing across the cristae and driving ATP synthase is called **chemiosmosis**.

The proton motive force and chemiosmosis are responsible for ATP production in mitochondria and chloroplasts.

Figure 8.17.1

Proton Motive Force
The membrane of the cristae contains two proteins relevant to our discussion. One is a protein which pumps hydrogen (protons) to one side of the cristae membrane. This is called a proton pump. The other is the enzyme ATP synthase. The proton pump protein is able to harness the energy from the activated electrons of NADH and $FADH_2$ and use it to pump protons against their gradient. This causes a high concentration of protons on one side of the membrane. As the hydrogen ions flow back across the membrane, they do so through a gated channel: the ATP synthase. The protons move through the ATP synthase down their concentration gradient. This movement provides the energy for ATP synthase to drive the endergonic reaction of linking a phosphate group to ADP, generating ATP, and is called chemiosmosis.

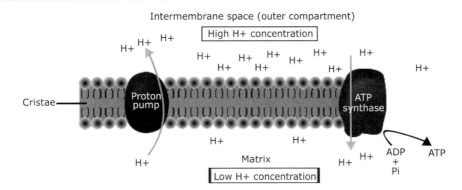

8.18 PEOPLE OF SCIENCE

Sir Hans Krebs (1900-1981) was a German physician. He did research in Germany until Hitler came to power. Once Hitler took control, Krebs was forbidden to practice medicine simply because he was Jewish. Leaving Germany, he went to England, where he studied biochemical processes extensively and discovered both the citric acid cycle (the Krebs cycle) and the urea cycle. He was knighted in 1958 and was professor of biochemistry at University of Sheffield until his death.

8.19 KEY CHAPTER POINTS

- Photosynthesis generates molecules of glucose. Glucose cannot be used by organisms as a direct energy source, though.

- Glucose is processed further by all organisms through the chemical reactions of cellular respiration. Cellular respiration extracts the energy contained in glucose and uses it to make molecules of ATP.

- ATP is the energy source which organisms use to fuel the endergonic reactions of life.

- Enzymes hydrolyze the phosphate bonds of ATP, which releases energy. The enzymes then couple that energy to fuel the reactions they catalyze.

- Cellular respiration can be performed using oxygen or not using oxygen, depending on the conditions of the cell. Cellular respiration using oxygen is called aerobic respiration. Cellular respiration not using oxygen is called anaerobic respiration.

- Aerobic respiration, like photosynthesis, is a set of related chemical reactions. There are three steps—the first occurs in the cytoplasm, while the second and third occur in the mitochondria.

- The first step of cellular respiration, glycolysis, occurs in the cytoplasm and is technically not considered aerobic respiration. It is not considered part of cellular respiration because glycolysis is performed by the cell at other times and for reasons other than aerobic respiration.

- The next two steps, the Krebs cycle and the electron transport chain, occur in the mitochondria. Both are aerobic respiration.

- Aerobic respiration generates thirty-six molecules of usable ATP per molecule of glucose metabolized.

- The structure of mitochondria is specialized to perform aerobic respiration efficiently.

- Mitochondria use the proton motive force to drive the enzymes which make ATP, called ATP-ase.

- Oxygen is consumed and carbon dioxide is produced during aerobic respiration.

- Anaerobic respiration occurs in the cytoplasm and generates two molecules of usable ATP per molecule of glucose metabolized.

8.20 DEFINITIONS

acetyl Co-A
A co-enzyme that carries the carbon atoms of pyruvate through the Krebs cycle, during which the bonds of pyruvate are broken and ATP, NADH, and $FADH_2$ are produced.

acetyl group
The two-carbon molecule made from pyruvate during pyruvic acid oxidation (the transition reaction).

ADP (adenosine diphosphate)
Two phosphate groups linked to an adenosine molecule. Converted by ATP-ase into ATP by the linking of another phosphate group onto ADP.

aerobic respiration
The biological process in which ATP is made from glucose, using oxygen as the final electron acceptor.

anaerobic respiration
The biological process in which ATP is made from glucose without oxygen. Oxygen does not serve as the final electron acceptor.

ATP synthase/ATP-ase
The enzyme that makes ATP from ADP.

chemiosmosis
The process of the hydrogen flowing across the cristae and driving ATP synthase.

citric acid cycle (or tricarboxylic acid cycle)
Other names for the Krebs cycle.

co-enzyme A
The coenzyme that carries carbon molecules from pyruvate through the Krebs cycle.

FAD
Flavin Adenine Dinucleotide, an energy capturing coenzyme. It captures energy in the form of electrons; an electron carrier.

fermentation
Anaerobic respiration.

glycolysis
The initial step in the metabolism of glucose in which glucose is broken into two pyruvate molecules.

inner membrane
Refers to the inner membrane of mitochondria. It contains the molecules which produce most of the ATP.

intermembrane space (a.k.a. outer compartment)
   The space between the inner membrane and the outer membrane in mitochondria.

Kreb's cycle
   The second step of cellular respiration which occurs in the mitochondria. During this sequence of reactions, the remaining carbon molecules from glucose are oxidized to form carbon dioxide, generating ATP, NADH, and $FADH_2$.

matrix
   The space on the inside of the mitochondria between the cristae.

NAD
   Nicotinamide adenine dinucleotide, an energy capturing coenzyme. It captures energy in the form of electrons (hydrogen ions); an electron carrier.

NADH
   The activated form of NAD; also referred to as the reduced form.

outer membrane
   Protects the inside of the mitochondria from the contents of the cytoplasm.

oxidation reaction
   Removing a hydrogen atom with its electron from a molecule.

proton motive force
   The ability of a hydrogen ion gradient to perform work.

proton pumps
   protein pumps embedded in the cristae which pump hydrogen into the intermembrane space from the matrix.

pyruvate
   The three-carbon molecule that is formed as a result of glycolysis.

pyruvic acid oxidation
   The transition reaction.

transition reaction
   The reaction that links glycolysis to aerobic respiration.

STUDY QUESTIONS

1. What is cellular respiration? Why do organisms need to perform cellular respiration?

2. What is important about the phosphate bonds of ATP?

3. What is the association between endergonic reactions and ATP?

4. What does the hydrolysis of the phosphate bonds of ATP result in? (Think in terms of chemistry and energy.)

5. Write the general chemical reaction which enzymes use to couple the energy released from ATP to fuel endergonic reactions.

6. Write the balanced equation of cellular respiration.

7. What is the process of making ATP from glucose when oxygen is plentiful called?

8. What is the process of making ATP from glucose when oxygen is scarce called?

9. What benefit does making ATP when oxygen is plentiful have as compared to when oxygen is not plentiful?

10. What is glycolysis? What are the products of glycolysis? Why is glycolysis important?

11. True or False? Glycolysis occurs in mitochondria.

12. True or False? Glycolysis is part of aerobic respiration? Why did you answer as you did?

13. True or False? Glycolysis requires oxygen.

14. True or False? When oxygen is plentiful in the cell, pyruvate enters aerobic respiration.

15. Draw and label the major structures of a mitochondrion. Include a brief description of the function of each part.

16. What is an oxidation reaction?

17. What happens to pyruvate after it is oxidized?

18. Describe the events which occur in the Krebs cycle. Include the products of the reactions.

19. What are the two energy–capturing co-enzymes in the Krebs cycle?

20. Which produces more ATP, the Krebs cycle or the electron transport chain? How many molecules of ATP are produced in each?

21. What is another name for anaerobic respiration?

22. What benefit(s) does anaerobic respiration have over aerobic respiration?

23. How does a proton pump work? How does it contribute to the proton motive force and chemiosmosis?

PLEASE TAKE TEST #3 IN TEST BOOKLET

DNA, RNA, and Proteins

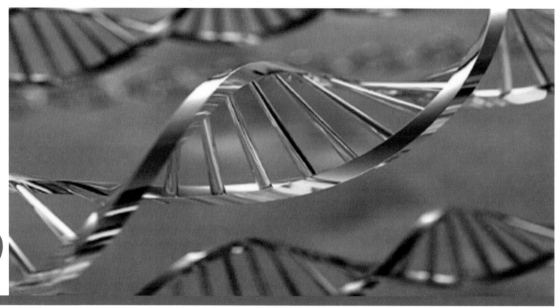

9

9.0 CHAPTER PREVIEW

In this chapter we will:

- Investigate the structure and function of DNA and RNA.

- Discuss the organization of DNA into chromosomes and genes.

- Study the concept that one gene codes for the production of one protein.

- Introduce the concept that genes control all traits of an organism or cell.

- Explore the biological processes of eukaryotic transcription and translation.

- Discuss transcription and translation in prokaryotes.

- Learn what the genetic code is and become comfortable using it.

9.1 OVERVIEW

In Chapter 3, we discussed the basic structures of protein and of the nucleic acids DNA (deoxyribonucleic acid) and RNA (ribonucleic acid). These molecules are intimately linked, and in this chapter we will explore their connections more closely. Because this is fairly complicated, this chapter is designed to be read once, then re-read and studied. This method will allow you to comprehend what you may have missed the first time.

Figure 9.1.1

General Structure of DNA Nucleotides

This represents the general structure of the four nucleotides which make up DNA. The nucleotides are also referred to as **bases**. Each nucleotide of DNA is composed of a central sugar composed of five carbon atoms arranged in a ring. This sugar is called deoxyribose. It has a phosphate group attached to it on one end and a nitrogen base attached on the other. A nitrogen base is a molecule that contains nitrogen and has a basic pH. Every molecule of DNA is made up of thousands to millions of nucleotides linked to one another.

DNA is the molecule in prokaryotes and eukaryotes that contains the genetic information. DNA contains the information instructing the cell which polypeptides to make and when. These polypeptides are then assembled in the cell to form proteins or enzymes, and the proteins and enzymes that the cell makes determine what type of cell it is. For example, a liver cell does not manufacture the same polypeptides, proteins, and enzymes that a lung cell does and a *Streptococcus* bacterium does not manufacture the same polypeptides, proteins, and enzymes that a *Salmonella* bacterium does. DNA contains the information regarding how tall we will be, whether or not an organism is a dog or a bacteria or a walrus. Any characteristic of an organism you can think of is determined by their DNA content.

Over time, through extensive research, investigators have found that it is the full compliment of polypeptides a cell/organism manufactures that makes it unique. Indeed, it is precisely this information, encoded in the DNA, that gives a cell or organism its physical, biochemical, and physiological properties and, to some extent, its behavioral properties.

How does the DNA communicate to the rest of the cell and direct protein synthesis? The process is remarkably similar in prokaryotes and eukaryotes, with the only major difference due to the presence of the nucleus in eukaryotes. Basically, the information contained in DNA is contained in a code. This code is read by enzymes and made into a code contained in RNA. This RNA serves as a messenger and takes the message from the DNA to ribosomes, which then manufacture the protein as directed by the RNA message. When the RNA reaches a ribosome, the message from the DNA is read, decoded, and made into a protein by the ribosome. This protein then influences the cell to behave in a certain way (in plain words, the protein tells the cell to "do something" or to "stop doing something").

9.2 DNA GENERAL

DNA is a macromolecule, a nucleic acid composed of between thousands and billions of molecules of nucleotides. In prokaryotes, DNA is found free in the cytoplasm. Eukaryotes contain much more DNA than prokaryotes. In fact, there is so much DNA in eukaryotes that it has its own special packing system. Eukaryotic DNA is tightly coiled and packed around nuclear proteins within the nucleus. These proteins are called **histones**. Histones allow for the DNA to be coiled tightly so it takes up less room than it otherwise would. Think of how difficult it would be to manage a tape measure if it were not all wound tightly inside of the tape measure housing. Histones provide an effective way to tightly package huge molecules of DNA into the nucleus.

Even though it is large, DNA is made up of only four different **nucleotides—adenine (A), thymine (T), guanine (G), and cytosine (C)**. The basic structure of DNA is nucleotides linked to one another repeatedly. These four nucleotides repeatedly link together forming a DNA molecule as small as 5,000 nucleotides (in the case of bacteria) or as large as over 6,000,000,000 nucleotides (in the case of humans). If the information contained in human DNA were printed like a book, it would be like reading the *Lord of the Rings* trilogy books four hundred times (which the cell is able to do in about four hours!).

Figure 9.2.1

The Four Nitrogenous Bases of DNA

Below are the four nitrogen containing bases of DNA. Each nucleotide is named for the nitrogenous base which it contains. Figures (a) and (b) show the structure of the two purine bases, adenine (A) and guanine (G), respectively. The purines are two-ringed molecules. Their pyrimidine counterparts, thymine (T) and cytosine (C), are shown in figures (c) and (d), respectively. They are both single-ringed molecules. You do not need to know the chemical structure of these molecules, but you do need to know that the purines are two-ring structures and the pyrimidines are single-ring structures.

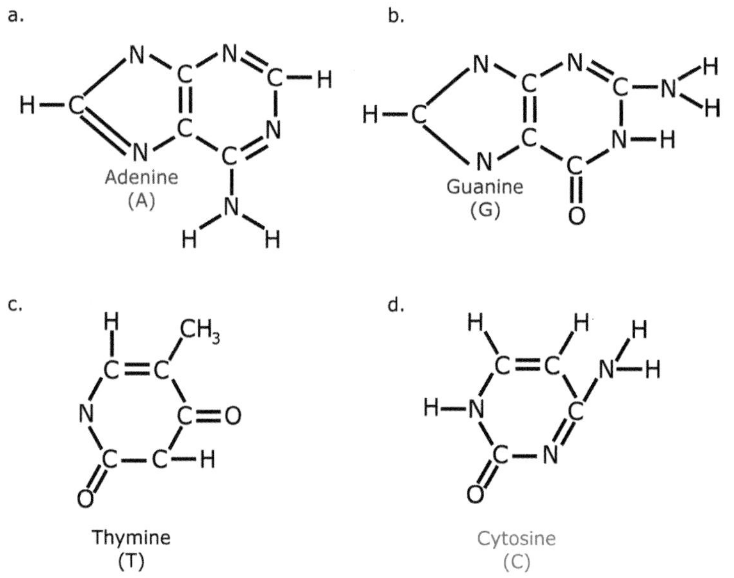

9.3 DNA IS MADE OF PURINES AND PYRIMIDINES

Recall that a nucleotide has three separate components—a phosphate group, a nitrogenous base (meaning a molecule whose pH is greater than seven and contains nitrogen), and a **sugar**. The sugar in DNA is deoxyribose and the four **nitrogenous bases** are **adenine, thymine, cytosine, and guanine**. The nucleotides are named after the base they contain, so the nucleotide that contains the base adenine is called adenine, etc. C and T belong to a group of nucleotides called **pyrimidines**, and A and G belong to a group called **purines**. As you can see from Figure 9.2.1 and 9.3.1, the nitrogen base of the purines contain a double-ring structure. The pyrimidines have a single-ring structure. Even though it seems simple now, it took scientists over 100 years to fully understand the structure and make up of DNA. It was not until the early 1950s that James Watson and Francis Crick were able to put together all the information known about DNA and correctly deduce the structure of the molecule.

Figure 9.3.1

Complete Structure of the Four Nucleotides of DNA

Adenine (a) and guanine (b) are purines. The nitrogen base of the purines is a two-ring structure. Thymine (c) and cytosine (d) are pyrimidines. Pyrimidines have a nitrogen base with one ring.

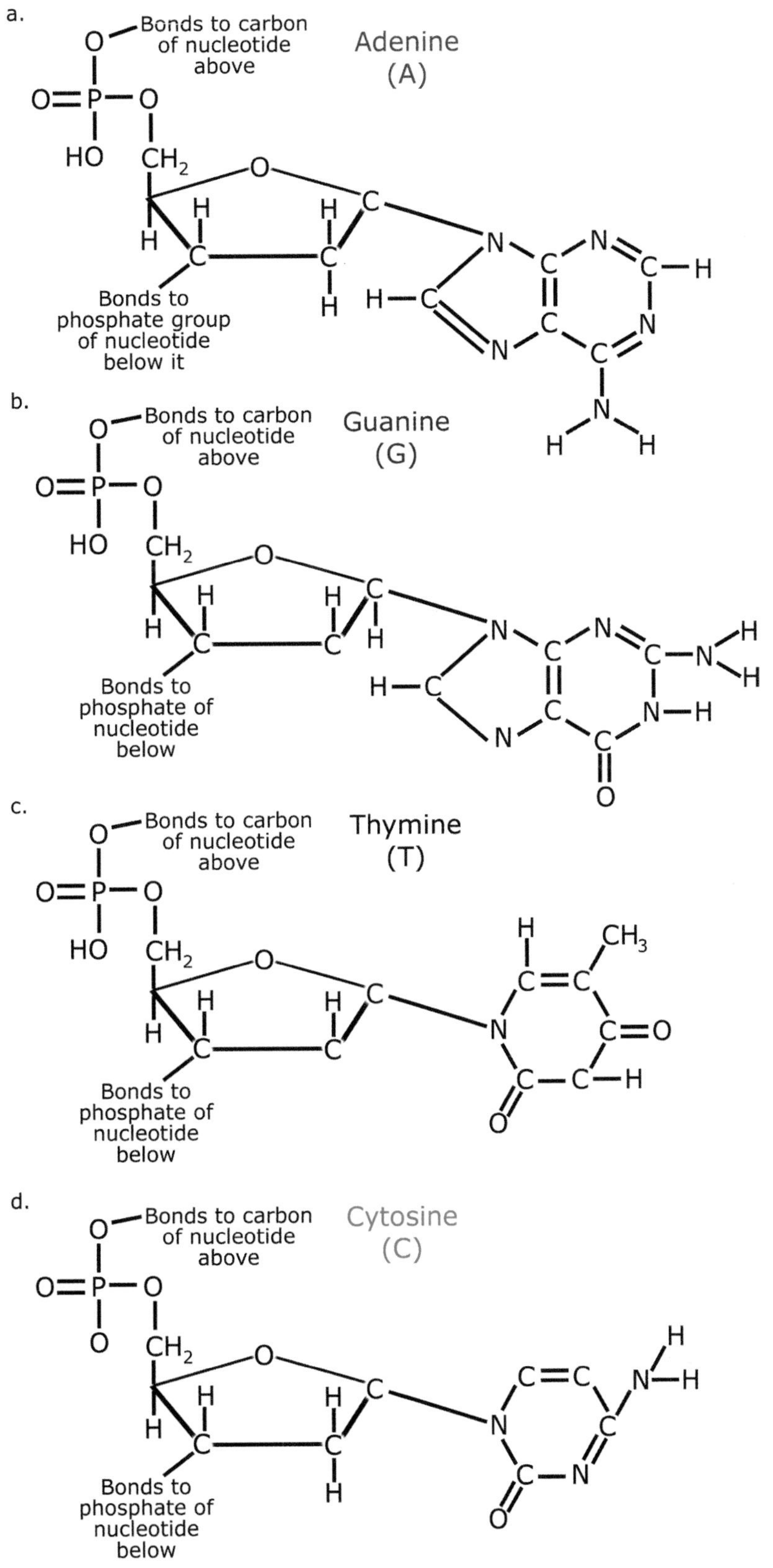

9.4 DNA IS A DOUBLE STRANDED HELIX

Thanks to Watson and Crick's elucidation of the structure of DNA, and the work of many scientists before them, we now know that the three dimensional structure of DNA is a **double-stranded helix**. It looks like a spiral staircase. Double-stranded means that DNA has two individual chains of nucleotides. Each chain is called a **strand**. Each strand is a long chain of nucleotides linked to one another. Nucleotides of a strand are linked together by covalent bonds. Each strand is held to the other by hydrogen bonds that form between the nucleotides of one strand and the nucleotides of the other strand. A hydrogen bond forms between a hydrogen atom on one strand of DNA and a nitrogen or oxygen atom on a base on the opposite strand of DNA.

The strands of DNA are called **complementary strands**. They are not complementary because one is nice to the other. They are complementary because the sequence of one strand contains the proper nucleotide sequence so the opposite strand can form hydrogen bonds with it. The process of nucleotides forming hydrogen bonds with one another is called **base-pairing**. When two strands of DNA are complementary, nucleotides base-pair and the two strands bond together. This forms a double-stranded molecule of DNA.

Base-pairing occurs in a very specific manner. A purine can only form a base-pair with a pyrimidine. Further, only the purine A and the pyrimidine T can form hydrogen bonds with one another, and only the purine G and the pyrimidine C can form hydrogen bonds with one another. Therefore, it is said that only A and T can "base-pair" with one another, and only C and G can "base-pair" with one another. For example, adenine never pairs with cytosine, guanine, or itself. This pairing relationship means that a nucleotide with a two-ringed nitrogenous base always base-pairs with a one-ringed nucleotide, which in part gives DNA its double-stranded helical shape.

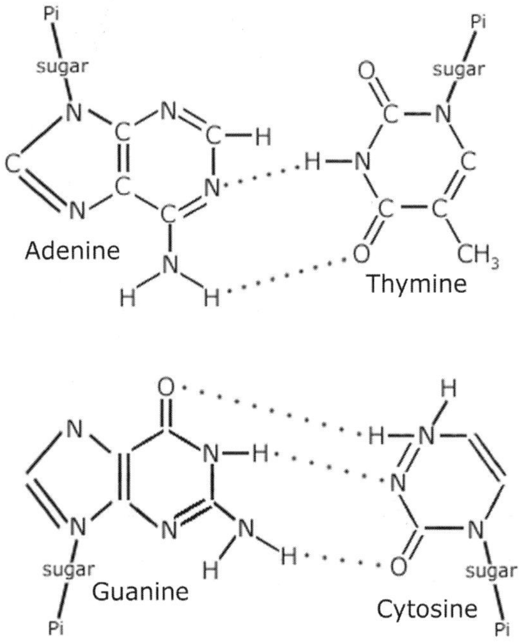

Figure 9.4.1

Base-pairing and Hydrogen Bonding of the Purines and Pyrimidines

Base-pairing is the property that nucleotides exhibit in DNA. Base-pairing is possible through the formation of hydrogen bonds. (Recall the process of hydrogen bonding that we discussed relating to water in chapter 3.) A hydrogen bond forms between a hydrogen atom on one nucleotide and a nitrogen or an oxygen atom on the base of the complementary strand (the hydrogen bond forms between one nucleotide and the base across from it on the other strand of DNA). A hydrogen bond is not as strong as a covalent or ionic bond, but is plenty strong to hold the two strands of DNA together. The purine A base-pairs with the pyrimidine T. The purine G base-pairs with the pyrimidine C. This represents the hydrogen bonding relationships between adenine/thymine and guanine/cytosine. Note that adenine and thymine have two hydrogen bonds and guanine and cytosine have three.

One of the big pieces of information which helped Watson and Crick figure out the shape of DNA is called **Chargaff's rule**. Erwin Chargaff studied DNA from a number of different animals. He found the amounts of the thymine and adenine components in DNA were always of equal percentage, as were the amounts of cytosine and guanine. This was true no matter which species' DNA was being studied, although the percentages for each change from species to species. For example, in humans, Chargaff found that the four bases were present in these percentages: A = 30.9%; T = 29.4%; C = 19.8%; and G = 19.9%. The fact that the percentage of A and T are equal in DNA, and the percentage of C and G are equal in DNA, is called Chargaff's rule. Watson and Crick knew this and used that information to help them build DNA structural models.

Figure 9.4.2

Molecular Structure of DNA

The molecular structure of DNA is called a double-stranded helix. Due to the chemical structure of the nucleotides, only adenine and thymine form hydrogen bonds with one another, and guanine and cytosine only form hydrogen bonds with one another. Adenine is said to "pair" with thymine, and guanine "pairs" with cytosine. After reading further into the chapter and reviewing the structures of the DNA nucleotides in the next few figures, return to this one and study it further. Because of the structures of the nucleotides and the way they bind together, DNA forms as two chains of molecules; hence, it forms a "double strand." Each blue chain in the figure is a "strand." Due to the hydrogen bonding interactions between nucleotides of opposite strands, the shape of the DNA becomes twisted, as shown. This gives rise to the "helix." Note from the diagram that A and T always pair across from one another, and C and G always pair across from one another. Normally, A and T do not pair with C or G, and C and G do not pair with A or T. The wrong bases can sometimes pair, though, as the result of an error in copying the DNA. This is a type of mutation, which we will discuss later in the genetics chapter. Because of this constant, pairing relationship, the two strands are said to be complementary. The only way that DNA can form the proper double helix structure is for each strand to contain the proper sequence of nucleotides so the As, Ts, Cs, and Gs all line up across from one another properly.

The exact reason Chargaff's rule occurred was not known until Watson and Crick's model of the double-stranded helix. They hypothesized the structure of the nucleotides means that only A can form hydrogen bonds with T, and only C can form hydrogen bonds with G. This has been confirmed over and over since the 1950s. The orderly base-pairing allows for accurate predictions of the sequence of nucleotides in one strand of DNA, as long as the sequence of the other strand is known. For example, if the sequence of nucleotides on one strand is TAACCGTACG, then we know that the sequence of the complementary strand will have the sequence ATTGGCATGC. This is the reason that Chargaff's rule is true. For every T in one strand of DNA, there is always an A hydrogen bonded to it in the opposite strand. For every C in one strand of DNA, there is always a G base-paired with it on the opposite strand.

Realize that since A and T only hydrogen bond to one another, each place an A appears on one strand, there has to be a T directly across from it on the other strand, allowing them to base-pair. The same is true for C and G. For every C that is on one strand, there is always a G across from it on the other strand, so they can base-pair. That is what is meant by complementary.

Let's say you had one single strand of DNA which was not complementary to another single strand of DNA. That means that the nucleotide sequence of one strand does not match the nucleotide sequence of the other. Therefore, hydrogen bonding could not occur properly because A and T would not be across from one another in the proper order, just as C and G would not be across from one another in the proper order. The only way that the nucleotides of DNA can form hydrogen bonds is if the A in one strand is across from the T in the other strand. The same holds true for C and G. If I took these two strands of DNA and placed them into a beaker, they would not form into a double-stranded DNA molecule because they are not complementary. The two strands would stay as individual strands in the beaker because one strand is not complementary to the other.

Now let's say you had two single-strand molecules of DNA which are complementary. This means the sequences of the nucleotides on one strand line up properly with the nucleotide sequences of the other strand. This allows A to hydrogen bond to T, and C to hydrogen bond to G. If I place these two strands in a beaker, since they are complementary, they would form hydrogen bonds together and form the double stranded helix of a normal DNA molecule. This concept of complementary strands will come up later, so be sure you understand it.

9.5 DNA ORGANIZATION

The DNA of eukaryotes may contain more than four or five billion base pairs. Human DNA contains more than six billion base pairs. Because there is so much genetic material, DNA does not exist as one continuous molecule. Rather, it is housed as smaller pieces called **chromosomes**. Think of DNA as an encyclopedia. Encyclopedias do not come in one book. There is too much information to fit into one book. Rather, encyclopedias are broken into smaller books called volumes—there is a volume for subjects starting with "A," a volume for "B," etc. Chromosomes are like the volumes of an encyclopedia. The information is broken into smaller pieces because it is easier to manage and use. There is way too much information in eukaryotic DNA to be housed in one continuous molecule. Chromosomes are simply smaller pieces of DNA. DNA exists as chromosomes because they are easier to manage than one huge molecule.

Chromosomes can appear in two different forms. Normally, during most of the cell's life, the chromosomes are wound loosely. They can be seen under a light microscope as material called **chromatin**. Although chromatin looks like it is scattered haphazardly in the nucleus, it is actually very organized. However, during mitosis, chromatin becomes compacted. This means the chromatin becomes tightly wound. At that time, when the chromatin becomes a tightly coiled structure, it is called a chromosome. Think of a chromosome and chromatin like a slinky. A chromosome is tightly wound, like a slinky at rest, while chromatin resembles a slinky stretched to its limit.

Figure 9.5.1

DNA as Chromosomes
Below left is a graphical representation of a human karyotype. A karyotype is an orderly presentation of chromosomes from one individual cell. The cells are prepared in the lab in such a way that all forty-six chromosomes can be removed from the cell and placed on a microscope slide. A picture is then taken with a special microscope camera so the chromosomes can be viewed. Humans have their DNA housed in forty-six individual chromosomes and they are arranged in 23 pairs. Eukaryotic chromosomes are arranged in pairs because pairs of chromosomes contain the same information. You can see the chromosomes are different sizes and different shapes because they contain different amounts of nucleotides. Generally, chromosomes that are larger contain more genes than smaller ones. A chromosome is the form of DNA that is wound and condensed as tightly as it can be. At other times, chromosomes are not as condensed; therefore, they are harder to see. Chromosomes which are not in the tightly-condensed form are called chromatin. The right micrograph shows what chromatin looks like. It is usually housed around the periphery of the nuclear membrane.

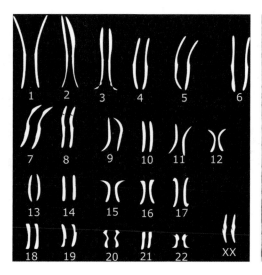
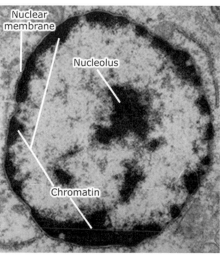

All organisms of the same species have the same numbers of chromosomes, but organisms of different species usually have different numbers of chromosomes. That is to say that normally all humans have 46 chromosomes, all earthworms have 32 chromosomes, all fruit flies have 8 chromosomes, and all ferns have about 1200 chromosomes. Regardless of the numbers of chromosomes, the function of the chromosome is the same in all species—to house the genetic material in an orderly fashion. This is so that the DNA is easy to reproduce and transcribe.

9.6 CHROMOSOMES, GENES, AND TRAITS

Chromosomes are further broken into smaller units called **genes**. A gene is considered the basic, functional unit of DNA. A gene is a linear section of a chromosome that contains coded instructions for making a protein. In that respect, DNA is like a huge recipe book that contains the exact information for all of the ingredients for making proteins. The instructions for making the protein are contained in the orderly arrangement of nucleotides. This orderly nucleotide arrangement is called the **genetic code**.

One gene codes for the production of one protein only. These proteins determine hundreds, even thousands, of the organism's **traits**. A trait is a characteristic of an organism. Each trait is controlled by one or more genes. Since genes contain information for making proteins, and one or more genes control a trait, traits are controlled by the proteins that a cell and organism makes. Some traits of an organism are visible, such as height, hair color, foot size and teeth whiteness. Other traits are not visible, such as the specific biochemical reactions a cell is performing. Whether traits are visible or not, they are all controlled by genes.

For example, in humans there is a gene which codes for straight or curly hair. If a person has the gene for curly hair, they make a specific protein that causes their hair to be curly. People that have straight hair do not have the gene that codes for curly hair; their hair straightness gene codes for a protein that makes their hair straight. In humans, there are probably 30,000 genes or more controlling different traits. We will learn more about these in upcoming chapters.

Figure 9.6.1

The Orderliness of DNA and Genes

Two graphical representations of the organization of DNA are shown. The left figure represents that way that DNA is ordered from a larger to a smaller scale. The largest unit of DNA is the chromosome. Chromosomes are long strands of DNA which are tightly wound around proteins called histones. As the DNA is unwrapped from around the histones, the individual, double helix shape of the DNA molecule is revealed. In the right figure, DNA is shown as a chromosome and then an individual segment of DNA. A gene represents a segment of DNA that contains coded information for making a protein. A gene is a linear sequence of nucleotides on one strand of DNA that codes for the production of one protein. Genes are the individual unit of the genetic code.

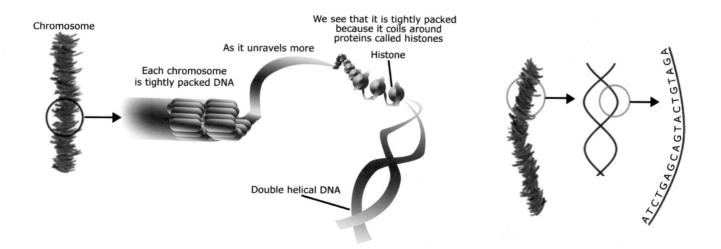

Chromosome

Each chromosome is tightly packed DNA

As it unravels more

We see that it is tightly packed because it coils around proteins called histones

Histone

Double helical DNA

ATCTGAGCAGTACTGTAGA

9.7 RNA

RNA stands for ribonucleic acid. There are several different types of RNA molecules in the cell and they are all involved in making proteins. Like DNA, RNA is composed of repeating sequences of four nucleotides. The nucleotides all share a common structure. RNA contains the sugar ribose instead of DNA's deoxyribose. A phosphate group is linked to ribose on one end. One of four nitrogenous bases is linked to the ribose on the other end. The four RNA nucleotides are the purines adenine and guanine, and the pyrimidine cytosine. However, instead of the other pyrimidine being thymine like in DNA, the pyrimidine which pairs with adenine in RNA is **uracil** (U). RNA is a single-stranded molecule. The nucleotides are all linked to one another by covalent bonds.

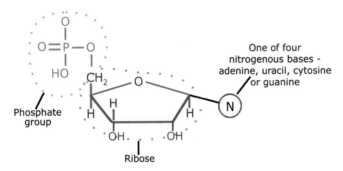

One of four nitrogenous bases - adenine, uracil, cytosine or guanine

Phosphate group

Ribose

Figure 9.7.1

RNA Nucleotides
There is a close similarity in structure between DNA and RNA nucleotides.

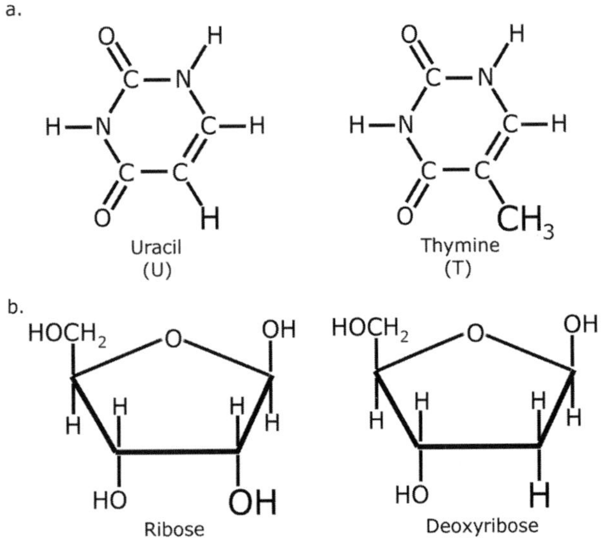

a.

Uracil
(U)

Thymine
(T)

b.

Ribose

Deoxyribose

Figure 9.7.2

The Structure of Thymine, Uracil, Deoxyribose, and Ribose Compared
The structures of thymine and uracil are similar. Uracil has a hydrogen atom attached to it in place of the methyl group (the "CH_3") on the thymine. Thymine is the pyrimidine that pairs with adenine in DNA, but uracil is the pyrimidine that pairs with adenine in RNA. In figure (b), you can see the minor difference between ribose and deoxyribose. "Oxy" relates to oxygen. You can see that ribose has an OH group, while deoxyribose has only an H molecule. The oxygen has been removed, or "deox-ied."

9.8 mRNA

There are two important types of RNA that we will learn about—**messenger RNA** and **transfer RNA**. Messenger RNA, or **mRNA**, is responsible for carrying a coded message from the DNA to the ribosomes in the cytoplasm. The message instructs the ribosomes which protein should be made. We will look at the structure of mRNA in the next few sections.

The coded message from the DNA molecule is made into a molecule of mRNA. (Realize that the mRNA is made from a DNA template.) The mRNA then leaves the nucleus through the nuclear pores and goes into the cytoplasm. In the cytoplasm, one or more ribosomes bind to the mRNA. The ribosomes read the code in the mRNA and make the protein indicated by the code in the mRNA.

Figure 9.8.1

mRNA
mRNA is a single-stranded molecule in the shape of a helix. Note the presence of uracil (U) instead of thymine.

9.9 tRNA

Transfer RNA, or **tRNA**, is responsible for bringing the appropriate amino acids to the ribosome for polypeptide assembly. The tRNA molecule is typically eighty nucleotides long, but some organisms have tRNA molecules as short as 74 nucleotides and others as long as 90. It is folded back on itself like a cross. The structure of the tRNA is maintained by hydrogen bonding between nucleotides. tRNA has two "ends." One end helps the ribosome identify which amino acid is being called for by the code in the mRNA. The other end of the tRNA carries the amino acid. Let's find out how the ribosome knows which protein is being coded for by the mRNA.

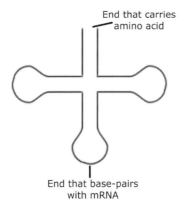

End that carries amino acid

End that base-pairs with mRNA

Figure 9.9.1

tRNA

tRNA is a molecule that is shaped like a lower case "t". The shape of tRNA occurs because of hydrogen bonding between nucleotides. tRNA's have two distinct ends. One end carries the amino acid. The other end helps the ribosome identify whether or not the amino acid the tRNA carries is the specific amino acid for which the mRNA code is calling. The ribosome knows that a specific tRNA molecule is carrying the right amino acid if the tRNA can base pair with the mRNA. We will see how this works in the next few sections.

9.10 FROM DNA TO PROTEIN

We know that genes are sequences of DNA which code for a specific protein. Genes make one organism different from another by directing the cell/organism to produce different polypeptides. Once the polypeptides are made in the cytoplasm, they are assembled to form proteins or enzymes. These proteins or enzymes then cause the cell to perform other biochemical processes. One gene codes for only one polypeptide chain or protein. This is called the "one gene, one polypeptide" or "one gene, one protein" hypothesis.

How does the information contained in the genes get from the nucleus to the cytoplasm? The pathway of information transfer looks like this:

- the sequence of a gene's nucleotides is read by enzymes

- the sequence of gene nucleotides is made into a complementary sequence of mRNA nucleotides in the nucleus

- mRNA is processed in the nucleus

- the mRNA moves from the nucleus into the cytoplasm

- one or more ribosomes bind to the mRNA

- the coded sequence of nucleotides in the mRNA is read by the ribosomes

- tRNA brings amino acids to the ribosomes for protein synthesis

- the protein is synthesized by ribosomes in the cytoplasm

We know that DNA is composed of a long series of nucleotides linked together. Similarly, we also know that proteins are composed of a long series of amino acids linked together. How then does the cell know what sequence of amino acids to make based on a sequence of nucleotides? The sequence of nucleotides in DNA serves as the code for the sequence of amino acids in proteins.

9.11 CODONS

A gene is composed of a certain number of nucleotides and the arrangement of nucleotides—the **sequence**—determines which polypeptide will be made. That means the sequence of nucleotides has something to do with the sequence of amino acids in the protein. However, there are four nucleotides in DNA, but twenty different amino acids, so one nucleotide cannot code for one amino acid.

Figure 9.11.1

DNA Codons

In order for the information in DNA to be accessed, the complementary strands need to be separated so the "inside" of the DNA is accessible. An enzyme called helicase is able to break the hydrogen bonds between the base pairs and "unzip" the DNA. When the DNA is unzipped, the codons are exposed and are able to be made into a complementary molecule of mRNA. Codons are linear runs of a gene's nucleotides organized into groups of three. Each group of three nucleotides is called a codon. Each codon codes for a specific amino acid to be placed into a protein at a specific location. Some codons that tell helicase where to bind to the DNA to start unzipping it. These are called replication origins. Other codons tell enzymes where to start making RNA or proteins. These are called start codons. Other codons tell the enzymes when to stop making RNA or proteins. These are called stop codons. The codons of DNA are not directly read and made into proteins, however. First, the DNA codons are made into mRNA codons in a process called translation. Then, the mRNA codons are read by ribosomes and made into the appropriate protein.

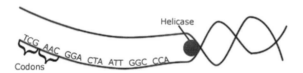

Therefore, the genetic code must be a combination of nucleotides that codes for each amino acid. After a lot of research in the 1960s, it was found that **groups of three nucleotides** provide the code for the sequence of amino acids in a protein. There are four nucleotides, and when taken in groups of three, the possible number of amino acids coded for is 4^3, or 64. This is more than enough combinations to code for the twenty known amino acids.

The sequence of three nucleotides which code for a specific amino acid is called a **codon**. There are three types of codons. Most codons code for the insertion of a specific amino acid in a specific location in a protein. Some amino acids are encoded by more than one codon, as can be seen from the codon table at the end of the chapter. Other codons are called start codons and stop codons. The mRNA codon AUG instructs the ribosomal enzymes where to start reading the mRNA to start synthesizing the protein. AUG is a **start codon**. The ribosomes always begin to read the mRNA at the AUG codon. Also, there are three codons—UAA, UAG, and UGA—that do not code for any amino acids and function as **stop codons**. Since stop codons do not code for any amino acid, when a ribosome reads a stop codon, no tRNA presents itself with an amino acid and so the ribosome simply stops making the protein.

9.12 READING FRAMES AND CODONS

It is important to understand that the gene codons are read by enzymes as linear. That means the gene is read in a straight line on the DNA beginning at the start codon all the way through the stop codon. No nucleotides are skipped and none are repeated, they are read as one continuous line, just like you read a book. This concept is called the **reading frame**. The proper reading frame must be maintained when making mRNA. If it is not, the protein which the mRNA codes for will not be the correct one. This must be kept in mind when the next section—making RNA from DNA and proteins from RNA—is presented.

9.13 TRANSCRIPTION

Transcription is the process of making mRNA from a DNA template. **RNA polymerase** is the enzyme which makes mRNA from DNA. Here is how transcription works. Helicase unwinds the segment of DNA which contains the gene to be transcribed into mRNA. RNA polymerase binds to the DNA and starts making mRNA. The RNA polymerase moves along the gene. As it does, it forms the mRNA molecule by base-pairing mRNA nucleotides across from the DNA nucleotide template. That means that when the RNA polymerase moves over an A in the DNA sequence, it base-pairs it with U and inserts a U into the mRNA molecule. If the next nucleotide in the DNA is a C then RNA polymerase adds a G to the mRNA molecule. This continues until the RNA polymerase reaches an area of the DNA which instructs the RNA polymerase to stop making mRNA. (The DNA start and stop sites of transcription are a bit too complicated for this course.) *Remember that since RNA does not use the nucleotide thymine, every time the RNA polymerase reaches an A on the DNA, it base-pairs it with a U on the mRNA.*

9.14 DNA CODONS ARE MAINTAINED IN mRNA

Since mRNA is made from a DNA template, it retains the nucleotide order of the gene of the DNA. In this way, the codon sequence is preserved in the mRNA. The mRNA codons still code for the same amino acids in the protein in the same order as the DNA codons do.

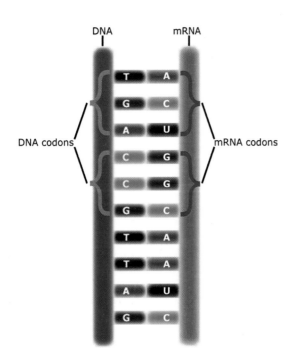

Figure 9.14.1

DNA to mRNA Codons
During DNA transcription, DNA codons are converted into mRNA codons. The DNA is shown here on the left and the mRNA is on the right. Notice that the mRNA retains the appropriate sequence of nucleotides, but U is substituted for T since RNA does not use the T base. The mRNA is complementary to the DNA from which it was made.

Let's look at a simplified example of what is occurring. Say that part of the gene's sequence for a particular protein reads "ATGGCTCTTCGTATT." This is the sequence of nucleotides in the DNA. The correct reading frame, in codons, from left to right, would be "ATG"—"GCT"—"CTT"—"CGT" and lastly "ATT." This is how the RNA polymerase would read the codon and assemble the mRNA nucleotides. mRNA does not go back and read any nucleotides again, nor does it skip any, it simply reads them in order as it proceeds down the gene. The mRNA molecule would be made in this order "UACCGAGAAGCAUUA" by the RNA polymerase. When the ribosome reads the mRNA, the correct reading frame is "UAC"—"CGA"—"GAA"—"GCA"—"UAA."

9.15 mRNA PROCESSING OCCURS AFTER TRANSCRIPTION

Since prokaryotes have no nucleus, often translation of mRNA occurs as the mRNA is being synthesized. In eukaryotes, though, once the mRNA is made, it undergoes **processing**. Eukaryote mRNA is made up of two components—parts of the mRNA that will be **ex-**pressed, called **exons**, and parts of the mRNA that **in-**tervene between the exons called **introns**. The mRNA processing occurs in the nucleus after the initial mRNA molecule is transcribed. It results in enzymes removing the introns, then splicing the exons back together to form the completed molecule of mRNA. Once the introns are removed, the mRNA moves into the cytoplasm.

Figure 9.15.1

Transcription

On top of the figure, the DNA has been unzipped and RNA polymerase has started to make a molecule of mRNA. DNA serves as a template for the production of mRNA. RNA polymerase reads the sequence of bases on the DNA in a linear fashion and base-pairs the appropriate RNA base to its DNA counterpart, making an mRNA molecule that is complementary to the gene being read transcribed. In this way, the DNA codons are transcribed into mRNA codons. Once the mRNA polymerase is finished making mRNA, the mRNA "falls off" the DNA and enters the nucleoplasm. Introns are parts of mRNA that are not made into proteins. Exons are the sections of mRNA that will be read into proteins. It is unclear why sections of mRNA are removed immediately following mRNA production. Introns are cut out of the mRNA molecule and then the exons are linked back together. Removing the introns and linking the exons is performed by enzymes and is called mRNA processing. mRNA processing only occurs in eukaryotes. Once the mRNA finishes being processed, it moves through the nuclear pores into the cytoplasm. Once in the cytoplasm, ribosomes will bind to it and begin reading the codons. The codons are read and the appropriate amino acids are linked together by the ribosome to form the protein.

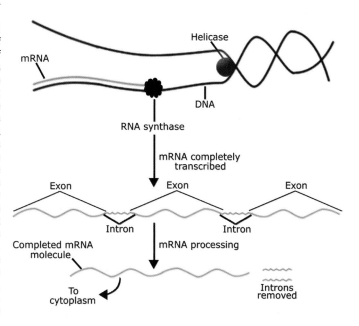

9.16 TRANSLATION

The process of the ribosome making a protein from an mRNA template is called **translation**. This is because the ribosome translates the coded message in the mRNA into a protein. Once in the cytoplasm, the mRNA will attach to a ribosome. Depending on the protein to be made, the ribosome may be free in the cytoplasm, or may be attached to ER. When the mRNA attaches to the ribosome, the ribosome begins to read the codons on the mRNA and assemble the proteins accordingly. The ribosome begins to make the protein at the start codon—AUG. The ribosome moves along the mRNA in a line, reading each mRNA codon in order. The reading frame is maintained.

9.17 THE RIBOSOME PAIRS THE mRNA CODON TO A tRNA ANTICODON

The proper amino acids are brought to the ribosomes by the tRNA. mRNA recognizing the proper tRNA depends upon the mRNA's codon's interaction with the tRNA. As previously stated, each tRNA molecule has two separate ends. On one end the tRNA carries the amino acid. The other end of the tRNA is the end that helps the ribosome identify whether or not a given tRNA molecule is carrying the proper amino acid. This tRNA section consists of a three nucleotide sequence called the **anticodon**. Anticodons of tRNA that are carrying the proper amino acid are complementary to mRNA codons which code for the amino acid. When a tRNA presents itself to the ribosome, the ribosome knows it is the correct tRNA if the codon of the mRNA can be base-paired with the anticodon of the tRNA.

For example, let's say the sequence of the mRNA codon is "CUC." A tRNA molecule comes along with the anticodon "UUU." "UUU" is not complementary to "CUC," so the two cannot base-pair properly. Since the ribosome cannot base pair the anticodon to the codon, it knows the amino acid carried by that tRNA is not the one the mRNA code calls for to be next in the protein. Another tRNA presents to the ribosome with the anticodon "GAG." GAG is complementary to CUC. The anticodon and the codon temporarily form hydrogen bonds to one another. This holds the two amino acids next to one another while the ribosomal enzymes catalyze the dehydration synthesis reaction to link them together.

Figure 9.17.1

Translating mRNA

The tRNA anticodon site is located opposite the site which carries the amino acids. The anticodon is complementary to the mRNA codon which allows it to "fit" to the codon of the mRNA. When a tRNA with the proper anticodon comes along, it forms hydrogen bonds, or base pairs, to the mRNA codon. This, in effect, brings the proper amino acid to the ribosome. As the ribosome moves along the mRNA molecule, it sequentially decodes the message in the mRNA codons. In this diagram, the ribosome is moving along the mRNA molecule from right to left. When the tRNA is bound to the mRNA, this allows the ribosomal enzymes to catalyze a dehydration synthesis reaction between the amino acid on the tRNA and the growing polypeptide chain. While this is occurring, the next tRNA hydrogen bonds to the codon. The ribosome moves linearly along the mRNA molecule, making the protein as it goes.

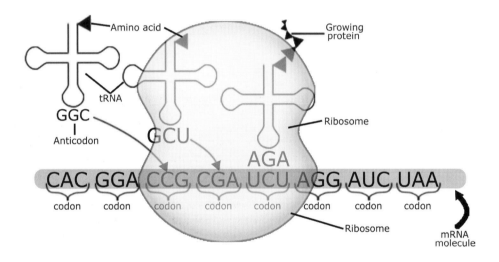

The mRNA codon and tRNA anticodon areas temporarily link together since they are complementary. They are held together by hydrogen bonds between the complementary nucleotide bases of the codon and the anticodon. This allows the ribosome to attach the amino acid on the tRNA to the growing polypeptide chain. The tRNA stays there until the next codon is read and matched with the proper tRNA anticodon. Now there are two tRNA's attached to the mRNA, each with the proper amino acid sitting right next to each other. The ribosome catalyzes the dehydration/condensation synthesis reaction between the two amino acids. The first tRNA falls off, but the second stays attached. The ribosome moves to the next codon. It is read by the ribosome, the proper tRNA anticodon is found and binds to the mRNA. The amino acids are bonded and the second tRNA falls off. This process continues until the codons UAG, UAA or UGA are reached. These are the stop codons. They cause protein synthesis to stop because there are no tRNA molecules which have matching anticodons and so protein synthesis stops.

Figure 9.17.2

Prokaryotic Transcription and Translation Occurs Simultaneously
Since prokaryotes do not have a nucleus separating the DNA from the protein-making machinery, often transcription and translation occur at the same time. This figure represents RNA polymerase transcribing mRNA, while ribosomes are simultaneously translating the mRNA codons into the appropriate protein. The genetic code is universal from bacteria to humans, with occasional, minor variances. Prokaryotes do not perform mRNA processing of introns and exons.

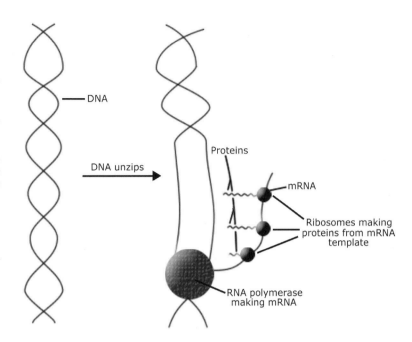

9.18 PROTEINS ARE PROCESSED AFTER THEY ARE TRANSCRIBED

Once synthesized, the polypeptides or proteins usually enter into the endoplasmic reticulum and Golgi apparatus. Inside the ER and Golgi, the protein is modified. One of the major modifications which the protein undergoes is the addition of sequences of amino acids which are needed to get the protein to the correct location in the cell. These are called **signal sequences**. Signal sequences tell the cell where the protein is supposed to go. Signal sequences are not needed for the protein to function normally, though. A signal sequence is like a zip code for a protein. A zip code tells the post office where to route a letter; a signal sequence tells the cell where to route a protein. The protein is transported through the cytoplasm by the cell wherever the signal sequence indicates it should go. They are later removed once the protein gets where it belongs.

9.19 GENE EXPRESSION

When a gene is **expressed**, it means the protein the gene encodes is being made. Since genes code for traits of an organism, when a gene is being expressed, the trait the gene codes for is visible in some way. This exerts some effects on the cell and the organism. For example, when the gene coding for skin color is expressed, the person's skin appears a certain color. Or, if a gene codes for curly hair, the person's hair will be curly when that gene is expressed. Or, if the gene which codes for the production of insulin is being expressed (insulin is a hormone which is released in our blood after we eat to help to properly metabolize sugar), that means insulin is being made.

Because all cells of the same organism contain the same exact information in their DNA, it is important to understand that in multi-cellular organisms, not all genes are expressed by every cell. This means that not all areas of the DNA that code for proteins are transcribed into mRNA. If they were, then every cell would have the same exact function and make the same exact proteins. But they do not. Each cell knows exactly what type of cell it is and which proteins it should make. This fact allows cells to be grouped into tissue and organ systems. For example, the cells in nerve tissue all express—or make—similar proteins, just as skin cells express similar proteins.

9.20 THE PRACTICAL GENETIC CODE

Figure 9.20.1

Genetic Code for mRNA Codons
The table below lists the three nucleotide codons and the amino acids they code for. Codon tables such as this one can be shown using codons for DNA or RNA. However, since the DNA is complementary to the mRNA and vice-versa, one can determine the amino acid being coded for by looking at the DNA or RNA codon. Note there is only one start codon, AUG, which is the mRNA codon where protein synthesis always begins. Remember the genetic code is universal, and so the mRNA start codon is the same in bacteria, plants and animals. There are three stop codons. This table looks difficult to use, but once you get the hang of it, it is pretty easy. If you have the mRNA codon of "ACA," you look at the left column, the "First Nucleotide Base" heading. This first nucleotide base in our example is "A." You then start in the "A" row on the left and move to the right until you get to the "C" column in the middle under "Second Nucleotide Base" heading. Finally, look to the right and match the corresponding third nucleotide base with that in the "Third Nucleotide Base" row, and you will identify the amino acid coded for by the mRNA codon. The listing of the amino acid abbreviations is given below.

In addition, as noted above, if one knows the DNA codon, the amino acid can also be determined, but one must be careful. Since the sequence of the DNA codon is complementary to that of the mRNA, one cannot simply translate the DNA codon directly into a particular amino acid. Instead, the DNA codon must be first translated into the appropriate mRNA codon, which can then be used to identify the amino acid. For example, if the DNA codon was "TGT," you could obviously not translate that into an amino acid because mRNA does not contain T. What must be realized is that during the process of mRNA transcription in the nucleus, the DNA codon "TGT" is transcribed to the mRNA codon of "ACA," which is the example we used above. We will go over some more examples below.

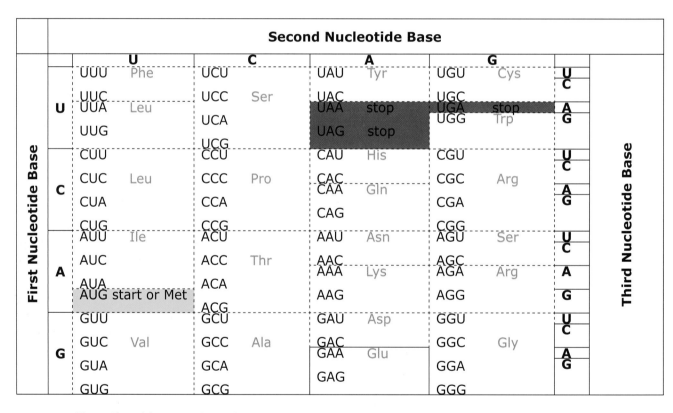

Phe = Phenylalanine
Leu = Leucine
Ile = Isoleucine
Val = Valine

Ser = Serine
Pro = Proline
Thr = Threonine
Ala = Alanine

Tyr = tyramine
His = Histine
Gln = Glutamine
Asn = Asparagine
Lys = Lysine
Asp = Aspartic acid
Glu = Glutamic acid

Cys = Cysteine
Trp = Tryptophan
Arg = Arginine
Ser = Serine
Gly = Glycine

Let's go over some examples using Figure 9.20.1 so you understand the genetic code a bit better.

Example 1:

What is the three-amino acid code of the mRNA codon "AUU-GCU-UUC"?

To determine the code for "AUU," look to the left, under the first nucleotide base code, and find the "A" row; then move to the right until you reach the "U" column under the second nucleotide base code. Now, you should look to the right and find the "U" row in the third nucleotide base. Here, you will find the amino acid coded for by the mRNA codon "AUU" is isoleucine. Follow the same procedure for the next two amino acids. You should find that "GCU" codes for alanine and "UUC" codes for phenylalanine. Therefore, the sequence of amino acids is "isoleucine-alanine-phenylalanine."

Example 2:

What are the tRNA anticodons for the above three codons?

We can determine the anti-codon of the tRNA for the same three mRNA codons. Since the tRNA anticodon is complementary to the codon, the appropriate anticodon for "AUU" is "UAA," because A pairs with U, and U pairs with A. Likewise, the anticodon for "GCU" is "CGA," since C and G pair together, and A and U pair together. The anticodon for the third codon is "AAG."

Example 3:

For which amino acid does the codon "TGA" code?

Note that since there is a "T" in the codon, we know automatically that this is a DNA codon because mRNA does not contain T. To obtain the answer, we must first figure out what the mRNA codon will be, which is simply the complementary sequence to the DNA codon. The DNA codon "TGA" will be translated into the mRNA codon "ACU." Then, look to the genetic code table above. "ACU" codes for the amino acid threonine, which is the correct answer to this question.

9.21 PEOPLE OF SCIENCE

James Watson (1928-) and **Francis Crick** (1916-2004) James Watson was born in Chicago and received his bachelor's degree in zoology at the age of nineteen from the University of Chicago, and his PhD in zoology from Indiana University at twenty-two years old. Francis Crick was born in England and received his bachelor's degree from University College in London, and his PhD in 1954 from Caius College in Cambridge, England.

Watson and Crick met in 1950 and found that they shared the common interest of the structure of DNA, which was as yet unknown. In 1953, they correctly deduced the double-stranded helix structure, as well as the correct base-pairing combinations for DNA. They received the 1962 Nobel Prize in chemistry for their work.

9.22 KEY CHAPTER POINTS

- DNA is the nucleic acid which contains the genetic code.
- DNA communicates to the rest of the cell and organism using messages in mRNA which code for the production of proteins.
- The highly-ordered nucleotides of DNA determine which proteins are made and when. This is called the genetic code.
- DNA is made up of four nucleotides—adenine, thymine, cytosine, and guanine. They link together in such a way that DNA forms a double-stranded helix.
- Each strand of DNA is complementary to the other.
- Genes are the smallest unit of the genetic code. Each gene codes for the production of one protein.

- DNA replicates itself using a variety of enzymes, including DNA polymerase, prior to the cell dividing.

- The code of DNA is contained in three-nucleotide sequences called codons. Each codon codes for one amino acid in a protein.

- DNA codons are transcribed into mRNA codons using a variety of enzymes, including RNA polymerase. mRNA then exits the nucleus and goes into the cytoplasm.

- mRNA is decoded by ribosomes, and the protein encoded by the mRNA is translated into a protein by ribosomes and tRNA.

- Following translation, proteins are processed further by the cell.

9.23 DEFINITIONS

adenine
A nucleotide found in DNA and RNA which contains the nitrogenous base adenine.

anticodon
The three-nucleotide sequence of tRNA which base-pairs with the mRNA codon.

Chargaff's rule
The finding that the percentage of A = T and G = C in DNA.

codon
A three-nucleotide sequence of DNA or mRNA which codes for the position of a specific amino acid in a protein.

complementary strands
The sequence of one DNA strand contains the proper nucleotide sequence to allow the opposite DNA strand to form hydrogen bonds between them, forming a double-stranded molecule of DNA.

cytosine
A nucleotide found in DNA and RNA which contains the nitrogenous base cytosine.

daughter strands
A DNA strand which is newly synthesized from a separate, parent DNA strand, with the parent strand acting as a template.

DNA polymerase
The enzyme that links new nucleotides across from the parent strand, forming a daughter strand. DNA polymerase makes new DNA.

double-stranded helix
The structure of DNA—two individual chains of nucleotides which twist around like a spiral staircase.

exons
The portions of the mRNA that will be expressed.

express
To make a gene product (protein).

gene
The individual unit of the genetic code; linear, orderly groupings of nucleotides on DNA that code for the production of polypeptides.

genetic code
The orderliness of nucleotides.

guanine
A nucleotide found in DNA and RNA which contains the nitrogenous base guanine.

helicase
The enzyme that "unzips" DNA for replication or mRNA synthesis to begin.

histones
Proteins that DNA is coiled around in eukaryotes.

introns
Parts of the mRNA that intervene between the exons; introns are excised and removed from the mRNA molecule before they leave the nucleus.

messenger RNA (mRNA)
Responsible for carrying the message from the DNA to the ribosomes in the cytoplasm.

parent strands
The DNA strands which serve as a template for DNA replication.

processing
Further modification of mRNA before it leaves the nucleus; specifically the excising of introns and splicing together exons.

purines
The nucleotides which have two-ring structures in the nitrogenous base.

pyrimidines
The nucleotides which have a one-ring structure in the nitrogenous base.

reading frame
The straight line in which the codons are read by enzymes.

replication origin
A sequence of nucleotides within DNA to which helicase binds and begins unwinding the DNA; replication begins at the replication origin.

RNA polymerase
The enzyme which makes mRNA from a DNA template.

sequence
The arrangement of nucleotides.

signal sequences
Sequences in polypeptides or proteins that instruct the cell where a protein is supposed to go within that cell after it is made. Signal sequences are not needed for the protein to function and are removed when the protein reaches its destination.

stop codons
The codons in DNA or mRNA which signal that the protein is completed. Stop codons do not code for any amino acid.

strand
A chain of nucleotides.

sugar
A carbohydrate molecule.

thymine
The nucleotide found in DNA which contains the nitrogenous base thymine.

transcription
The process of making mRNA from a DNA template.

transfer RNA (tRNA)
Responsible for bringing the appropriate amino acids to the ribosome for polypeptide assembly.

translation
>   The process of ribosomes synthesizing protein from mRNA.

uracil
>   The nucleotide found in RNA which contains the nitrogenous base uracil.

STUDY QUESTIONS

1.   What are the chemical names of DNA and RNA?

2.   What are the four nucleotides of DNA? Which ones form hydrogen bonds (base-pair) with one another?

3.   Describe the structure of the DNA molecule.

4.   How many different nucleotides form the structure of DNA?

5.   True or False? Adenine and thymine are purines.

6.   True or False? Purines normally always base-pair with pyrimidines in DNA.

7.   What is the genetic code? What does it "do"?

8.   What is the complementary DNA sequence to ATGCTTAACCGA?

9.   Describe the structure of a chromosome.

10. How are chromatin and chromosomes similar? How are they different?

11. True or False? Histones hold sister chromatids together.

12. What is the relationship between DNA, chromosomes and genes?

13. How can you distinguish RNA from DNA? (There are three answers to this question.)

14. What is the series of events which results in synthesis of a protein? Yes, this is a long answer and it covers almost everything we discussed!

15. Why does tRNA take on its characteristic "t" shape?

16. How does a ribosome know that a given tRNA molecule is carrying the amino acid called for by the mRNA?

17. If an mRNA molecule contains the codons UUU-ACA-AGC-GCA-UGG, what is the sequence of amino acids in the polypeptide?

18. At first, you may think you cannot do this problem, but you really can. What is the sequence of amino acids that the DNA codons of CTA-CCC-TTG-ATA-ACT codes for?

Cell Reproduction: Mitosis

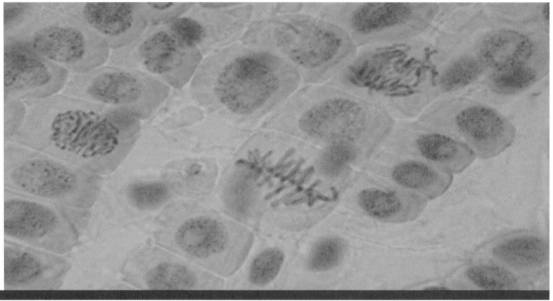

10

10.0 CHAPTER PREVIEW

In this chapter we will:

- Discuss the biological process of asexual cell division, called mitosis.
- Review the theory of spontaneous generation and how it was disproved.
- Review the Theory of Biogenesis.
- Investigate the process of DNA replication.
- Learn how DNA is packaged in the cell at various stages.
- Discuss the events of the cell cycle.

10.1 OVERVIEW OF CELL DIVISION

This chapter will serve as an introduction to the different ways cells reproduce. **Cell division** (or **cell reproduction**) is the way in which organisms make new organisms and make more cells. Cell division is the process of one cell dividing into two cells. But there are different types of cell division, called **mitosis, meiosis, budding,** and **binary fission**. This chapter will serve to describe the processes of mitosis; in the next chapter, we will discuss binary fission, budding, and meiosis.

Every organism starts from one, single cell. Therefore, in order to be able to grow in size, multicellular organisms make new cells, which all come from the one original cell. In addition, there must be a mechanism in place for multicellular organisms to repair injuries to tissues. For example, when we get a cut on the skin, there must be some way to repair the cut. The same is true of a broken bone or of any injury to the tissue. The organism must have some way to grow and regenerate tissue to repair damage. Multicellular organisms grow in size and make new cells to repair damage to tissues by mitosis.

10.2 ONE PARENT DIVIDES INTO TWO DAUGHTER CELLS

The process of cell division is common. It is the process of one cell dividing into two cells. The starting single cell is called the **parent cell**. The two cells the parent cell divides into are called **daughter cells**. Mitosis, meiosis, budding, and binary fission accomplish this, but in different ways. Recall that DNA is essentially the brain of the cell. DNA contains the information the cell and organism need to function properly. Therefore, it is important to understand that cell division is a process which distributes a complete copy of DNA from the parent cell to each of the two daughter cells. If DNA is not distributed so that each cell has a complete copy of DNA, the daughter cells do not work. Think of cell division—whether mitosis, meiosis, or binary fission—as the way cells divide to form more cells *and* distribute a complete copy of DNA into each new cell. In order for this to occur properly, the DNA of the parent cell must be copied before the cell divides. We discussed briefly the process of DNA replication in the last chapter. This is how the cell ensures that an exact copy of the DNA will pass from parent to daughter cell and that all daughter cells will have the exact same function as the parent.

In humans and animals, cell division is responsible for repairing cuts and broken bones, fighting infections, and replacing blood cells. The most rapid cell division occurs on the surface of the respiratory (nose, lungs) and GI tracts (mouth, stomach and intestines). All of these cells reproduce by mitosis. It is estimated that 25 million cells undergo mitosis every second in humans. In addition, mitosis is responsible for growth of the organism and of its organs and tissues as it grows in physical size from conception to adulthood.

Figure 10.2.1

A Parent Cell Dividing
This is the general scheme showing how a parent cell divides into two daughter cells. The parent cell begins to elongate and the cell membrane begins to pinch inwards. It continues to pinch inwards until two separate cells have formed. The two new cells are called daughter cells. This is the basic process of how all new cells are formed whether the process is mitosis, meiosis, or binary fission. One important structure is not shown in this graphic, though—the DNA. Before the cells divide, all of the chromosomes need to be copied. We are going to learn how the DNA is copied and distributed to the daughter cells in this chapter.

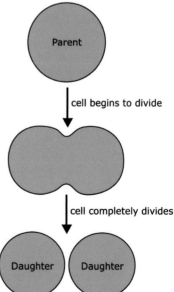

10.3 SPONTANEOUS GENERATION

Before microscopes allowed scientists to see individual cells, the way in which new life forms arose was a mystery. There was not an understanding of how mold seemed to "magically" appear on bread if it was left out in the open air. As well, the way in which the body healed a cut was unknown. For hundreds of years, it was commonly thought that living things arose from non-living things. This concept is referred to as **spontaneous generation** and took several centuries to thoroughly disprove. It was not until excellent scientific experiments were devised and carried out from the mid 1600s to the mid 1800s that spontaneous generation was proven false.

The concept of spontaneous generation no doubt arose in ancient times for fairly good reason. The most likely reason people thought spontaneous generation was how new life forms were generated was a result of what occurs when meat putrefies (spoils). It was noted for centuries, thousands of years ago, that if meat was left out for too long, it started to get smelly and "spoil." After a few days of being left out, maggots seemingly appeared out of nowhere all over the meat. Maggots are immature forms of flies and look like small, white worms, if you have never seen one. Scientists of the time were at a loss as to where the maggots came from. It was thought there was some factor in the air that caused this to happen. More than two thousand years ago, the Greek philosopher and scientist Aristotle taught that flies arose from putrid meat, mice came from dirty hay, and plant lice came from dew. Literally, he taught that the hay produced mice. Another common contributor to this theory was moldy bread. The scientists knew that if bread sat in the open for several days, mold seemingly sprouted on it out of nowhere. Since there was no other way of explaining the observable facts at the time, the concept that life sprang from non-living things was accepted as truth for many centuries.

However, in 1668, a physician named Francesco Redi seriously doubted that spontaneous generation occurred. He set out to design an experiment to disprove spontaneous generation. He had noted that as meat sat out, it was visited by many flies. Soon thereafter, maggots formed (maggots are the immature forms of flies). Redi postulated that the flies laid eggs on the meat when they came to feed on it, and then the maggots hatched from the eggs. To test his hypothesis, he let meat sit out in two different dishes. One of the dishes was uncovered and left uncovered. This allowed the flies to get to the meat as it spoiled. The other dish was covered with a mesh that allowed the air to get to the meat but not flies. Since the popular theory at the time was that some "factor" in the air caused the maggots to form, this design would properly test it. His experimental design allowed the air to touch both dishes of meat but only allowed the flies to touch the uncovered meat. If some sort of air factor was the cause of the maggots growing, then both dishes should have maggots on them. But if it was the flies, only the meat the flies could get to should have maggots.

Redi found that the meat that was uncovered grew maggots, but the covered meat did not. Only the meat which the flies were able to land on grew maggots. This proved his hypothesis that spontaneous generation did not occur. There was no "factor in the air" which caused the maggots to form. Although he was not able to see the flies' eggs with his naked eye, Redi theorized the flies laid eggs on the meat. The eggs then hatched into maggots. He was right. But there was a twist, of course.

Figure 10.3.1

Spallanzani's Experimental Design

In the top experimental design, Spallanzani left the flasks open after he had boiled them. This allowed microscopic organisms to fall into the broth through the opening and grow in the broth. The bottom experimental design did not allow anything to fall into the broth since the top was plugged. This simple but elegant design added to the slowly growing information that eventually led to proving that spontaneous generation did not occur. If spontaneous generation did occur, then both sets of flasks should have spontaneously grown organisms in the broth. However, only the uncovered flasks grew microscopic organisms in the broth. The lack of spontaneous growth in the covered flasks clearly indicated spontaneous generation cannot occur. However, the scientists of the day were not completely convinced until almost one hundred years later following Pasteur's experiments.

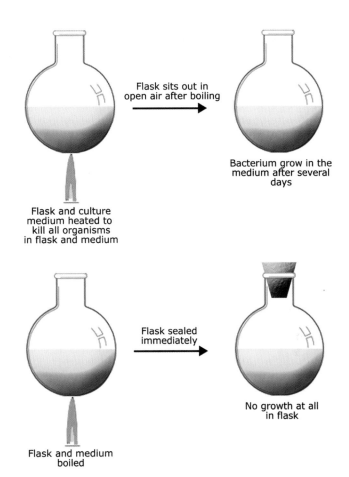

Flask sits out in open air after boiling

Bacterium grow in the medium after several days

Flask and culture medium heated to kill all organisms in flask and medium

Flask sealed immediately

No growth at all in flask

Flask and medium boiled

Soon after Redi's experiment, bacteria were discovered by Leeuwenhoek in 1683. It was then postulated that perhaps the visible life forms are generated from life forms of their kind, but perhaps that spontaneous generation theory seemed to be true in the case of micro-organisms. It appeared that the microbes appeared from nowhere. It was easy to prove that, in the case of complex multicellular organisms, spontaneous generation was not true, but disproving spontaneous generation for micro-organisms was much more difficult. A biologist named Lazzaro Spallanzani did perform some experiments in 1768 which cast doubt on the spontaneous generation theory in the case of microbes, but his work was not completely convincing at the time. However, his work paved the way for Louis Pasteur.

In 1864, Louis Pasteur was able to devise an experiment that would effectively test the spontaneous generation theory in the case of micro-organisms. The big micro-organisms in Pasteur's day (and today, for that matter), were yeast and bacteria. Yeasts are unicellular eukaryotes and bacteria are unicellular prokaryotes. Pasteur thought that the air contained **spores** (like the micro-organism equivalent of an egg) of yeast and bacteria that would develop into micro-organism when exposed to favorable conditions (like rotting meat). He felt, therefore, that spontaneous generation was not true, and sought to design an experiment to completely test his hypothesis.

He designed flasks with a gooseneck in them. In this way, he could fill the flask with broth that would provide favorable conditions for the growth of the spores and leave the flask exposed to the air. However, he thought the gooseneck would trap any microscopic organisms and prevent them from ever reaching the broth. He boiled the broth, killing all the organisms (and their spores) that were in the broth and trapped in the neck of the flask. After boiling the broth, he waited for a week, and there was no growth of microbes in the broth. He then tipped one of the flasks to let the broth touch the bend, thinking this would contaminate it with all of the microbes that had been trapped there.

Very quickly, microbes grew in the broth. But there was never any growth in the boiled flasks which were not tipped. If spontaneous generation was true there would have been growth in the broth regardless of the gooseneck. Today, there are original flasks in the Pasteur Museum in Paris that still do not have any growth in them.

Figure 10.3.2

Pasteur's Experimental Design

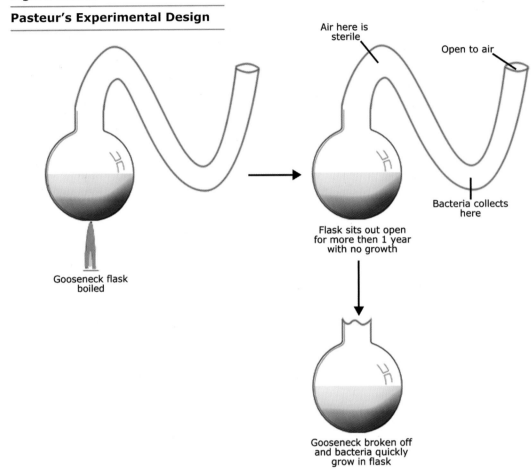

Air here is sterile

Open to air

Bacteria collects here

Flask sits out open for more then 1 year with no growth

Gooseneck flask boiled

Gooseneck broken off and bacteria quickly grow in flask

10.4 THE THEORY OF BIOGENESIS

Pasteur's experiments eloquently disproved the theory of spontaneous generation as it related to micro-organisms. Redi had disproved the theory two hundred years earlier as it related to complex organisms. Spallanzani and Pasteur then disproved spontaneous generation in the case of microbes. The result of showing that spontaneous generation did not occur led to the development of the **theory of biogenesis**. This theory states that all **life comes from life**. Since we know that cells are the functional unit of life, we can also state that **all cells come from cells**.

10.5 CELL DIVISION—BASICS

There are two basic ways that cells reproduce, or divide—sexually and asexually. **Asexual reproduction** is a biological process in which cells and organisms are made by duplicating their DNA and then splitting into two cells. Asexual reproduction results in the formation of cells which are genetically identical to the parent cell and to one another. Mitosis, the topic of this chapter, is a type of asexual reproduction. Mitosis is the biological process in which a parent cell copies its DNA and then divides into two cells, passing on an identical copy of DNA to each daughter cell. Also, two processes we are going to learn about next chapter—budding and binary fission—are types of asexual reproduction.

Sexual reproduction is the biological process in which offspring (new organisms) are formed by combining DNA. Organisms which reproduce by sexual reproduction have male and female organisms. The chromosomes from the male are combined with the chromosomes from the female which generates a new organism. Since sexual reproduction is the result of combination of genetic material from two different organisms, the offspring are genetically different from both parents. In order for sexual reproduction to work, though, a special type of cell division occurs called meiosis. The next chapter will be all about forming new organisms through binary fission, budding, and meiosis (but remember that binary fission and budding are asexual forms of cell reproduction).

All multicellular organisms perform mitosis. It is the same regardless of the organism performing it—the DNA must be replicated in the parent cell and a complete copy distributed to each daughter cell. It is critical that cell division occur in a precise way to pass on a complete set of chromosomes from the parent cell to both daughter cells. For this to occur, the chromosomes all need to be replicated. Once all chromosomes are copied, they need to be passed from parent cell to both daughter cells so that each daughter cell receives exactly the right number of chromosomes. From this point on in this chapter, we are going to be discussing human mitosis unless otherwise indicated. Mitosis is the cell division process that eukaryotes use to grow new cells.

Figure 10.5.1

Mitosis, An Overview

Mitosis is the phase of a cell's life when it divides to form two daughter cells. This graphic represents what happens to the DNA before, during and after mitosis. Prior to beginning mitosis, the DNA of the parent cell is replicated. There are now two complete copies of chromosomes in the cell. The forty-six chromosomes of humans are copied into ninety-two chromosomes following DNA replication. In this figure, the usual state of forty-six chromosomes is represented by "DNA". After the chromosomes are duplicated, the cell enters mitosis. All chromosomes line up in the middle of the cell. Then they are pulled apart so that one complete set is pulled to one side of the cell, and the other complete set is pulled to the other side of the cell. The process of the chromosomes getting pulled apart is called karyokinesis. In order for the chromosomes to be pulled apart, the nuclear membrane disintegrates, which is why there is no nucleus in the third cell. The cell membrane then pinches inward in the middle. The formation of two cells from one cell is called cytokinesis. This results in the formation of two daughter cells from one parent cell. Each daughter cell has an exact copy of DNA, and this DNA is identical to the DNA of the parent cell. Mitosis ensures that the normal numbers of chromosomes are passed from parent cell to daughter cell during cell reproduction. Mitosis is completed when the daughter cells have completely separated. The nuclear membrane re-forms and each cell continues on in its life cycle until it is time to divide again.

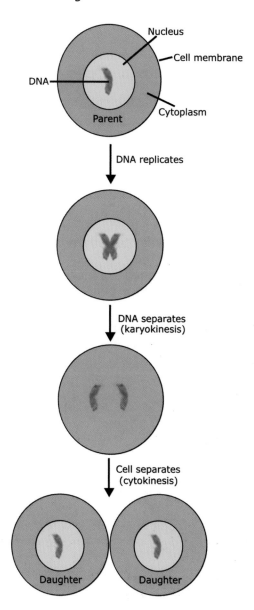

10.6 CELL LIFE CYCLE

The life of a cell has been divided into **phases** depending upon where the cell is in the process of reproducing itself. This is called the **cell cycle**. The cell cycle is the cycle of events which occurs in a eukaryotic cell from one cell division to the next. Some human cell cycles can last for years. Other human cells divide every twenty hours or so. The cell cycle is broken into interphase and mitosis. Because so much occurs in the cell during mitosis, it is further divided into **prophase**, **prometaphase**, **metaphase**, **anaphase**, and **telophase**. We will discuss these phases in detail.

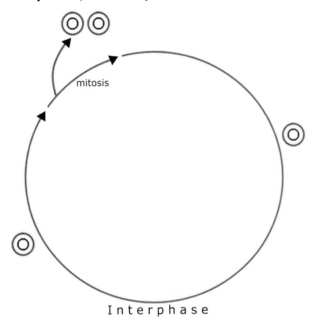

Interphase

Figure 10.6.1

The Cell Cycle
Cells spend more than 90% of their lives in interphase. The life cycle of a cell is called the cell cycle. The cell cycle describes what a cell is doing during the time it is alive. During interphase, the cell has one complete copy of chromosomes. It performs the various functions to keep itself alive and contribute to the health of the organism. DNA replication occurs at the end of interphase and signals that the cell is about to enter into mitosis. Following DNA replication, the cell has two complete copies of chromosomes for a short time. Once the DNA is replicated, the cell enters mitosis. During mitosis, the cell divides into two cells. This forms two daughter cells, each of which receives one copy of DNA from the parent cell. Once the daughter cells are completely formed, they each enter interphase and restart the cell cycle. This cycle is true for most eukaryotic cells.

10.7 DNA REPLICATION

The first step of cell division is replication of the DNA. It occurs at the end of interphase. As soon as the DNA is copied, the cell enters mitosis. DNA replication accurately generates an exact copy of a cell's DNA. Chromosomes take the form of chromatin during interphase. Just before they are replicated the chromosomes condense into their super-wound forms of recognizable chromosomes. Since DNA is housed as chromosomes, when the DNA is replicated, that is the same as saying the chromosomes are replicated. Since genes are contained on chromosomes, when the chromosomes are replicated, so are all of a cell's genes. In this way, an exact copy of genes is passed from parent cell to daughter cells. Replication requires more than a dozen different enzymes and takes the human cell about four hours to complete.

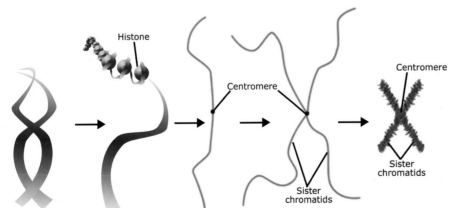

Histone

Centromere

Centromere

Sister chromatids

Sister chromatids

Double stranded DNA | Double stranded DNA wraps around histones | Condensed DNA in interphase | Duplicated DNA early prophase loosely coiled chromosome | Condensed chromosome metaphase

Figure 10.7.1

Condensing Chromosomes
This graphic shows what happens to a chromosome as it condenses into a formal chromosome from chromatin during the last stages of interphase. Sister chromatids are the duplicated chromosome copies. One sister chromatid is identical to the other.

Figure 10.7.2

Initiation of DNA Replication

DNA is shown in its normal double-helical form on the left. Whenever information from DNA needs to be accessed, the DNA needs to be opened up so the inside is accessible. This is like unzipping a zipper. The parts of a zipper that lock together are like the hydrogen bonds which form between the bases on opposite strands of DNA. In order for DNA to unzip, the hydrogen bonds between the bases of the two strands must be broken. The enzyme helicase is able to do this. Helicase binds to the DNA at one of the many replication origins and begins to unwind and unzip by breaking the hydrogen bonds between the strands. Other enzymes serve to hold the DNA open and stable while the helicase moves its way along the DNA. Once the DNA is opened, the bases are accessible to other enzymes which use the DNA as a template to make RNA or to duplicate the DNA before the cell divides. When the DNA is done being read, it is re-zipped by other enzymes.

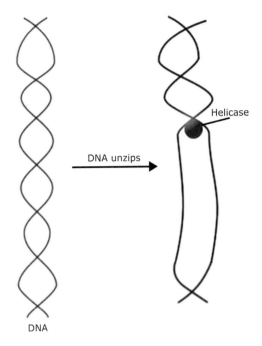

Helicase

DNA unzips

DNA

Replication begins at the end of interphase with an enzyme called **helicase** binding to the DNA at the **replication origin**. Helicase binds to DNA at the replication origin and begins to "unzip", or unwind, the DNA. It is able to unzip DNA by breaking the hydrogen bonds between base pairs. When information needs to be accessed from DNA, the DNA must first be unzipped. There can be hundreds or thousands of replication origins on one molecule of DNA. This allows DNA to be unzipped at many different places, which allows DNA to be replicated more quickly. Normally, there are proteins bound to the replication origin to prevent helicase from being able to unwind the DNA. When the DNA needs to replicate, the proteins come off the origin, which allows helicase to bind and unzip the DNA. Remember, this occurs simultaneously at the multiple replication origins.

Once the DNA begins to be unzipped, a complicated enzyme, called **DNA polymerase**, binds to the unzipped DNA (called **parent strands**) and begins linking new nucleotides across from the parent strand, forming a complementary **daughter strand**. DNA polymerase moves from one nucleotide to another on the parent strand, in a linear fashion, linking more and more complementary nucleotides to the growing daughter strand. In this way, the parent strand serves as a template for the daughter strand to be made, just as DNA serves as a template for mRNA to be made. This process occurs simultaneously on both parent strands, but in opposite directions. Human DNA polymerase can link about fifty bases per second, while bacteria can link about five hundred.

Once the entire parent strand has been traversed by DNA polymerase, the DNA has been replicated. There are now two copies of the original DNA molecule in the cell. Each replicated copy of DNA is composed of one parent strand and one daughter strand.

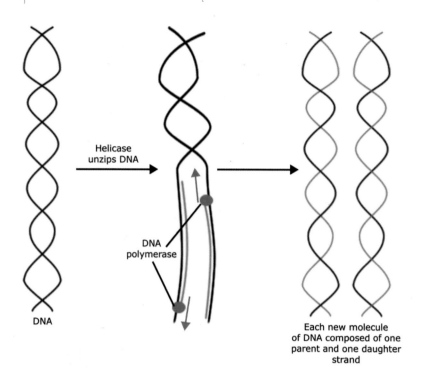

Figure 10.7.3

DNA Replication
At the end of interphase, DNA replication begins with helicase breaking the hydrogen bonds between complementary nucleotides. Once the nucleotides are exposed by helicase, DNA polymerase binds to the DNA and begins to base-pair complementary nucleotides across from each parent strand. The new strand that is made using the parent strand as a template is called a daughter strand. This occurs simultaneously at many sites along the DNA. When completed, there are two new strands of DNA, each composed of one parent strand and one daughter strand. Following DNA replication, the cell enters mitosis.

Helicase unzips DNA

DNA polymerase

DNA

Each new molecule of DNA composed of one parent and one daughter strand

10.8 CHROMOSOME TERMINOLOGY DURING CELL REPRODUCTION

Identical replicated chromosomes stick together. Each replicated chromosome has two strands. Each strand of the chromosome is referred to as a **chromatid**. The two chromatids of the same chromosome are called **sister chromatids**. The site where the sister chromatids are held together is called the **centromere**. We are able to see chromosomes in this way because DNA is densely packed during mitosis. It coils around special proteins called histones. When the DNA becomes compacted, it forms into structures that are able to be seen under a light microscope, and that is when chromosomes are able to be easily identified. In prokaryotes with little genetic material and no nucleus, the DNA is formed as one long, circular molecule in the cytoplasm.

Figure 10.8.1

Duplicated Chromosome
The graphic on the left is conceptually what a chromosome looks like after it has been replicated. The identical strands are held to one another. The chromosome on the right of the figure is an electron micrograph of an actual chromosome after it has been replicated and is in its completely condensed form. There are two strands which are held together in the middle. Each strand is an individual chromosome. One strand is the original chromosome and the other strand is its identical copy. Each strand is called a sister chromatid. Sister chromatids are held together in the middle at an area called the **centromere**. The centromere is also the area where the microtubules attach to pull the sister chromatids apart. Since sister chromatids are identical copies of one another, the genetic content of each of the two strands is identical.

Duplicated chromosome

Centromere

Sister chromatids

Centromere

Sister chromatid

Sister chromatid

10.9 INTERPHASE

Interphase starts immediately after the cell divides. It was originally thought that during **interphase** the cell was quiescent, or relatively inactive. Nothing could be further from the truth. The cell spends about 90% of its lifetime in interphase. During this period, the cell performs whatever vital functions it is programmed by the DNA to perform for the organism – making antibodies, absorbing nutrients, synthesizing hormones, etc. It is definitely not a period of inactivity for the cell.

Figure 10.9.1

The Cell's Appearance During Interphase

The cell spends most of its life in interphase. During interphase, the cell performs its everyday functions with the DNA in the form of chromatin. During the last stages of interphase, the cell replicates the DNA. This results in two exact copies of DNA. When the single parent cell divides into two cells, each daughter cell receives a copy of the DNA. The cell in the top diagram shows that the DNA has started to condense into chromosomes. It is not yet quite as compact as it will get, though. The red strands are individual chromosomes but they have not been duplicated yet. In the bottom left diagram, the DNA is now replicated—the red strands of DNA represent the original chromosomes and the blue strands represent the duplicated DNA. This cell is in late interphase. The cell on the bottom right is a micrograph taken from an onion cell in a similar state of interphase. The nucleus is in the center of the cell and the hazy blue material is chromatin.

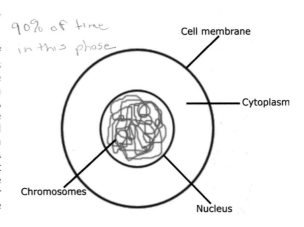

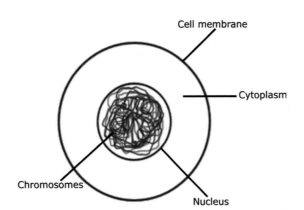

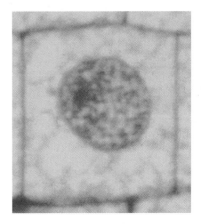

A cell that is in rapidly reproducing tissue, such as the lining of the GI tract, has a cell cycle that lasts approximately twenty hours. This means the cell reproduces itself and forms another cell every twenty hours. Therefore, usually the cell is in interphase for eighteen hours and actively duplicating (mitosis) for two hours.

During most of interphase, the cell performs its functions as directed by the DNA in the nucleus. Recall that all of the genetic material is contained in the DNA within the nucleus of the eukaryotic cell. During the later period of interphase, the cell replicates the DNA, making exact copies of each of the chromosomes. This means that the cell now has ninety-two chromosomes inside of it. At this point, the cell has two, fully functional, exact copies of its DNA. Another way to state this is that the cell has two exact copies of each chromosome contained in the nucleus. During mitosis, the cell will evenly distribute one complete set of chromosomes to each daughter cell.

10.10 PROPHASE

Prophase, the first stage of mitosis, begins after the chromosomes are copied. The nucleoli begin to disappear and the DNA begins to condense and become visible. As the chromatin continues to condense, it forms distinct chromosomes before prophase is over. Centrioles begin to form at each pole of the nucleus. Recall that centrioles are composed of microtubules and are capable of rapidly assembling/disassembling microtubules. Most non-animal cells do not form centrioles, but all animal cells do.

As you can see from figure 10.10.1 microtubules begin to extend out from each centriole in a star like pattern. As the microtubules elongate, they begin to form the **spindle**. The spindle is composed of microtubules and will attach to the chromosomes and function to pull the chromosomes apart as the cell divides. Although non-animal cells do not form centrioles, they do form the spindle.

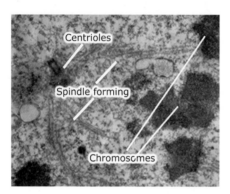

Figure 10.10.1

The Spindle

This electron micrograph shows the spindle forming. The spindle is composed of microtubules and they extend out from the centrioles towards the chromosomes. You know this is from an animal cell, because plant cells do not have centrioles, but they do form a spindle.

Figure 10.10.2

The Cell in Prophase

The DNA has condensed into chromosomes. They are the little "X" shaped structures in the nucleus. As you can see, each original chromosome is attached to its replicated sister chromatid. Again, the red chromatids represent the original chromosomes and the blue chromatids represent the duplicated chromatids. Also, the spindle has formed from the centrioles. The spindle consists of microtubules and other proteins which attach to one another and to the centromere of the chromosomes. The spindle is responsible for properly lining up and separating the sister chromatids. The onion cell on the right is in prophase. The chromosomes are condensed, but are not lined up along the equator of the cell yet.

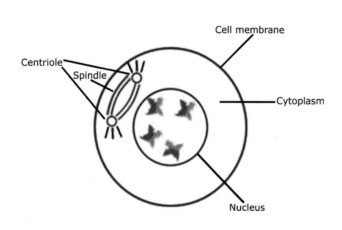

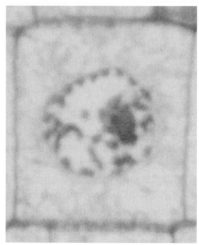

At this point in prophase, the chromosomes are distinctly visible as two sister chromatids held together at the centromere.

10.11 PROMETAPHASE

Some geneticists refer to this stage as late prophase or early metaphase. Other geneticists refer to this as **prometaphase**. It begins with the nuclear membrane already starting to disintegrate. The spindle fully forms and attaches to the centromere of each pair of sister chromatids. As prometaphase ends, the nuclear membrane has completely disintegrated. During prometaphase, the chromosomes completely condense, but they are not quite fully lined up at the equator of the cell.

Figure 10.11.1

Prometaphase
The centrioles have moved to opposite poles of the cell and the chromosomes are lining up along the equator. The spindle attaches to the chromosomes at the centromeres. The spindle is formed by proteins which connect the centromere to the centriole. The nuclear membrane is dissolving. The centrioles, through the contractile actions of the spindle, are about ready to pull the chromosomes apart.

10.12 METAPHASE

The third step of mitosis is called **metaphase**. The chromosomes line up completely along the equator of the cell. As the spindle fibers contract and tug at the chromosomes to move them into place, they seem to dance. The alignment of the chromosomes by the spindle ensures that each daughter cell will receive only one copy of each chromosome (you could also say one daughter cell will receive one complete copy of sister chromatids, and the other daughter cell will receive the other complete copy).

Figure 10.12.1

Metaphase
The centrioles are lined up at opposite poles and completely connected to the centromeres by the spindle. The chromosomes are also lined up at the equator, and the nuclear membrane has completely dissolved. The photo at the right is taken from a cell in an onion which is in metaphase. The chromosomes are the bands lined up across the nucleus. The electron micrograph shows more detail.

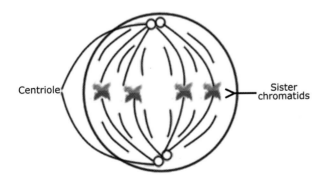

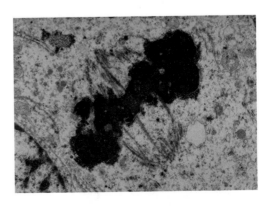

Centriole

Sister chromatids

10.13 ANAPHASE

During the next step, **anaphase**, the sister chromatids are pulled apart due to the contractile action of the spindle. As the chromatids are separated, they move to opposite poles of the cell. Anaphase ends with the one set of sister chromatids, each a fully functional and complete copy of the cell's DNA, at opposite ends of an elongated cell. At this point, each chromatid is again referred to as a chromosome. The process of the chromatids separating is called **karyokinesis**.

Figure 10.13.1

Anaphase
The spindle is pulled toward each centriole, which separates the chromosomes. This is possible due to the actions of the motor proteins tubulin and actin and others. These proteins function to shorten the spindle fibers. As the fibers shorten, the chromosomes are pulled from the middle to the edge of the cell. Also during anaphase, the cell begins to elongate as it gets ready to divide. On the right is a picture from an onion. The chromosomes have moved to opposite ends of the cell through the pulling action of the spindle. The bottom is an electron micrograph.

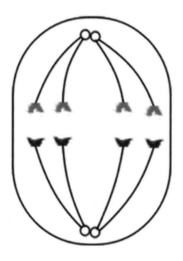

10.14 TELOPHASE

In the last phase of mitosis, **telophase**, two cells form from one. In animal cells, through the contractile action of the microfilaments, the cell membrane pinches in at the equator, forming two complete cells in the process. The process of the cell membrane pinching inward and forming two cells is called **cytokinesis**. The nuclear membrane re-forms. Once telophase is completed, the parent cell has effectively and evenly distributed exact copies of its DNA to two daughter cells. These two daughter cells then enter interphase and eventually repeat the mitosis.

Figure 10.14.1

Telophase
Early telophase is shown on the top left. The chromosomes have moved to opposite ends of the cell. The nuclear membrane begins to re-form around the chromosomes as a cleavage furrow forms. As the nuclear membrane re-forms, the chromosomes will begin to de-condense and form back into chromatin. The cleavage furrow gets deeper and pinches inward. This will ultimately form two daughter cells, each with their own complete set of chromosomes. In the top center, the two cells have separated completely, the nuclear membrane has re-formed, and the chromosomes are starting to unwind back into chromatin. Each cell is now back into interphase. The figure on the top right shows an onion cell in early telophase. The chromosomes in the right half of the cell are beginning to condense, and those on the left half have condensed. A definite cleavage furrow has not yet formed. Two electron micrographs are shown on the bottom. The one on the left is a detail view of the two membranes separating. The one on the right is a SEM view of a more global picture of two cells completing cytokinesis. The last remnants of the cell membrane are pulling apart.

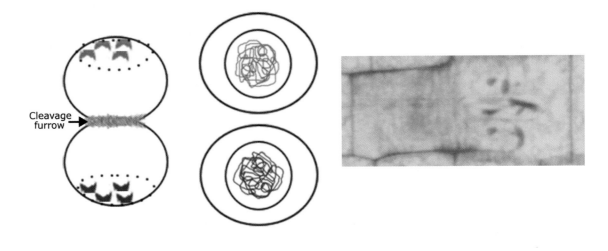

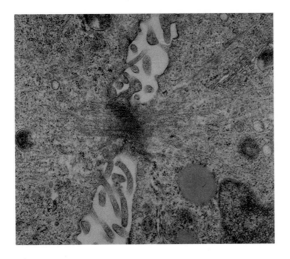

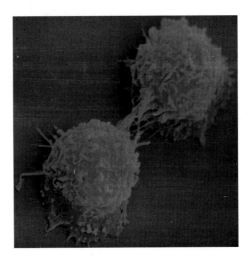

Figure 10.14.2

Mitosis Overview
Here is the whole mitotic process in one large graphic.

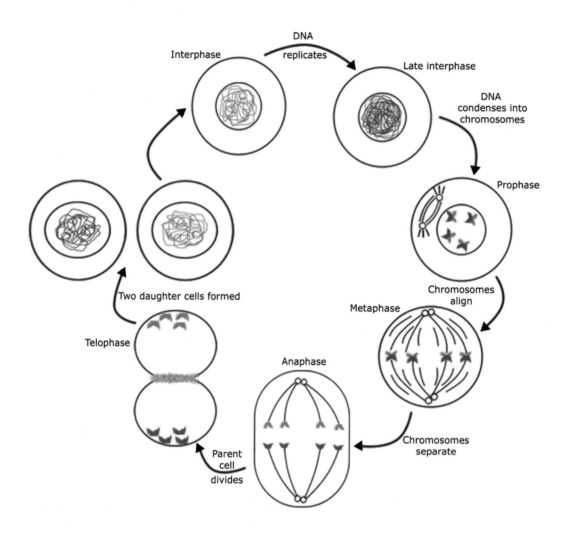

10.15 PLANT CELL DIVISION

Recall that plant cells have a rigid cell wall. The cell wall cannot pinch inward to form two new cells. During plant mitosis, the cell divides inside the cell wall and forms two daughter cells. Then, in between the daughter cells, a **cell plate** forms from the Golgi apparatus or ER at the equator of the cell. Following that a membrane forms at the site of the cell plate. As the daughter cells mature, the cell plate eventually forms into the new cell wall.

Figure 10.15.1

Plant Cell Division
Cell division occurs in plants the same way as in animal cells. However, the presence of the cell wall puts a twist on the process. The cell proceeds through the same five stages of mitosis as already described. After karyokinesis, the cell performs cytokinesis. However, along the site where the cell membranes actually separate, a structure called the cell plate forms. The cell plate organizes into a new cell wall.

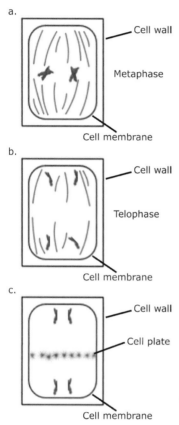

10.16 ADVANCED

As you have read this past chapter, this may or may not have come to your mind: cell division is an extremely complicated process that occurs billions and billions of times per day in a human being! How can cells keep dividing at the proper rate and time? This is an area of intense research and is a subject that is not totally understood. One can imagine how important more and more knowledge in this area is, since all types of cancer are essentially cellular reproduction out of control.

As intensive research into what causes cancer has progressed; there have been substances identified that function to stimulate the cell to move from interphase to mitosis. Two of these substances are cyclin and cyclin-dependent protein kinases. During interphase, the level of a protein called **cyclin** slowly builds up inside the cell. Cyclin functions to bind to a group of enzymes called **cyclin-dependent protein kinases** (CDPK). Protein kinases are enzymes that control the activity of other enzymes. Cyclin-dependent protein kinases are inactive until the molecule cyclin binds to it.

As the level of cyclin slowly builds during interphase, eventually the concentration reaches a critical level. This causes cyclin to bind to CDPK. Once cyclin has bound to CDPK, this enzyme complex activates and hydrolyzes one of the phosphate bonds from ATP. Using the energy released from the ATP, the enzyme complex adds the inorganic phosphate to another protein. This protein with a phosphate group attached to it is called a **phosphorylated protein**. This newly-phosphorylated protein then stimulates the cell to move from interphase into prophase. This initiates mitosis.

Another control mechanism occurs when cells come into contact with one another. Usually when cells come into contact with other cells of the same type, they stop dividing. We do not understand why this happens, but it is another check to keep cells from excessively growing.

A third control mechanism is called **apoptosis**. Apoptosis is other wise known as "programmed cell death." Cells seem to have a built in mechanism which allows them only to live for twenty-five to fifty cell division cycles. Following that, they die. For the most part, we don't understand how the cell "knows" it is supposed to die after so many cell cycles, but it is thought that this is one way for the organism to maintain homeostasis.

Cancer cells do not respond to the normal stimuli to stop growing. They do not exhibit the property of ceasing cell division when coming into contact with other cells, they also do not follow the cyclin dependent protein kinase mechanism or show the property of apoptosis. Cancer cells are often called "immortal" because many types of cancer cells are able to divide forever. There is even a tumor cell line that has continuously been reproducing since 1951.

Figure 10.16.1

More Detailed Cell Cycle
This represents what is going on biochemically during the cell cycle. At the beginning of interphase, kinases are present in the nucleus, but are inactive. During interphase, levels of cyclin slowly build. Eventually, the cyclin levels reach a certain level. When this level is reached, cyclin binds to kinase. The kinase is now activated and phosphorylates proteins. The phosphorylated proteins then activate the pathway toward mitosis.

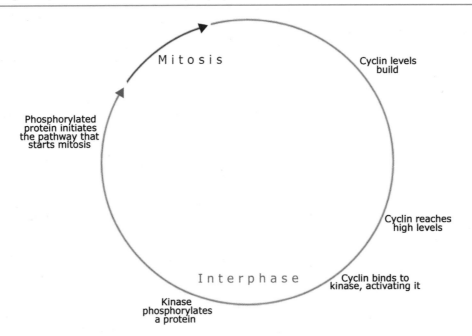

10.17 PEOPLE OF SCIENCE

Louis Pasteur (1822-1895). Born in France, Louis Pasteur is commonly referred to as the "father of microbiology and immunology" as a result of the work he did in studying micro-organisms and the role they play in transferring disease to humans. The contributions he made to conceptions of sterility and disease transmission/prevention are too numerous to list. However, he was the first to recognize that diseases were passed from infected patients to uninfected patients in hospitals by the hospital staff not washing their hands as they performed their rounds, and that various diseases obtained from liquids could be rendered sterile simply by heating the liquid to a certain temperature for a certain amount of time. As a result of his work, the process of reducing the bacterial load in milk by heating, causing it to last longer and not transmit disease to humans, is called pasteurization. He was also the first to develop effective vaccines.

10.18 KEY CHAPTER POINTS

- All cells reproduce themselves, or divide. One parent cell divides into two daughter cells.

- The idea of spontaneous generation was disproved by Redi, Spallanzani, and Pasteur.

- The Theory of Biogenesis states that living things can only come from other living things; or "life begets life".

- The purpose of cell reproduction is to create more organisms or more cells of an organism. Each newly created cell must receive a complete and fully functional copy of DNA from the parent cell.

- There are two types of cellular reproduction: asexual and sexual reproduction.

- Asexual cell reproduction results in the formation of two daughter cells that are genetically identical to one another and the parent cell.

- Mitosis, binary fission and budding are examples of cell division by asexual reproduction.

- Sexual reproduction results from the combination of genetic material from a male parent and a female parent and results in the formation of a new organism that is genetically different than either the male or female parent.

- Meiosis is an example of cell division for means of sexual reproduction.

- The cell cycle is a way of describing events of the cell's life. The cell cycle consists of interphase and mitosis. Interphase is the time when the cell is not dividing and mitosis is the time when the cell is dividing.

- The purpose of mitosis is to first create an exact copy of DNA in the parent cell and then distribute a complete copy of DNA to each daughter cell.

- DNA is replicated at the end of interphase, before the cell enters mitosis.

- DNA replication requires many enzymes, including helicase, which unzips DNA, and DNA polymerase, which copies the parent strands.

- Following DNA replication, each chromosome is attached to its identical copy at the centromere. The identical chromosome copies are called sister chromatids.

- Mitosis is broken into prophase, prometaphase, metaphase, anaphase and telophase. Each phase of mitosis is determined based upon what is happening to the chromosomes.

- Plant cell division occurs very similar to animal cell division except that plant cells do not have centrioles and a cell plate forms between the daughter cells. The cell plate later becomes the cell wall.

- Although the exact mechanisms that control the timing of the cell cycle are not well understood, it is known that the levels of cyclin, cyclin-dependent protein kinase, direct cell contact, and apoptosis all play roles in governing mitosis.

10.19 DEFINITIONS

anaphase
  The fourth phase of mitosis when the chromosomes are separated.

asexual reproduction
  The biological process of forming new cells or organisms without combining genetic material from two organisms; asexual reproduction leads to the formation of clones.

binary fission
  An asexual process of reproduction used by prokaryotes and some eukaryotes.

budding
An asexual process of reproduction.

cell cycle
A way of breaking up the life of a cell based on its activities; the phases a cell goes through in relation to the state of the chromosomes.

cell division (cell reproduction)
The way in which organisms make new organisms and/or new cells; one cell "splits" into two.

cell plate
The area that forms between two plant cells following mitosis and will become the new cell wall between the two cells.

centromere
The site where the sister chromatids are held together and the spindle attaches.

chromatid
Each strand of a chromosome.

chromosomes
Smaller pieces of DNA.

cyclin
A protein that functions to bind to a group of enzymes called cyclin-dependent protein kinases.

Cyclin Dependent Protein Kinases (CDPK)
An enzyme which is activated when cyclin binds to it, causing the cell to proceed into mitosis from interphase.

cytokinesis
The process of the cell membrane pinching inward to form two cells.

daughter cell
During cell division, two cells are formed. The original cell is called the parent cell, and the new cell formed from the parent cell is the daughter cell.

interphase
The period where the cell performs whatever vital functions it is programmed by DNA to perform for the organism. DNA is in the form of chromatin for most of interphase.

karyokinesis
The biological process of the chromatids or chromosomes separating.

meiosis
Cell division which occurs to make a special kind of new cell for sexual reproduction.

metaphase
The third stage of mitosis; when the chromosomes are completely lined up along the cell equator.

mitosis
An asexual means of cellular reproduction to make new cells for organism growth and tissue repair.

parent cell
During cell division, two cells are formed. The original cell is called the parent cell, and the new cell formed from the parent cell is called the daughter cell.

phases
Stages of cell division.

phosphorylated protein
A protein that has had a phosphate group attached to it. Phosphorylated proteins are active.

prometaphase
The second stage of mitosis, during which the chromosomes are coming near complete alignment along the equator of the cell.

prophase
The first stage of mitosis, during which time the chromosomes are condensing.

sister chromatids
The two chromatids of the same chromosome, after the chromosome has been copied.

spindle
Composed of microtubules; will attach to the chromosomes and pull them apart before the cell divides.

spontaneous generation
The now disproved theory that living things arise from non-living things.

spores
A small structure produced by bacteria and other organisms which is resistant to drying out and other harsh environmental conditions. Spores have the ability to grow into a new organism when conditions are right.

telophase
The last phase of mitosis, during which the chromosomes begin to unwind and cytokinesis occurs.

Theory of Biogenesis
States that all life comes from life.

trait
A characteristic of an organism.

STUDY QUESTIONS

1. What is cell division? What are the two types of cell division?

2. What is a parent cell?

3. True or False? Normally, after cell division is completed, one daughter cell has no functional DNA and the other daughter cell has a normally functioning copy of DNA.

4. What is the purpose of mitosis?

5. Define spontaneous generation. Does it occur?

6. What is the theory of biogenesis?

7. True or False? The enzyme helicase induces DNA to form a helix.

8. What is the function of DNA polymerase?

9. Imagine the process of DNA replication. Draw a picture of what a DNA molecule looks like after helicase has unzipped it, and the DNA polymerase has linked together several nucleotides of the daughter strand. Be sure to label the components of the diagram. You can use whatever base sequences you would like, but be sure they are complementary.

10. Is mitosis a form of sexual reproduction?

11. What happens at the replication origin?

12. What are the two phases of the cell cycle?

13. List the phases of mitosis in the order they occur and describe what happens in each phase. This is necessarily a long answer—be specific!

14. True or False? The cell spends 90% of its time in prophase.

15. What is the spindle's function?

16. True or False? Cytokinesis is the name given to the process of pulling the chromosomes apart.

17. What is a cell plate?

18. List two ways in which cancer cells may develop.

19. What happens when the level of cyclin builds up inside of a cell? (Describe the whole process—do not just answer "mitosis starts".)

Organism Reproduction: Binary Fission, Budding, and Meiosis

11

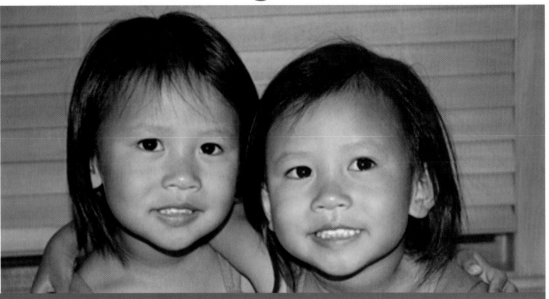

11.0 CHAPTER PREVIEW

In this chapter we will:

- Investigate the asexual cell/organism reproductive processes of binary fission and budding.

- Review more information regarding chromosomes and how they align during the sexual reproductive cell division process of meiosis.

- Completely define the meaning of diploid and haploid as it relates to meiosis.

- Investigate the two stages of meiosis—meiosis I and II.

- Define the differences between male and female meiosis in humans.

- Discuss ways in which genetic variation occurs.

11.1 OVERVIEW

In the previous chapter we learned basic information about chromosomes, as well as detailed information about mitosis. We also learned that spontaneous generation does not occur. Indeed, the basic idea behind disproving spontaneous generation is that life comes from life. Further, we know from experience that "like begets like," or that olive trees produce more olive trees, dogs produce dogs, and humans produce humans. Elephants are never produced from pumpkin plants, and blue whales never produce a blue-footed boobie bird.

In this chapter, we will learn how new organisms are formed. Formation of new organisms is also a type of cell division. New organisms can be formed through sexual or asexual reproduction. Whether the process is sexual or asexual reproduction, like begets like. Last chapter, we discussed the asexual cell reproductive process of mitosis. In this chapter, we will discuss the asexual cell reproductive processes of binary fission and budding. In this chapter, we will learn how prokaryotes form new organisms through binary fission. We will also discuss the asexual cell reproductive process of budding. Budding is performed by eukaryotes. Asexual reproduction creates cells or organisms which are **genetically identical**. Genetically identical organisms are also called **clones**.

We will also learn about meiosis, which is a critical process to form cells to participate in sexual reproduction. Meiosis is an interesting form of cellular reproduction. Meiosis is necessary because when a new organism is formed through sexual reproduction, genetic material is combined. An offspring produced through sexual reproduction receives half of their chromosomes from their mother and half from their father. This requires a special cell division process—meiosis—to form reproductive cells with the proper numbers of chromosomes. In this chapter, we will learn exactly how this process works.

11.2 ASEXUAL REPRODUCTION: PROKARYOTIC BINARY FISSION

Recall that prokaryotes (bacteria) have only one circular strand of DNA. Still, the DNA needs to be replicated and evenly distributed to two daughter cells in order for the cell to reproduce. Because bacteria are unicellular without a male and female of the species, they reproduce through asexual reproduction. Asexual reproduction in prokaryotes is called **binary fission**. Binary fission results in the production of two genetically identical cells from one parent cell.

Figure 11.2.1

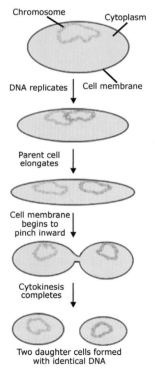

Binary Fission

Prokaryotes divide through binary fission. This is a type of asexual reproduction. The graphic to the right represents what is occurring inside the bacterial cell during binary fission. The organism's initial strand of DNA is colored red. The circular DNA replicates, which leads to two exact copies of DNA in the cytoplasm. Each copy of DNA attaches to the cell membrane at slightly different locations. The cell begins to elongate after the DNA attaches to the cell membrane. This pulls the two copies of DNA apart. As the cell continues to elongate and the DNA strands are far enough apart, cytokinesis occurs. The single cell separates into two daughter cells. Each cell now has its own copy of DNA. Two genetically identical, single-cell organisms have been formed. Usually the two daughter cells are not exactly the same size immediately after binary fission is completed. The cell which retains the original copy of DNA is usually a bit larger than the cell which receives the replicated copy. However, the two cells grow rapidly to the normal size for their species. The electron micrograph below is of a bacterial cell nearing completion of binary fission. You can see that one parent cell has almost finished dividing into two daughter cells. The nucleoid is not clearly visible in either cell.

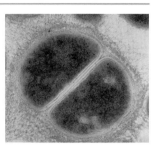

As can be seen from the figure, the first step in binary fission is DNA replication. One exact copy of the DNA is made in the cytoplasm. At this point, then, there are two exact copies of DNA inside the cell. Recall a prokaryote has no nucleus. When a prokaryotic cell needs to divide, a small section of its circular DNA attaches to a site on the interior of the cell membrane. The DNA is then replicated and the new copy also attaches onto the interior of the cell membrane, close to the original copy of DNA. The cell (and the cell wall if it has one) then begins to elongate, causing the two copies of DNA to move apart from one another. Once the cell gets about twice as long as it started, the cell membrane (and wall) pinch inward and cytokinesis occurs. Two daughter cells have been formed, each with its own copy of the parent cell's DNA strand.

11.3 ASEXUAL REPRODUCTION: EUKARYOTIC BUDDING

Budding is a common way many unicellular eukaryotes and some multicellular eukaryotes can reproduce to form an identical and new organism. Many plants can perform this, as can unicellular yeast. Even some microscopic multicellular animals, such as the *Hydra* species, can generate new organisms through budding. Like mitosis and binary fission, the organisms formed following budding are clones to the parent cell/organism. It is important to remember there is no combining of genetic material during asexual reproduction.

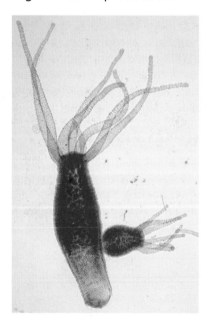

Figure 11.3.1

Budding

The budding process for a multicellular organism is shown on the left. *Hydra* is a microscopic species which lives in water. It may look more like a plant than an animal, but it is an animal. In this budding process, a genetically identical, miniature version of the parent animal sprouts from the side of the parent. It grows as a miniature and genetically identical multicellular version of the parent on which it is growing. The small bud grows by mitosis. The mini version falls off and is a fully functional organism.

11.4 CHROMOSOMES

Recall our discussion about chromosomes from last two chapters. As noted, most bacteria have only 1 chromosome, which is arranged in a circle. Some bacteria have 2 chromosomes. All eukaryotic cells have more than 2 chromosomes; some have more than 1000.

Notice from Figure 11.4.1 that there is a wide range in numbers of chromosomes. All cells of a particular organism have the same number of chromosomes (except the sex cells, which we will get to in a minute). For example, all of the cells in your body (except the sex cells) have forty-six chromosomes in them. All of the millions of liver cells in you each have forty-six chromosomes, just as all of the millions of bone cells, billions of nerve cells and millions of muscle cell. Also, normally, all of the other organisms within the same species have the same number of chromosomes. For example, every fruit fly has 8 chromosomes, just as every human normally has 46 chromosomes. Notice also that "more complex" organisms do not necessarily have more chromosomes than "less complex" organisms (by that I mean a fern plant has 1200 chromosomes and humans "only" have 46). Human chromosomes are fairly large and carry a lot of genetic information while the chromosomes of a fern are all small and carry less genetic information.

Figure 11.4.1

Chromosome Numbers in Selected Species

Species	Number of Chromosomes
fruit fly	8
rye	14
dove	16
earthworm	32
pig	40
wheat	42
human	46
gorilla	48
sand dollar	52
horse	64
carp	104
fern	>1200

The most important thing to learn about chromosomes right now is that **chromosomes are arranged in pairs**. Inside of almost all eukaryotic cells are a specific number of paired chromosomes. Why are they paired? Two reasons: one is that each pair of chromosomes contains the same sequence of genes. That means that chromosome pairs contain genes that code for the same information (except for the sex chromosomes which we will get to later). For example, both chromosome number 1's in humans contain genes that code for the same traits, just like both chromosome number 2's code for the same traits, etc.

The second reason is that half of an organism's chromosomes come from the male parent and half from the female parent. If we look at the Figure 11.4.1, the plant organism rye has fourteen chromosomes. That means it has seven pairs. It receives one set of seven chromosomes from the male parent rye plant and one set of seven chromosomes from the female parent rye plant. That gives the rye plant fourteen total, or seven pair, of chromosomes.

Also, chromosomes are numbered by geneticists to help keep track of them. Since we will be using humans as an example quite a bit, let's look at them for a second. Normally, humans have forty-six chromosomes arranged as twenty-three pairs. Each human receives half of the chromosomes from their mom and half from their dad. That means that twenty-three chromosomes come from the mom and twenty-three from the dad. Each person receives one set of chromosomes, numbered 1-23, from their mom and one set from their dad. We all have two pairs of every chromosome in our cells. Be sure that you understand this!

11.5 KARYOTYPE, AUTOSOMES, AND SEX CHROMOSOMES

Chromosomes vary significantly from species to species in more ways than their numbers. Chromosomes also vary greatly in their size and shape. This is true not only from species to species, but also within the same organism. For example, look at the human **karyotype**. A karyotype is an orderly presentation of chromosomes after preparing and staining them a special way. Chromosomes are extracted from a cell using special techniques. Then, a scientist aligns the chromosomes according to their size. Chromosome number 1 is the largest chromosome, number 2 is slightly smaller than 1, number 3 is slightly smaller than number 2, and so on. The chromosomes are arranged in pairs and then a picture is taken of them. You will notice that the chromosomes are of varying shapes and sizes, but they all came from the same cell (the same person). Notice that they are arranged in pairs—twenty-two pairs of chromosomes, and one pair of sex chromosomes, for a total of forty-six individual chromosomes. Almost all eukaryotic chromosomes are arranged in pairs. They are arranged in pairs because each pair contains information for the same trait. For example, each chromosome number 7 contains a gene which codes for the production of a certain type of transmembrane channel.

There are two basic types of chromosomes—those that do not determine sex and those that do. The chromosomes that do not determine sex are called **autosomes**. Chromosomes that do determine the sex of the organism are called **sex chromosomes**. Thus, humans have twenty-two pairs, or forty-four individual, autosomes; they also have one pair, or two individual, sex chromosomes. Fruit flies have six pairs of autosomes and two pairs of sex chromosomes. Doves have sixteen total chromosomes—seven pairs (fourteen total chromosomes) are autosomes and one pair (two chromosomes) are the sex chromosomes.

Notice that the **female sex chromosomes** look somewhat the same. They are the same size and shape. However, the male sex chromosomes do not look at all alike. One is large and the other is quite small. Why is this? Females contain two **X chromosomes**; they are said to be "XX" in regard to their sex chromosomes. Because all X chromosomes are generally the same shape and size, the paired sex chromosomes in the female look the same. But notice in the male karyotype that there is one X chromosome, but the chromosome paired with it is much smaller. Is this a mistake? No, the **male sex chromosomes** consist of one X and one **Y chromosome**; males are said to be "XY" in regard to their sex chromosomes. Even though the sex chromosomes in a male look different, they are still considered pairs because both the X and the Y chromosomes code for sexual information. In most eukaryote species, organisms that have the Y chromosome are male.

Figure 11.5.1

Human Karyotype

These are graphical representations of a female (left) and male karyotype (right). Notice the chromosomes are numbered and are arranged in pairs. Both chromosomes of a pair contain genes which code for the same traits. The same pairs are also the same size, except for the male sex chromosomes. In a karyotype, the sex chromosomes are almost always paired in the bottom right corner of the karyotype. The X chromosome is much larger than the Y. This is because the Y chromosome does not contain as many genes as the X chromosome. This fact will be important when we discuss human genetic diseases in a few chapters. After you have read ahead, come back to this figure. The origin of a chromosome—i.e. which chromosome of a pair came from the mom and the dad—cannot be identified just by looking at the chromosome. There are other special tests that can be performed to discover that. Each chromosome of a pair is called a homologue. Since karyotypes pair chromosomes that code for the same information, karyotypes display chromosomes organized by homologues. The two number 1 chromosomes are homologues; the two number 2 chromosomes are homologues, etc. In females, the two X chromosomes are homologues, as are the X and the Y in the male.

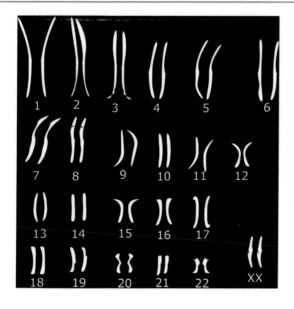
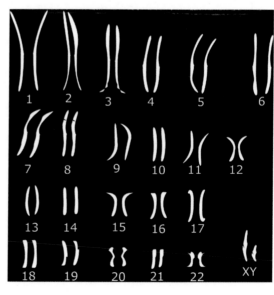

11.6 SEXUAL REPRODUCTION

Organisms which contain sex chromosomes pass their genetic material to their offspring via sexual reproduction. Another way of stating that is that all species which have male and female organisms reproduce through sexual reproduction. Sexual reproduction is the generation of a new organism by combining DNA from a male and DNA from a female. Since DNA is housed in the form of chromosomes, another way to state this is: combining chromosomes from the male with chromosomes of the female results in offspring. This is the process by which many plants and almost all animals reproduce. This is the process by which you and I and snakes and bears and fish were made. It is also the process by which roses and trees and grass are made.

Remember that chromosomes in most eukaryotes are in pairs! The fruit fly has eight total chromosomes which are arranged as four pairs. A human has forty-six total chromosomes arranged as twenty-three pairs. Each chromosome of a pair is called a **homologue**. For example, humans have two number 11 chromosomes. Each number 11 chromosome is a homologue to the other. (Some plants, moss, and fungi do not have paired chromosomes because they do not reproduce through sexual reproduction.) Take a look back at the karyotype figure for a little better understanding. The karyotype is laid out so that the homologues are next to one another. Each chromosome of a pair in the karyotype is a homologue to the other chromosome of the pair.

11.7 DIPLOID AND HAPLOID

Cells that have paired chromosomes are called **diploid cells:** "di" means "paired," and "ploid" means "chromosome. Diploid cells contain two copies of every chromosome. As we have stated, one copy of the chromosomes comes from the mom and one copy from the dad. Normal human diploid cells contain forty-six total chromosomes. This is called the **diploid number**, referred to as **2n**. The "n" refers to "copies of chromosomes" (in that there are twenty-three individual copies of chromosomes) and the "2" means "two times." $2 \times 23 = 46$ total chromosomes.

Take note that a diploid cell is not defined by the *number* of chromosomes that it contains. By definition, a diploid cell contains one set of chromosomes from the female parent and one set from the male parent. For example, just because a human cell contains forty-six chromosomes does not mean it is a diploid cell, as we will see in the upcoming sections. What defines a diploid cell is having one complete copy of chromosomes from the male parent and one complete copy of chromosomes from the female parent contained within the cell.

There are two types of cells in eukaryotes—**somatic** and **reproductive** cells. Somatic cells are also called body cell and are the cells of the skin, muscle, heart, bones, organs, etc. Somatic cells of almost all eukaryotes are diploid, or 2n. For example, since the diploid number for humans is forty-six, all human somatic cells have forty-six chromosomes in them.

Diploid cells are contrasted to **haploid cells**, or cells which have only one chromosome of a pair (instead of two). Haploid cells only contain one copy of every chromosome. Just as diploid cells are referred to as 2n, haploid cells are referred to as n. Why is this concept of diploid and haploid important? We know that in organisms that sexually reproduce, a cell containing chromosomes from the female parent is combined with a cell containing chromosomes from the male parent. Some of you may have had the thought that if forty-six chromosomes from the mother are combined with forty-six chromosomes from the father, then the offspring would have ninety-two chromosomes. Good thinking, but that is true only if the reproductive cells have forty-six chromosomes in them. Above, we stated that all cells of an organism have the same number of chromosomes *except the reproductive cells*.

Reproductive cells, also called sex cells or **gametes**, are cells that participate in sexual reproduction. The male gamete is called **sperm**; the female the **egg** or **ovum**. Sperm and eggs are not diploid cells; they are haploid, or n. Gametes contain only half the number of the usual chromosomes, or twenty-three in the case of humans. That means that each sex cell only has one chromosome of each pair. That way, when the chromosomes from the sperm and egg combine, the diploid number is restored—twenty-three chromosomes from the male haploid gamete combined with twenty-three chromosomes from the female haploid gamete equals 46 chromosomes. The gametes of all sexually reproducing organisms are n.

Figure 11.7.1

Haploid and Diploid
The difference between a haploid and a diploid cell is shown here. A "normal" cell should have two pairs of every chromosome in it. That is known as a diploid cell, said to be 2n. A diploid cell has two copies of every chromosome, one from the male parent and one from the female parent. Normal body cells, or somatic cells, are diploid. A cell that has only one copy of every chromosome is a haploid cell. A cell which has half the normal number of chromosomes is called a haploid cell and is said to be n. A haploid cell has one copy of every chromosome. Normal sex cells—eggs and sperm—are haploid. That way, when the chromosomes of the sperm (n) are combined with the chromosomes of the egg (n), the resulting offspring is diploid—n + n = 2n.

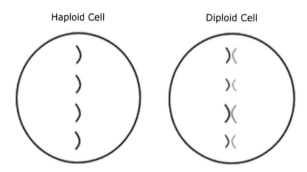

Haploid Cell   Diploid Cell

11.8 MEIOSIS

Mitosis results in the formation of diploid daughter cells from diploid parent cells. Haploid cells cannot be formed from mitosis. How do haploid male and female gametes form? **Meiosis** is the biological process of forming haploid gametes from diploid somatic cells. Please note that meiosis does not occur just anywhere and everywhere in an organism. Meiosis occurs only in the **reproductive organs** of the organism. In the female, meiosis occurs in the **reproductive cells** of the ovary while in the male, meiosis occurs in reproductive cells of the testes.

The purpose of meiosis is to ensure that the proper number of chromosomes is dispersed into the gametes. In order for sexual reproduction to result in the production of new offspring that can survive, it is critical that every sperm and every egg receive the proper numbers of chromosomes during meiosis. A gamete that has too many or too few chromosomes results in the production of a new organism that is not **viable**. To not be viable means "cannot live".

The starting point for all cells entering meiosis is the diploid number. In humans, that means the starting point is the 2n number 46. This means that during meiosis, the diploid number is reduced to the haploid number, from 46 to 23. The process of the sperm fusing with the egg and combining chromosomes is called **fertilization**. When a sperm fertilizes an ovum, the chromosomes are **fused** (or joined), forming a diploid cell from two haploid cells. As we said, n + n = 2n. After fertilization, a new single cell, called a **zygote**, is formed. The zygote then grows into the mature organism through repeated rounds of mitosis.

Figure 11.8.1

Chromosome Numbers During Meiosis and Mitosis
The drawing below represents the relationship of the number of chromosomes to mitosis and meiosis. Every sexually reproducing organism is a diploid organism. However, diploid cells cannot participate in fertilization. Cells that participate in fertilization are called gametes, and gametes must be haploid cells. Each sexually reproducing organism produces gametes through meiosis. The function of meiosis is to form haploid sperm and eggs. Since every sexually-reproducing organism needs to have two copies of every chromosome to function normally, one egg needs to combine with one sperm. This is called fertilization. When this happens, the chromosomes from the egg and sperm fuse and form a diploid cell. This new diploid cell is called a zygote. It is the starting cell from which a fully functional organism will form. The zygote grows in size through trillions of cycles of mitosis. The function of mitosis is to form more diploid cells. As the zygote grows and the number of cells increases, cells will begin to group together and form tissues and organs in a multicellular organism.

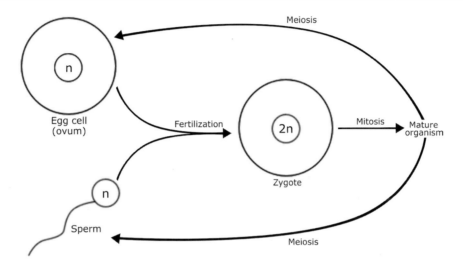

11.9 MEIOSIS DIVIDED

Meiosis is a two-step process, broken into **meiosis I** and **meiosis II**. Remember, the purpose of meiosis is to distribute the proper numbers and types of chromosomes to the gametes. During this discussion, we will not be so concerned with what is happening structurally to the cell, but more so with what is happening to the chromosomes. Meiosis I is broken into interphase I, prophase I, metaphase I, anaphase I, and telophase I. Meiosis II is broken into interphase II, prophase II, metaphase II, anaphase II, and ends with telophase II. The process is the same for the male and female organisms, but some exceptions will be noted where appropriate. The entire process of meiosis includes one DNA duplication event and two karyokinesis events.

Figure 11.9.1

Overview of Meiosis
Meiosis starts with the diploid reproductive cells replicating the chromosomes. This forms a 4n cell from a 2n cell. Another way of saying this is a cell with four copies of chromosomes is formed from a cell with two copies of chromosomes. (When two copies of chromosomes are replicated, the result is four copies—two copies of each chromosome from the male parent and two copies of each chromosomes form the female parent.) Unlike mitosis, the same chromosomes stay together during meiosis. That means there are four copies of chromosome 1 grouped together, four copies of chromosome 2 grouped together, etc. Once meiosis I and II are completed, the single diploid reproductive cell has generated four haploid cells.

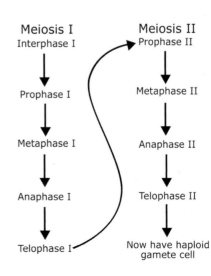

11.10 INTERPHASE I

In **interphase I**, the reproductive cell duplicates its chromosomes, as in mitosis. This is the only time during meiosis that the chromosomes are replicated. At this point, the cell has ninety-two chromosomes in its nucleus. In mitosis, the chromosomes line up along the equator of the cell to be pulled apart independent of one another, but in meiosis I, homologous chromosomes cluster together before they are separated.

Let's take chromosome number 25 as an example. In the diploid state, there is one pair (two total) of chromosome 25 in the nucleus. One chromosome 25 is from the organism's father, and one from the mother. These two number 25 chromosomes are homologues. The cell then replicates the chromosomes, and now there are two pair—or four total—chromosome 25s in the nucleus. These four homologous chromosomes are now referred to as **homologous pairs,** or **tetrads**.

To be clear, during the duplication process, each chromosome of a pair is copied. The identical copy of each chromosome is called a sister chromatid. For example, chromosome 25 from the male parent is copied and that results in two copies of chromosome 25 from the male parent. The same thing happens to chromosome 25 from the female parent as well as all other chromosomes. The sister chromatids remain attached to one another at the centromere just as in mitosis. Further, all four of the copies of every chromosome remain together. Another way of stating that is all of the tetrads, or homologous pairs, remain together (until they are pulled apart later in meiosis) after they are replicated. Each tetrad, or homologous pair, is made up of two copies of the chromosome from the male parent and two copies of the chromosome from the female parent. The two copies are sister chromatids attached at the centromere.

Figure 11.10.1

Relationship of Homologues and Homologous Pairs
Chromosomes are arranged in pairs. That is because it just so happens that each chromosome of a pair contains genetic information for the same characteristics. One chromosome in each pair comes from, or is inherited from, the male parent and other chromosome of a pair is inherited from the female parent. The paired chromosomes are called homologues. Homologues are not held together at the centromere; they are individual. Chromosomes do not "stick" together at the centromere until they have been duplicated. Once the homologues are duplicated, the identical strands are held to one another at the centromere. The attached, identical chromosomes are referred to as sister chromatids. When the duplicated chromosomes align during mitosis, they do so without regard to the homologue relationship. During meiosis I, the chromosomes align such that the homologous pairs, or tetrads, line up across from one another before the first karyokinesis event. During karyokinesis, one set of homologous pairs is pulled to one pole of the cell, and the other set of homologous pairs is pulled to the opposite pole. This effectively separates the chromosomes inherited from the male parent from those inherited by the female parent. Following meiosis I, all of the cells that are formed are haploid cells because they do not contain a copy of each chromosome from each parent; they contain two copies of the chromosome inherited form the male parent or two copies of the chromosomes inherited from the female parent.

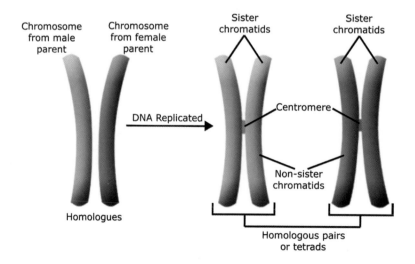

Chromosome from male parent   Chromosome from female parent   Sister chromatids   Sister chromatids

DNA Replicated

Centromere

Non-sister chromatids

Homologues

Homologous pairs or tetrads

11.11 PROPHASE I

Prophase I begins following chromosome duplication and the homologous pairs (tetrads) begin to move closer to one another. The chromosomes continue to wind more tightly around the histones and condense. During prophase I, the same structural changes that occurred to the cell during prophase of mitosis are occurring (for example, the centrioles are beginning to form the spindle, the nucleoli disappear, and the nuclear membrane disappears).

11.12 METAPHASE I

During **Metaphase I**, the tetrads align along the equator of the spindle across from one another. This process is called **synapsis**. During synapsis, the individual chromosomes of the tetrads often wind around one another. Note that in mitosis, the lining-up process of the chromosomes is random, and homologous pairs do not associate with one another as they do during meiosis. This alignment is the critical part of meiosis. Since the two copies of the chromosomes inherited from the male parent always line up across from the two copies inherited from the female parent, when they are separated, one cell receives two copies of the male-inherited chromosome and the other cell receives two copies of the female inherited chromosome. This is the point where the diploid number is reduced to the haploid number.

11.13 ANAPHASE I

Anaphase I begins as the homologous pairs are pulled apart by the spindle to opposite ends of the cell. Notice that at this step, the diploid number is reduced to the haploid number. This seems confusing because there are still two copies of the chromosomes at each end of the cell. However, they are copies of the same chromosome.

In our example above, the two copies of chromosome number 25 from the father move to one end of the cell, and the two copies of chromosome 25 from the mother move to the other end of the cell. This process splits the diploid number (one chromosome from the father and one from the mother) into the haploid number. However, there are two copies of each chromosome at either end of the cell. Another aspect to remember is that there are forty-six chromosomes undergoing this process at the same time. Although the homologous tetrads always line up with one another, sometimes the homologous pair from the father is on one side of the spindle equator, and sometimes it is on the other. In other words, during synapsis, maybe the father's chromosome 25 is on the "top" of the equator, while the father's chromosome 26 may be on the "bottom" of the spindle equator, and so on for the other forty-four chromosomes. This ensures that there is random dispersion of the chromosomes during meiosis. I do not want you to get the idea that the chromosomes always line up the same way so the chromosomes from the father always get separated from the chromosomes of the mother. They do not. There are 2^{23} (or over 8 million) different possibilities for the arrangement of the tetrads during synapsis. That means there are over 8 million different combinations of chromosome separation during meiosis I.

11.14 TELOPHASE I

Telophase I then begins with the formation of cytoplasm around the chromosomes at each end of the cell, forming two new cells. Again, each cell now has two copies of the haploid number arranged as sister chromatids. **Meiosis II** is ready to begin. Some organisms have a brief interphase, **interphase II**, during which a nuclear membrane forms around the chromosomes, and some proceed directly onto prophase II. *There is no duplication of chromosomes during interphase II.*

Figure 11.14.1

Meiosis I

The figure below depicts what happens to two chromosomes during meiosis. During interphase I, the chromosomes are replicated. The cell nucleus shown in interphase I contains two sets of homologues. **The black and yellow chromosomes are homologues, and the blue and red chromosomes are homologues.** Let's just say that the black and red chromosomes are inherited from the father and the yellow and blue are from the mother. The cell shown in prophase I has replicated its chromosomes. Each chromosome now consists of two sister chromatids held together at the centromere. The black and yellow chromosomes are homologous pairs, as are the red and blue chromosomes. In metaphase I, the homologous pairs have lined up across from one another along the equator of the cell. Anaphase I separates the homologous pairs from one another. It is important to realize that each homologous pair is made up of two copies of the chromosome either from the father or the mother. Therefore, when the chromosomes separate in anaphase I, the diploid chromosomes are separated from one another. Although the two cells in telophase I contain two copies of chromosomes, they only have two copies of "n" chromosomes. The cells in telophase are haploid, but they have two copies of a haploid number of chromosomes. Remember that a diploid cell is defined not by having two copies of every chromosome, but by having one copy of every chromosome from the male parent and one copy of every chromosome from the female parent. Following meiosis I, the two daughter cells do have two copies of every chromosome in them, but they are two copies of either the male parent's chromosomes or the female parent's chromosomes. That is not a diploid cell, but haploid. Look at the cell in interphase I. It is a normal, diploid cell. There is one copy of the blue chromosome (inherited from the mother) and there is one copy of its homologue, the red chromosome (inherited from the father). There is also one copy of the yellow chromosomes (from the mother) and its homologue the black chromosome (from the father) That is a normal diploid cell. When the chromosomes are duplicated, the cell in prophase I and metaphase I still each have a set of chromosomes inherited from the mother and a set from the father. However, they have two copies of each of the chromosomes. So those cells have two copies of the diploid (or 2n) chromosomes. Because of the way the chromosomes align in meiosis, the father's homologous chromosomes are always separated from the mother's homologous chromosomes during anaphase I. This generates the haploid number. Notice that the cell in telophase I does not contain four chromosomes of different colors like the diploid cell in interphase I did. The cell in interphase I was diploid because it contained the normal numbers of chromosomes with one of the pair being from the father and one from the mother. Now, while the cell in telophase I does contain four chromosomes like the one in Interphase I did, there are only **two** different chromosomes, each with two copies. The cell in telophase I does not have the normal diversity of chromosomes that a normal diploid cell does; it only has half the normal diversity of chromosomes. We call that condition haploid, so even though the cell in telophase I has two copies of chromosomes in it, there is one copy each of two identical chromosomes. The cell in interphase I has one copy each of two different chromosomes.

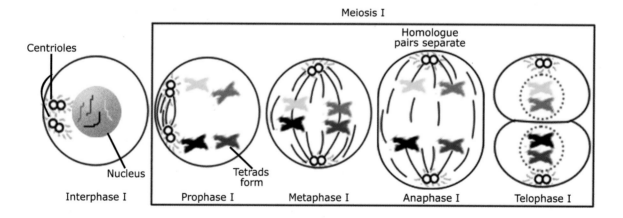

Meiosis I

11.15 MEIOSIS II

The spindle begins to assemble during **prophase II** and then the chromosomes—now properly called sister chromatids—line up along the equator of the spindle during **metaphase II**. The sister chromatids separate and are pulled to opposite ends of the cell during **anaphase II**. This process has separated two copies of the haploid number into two cells with one copy of the haploid number. During **telophase II**, the nuclear and cell membranes fully form; there are now **four** haploid cells that have formed from one diploid cell. These haploid cells are called gametes. The male gamete is the sperm and the female is the egg (or ovum).

Figure 11.15.1

Meiosis II
There is no chromosomal duplication between meiosis I and meiosis II. The starting point of meiosis II is the two cells formed in Telophase I, and the chromosomes are divided directly from the chromosome material left in the cell. The chromosomes line up along the equator of the cell. The spindle forms and attaches to the centromeres. The chromosomes are pulled apart into separate cells. This effectively completes the process of forming four haploid sex cells from one diploid reproductive cell.

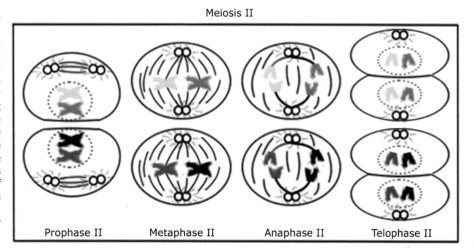

Meiosis II

Prophase II   Metaphase II   Anaphase II   Telophase II

To summarize, the events of meiosis I separate the tetrads, or homologous pairs, into two cells which have two copies of the haploid number. The events of meiosis II separate the two n copies of sister chromatids into a total of four cells (because each of the two cells produced from meiosis I now separate, giving rise to a total of four cells from the one cell starting point). This is how haploid gametes are generated from diploid somatic cells.

11.16 MEIOSIS IN HUMAN MALES

In humans, meiosis is different in males from meiosis in females. Although the same pattern is followed, it occurs at different times and with notable differences between men and women. In men, meiosis is an ongoing process that does not start until reaching sexual maturity. Sexual maturity is the point at which an organism can reproduce. Once sexual maturity is reached, meiosis results in the formation of four fully functional sperm cells from one diploid reproductive cell. This takes place in the testes and occurs nearly continuously throughout life. Once the haploid sperm cell has been made, a flagellum then grows out of the cell from one of the centrioles and functions to propel the sperm toward the ova.

Figure 11.16.1

Meiosis in Males
Meiosis in males results in the production of four haploid sperm cells.

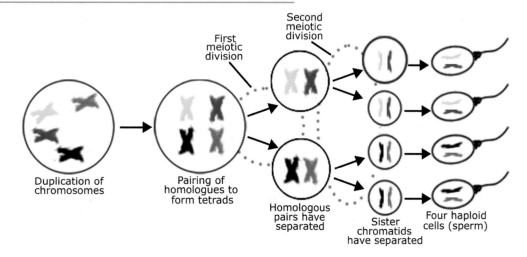

Duplication of chromosomes

First meiotic division

Pairing of homologues to form tetrads

Second meiotic division

Homologous pairs have separated

Sister chromatids have separated

Four haploid cells (sperm)

11.17 MEIOSIS IN HUMAN FEMALES

Meiosis is a bit more complicated in women. In females, the pattern of meiosis is followed as outlined above, but with interesting differences. Meiosis actually begins in the female when she is a fetus. In the womb, cells in the ovary undergo meiosis, but then stop after meiosis I is completed. The cells stay suspended between meiosis I and II until sexual maturity is reached. Once sexual maturity is reached, normally one of the original cell groups that started meiosis I proceeds with meiosis II. This occurs cyclically once per month.

One of the most interesting aspects of meiosis in females is that during meiosis I, there is an unequal splitting of the first cell, such that one cell receives more cytoplasm than the other cell. This results in the formation of one smaller and one larger cell. Then, when meiosis II starts, both of these cells continue through meiosis, and when the cells divide into four cells, the two smaller cells divide into two small cells. The larger cell again divides unequally into a larger and smaller cell. The larger cell is the ovum and is ready to be fertilized. The three smaller cells are called **polar bodies**. Polar bodies do not get fertilized and degenerate.

Figure 11.17.1

Meiosis in Females
Meiosis in females follows the same chromosomal pattern as in males. However, both the first and the second meiotic divisions occur unequally. In each division, each of the cells receives the same number of chromosomes, but one cell gets a larger portion of cytoplasm than the other. The cell that receives the larger amount of cytoplasm forms into the egg, and the other three form into degenerative cells called polar bodies.

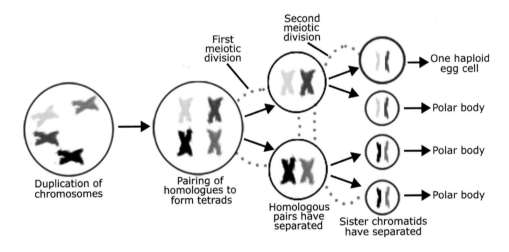

To summarize meiosis in humans, four haploid sperm are formed from one diploid cell in the male and one ovum and three polar bodies are formed from one diploid cell in the female.

11.18 ADVANCED: GENETIC VARIATION

Genetic variation, in general, is good for a species. **Genetic variation** describes the small differences between genes in any given population. The more genetic variation that exists in a population, the healthier the population is over time. It has been found that when there is relatively little genetic variation within a population, more birth defects occur. For example, there are religious groups that forbid their members from marrying outside of that group. Over time, the genetic "pool" does not change much. A **genetic pool** is the total amount of genes available within a population. When there is a smaller genetic pool, there are more detrimental effects on the organisms within the population. Some of these religious groups have high incidences of genetic alterations leading to things such as extra fingers or toes on the hands or feet.

There are many ways that genetic material can be altered during meiosis. As we have seen, about six base pairs of the DNA will be wrong after DNA is replicated. This leads to a small amount of change in the genes and DNA. The other two ways genetic material can be altered are: 1) crossing over and 2) independent alignment of the tetrads during synapsis.

During the period of synapsis in meiosis I, the tetrads associate with one another so that their DNA "lines up." This means that genes for the same trait line up next to one another. Recall that the strands of the tetrads often twist around one another. Because the sequence of DNA for the same genes is similar, the strands twisting around one another often allows for sections of DNA to be "swapped" from one strand to another. Due to the way the tetrads align, it results in a transfer of DNA between the father's and the mother's chromatids. This process is called **crossing over**. Sometimes large segments of DNA cross over, making this an important contributor to genetic variation.

Figure 11.18.1

Crossing Over
This figure is exaggerated, but will help to make the process of crossing over clearer. When homologous pairs line up along the equator during meiosis I, segments of chromosomes of non-sister chromatids are close to one another. Because these areas code for the same traits, the sequence of DNA is similar, but not exact. They are close enough in sequence, though, that sometimes segments of entire chromosomes swap from one sister chromatid of one homologous pair to the other. Then when the chromosomes undergo karyokinesis, the chromosomes which separate are genetically different than either of the starting chromosomes. This results in the generation of increased genetic diversity.

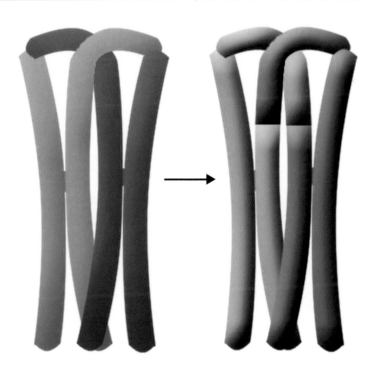

Another important factor leading to genetic variation was described above in the section on meiosis. This refers to the independent alignment of the tetrads along the equator of the spindle during meiosis I. As noted, there are over 8 million possible combinations for how chromosomes can align, which leads to the production of different gametes from the DNA stand point. We will learn more causes of genetic variation in the upcoming chapters.

Figure 11.18.2

Genetic Variation During Meiosis I
Notice the relatively large number of gametes produced with just four chromosomes. This occurs because of the independent alignment of chromosomes during meiosis I.

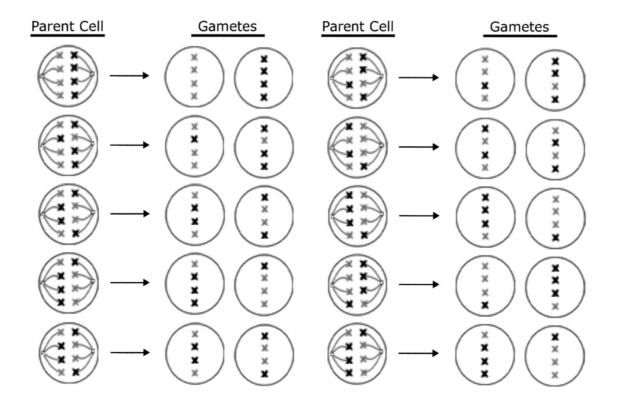

11.19 PEOPLE OF SCIENCE

Rosalind Franklin (1920-1958) was a British researcher who used x-rays to study the structure of DNA and viruses. Her work on the structure of carbon in coal led to the idea that carbon could form lightweight strong bonds. This eventually led to carbon fiber being used in everything from bullet proof vests to golf club shafts. In addition, her work on the x-ray structure of DNA was critical to helping Watson and Crick understand the double helical nature of the molecule. Unfortunately, she died in 1958 from ovarian cancer before the Nobel Prize was awarded for the discovery of the structure of DNA; many think she would have shared the award if she had been alive.

11.20 KEY CHAPTER POINTS

- Budding and binary fission create new cells without combining DNA from two separate organisms. Together with mitosis, these processes represent forms of asexual reproduction. Asexual reproduction produces clones.

- Sexual reproduction creates new organisms by combining DNA from two separate organisms. Sexual reproduction requires the formation of special cells called gametes.

- Meiosis is the specialized form of cell division which creates gametes. Gametes are the cells which fuse together and combine their DNA, creating a new organism.

- All organisms that sexually reproduce have their DNA broken into smaller segments called chromosomes. Each species has a unique number of chromosomes that all organisms of that species contain. For example, all humans have forty-six chromosomes.

- Every chromosome contains multiple genes that code for different traits.

- All sexually-reproducing organisms have two sets of genes for the same trait. One set of genes is contained on one chromosome which comes from the father, and the other set is contained on a chromosome which comes from the mother. These chromosomes are called homologues.

- All somatic cells are diploid, 2n, while all gametes are haploid, 1n or n.

- During meiosis, diploid reproductive cells generate haploid gametes.

- Meiosis is broken into two parts, meiosis I and meiosis II. Meiosis I creates cells which contain two sets of the haploid number. Meiosis II results in those cells producing gametes with one set of the haploid number of chromosomes.

- Meiosis in human males results in the production of four sperm cells (the male gamete) from one reproductive cell.

- Meiosis in human females results in the production of one ova, or egg (the female reproductive cell), and three polar bodies from one reproductive cell.

- Meiosis results in significant genetic variability between gametes from the same individual. Genetic variation is good for a species.

11.21 DEFINITIONS

anaphase I
The stage of meiosis I when the chromosomes (as homologous pairs) separate.

anaphase II
The stage of meiosis II when the sister chromatids are pulled apart.

autosomes
The chromosomes that determine all non-sexual characteristics.

clones
Offspring that are genetically identical to the parent.

crossing over
Transfer of DNA between the father's and mother's chromatids that usually occurs during meiosis I when the homologous pairs are lined up next to one another.

diploid cells
Cells that have paired chromosomes, or are 2n.

diploid number (2n)
Twice the haploid number of chromosomes. 2n is the state of all non-sex cells in eukaryotic organisms.

eggs (ova)
Animal gametes in the female.

female sex chromosome
A female organism contains two X chromosomes.

fuse
To join together, as when the sperm fuses with the ovum, allowing the chromosomes of each to unite and form an embryo.

gamete
A sex cell; a cell used for sexual reproduction.

genetically identical
Cells or organisms created by asexual reproduction; clones.

haploid cells (n)
Cells that contain only one copy of chromosomes.

homologous pairs (tetrads)
The name given to homologous chromosomes after they have replicated and are aligned with one another in metaphase I.

homologue
An individual chromosome of a homologous pair.

interphase I
The stage of meiosis I when the cell duplicates its chromosomes.

interphase II
The stage of meiosis II that occurs after telophase I and before metaphase II. No chromosomal duplication occurs during interphase II.

karyotype
An orderly presentation of chromosomes after staining them a special way.

male sex chromosome
The Y chromosome. A male organism has one X and one Y sex chromosome.

meiosis I
The stage of meiosis when the homologous pairs are separated, forming two cells, each of which has two copies of the haploid (n) number.

meiosis II
The stage of meiosis when the sister chromatids are separated, forming four cells with the haploid number (n).

metaphase I
The stage of meiosis when the homologous pairs line up with one another along the cell's equator.

metaphase II
The stage of meiosis when sister chromatids are separated.

polar bodies
The three smaller cells formed during meiosis in females; these do not get fertilized and will degenerate.

prophase I
The stage of meiosis when the duplicated chromosomes (as homologous pairs) begin to condense.

prophase II
The stage of meiosis when the sister chromatids condense.

reproductive cells
Cells which are used for sexual reproduction.

reproductive organs
The organs that perform sexual reproduction.

sex chromosomes
Chromosomes that determine the sex of the organism. In most eukaryote species, the sex chromosomes are X and Y.

somatic cells
Body cells such as skin, muscle, heart, etc.

sperm
Animal gametes in the male.

synapsis
The process of tetrads aligning along the equator of the spindle next to one another.

telophase I
The stage of meiosis when cytokinesis occurs, forming two cells from one.

telophase II
The stage of meiosis when the second cytokinesis event occurs, forming four cells from two.

X chromosome
   The female sex chromosome.

Y chromosome
   The male sex chromosome.

zygote
   The cell formed when chromosomes are fused.

STUDY QUESTIONS

1. True or False? All bacterial cells have more than one chromosome.

2. True or False? All eukaryotic cells have more than two chromosomes.

3. True or False? All living organisms have the same number of chromosomes.

4. True or False? All organisms of the same species normally have the same number of chromosomes.

5. What are autosomes?

6. What is a karyotype?

7. How many pairs of sex chromosomes do humans normally have? What are they called?

8. True or False? A person with the karyotype XX is female.

9. What is sexual reproduction?

10. Describe what is meant first by a cell which is n, then by a cell which is 2n.

11. What are the n and 2n number for the sand dollar? The fruit fly?

12. True or False? Male and female gametes are n, so when the male gamete fertilizes the female gamete the new organism is 2n.

13. What is meiosis? What is its purpose?

14. What is the end result of meiosis I?

15. What is the end result of meiosis II?

16. How many functional gametes are produced as a result of human male meiosis?

17. How many fully functional gametes are produced as a result of human female meiosis?

18. What are polar bodies?

19. Describe the process of crossing over.

20. What is a clone? Are they produced as a result of sexual or asexual reproduction?

PLEASE TAKE TEST #4 IN TEST BOOKLET

Genes and Heredity

12

12.0 CHAPTER PREVIEW

In this chapter we will:

- Discuss how genes are related to traits.

- Define what alleles are.

- Learn the basic processes—such as gene segregation and independent assortment—that govern how genes are passed from generation to generation.

- Become comfortable using the technical jargon of geneticists.

12.1 OVERVIEW

We have learned that DNA is organized into smaller and more manageable units called chromosomes. Within each chromosome are smaller and well-defined sequences of DNA that encode proteins. These sequences are called genes. During mitosis and meiosis, the chromosomes (genes) are copied and then dispersed to daughter cells. For those of you who like definitions, a gene is a segment of DNA which encodes the instructions for making one polypeptide (protein) chain.

Chromosomes, subdivided as genes, contain the information that instructs an organism how to look and function. Genes contain the information that makes an organism what it is. Gene-containing chromosomes are passed from parent to offspring in a two-step process. First, meiosis generates the male and female gametes. Second, the male and female gametes fuse to form a diploid zygote. Then the zygote develops through mitosis into a mature multicellular organism. As such, genes are the physical carriers of the information from generation to generation. This passing of genes from generation to generation, along with the traits they carry, is called **heredity**. Therefore, genes are the units of heredity.

In this chapter, we will learn more about the gene and how it is passed from parent to offspring through meiosis. We will also learn how this influences the characteristics (traits) of the offspring and how to predict the ways genes are passed from one generation to the next.

12.2 GENES

As was discussed in Chapter 9, a gene is a specific segment of DNA contained on a chromosome which codes for the production of one protein. Remember "one gene one protein." Recall that in eukaryotic cells, the gene is "read," or transcribed, while inside the nucleus to a molecule of mRNA. The mRNA then enters the cytoplasm and attaches to a ribosome. Here, it is "made into a protein," or translated. The protein then acts to direct the cell to do something or make something or behave in a certain way. When a gene is active, it is said the gene is being **expressed**. Any time a gene is expressed, that means the protein the gene codes for is being made or that the trait the gene codes for is visible in some way. An expressed gene is "doing its thing," whatever its thing is.

For example, if the cell is a hair cell, the gene that codes for hair growth may be read, or **expressed**. When the gene for hair growth is expressed, the gene is transcribed into mRNA, then the mRNA is translated into protein. The protein then signals the cells to make more hair. This causes the hair to get longer. Or, the gene that codes for hair color may be "turned off." In this case, the gene is no longer expressed (meaning its protein is no longer made) and the hair cell will stop depositing pigment into the hair, causing the hair to turn gray.

Another example can be seen with injured bone. There is a protein that is made by bone cells when a bone is broken. When the bone is not broken, this protein is not made. Therefore, normally, the gene for this protein is not expressed. However, if a bone is broken, this gene "turns on" and is expressed. The bone cells around the break start to make this protein because the gene is being expressed. This protein then stimulates the bone cells to make new bone and heal the fracture.

In reality, though, gene expression is a much more complicated process than what is described above. It is so complicated, in fact, that we still do not understand exactly how it works, but the concept presented above is quite accurate.

12.3 THE GENOME

There is a huge amount of information that is coded into chromosomes and their genes. The entire sequence of DNA in an organism is referred to as its **genome**. Another way of saying this is that the genome is the total number of genes the DNA of an organism contains. The human genome has at least 30,000 genes. Genomes are so large, even in simple organisms, that not all of the information is ever expressed in any one cell. Each cell only expresses those genes specific for the cell type. For example, a liver cell does not express the same genes that a brain cell does. That trait is what establishes the basis for tissues and organ systems. If every cell expressed every gene that was contained in the chromosomes, there would be no order and life would cease to exist.

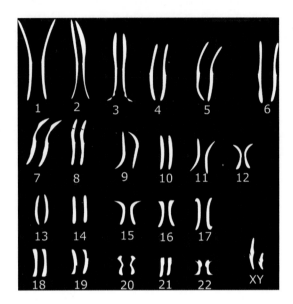

Figure 12.3.1

Human Genome
This is another look at a human karyotype to illustrate another genetic concept. The genome is the sum of all of the genes contained in an organism. All 30,000+ human genes are contained on the twenty-three pairs of human chromosomes. They carry the information which codes how tall a person will be, what color their eyes and hair are, how long they will live and so much more information regarding a person's traits that we cannot even list it all. Interestingly, only about 1% of the DNA of a human actually codes for a gene. Part of the rest of human genetic material codes for the production of mRNA, tRNA, and ribosomes. Therefore, whenever you see a karyotype, you are looking not only at "genes," but also at DNA which codes not only for proteins, but also for ribosomes, mRNA, and tRNA. The majority of DNA seen in a karyotype does not code for the production of any type of molecule, at least as far as we know.

Also, since genes are contained within chromosomes, and chromosomes are the carriers of information passed from one generation to the next, genes are the individual units of heredity. Heredity is the passage of genes from one generation to the next. Since genes code for traits, heredity can also be defined as the passage of traits from one generation to the next.

Recall that in diploid organisms, one set of chromosomes is inherited from the mother and one set from the father. Also, remember that meiosis is responsible for the dispersion of the chromosomes (genes). In sexually-reproducing species, a new organism is formed by the uniting of one set of chromosomes from the father and one from the mother. This is critical to remember when discussing the properties of heredity.

12.4 GENETICS

Genetics is the study of genes and heredity. **Geneticists** are scientists who study genetics. They evaluate many factors besides genes. Initially, the fact that genes and chromosomes were involved in inheritance was not even known. However, it has been noted for thousands of years that the traits, or characteristics, of the parents in some part influence the traits of the offspring. Therefore, the passage of traits from one generation to the next—called **inheritance**—was studied by scientists. **Characteristics** such as skin color, height, flower color, eye color, etc. are inheritable features. **Traits** are a variant of the character, such as brown or white skin, tall or short stature, yellow or purple flower, blue or brown eyes,.

Figure 12.4.1

Heredity and Traits
All of the organisms shown below were produced by other organisms which looked like they look. The polar bear was not the offspring of a bird of paradise mother and a ladybug father. The bird of paradise flower on the left is the offspring of bird of paradise parents. The ladybug in the middle was made by ladybug parents and the polar bear came from polar bears. This is the concept of "like begets like." Why is that? Because every organism receives its DNA from its parents, one set of chromosomes comes from the male parent and one from the female parent. Another way of stating this is that one set of chromosomes is inherited from the mother and one set of chromosomes is inherited from the father. The genes which make the organism are inherited from the parents. The ways in which an organism looks, acts, and functions are called characteristics, or traits. Traits are almost completely controlled by genes (there are some environmental conditions which can modify the ways genes and traits are expressed). The gene is the fundamental unit of heredity.

12.5 GREGOR MENDEL

Any discussion of genetics, genes, and chromosomes must begin with Gregor Mendel. He was a monk who lived in Austria from 1822-1884. He is considered the father of genetics because of the work he did studying the common pea, *Pisum sativum*. Mendel's work not only was revolutionary and creative, but also demonstrated concepts of excellent scientific process. His results were so completely not understood by the scientists of the time that they were largely ignored until 1900 when other researchers began to find similar results as Mendel had 40 years prior.

Figure 12.5.1

Characteristics and traits of the pea studied by Mendel

Characteristic	Trait
seed shape	round or wrinkled
seed color	yellow or green
flower color	purple or white
flower position	axial (side) or terminal (tip)
pod color	green or yellow
plant height	tall or short

Mendel observed the passage of the traits listed in Figure 12.5.1. He followed how offspring inherited these traits for many generations. He had observed that many different traits are displayed from one individual to another between organisms of the same species. Some pea plants were tall, just as some people were tall. Some pea plants had white flowers but it seemed that a larger percentage had purple flowers. Mendel devised experiments to see if he could identify why that was the case, and how the traits were passed from generation to generation.

The pea plants that Mendel first observed were in their natural state, and part of the nature of the pea plant is they self pollinate. That means that even though peas reproduce by sexual reproduction, they do so normally by the same plant pollinating itself, rather than another plant. So the plants that Mendel started with were "pure." Plants with purple flowers always produced offspring that had purple flowers. Plants that were tall always pollinated plants that were tall, and so on for all seven characteristics. He studied the traits of offspring of the pea plants that were allowed to reproduce naturally, and also of those plants he "**crossed**." Crossing is the process of a person transferring pollen from one flower to another rather than letting that happen naturally. This is also called **cross pollination**. By doing this, Mendel could control the traits of the plants that mated with one another. He meticulously recorded which plants mated with which and what the traits of the parents and offspring were through several generations.

12.6 MENDEL DID NOT KNOW IT, BUT HE DISCOVERED ALLELES

Mendel did not know of chromosomes and genes and DNA, but he surmised there were "factors" that controlled the traits of the plants. He thought these factors were passed from one generation to the next. We now know these "factors" are genes, and we will refer to them as genes even though Mendel did not know this concept or term in his time. At this point it is critical for you to remember what we have learned about genes and chromosomes; namely, that every sexually reproducing organism has two chromosomes that contain information for the same trait. One gene for a trait is inherited on the homologous chromosome from the male parent and the other gene for the same trait is inherited on the homologous chromosome from the female parent.

Through his research, Mendel also developed the theory of what we now call **alleles**. An allele is an alternate form of the same gene that codes for a trait. The gene that codes for flower color, for example, has two forms, or alleles. One allele codes for a white flower, the other codes for a purple flower. The gene which codes for plant height has two forms, or alleles. One allele for plant height codes for a tall plant trait, while the other allele codes for short height trait. The same is true for the other five characteristics that Mendel studied.

As we stated, Mendel started with parent plants that were pure, and these are called the **P generation**. For example, the plants of the P generation all had purple flowers. These plants with purple flowers were mated with plants which had only white flowers. Mendel had studied the plants for several generations prior to starting his experiments to be sure that the plants with purple flowers only produced plants with purple flowers when they were crossed and that plants with white flowers only produced other plants with white flowers when they were crossed. He did the same for the other traits he studied. This is how he ensured they were "pure."

The generation produced by crossing the P generation plants is referred to as the **F1 generation**, or first filial. The generation produced by crossing the F1 generation plants with one another is called the **F2 generation**, and so on. Mendel generally studied the mating results of the P, F1 and F2 generations. By selectively crossing plants with different traits, he was able to systematically follow the effects of mating plants with different traits with one another. He kept very meticulous records of the results.

12.7 RECESSIVE AND DOMINANT ALLELES

Through his experimentation, Mendel found that one trait always dominated the other trait. For example, when he crossed the plants with white flowers and those with purple flowers—the P generation—he found that all the offspring—the F1 generation—had purple flowers. Mendel knew that the purple trait always dominated the white trait, but today we know that the purple allele always "dominated" the white allele. He found the same findings for all of the traits he studied as summarized in Figure 12.7.1.

The trait that was dominated in the F1 generation is called a **recessive trait**. Recessive traits are caused by a **recessive allele** of the gene which codes for the trait. For example, the allele that codes for a white flower is recessive to the allele that codes for a purple flower. The trait that was dominant in the F1 generation is called a **dominant trait** and is caused by a **dominant allele**. The purple flower allele is dominant to the white flower allele. In other words, the presence of the dominant allele prevents the expression of the recessive allele altogether. In genetics, a dominant allele is indicated by a capital letter, and a recessive allele is indicated by a lower case letter.

Figure 12.7.1

Results of P Crosses

P Generation Trait	F1 Generation Trait	Dominant Trait
purple flower plants with white flower plants	all purple flowers	purple flower color
tall plants with short plants	all tall plants	tall plant height
yellow pea plants with green pea plants	all yellow peas	yellow pea color
round pea plants with wrinkled pea plants	all round pea plants	round pea shape
axial flower position with terminal flower position	all axial positioned flowers	axial positioned flowers
yellow pea pod plants with green pea pod plants	all yellow pea pods	yellow pea pod color
inflated pea pod plants with wrinkled pea pod plants	all inflated pea pod plants	inflated pea pod shape

12.8 THE GENOTYPE CONTROLS THE PHENOTYPE

The **genotype** is the genetic makeup of an individual. Another way of looking at this is that the genotype is the specific gene content of an individual. The **phenotype** is the expression of the genotype. The phenotype is what you can "see" as a result of the genotype; it is how the genotype is expressed. For example, the genotype of the purple flowers was that they contained the genes which code for purple flowers. The phenotype of the purple flowers was, of course, purple flowers. The genotype of white flowers is that they contain the alleles which code for the phenotype of white flowers.

By convention, geneticists give the alleles for flower color in Mendel's pea plants the symbols W and w. The W allele codes for purple flowers and the w allele codes for white flowers. Remember, a capital letter denotes a dominant allele and a lower case letter a recessive allele. Since the plants of the P generation were pure, and every sexually reproducing organisms has two genes for the same trait (one on each chromosome), every P generation pea plant in Mendel's experiment either had a genotype of WW or ww. We now know that the genotype of the P plants with the purple flowers was WW. Another way of stating that is that the P generation plants with purple flowers had two dominant purple alleles. The genotype of the plants with the white flowers was ww. Another way of stating that is the P generation white flower plants had two recessive white alleles. The genotype WW results in the phenotype of purple flowers. The genotype ww results in the phenotype of white flowers. Therefore, the phenotype of WW is purple, and the phenotype of ww is white. Realize that since W is dominant to w, plants with the genotype Ww will have the phenotype of purple flowers. Why? Because the purple allele is dominant to the white allele and so suppresses the expression of the white allele.

Figure 12.8.1

Alleles and Flower Color

Mendel found that one trait always dominated the other during his study of the pea plants. For example, he found that the purple allele for flower color always dominated the white allele. We now know that the purple allele is dominant, and the white allele is recessive. The effects of mixing the alleles with one another are shown here. The plants which have two purple alleles produce purple flowers as do the plants with one purple and one white. Since the white is recessive, the presence of the purple allele causes the white not to be expressed and all of the flowers are purple. The genotype of the purple flower P generation plants was WW. The genotype of the white flower P generation plants was ww. The only way that a pea flower can be white in color is if there are two recessive white alleles. In fact, the only way that any recessive trait can be expressed is if the organism contains two recessive alleles.

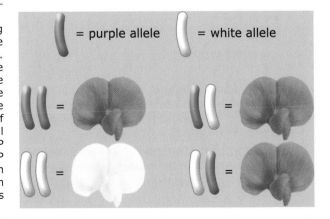

12.9 HOMOZYGOUS AND HETEROZYGOUS CONDITIONS

In genetics, when an organism has two copies of the same two alleles, it is said to be **homozygous**. If the two alleles are dominant, that is a **homozygous dominant** condition. If the two alleles are recessive, that is a **homozygous recessive** condition. When the organism has two different alleles, the organism is considered to be **heterozygous**. In applying this concept to the above situation for flower color, the P generation purple flower plants are homozygous dominant, *WW*. The white flower plants are homozygous recessive, *ww*.

At this point, realize that an organism which is homozygous dominant or heterozygous will express the dominant trait. The only way in which an organism can express a recessive trait is if its genotype is homozygous recessive.

Figure 12.9.1

Alleles, Genotypes, and Phenotypes

The simplest relationship that genes have to one another is dominant and recessive. One of the traits Mendel studied was the color of the peas the plants produced. Pea plants made peas with one of two phenotypes, or colors, of the pea seed —green or yellow. Mendel found that the yellow trait was always dominant to the green trait. He knew this because any time he crossed a plant with yellow peas with one that had green peas, the offspring always made yellow peas. We know now that there are two alleles for pea color—yellow and green. Yellow is dominant and is termed *Y*. Green is recessive and is termed *y*. A pea which has two dominant yellow alleles produces yellow peas. They are said to be homozygous dominant because they contain two of the dominant alleles. The genotype of homozygous dominant plants for pea color is *YY*. They have two dominant *Y* alleles. Peas can also be yellow in color if they contain one yellow allele and one green allele. That is because the yellow dominates the green and so the green trait is not expressed. If an organism contains a dominant allele and a recessive allele, it will take on the trait of the dominant allele. An organism which contains two different alleles for the same trait is called heterozygous. Peas can be yellow if they are homozygous dominant or heterozygous. Peas which are heterozygous for pea color are termed *Yy*. Another way of stating this is that the genotype for yellow peas can either be *YY* or *Yy*. Also, the phenotype of the peas which have the genotype of *YY* or *Yy* is yellow peas. This is the same concept as flower color. Homozygous dominant peas for flower color are said to be *WW*. They will always be purple since purple is the dominant allele. Likewise, plants which are heterozygous for flower color are said to be *Ww*. They will also have purple flowers since the purple allele dominates the white allele. The only way a pea plant can produce green-colored peas is if it is homozygous recessive for pea color. The allele which codes for a green pea is recessive. Therefore, a plant which is homozygous recessive for pea color has two alleles which code for a green pea and so will produce green peas. Homozygous recessive pea plants for pea color are termed *yy*. The same is true for flower color. The only way that a pea plant can make white flowers is if it contains two of the recessive white alleles, or is homozygous recessive for flower color. They are termed *ww*.

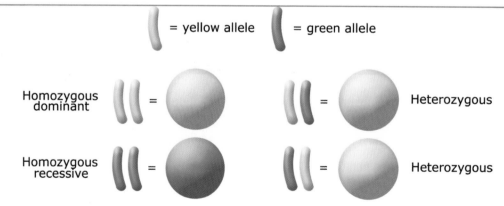

12.10 GENE SEGREGATION

Gene segregation is the process of two alleles that code for the same trait separating from one another during meiosis. Remember when we discussed meiosis, the critical event was when the homologous pairs (tetrads) lined up across from one another before metaphase I. After metaphase I, the genes inherited from the male parent are separated into a different cell from the genes that were inherited from the female parent that code for the same traits. This ensures that no gamete receives two alleles for the same trait. For example, when the *WW* plants undergo meiosis, each gamete receives a *W* gene. When each *ww* plant undergoes meiosis, each gamete receives a *w* gene. The fact that the traits separated form one another during gamete formation was understood by Mendel. We now call that process gene segregation.

Gene segregation simply means that one of the parental gametes receives one allele for a particular trait, while the other gamete receives the other allele. When the homozygous dominant plants, *WW,* undergo meiosis, one gamete receives a *W* allele and the other gamete receives a *W* allele. When the *ww* plant undergoes meiosis, each gamete receives a *w* allele. This is gene segregation. When Mendel crossed the P plants, all of the purple plants had produced a *W* gamete, and all of the white flower plants had produced a *w* allele. When these two gametes joined their genetic material, the genotype of the offspring was *Ww*. All of the F1 pea plants were heterozygous, *Ww*. Since the purple allele dominates the white allele, all of the flowers of the F1 generation were purple.

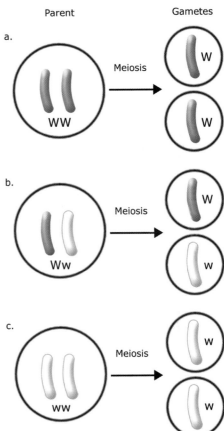

Parent   Gametes

Figure 12.10.1

Gene Segregation

Gene segregation is simply how the genes separate from one another during the formation of gametes. During meiosis the genes coding for the same trait inherited from the male parent and those from the female parent are separated. In the case of flower color, that means that one gamete receives one allele for flower color and the other receives the other allele. In figure (a), the parent cell is homozygous dominant for flower color, or *WW*. The genotype is *WW* and its phenotype is purple flowers. During meiosis, a gamete receives one of two of the alleles. Since the parent is homozygous dominant, *WW*, each gamete receives a *W* allele. In figure (b), the parent plant is heterozygous. Its genotype is *Ww* and its phenotype is purple flower color. During meiosis, each gamete receives one of the alleles. That means that one gamete receives a *W* allele and the other gamete receives a *w* allele. Figure (c) represents gene segregation in the case of a homozygous recessive plant for flower color. The genotype is *ww*, and the phenotype is white flowers. During gene segregation, each gamete receives one *w* allele. For Mendel's experiments, the P generation purple flowers had the genotype *WW* and the white flowers *ww*. All of the F1 generation had the genotype of *Ww*. Gene segregation is important to understand to fully comprehend the principles of genetics.

12.11 GENE SEGREGATION AND THE F2 GENERATION

During his experiments, Mendel found something that he did not expect to find. When he allowed the F1 plants to pollinate normally, the results were plants with purple flowers *and* plants with white flowers. In fact, he found that the ratio of plants with purple flowers to white flowers was almost 3 to 1. He found similar ratios for the other characteristics.

Why did the recessive trait come back in the F2 plants after completely disappearing in the F1 plants? The answer lies in meiosis and gene segregation. We know that all of the F1 plants' genotypes were *Ww*. They were heterozygous for flower color. During meiosis, all of the F1 plants formed gametes which were *W* and *w*. This is shown graphically in Figure 12.10.1b.

When the F1 plants were mated, there were one of three genotypes which resulted in the F2 generation. The three possible genotypes are *WW, Ww* and *ww*. It can be confusing to imagine all this at once. Fortunately, a British scientist named Reginald Punnett figured out an easy way to keep track of genotypes and phenotypes from generation to generation, as we are about to see.

12.12 PUNNETT SQUARES

A **Punnett square**, named after the man who invented it in the early 1900's—Dr. Reginald Punnett—is often used in genetics to visualize better how genotypes and phenotypes are passed from parent to offspring. It can also be used to predict genotypes and phenotypes of offspring when the same information is known about the parents. In the square, the genotypes of the gametes from one parent are written along the top, and of the other parent along the left side. The genotypes resulting from the joining of the gametes are written in the box as indicated.

Once Mendel came up with his theory of how traits segregated during gamete formation (now called gene segregation), he tested it. First, he predicted the results of the cross of the F1 generation, then he performed the cross. Since all of the plants from the F1 generation were *Ww*, according to the gene segregation theory, one gamete received a *W* allele and the other a *w* allele. Therefore, the resultant genotypes of the F2 generation are *WW*, *Ww*, *Ww*, and *ww*. That means the phenotype of three of the flowered plants is purple, and the phenotype for one of the flowered plants is white, or a ratio of three purple to one white. Mendel had predicted this result. This is gene segregation at work and is the basis of heredity and genetics.

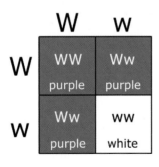

Figure 12.12.1

Punnett Square for the P Cross and Resulting F1 Generation for Flower Color
The F1 generation is the product of mating the P generation. Recall Mendel made sure the P generation plants were "pure." That means they were all either homozygous dominant (*WW*) or recessive (*ww*). Look at Figure 12.10.1a for the gene segregation of the homozygous dominant parent and Figure 12.10.1c for the gene segregation of the homozygous recessive parent. The Punnet square lists the possible gamete genotype for one parent along the top and the genotype of the other parent's gametes along the left side. We have arbitrarily placed the gamete for the homozygous dominant parent along the top and for the homozygous recessive parent on the left side. You could do it the other way, though, and still get exactly the same results. According to the gene segregation theory, the possible gamete phenotypes of *WW* are *W* and *W*. The possible gamete phenotypes of *ww* are *w* and *w*. These expected gamete phenotypes are filled in the spaces as indicated. In this example, all offspring of the P generation will be heterozygous for flower color, or *Ww*. They will all have purple flowers.

Figure 12.12.2

Punnett Square for the F2 Generation of Flower Color
The F2 generation is the product of mating between the F1 generation plants. All of the F1 generation plants had the heterozygous genotype for flower color, or were *Ww*. The gene segregation of heterozygous parents for flower color is shown in Figure 12.10.1b. According to gene segregation theory, the possible gamete genotypes of the F1 generation are *W* and *w* for both F1 parents. The genotypes of each parent's gametes are written as indicated. The offspring have the indicated genotypes and phenotypes. Notice that the ratio of plants with purple flowers to plants with white flowers is 3 to 1. This also explains why the recessive trait of white flowers returns in the F2 generation.

12.13 INDEPENDENT GENE ASSORTMENT

Mendel also discovered another principle of genetics, now called **independent assortment.** He realized that when he studied the hereditary patterns of two or more traits at the same time, the traits of the offspring seemed to be inherited independent of one another. For example, he noted that if he were studying seed shape and seed color at the same time, sometimes F1 plants had round yellow seeds, yellow wrinkled seeds, round green seeds, or wrinkled green seeds. He reasoned that during gamete formation, the traits (genes) separated independent of one another and are not connected. This theory has also been proven true.

The dominant trait for seed shape is round, or *R*, and the recessive trait is wrinkled, *r*. The dominant trait for seed color is yellow, *Y*, and recessive is green, *y*. Mendel took P generation plants with seeds that were all round and yellow, or homozygous dominant *RRYY*, and crossed them with plants that were all wrinkled and green, or homozygous recessive *rryy*. Based on the principle of gene segregation, the possible gamete phenotypes are only *RY* or *ry*. He predicted the F1 generation would all have round and yellow seeds. They did and we now know the genotypes of the F1 generation were all *RrYy*.

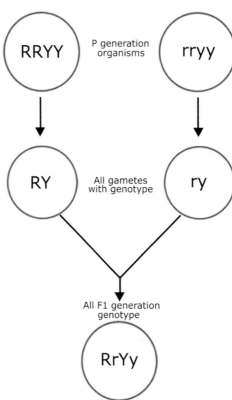

Figure 12.13.1

Gamete Formation of P Generation With Two Traits and Resulting F1 Generation Genotype

Gamete formation for the P generation of the homozygous dominant and homozygous recessive parent plants for two pea plant characteristics—pea color and pea shape. The pea color trait of yellow—*Y*—is dominant to that of green—*y*. The pea shape trait of round—*R*—is dominant to that of wrinkled—*r*. The parent plant of *RRYY* is a yellow round pea; *rryy* is a wrinkled green pea. Since the parents contain the same allele for each of the two traits, each one can produce gametes only as shown. When the plants were crossed by Mendel, all of the offspring had the genotype of *RrYy* and a phenotype of yellow, round peas.

Figure 12.13.2

Punnett Square for the Cross of the P Generation with Two Homozygous Dominant Traits

Sometimes the Punnett square helps to keep the gamete formation straight. The P generation parent plants are either homozygous dominant, *RRYY*, or homozygous recessive, *rryy*, for their genotypes. Homozygous dominant P plants have the phenotype of round yellow peas. Homozygous recessive P plants have the phenotype of wrinkled green peas. See Figure 12.13.1 for gamete formation of the parent organisms. The homozygous dominant parent's gamete genotypes are written at the top, and the recessive parent's are on the left. All of the F1 offspring are heterozygous and have the same genotype, *RrYy*. They will have round yellow peas. Even though we are working with two genes, the result of the P cross is the same as it was for the flower color. All of the F1 offspring are heterozygous and display the dominant allele's traits.

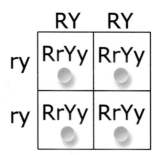

Mendel then performed the F1 cross, and predicted the resulting phenotypes of the plants would be in the ratio of 9 plants with seeds round and yellow, 3 plants round and green, 3 plants wrinkled and yellow, and 1 plant wrinkled and green. He was again correct. Since the F1 generation plants are all heterozygous *RrYy*, there are four possible genotypes for the gametes, *RY, Ry, rY,* and *ry*. Figures 12.13.3, 12.13.4, and 12.13.5 all pertain to the F1 cross.

Gametes

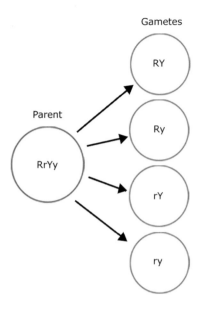

Figure 12.13.3

Independent Assortment of the F1 Generation Heterozygous for Two Traits

Independent assortment is the property of alleles of one gene to segregate independently of alleles for other genes. For example, the round allele does not always separate with the green allele. The principle of independent assortment is seen clearly when performing the F1 cross. This figure shows the possible gametes that are formed when the F1 plants from the cross of *RRYY* and *rryy* form gametes. All F1 plants have the genotype of *RrYy*. Independent assortment states that: *R* will segregate independently of *Y* and *y*; *r* will segregate independently of *Y* and *y*; *Y* will segregate independently of *R* and *r*; and *y* will segregate independently of *R* and *r*. As shown, the allele *R* does not always segregate with *Y*, nor does it always segregate with *y*. Rather, sometimes it segregates, or separates, with *Y* and other times it segregates with *y*. Likewise, sometimes *y* is segregated with *R* and sometimes with *r*. However, you will note that alleles of the same gene always separate from one another. That is because of meiosis. Normally, alleles for the same gene are separated from one another during gamete formation, but segregate independently of alleles for other genes.

Figure 12.13.4

Punnett Square for the F1 Cross of *RrYy*

Below is the Punnett square for the expected offspring genotypes and phenotypes of the F1 cross. The F1 parents have the genotype *RrYy*, and their gamete formation is shown in Figure 12.13.3. Please use Figure 12.13.3 and this one for complete understanding; they are meant to compliment one another.

	RY	Ry	rY	ry
RY	RRYY	RRYy	RrYY	RrYy
Ry	RRYy	RRyy	RrYy	Rryy
rY	RrYY	RrYy	rrYY	rrYy
ry	RrYy	Rryy	rrYy	rryy

Figure 12.13.5

Gamete Formation for the F1 Generation, Genotype *RrYy*

During gamete formation, each of the F1 parents can produce four possible gametes, as shown. This is a little more detailed example of what happens when two F1 plants with the genotypes of *RrYy* are crossed. As can be seen, there are four different types of peas that their offspring, the F2 generation, will have: the dominant form, round and yellow; round and green; wrinkled and yellow; and the recessive form, wrinkled and green. The numbers indicate that: 9 of the 16 offspring will be round and yellow; 3 of 16 offspring will be round and green or wrinkled and yellow; and 1 of 16 offspring will be wrinkled and green.

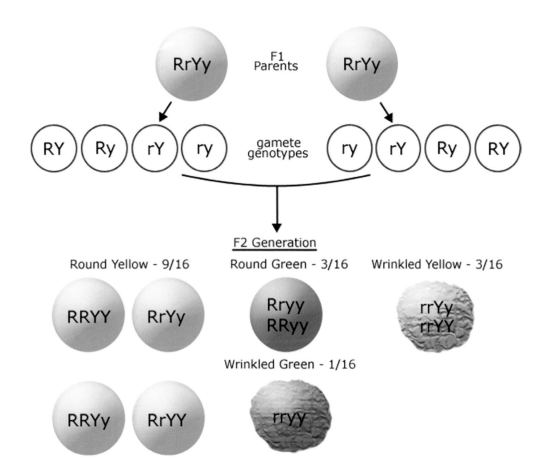

Through looking more closely at the gene and alleles, we have explored how traits are passed from one generation to the next using **Mendelian principles**. Mendelian principles are the basic rules—such as gene segregation and independent assortment—that govern the passage of alleles (traits) from generation to generation. These principles are as true today as they were 150 years ago. However, our understanding of the process of genes passing from one generation to the next, called heredity, has increased greatly over the past one hundred years.

In the next chapter, we will look more deeply into inheritance patterns using the principles we have established in this chapter. One of the key ideas to understand about genetics is independent assortment. Since genes and chromosomes assort independently and are distributed to gametes independent of one another, which means the process of meiosis is completely random from a mathematical standpoint. Therefore, the principles of statistics can be applied to genetics. We will learn much more about this in the next couple of chapters, but it is important to understand that the way chromosomes and genes are distributed during meiosis is random.

12.14 PEOPLE OF SCIENCE

Hugo de Vries (1848-1935) was a Dutch researcher who spent most of his career at the University of Amsterdam. While he was there, he found similar results in his plant experiments to Mendel's. While searching the available literature, he also rediscovered the work of Mendel that had been published almost 40 years earlier and, with John Bateson, brought this knowledge to the forefront. Through his work, Dr. de Vries developed the theory of gene mutation, which we will discuss in upcoming chapters. The theory of gene mutation has been embraced by evolutionists who use it to explain how all life on earth came from one single-cell organism.

12.15 KEY CHAPTER POINTS

- Genes are the smallest unit of heredity. They are passed from parent to offspring through sexual or asexual reproduction.

- When a gene is expressed it means that the gene is being transcribed into mRNA, and the mRNA is being translated into the gene's protein. Basically, it means that whatever trait the gene codes for will be active or visible.

- The entire amount of DNA in any given organism is referred to as the genome.

- Geneticists study the passage of genes from parent to offspring and learn to predict the patterns of the traits being passed. The passage of genes (traits) from parent to offspring is called heredity; therefore, geneticists study hereditary patterns.

- Gregor Mendel laid the foundations of modern genetics by studying the passage of traits in pea plants.

- Alleles are forms of the same gene that code for a slightly different trait.

- The simplest relationship genes can have with one another is dominant/recessive, which is the relationship Mendel was studying.

- Genotype is the genetic makeup of an individual; phenotype is the way the genotype is expressed. Another way of stating this is the genotype are the genes and the phenotype is the trait the genotype creates.

- Gene segregation splits up alleles so that each gamete receives one allele for each gene.

- Punnett squares are commonly used in genetics to follow and predict hereditary patterns.

12.16 DEFINITIONS

alleles
    An alternate form of the same gene that codes for a slightly different trait than another allele.

characteristics
    Inheritable features such as skin color, height, flower color, etc.

cross pollination
    Taking pollen from one flower and pollinating another plant with it.

dominant allele
    A form of a gene whose trait is always expressed.

dominant trait
    The trait coded for by a dominant allele. Dominant traits are always expressed.

expressed
    Refers to the condition where the trait for which a gene code is able to be seen, or is being exhibited.

F1 generation
    The resulting generation from the cross of the P generation

F2 generation
The resulting generation form the cross of the F1 generation.

gene segregation
The fact that when gametes are formed, the two alleles (or genes) that code for the same trait separate from one another.

geneticists
Scientists who study genetics.

genetics
The study of genes and heredity.

genome
The entire sequence or content of DNA in an organism.

genotype
The genetic makeup of an organism. The genotype is the actual nucleotide sequence (or gene) which codes for a particular trait.

heredity
The passing of genes, and the traits they carry, from generation to generation.

heterozygous
The condition where an organism has two different alleles for the same trait.

homozygous
The condition where an organism has the same two alleles for a trait.

homozygous dominant
When both alleles that an organism has for a given trait are dominant.

homozygous recessive
When both alleles an organism has for a given trait are recessive. The only way a recessive condition can be expressed is if an organism is homozygous recessive.

independent assortment
The genetic property that genes and chromosomes assort, or are distributed, independent of one another during meiosis. This is a totally random process which allows the principles of statistics to be applied to genetics.

Mendelian principles
Principles of genetics first studied by Gregor Mendel; namely the property of independent assortment and dominant/recessive relationships.

P Generation
The starting generation when looking at heredity.

phenotype
The expression of the genotype. The phenotype is what you can "see" in the organism.

Punnett square
A tool used in genetics to understand and predict genotypes and phenotypes passed from parent to offspring.

recessive allele
An allele which is not expressed unless an organism has two of them.

recessive trait
The trait coded for by a recessive allele. Recessive traits are never expressed unless an organism has two recessive alleles for the same condition.

STUDY QUESTIONS

1. What is a gene? Why is it important?

2. What does it mean to say a gene is "expressed"?

3. If a gene codes for blue eyes, what does it mean to say this gene is being expressed?

4. _____ is the term used to mean the total number or total amount of genes an organism contains.

5. How are genes and heredity related?

6. True or False? Humans inherit one set of chromosomes from their mother and one set from their father.

7. How are traits and characteristics not quite the same in genetics? You can use an example if that helps.

8. What is a trait? How is it related to a gene?

9. Why is Gregor Mendel an important figure in genetics?

10. True or False? An allele is an alternate form of a gene.

11. In a diploid organism, how can a recessive allele be expressed?

12. True or False? If a person has a dominant allele and a recessive allele, the recessive allele will be expressed.

13. What is a genotype? How does it relate to the phenotype?

14. What is a P generation? An F1 generation? An F2 generation?

15. There are two alleles for nail color in brown bears—*N* and *n*. *N* codes for a brown nail and *n* codes for a black nail. A bear is homozygous recessive for nail color. How is this written genetically? What color would the bear's nails be?

16. The bear in question #15 mates with a bear who is homozygous dominant for nail color. Write the Punnett square for the gametes and the genotypes and phenotypes of the potential offspring of these two bears.

17. A bear from the F1 generation of the bears mentioned in question #16 mates with another bear that has the exact same genotype and phenotype for nail color. Write the Punnett square for the gametes and the genotypes and phenotypes of the potential offspring of these two bears.

18. A plant species has two traits for leaf shape—round and oval. Round is dominant to oval. Assign a letter to indicate the allele for the round and oval trait.

19. If you crossed the plants that are homozygous dominant for leaf shape with the plants that are homozygous recessive for leaf shape, what leaf shape would you expect the offspring to have? Use a Punnett square if that is helpful.

20. What does independent gene assortment mean?

21. List at least two processes we discussed in this chapter that are considered Mendelian principles.

Inheritance Patterns

13

13.0 CHAPTER PREVIEW

In this chapter we will:

- Discuss the importance that probability plays in the study of genetics.

- Investigate the inheritance patterns of:
  - incomplete dominance
  - multiple alleles
  - co-dominance
  - continuous variation
  - epistasis

- Evaluate the impact the environment can have on the phenotype.

13.1 OVERVIEW

In Chapter 12 we reviewed principles of genetics that were first established by Gregor Mendel 150 years ago, but which are still true today. However, we have learned more and more about chromosomes and the ways in which genes interact with one another to affect traits. We have learned that the simple dominant-recessive relationship that Mendel's peas displayed is often not the case in most traits. There are often many genes which interact to influence traits. Also, we have learned how to predict genotypes and phenotypes of offspring based on those of the parents. In technical terms, we have learned that there are complex ways in which the genotype affects the phenotype. There are ways in which genes interact with one another that are very complex and still not well understood.

Figure 13.1.1

Complex Nature of How Genotype Affects Phenotype
All of the people shown below have genotypes that specify they are to be human beings. Their genes contain the information that causes them to develop into humans instead of bumble bees or cabbages. But why does one have light skin and straight hair, the two in the middle have darker skin and the other have dark skin and curly hair? Traits such as skin color and hair color in humans are controlled by many genes, and we still do not understand why a person's skin or hair is exactly the color that it is. We all have the same general genetic material that causes us to develop into human beings. However, slight variances in the genes cause people of Asian descent to develop epicanthal folds (little folds of skin above the eyes) that people of African or European descent do not have. We do know that all of a person's traits—and any organism's, for that matter—are passed from parent to child. Traits of sexually reproducing organisms are inherited—or passed on—from parent to offspring. Therefore, the traits of the parents in some way affect the traits of their offspring. Sometimes the way in which the parent's traits affect the traits of their offspring is rather easy to understand, as in the case of Mendel's peas. Other times, the way in which the parent's traits are inherited and expressed in the offspring is more difficult to comprehend, such as when two tall parents have one or more short children. Even more complex is the relationship inheritance has with genetic diseases—diseases caused by abnormal alleles passed from parents to child.

The most important thing we know is how little we know about the ways in which genes influence traits, or how the genotype truly affects the phenotype. This is because the influence on the phenotype by the genotype is usually not as simple as two alleles affecting flower color in a dominant-recessive relationship. In fact, most of the relationships between genotype and phenotype are much more complicated than one trait being recessive to another. The ways in which traits are passed from parent to offspring—called **inheritance** or **inheritance patterns**—are even more complicated. Based on the work started by Mendel and advanced over the past one hundred years, geneticists have developed ways to track inheritance of normal traits and diseases. This chapter will be the foundation of understanding for human genetics and how diseases caused by abnormal genes can be understood and even predicted to some degree.

13.2 PROBABILITY

Probability is the measure of how likely something is to happen. Probability principles are applied to events which occur randomly. As we learned at the end of the last chapter, passage of genes from parent to their gametes occurs in a random fashion. Therefore, probability and the mathematical principles associated with statistics can be applied to genetics. This is an important concept because genetics deals with the likelihood of organisms inheriting genes for certain traits from their parents. Understanding probability is the first step in understanding how to predict inheritance patterns. Why? Because, from a purely scientific standpoint, the patterns of inheritance are completely random events, as we will see.

Figure 13.2.1

Genetics and Probabilities
Figuring probabilities in genetics is like estimating probabilities in any other endeavor. In assessing probabilities, the outcome you are looking for is divided by the total number of possible outcomes. In the case of flipping a quarter, there are two possible outcomes—heads or tails. On any given flip of the quarter, the probability of heads "winning" is 50%, or one-in-two, or 1/2. That means that for any given flip of the coin there is a 50% chance of getting heads and a 50% chance of getting tails. The probability of getting a head or a tail on any given flip, is 1/2. Probabilities are used in genetics to estimate the likelihood of passing a genetic disease from parent to offspring for persons who either have or are carriers of a genetic disease.

The easiest way to understand probability is with the example of tossing a coin. In assessing probabilities, a question is asked about the likelihood of a particular event happening. If a quarter is tossed in the air, what is the probability of getting heads? What is the probability of getting tails? In order to assess that, one needs to know all of the possible outcomes of tossing a coin in the air. In this example, the number of possible outcomes is two. When a coin is tossed in the air, you will either get heads or a tails. That means there is a one-in-two chance, or 50%, of getting heads and a one-in-two chance, or 50%, of getting tails each time a coin is tossed. Probability simply addresses the likelihood of one outcome happening as compared to the number of total possible outcomes.

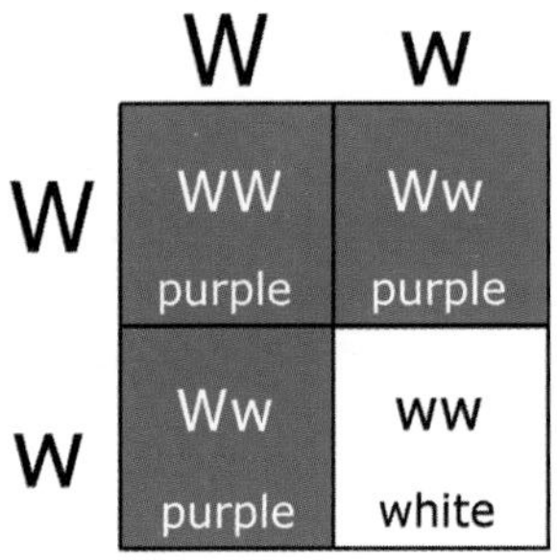

Figure 13.2.2

Probability and Mendel's Peas

On the left is the Punnett square for the heterozygous (F1) cross of Mendel's peas. As you can see, there are three possible genotype outcomes for this cross—*WW*, *Ww* and *ww* (note that *Ww* occurs twice). Since *W* is dominant to *w*, we know the phenotypes of *WW* and *Ww* will be purple flowers. How would we predict the probability of the flower colors of the cross between organisms with the *Ww* and *Ww* genotypes? We know there are four genotypes possible, *WW*, *Ww*, *Ww*, and *ww*. Three of those genotypes result in purple flowers and one of those genotypes result in white flowers. We would predict a 3:1 ratio, or that 75% of the organisms would have purple flowers and 25% would have white flowers. That means that there is a 75% probability that a pea plant offspring of *Ww* parents will inherit the genotype, which will give it purple flowers. There is only a 25% chance, though, that the offspring will inherit the genes for white flowers. That prediction is close to the actual results which Mendel obtained when he performed the crosses. In nature, rarely are the exact prediction probabilities actually observed. For example, with Mendel's peas, he found 3.15 purple flowers for every 1 white flower. This is close to the predicted probability of 3:1 ratio. The numbers are usually close, but not exactly what is predicted. This is due to the randomness of nature. Of course, Mendel did not know all of this. It is only the genetic research of the past seventy-five years which has allowed us to understand Mendel's results. Further, we have learned how to predict probabilities through the research.

Figure 13.2.3

Probabilities and Inheritance
This is also from the last chapter. Probabilities are simply predictions of what is likely to occur based on what is known. The Punnett square to the right indicates that there are sixteen different possible genotypes from the mating of parents with the genotypes of *RrYy*. That tells us there are sixteen different possible genotype outcomes of the mating of *RrYy* parents. If you were asked the probability of the offspring being of the genotype *RRYY*, you would construct a Punnett square and see that only 1 of 16 offspring have that phenotype. Therefore, the probability is 1 in 16, or 6.2%, that the offspring will be *RRYY*. The probability of the genotype *RRyy* is also 1 in 16. The probability of the genotype *RRYy* is 2 in 16, or 12.5%.

However, if you are asked about phenotype, you need to know the dominant recessive relationship. At right is a summation of the possible phenotypes for the mating of two *RrYy* parents. As you can see, there are several different genotypes that result in a round and yellow pea phenotype. If you were asked what the probability was of an offspring being of the phenotype of a yellow and round pea, you see there are 9 possible genotypes which would result in a round and yellow pea. That means there is a 9 in 16, or 56%, chance that an offspring of *RrYy* parents will have round and yellow peas. You are able to predict this before hand if you know the genotypes and phenotypes of the parent organisms. On the other hand, there is only one genotype which will result in a wrinkled and green pea. This is because the wrinkled trait and the green trait are both recessive traits. That means that a pea plant must have inherited recessive alleles from both parents for both traits. Probabilities in genetics almost always deal with the likelihood that certain genes will be inherited from one or both parents and passed on to their offspring.

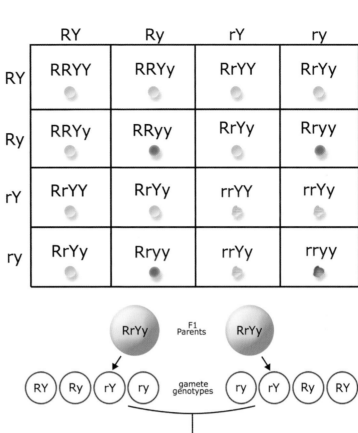

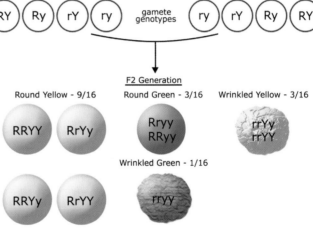

13.3 PROBABILITY AND INHERITANCE

"What does this have to do with inheritance?" some of you may be wondering. From the example and figures, you can see that the genotype of the offspring depends directly on the genotype of their parents. Since the phenotype is an expression of the genotype, the phenotype is also passed from parent to offspring. All offspring receive, or inherit, their chromosomes from their parents. One half of their chromosomes come from their mother and one half from their father. Carried on the chromosomes are the genes for every trait which makes up the organism. That is why the gene is called the hereditary unit. Everything about an organism is directed by its genes. By knowing the genotype and corresponding phenotype, we can fairly accurately predict which traits and genes the offspring can possibly inherit from their parents.

Probability comes into play directly when looking at gene segregation. Gene segregation occurs randomly. That means that we can apply the principles of probability to gene segregation. When genes segregate, one allele goes into one gamete, and the other allele goes into the other gamete. That is why we are able to make Punnett squares. According to probability, since gene segregation occurs randomly, each gamete has a 50% chance of receiving a given allele. Also, each gamete has a 50% chance of fusing with the other parent's gamete. The probability of an organism inheriting genes from the parents is based purely on these mathematical relationships, which occur at random. We can apply these to study and predict inheritance.

Figure 13.3.1

Figuring Successive Probabilities

If you wanted to know what the likelihood of tossing two heads in a row, you would multiply the probabilities of each independent event happening, as shown below. If you wanted to know the probability of tossing three successive heads, you do the same thing. Many times, genetics deals with probability. Geneticists usually work with families who have histories of diseases or unusual traits which are transmitted in their genes and so inherited from one generation to the next. If a child is born with one of these traits or diseases, the parents may seek counseling from a geneticist to try to figure out what the likelihood is that their next child will have a particular disease.

Further, genetics also deals with probabilities of successive events happening. For example, parents who have a child who was born with a disease may wish to know the probability of their next child having the same disease. This is similar to asking "what are my chances of tossing two successive heads?" To determine that, the probability of the first event, tossing a heads, is multiplied by the probability of the second event, tossing a heads. Each individual event has a 1/2 chance of happening. However, *the probability of getting two heads in a row is the product of the individual events occurring*. This results in multiplying 1/2 times 1/2, or 1/2 x 1/2 = 1/4, or a probability of 1/4. This means there is a 1 in 4 (25%) chance of tossing heads twice in a row. The probability of tossing heads three times in a row is 1/2 x 1/2 x 1/2 = 1/8. This means there is a 1 in 8 (12.5%) chance of tossing three successive heads.

A common application of these principles is seen in the following example. The parents of a child born with a genetic disease may be wondering what their chances are of having another child with the same disease. A genetic disease is a disease caused by abnormal genes. Most genetic diseases are cause by recessive alleles. The nature of our current example disease is that it is also caused by a recessive allele. Therefore, in order to have the disease, the child would need to inherit one recessive allele from the mother and one from the father. (Remember, the only way for a recessive trait to be expressed is for the organism to be homozygous recessive). When the parents form gametes, there is a 50-50 chance that one gamete receives the normal allele or the abnormal, recessive allele. That is true for both parents. The likelihood that the child will inherit a recessive allele from each of his parents is 1/2 x 1/2 = 1/4, or a 25% chance.

Figure 13.3.2

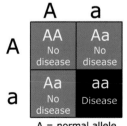

A = normal allele
a = disease allele

Figuring probabilities for the inheritance of a genetic disease.

Parents of children born with a disease caused by abnormal genes are always very interested to know what the chance is that their next child may have the disease. The chance can be estimated using simple probability principles. The disease is caused by a recessive allele – a. The normal allele is A. Since this is a recessive disease, and their first child has the disease, we know that both parents have the recessive allele. The geneticist can use a simple Punnett square to estimate that the risk of their next child having the disease is 1 in 4, or 25%. Or, you can look at the Punnett square and see there are four possible outcomes—three of which do not result in the disease and one that does. You divide the number of outcomes you are looking for—in this case 1—by the total number of out come—four—and get the same answer—1/4. However, the chance that the couple will have two consecutive children born with the disease is 1/4 x 1/4 = 1/16, or a 6.3% chance.

This is like the color results when the F1 generation flowers were crossed with one another. In order for the white flowers to re-appear in the F2 generation, they needed to inherit one recessive allele from one F1 parent and one recessive allele for flower color from the other F1 parent. In order for a child to have a disease, he would need to have both recessive alleles. The genetic counselor would tell them that the chance of their next child having the disease is 1 in 4, or 25%. However, the chance of having two children with the same disease in a row is 1/4 x 1/4, or 1/16, or a 6.3% chance. The probabilities all depend from what standpoint you are viewing the problem.

Thus far, we have been discussing the traits controlled by one gene with only two alleles that are transmitted in a simple dominant/recessive nature. However, there are many relationships which alleles can exhibit in nature that are not of a dominant/recessive nature. These are:
- incomplete dominance
- codominance
- sex-linked
- multiple genes causing continuous variation
- modifier genes

These types of relationships between genes make genetics a challenging field because it is hard to accurately predict what the phenotype will be based on the genotype.

13.4 INHERITANCE PATTERNS: INCOMPLETE DOMINANCE

Incomplete dominance occurs when there are no forms of the gene that are dominant. The resulting trait is a blend of the two traits. This occurs often in nature, but flower colors provide the classic example. White and red carnations, when crossbred, will give pink flowers. Red flowers are homozygous, *RR*, as are white flowers, *WW*. These plants are crossed, and the F1 heterozygous crosses, *RW*, are pink. These are called **monohybrid** crosses. A monohybrid cross is formed by crossing organisms that differ in only one allele that has two different forms. The experiments Mendel performed in which he looked at only one trait, such as flower color, were also examples of monohybrid crosses.

Figure 13.4.1

Carnations and Incomplete Dominance
Carnations offer the classic example of incomplete dominance. The red and white colors are controlled by separate genes. When a carnation plant is homozygous for the red allele, the flower is red. If the plant is homozygous for the white allele, then the flower is white. However, if the plant is heterozygous, *RW*, they do not show a dominant-recessive relationship like the flower colors did for Mendel's pea experiments. Instead, the red and white colors are "blended" (i.e. both colors are expressed in the same flower), and the resulting flower is pink.

a.　　　　　b.　　　　　c.

These heterozygous pink carnations are then crossed producing an F2 generation. When the heterozygous *RW* plants undergo meiosis, one gamete receives a *R* allele and the other gamete receives a *W* allele. The results of their offspring are as shown in Figure 13.4.2.

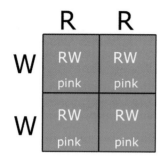

Figure 13.4.2

Punnett Square for the F1 and F2 Generation of Red and White Carnations with Incomplete Dominance Demonstrated

Top, F1 generation resulting from the cross of all red carnations, *RR*, with all white carnations, *WW*, resulting in all pink carnations, *RW*, demonstrating incomplete dominance.

Bottom, F2 generation resulting from the F1 cross of the pink carnations.

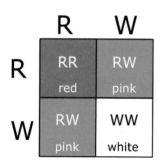

13.5 INHERITANCE PATTERNS: MULTIPLE ALLELES AND CO-DOMINANCE

So far, we have been discussing traits that have only two alleles that code for the trait, such as flower color, plant height, seed color, etc. However, within a population, there may be three or more alleles that code for the same trait. This condition is called **multiple alleles**. Sometimes multiple alleles exhibit simple dominance relationships, as we have already discussed, in which one allele is dominant over the other alleles. Other times there are alleles that are not dominant or recessive to one another, and both traits of the allele are expressed. This is called **codominance**.

The classic example of codominance and multiple alleles is blood types in humans. There are three alleles that code for blood types, called I^A, I^B, and *i*. I^A and I^B are dominant over *i* in a simple, dominant-recessive fashion, but neither I^A nor I^B is dominant over the other, so both are expressed at the same time. This is in contrast to incomplete dominance where the traits of both would be equally expressed. This results in four different blood types as shown in Figure 13.5.1.

Figure 13.5.1

Genotypes and Phenotypes of the Four Blood Groups in Humans

Phenotype	Genotype
blood type A	$I^A I^A$, $I^A i$
blood type B	$I^B I^B$, $I^B i$
blood type AB	$I^A I^B$
blood type O	ii

The four human blood types are shown on the right. There is both dominant-recessive and co-dominance demonstrated. Note that i is always recessive to I^A and I^B. When the i allele pairs with I^A, the blood type is always A; when it is paired with I^B, the blood type is always B. However, when I^A and I^B are both paired together, neither one is dominant, and the traits of both are expressed. This is the AB blood type. The recessive ii blood type results in the phenotype of type O blood.

Even though there is more than one blood type, the use of a Punnett Square is still helpful to determine expected blood types of offspring. For example, if a woman with blood type O (*ii*) marries a man with blood type AB ($I^A I^B$), what are the expected genotypic and phenotypic ratios in their children? Look at Figure 13.5.2 for details.

Figure 13.5.2

Punnett Square for the Mating of a Parent with Type O Blood and a Parent with Type AB Blood

Let's say we wanted to determine the probabilities of a child having a certain blood type. The mother is type O blood; therefore, her genotype is ii. Her expected gametes are written on the top of the square. The father is type AB blood. His gametes are written on the left side of the square. Remember that each gamete has a 50-50 chance of receiving a given allele, and that each gamete has a 50-50 chance of fusing with the gamete of the opposite sex. The resulting phenotypes and genotypes of the offspring are filled in. We would expect that half of the offspring would have blood type A, and half would have blood type B. Another way of looking at it is by stating that there is a 50% chance the child will be blood type A and 50% the child will be blood type B.

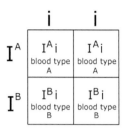

13.6 INHERITANCE PATTERNS: SEX-LINKED TRAITS AND DISEASES

Sex-linked traits are traits which do not determine the sex of the individual, but are carried on the sex chromosomes. There are many traits that are sex-linked. This is particularly important when dealing with human genetics, since many genetic diseases affecting humans are transmitted in a sex-linked manner. We will be talking about sex-linked diseases in Chapter 15. Sex-linked inheritance patterns are different than those seen for the autosomes. However, the hereditary pattern still follows Mendelian principles once the fact that the trait is sex-linked is understood.

Recall that in most animal species, the female chromosome is designated *X* and the male *Y*. Females are therefore *XX* and males are *XY*. The *Y* chromosome is small and does not carry much information for non-sex, related traits. The *Y* chromosome codes mainly for male sex-related traits. The *X* chromosome is much larger and is the sex chromosome that carries genes for many non-sex-related traits. Since the *X* chromosome is the sex chromosome that carries most sex-linked traits, sex-linked genetic diseases are also often referred to as **X-linked diseases**. If a gene is abnormal on the *X* chromosome, there is not a corresponding normal allele to counteract it on the *Y* chromosome which is why males have far more sex-linked diseases than females. However, the point not to be lost is that there are non-sex linked genes on the *X* chromosome without the corresponding normal allele on the *Y* chromosome.

The *X*-linked nature of traits was first discovered in the early 1900s by a man named Thomas Morgan, who was studying fruit flies, species *Drosophila*. Fruit flies are often studied in genetics because they have a rapid reproductive cycle and only have 8 paired chromosomes. Morgan noticed one day that a male with white eyes had been produced from a strain of flies that only had red eyes. In genetics, the "normal" trait is referred to the "**wild type**" because it is the trait found in the wild. The wild type eye color for fruit flies is red. The abnormal type is called the **non-wild type**. The non-wild type eye color for fruit flies is white. He hypothesized that the gene for eye color was on one of the sex chromosomes. Further, he thought that the non-wild type allele for the white eyes must be recessive to the wild type allele since there was only one male with the white eyes.

Dr. Morgan called the gene for eye color *R*, such that *R* was the wild type allele; it coded for red eyes and was dominant to the non-wild type allele, *r*. He thought the gene was located on the *X* chromosome. Therefore, the genotype $X^R X^R$, $X^R X^r$, and $X^R Y$ all would result in the red-eye phenotype, while the fly he saw with the white eyes was $X^r Y$. He then crossed the red eyed females, $X^R X^R$, with the white eyed male $X^r Y$ to obtain the F1 generation, all of which had red eyes. He then crossed the F1 generation with itself to get the F2 generation. This resulted in 3/4, or 75%, red eye flies (both male and female) and 1/4, or 25%, males with white eyes.

If his theory that the gene for eye color was a recessive allele on the *X* chromosome was accurate, in the end, he should be able to obtain white-eyed females having the genotype X^rX^r. Therefore, he crossed F1 females, X^RX^r, with white-eyed males, X^rY and did indeed get white-eyed females. See figure 13.6.1 for full details.

Figure 13.6.1

Punnett Squares for Fruit Fly Crosses F1 and F2 Demonstrating Sex-linked Traits

a. The P generation cross of the white-eyed males (X^rY) with the red-eyed females (X^RX^R) resulted in the F1 generation all with red eyes. Sex-linked traits initially confused geneticists. However, as this figure shows, once the inheritance patterns of the white-eye trait in fruit flies was carefully studied, the presence of genes on one sex chromosome (the X) and not the other (the Y) was better understood.

b. Crossing the F1 generation resulted in the F2 generation of red-eyed males and females and white-eyed males. There are three red-eyed male for every white-eyed organism (male or female).

c. The cross of the white-eyed males with the females of the F1 generation resulted in white-eyed females as Morgan had predicted. There are many sex linked diseases which affect humans. We will discuss these more in the upcoming chapter. It is fascinating that there are sex-linked traits in all animal species from fruit flies to humans. Interestingly, many sex-linked traits have to do with eye conditions.

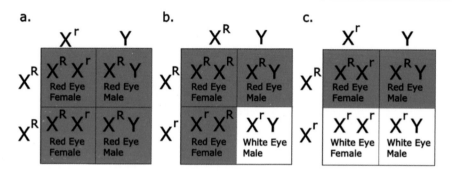

13.7 INHERITANCE PATTERNS: CONTINUOUS VARIATION

Many traits are not controlled by one gene, but by many. This results in **continuous variation**. In this situation, there is a gene that codes for a certain trait, and there are other genes that act to modify the way the trait is expressed (called **modifier genes**). There are no genes that are dominant over the others; they all act together to give the final trait. This results in phenotypes which fall within a range of phenotypes. With continuous variation, there are two phenotype "extremes" within which all of the phenotypes fall.

Figure 13.7.1

Continuous Variation
Corn plants exhibit the property of continuous variation. As can be seen from this picture, ears of corn have differing lengths. This range of corn lengths is not by chance, it is controlled by two separate genes, each with two alleles. Each allele codes for a slightly different length of an ear of corn. The exact length of the ear depends on the exact genotype of the plant. This is due to the property of continuous variation. The length of the pieces of corn is determined by the interactions of several different genes. Depending on the mix of genes present, the length of the corn can be short, medium-short, medium, long, or extra long.

For example, the phenotypes of Mendel's flowers did not fall within a range; they were either white or purple. The phenotypes of the carnations we have discussed do not have a range; they are red, white, or pink. These are not examples of continuous variation. Human height, though, is an excellent example of continuous variation. The tallest recorded human was 8 feet 11 inches tall. The shortest recorded adult was under 2 feet tall (22.5"). The heights of all other human beings fall between these extremes.

For example, let's say that there are two genes—not two alleles of the same gene, but two separate genes on different chromosomes—that determine the length of a grizzly bear's fur. Let's call these genes *L* and *S*. Each gene for fur length has two alleles, one that is dominant (*L* and *S*) and one that is recessive (*l* and *s*). *L* and *S* code for long fur while *l* and *s* code for short fur. If the genotype is *LLSS,* the grizzly bear would have the longest fur, and if the genotype is *llss* the grizzly would have the shortest fur. A genotype of *LlSs* would have fur that is medium length.

 Being careful during the crossbreeding process, we are able to cross the grizzlies with the longest fur, *LLSS,* and the grizzlies with the shortest fur, *llss.* The F1 cross results in grizzly bears with the phenotype of *LlSs,* all having medium-length fur. We initially assume that this is incomplete dominance and the fur length is a blend of the long and the short lengths. We then wish to perform the F1 cross to further understand the relationship of the genes to one another. Based on the phenotypes of the F1 parents, *LlSs,* the gametes of the F1 parents can have one of four different phenotypes—*LS, lS, Ls,* and *ls.*

Figure 13.7.2

P Generation Grizzly Bear Cross
In our hypothetical study of continuous variation, the crossing results of *LLSS* grizzlies with *llss* grizzlies is shown. All F1 organisms have the genotype LlSs and the phenotype of medium length fur.

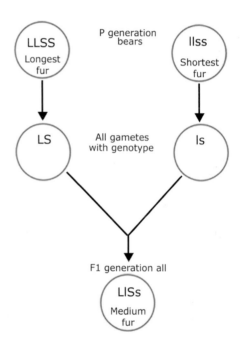

This is an example of a **dihybrid cross**. A dihybrid cross examines the effects of crossing two genes with two alleles each. (If you look at the figures in section 13 of chapter 12 you will see that Mendel also performed dihybrid crosses. When he crossed pea plants looking at the color and the shape of peas, he was performing dihybrid crosses.) After geneticists have thoroughly analyzed continuous variation, we see that the trait and inheritance relationships are governed by more than one gene. This has been found to be the case in the length of ears of corn, and is probably the way skin color is determined in humans.

Figure 13.7.3

Hypothetical Dihybrid Cross in Grizzly Bears Resulting in Continuous Variation in Fur Length: F1 Cross

Continuing with our grizzly crossing, we now perform the F1 cross using the animals obtained in Figure 13.7.2. All of the F1 generation organisms have the genotype *LlSs*. During gene segregation of meiosis, the gamete genotypes for each F1 animal are *LS*, *Ls*, *lS* and l*s*, as shown. The Punnett square shows the gamete genotype for the F1 bear parents and the expected possible genotypes and phenotypes of the resultant F2 generation. The F2 generation grizzly bears have five different fur lengths: shortest, short, medium, long, and longest. As you may imagine, the presence of modifier genes which result in continuous variation is a difficult situation to predict until the exact relationships of the genes are understood. Modifier genes are one of the main reasons that geneticists have a difficult time in some cases accurately predicting heredity patterns.

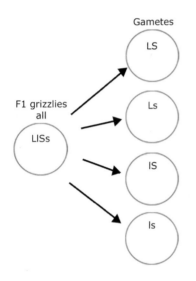

	LS	Ls	lS	ls
LS	LLSS longest	LLSs long	LlSS long	LlSs medium
Ls	LLSs long	LLss medium	LlSs medium	Llss short
lS	LlSS long	LlSs medium	llSS medium	llSs short
ls	LlSs medium	Llss short	llSs short	llss shortest

13.8 INHERITANCE PATTERNS: EPISTASIS

Modifier genes cause what is referred to as **epistasis**. Epistasis occurs when one or more genes that do not code for a trait modify or change the way the trait is expressed. Modifier genes do not code directly for a trait, but influence how the gene or genes that do code for the trait are expressed. Modifier genes can make accurately predicting heredity patterns difficult for geneticists. This is because when epistasis is present, a gene which has been identified to code for a certain trait does not always completely control that trait. Modifier genes cause the phenotype to vary—sometimes a little and sometimes a lot—from what one would expect. Often times the epistatic relationship is that one gene which does not code for a trait suppresses the expression of a gene which does code for a trait. So even though an organism may have a gene coding for a trait, that trait may not be expressed because of the epistatic interaction causing suppression of the trait for which the gene codes.

Eye color is the classic example of epistasis. There are only two alleles for human eye color, *B* and *b*. The *B* allele codes for brown eyes and is dominant. The *b* allele codes for blue eyes. If eye color were determined by a simple dominant-recessive relationship, everyone would either have brown or blue eyes. If the relationship was incomplete dominance, everyone would have one of three eye colors—brown, blue, or a dark brownish color resulting from a blend between blue and brown. But there are many different eye colors that humans exhibit—brown, blue, green, gray, and others because of epistasis caused by modifier genes.

Geneticists learned long ago that "something else" influences the trait for eye color other than the *B* and *b* alleles. That "something else" is the presence of modifier genes. This means that the strict genotype does not always control the phenotype. Even though a person may have the genotype *bb*—so should have blue eyes—they may have the phenotype of green eyes because of modifier genes. Epistasis is a difficult area to study and is not completely understood. We still do not completely understand how eye color is determined, even though there are only two alleles that code for it.

Another example of epistasis is seen in the colors of mice. Mice have two coat colors: black and brown. Black is dominant to brown. A mouse that is homozygous for the black coat color, or heterozygous will have a black coat. A mouse that is homozygous for the brown color will have a brown coat. However, there is another gene which determines whether the pigment will deposit in the hair or not. The allele for pigment deposition the hair is dominant to the allele for no deposit of pigment in the hair. A mouse which is homozygous for the recessive non-deposition allele will appear white no matter what the genotype is for coat color. The gene for deposition of coat pigment is a modifier, or is said to be epistatic, to the gene which codes for coat color.

13.9 INHERITANCE PATTERNS: ENVIRONMENT

Finally, phenotypes can also be affected by the environmental conditions such as nutrition and temperature. For example, if a corn plant has genes that code for long ears of corn, they may not be able to grow long because of poor soil conditions. The genes of the corn plant did not undergo some kind of change which resulted in the genotype changing from one which coded for longer corn plants to one which coded for shorter corn plants. The corn plant did not grow as tall as the gene code instructed it to because of poor nutrition in the soil. The poor soil condition could not provide enough nutrients for the corn to grow as tall as the genes coded.

Or, if a person with the genotype for light-colored skin moves to the tropics and is in the sun all of the time, their skin will tan and turn much darker than their genotype codes for. The reason their skin becomes darker is not because their genes have changed. It is because of the environmental change they are exposed to. The more sun you are exposed to, the darker your skin gets (i.e., it tans).

Environmental factors can also result in changes in behavior. For example, a person's response to their environment and to those around them is in part determined by genes. If a person's genes code for them to be easygoing, then usually they are easygoing. Even the most genetically easygoing person can become grumpy if they are exposed to enough stress. That person's genes have not changed; their environment is simply causing their normally easygoing nature to temporarily change.

It is important to realize that environmental factors cannot change the genetic material. A genetically tall corn plant which is nutritionally short still contains the genes to be a tall corn plant. The genes do not change. When that corn plant reproduces, it passes along its genes to be tall to its offspring. The offspring do not inherit genes to be short because the parent plant suffered nutritional problems in the soil. The offspring will inherit the genes to be tall because that is the information contained in the genes. Likewise, a person who is genetically light skinned, but is tan because they are living in the tropics, does not pass genes to their children to be dark skinned. Rather, the genes for light skin are passed to the offspring because that is the genetic material of the parent. Inherited genetic material can only contain the genes which the parent organism has. Changes in an organism due to environmental factors are never passed from parent to offspring.

This chapter has helped to further identify patterns of inheritance and how they can be predicted. It is amazing to think that everything we have been discussing regarding phenotype—how something looks or acts because of their genes—is governed by molecules that direct the making of proteins. We will continue to explore the properties of genes and chromosomes in the next chapter, then apply that knowledge to human genetics.

13.10 PEOPLE OF SCIENCE

Thomas Morgan (1866-1945) was an American researcher who was born in Kentucky. He received his bachelor's and master's degrees from the University of Kentucky and his PhD from Johns Hopkins. Dr. Morgan utilized Mendel's principles to prove that chromosomes were the carriers of genes. He received the 1933 Nobel Prize for his work.

13.11 KEY CHAPTER POINTS

- The relationship of genotype and phenotype is usually more complex than dominant-recessive relationships.

- Probability is predicting how likely an event is to occur. Probability is commonly used in genetics to predict how likely it is that offspring may inherit a certain trait or disease from their parents.

- Incomplete dominance is an inheritance pattern in which no allele for a particular gene is dominant or recessive. Traits controlled by alleles showing incomplete dominance demonstrate a blend of the phenotypes of the two traits.

- Some traits are controlled by genes with more than two alleles. This situation is called multiple alleles.

- Codominance is an inheritance pattern in which neither allele for a gene is dominant over the other. Codominant traits result in the organism expressing the phenotypes of both genes equally.

- Sex-linked traits are non sex-related traits that are carried on the sex chromosomes.

- Continuous variation is an inheritance pattern in which the phenotypes fall within a range rather than in exact categories.

- Epistasis is the influence of one or more genes on phenotype expression for a trait (or traits) coded for by another gene.

- Environmental conditions can alter the phenotype.

13.12 DEFINITIONS

codominance
   When alleles are not dominant or recessive to one another, and both traits of the allele are expressed, but not in a blending pattern.

continuous variation
   When a gene that codes for a certain trait is modified by other genes, this results in the phenotypes that are expressed falling within a continuous range between two extremes.

dihybrid cross
   Examines the effects of crossing two genes with two alleles each.

epistasis
   The condition where one or more genes which do not code for a trait affect the expression of the trait.

incomplete dominance
   Inheritance patterns that occur when there are no forms of the gene that are dominant. The resulting phenotype is a blend of the allele phenotypes.

modifier genes
   Genes that modify the way a trait is expressed and are responsible for epistasis.

monohybrid cross
   Crossing organisms that differ in only one allele that has two different forms.

multiple alleles
   Three or more alleles that code for the same trait within a population.

sex-linked
   Genetic traits that are transmitted from parent to offspring by the sex chromosomes.

STUDY QUESTIONS

1. There are two alleles for a certain gene, a dominant and recessive form. An organism has both alleles. During meiosis, what is the probability that a gamete will receive the dominant allele? What is the probability that a gamete will receive the recessive allele?

2. A family has a history of a genetic disease that is caused by a recessive allele. Their first child, a girl, was not born with the disease, but their next two children, a boy and a girl, were. Is it likely this disease is a sex-linked disease? Why or why not.

3. The family in question 2 would like to know what the probability is of having another child with this disease. You tell them that the likelihood of having three children in a row born with the disease is_____, but that the probability of the next child being born with the disease is _____?

4. What is incomplete dominance? If the color of a particular dog species was controlled by one gene with two alleles in an incomplete dominance relationship, what color would you expect the offspring to be of a black female and white male dog?

5. What is the difference between incomplete dominance and codominance?

6. True or False? Sex-linked traits are almost always carried on the X chromosome.

7. What is epistasis?

Genetic Variation

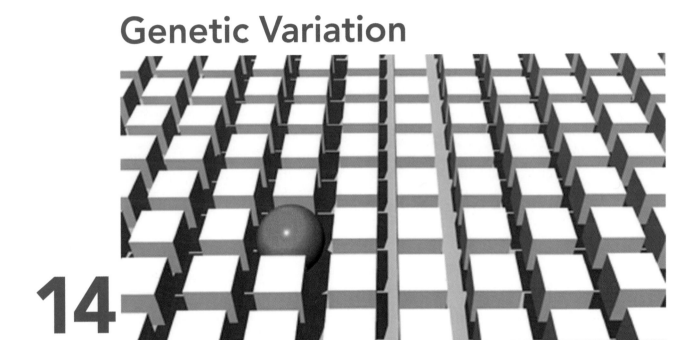

14

14.0 CHAPTER PREVIEW

In this chapter we will:

- Discuss normal genetic variation and how it is generated.
- Investigate point mutation and chromosomal mutation types.
- Learn the difference between somatic and germ cell mutations.

14.1 OVERVIEW

We have been discussing genes and different forms of genes, called alleles, for the past couple of chapters. Hopefully by now it is evident that alleles and their interactions provide some degree of genetic variation. That is, there are alleles that code for different characteristics of the same trait. Alleles cause eyes to be different colors, carnations to be pink, red, or white, and pea plants to have either wrinkled green seeds or round yellow seeds. This variation occurs naturally as a result of gene expression and epistasis. This results in normal genotypic and phenotypic variation.

However, genetic variation can occur in which genes are altered from their normal sequence. Genes become altered from their normal sequence by a process called mutation. Mutation almost always leads to a gene that does not work properly. Sometimes the gene that is mutated is so important that the organism cannot survive. So, genetic variation can be considered "normal" at times (such as described in the first paragraph) and "abnormal" at other times (due to mutation). If a mutation alters a gene so it is harmful to the organism, then it is considered an abnormal allele. Sometimes, though, mutations may lead to normal genetic variation. If a mutation alters a gene so the gene is still functional and no harm comes to the organism, then it may be considered a normal allele. In this chapter, we will discuss what is considered to be normal and abnormal genetic variations and how these variations arise.

Figure 14.2.1

Normal and Abnormal Variations

No one would argue that the giraffe on the left is considered normal in color and shape. It is within normal limits as far as one can tell by looking at it. We therefore assume it is unlikely to have a major genetic disease because if it did, it would either be unhealthy or look abnormal in some way. However, if you were to walk by a flower bed and see the carnation on the right growing there, you would immediately stop and look at it. Why? Because its color falls outside the limits of normal. Only a mutation in the gene that codes for coloring could result in a carnation as shown. (Actually you can also make the flower this color in Photoshop.) However, if this flower color was highly desirable, then you may try to reproduce this color by selective breeding. If you had two flowers like this, you could artificially pollinate them with one another and soon would have a line of carnation plants, all of which had flowers of this color. Although the flower originally arose as the result of a mutation, if the flower line is kept going long enough, this color could gradually become "normal."

14.2 NORMAL GENETIC VARIANCE

There are variances in genotypes and phenotypes for a species that are considered normal. Genes which have different alleles that do not cause harm to the organism are said to be **normal variants**. That means that although there are different genotypes which result in different phenotypes, they are still considered normal for a population. For example, carnations can come in many colors—red, pink, white, yellow, etc. The genes that code for these colors are different normal alleles for carnation flower color.

Even though the colors are not the same, these colors are considered normal variants. However, if a carnation pops up that looks like the one in Figure 14.2.1, that would not be normal. Therefore, the phenotype of a black carnation with bright green tips for a flower color is not considered a normal variant of carnation flower color. Also, the genotype causing that abnormal phenotype is also considered abnormal.

Normal genetic variation arises during meiosis through the processes of independent assortment. Remember that during human meiosis, there are 2^{23} (or about 8 million) possible ways that the maternal and paternal chromosomes can segregate. That results in a lot of variation. It is unlikely that multiple offspring of sexually reproducing organisms will have exactly the same genetic makeup. This is the essence of normal genetic variation.

Figure 14.2.2

Independent Assortment

We have seen this graphic before, but it is important to understand the concept of independent assortment as it relates to normal genetic variation. Some of the possible gametes genotype combinations that can be formed from a hypothetical organism with only 4 chromosomes is shown below. This results in normal genetic variation, which is healthy for a population.

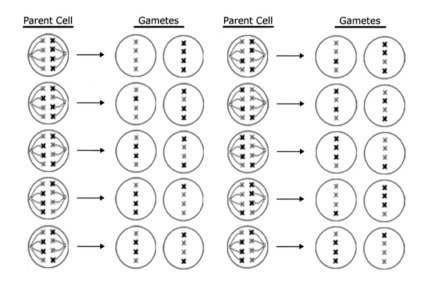

Why is genetic variation important? It has been found that reducing the genetic variation in a population makes it unstable. The less normal genetic variation occurs in a population, the less healthy the population becomes over time. This results in birth defects and other problems which can occur in genetically isolated populations. Normal genetic variation is critical to the healthy survival of all organisms.

14.3 ABNORMAL GENETIC VARIANTS: MUTATION

Any process, condition, or event which alters a gene is called a **mutation**. Mutations change the normal nucleotide sequence of the offspring as compared to that of their parents. A change in the sequence of a gene has the potential to alter one or more codons. If a codon is altered as a result of a mutation, the protein which the gene codes for may be altered. In fact, almost all observed mutations that alter the protein which a genes codes for alter the protein so much that it does not work properly. Most mutations cause severe problems with the way an organism functions and often result in the death of that organism.

Rarely, a mutation may alter some single nucleotide or nucleotide sequence within a gene and nothing observable or harmful happens. Other times mutations occur and the result is a change in the phenotype which is considered normal, but not one that would be expected given the phenotype and genotype of the parents. It is believed that many mutations occur naturally and are never noticed because the resulting phenotype is not outside the limits of normal. If there is no observable change in the phenotype then everything works as it should. Mutation, then, can rarely be a source of normal genetic variation.

The rule of inherited mutations is that they are harmful, at best; fatal, at worst. Sometimes a mutation leads to an organism with a defective gene product, but the organism does not function properly. Other times, the mutation does not kill the organism, but causes genetic variation outside normal limits. These types of mutations result in abnormal phenotypes. Abnormal phenotypes, of course, result from abnormal genotypes. The abnormal genotype comes from the mutation. Most times, though, mutation leads to a non-viable organism. In those cases, the organism which inherits a mutation does not survive.

Figure 14.3.1

The Basset Hound, Mutation Considered Normal
Bassets are thought to have developed from a mutation in the gene or genes which code for leg length. A mutation occurred which gave the dogs their short legs. This breed has been in existence for at least 450 years. Even though their short legs are due to a mutation, they are considered "normal."

There are many examples of organisms that inherit mutations from their parents but are able to survive. A very common type of mutation causes an inability for an animal to produce pigments of the skin, hair, and eyes. Animals with this type of mutation do not have any color to their skin, hair, or eyes. This genetic condition is called **albinism**, and individuals who have this are called **albinos**. Albinos appear to have pale, nearly white skin and blue or pink eyes. The hair or fur is a soft white color in pure albinism. Almost every animal species is thought to have albino individuals—lobsters, tigers, gorillas, squirrels, rats, mice, kangaroos, and humans are only a few of the species that have documented albinos. Although people (and animals) with albinism have an alteration in their genetic material so that their appearance is outside normal limits, they are usually perfectly functional in every other way. The mutation that leads to albinism is one that is compatible with a normal life and does not cause any direct harm to the affected individual. Albinism is a recessive condition, so the recessive gene must be inherited from the father and mother. Most parents of albinos appear to have the usual coloration of the species.

Figure 14.3.1

Albinos
Albino animals have a mutation which does not allow them to produce normal skin pigments. Without these pigments, they do not have "normal" coloring, appearing white or pinkish instead. Albino individuals have been described for almost every animal species. In nature, albino animals are often killed because of their different appearance.

14.4 DNA: THE MOLECULE REVISITED

Recall the structure of DNA from earlier chapters. Remember that within the continuous lengths of the chromosomes are smaller segments, some of which are genes and some of which have other functions. You may be surprised to learn that only about 1% of human DNA actually codes for protein production. That means only about 1% of the human genome is made up of genes. What does the remainder of the DNA do? Several functions have been identified for the remainder of the DNA, but the function of most of the human DNA sequences is still unknown.

Figure 14.4.1

Gene Segments on Chromosomes

Gene segments are spread out along chromosomes as shown below. Humans have more than 30,000 genes on their forty-six chromosomes. That averages out to more than 650 genes per chromosome. By far, the largest portion of DNA does not code for any proteins at all, but is composed of tandem repeats and introns. The function of these segments is unknown.

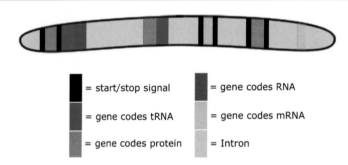

■ = start/stop signal	■ = gene codes RNA
■ = gene codes tRNA	■ = gene codes mRNA
■ = gene codes protein	■ = Intron

Part of the DNA is made up of segments that code for ribosomal RNA (rRNA) and transfer RNA (tRNA). These segments are referred to as **RNA genes**. Often these sequences are repeated multiple times on the chromosome so that the cell can quickly make RNA.

There are other areas of the chromosome that serve as start and stop signals for the transcription of RNAs and proteins. Still other segments are introns that are later removed from the mRNA. Some segments are known as **tandem repeats**. They often contain two or more nucleotides in a row which are repeated again and again. For example, the pattern—CATTGCATTGCATTG—is repeated hundreds or millions of times. Their function is not completely understood.

Some sequences of DNA are similar to that of actual genes, yet they do not code for a protein or RNA. These are called **pseudogenes**. Their function also is not understood. About 69% of human DNA codes for pseudogenes; 30% are tandem repeats.

14.5 MUTATION

Mutations are simply errors in the normal sequence of DNA; they result from a number of factors. There are many different types of mutations, which we will discuss. During the discussion of mitosis, we mentioned that after DNA replication and repair, as many as 1 base per 1 billion replicated may be incorrect. That means that following the completion of mitosis or meiosis in a human, there may be as many as six nucleotides that are incorrect. These are known as **copying errors**.

It seems quite possible that the reason there is such an excess of genetic material is to "pad," or protect, the genes from the mutation process. Recall our discussion of probability. If genes make up only 1% of the total sequence of DNA, and the rest of DNA is "extra," where is it most probable that a mutation event will occur? It is much more likely that a mutation will occur in the 99% of the DNA that has no known function. Conversely, it is unlikely that the DNA of a gene will be involved in a mutation event, since this portion of the DNA accounts for only 1% of the DNA. Therefore, most of the mutation events probably go completely unnoticed and have no effect on the organism. The redundancy of DNA is probably protective from mutation to a large degree. However, genes inevitably are involved in mutations, and we will discuss how this occurs and what it means to the organism.

The proteins that genes code for are finely tuned. This means the proteins must be made properly for them to work properly. The function of a protein depends on the proper sequence of amino acids, which depends on the proper sequence of DNA nucleotides. If a mutation occurs within a gene segment, and only one nucleotide is copied wrong, that would mean the codon of only one amino acid would be different. That does not sound too bad. However, when you combine an amino acid in the wrong place with the highly tuned nature of proteins, altering only one nucleotide in the gene of one protein can often make an organism die. Almost every observed mutation has resulted in an organism that has not survived. That is to say that **almost all** naturally occurring gene mutations kill the organism before it is born or shortly after. However, a mutation that occurs within the remaining 99% of the non-gene-encoding DNA **may** not necessarily be detrimental to the organism. Understand that genetic mutations are almost always fatal to the organism. If they are not fatal, they almost always result in an organism with a shortened life span, during which reproduction is impossible because of the mutation.

Mutations, once they occur, are permanent. If the mutation occurs in the sex cells during meiosis, then the mutation potentially could be passed from the parent to the offspring, and so on, for generations. Mutations that occur and are transmitted to gametes are celled **germ cell mutations**. Germ cell mutations are passed to every cell in the organism formed from a mutated gamete. But recall that there are two alleles for each gene; often the normal allele inherited from the other parent can produce enough of the protein product to compensate for the mutated form. Sometimes, though, the product of the mutated allele is toxic to the cell and could possibly cause the organism to die.

The other type of mutation is a **somatic mutation**. This is a mutation that occurs in the organism after it is formed. Somatic mutations are not passed from generation to generation like germ cell mutations can be. However, somatic mutations often cause cancer. Mutations in the DNA have been found to be quite prominent in some forms of the blood cancer **leukemia**. It appears that mutations of a certain gene in a certain chromosome results in the body producing some blood cells out of control. It is likely that all cancers will be found to arise from specific mutations once we are able to study them enough.

Mutations can generally be divided into those that affect one nucleotide of the DNA—called point mutations—and those that affect larger segments of the chromosomes—called chromosomal mutations.

14.6 POINT MUTATION TYPES

Point mutations result in the replacement of one normal DNA nucleotide with an incorrect one. This type of mutation occurs when DNA is replicated during mitosis and meiosis, and a mistake occurs. For example, let's say the normal sequence of part of a gene is A-T-A-G-G-G-C. If a point mutation occurs in this sequence, then the sequence may change to A-T-A-**A**-G-G-C. Notice that the sequence of the entire segment is normal except for one nucleotide. This is a point mutation, but there are several different types of mutations. Point mutations can be caused by **substitutions**, **deletions**, and **additions**.

Substitutions are just that: the wrong nucleotide is inserted into the DNA instead of the correct one. The example in the paragraph above is a substitution mutation. During DNA replication, the G was substituted by an A.

Recall when we were studying protein synthesis that there are many amino acids which are coded for by more than one codon. If a substitution mutation occurs so that the normal sequence of the codon changes, but the amino acid for which the codon codes is not changed, then the mutation has not caused any change in the protein. This is called a **silent mutation**. For example, both AAA and AAG code for the amino acid phenylalanine. If the third A in the AAA codon undergoes a substitution mutation changing the A to a G, then the codon still codes for phenylalanine. A mutation has occurred because the normal sequence of the gene is altered, but the amino acid is the same because of the redundant nature of the genetic code.

At other times, a substitution mutation can occur which alters a codon so that the amino acid is changed. However, if the new amino acid has similar properties to the original amino acid, then the protein may still function normally. This is another example of a silent mutation.

However, a substitution mutation may change the codon in such a way that the amino acid the codon calls for is changed. For example, there is a particular substitution mutation in the gene coding for the hemoglobin molecule. Hemoglobin is a huge molecule made up of four different polypeptide chains that kind of wrap around one another. Hemoglobin is the molecule that carries oxygen to our cells and carbon dioxide away from our cells. This well-known substitution mutation changes the "A" in the "GAG" codon to a "T" in only one codon of the DNA that encodes one of the four polypeptides. During translation of the protein, this results in the amino acid valine being inserted into the protein, rather than the correct amino acid, glutamic acid. Because of what seems to be a relatively minor change in the amino acid sequence, a completely dysfunctional hemoglobin molecule is formed. This is exactly the mutation that causes sickle cell disease (which we will cover more in the next chapter), a very severe blood disease that affects people of Mediterranean and African descent. So point mutations can have severe effects on an organism.

Deletions occur when a nucleotide is left out of its proper sequence. If the normal sequence is G-G-T-A, and a deletion mutation occurs, the sequence would change to G-T-A. The G was deleted from its normal position during replication.

Additions occur when a single nucleotide is added during replication. If the normal sequence is G-A-A-T, and an addition point mutation occurs, the sequence could change to G-C-A-A-T. A "C" was added in the sequence where it is not supposed to be.

14.7 MISSENSE MUTATIONS

Missense mutations are caused by substitution mutations. Deletion and addition mutations do not cause missense mutations. A **missense mutation** is the term used when a substitution mutation causes an incorrect amino acid to be inserted into the protein. This often causes the protein to function improperly. Sometimes the result of a missense mutation is severe, as in the case of sickle cell disease (caused by a missense substitution mutation). At other times, the missense mutation may be completely unnoticed (i.e., a silent mutation).

For example, let's say the normal DNA codon sequence is:

TAT GGC TCA TTT

This DNA codon would be transcribed into the mRNA sequence:

AUA CCG AGU AAA

The proper amino acid sequence would be:

Isoleucine - Proline - Serine - Lysine

Let's say that a point mutation occurred in which the first T in the TAT codon was changed to a C. The DNA codon sequence now changes to:

CAT GGC TCA TTT

And the mRNA codon changes to:

GUA CCG AGU AAA

This would give an amino acid sequence:

Valine – Proline - Serine - Lysine

Missense mutations allow the mRNA and the protein to be synthesized properly with the exception of the incorrect amino acid that is inserted. All of the other amino acids are still in their usual positions. In the above example, the amino acid isoleucine has been changed to valine as a result of the substitution. Depending on the change in the structure of the protein as a result of the mutation, one of two results may occur: no observable change in the protein function; or, the protein is minimally or non-functional.

14.8 NONSENSE MUTATIONS

Sometimes a substitution mutation occurs such that a codon which normally codes for an amino acid is mutated into a stop codon. This is called a **nonsense mutation**. This also allows the DNA to be read correctly and transcribed into mRNA. However, when a nonsense mutation occurs, amino acid-encoding codon is converted into a stop codon. When the mRNA is read by the ribosome, the protein will stop being made too early. The result of this is a protein that is generally much smaller and often minimally functional.

For example, let's say that the normal DNA codon sequence is:

TAC TGA GTG GCT CGC GCA TCG ACT.

The mRNA of this segment would read:

AUG ACU CAC CGA GCG CGU AGC UGA

and the amino acid sequence of this would be:

methionine - threonine - histine - arginine - alanine - arginine - serine - stop

If a nonsense mutation occurred at the GCT codon changing the G to an A, then that codon would read ACT. When the mRNA is transcribed, it would have the sequence:

AUG ACU CAC U**G**A GCG CGU AGC UGA

When the ribosome transcribes this mRNA, the protein will have the amino acid sequence:

methionine - threonine - histine - stop

The nonsense mutation obviously shortens the protein due to the premature appearance of the stop codon.

14.9 POINT MUTATIONS, THE READING FRAME, AND FRAME SHIFT MUTATIONS

Since the DNA and RNA are read in three codon sequences, it is important that the exact sequence be maintained. This is the reading frame. Recall the discussion of the reading frame from chapter 9. When a substitution mutation occurs, it does not cause a change in the reading frame. Since a substitution mutation simply substitutes one nucleotide for another, there are still the same numbers of nucleotides, and they are still read in the proper order. However, one of them is not the correct nucleotide. This would be like changing one letter in the sentence "He went to the store and bought a dog." If a substitution mutation occurs, the sentence may change to "He went to the store and bought a **b**og." The DNA, like the sentence, is able to be read properly for the most part, but the meaning changes somewhat. This is similar to what occurs when a substitution mutation occurs in a gene. Substitution mutations do not cause changes in the reading frame.

Deletion and addition mutations do cause changes in the reading frame. These are called **frame shift mutations**. Deletion mutations remove a nucleotide from the gene. This leads to the DNA being read by the DNA polymerase incorrectly. This would be like removing a letter from a sentence. Addition mutations add a nucleotide to the gene. This is like adding a letter to a sentence. Both of these change the reading frame and have much more severe effects on the protein the gene codes for than substitution mutations.

Think of a frame shift mutation as being similar to inserting or removing a random letter in the following set of three-lettered words: dog, cat, tip, yip. When the letters are in that exact order, you can read them properly. If an addition mutation were to occur in this sequence, a frame shift mutation would result. Let's say a "k" were added after the "o" in "dog." The sequence of letters would then read: "do**k** – gca – tti – pyi – p." The letters no longer make sense to you, just as DNA which has had a frame shift mutation occur to it no longer codes for a protein which has the correct sequence of amino acids. Usually proteins made as a result of frame shift mutations do not work correctly.

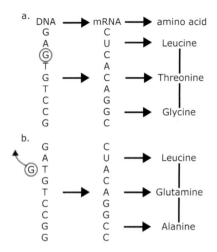

Figure 14.9.1

Deletion Mutation

The normal DNA sequence of a protein is shown in figure (a). Read the DNA sequence, mRNA sequence, and amino acids from top to bottom. When the DNA is replicated, the G (which is circled) is deleted. This is a deletion mutation. As you can see, this alters the codon sequence from GAG-TGT-CCG to GAT-GTC-CGG. This causes a frame shift. This results in the wrong amino acids being inserted into the protein from the point of the mutation until the protein is completely synthesized. As you can imagine, a frame shift mutation which occurs near the beginning of a gene results in a protein with more incorrect amino acids than frame shift mutations which occur near the end of a gene.

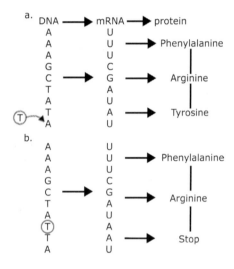

Figure 14.9.2

Addition Mutation

Figure (a) shows part of the normal sequence of a gene. The DNA sequence should read, from top to bottom, AAAGCTATA. The mRNA is transcribed and the protein sequence is shown on the right. As indicated, a thymine is added into the DNA segment during DNA replication. This alters the normal sequence of the codons. Now the DNA codon of ATA (ATA codes for tyrosine) is changed to the DNA codon of ATT. ATT is a stop codon and is transcribed into the mRNA codon of UAA. This means that when the ribosome is reading the mRNA and reaches the codon UAA, it will stop making the protein when it should have inserted the amino acid tyrosine. This is a nonsense mutation because the mutation has caused the codon to change from an amino acid-encoding codon to a stop codon.

14.10 CHROMOSOMAL MUTATION

The mutations we have been discussing thus all concern the change of one nucleotide in the DNA. However, there are other forms of mutations that can occur which involve larger segments of the DNA. These are called **chromosomal mutations** and often involve changes in thousands or millions of nucleotide sequences of DNA. Most of the chromosomal mutations occur during mitosis and meiosis when the DNA is heavily condensed into chromosomes. Also during mitosis and meiosis, the chromosomes are close together, and it is easy for genetic material to be exchanged.

Generally the chromosomal mutation patterns involve a piece of the chromosome breaking off during prophase or metaphase. The broken piece then re-inserts somewhere in a different chromosome or into the same chromosome it came from, but in the incorrect sequence. Other times, pieces from two chromosomes break off, and the material is swapped.

Keep in mind that during the period of prophase and metaphase, the chromosomes are closely aligned. Also, it is a time of great forces being placed on the DNA as they are moved around by the spindle. Chromosomal mutations result in one chromosome losing material, called a deletion, and another chromosome gaining material. The chromosome that gains material does so in a number of different ways, which will be discussed below.

14.11 CROSSING OVER

One mechanism of a chromosomal mutation we have already discussed is called crossing over. Recall that during meiosis, the homologous chromosomes are aligned next to one another, their arms often wrapped around one another. Crossing over occurs when homologous chromosomes exchange pieces of the chromosomes as they are twisted around one another. This effectively results in a fairly equal "swap" of the genes involved and usually is not detrimental to the organism, but does change the original sequences of the nucleotides involved.

Figure 14.11.1

Crossing Over
Crossing over involves homologous chromosomes. This occurs during meiosis I, when the homologous pairs are all lined up together during late prophase or metaphase. Crossing over usually results in a fairly even "swap" of genetic material from one chromosome to another and so there is often no harmful change to the genes.

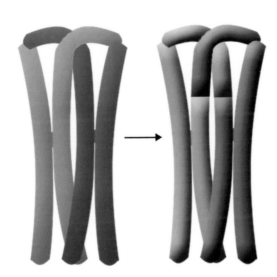

14.12 CHROMOSOMAL DELETION MUTATION

A **deletion mutation** occurs when an entire segment of the chromosome is deleted, or removed, from the chromosome during DNA replication. This can occur during meiosis or mitosis. The chromosome which has a segment break off loses whatever genes are contained in that chromosomal segment. Usually, the segment of DNA then reinserts into another chromosome. This type of mutation generally causes a mutation that is considered "incompatible with life," meaning the organism dies. This is because there is usually critical information that the organism cannot live without removed from the genetic material. Where the chromosome segments end up after breaking off is the next topic.

Figure 14.12.1

Chromosomal Deletion
The chromosome below has lost a section of its genes, labeled "2." This results in loss of genetic material and usually kills the organism that is formed from a gamete carrying this type of mutation.

14.13 CHROMOSOMAL INVERSION MUTATION

Occasionally, the broken-off piece inserts back into the chromosome in the correct order, and no change in the DNA occurs. Other times, the broken-off segment reattaches at the end of the chromosome, or within the chromosome, but in the reverse orientation. This is called an **inversion mutation**. Inversion mutations may not harm the organism, depending upon where they occur in the chromosome.

Figure 14.13.1

Chromosomal Inversion

In a chromosomal inversion mutation, a piece of the chromosome breaks off, then reinserts back into the same chromosome. However, it is inserted in the wrong place.

14.14 CHROMOSOMAL DUPLICATION MUTATION

A **duplication mutation** results when the piece of a broken off chromosome inserts into the homologous chromosome. This results in two copies of the same segment within the same chromosome. The chromosome which receives the extra chromosomal material is usually not adversely affected. However, the chromosome that donated the chromosomal material has lost genes, or undergone a deletion mutation. It is thought that this may be a fairly common occurrence and is the reason there are so many repeated segments of DNA. An organism formed from a gamete that has a chromosome with a duplication mutation would likely be able to survive normally. The additional genetic material then is available to passed onto that parent's offspring.

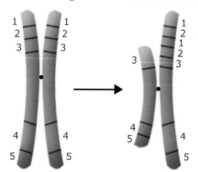

Figure 14.14.1

Duplication Mutation

Gene duplication involves the donation of genetic material from one homologous chromosome to another. As can be seen, one homologue has lost part of its DNA while the other has gained it. Note that there is no exchange of the chromosomal segments; one chromosome essentially "gives" its genes to the other. Since the chromosomes are homologues, the one that receives the chromosomal segment has duplication of the genes contained in the genetic material transferred. The chromosome that loses the information undergoes a chromosome deletion mutation.

14.15 CHROMOSOMAL TRANSLOCATION MUTATION

A **translocation mutation** is the final way that chromosomal material is exchanged after breaking off. This occurs when a chromosomal piece breaks off and inserts itself into a non-homologous chromosome.

Figure 14.15.1

Translocation Mutation

Two non-homologous chromosomes are shown below. As can be seen, a section of one of the chromosomes is removed from the normal chromosome and inserted into the non-homologous chromosome. There is no overall loss of genetic material; it changes location.

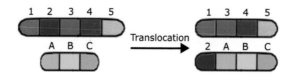

14.16 NONDISJUNCTION CHROMOSOMAL MUTATION

Occasionally, the homologous chromosomes do not separate during meiosis I. There is a failure in karyokinesis. Basically, the chromosomes stick together and do not separate. This is called **nondisjunction** and results in one gamete receiving too many chromosomes and the other gamete not receiving enough. Usually, one gamete receives two chromosomes of a pair and the other receives none. This is the type of mutation that causes **Down's Syndrome** (also called **trisomy 21**), which we will discuss next chapter. There are also other types of trisomy conditions which affect humans, but trisomy 21 is the most common.

Figure 14.16.1

Nondisjunction and Trisomy-21
This is a graphical representation of a karyotype from a person with Down's syndrome, or trisomy 21. Note the three chromosome number 21 in the bottom row. Down's syndrome results from a nondisjunction of chromosome 21 during meiosis in one of the parent's gametes. This results in that parent's gamete receiving two chromosome 21's instead of the usual one. If that gamete participates in fertilization, the child will end up with three number 21 chromosomes. This is not lethal to the child, but does cause the child to have common abnormalities associated with the mutation such as mental retardation, a characteristic facial appearance, common defects in the way the heart forms, and a large tongue.

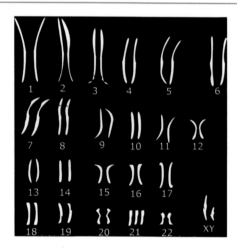

14.17 MUTAGENS

Finally, there are environmental conditions, called **mutagens**, which can cause changes in the normal DNA structure. Cigarette smoke, X-rays, UV rays, and some chemicals are all types of mutagens. Mutagens can break the hydrogen bonds of DNA, altering the structure. Other mutagens cause an abnormally high number of point mutations to occur and inhibit the repair process. Still other mutagens can cause abnormal bonds to form with the DNA. The damaging effects of UV rays on the skin are due to changes in the DNA structure which can lead to skin cancer.

Figure 14.17.1

The Effects of Mutagens on Life
Several years ago, frogs with mutated DNA were found all over the United States and Canada. It is thought that their mutations were caused by the effects of pesticides on the frog DNA, altering the DNA during meiosis. Chemicals were absorbed into the frog eggs shortly after they were laid. The chemicals caused changes in the normal sequence of the genes. Due to the changes in the DNA, unusual traits were coded for—such as legs growing in places they did not belong.

14.18 ADVANCED

Let's go back to the germ cell versus somatic tumor concept. Recall that all organisms start out as one single cell. In sexually reproducing organisms, that single cell is formed when the male gamete fuses with the female gamete. When that occurs, the chromosomes combine. Then, through millions to trillions of mitotic events, the organism grows from a single cell into a multicellular life form. All cells of an individual grow from the single cell formed when a male gamete fuses with a female gamete. If one of those gametes has a mutation, then the cell formed when that gamete fuses with another gamete will have the mutation. As the single cell undergoes millions to trillions of mitotic events to grow in size from a single cell to a multicellular organism, that mutation is passed to all of the cells every time a cell divides. Then, assuming the organism lives to adulthood, half the gametes the organism produces will also have the mutation; the mutation could be passed on indefinitely.

Figure 14.18.1

Mutation in Somatic vs. Germ Cells
There are two types of cells in all sexually reproducing organisms: **germ cells** and **somatic cells**. Germ cells are the cells we have been calling gametes (sperm or eggs). Germ cells are formed during meiosis and are the cells that fuse with another gamete from an organism of the opposite sex to make a new organism. Somatic cells are all the other cells in the body or organism. Muscle cells, bone cells, skin cells, brain cells—you get the idea—are somatic cells. Figure (a) represents the usual condition in which the somatic cells and the germ cells are normal; that is, they have no mutations present in them. As the organism grows, all of the organism's growing and reproducing cells replicate normal DNA and pass normal genes on to offspring cells. When the organism makes new gametes, they are all normal. Figure (b) represents what occurs in a gamete's mutation. Since the new organism is formed from the fusion of the male and female gametes, if one (or both) gametes have a mutation, that mutation is present in all the cells of the organism. If the mutation does not cause some problem that is incompatible with life, the organism can live and possibly reproduce. However, it is possible for the mutation to be passed on to the offspring, because the gametes will also carry the mutation. This concept forms the basis of human genetics, which we will be studying next chapter.

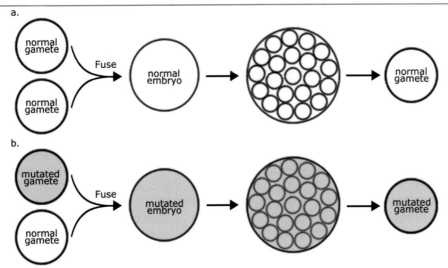

As you can imagine, a mutation which is passed from parents to offspring in this fashion almost always results in an organism which cannot survive. If the organism survives, then that mutation is passed to its offspring. It is important to remember that if a mutation occurs in the gametes, then the offspring resulting from those gametes will be born, hatched, or grown with that mutation. That is, it will be born, hatched, or grown if the mutation does not result in its death. If the organism with a mutation does live and can reproduce, the mutation is then passed down from generation to generation. All of the types of mutations we have just discussed are involved in creating various human genetic disorders, which we will discuss in the next chapter.

14.19 PEOPLE OF SCIENCE

William Bateson (1861-1926) was a British geneticist. Dr. Bateson researched plant genetics and also was one of the scientists (along with Dr. de Vries) who "re-discovered" work done years earlier by Gregor Mendel. Dr. Bateson made many contributions to genetics, including founding the *Journal of Genetics*. He was also the first person to use the word "genetics" as it related to the study of chromosomes and heredity.

14.20 KEY CHAPTER POINTS

- Sometimes mutations arise in the DNA and genes during meiosis or mitosis. Mutations are changes in the normal sequence of DNA.

- Normal genotype variances arise through the process of independent assortment and crossing over during meiosis.

- Abnormal genetic variances occur due to mutation.

- Mutations are almost always fatal or, at best, detrimental to the organism that inherits the mutated gene(s).

- It is estimated that 1% of an organism's DNA sequences are actual genes. The remainder of the DNA codes for RNA, ribosomes, tandem repeats, and pseudogenes.

- Point mutations result in a change of only one nucleotide in DNA. There are three types of point mutations: addition, deletion, and substitution.

- Addition and deletion mutations cause frame-shift mutations.

- Missense mutations are point mutations which result in the insertion of the wrong amino acid into the protein for which the gene codes.

- Nonsense mutations are point mutations which result in the insertion of a stop codon into the gene. This leads to premature termination of protein translation.

- Chromosomal mutations occur when there are large segments of chromosomal material gained or lost by a chromosome. The types of chromosomal mutations are: crossing over, deletion, inversion, duplication, translocation, and nondisjunction.

- Mutagens are things which are known to cause genetic mutations.

14.21 DEFINITIONS

addition
A single nucleotide is added into the DNA sequence during replication.

albinism
A type of mutation that makes an animal unable to produce pigments of the skin, hair, and eyes.

albinos
Individuals who have albinism.

chromosomal mutations
Mutations which can occur involving larger segments of the DNA and, often, cause changes in thousands or millions of nucleotide sequences of DNA.

deletion mutation
When an entire segment of the chromosome is duplicated, added, or deleted from the chromosome during DNA replication.

deletion
A nucleotide is left out of its proper sequence in the DNA during replication.

down's syndrome
DNA mutation caused by nondisjunction of chromosome 21 during meiosis I.

duplication mutation
When a piece of broken-off chromosome inserts into the homologous chromosome. This results in two copies of the same DNA segment within the same chromosome.

frame shift mutation
A change in DNA sequence resulting in the DNA polymerase reading codons incorrectly.

inversion mutation
When a broken-off segment of DNA reattaches at the end of the chromosome, or within the chromosome, but in the reverse orientation.

leukemia
A form of blood cancer that is often caused by chromosome mutations.

missense mutation
The term used when a substitution mutation causes an incorrect amino acid to be inserted into the protein.

mutagens
Environmental conditions which can cause changes in the normal DNA structure.

mutation
Any process, condition, or event which alters a gene or segment of DNA.

nondisjunction
When homologous chromosomes do not separate during metaphase I of meiosis.

nonsense mutation
A substitution mutation that changes a codon from coding for protein to a stop codon.

normal variants
Variances in genotypes and phenotypes for a species that are considered normal.

point mutations
The replacement of one normal DNA nucleotide with an incorrect one. This can be caused by substitution, deletion, or addition type of mutations.

pseudogenes
Sequences of DNA that are similar to those of actual genes, yet they do not code for a protein or RNA.

RNA genes
Segments of DNA that code for ribosomal RNA (rRNA) and transfer RNA (tRNA).

silent mutations
Mutations that occur, but go unnoticed. The term generally refers to a substitution mutation that does not alter the amino acid encoded by the codon.

substitution
The wrong nucleotide is inserted into the DNA instead of the correct one.

tandem repeats
DNA segments that often contain two or more nucleotides, which are repeated over and over again along a continuous segment of DNA.

translocation mutation
A type of chromosomal mutation that occurs when a chromosomal piece breaks off and inserts into a non-homologous chromosome.

STUDY QUESTIONS

1. List at least two ways that genetic variation can occur.

2. True or False? RNA genes code for the production of tRNA and mRNA.

3. True or False? Most human DNA codes for protein production.

4. Give an example of a tandem repeat. Do tandem repeats code for protein production?

5. What is a gene mutation? Why might the fact that genes only comprise 1% of the human genome be a protective feature in light of mutation?

6. Why are organisms sometimes unaffected by mutations?

7. Indicate the type of point mutation which has occurred:

sequence before replication	sequence after replication	type of mutation
A-T-T-G-C	A-A-T-T-G-C	_____
G-T-T-T-G	T-T-T-G	_____
C-G-T-A-T	C-G-A-A-T	_____

8. True or False? Addition and substitution point mutations can cause shifts in the reading frame.

9. If a point mutation causes an amino acid codon to be mutated into a stop codon, it is called a _____ mutation.

10. What is a missense mutation?

11. True or False? Chromosomal mutations result in changes in more DNA than point mutations.

12. True or False? A mutation occurs in a female gamete. That gamete is able to be fertilized by a normal male gamete. The organism which grows from this fertilization is a male of the species. He would be expected to have the mutation in only a few cells when it is mature.

13. The organism from question #12 mates with a female and produces offspring. What is the likelihood that the mutation will be passed from the male to the offspring?

14. What is the difference between normal genetic variation and abnormal genetic variation?

15. True or False? Somatic mutations may be passed on to offspring.

16. What is a non-disjunction chromosomal mutation?

PLEASE TAKE TEST #5 IN TEST BOOKLET

Human Genetics

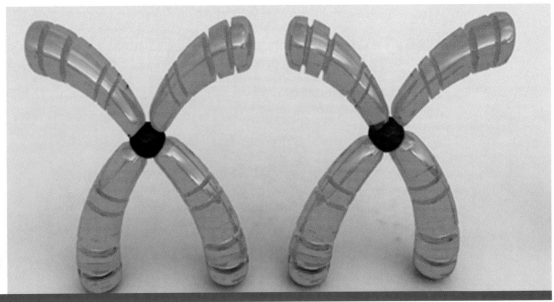

15

15.0 CHAPTER PREVIEW

In this chapter we will:

- Define congenital genetic diseases.

- Learn why most genetic diseases are inherited as an autosomal recessive pattern.

- Discuss the meanings of carriers, affected and unaffected individuals as it relates to genetic disorders.

- Learn how to use a pedigree analysis.

- Investigate:
  - the autosomal recessive genetic diseases of phenylketonuria, cystic fibrosis and sickle cell anemia.
  - the autosomal dominant genetic disease of Huntington's chorea.
  - the X-linked diseases of hemophilia and color blindness.
  - the polyploid condition of Down's syndrome.

15.1 OVERVIEW OF CONGENITAL DISEASES

We have just learned that as a result of mutations, DNA is permanently altered. Sometimes the changes go unnoticed. Other times, the mutations cause problems for the organism that range from relatively minor enzyme malfunctions to abnormalities that are incompatible with life. Once a mutated allele is formed, as long as it does not result in the organism's death, or cause the organism to be sterile, the mutated allele may be passed from generation to generation.

The study of human genetics is the fastest growing area of interest in terms of understanding and trying to cure **congenital genetic diseases**. A congenital disease is a disease that a person is born with. Congenital genetic diseases are abnormalities that people are born with due to mutations in the DNA. The mutation may be a point mutation or a chromosomal mutation. Most genetic diseases are caused by mutations to the somatic chromosomes and not mutations to the sex chromosomes. Recall that somatic chromosomes are also called autosomes. Since almost all genetic diseases are transmitted on autosomes in a recessive fashion, most genetic diseases are inherited in an **autosomal recessive** fashion. However, there are some genetic diseases that are transmitted in a sex-linked fashion. These are called **sex-linked diseases**. We learned about these in Chapter 13, but will learn more about them in this chapter. Doctors who specialize in studying genetic diseases are called **geneticists**.

Most congenital genetic diseases are caused by already described and known alterations in the DNA structure. There are very rarely new cases of a congenital genetic disease that have never been seen before. Most people affected by the known congenital genetic diseases exhibit similar traits. Diseases that display similar symptoms and problems associated with the disease are called **syndromes**. Probably the most well known of the congenital genetic diseases is Down's syndrome. This is also called Trisomy 21 because people born with this disease have three number 21 chromosomes instead of two.

There are some congenital abnormalities are not caused by mutations. For example, some babies are born with abnormally-formed body parts. These include cleft lip and palate (where the upper lip and roof of the mouth do not fuse together, forming a "hole"), or abnormally formed organs such as hearts or kidneys. Structural abnormalities are usually not genetic problems. They result from abnormal tissue growth while the baby is developing in the mother.

In 1990, the Human Genome Project was started. This has many purposes, but one of the initial purposes was to identify the entire nucleotide sequence of the approximately 30,000 genes in human DNA. This goal was completed in 2003. The hope is that by knowing what "normal" gene sequences are, we will be able to determine what "abnormal" sequences are. This will allow for increased understanding of genetic diseases and possibly lead to cures for some.

It also seems likely that there are diseases which have not been generally thought of as genetic but, in fact, are. There are many diseases that run in families such as high blood pressure, certain types of arthritis, and the adult form of diabetes. It is possible that changes in the normal DNA pattern result in these diseases in many people. The only way to know for sure is to know the entire normal sequence of nucleotides in human DNA. Now that this is known, we hope to find cures, rather than treatments, for many human diseases.

In this chapter we will be studying different genetic diseases to learn about the practical applications of genetics to a human population.

15.2 UNAFFECTED, CARRIERS, AND AFFECTED

Most genetic diseases are transmitted in an autosomal recessive fashion. Again, this means that in order to have a particular genetic disease, one recessive autosomal allele for the disease must be inherited from the father and one recessive autosomal allele for the same disease must be inherited from the mother. There are three types of people in this regard from a geneticist's standpoint: unaffected, carriers and affected.

Individuals who do not have a gene for a genetic disease are called **unaffected**. Unaffected persons have two normal alleles and can only pass on normal alleles to their offspring. Individuals who have only one copy of the recessive, disease-causing allele for a particular genetic disease are said to be **carriers**. Since carriers have one normal allele, they do not exhibit the disease because the normal allele makes up for the recessive, defective copy. However, it is possible for a carrier to pass along the recessive allele to their offspring. Those that have both copies of the recessive and defective allele have the disease. They are said to be **affected**. Therefore, the parents of a child born with a recessive genetic disease have one of three phenotypes: both are carriers; one is a carrier and one is affected; both are affected. The presence of one of these three parental phenotypes is the only way a child can inherit an autosomal recessive genetic disease because the child *must* inherit a defective, recessive allele from each parent to have the disease.

Let's review some definitions again for this section. A person who is homozygous-dominant for a condition carries two dominant alleles for the condition. Homozygous-dominant individuals do not have a genetic disease, nor do they carry an allele for the disease. A person who is heterozygous for a condition carries one normal, dominant allele and one abnormal, recessive allele for the disease. All carriers are heterozygous for a particular condition or disease. An affected person has two abnormal, recessive alleles for the condition. All affected people are homozygous recessive.

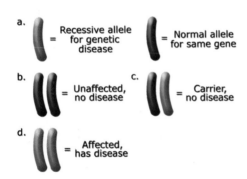

Figure 15.2.1

Terminology in Genetic Diseases

Genetics uses the following terms often, and you should be familiar with them. Figure (a) shows two alleles that represent two different alleles for a particular trait. The trait may be a disease or may be a recessive condition. For example, in order for a person to have the genetic disease cystic fibrosis, they must have two recessive alleles which code for that disease. Or, the trait may be something considered a normal variant, but it is transmitted in a dominant-recessive fashion. Recall Mendel's experiments. The trait for purple flowers was dominant, and the trait for white flowers was recessive. The trait carried by the recessive allele is suppressed by the normal, dominant allele. This is true whether the trait is a genetic disease or a normal variant. In figure (b), an organism which has two of the normal alleles is said to be normal, or "not affected" by a particular disease or trait. In figure (c), an organism which has one of the normal, dominant alleles, and one of the recessive alleles, is said to be a carrier of the trait the recessive allele codes for. Since that organism has one normal allele, they do not express the trait of the recessive allele. For example, the flowers that had one purple allele and one white allele were purple in color. This organism is said to be a carrier of the white trait. In figure (d), an organism which has two recessive genes will have the trait coded for by the recessive alleles. If the trait is a genetic disease, the organism will have the disease. If the trait is a recessive but normal trait, then the organism will have that trait (such as white flowers). The main point here is that carriers of a recessive condition can pass the recessive allele to their offspring.

There are also many genetic conditions which do not result in a "disease," but are transmitted in a recessive fashion. The same terminology is used for these conditions when describing people who have the recessive condition. We will discuss some of these below, but one example is the trait of earlobes being attached to the side of the head. This is a recessive condition. The dominant condition is for earlobes to be hanging. People who have attached earlobes are said to be affected by the recessive condition.

Take a look at your earlobes and those of family and friends. Are they attached or do they hang? If they are attached, then that person is affected by the recessive condition of attached earlobes. This means that person has two recessive genes, both of which code for the earlobes to be attached. This is obviously not a "disease," but a normal variant. It is possible that a person with attached earlobes had a mom and a dad who did not have attached earlobes. How? The parents could have both been heterozygous for the condition. That means that both the mom and the dad had one dominant gene and one recessive gene for earlobe attachment. In this case the mom and dad would both have had hanging earlobes, but each passed their recessive gene to their child with attached earlobes. The parents were carriers of the recessive condition of earlobes being attached, even though both parents did not have attached earlobes.

Figure 15.2.2

Unaffected, Carrier, and Affected

Using Mendel's peas, there are two alleles for flower color. Recall the purple allele is dominant to the white allele. The dominant condition is purple flowers, and the recessive condition is white flowers. The plant which is homozygous-dominant is unaffected by the recessive condition since it only contains the dominant allele. Therefore, the homozygous dominant plants all have purple flowers. The plant which is heterozygous has the same phenotype as the homozygous dominant plant (i.e., the flowers are purple), but it carries one of the recessive genes. It is a carrier of the recessive condition, or a carrier of the white allele. The plant which is homozygous recessive for the flower color has white flowers. It is affected by the recessive condition (gene) and has the recessive phenotype of white flowers. Both homozygous recessive and heterozygous organisms can pass recessive traits to their offspring.

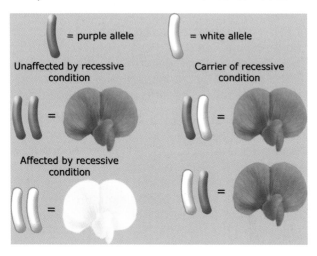

Figure 15.2.3

Possible Hereditary Patterns of Autosomal Recessive Genetic Diseases (and of recessive traits)

Figure (a) shows the gamete formation of a carrier parent and an unaffected parent. As can be seen, one would predict that 50% of the offspring would be carriers of the recessive trait or disease, while 50% would be unaffected. Figure (b) shows what one would expect if both parents were carriers. 50% of the offspring would be carriers, 25% would be unaffected, and 25% would have the disease or condition for which the recessive gene codes. Figure (c) represents the possible genotypes and phenotypes of an affected parent with an unaffected parent. All of the offspring would be carriers. Figure (d) represents the offspring of a carrier parent and an affected parent. 50% of the offspring are expected to be affected and 50% to be carriers. This relationship is important to understand. You can imagine how critical it is for geneticists to be able to accurately predict expected genotype outcome probabilities for families who have histories of genetic diseases.

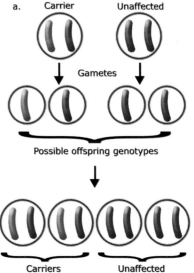

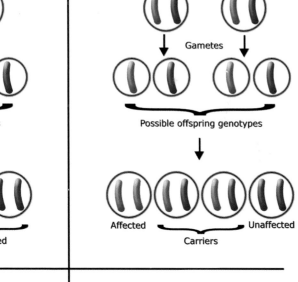

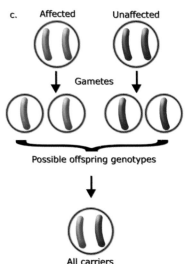

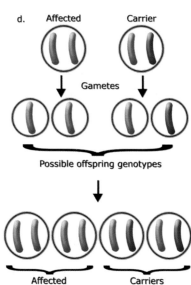

15.3 PKU

The genetic disease called **phenylketonuria**, or **PKU**, is inherited as an autosomal recessive disease. This is a disorder in which the enzyme which breaks down the amino acid phenylalanine is defective. This genetic disease is caused by a mutated gene which codes for the enzyme phenylalanine hydroxylase. People with PKU do not make this enzyme correctly because the gene that contains the code for making the enzyme has been mutated. The enzyme is synthesized with the incorrect amino acid sequence and does not work properly. Therefore, affected individuals do not metabolize phenylalanine. Phenylalanine levels build up in the blood stream and get deposited in the brain. This causes mental retardation and other problems. It is a completely treatable disease, as long as its presence is known.

Since PKU is caused by a recessive autosomal allele, the only way for the child to have PKU is to inherit one recessive allele from his carrier or affected mother and one from his carrier or affected father. If both parents are carriers for PKU, neither one of them will have PKU. They may not even know they are carriers. They do not have problems metabolizing phenylalanine because they also have a normal copy of the gene for the enzyme that breaks phenylalanine down. The enzyme product of the normal allele compensates for the lack of enzyme coded for by the abnormal allele. However, the child with PKU inherits two abnormal alleles, one from each parent, and so cannot metabolize phenylalanine.

15.4 PEDIGREE ANALYSIS

Because most genetic diseases are caused by recessive alleles, the disease may "skip" a generation or two, then reappear, making tracking the disease difficult. Therefore, geneticists use a **pedigree analysis** to follow the disease through generations. A pedigree analysis is a family tree that tracks the inheritance of traits over many generations. It shows the phenotypes of parents and their children over many generations. A pedigree analysis can be used to track genetic diseases or normal traits in families. (This is one way of determining the wild type phenotype and genotype.) The most practical application of a pedigree analysis is to track autosomal recessive and sex-linked genetic diseases in families.

For example, the presence of a "widow's peak" can be tracked using a pedigree analysis. The widow's peak refers to the appearance of the hairline across the forehead. A person with a widow's peak has the hair come to a small point in the middle of the forehead. A person without a widow's peak has a hairline that is straight across. The widow's peak is the dominant hairline in humans, while the straight across hairline is recessive. We will call the gene for a widow's peak W. Therefore, a person with a widow's peak may be homozygous dominant, WW, or heterozygous, Ww. A person without a widow's peak must then be homozygous recessive, ww.

In the case of widow's peaks, many individuals have been studied for the presence or absence of that trait. By tracing the inheritance pattern for the widow's peak through a pedigree analysis, we can identify which phenotype is recessive and which is dominant. This is a common problem of genetics.

In the pedigree analysis of the widow's peak, we know that the P generation, or grandparents, who did not have a widow's peak were homozygous recessive, ww. In addition, since the mating of the P generation resulted in offspring who also did not have widow's peaks, both grandparents who had a widow's peak were heterozygous, Ww. We know that if the grandparents who had a widow's peak were homozygous dominant, then all of the offspring would have had a widow's peak. But as you can see from the pedigree analysis, there was at least one child who was homozygous recessive and did not have a widow's peak

Figure 15.4.1

Widow's Peak

The presence of a widow's peak is genetically determined (at least before hair starts falling out!). It is not a genetic disease, but having a widow's peak is inherited as a dominant trait, and not having a widow's peak is a recessive trait. The right photo shows the dominant condition of a widow's peak. The left photo is the recessive condition of no widow's peak. The bottom figure is a pedigree analysis for a widow's peak. The analysis is read from the top down. A square represents a male and a circle a female. A line drawn between a square and a circle horizontally represents a marriage between the two individuals. Lines drawn down from a union indicate the number and sex of the children. The genotypes of the individuals are written inside of the square or circle. *WW* is the homozygous dominant condition, and people with that genotype have the phenotype of a widow's peak. *Ww* is the heterozygous condition and people with that genotype also have the phenotype of a widow's peak. However, they are carriers of the recessive gene for no widow's peak. Individuals with the genotype *ww* have both recessive genes for no widow's peak and so have the phenotype for a straight across hairline. One parent on the top left of the pedigree analysis is a carrier for no widow's peak, while the other has the homozygous recessive condition (or no widow's peak). The same is true for the parents at the top right of the analysis. The trait can be followed through the first and second generations as indicated using a pedigree analysis. In the first generation, you can see that two carriers of no widow's peak from each family were married and had two children. One child was born with the recessive condition of not having a widow's peak, and the other is a carrier. Pedigree analyses like this are used all of the time in genetics to follow inherited traits.

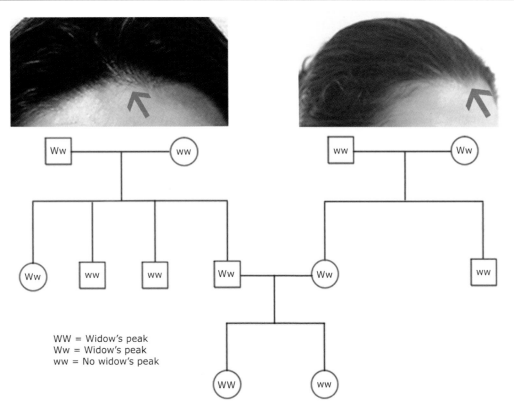

WW = Widow's peak
Ww = Widow's peak
ww = No widow's peak

Figure 15.4.2

Use of a Punnett Square to Help with Understanding Inheritance of Traits in Pedigree Analyses

Punnet squares can be helpful in determining whether a trait is dominant or recessive. One would first identify a trait that can be studied. In this case, we are still discussing the widow's peak trait. During the discussion of this figure, refer back to the pedigree analysis as needed.

a. Incorrect identification of genotypes and phenotypes for the presence of a widow's peak. The incorrect assumption was that each grandparent (the P generation) from the pedigree analysis in Figure 15.4.1 who had a widow's peak was homozygous dominant, *WW*. If that were true, then all of the F1 offspring would have had a widow's peak, as shown here, but they did not. Therefore, the data must be re-evaluated as below.

b. Correct identification of genotypes and phenotypes for the presence of a widow's peak. Since it is known that in each arm of the F1 generation, at least one child did not have a widow's peak, we know the grandparent with a widow's peak had to be heterozygous, *Ww*, in order to pass along a recessive allele to the child without a widow's peak.

a.

	W	W
W	Ww widow's peak	Ww widow's peak
W	Ww widow's peak	Ww widow's peak

b.

	W	W
W	Ww widow's peak	Ww widow's peak
W	ww no widow's peak	ww no widow's peak

A final note about this analysis: notice that even if all you knew about the 3rd generation was that one of the offspring did not have a widow's peak, you would be able to figure out the genotype of the 2nd generation (the F1 generation) parents. Notice that in the 3rd generation (the F2 generation), there is one child with a widow's peak—we know that this child has the genotype of *WW* or *Ww*—and one child without, who has the phenotype of *ww*. Since both second generation parents had a widow's peak, the only way they could have had a child with the recessive condition of no widow's peak would be if both of the second generation parents were heterozygous, *Ww*. In that instance, each parent would have a recessive allele to pass along to the child who is homozygous recessive without a widow's peak. A child cannot have a recessive condition unless he or she inherits a recessive allele for the condition from both parents.

15.5 CYSTIC FIBROSIS

Cystic fibrosis (CF) is the single most common inherited disease among Caucasians of European descent. 1:25 people are carriers of this disease. It is an autosomal recessive disorder. The child with CF inherits a recessive copy of the gene from the mother and one from the father. Assuming both parents are carriers, the chance of that happening is 1:4 (1:2 chance the gene comes from the mother and a 1:2 chance the gene comes from the mother, multiply together and you get a 1:4 chance). There are two forms of CF, both cause similar symptoms. One form is worse than the other as far as symptoms are concerned. In the 1960s, the life expectancy of a child with CF was three years. Now, with the advent of better treatments and an increased understanding of this disease, the life expectancy has improved to thirty-two years.

Figure 15.5.1

Inheritance of the Recessive CF Allele
Since cystic fibrosis is a recessive genetic disorder, in order for a child to be born with CF, he or she must receive a recessive allele for CF from both the mother and the father. There are two ways in which this can happen, as shown below. The most common way for a child to have CF is to be born from parents who are both carriers. As shown in figure (a), the child has a 1:4 (25%) chance of being born with CF when both parents are carriers. The situation in figure (b) is less common because most all people who have cystic fibrosis are **sterile**, which means they cannot reproduce. In that situation, one parent has CF; the other is a carrier. There is a 2:4 (50%) chance the child will be born with CF.

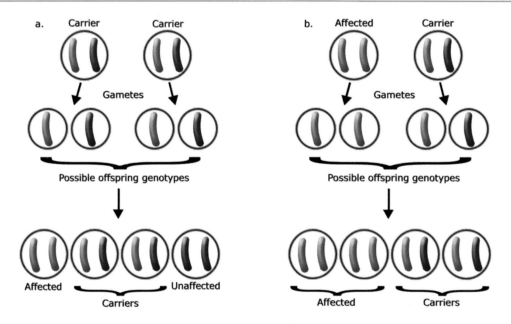

The **pathology** (or genetic/medical problem) in CF is a defective membrane protein. Recall from our discussion on membrane function that there are proteins in the membrane which facilitate the movement of molecules across the membrane. Patients with CF cannot properly move chloride ions across the cell membrane in the lungs and pancreas. As a result, a thick, sticky mucus builds up outside the cell.

Clinically, patients with CF have a difficult time clearing this secretion; that makes them susceptible to problems in the organs involved. In the lungs, they have frequent infections and do not exchange oxygen and carbon dioxide properly. They are also chronically short of breath. In the pancreas, the secretions build up in such a way that the release of digestive juices into the small intestine is blocked. This results in poor absorption of their food and malnutrition. In addition, the production and release of insulin is blocked, and CF patients often develop diabetes. Improvements in antibiotics to treat infections and medications to treat malabsorption and diabetes are largely responsible for the increase in life expectancy of CF patients.

From a genetic standpoint, there are actually thousands of mutations that have been described in the gene that codes for the membrane protein. However, all of the mutations have the same effect: they significantly impair the protein's function. The result is the build up of thick secretions that are hard to clear from the lungs and intestinal tract. Just remember, although there are many mutations of the membrane protein gene, all of them occur within the same gene, but at different locations. Although there are many separate mutations which have been seen in the CF gene, almost all of the mutations are point mutations in the CF membrane protein gene.

Because CF is a homozygous recessive disorder, we know that all of the children with CF have both recessive alleles. Let's call the dominant allele for the membrane protein *P*, and the recessive allele *p*. Therefore, someone who does not have CF (meaning they have at least one dominant or wild type allele for the membrane protein) will have the genotype of *PP* or *Pp*. Individuals affected by CF will have the genotype *pp*. Therefore, we know that in order for the child to have CF (genotype *pp*), both parents need to be heterozygous (genotype *Pp*) for the condition.

Figure 15.5.2

Pedigree Analysis for CF
One can follow the hereditary patterns of a recessive genetic disease like cystic fibrosis with a pedigree analysis.

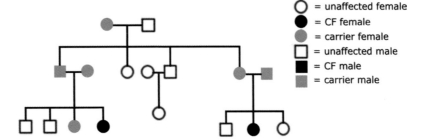

○ = unaffected female
● = CF female
◔ = carrier female
☐ = unaffected male
■ = CF male
◪ = carrier male

Oftentimes in pedigree analyses, we use an unshaded circle or box to indicate an unaffected individual. A lightly shaded–in box or circle indicates a carrier of the mutated allele. The solidly colored shape indicates an individual with the disease. Note that parents who are both carriers of the CF allele have a 25% chance of having a child with full-blown cystic fibrosis. Also, there is a 25% chance a child will not have the CF allele at all, and a 50% chance the child will be a carrier.

15.6 SICKLE CELL DISEASE

Sickle cell disease is the most common inherited disorder seen in individuals of African descent. In the United States, it is estimated that 1:13 people of African descent are carriers of the sickle cell gene. Like CF, sickle cell disease significantly reduces the life expectancy. People affected by sickle cell disease have a life expectancy of around forty years.

The pathology in patients with sickle cell disease is a defect in one of the four chains of proteins that make up the hemoglobin molecule. Hemoglobin is a complex molecule which is made up of four different protein chains. Sickle cell is caused by a substitution point mutation at the 6th codon of one of the four protein chains. This causes the amino acid valine to replace glutamic acid in the sixth position of the protein. The other three proteins which make up the hemoglobin molecule are normal, as is the remainder of the protein which has the point mutation. The only thing altered is the 6th amino acid of one of the four protein chains of the hemoglobin.

Even though this seems relatively minor, this mutation causes an abnormal structure of the hemoglobin macromolecule. The other three protein chains can no longer interact appropriately with the one, abnormal protein. This results in an abnormal shape of the hemoglobin in persons affected with sickle cell disease. This actually distorts the shape of the red blood cell. Instead of being ovals with a little dent in the middle on each side, the red blood cells look like a sickle. This change in the shape of the hemoglobin and the red blood cell severely limits the oxygen and carbon dioxide-carrying function of the hemoglobin and red blood cell.

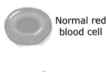

Normal red blood cell

Sickled red blood cell

Figure 15.6.1

Normal and Sickled Red Blood Cells
A graphic of normal red blood cells and the red blood cells of a sickle cell patient are shown here. The normal red blood cells contain normal hemoglobin. As a result, the structure of the cell is normal. It is a disc with little indentations on both surfaces. The sickle-shaped red blood cells are deformed because the hemoglobin molecules inside the cell are not normally shaped. Since the structure of the red blood cell is maintained by the presence of a normal hemoglobin molecule, the deformed hemoglobin molecule results in a deformed red blood cell.

Clinically, patients with sickle cell disease have problems carrying the oxygen to the tissues and the carbon dioxide away from the tissues. This results in chronic shortness of breath and fatigue. Also, because the red blood cells are no longer nice and round and smooth, they tend to get stuck in the capillaries and other small blood vessels. This leads to strokes. A stroke is an injury to the brain tissue caused by the blood supply getting cut off. Also, people with sickle cell disease often go into "crisis," which is severe pain in organs and bones induced by too little blood flow and too little oxygen supply to the tissues.

Because sickle cell disease is transmitted in a dominant-recessive fashion as CF is, both parents need to have the disease or be carriers of the disease to pass it on to their children. For example, two carriers of the disease mating leads to a 25% probability the offspring will either have sickle cell disease, or will not have the sickle cell allele at all; it leads to a 50% chance the child will be a carrier of the sickle cell trait. If one parent has sickle cell disease and the other parent is homozygous dominant, the children would all be carriers of the disease.

15.7 HETEROZYGOUS SUPERIORITY

You may be wondering why such deadly allele forms such as CF and sickle cell exist. It has been estimated that any one person carriers between five and eight harmful genes. However, they do not feel the effects of these genes because they have another normally-functioning gene to counteract the harmful one. In a sense, the presence of the CF gene and the sickle cell gene is due to a protective effect.

The CF gene has been traced back to Caucasians of European descent. People in this part of Europe have had to deal with a disease called cholera. Cholera is an infection of the intestines. It causes severe diarrhea. Prior to the antibiotics and good sewage, most people died as a result of dehydration when they developed cholera. Individuals who are heterozygous, or carriers, for the CF allele have been found to be protected from the extreme water loss and subsequent dehydration associated with cholera. Having one copy of the gene for CF actually protected people for many years from dying of cholera. Therefore, the recessive allele for CF lived on.

Sickle cell disease, recall, is most prominent in people with African roots, but is also found in populations surrounding the Mediterranean. Being a carrier for the sickle cell trait, or heterozygous, has been found to be protective against disease, just as carriers of the CF allele were protected against cholera. Africa and the countries surrounding the Mediterranean Sea are areas where malaria is a huge problem. Malaria is also an infectious disease, like cholera, but the affected tissue is the blood (yes, blood is a tissue). Untreated malaria generally kills the person it infects. The agent that causes malaria infects red blood cells. However, the red blood cells of carriers of the sickle cell trait are protected from being infected with malaria. For reasons beyond the scope of this course, the organism that causes malaria is not able to establish a severe infection in the red blood cells of carriers of sickle cell disease. Being heterozygous for the sickle cell allele was protective against malaria and the recessive allele lived on.

In many inherited diseases, the recessive allele imparts some protection against a disease or condition that exists in the area where the recessive allele originated. The condition of the heterozygous form being protective against some disease or illness is called **heterozygous superiority**.

Figure 15.7.1

Recognized Patterns of Inheritance
This table lists a few of the known heritable genetic diseases. Note that there are a variety of phenotypes included in this table, not all of them are due to mutations. As a result of identifying the normal nucleotide sequence in humans through the Human Genome Project, we are now able to exactly pinpoint the mutation(s) involved in creating various genetic diseases. All of these traits can be traced using the principles of genetics that we have learned thus far. In most genetics problems you are asked to solve, you will need to predict the probability of a child being born with a particular disease or the type of inheritance pattern the allele or trait shows, given particular information—including a pedigree analysis.

Single Allele Dominant
Huntington's Disease
dwarfism
cataracts
polydactyly (multiple digits)
Single Allele Recessive
albinism
cystic fibrosis
sickle cell disease
phenylketonuria (PKU)
deafness
X linked
colorblindness
hemophilia
muscular dystrophy
Polygenic
skin/hair/eye color
foot size
nose length
height
Multiple Alleles
blood type

15.8 HUNTINGTON'S DISEASE

Huntington's disease is an inherited disorder which is not caused by a recessive allele, but by a single dominant one. It is caused by a dominant somatic allele. It is called an **autosomal dominant genetic disease**. Since it is caused by a dominant allele, a person only needs to have one copy of the gene which causes Huntington's to be affected by the disease. It is caused by a mutation of a gene on chromosome 4.

Clinically, individuals with Huntington's disease (also called Huntington's chorea) generally do not show symptoms of the disease until they are at least forty. Huntington's causes a degeneration of the brain cells which results in personality changes; uncoordinated movements of the body, arms, and legs (called chorea); memory loss; and early death. Because Huntington's is caused by a dominant allele, children of a person with this disease have a 50% chance of having the disease. Therefore, many people who know they have Huntington's choose not to have children so their kids will not have the disease. Unfortunately, the onset of symptoms after the age of forty means that many people have children before knowing they have the disease. If a person knows of a family history of Huntington's, they can be tested to see if they have the gene.

Figure 15.8.1

Huntington's Disease Pedigree Analysis
Often, it is easy to spot a genetic disease that is inherited in a dominant fashion. When looking at the pedigree analysis of a dominant genetic disease, there are many more affected individuals than in a recessive disease. As you look below, you can see that is the case with Huntington's.

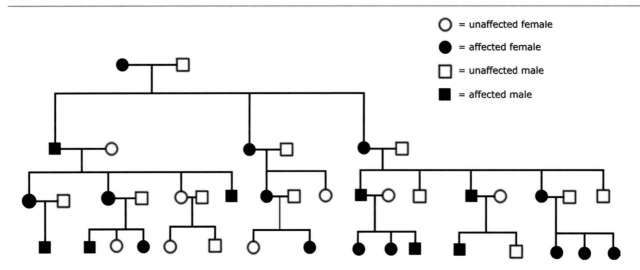

- ○ = unaffected female
- ● = affected female
- □ = unaffected male
- ■ = affected male

Diseases inherited in a dominant fashion are easier to track in families than are recessive diseases. Note that because it is caused by a dominant allele, the probability of a child whose parent has Huntington's disease being born with the disease is 50%.

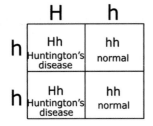

Table 15.8.2

Punnet Square Analysis in Huntington's Disease
Here, for example, the dominant allele for Huntington's Disease is designated *H* and the recessive is *h*. Probability states that 50% of the offspring will have Huntington's and 50% will not. Nature rarely follows probability, as the pedigree analysis for Huntington's shows. Note the differences in the inheritance patterns between the recessive diseases like CF or sickle cell disease, and the dominant nature of Huntington's (i.e., many more individuals are born with genetic diseases that are transmitted in a dominant fashion).

15.9 SEX-LINKED DISEASES

Recall from our previous discussions that there are number of sex-linked traits. Sex-linked traits are traits that are carried on the sex chromosomes, but do not determine the sex of the individual. When these sex-linked genes become mutated, they can result in a disease because of the mutated chromosome. These are genetic diseases that are transmitted from parent to offspring by the sex chromosomes.

Recall the Y chromosome is small. It almost exclusively contains information regarding sex characteristics. There are no recognizable Y-linked genetic diseases. The X chromosome, however, is larger than the *Y* and contains many more genes than those for sexual information. Because of this, the sex-linked diseases are referred to as **X-linked diseases**. What this means is that many more males than females are affected by sex-linked diseases. Ironically, because males always receive their *Y* chromosome from their father, they always inherit their X-linked disease from their mother. Females can be affected by X-linked diseases, but it is unusual.

Sex-linked disorders are, by their nature, recessive. This means you need to have two alleles present to have the disease. Since males have only one *X* chromosome, and the *Y* chromosome does not have the corresponding normal allele to counteract the mutant form, all males who inherit a sex-linked trait from their mother will have the disease. Females, on the other hand, show the true recessive pattern and must be homozygous recessive for the trait to have the disease.

Hemophilia and **color-blindness** are classic examples of sex-linked/x-linked genetic diseases. Hemophilia is a disease that causes the body to be unable to clot properly, which leads to excessive bleeding. Patients with hemophilia require multiple transfusions over their lifetime and often bleed to death. Also, as diseases transmitted in the blood such as HIV and hepatitis have become more and more common, many patients become infected with these illnesses through the transfusion. Blood donation centers try as hard as they can to screen blood donors and limit the donation of infected blood.

Color-blindness is exactly what it says it is—the inability to see colors (it is rare to have complete color-blindness, though). It is caused by a defect in the way the color-receiving cells in the eye work. There are many forms, but **red-green color-blindness** is the most common. People with red-green color-blindness are unable to distinguish the colors red and green. When they look at these two colors, they see a kind of brownish.

Table 15.9.1

Punnett Square Analysis of the Sex-linked Genetic Diseases Color-Blindness and Hemophilia

(a) *The expected genotype and phenotype of offspring of a father without color- blindness and a carrier mother:* We will call the normal gene X^B and the mutant allele X^b. Note that there is a 25% chance the child—always a male in this particular case—will be color–blind, and a 75% chance the children have normal vision. Note, also, that there is a 50% chance a male child will be color-blind and a 0% chance a female child will be color-blind.

(b) *The expected genotype and phenotype of possible offspring of a father with color-blindness and a carrier mother*: This demonstrates that a female can inherit an X-linked disease, but it is rare. In order for that to happen, the father needs to be color blind and the mother must be a carrier.

(c) *The expected genotype and phenotype of offspring of a father without hemophilia and a mother with the x-linked trait:* Note the probabilities of having normal children and affected males are the same as for the color-blindness example.

(d) Although it is rare, females with hemophilia do exist. It is only possible for this to happen if a carrier or affected female marries an affected male and they have children. The example on the right shows the situation of a hemophilic male and a carrier female having children.

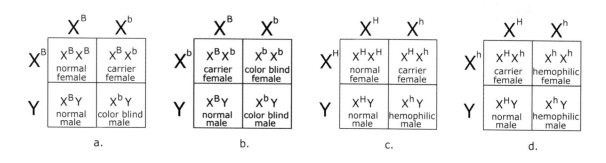

a.   b.   c.   d.

15.10 ANEUPLOIDY

You may recall we used the ending "-ploid" in reference to chromosomes when discussing mitosis and meiosis. The normal number of chromosomes in humans is forty-six, or two sets of twenty-three. Forty-six is the **diploid** number of chromosomes in humans; it is the normal number of chromosomes. **Haploid** refers to half the normal number of chromosomes present in the cell during meiosis. **Aneuploid** refers to any abnormal number of chromosomes in a cell. There are a number of genetic conditions that result in too many, or too few, chromosomes being transmitted from one parent to the offspring. **Polyploidy** is the term used by geneticists when cells contain too many chromosomes.

As you may recall from the last chapter, the process of nondisjunction causes either too many or too few chromosomes to be dispersed to the gametes. This is the cause of aneuploid organisms. Aneuploid genetic diseases are caused by nondisjunction during meiosis. Most aneuploid conditions are not compatible with life. Generally, the pregnancy ends early in miscarriage, or the baby dies soon after birth.

Down 's syndrome, **Kleinfelter's syndrome**, and **Turner's syndrome** are all examples of aneuploid conditions. Most of the people with these genetic diseases can live, but their life span is usually shortened. Individuals affected by these genetic disorders have consistent, observable abnormalities.

Down's syndrome is caused by a nondisjunction event of chromosome 21. It occurs in about 1:660 live births. During nondisjunction, one gamete in one of the parents receives two chromosome 21s, and the other gamete does not receive any. Individuals with Down's syndrome are formed from the abnormal gamete that has two chromosome 21s, and a normal gamete with one chromosome 21. This means they have three chromosome 21s, a condition referred to as **trisomy 21**. There is an unusually high rate of babies with Down's syndrome born to mothers older than 40. In women in their 20s, the incidence of Down's syndrome is about 1:1490 live births, but in women over 49, it is 1:11.

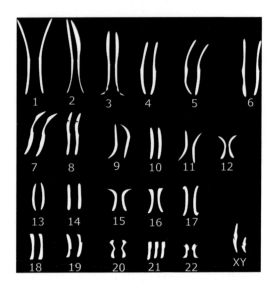

Figure 15.10.1

Trisomy 21, Down's syndrome
Trisomy 21 is the most common human polyploid condition. Its karyotype is shown here. People with Down's syndrome have three number 21 chromosomes. This means they have forty-seven total chromosomes. People who have genetic syndromes have common observable differences in the way they look or the way they function biochemically. Individuals with Down's syndrome have the common appearance of a wide forehead, epicanthal folds (small foldings of skin at the corners of their eyes) and large tongues. The large majority of people with trisomy 21 are also mentally retarded (but not all) and are sterile.

Trisomy 21 is not incompatible with life. However, there are common observed conditions which are associated with it. People with this disease are almost always mentally retarded, have large tongues, prominent epicanthal folds (skin folds above the eyes) and, often, cardiac defects. When given the proper environment, people with Down's syndrome are productive members of society and have a fairly normal life expectancy.

Both Turner's syndrome and Kleinfelter's syndrome are caused by nondisjunction events of the sex chromosomes during meiosis. Individuals with Turner's syndrome are always girls and have only one *X* chromosome. They often are short in stature, have small sex organs, webbed necks, kidney problems, and heart defects. Individuals with Kleinfelter's syndrome are always male and have the genotype *XXY*. They usually have long legs, small testes, and are mentally retarded.

15.11 ADVANCED

The study of genetics has led to significant ethical and moral questions that we all should be aware of, no matter which side of the issues you find yourself on.

As a result of expanding our knowledge of the genetic basis of disease, and the rapid growth of technological advancement, we are now able to detect genetic diseases before a baby is born. Genetic counselors are people who have been trained in human genetics and help prospective parents determine the risks associated with a pregnancy. In addition, there are tests and procedures that can be performed—**chorionic villus sampling**, **amniocentesis**, **ultrasound**, and **fetoscopy.**

Chorionic villus sampling can be done after the eighth week of pregnancy. It involves taking a small amount of tissue from a specific area of the placenta (the connection between the fetus and the mother) called the chorion. The chorion has the same genetic make-up as the fetus. In chorionic villus sampling, the DNA in the cells from the tissue sample is extracted and sequenced to check for abnormalities.

Amniocentesis involves obtaining a sample of the fluid surrounding the fetus, called the amniotic fluid. This procedure can be performed following the fourteenth week of pregnancy. The fluid contains cells from the fetus. DNA is extracted from these cells and sequenced to check for abnormalities. Both chorionic villus sampling and amniocentesis can harm the mother or the unborn baby, so they must be done only if absolutely necessary.

Ultrasound and fetoscopy are both ways of looking at the fetus before it is born to try to identify any obvious abnormalities. Ultrasound uses sound waves which are sent to the fetus and then bounce back, creating a picture of the fetus. Fetoscopy uses a small camera inserted into the uterus to look directly at the fetus. Ultrasound is safe as far as we know, but fetoscopy is a surgical procedure and as such does involve some danger to mother and child.

I started this section off by stating there are moral and ethical issues that advancing medical technology brings. You may be wondering what the moral and ethical issues are since the above information does not seem too controversial. The most significant moral/ethical issue is this: what is done if one of these tests is not normal? What happens if a pregnant woman finds out that her baby has a genetic disease or is deformed in some way? Unfortunately, many in our society have chosen to deal with the information that their unborn child has a genetic disease by killing the unborn baby. An abortion is a medical procedure (sadly performed by the same physicians who have taken an oath not to harm human life) that ends a pregnancy by killing the baby. This is an area that deserves a discussion with your parents.

Figure 15.11.1

Fetal Ultrasound
Medical imaging has come a very long way the past 20 years. This image was obtained using ultrasound and is of a fetus that is 20 weeks old. A fetus is a developing baby that is still in the womb.

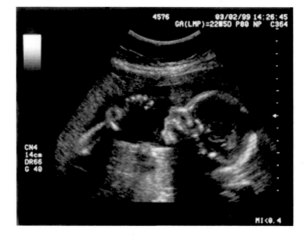

15.12 PEOPLE OF SCIENCE

Francis Collins MD, PhD, is a former homeschooled student and the director of the National Human Genome Research Institute. He oversees the Human Genome Project and has made many discoveries in the area of genetics, including isolating the genes which code for Huntington's disease, neurofibromatosis, and a type of adult leukemia. He is trying to apply the knowledge gained through mapping the entire human genome so that diseases such as diabetes, cancer, and heart disease may be cured rather than just treated.

15.13 KEY CHAPTER POINTS

- Congenital genetic diseases are diseases which are transmitted from parent to offspring. Most congenital diseases are cause by recessive genes.

- Affected individuals are said to have a genetic disease or recessive trait. A disease or trait caused by recessive alleles requires that the affected individual have both recessive alleles in order to have the condition.

- Carriers of a recessive condition have one recessive allele and one dominant allele for the condition for which the gene codes.

- Unaffected individuals have two dominant alleles for the condition for which the gene codes.

- A pedigree analysis is a way of tracking traits through multiple generations in a family.

- Cystic fibrosis is the most common inherited genetic disease among Caucasians. It is transmitted as a recessive condition.

- Sickle cell disease is the most common inherited genetic disease among people of African descent. It is transmitted as a recessive condition.

- Recessive alleles exist due to heterozygous superiority.

- Huntington's disease is transmitted in a dominant fashion.

- Sex-linked diseases, such as hemophilia and color-blindness, are carried on the X chromosome. They also follow a recessive hereditary pattern, but since males only have one X chromosome, they will have the disease if they inherit the recessive allele from their mother.

- Aneuploidy is the condition of having the incorrect number of chromosomes. The most common polyploid condition is trisomy 21.

- There are a number of ways to test a fetus for the presence of genetic diseases. These include fetal ultrasound, amniocentesis, and fetoscopy. However, there are serious ethical and moral questions to these practices regarding what is done with the results.

15.14 DEFINITIONS

affected
Individuals who have both copies of a recessive allele and therefore display the recessive condition.

amniocentesis
Obtaining a sample of the amniotic fluid surrounding a fetus by inserting a needle through the abdomen into the uterus. Used to check for DNA abnormalities.

aneuploid
A condition of an abnormal number of chromosomes in a cell.

carriers
Individuals who have one allele of the gene for a particular genetic disease or recessive condition.

chorionic villus sampling
Taking a small amount of tissue from a specific area of the placenta, called the chorion, to check for DNA abnormalities.

color-blindness
The inability to see colors.

congenital genetic diseases
Those abnormalities that people are born with and are the result of gene abnormalities.

diploid
The normal number of chromosomes being present in a cell.

fetoscopy
A procedure in which a small camera is inserted into the uterus to look directly at the fetus.

haploid
Half the normal number of chromosomes being present in a cell.

hemophilia
A disease that causes the body to be unable to clot properly, leading to excessive bleeding.

heterozygous superiority
The condition of the heterozygous genotype being protective against some disease or illness.

pathology
The nature of the disease or illness in a medical condition.

pedigree analysis
A family tree that tracks the inheritance of traits over many generations.

phenylketonuria (PKU)
A disorder in which the enzyme assigned to break down the amino acid phenylalanine is defective.

red-green color-blindness
The most common form of color-blindness leaving people unable to distinguish the colors red and green.

sterile
Unable to reproduce.

syndromes
A medical condition in which those affected have a characteristic appearance as well as behaviorial and other associated problems. Many syndromes are caused by congenital genetic disorders.

trisomy 21
The condition of having three chromosome 21s; also called Down's syndrome.

ultrasound
A test that sends sound waves to a fetus, then bounces them back to create an image of the fetus.

wild type
The "normal" phenotype.

X-Linked Diseases
Sex-linked diseases.

STUDY QUESTIONS

1. What is a geneticist?

2. What is a genetic disease?

3. Why is understanding the normal sequence of the human genome important?

4. True or False? Most genetic diseases are caused by dominant alleles.

5. What is a person called who has an allele for a certain disease and a copy of the normal gene? Since this person has the allele for the disease, do they have the disease?

6. Why are pedigree analyses helpful in understanding genetic diseases?

7. True or False? Cystic fibrosis (CF) is a genetic disease in which 1:25 people of African descent are affected.

8. If two people who have CF get married and have a child, what is the chance their child will have CF? (In reality, most males with CF are sterile because of the effects of the disease, but I would like you to answer this problem for the sake of the thought that goes into it).

9. CF usually results from a _____ mutation in the gene which codes for a _____ protein which is responsible for transporting _____ across the membrane.

10. Draw the Punnet square for the mating of one parent with sickle cell disease with one parent who is homozygous dominant. Call the normal hemoglobin gene *S* and the sickle cell allele *s*.

11. Why do some recessive alleles exist? What is that called?

12. Why do children of a parent with a dominant genetic disease have a higher likelihood of having the disease as compared to kids of parents who are carriers of a recessive gene?

13. True or False? Sex-linked genetic diseases always affect females more than males since they are transmitted by the *X* chromosome.

14. True or False? Trisomy 21 (Down's syndrome) is caused by a nondisjunction of chromosome number 21 and is a type of aneuploid condition.

15. _____ _____ _____, _____, _____ and _____ are all ways of evaluating a baby for congenital birth defects before they are born.

DNA Technology

16

16.0 CHAPTER PREVIEW

In this chapter we will:

- Define the terms associated with DNA technology.

- Discuss the process of transformation.

- Investigate the common methods for making recombinant DNA and inserting it into appropriate hosts.

- Review several ways in which recombinant DNA technology is being applied on a daily basis.

16.1 OVERVIEW

As the knowledge of the structure and function of DNA has grown since the time of Mendel, there have been extensions of this knowledge into practical applications. More specifically, there has been a huge growth of knowledge as to how to manipulate DNA. Yes, we have the ability to change the genetic structure of virtually any organism based on what we have learned over the past 150 years. (One of the problems, though, is what to do with that knowledge!)

The field of **genetic engineering**—or the application of molecular genetics for practical purposes—is a rapidly growing field in science. **DNA technology** involves the application of everything known about DNA for genetic engineering. Genetic engineering has been used to try and replace defective genes with the correct one. This has already been tried on humans—particularly to treat cystic fibrosis. There is much to be learned, as the initial trials of giving a normal allele to a person with a defective one has not been very successful in the long term treatment of those born with genetic diseases. However, genetic engineering likely holds the key to cure many diseases, both genetic and not, because the disease should be able to be cured by giving the person the normal gene.

16.2 TRANSFORMATION

Modern DNA technology was born out of the work of Fred Griffith and his 1928 study of *Streptococcus pneumoniae* (*Strep pneumo* for short). *Strep pneumo* is a bacteria that causes pneumonia, an infection in the lungs. Untreated, it leads to death in a majority of people and animals. There are two forms of *Strep pneumo*—a form that has the trait of a smooth, jelly-like capsule around the outside of it (called smooth), and a form that does not have that trait (called rough). Only the smooth form of *Strep pneumo* is pathogenic. "Pathogenic" is another way of saying "it causes disease." The rough *Strep pneumo* do not cause disease, the smooth *Strep* does.

Dr. Griffith injected the smooth *Strep* bacteria into mice, and they all got sick and died. After the mice died, he isolated the smooth *Strep* from their blood. He injected the rough *Strep* into mice and they did not get sick or die. He then took the smooth *Strep* and heated them to the point that they all were dead. He took these dead smooth *Strep* and mixed them with live rough *Strep*, then injected the mixture into the mice. Many of the mice became sick and died; he isolated smooth *Strep* from the blood of those that died even though he had injected rough cells into the mice.

From this experiment, he deduced that something from the dead smooth cells was able to make the rough cells cause the disease. He thought it was a part of the dead smooth bacterial cells, or some molecule from the dead cells. To identify what it was, the smooth cells were completely ground up and allowed to settle. The fluid was separated from the more solid cell components. Only molecules were contained in the fluid as the cell parts were left out. The fluid was then added to a live culture of rough cells. The rough cells were able to reproduce in this environment for several generations, and soon smooth bacterial colonies were growing. This proved that some type of chemical or molecule was the factor that caused the rough cells to develop the smooth trait. These smooth cells were then injected into the mice, and the mice became sick and died.

It has since been proven that the molecule that caused this to happen is, of course, DNA. In 1928, Dr. Griffith called the process of a change in a trait in an organism **transformation**. The modern definition of transformation is the genetic alteration of a cell resulting from the uptake and expression of foreign DNA. What Dr. Griffith had done was to supply the rough *Strep* cells with DNA from the smooth *Strep* cells. This DNA, including the gene coding for a capsule around the bacteria, was taken up by the rough *Strep*, incorporated into its genome, then expressed. Rough *Strep* cells were transformed into smooth strep cells. This technology is currently used by genetic engineers all the time.

Figure 16.2.1

Transformation
The principle of bacterial transformation created a revolution in genetics. Transformation is the ability of cells to take up foreign DNA, then begin to express whatever genes that DNA contains. Below is how transformation was discovered. The S bacterial cells are covered with a capsule. The cells with a capsule are able to cause disease. The R bacterial cells do not have a capsule and cannot cause disease. When the S cells are injected into mice, the mice become infected and die. Injecting the R cells or heat killed S cells does not cause infection. However, when heat-killed S cells and live R cells are injected into mice, the mice die. This is because the heat-killed S cells release their DNA inside of the mouse. Some of the R cells are able to absorb this DNA into their own DNA. After the R cells take the S DNA up, they are referred to as transformed R cells. The transformed R cells begin to express the genes contained in the absorbed S DNA. Some of the genes contained in the absorbed S DNA code for the production of the capsule. When the transformed S cells begin to express the capsule genes, they make a capsule and become infectious. Also, when the transformed R cells divide, the absorbed S DNA is passed along to the new cells. The transformed R cells are all able to cause disease, so the mice die. Further, when the scientists recovered blood from the mice injected with the heat killed S cells and the R cells, they were able to isolate bacteria with capsules. This effectively led to researchers learning how to get various prokaryotes to incorporate foreign DNA into their cells. Also, there is great research on how to effectively get eukaryotic cells (such as human cells) to incorporate foreign DNA, in order to cure genetic diseases.

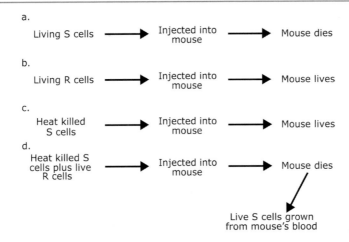

16.3 RECOMBINANT DNA

The transformation process has been studied and modified extensively over the past thirty years. It has subsequently been applied to many different areas, as noted in the beginning of the chapter. The usual purpose of utilizing DNA technology is to clone a gene. This means to isolate a gene and make many copies of it. Then the many copies are made into many, many protein molecules the gene codes for. In order to understand DNA technology, it is critical to understand that once an outside gene has been incorporated into an organism, the gene is then transcribed and translated as if it were a normal gene in the organism. This is the principle of transformation and the reason the rough *strep* bacteria were able to develop traits of smooth *strep* bacteria.

Recombinant DNA is the name given to DNA that is made up of DNA derived from two or more organisms. One molecule of DNA which contains DNA from two or more organisms is recombinant DNA. The DNA of the rough *Strep* cells, after they were grown in the presence of the fluid from the busted up smooth cells, would properly be referred to as recombinant DNA. Inside the rough cells, the DNA of the rough *Strep* combined with the DNA of the smooth *Strep* and formed recombinant DNA. Then the newly changed organism began to express the traits given to it by the new DNA.

For a historical perspective, let's briefly examine how scientists used to isolate genes and make recombinant DNA. In the beginning of DNA technology, in order to obtain a specific gene that coded for a specific protein, scientists started with the cells that normally made a lot of the protein whose gene they wished to isolate. Then they obtained as much mRNA that coded for the desired protein from the cells as possible. Once they had the mRNA, they then made DNA from the mRNA. In essence, they made DNA backwards by starting from the protein and ending with the DNA which codes for that protein.

The most common use of recombinant DNA is to isolate a gene which codes for a protein or enzyme of interest. Once the gene is isolated, it can then be inserted into another organism—usually a bacteria—which makes a lot of the protein for which the recombinant gene codes. There are two ways to make a recombinant gene (recombinant DNA)—"work backwards"—using the mRNA which codes for the protein of interest or "work forwards" using the actual DNA which contains the gene of interest. We will discuss "working backwards" in 16.4 and "working forwards" in the sections following.

16.4 REVERSE TRANSCRIPTASE

The mRNA route is called working backwards because when you start with an mRNA molecule, you must make a molecule of DNA from it. You should realize that the mRNA molecule is the complimentary base sequence of the DNA which contains the gene. That means if you can make a molecule of DNA from the mRNA, you will in effect be making the gene. It is called backwards because instead of making mRNA from a DNA template like normal, a DNA molecule is made from an mRNA template. Fortunately, there is a way to do this.

In the early days of making recombinant DNA, scientists first started with cells from the pancreas. A protein hormone called insulin is made in the pancreas, and a way to make human insulin was needed. The scientists first needed to isolate the mRNA for insulin. If this mRNA which coded for the insulin could be "backward" made into DNA, then the molecule of DNA made from the mRNA would be the gene for insulin. Scientists are able to make DNA from mRNA by using an enzyme called **reverse transcriptase**. Reverse transcriptase is an enzyme which can make a single-stranded DNA molecule using an mRNA template. This enzyme itself was taken from viruses. Reverse transcriptase was added to the mRNA which coded for insulin, along with the nucleotides A, T, C, and G. Reverse transcriptase base-pairs the nucleotides of DNA across from their complimentary mRNA bases. After a while, there was single-stranded DNA made. This single-stranded DNA molecule represents the gene for the insulin. The single-stranded DNA molecule was then mixed with DNA polymerase and more A, T, G, C. DNA polymerase makes double stranded DNA from a single-stranded DNA template. After a while, the single-stranded DNA would be made by the DNA polymerase into a double-stranded DNA molecule. This double-stranded DNA molecule could then be studied further. This was a slow and methodical method, but was effective at making recombinant DNA.

Figure 16.4.1

Reverse Transcriptase
Figure (a) In cells, mRNA is normally made from a DNA template. Then the mRNA is translated into the protein. This is known in DNA technology as "working forwards". Figure (b) However, in the early days of recombinant technology, the protein would be made by making the gene from an mRNA template. Since mRNA is normally made from a DNA template, this is called "working backwards". Working backwards is possible because some viruses contain an enzyme called reverse transcriptase. This enzyme makes a molecule of single-stranded DNA (ss DNA) from an mRNA template. Once the gene is made from the mRNA template, it can be transcribed and translated into the desired protein. Reverse transcriptase has been an essential tool in genetics and recombinant technology.

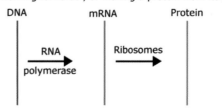

a. "working forwards", or making a protein from its gene

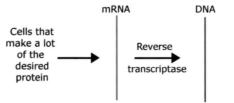

b. "working backwards", or making a gene from its protein

16.5 BRIEF OVERVIEW OF MODERN RECOMBINANT TECHNOLOGY

Although reverse transcriptase is still used in DNA technology, there are newer and quicker ways to make recombinant DNA. Current methods to make recombinant DNA do not usually "work backwards" making the gene from its complimentary mRNA using reverse transcriptase. Instead, most genes that need to be isolated and made into recombinant DNA are directly isolated. That is, the gene is removed from the DNA which contains it by chemically cutting the DNA on either side of the desired gene. Then the gene can be transcribed and translated into the desired protein. This is called working forwards because the desired protein is made the same way as it is in cells—the DNA is transcribed into mRNA and then mRNA is made into the desired protein.

Modern methods for synthesizing recombinant DNA require three things: restriction enzymes, a vector and an appropriate host organism. Restriction enzymes cut DNA at specific places. This is critical to linking pieces of DNA together. A vector is the unit used to get the recombinant DNA into the host. The host is the organism the DNA is introduced into. The host then makes a lot of the product of the gene which is introduced into it. We will look at these three components in more detail, individually.

16.6 RESTRICTION ENZYMES

The process of isolating genes from normal DNA, rather than making the gene from the corresponding mRNA segment, is possible only because of **restriction enzymes**. Restriction enzymes cut DNA at specific nucleotide sequences. There are several hundred restriction enzymes known to exist. Restriction enzymes are normally found in bacteria and protect the bacteria's DNA from invading virus DNA. If a bacterium is infected by a virus which contains DNA, the restriction enzyme cuts the viral DNA, which inactivates it, protecting the bacterium.

Restriction enzymes are very precise because they will only cut DNA at specific nucleotide sequences, typically four to eight nucleotides long. For example, the restriction enzyme EcoRI will only cut DNA at the sequence "GAATTC." If there is no segment of the DNA with the sequence of GAATTC, then EcoRI cannot cut it. BamHI will only cut DNA at "GGATCC." It does not matter what the source of the DNA is (animal, plant, bacterium, or virus) for a restriction enzyme to cut it. If the DNA nucleotides are in the proper sequence it will be cut.

Figure 16.6.1

Restriction Enzymes
Restriction enzymes are another essential tool used in recombinant DNA technology. Restriction enzymes are normally found in bacteria to cut foreign viral DNA that has infected the bacteria. There are many different restriction enzymes currently used. They all have the ability to cut any double-stranded DNA molecule at a specific site. DNA from a bacterium or animal can be cut with these enzymes. The key to the cut is that it always occurs at the same nucleotide sequence for any given restriction enzyme. Also, the enzyme cuts the DNA into short sequences, which are not base paired at the ends. This results in the formation of sticky ends, which can then stick onto other sequences of DNA that are complimentary to the sticky ends. The restriction enzyme shown below is EcoRI and cuts DNA at the sequence of GAATTC.

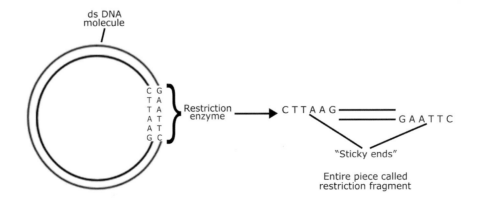

Two critical properties of restriction enzymes are a key to their usefulness in DNA technology. First, the sites that are cut by restriction enzymes are specific and well-mapped by geneticists. This enables scientists to use a specific restriction enzyme for a specific purpose, depending on the nucleotide sequence of the gene being used. The second critical property of the restriction enzyme is that it cuts the DNA so that each double-stranded end of the cut DNA has a short length of a single strand hanging off of it. These are called **sticky ends**. We will see the importance of sticky ends in the next section.

16.7 VECTORS

Once a gene has been isolated using a restriction enzyme, there needs to be a way to get the gene into the host organism. A vector is the second piece of the recombinant DNA puzzle. A **vector** is a unit which introduces DNA into a host. Often, recombinant hosts are bacteria. You have some DNA which you have cut with a restriction enzyme, but have no effective way to get the DNA into the bacterium. If you put the DNA into the fluid in which the bacterium lives, the bacterium may take the DNA up into its cytoplasm. Then again, it may not. If it does take the DNA up, it will recognize the DNA as foreign and cut it with a restriction enzyme before it has a chance to be inserted into the bacteria's DNA. There needs to be a more effective way to get the DNA into the host and protect it from the bacteria's normal restriction enzyme defenses.

Vectors are the way in which DNA is introduced into the host. There are two common vectors in use today, **viruses** and **plasmids**. Both of these particles exist normally in nature. They are small pieces of DNA surrounded by a protective covering. Both plasmids and viruses normally inject their DNA into bacteria. They are effective at delivering DNA into a bacterial cell. Because plasmids are most commonly used, we will discuss them, but be aware that a virus can work just as well.

Figure 16.7.1

Plasmids

Plasmids are sequences of double-stranded DNA found in bacteria. Plasmids are not living organisms; they are simply circular pieces of DNA found in the cytoplasm separate from bacterial DNA. Plasmids can easily enter into bacteria, and then their DNA is copied inside the bacteria. Plasmids are a commonly-used vector in recombinant DNA technology to get the desired DNA into the host organism.

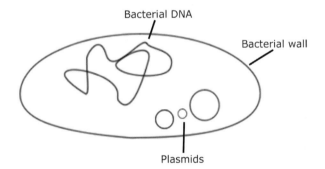

Normally, plasmids are double-stranded, circular pieces of DNA that exist within the cytoplasm of bacteria. They are separate from the bacterial DNA and are able to replicate themselves independently of the bacterial DNA. Some bacteria have only one copy of one type of plasmid inside it; others may have several copies of many different plasmids. However, the machinery to replicate and to transcribe and translate the plasmid genes belongs to the bacteria. There are many different plasmids in use with recombinant DNA technology. They are chosen by the researcher as carefully as the restriction enzyme is.

When researchers want to make a recombinant plasmid or virus, the process is as follows:

- The DNA containing the gene is cut by the desired restriction enzyme.

- This results in a linear DNA molecule with sticky ends.

- The vector DNA is cut with the same restriction enzyme.

- This also makes a linear DNA molecule with sticky ends. The sticky ends of the gene are complimentary to the sticky ends of the vector.

- An enzyme called **ligase** is then added to the cut gene DNA and the cut vector DNA.

- Ligase is an enzyme which links together DNA nucleotides that are complimentary to one another.

- When the vector and gene DNA are mixed together with the ligase, ligase links together the sticky ends of the gene DNA to the sticky ends of the vector DNA.

- This forms one circular piece of recombinant DNA.

Now a **recombinant plasmid** has been made. This process is repeated until thousands or millions of plasmids have been made, each containing the same gene.

Figure 16.7.2

Making a Vector for Recombinant DNA

Below is one of the multi-step processes which can be used to make a vector. Once the vector is made, it is used to introduce the foreign DNA it contains into another organism. Although there are several ways to do this today, the slightly older way of starting with a molecule of mRNA is shown below. mRNA is obtained from a source which is rich in the desired protein. For example, if one wanted to make a lot of insulin, then cells from the pancreas would be crushed, and the mRNA extracted. The mRNA is added to a vial with the enzyme reverse transcriptase. Reverse transcriptase is an enzyme found in viruses. Also added to the vial with the mRNA and reverse transcriptase are the four DNA nucleotides. As the broth sits, the reverse transcriptase synthesizes single-stranded DNA (ss DNA) from the mRNA template. This process then makes the DNA gene for the desired protein using the mRNA. Once the ss DNA was made, then DNA polymerase was added. DNA polymerase made a complimentary DNA strand, effectively turning the ss DNA into double-stranded DNA (ds DNA). Then, a plasmid is cut using a restriction enzyme. Scientists use the appropriate restriction enzymes so the sticky ends of the cut plasmid DNA are complimentary to the ends of the synthesized ds DNA. When the cut plasmid DNA and the ds DNA are mixed, the ds DNA sticks to the plasmid DNA. This plasmid is now called a vector and will be used to get the DNA into the host. The vector is added to a vial containing a host, often the bacteria *E. coli*, and a broth solution that provides nutrients for the *E. coli* to replicate. Once the plasmid gets inside the host, the host begins to make the gene product of the recombinant DNA. In our example, if the gene for insulin was made from the mRNA for insulin, once the plasmid containing the recombinant insulin gene was inserted into the host, insulin would start to be produced. That insulin can then be collected, purified, and used to treat diabetics.

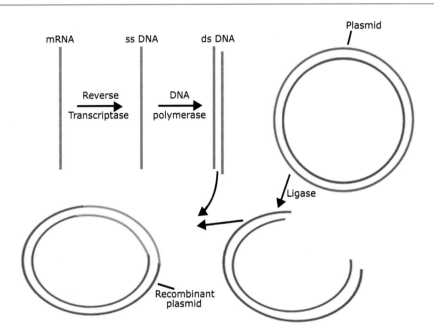

16.8 GETTING THE RECOMBINANT DNA INTO THE HOST

Now that the recombinant plasmid has been made, it needs to get into the host. A **host** is a suitable organism to receive the recombinant DNA. Once the host receives the recombinant DNA, the host has to further allow the recombinant DNA to insert into the host's DNA. A host is usually a bacterium. However, there is no limit to which type of organism can be a host. Even humans have served as hosts in attempts to cure genetic diseases (we will get to that later). A good host is one that has well understood biochemistry and is hardy (meaning it does not die easily). A common host is the bacterium *Escherichia coli*, a bacteria normally living in the intestines.

Figure 16.8.1

Bacteriophage
This is an electron micrograph of a bacteriophage on the surface of a bacterium. Bacteriophages are a type of virus and are used as vectors. Viruses are specialized at injecting DNA or RNA into cells and infecting them. Bacteriophages are engineered to attach to the surface of the bacterial cell and inject the recombinant DNA into the bacteria. Once injected, the DNA is taken up into the bacterial DNA. The gene product of the recombinant DNA is then made by the bacterial cell.

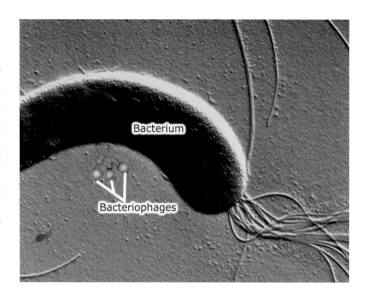

The recombinant plasmids are then added to the host in a solution of chemicals that helps the host grow well and the plasmids to be incorporated into the host. When the recombinant DNA enter the host's DNA, the host is called a **transgenic** organism. A transgenic organism contains DNA from another species, which has been introduced into it by a vector. Once the plasmid has been taken into the host, the bacteria then makes the protein which is coded for by the recombinant gene. This protein is then purified and studied further, or used for medical and other purposes. The process of making a recombinant plasmid and inserting it into a vector (plasmid or virus) to make the gene's protein is called **gene cloning**.

16.9 RFLP ANALYSIS AND DNA FINGERPRINTING

In order to accomplish DNA fingerprinting, a process called **restriction length polymorphism**, or **RFLP analysis** is used. RFLP analysis works by first breaking larger pieces of DNA into smaller pieces using restriction enzymes. These smaller pieces are referred to as **restriction fragments**. Restriction fragments are highly specific to an individual. That means the fragments of DNA generated from one person are different than those generated in another person when their DNA is cut by the same restriction enzyme. Typically, five fragments are studied from one person. The chance that the same five restriction fragments would match in two unrelated people is 1:1,000,000. This accuracy improves when more fragments are studied. Because it is highly specific, DNA fingerprinting is commonly used to try to link suspects to crime scenes when there is not much other evidence to do so.

After the restriction fragments are generated, they are placed onto a gel and subjected to electrical current. This is called **electrophoresis**. The electrical current makes the restriction fragments move into the gel; how far depends both on the size and the charge of the fragment. Then, the double stranded DNA on the gel is split into single chains, and a radioactive **probe** is added to the gel. The probe consists of short segments of DNA that will stick to specific areas on the single-stranded DNA in the gel. Once the probe has been added, a picture is taken of the gel with a special camera. When the probe sticks to the gel, dark bands form in that area. These bands are called **DNA fingerprints**; like normal fingerprints, they are unique to the individual from which they came. The location and darkness of the bands are matched from suspect to crime-site sample. If there is a match in the banding pattern, there is a high probability that the suspect was there at some point in time.

Figure 16.9.1

DNA Fingerprint Technology and RFLP Analysis

DNA fingerprinting takes advantage of the fact that certain DNA sequences are highly personal in certain segments of the DNA. For example, the exact sequences of nucleotides in DNA are not exactly the same as they are in you or anyone else. In our example below, vial #1 contains a DNA sample from a suspect of a murder. Vial #3 contains DNA from another suspect. Vial #2 contains DNA found at the scene of the crime.

(a) DNA which tends to show the most variability is cut into small pieces. These are called restriction fragments.

(b) The restriction fragments are placed into a gel and subjected to electrical current. This is called electrophoresis. The electricity causes the restriction fragments to move into the gel. Depending on how large and how charged the fragments are, they move different distances into the gel.

(c) A radioactive marker is added to the gel after electrophoresis. The marker sticks to the DNA fragments so they "light up" when exposed to a special kind of camera film.

(d) A picture is taken of the gel. The bands seen on the gel correspond to the restriction fragments and how far they moved into the gel during electrophoresis. The banding patterns of numbers 1 and 3 are compared to the sample taken at the crime scene. You can see the banding patterns for numbers 1 and 2 do not match up at all, but the patterns for numbers 2 and 3 do match. Therefore the suspect whose DNA sample was in the vial #3 was at the crime scene.

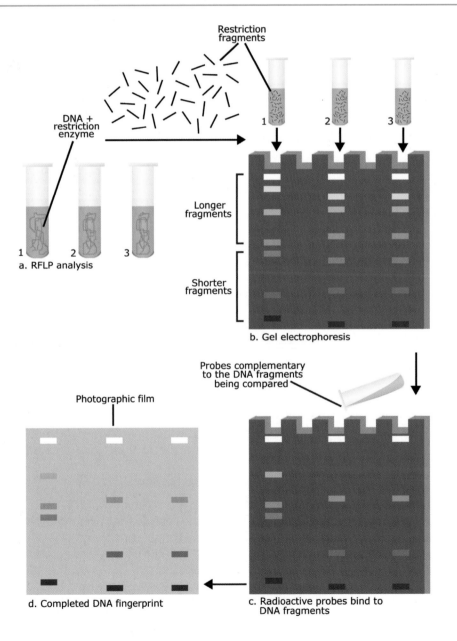

16.10 POLYMERASE CHAIN REACTION

Sometimes, whether the sample is from a crime scene or a 4,000 year-old mummy, there is not enough DNA to obtain a DNA fingerprint. If there is even a little DNA, though, that amount can be amplified by a process called **polymerase chain reaction**, or **PCR**. PCR is a technology used to make a lot of DNA from a sample which contains little DNA.

In PCR, the small amount of DNA is mixed with the four DNA nucleotides (A, T, G, and C), the enzyme to make DNA (DNA polymerase) and a primer (a small sequence of DNA to get the process started). In short time, the sample DNA is copied, as it would be in the nucleus before mitosis or meiosis, with the amount of DNA doubling about every five minutes. In this way, enough DNA can be made in a relatively short time to be used for RFLP analysis.

Figure 16.10.1

PCR

Polymerase chain reaction can be used to "amplify" small amounts of DNA. The DNA sample is mixed with DNA polymerase, the four DNA nucleotides and primers. Primers are proteins which help to get DNA synthesis started. The materials are mixed together and, as they sit, the DNA polymerase makes more and more copies of the original DNA sample. Relatively quickly, many copies of DNA can be made from a few.

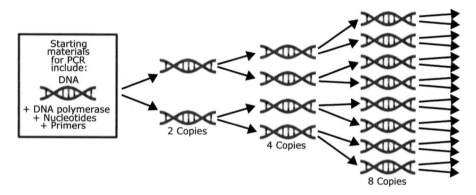

Finally, the ultimate in DNA technology is not in cloning a gene, but cloning an entire organism. This involves taking DNA from an adult organism, then manipulating it in such a way that it grows into a new organism that is genetically identical to the organism it came from. You may have heard of the sheep called "Dolly." Dolly was the first organism to be cloned from a somatic cell. She was cloned in Scotland. She was born in 1996 and lived until 2003. Her health was not good, though, and she did not live a normal lifespan for a sheep. That is typical of cloned animals. Sheep, goats, cows, mice and pigs have successfully been cloned in laboratories. They appear to function normally, but do not have a normal life span and may be susceptible to disease at earlier ages than usual.

16.11 APPLIED DNA TECHNOLOGY: GENE ISOLATION

There are four main areas of the use of DNA technology. The first one is isolating a particular gene of interest. Recall that genes code for the production of proteins, and the proteins then influence the organism to behave or respond in a certain way. Once a gene has been isolated, it may be studied or used in a number of ways. This helps us understand why a protein does not work properly when its gene is mutated. Also, in order to make a transgenic organism the desired gene needs to be isolated so it can be inserted into the host.

16.12 APPLIED DNA TECHNOLOGY: SELECTIVE BREEDING

A second area of application is to give an organism a trait that it did not previously have. Humans have been doing this naturally for thousands of years with domesticated animals and plants in the process of selective breeding (there was originally only one type of dog or cow or chicken). **Selective breeding** is a process by which organisms that contain a particular trait, or traits, are bred with one another across many generations in order to make that trait more obvious. Eventually, a pure-bred line is established with traits different than those of its ancestors.

Until recently, humans did not realize that selective breeding was a form of DNA technology. Although selective breeding does not seem technologically advanced, it does take advantage of genes and the traits that genes impart upon individuals in order to obtain a desired characteristic or trait. One example is, again, the basset hound. There have not been basset hounds running around the earth for thousands of years. Rather, these animals were bred to look like they do. Dogs that were a bit shorter and had larger ears than other dogs were bred together. The traits for shortness and larger ears were passed from parent to offspring. Always the shortest of the animals with the largest of ears were bred with one another from generation to generation. Over time, bassets eventually came to look as they do. This process is (and has been) practiced for thousands of years by horse breeders, bird breeders, dog breeders, cat breeders, etc.

16.13 APPLIED DNA TECHNOLOGY: GENE CLONING

The third area DNA technology is used for is to clone a gene in order to make a large amount of the protein the gene codes for. We have previously discussed this at length. Gene cloning is the DNA technology in which a gene is first isolated; then exact copies of that gene are made and inserted into a vector. There are many examples of DNA technology being used to clone genes for medical purposes.

We spoke earlier of insulin and its relationship to diabetes. Diabetics cannot control their blood sugar properly because they do not make any or enough insulin. As a result, many diabetics need to inject insulin under their skin to control their blood sugar. Recombinant technology has been applied to the manufacturing of insulin. The human gene which codes for insulin has been cloned. It has been inserted into billions of bacteria, which are now producing human insulin. This insulin is then purified, packaged, and ultimately injected under the skin by diabetics to treat their diabetes.

DNA technology is also commonly in use to make vaccines. In this application, there is a particular organism that causes disease in humans or domestic animals. Many of these diseases are preventable with vaccines. A **vaccine** is something which is injected into a person or animal. This injected material then causes the person or animal to develop resistance against the disease that is targeted for prevention. In order for a vaccine to be effective, it must cause the person who receives the vaccine to develop immunity against the organism. There are two ways to develop immunity to a contagious disease—contract the disease, or get vaccinated against it.

What confers immunity to the disease is the development of antibodies. Antibodies are made whenever we are exposed to a contagious illness or a vaccine. Antibodies act to deactivate the disease-causing organism. They also act to protect us from being infected by the same organism twice. Antibodies are made to various proteins on the surface of the infectious disease-causing cell. Then, if we are exposed to the same organism again, the antibodies deactivate so we do not get sick.

Recombinant technology takes the genes for various cell surface proteins found on infectious agents and inserts the genes into another organism that does not cause illness to develop when exposed to it. This organism then expresses the proteins for the infectious agent on its cell surface, allowing antibodies to be made to these proteins without getting sick. Later, if the person is exposed to the infectious agent, it is cleared from the body without becoming ill, because of the antibodies generated to the recombinant organism.

16.14 APPLIED DNA TECHNOLOGY: GENE THERAPY

Gene therapy is another extension of recombinant DNA technology. Gene therapy is being studied as a way to cure genetic diseases. In gene therapy, a person born with a defective gene is given the proper gene through recombinant technology, hopefully curing the genetic disease. All of the treatments using recombinant technology to treat human diseases are still in the trial stages and will take a number of years before they are perfected. However, gene therapy appears to be the future of treating many medical illnesses.

The first application of gene therapy in a human was in 1990. A child with adenosine deaminase deficiency (ADA: a rare hereditary immune disorder) was given recombinant DNA containing the gene which coded for a normal adenosine deaminase enzyme. Since that time, research has taken off, trying to perfect recombinant technology to treat genetic disease.

Cystic fibrosis is an example in which DNA recombinant gene therapy is actively being pursued. Like ADA, CF is one of the nearly 4000 human genetic diseases known to be caused by a single faulty gene. We know where the defective CF gene is located (on chromosome 4). We also can remove a normal gene for the channel protein by using restriction enzymes. This gene could then be given to a person with CF in order to try to induce the patient to make a normal channel membrane protein and cure the disease. This has in fact been done, using a virus as the vector (the host is the human with CF). Early results are promising that recombinant technology will be effective against all genetic diseases such as sickle cell, CF, muscular dystrophy, and PKU. Also, common diseases such as diabetes may be treatable using gene therapy. There is extensive research into using gene therapy to treat cancers, since cancer results from some genes not turning off.

There are many agricultural applications for genetics, as well. Plants have been treated with gene therapy. They have been genetically engineered to bear fruit with no seeds or fruit that takes longer to ripen, so it does not spoil easily. Also, genes have been introduced into plants to make then resistant to certain diseases and herbicides (chemicals used to kill weeds).

16.15 APPLIED DNA TECHNOLOGY: FORENSICS

The fourth application of DNA technology is in forensics. More and more frequently, DNA is being used to link suspects to a crime scene. This is particularly true if there is not much evidence, or if the evidence is disorganized and difficult to interpret. Samples of hair or blood can be used to identify who was at a crime scene. This information can then be used to identify whether potential suspects should be actual suspects. Unless a criminal has an identical twin, there is no one else on the planet that has the same DNA sequence. If a person's DNA is found somewhere, that person was there. This is frequently where DNA fingerprinting is performed.

16.16 ETHICS

Rather than a "People of Science" section, I thought we would have a short discussion on the ethics involved in cloning, whether genes or entire organisms. Opponents of cloning state, rather correctly, that cloners have the power to "play God" by creating and manipulating life. Also, it is not understood how safe the genetically engineered organisms are. People who are disagreeable with cloning are afraid that animals—humans in particular—will be made by cloners simply to fulfill medical needs. For example, there are legitimate concerns that cloned humans would be used to supply needed organs for transplantation or to be used as research subjects. The potential moral and ethical dilemmas are felt to be too much to overcome by opponents of cloning.

Proponents of cloning, while they recognize that there are ethical dilemmas to be faced, see cloning as a benefit to all involved. The benefit is felt to outweigh any possible drawbacks of the procedure. Also, they feel any moral or ethical dilemmas are far off at some time in the future, so there will be plenty of time to deal with them as they crop up.

16.17 KEY CHAPTER POINTS

- Genetic engineering is the application of molecular genetics and DNA technology for practical purposes.

- Transformation is the genetic alteration of a cell by introduction, uptake, and expression of foreign DNA into a cell. This process has the ability to change or introduce new traits into a cell.

- Recombinant DNA is DNA made up of genetic material from two or more unrelated organisms.

- Reverse transcriptase is an important enzyme in recombinant DNA technology. It makes DNA from an mRNA template.

- A vector is used to introduce recombinant DNA into an appropriate host.

- Restriction enzymes are used to cut DNA at precise locations.

- Common vectors are plasmids and viruses.

- Common host organisms are bacteria, particularly *E. coli*.

- Recombinant DNA can be used to make large amounts of a particular gene product (protein). It can also be used to introduce normal genes into organisms which contain abnormal genes.

- Gene therapy may be able to cure genetic diseases such as cystic fibrosis and muscular dystrophy. Gene therapy also has the potential to cure cancer and diabetes.

- DNA technology of RFLP analysis, which makes a DNA fingerprint, can be used to identify people and to link criminals to crime scenes.

- There are serious moral and ethical issues which need to be addressed regarding the use of DNA technology.

16.18 DEFINITIONS

DNA fingerprints
Sections of DNA which are unique to the person or organism they came from.

DNA technology
The practical application of everything known about DNA.

gene cloning
The DNA technology in which a gene is isolated, then copied, exactly, manytimes over.

gene therapy
A treatment where a person born with a defective gene is given the proper gene through recombinant technology.

genetic engineering
The application of molecular genetics for practical purposes.

ligase
An enzyme which is able to base-pair segments of DNA.

plasmids
Naturally occurring (now, also man-made) segments of DNA that are taken up by bacteria and remain in bacteria indefinitely.

polymerase chain reaction (PCR)
A method of amplifying a small sample of DNA.

probe
Short segments of DNA that will stick to specific areas of single-stranded DNA.

recombinant DNA
A DNA molecule that is made up of DNA derived from two or more organisms.

recombinant plasmid
A plasmid made from two or more sources of DNA (one of the sources being the initial plasmid DNA).

restriction enzymes
Enzymes normally found in bacteria which cut foreign DNA entering the cell.

restriction fragment length polymorphism (RFLP)
A process to cut large pieces of DNA into smaller pieces for DNA fingerprinting.

restriction fragments
DNA segments obtained through **r**estriction **f**ragment **l**ength **p**olymorphism (RFLP).

reverse transcriptase
An enzyme which synthesizes DNA from an mRNA template.

selective breeding
A process by which organisms containing a particular trait, or traits, are bred with one another across many generations to refine the desired trait. The oldest form of genetic engineering.

sticky ends
The double-stranded end of a cut DNA with a short length of single-strand material hanging off of it.

transformation
The process of changing a trait in an organism as a result of the introduction of recombinant DNA into that organism.

transgenic
An organism that has DNA in it from another species.

viruses
A particle which contains DNA or RNA, but is not a living organism.

STUDY QUESTIONS

1. What are several ways that DNA technology is currently being used?

2. What is recombinant DNA?

3. Why is reverse transcriptase unusual? Why is this enzyme important in recombinant technology?

4. Why are restriction enzymes useful? (Please give at least two reasons.)

5. Why is a vector used in recombinant DNA technology? List at least two commonly-used vectors.

6. True or False? Plasmids normally exist in the cytoplasm of bacteria and use the bacteria's enzymes to replicate the plasmids DNA.

7. Describe the process of modern day gene cloning using restriction enzymes—start at the stage of obtaining the DNA and end with getting it into the host. Be specific in the description of the steps.

8. Describe the process of DNA fingerprinting.

9. Describe the process of PCR.

10. Why might gene therapy be able to cure a genetic disease like cystic fibrosis or sickle cell anemia?

PLEASE TAKE TEST #6 IN TEST BOOKLET

Introduction to the Creation and Evolution Origins Models

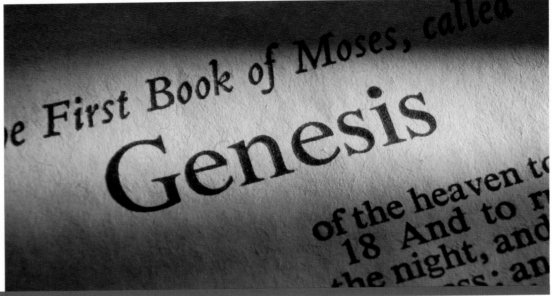

17

17.0 CHAPTER PREVIEW

In this chapter, we will:

- Introduce the creation and evolution origins models.

- Discuss biblical "kinds," "types" and "varieties" as clearer descriptions than "species" when referring to organism "speciation."

- Dive into the creation origins model, which is driven by the understanding that God's unerring Word accurately describes predicted and documented scientific observations.

- Learn that the objective scientific data are perfectly compatible with the creation origins model and frequently contradict the evolution model.

- Describe the difference between intelligent design and the intelligent design movement.

- Review the properties of "creation design" and its polar opposite, "evolution randomness," to clearly see that living systems display design properties and at the same time do not display random ones, implying that life is the result of specific design, not random events.

- Identify God as the perfect Intelligent Designer of life.

17.1 OVERVIEW

The next few chapters will be a little different than the previous sixteen because we will turn attention to the origins theories of creation and evolution. An **origin theory** explains "How we and everything else got here." So far, we have been dealing with rigorously tested, confirmed and undisputed scientific facts, processes, chemical reactions, etc. that you will find in any high school biology book. Studying origins theories is a little different because neither creation nor evolution are science as we typically think of "science." Scientific endeavors are usually defined by going in the field and making specific observations, digging up fossils or running laboratory experiments designed to test a certain hypothesis or study biology in a specific way. However, studying creation and evolution is very different because there is no way to directly "test" them. Instead, they are properly described as philosophical explanations to the "Where did we come from" question.

Creation theory, or the **creation model**, (believed by **creationists**) is an origins model that relies on God's inerrant Word, in which an all-powerful God created the universe and everything in it, simply by speaking the words, exactly as the Bible indicates.

> ***In the beginning, God created the heavens and the earth. The earth was without form and void, and darkness was over the face of the deep. And the Spirit of God was hovering over the face of the waters. And God said, "Let there be light," and there was light. And God saw that the light was good. And God separated the light from the darkness. God called the light Day, and the darkness he called Night. And there was evening and there was morning, the first day.*** *Genesis 1:1 – 5*

Evolution theory, or the **evolution model**, (believed by **evolutionists**) is an origins model specifically developed to explain the origin and diversity of life without God, relying on man's own determination of truth. Evolution theory is in direct opposition to the Bible and creation. *It was never meant to be an origins explanation consistent with belief in God*. According to evolution:

- Life first originated as single cells (prokaryotes), from nonliving chemicals, billions of years ago.

- Very slowly, over hundreds of millions of years, the "less complex" prokaryotes began to develop new characteristics so that they transformed into "more complex" eukaryotes. (Note – organism "complexity" is an evolutionary concept that completely disregards how incredibly complex life is even at the single cell level. Creationists generally do not pay homage to this one life being more or less complex than another concept. All life is extremely complex).

- This same process occurred hundreds or thousands of times over so that "less complex organisms" gained new traits, which caused them to transform into previously nonexistent kinds of "more complex organisms" (fish into amphibian, amphibian into reptile, reptile into birds and mammals).

- This occurred via completely random processes, termed "**naturalistic processes.**" Naturalistic processes are those that occur as a result of nature alone, making them purposeless from the evolutionists' viewpoint, and are what drive evolution.

- The foundation of modern-day evolutionary thought was laid down in 1859 by Charles Darwin when he published ***On The Origin of Species by Means of Natural Selection, or the Preservation of Favoured Races in the Struggle for Life***.

Although it is not possible to directly "test" creation and evolution as origins models, it is possible to evaluate the scientific predictions each model makes. The hallmark of any scientific model is how well or poorly the model explains or predicts scientific data, which then makes it possible to objectively assess how well or how poorly each one conforms to scientific observations. Ultimately, how well or how poorly a model predicts or explains the data is what allows one to conclude which model is accurate. To that end, a model that describes the data poorly should be discarded and one that describes the data well lives on. In this and the next two chapters, we will look at how well creation and evolution explain and predict scientific data.

This chapter will explain creation origins theory, Chapter 18 will address evolution origins theory and Chapter 19 will draw on these foundations in a compare and contrast type of discussion. Of course, these are very deep topics, with countless pages of material written on each subject. Therefore, we will only be able to briefly touch on many aspects. The intent is to provide an overview, hopefully stimulating further interest and self-study!

As we move through these next three chapters, keep in mind the over-riding truth that God's Word is entirely sufficient to explain origins. The fact that the science fits so well with the creation model simply reinforces that we can always trust the bible.

> **Sanctify them in the truth; your word is truth.**   John 17:17

17.2 "SPECIES" AND EVOLUTION, "KINDS" AND CREATION, A.K.A. "THE SPECIES PROBLEM"

I should point out that in the next three chapters, instead of using the word "species," I will be using the words "kind" and "type" or "variety" instead. You see, evolutionists have a serious problem. Despite a **"species"** being the fundamental unit of evolution, they self-admittedly don't know what a "species" is and creationists need to be fully aware of it since the species confusion can make origins model discussion very confusing. This confusion isn't new – it has been the case since Charles Darwin remarked in *The Origin of Species*:

> **"I was much struck how entirely vague and arbitrary is the distinction between species and varieties."**

Because "species" is confusing and there is simply no agreement amongst evolutionists about exactly "what a species is, " we will use the following terms and concepts:

Kind	Defining Characteristics
Bacteria	Prokaryotic, microscopic, single cell, self-reproducing, no nucleus
Fish	Aquatic, gills, scales, fins, cold-blooded
Amphibians	Water-permeable smooth skin through which respiration occurs, lay soft eggs that require water, two-stage development – tadpole and adult
Reptiles	Cold-blooded terrestrial organisms, lay shelled amniotic eggs, scales (different than fish)
Birds	Feathers, beaks, wings, warm-blooded
Mammals	Hair, provide milk to young via mammary glands, warm-blooded, almost all bear live young with placenta providing nourishment in fetal stage
Humans	Same as mammals, rational thought, permanently walk upright

Figure 17.2.1

Defining Characteristics, Kinds and Varieties
The concept of **defining characteristics** is very helpful to keep in mind during the evolution and creation discussion. A defining characteristic is a trait held by every member of the group of organisms such that if an organism posses it, you can assign it into that group. Like just about everything in biology, though, there are examples here and there that can confuse a person such that approaching "defining characteristics" overly dogmatically could cause confusion because sometimes it may appear that more than one group posses a certain trait. In cases like this, usually further trait and organism study allows one to confidently assign the group to which the organism belongs. "Gills," for example, can be a generic description of a "non-lung" structure to perform oxygen-carbon dioxide exchange and are commonly a defining characteristic of fish. However, "gills" are shared by organisms other than fish, but further study of the organism would clearly allow one to assign it into the appropriate group, if, indeed, it isn't a fish. For example some amphibians have gills, but their gills don't look like fish gills, amphibians don't have any other defining characteristics of fish and they do have defining characteristics of amphibians. Therefore, even though they have "gills" – a defining characteristic of fish – further study identifies some types of amphibians happen to have gills.

- "**Kind of organism**" or "**kind**" when referring to groups of organisms that when you see one organism from one kind and one from another, you know they are not the same kind, such as the "dog kind," the "bird kind," the "elephant kind," or the "flowering plant kind," etc. Members of a kind all share the same defining characteristics such that when you see an organism with certain defining characteristics, you know it is of a certain kind. When you see a dog, you know it is the dog kind and not the tree kind, the bacteria kind or the flea kind because the defining features of the dog – a rather certain body shape, fur, paws with nails, a tail, barking, etc – are different than those of trees, bacteria and fleas. Sometimes creationist literature calls kinds "**baramins**," but I am going to stick with "kinds."

  - This "kind concept" is based upon the Genesis 1, 7 and 8 description of "kinds" where God described the created plants and animals reproducing "each according to its kind."

  - "**Type**" or "**variety**" to differentiate between different organisms of the same kind, such as the type/variety of bird kind called the "robin," the type/variety of elephant kind called the "African elephant," etc. Types or varieties of the same kind all share the same defining characteristics of the kind, with the difference being that members of the same type all share the same attribute or feature of the trait. For example, the Newfoundland dog variety has the features of larger body, wide head, thick legs, long hair and floppy ears of the dog kind's defining characteristics whereas the Chihuahua dog variety has the features of small body, very short legs, thin head and short hair. They both share the same defining characteristics of the dog kind, but they vary in how those defining characteristics are expressed within each variety.

So, how is "species" defined? As noted, it depends on who you are and what scientific discipline you follow. It's really interesting to note that there is even a Wikipedia entry titled "Species Problem" that chronicles the difficulty evolutionists have had and

Figure 17.2.2

Kinds, Types/Varieties and Species

We all seem to inherently know organisms are of "different biblical kinds" virtually as soon as we see them. And, if they are of the same kind, you can further usually tell that they are different "types" or "varieties" within the kind. For example, when you look at any types of the "fish kind," you know they are not the same "kind" as organisms of the "amphibian kind." And, when you look at these two photos of different varieties/types of the fish kind, not only can you tell they are both the fish kind, but you can easily identify they are different types or varieties within the fish kind. The same is true of the two different types of the amphibian kind in the two photos on the right. The "species problem" evolutionists face is that both "kinds" and "types/varieties" are referred to as "species," which causes them great problems when they scientifically try to describe how evolution occurs. There are "fish species" and "amphibian species," just as there are the "clown trigger fish species" (left), the "barracuda species" (second from left), the "spotted salamander species" (second from right) and the "Eastern newt species" (right). Evolutionists believe that "one species evolved into another," but the confusion is clear – does that mean the "fish species evolved into the amphibian species" or that one fish species evolved into another fish species? The evolutionist would answer, "Yes" to both questions, but it is clear those two concepts represent two entirely different processes. A fish species "evolving into" an amphibian species means that the fish species lost the defining characteristics of the fish and gained those of the amphibian so that a new and previously nonexistent type of organism was formed. That is truly what evolution is. To add confusion to the picture, evolutionists also call the development of varieties within a kind (one type of fish transforming into another type of fish) "evolution." However, varieties forming within a kind is very different than one kind transforming into another kind because varieties within a kind are already that kind – fish are fish and amphibians are amphibians. If a new fish variety forms over time, nothing "new" has happened because "fish" already existed. We need to be very careful to define terms and concepts and, as we will see, evolutionists have a very difficult time presenting their case because they confuse these two elemental concepts – a new and previously nonexistent kind forming from a previously existing kind is a _very_ different process than new varieties forming within a kind.

continue to have defining "species." If one cannot define this critical and foundational aspect of evolutionary theory, there cannot be any rational discussion of the subject until a universally agreed-upon definition is made for this "currency of evolution?" Darwin's vague species arbitrariness continues to this date, according to evolutionist N. Bonde of the Institute of Historical Geology and Palaeontology (Denmark):

> *"An important aspect of any species definition whether in neontology or palaeontology is that any statement that particular individuals (or fragmentary specimens) belong to a certain species is an hypothesis (not fact)."*

Dr. Bonde is specifically saying that whatever the definition of "species" may be, it is an arbitrary one and so putting one "species" in direct line of evolution to/from another is arbitrary (i.e., it is a story, not science). Further, Massimo Pigliucci PhD, Chair of the Department of Philosophy at City University of New York (CUNY), ardent atheist, makes it clear that there is very likely no objective (empiric) way to define "species":

> *"First, the species problem is not primarily an empirical one, but it is rather fraught with philosophical questions that require – but cannot be settled by – empirical evidence."*

And Jody Hey, evolutionary geneticist from Rutgers University:

> *"The species problem is the long-standing failure of biologists to agree on how we should identify species and how we should define the word 'species.'...The species problem can be overcome if we understand our own role, as conflicted investigators, in causing the problem"*

Actually, the species problem can be overcome if we use God's word, rather than man's, as the ultimate source of truth. That "conflict" Dr. Hey discusses has always been the disconnect generated between discarding God's Word for man's and will never be resolved unless science backs away from its atheistic stance of evolution origins. By ignoring God's Word, evolutionists remain convicted by their inability to explain the origin and diversity of life without God and so ignore very obvious and irresolvable conflicts such as the species problem.

> *Praise the LORD! For it is good to sing praises to our God; for it is pleasant, and a song of praise is fitting. The LORD builds up Jerusalem; he gathers the outcasts of Israel. He heals the brokenhearted and binds up their wounds. He determines the number of the stars; he gives to all of them their names. Great is our LORD, and abundant in power; his understanding is beyond measure.*   Psalm 147:1 – 5

The whole creation/evolution debate scientifically hinges on the answer to the question, "Where did the 'species' come from," which is really evolution-speak for, "From where (and how) did all of the diverse life forms in existence now or ever come?"

Evolution answer: everything is here as a result of "common ancestry," which means all living organisms came from those before. Quite accidentally, the first cell formed, which transformed into a multicellular organism, and that into the fish species, the fish species into the amphibian species, the amphibian species into the reptile species, the reptile species into the bird species and mammal species (including humans, which evolutionarily are no different from animals). All life forms came directly from those before. This is viewed as an overall process in which "less complex species" evolve into "more complex species."

<u>Creation answer</u>: God created the kinds (for example, the bacteria kind, fish kind, reptile kind, bird kind, mammal kind, human kind) and, once created, as groups of organisms within each kind branched out from Eden (or from Mount Ararat after the Flood) into new habitats, different varieties developed within the kinds. This is an overall process in which God gave his created kinds tremendous built-in genetic ability to be different (meaning to form different types or varieties), which is manifest when organisms are exposed to different habitats, predators, food sources, etc.

Of course, the ultimate way to decide is to read God's Inerrant Word, the ultimate source of truth. Scientifically, the issue is, which one of these positions is best supported by the scientific data? Since the difference between the creation and evolution origins explanations are irreconcilably opposite one another, it is critical to hold these two positions up to the data and objectively determine the answer. Further, since God's Word is true, then we would expect that the scientific data is fully explainable by the creation model. Conversely, since evolution is 180 degrees opposite creation and God's Word is true, we would expect the evolution model would not be consistent with the scientific data.

This species problem has resulted in "species" being nothing more than a garbage can term that lacks clear scientific definition. As such, it is prone to manipulation (accidental or intentional) and misunderstanding; thus, it should be avoided. One would think there would be a very clear evolutionary definition of "species" since "species" is <u>the unit</u> of evolution! The main header of Darwin's book is *The Origin of Species*. Evolutionists constantly talk about how one species evolved into (or from) another and yet evolutionists admittedly do not know what a "species" is. If there is no clear understanding of what a species is, then one would expect "mass evolutionary confusion." And, indeed, that is what we have. Population geneticists define "species" one way, biologists another and some paleontologists yet slightly differently. Often science philosophers just avoid trying to define it altogether.

For decades, the biological definition of species was generally accepted to be "a population of organisms that doesn't interbreed in the wild." That seemed to work fine until various populations were studied more and more and it was found interbreeding was quite common in some! So, maybe "populations that don't interbreed" doesn't define a species. But, yet unknown, what does? Without proper definition, "species" is thrown around without regard and, if you are not careful, you will be deceived and perhaps think that evolution is something that it is not and start to think, "Maybe evolution *does* explain why we are here!" That is why we will consistently use the term "kind" instead of "species." You will certainly see creationist literature using the word "species," but "kind" and "variety" or "type" lead to less confusion.

To highlight this point, because it is central to this discussion, genetically speaking, there is a huge difference between the process of "a fish species evolving into an amphibian species" and the process of different types forming within a created kind. The evolution model calls both processes "evolution." They are absolutely two different biological processes and the failure to recognize that is instrumental to understanding why the evolution model consistently fails.

Figure 17.2.3

"Species," "Evolution" and "Speciation"

When evolutionists use the undefined term "species" when describing "how evolution works," confusion reigns. Now, I am going to be using creationist terms to describe evolutionary processes because it actually clarifies the concept quite nicely. Evolutionists refer to the process of an amphibian kind (what evolutionists call "species") evolving into a reptile kind ("species") and a reptile kind ("species") evolving into a bird kind ("species") as "evolution." Evolutionists refer to this process as "**speciation**," which is the process of species formation. Confusingly, though, evolutionists also refer to the process of varieties forming within a kind as "speciation" and, adding to the confusion, also call that evolution. This is confusing because these are two entirely different genetic processes. Remember that the genetic content of an organism is what contains the instructions for it to develop into that kind of organism. Darwinian evolution is specifically the process of a "less complex" organism ("kind" or "species") developing new previously nonexistent characteristics and transforming into a "more complex" previously nonexistent organism ("kind" or "species"), which can be viewed as "one kind evolving into another kind." That means that evolution is a model that describes how a less complex kind gained new DNA, providing new traits, so that the less complex kind could evolve into the more complex kind – the fish gaining new DNA to make it an amphibian. That is what Darwinian evolution is, but it is absolutely not the type of "speciation" where varieties/types form within an already existing kind. Why are they different? Because, when varieties form within a kind, the kind already exists. Different varieties forming within the fish kind doesn't lead to new and previously nonexistent kinds of organisms. Fish are already fish. Creationists clearly identify that there is proliferate evidence of new varieties forming within already existing kinds, and so have no qualms referring to that process as "speciation." But, that is not what evolution is! Varieties form within kinds, but Darwinian evolution is one kind evolving into another kind. There is no scientific evidence to support one kind evolving into another entirely new and previously nonexistent kind. As we move through the next three chapters, we will clearly identify why the "varieties-forming-within-a-kind" of speciation is not "evolution" and will learn that there is absolutely no scientific data that supports the "less-complex-kind-of-organism (or species)-gaining-new-traits-and-transforming into-a-new-and-previously-nonexistent-kind (or species)" of speciation that must exist in order for evolution to occur. This difference is foundational!

From the creation perspective, notice that no matter how differently varieties within the same kind may appear or behave, they are still all that same kind. A fish is a fish and an amphibian is an amphibian and a dog is a dog no matter what it looks like, what it eats, how big it is, what color it is or where it lives. The formation of different types/varieties within kinds – different types of fish within the fish kind, different types of bats within the bat kind or different types of snakes within the reptile kind – are explained by a process called **natural selection**. Natural selection is sometimes called "survival of the fittest," or the process that those organisms that are more fit for their environment – more fit for survival – live more often than those that are not and pass along their "fitter" traits to their offspring, which do the same to theirs, and so on. Over time, there are more and more organisms with the beneficial-for-survival traits and fewer with the "less-beneficial-for-survival-traits." One of the results of natural selection is that populations of slightly different appearing and behaving organisms arise here and there – varieties form within kinds, but not new kinds themselves. The effects of natural selection on the appearance and behavior of populations of organisms are observable scientific events, but never lead to the formation of entirely new and previously nonexistent kinds of organisms. Natural selection only modifies the appearance and behavior of already existing kinds.

Darwinian evolution demands new trait formation in an ancestor organism so that, over time, it transforms into a new and previously nonexistent kind of organism. When a new variety forms within a kind, that is not evolution because no new "more complex" organism with previously nonexistent traits has formed from a "less complex" one. Indeed, evolution can be properly defined:

A biological process in which a "less complex" ancestor organism acquires new and previously nonexistent traits such that, over time, as it accumulates more novel traits, it develops new defining characteristics and transforms into a previously nonexistent and more complex organism. For example, the fish ancestor organism gained the defining characteristics of the amphibian so that, over time, the ancestor fish transformed into the first amphibian.

Gerald Kerkut PhD (1927 – 2004), evolutionary zoologist from the University of Southampton, makes it clear that, as we have been discussing, there are two very different types of "evolution," one of which is supported by scientific data (varieties forming within kinds), and one of which isn't (one kind evolving into a new and previously nonexistent kind):

"There is a theory which states that many living animals can be observed over the course of time to undergo changes so that new species are formed. This can be called the 'Special Theory of Evolution' and can be demonstrated in certain cases by experiments. On the other hand there is the theory that all living forms in the world have arisen from a single source which itself came from an inorganic form. This theory can be called the 'General Theory of Evolution' and the evidence that supports it is not sufficiently strong to allow us to consider it anything more than a working hypothesis."

Dr. Kerkut makes it clear that evolutionists know that there are two different types of "evolution." One type, what he calls the "special theory of evolution," or varieties forming within a kind, is supported by scientific observations. Creationists agree, because this is not evolution. It is simply variation within a kind that arises as a result of natural selection. The other type, what he calls the "general theory of evolution," or one kind evolving into a new and previously nonexistent kind, has very little scientific evidence. Creationists agree, because this is what evolution is and there is absolutely no scientific evidence to support it.

Sometimes newer creationists are at first uncomfortable with the thought that different varieties could form from within a created kind, because "that sounds like evolution," but that discomfort highlights the effectiveness evolutionists and the media have had at confusing the two very different concepts. The main issue here is "species." What is it? Does a species of reptile evolve into a different species of reptile? "Yes," says the evolutionist. Does a species of reptile evolve into a species of bird? "Yes," says the evolutionist, "but we can't see it. Just take our word for it because it happens just like as reptile species formation occurs."

Well, which is it, though? The processes are two completely different biological processes. One is "evolution" – the reptile transforming into a bird – and one isn't "evolution" – reptile varieties forming within the reptile kind. This just shows how confusing the evolutionary picture is when "species" is thrown around without definition and clarity. We must keep the process of Darwinian evolution clearly defined as we walk through the next three chapters. Evolution is the process of a less complex ancestor organism acquiring, over time, new traits that previously did not exist such that the ancestor organism transforms into a previously nonexistent organism.

Since we can clearly see that there is evidence of considerable variation between kinds (hence the differing appearances of fish from salamanders from dogs from people), how does the Bible explain that? There is every reason to believe that God created every *kind* of organism ever present on earth, but no reason to believe that God created every single *type* or variety of organism within the kinds. Why? Because creating kinds is exactly what God said he did!

And God said, "Let the waters swarm with swarms of living creatures, and let birds fly above the earth across the expanse of heavens." So God created the great sea creatures and every living creature that moves, with which the waters swarm, according to their kinds, and every winged bird according to its kind. And God saw that it was good. And God blessed them, saying, "Be fruitful and multiply and fill the waters in the seas, and let the birds multiply on the earth." And there was evening and there was morning, the fifth day. And God said, "Let the earth bring forth living creatures according to their kinds – livestock and creeping things and beasts of the earth according to their kinds." And it was so. And God made the beasts of the earth according to their kinds and the livestock according to their kinds, and everything that creeps on the ground according to its kind. And God saw that it was good.   Genesis 1:20 – 24

© Malene Thyssen/Wikimedia Commons/CC-BY-SA-2.5

© Akse107/Wikimedia Commons/{{PD}}

© The Random Editor/Wikimedia Commons/{{PD}}

Figure 17.2.4

Varieties Form Within Kinds (And That Isn't "Evolution")
There are two entirely different processes that evolutionists refer to as "evolution" – "one kind evolving into another kind" (which has no supporting scientific data) and "varieties forming within a kind" (which has lots of supporting scientific evidence). For example, creationists and evolutionists alike believe that the many varieties of the "dog kind" we see today likely arose from one ancestor variety of dog that probably looked a lot like the Scandinavian grey wolf (top). Over time, this ancestor wolf-like variety was exposed to different conditions as it spread out geographically from other wolf-like populations, resulting in exposure to different environments, predators/prey, etc. As a result, different varieties formed, such as the German shepherd and the chocolate Labrador. Creationists view this process of varieties forming within a kind – "speciation" – as describing the way that God used to make the diverse appearances of varieties within kinds. All of the different kinds living today, or that ever have lived in the past, were first created and then, over time, developed into different varieties. Creationists and evolutionists believe this because it is supported by scientific data. However, it is very obvious that this "varieties-forming-within-a-kind" description of "evolution" is very different from the "one kind evolving into another kind" of "evolution" because when all of the different types of dogs formed from that ancestor wolf kind, nothing "new" resulted. All of the dog varieties are still dogs. They look a little different, but they all still share the same defining characteristics of the dog kind! They are all mammals, all have four legs, all bark, etc. Varieties forming within a kind does not lead to the formation of a new "more complex" organism that didn't previously exist and so that is not Darwinian evolution. You can see why the evolutionary practice of referring to "one kind evolving into another kind" and "varieties forming within a kind" as both being "evolution" not only does not foster true understanding of what evolution is and what it isn't, but it also seems to indicate that evolutionists do not understand their own "theory." Darwinian evolution simply is not the biologic process of "varieties forming within kinds."

As Dr. Kerkut mentioned, we have actually been able to see new varieties forming almost before our eyes. Over the centuries, new varieties of cats, dogs, horses and fish have arisen through the process of selective breeding, which is a sped up artificial form of varieties forming within a kind. This is direct evidence that varieties do form within kinds.

To creationists, a biblically compatable explanation is that the variation within the created kinds comes from "built-in" ability to vary given to the kinds by God at creation. Since the instructions to vary are contained in the DNA and since God is all-knowing, that means he knew the plans he had for everything he created and so he gave all life forms exactly the genetic variation they would need in order to fulfill his plans. Creationists believe that one kind can never "evolve into" another kind, but that variation within kinds is fully explainable by the biblically sound biological process of natural selection and all of the associated scientific processes. We will explore this in depth as we dissect the scientific data that supports the creation model.

17.3 CREATION AND EVOLUTION ARE PHILOSOPHIES

It is very important to clearly understand that neither creation nor evolution is "science" in the sense that we understand "science." Our understanding of "science" is that of a defined process in which hypotheses and theories are tested with well-designed experimental or observational study. As a result, data accumulates and is analyzed and interpreted with the end result of identifying whether or not the data supports said hypothesis or theory. If it does, the hypothesis/theory is strengthened, perhaps even being elevated to law. If the data does not provide support, the hypothesis or theory is weakened or perhaps even discarded and a new one may be developed to explain the data. Such science is called **operational** or **empiric science**.

However, the terms "empiric science" or "operational science" do not accurately describe creation or evolution. There is no way to "directly test" a theory in which it takes billions of years to get results (in the case of evolution), just as there is no way to "directly test" whether or not God created Adam out of the dust of the Earth (of course, there really is no need to test God's Word since he is all knowing and cannot lie and he has specifically told us how he created).

Therefore, evolution and creation are not operational science; instead, they are examples of **historical science** or **philosophy**. Historical science is when something has already happened, which left clues to its happening (i.e. observable scientific data such as fossils) and yet there is no direct way to test an hypotheses about how or why it happened. Instead, the historical data is logically interpreted based upon clues that are present in the form of scientific facts. Philosophy is the study or pursuit of causes, principles or knowledge based upon reasoning and not empirical methods. Since operational science is validated using empirical methods and neither creation nor evolution can be strictly tested using such methods, they are properly referred to as philosophical pursuits.

Of course, how the scientific data is interpreted is not just related to the data at which you are looking. It is also related to everything else about you. If you are a creationist, you would interpret all scientific data with the philosophical position that an all-powerful and all-knowing God exists and created the universe and everything in it out of nothing, just like the Bible says. In this belief system, all of the rules are written by God and everything that he does exists for his specific purpose. On the other hand, an evolutionist interprets scientific data with the philosophical position that an all-powerful and all-knowing God does not exist and somehow everything in the universe "just is." In this paradigm, there is no purpose and the "rules" governing evolutionary processes are random and all-natural. Clearly, when interpreting any type of scientific data, the philosophical position from which one operates heavily influences the conclusions at which one arrives.

Figure 17.3.1

How Your Origins Stance Affects Scientific Data Interpretation

Let's look at the following example to further understand how the philosophical positions underlying the creation and evolution models influence scientific conclusions. **Paleontology** is the study of life forms that existed in the prehistoric or geological past. A **paleontologist** (a person who studies paleontology) finds this fossil. If the paleontologist is an evolutionist, everything about that fossil will be explained in light of a billions-of-years-old Earth – God does not exist, life was not created and instead is here as a result of a series of accidental biological events. The evolutionist paleontologist concludes that, since this fossil was found in a rock layer thought to be 8 million years old, so then the fossil is 8 million years old. Further, when noting the apparent discrepancy between the 8 million years old age and the presence of a brown, woody stem and green leaves (which is clearly not consistent with a fossil that is more than several thousand years old), concludes that is a strange finding, indeed, and that the fossil was somehow preserved in highly unusual conditions in order for that to happen. If the paleontologist is a creationist, everything about that fossil will be explained in light of the fact that God created the universe and everything in it about 6,000 years ago and that this fossil, like most (but not all) others, was made during Noah's Flood. The creationist paleontologist examines the fossil and sees that the leaves are still green and the stem is still brown and concludes that this is not unusual at all for a specimen that is, at most, 4,000 years old. Which interpretation, evolution or creation, fits better with the observable scientific data seen in this specimen? That is that question that must always be answered!

17.4 WHY DISCUSS EVOLUTION AT ALL?

Since I am a Christian and creationist, some may think, "Why is he even discussing evolution?" A reasonable question, to which there are actually a number of answers:

1. Evolutionists and creationists use observable scientific facts and processes in order to arrive at their conclusions. Some of the observable scientific processes (such as natural selection), but not all (such as radiometric dating), creationists accept and it is important to break down the evolution/creation interpretation of these data, which we will do. As a result, we will clearly understand that creation is actually scientifically and rationally a better explanation for the majority of scientific observations than is evolution.

2. _So that you clearly know why you believe what you believe_. There are many problems with the evolution origins model, which are rarely ever reported in media and certainly not discussed in secular biology texts. It is important to logically dissect evolution so that you can see that the biblical sufficiency framework of "I believe in creation because the Bible is the inerrant Word of God and the Bible documents that God is the Creator" is _fully supported by scientific observations_ and rational thinking. The creation position is a quite-compelling origins explanation. There is no need to defer our belief in creation origins to the evolutionary scientific establishment!

3. It is important to be as well versed as possible about evolution so that when you are confronted with evolutionary dogma (which can be very subtle), you can identify it as such.

   > **You adulterous people! Do you not know that friendship with the world is enmity with God? Therefore, whoever wishes to be a friend of the world makes himself an enemy of God.** James 4:4

   It is important to know what the world looks like so that it can be excluded from our world views.

4. As a result of logically breaking down creation and evolution side by side, you will start to develop focused critical thinking skills so that you can easily present an academic defense of creation and argument against evolution. Such ability cannot exist if you do not understand the many places where logical thought does not support evolutionary interpretation of the scientific data.

5. The forbidden or unknown is tempting and the known is much less so.

17.5 CREATION IN MORE DETAIL

Biblical creation provides the framework of the creation origins model. It relies upon the Word of God to define truth, with the creation events described in Genesis 1. God created everything in six literal, twenty-four hour days:

Day 1: light and dark (Genesis 1: 1 – 5)

Day 2: expanse separating the waters above and below (Genesis 1: 6 – 8)

Day 3: land and plants, according to their kinds (Genesis 1: 9 – 13)

Day 4: "lights" including the stars, sun, and moon (Genesis 1: 14 – 19)

Day 5: water and flying organisms, reproducing according to their kinds (Genesis 1: 20 – 23)

Day 6: land animals and humans, reproducing according to their kinds (Genesis 1: 24 – 31)

After creating life forms on Days 3, 5 and 6, God blessed them, said it was "good" and "very good" and rested on Day 7.

In this viewpoint, there is nothing the Creator cannot do. The limitations of God are only those that we as humans assign to God due to our inability to understand how powerful He is. Using the Bible as the frame of reference, the creation model postulates that the Earth is about 6,000 years old and that humans have been on Earth essentially "from the beginning," since day 6. Note that this contrasts sharply to the decidedly anti-biblical evolutionist belief that life and death existed for billions of years before humans "arrived on the evolutionary scene." For reference, Noah's Flood, a truly global event in which the entire earth was simultaneously covered with water for a year, occurred about 4,500 years ago.

It is interesting to consider how God actually did the creating. When God created the heavens, the earth and all life forms, He created three different ways – by speaking, by forming and by making. By *speaking the words*:

> **And God said, "Let there be light," and there was light.** Genesis 1:3

> **And God said, "Let the earth sprout vegetation, plants yielding seed, and fruit trees bearing fruit in which is their seed, each according to its kind, on the earth." And it was so.** Genesis 1:11

> **For he spoke, and it came to be; he commanded and it stood firm.** Psalm 33:9

As with all miracles in which the "miracle-inducing action" is the spoken word (and when context permits), the response to God's Word was immediate. When God said "Let there be" it was there. The billions of stars and planets in the universe appeared on day 4. Everything that lives in the ocean and all flying creatures formed faster than a blink of the eye on day 5 and all land creatures on Day 6 when God spoke the words, all fully functional and very likely genetically perfect. The incomprehensibly intricate and still poorly understood biochemical reactions and the elusive genetic mechanisms of life and the complicated interdependence of life forms on each other and their ecosystems was created the very instant God spoke the words.

Figure 17.5.1

"And God Said..."

It's important to think a little deeper than just reading the words in order to appreciate what happened when God said, "Let there be...." or when he did his forming and making. Everything about every organism, all anatomy, every single biochemical reaction, the ability to open DNA for replication and transcription, the ability for kinds of organisms to vary genetically so that they could adapt and form the wide variety of organisms that have ever existed, _everything_ came to be instantaneously when God spoke the words. The intricate external anatomy of the eye (top left), the internal retinal gross anatomy (top right), the perfectly designed microscopic retinal anatomy (bottom left) all the way down to every detail like the structure, function and cellular positioning of the light-sensitive molecule rhodopsin (bottom right) immediately came into being for every single organism with a refractive eye (like ours). The retina is a series of one cell layer upon another with amazing properties: the world's smallest fiber optics (10 times smaller than anything man can make); specialized structure to limit light scatter (maximizing visual acuity); the world's first and smallest heat sink (protecting the light sensitive cells from excess damage). The dynamic range of the human eye is 10,000,000,000:1, which means we can see in the smallest possible amount of light (1 photon) up to very bright light (10,000,000,000 photons). The best photographic film has a dynamic range of 1,000:1 and the best LCD/LED TVs presently are 5,000,000:1. All of this was accomplished faster than the blink of an eye.

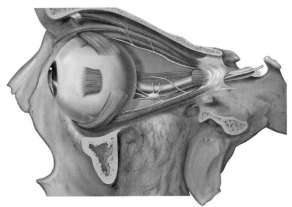

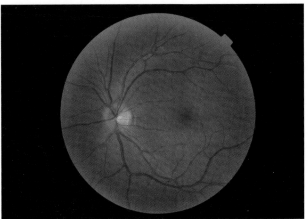

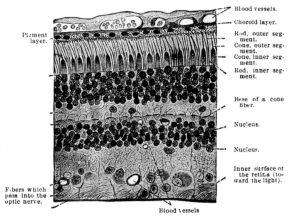

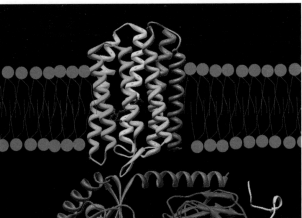

In addition to creating by speaking, God uniquely created man and woman in different ways than He created everything else, which is one of many indications of the special relationship human beings have with God. Adam was not created with the spoken word:

> ***Then the Lord God formed a man from the dust of the ground and breathed into his nostrils the breath of life, and the man became a living being.*** Genesis 2:7

So Adam was formed, which sounds a lot like God "used his hands" to make Adam! Likewise, Eve was made differently than everything else (note that God was the very first anesthesiologist and surgeon!). As with Adam's creation, the description is entirely consistent with God actually making direct contact when making Eve:

> ***So the Lord God caused the man to fall into a deep sleep; and while he was sleeping, he took one of the man's ribs and then closed up the place with flesh. Then the Lord God made a woman from the rib he had taken out of the man, and he brought her to the man.*** Genesis 2:21-22

17.6 TWO OF GOD'S CHARACTERISTICS IMPORTANT TO CREATION

Sometimes, it is hard to wrap our heads around the eternal biological implications of God's character. God is **omniscient**, which means that _He knows everything_ that can possibly be known, including what is going to happen in the future. God is **omnipotent**, which means that _He is all powerful and can do anything_. And, He has known everything forever, from the very beginning. That means that when He created everything, He had a plan. Important to this discussion, for example, He knew exactly how to design variety into all of the created kinds' DNA so they would be able to fulfill His plans of wonderful living organism diversity. He knew that he was going to cause a Great Flood to come and wipe everything off the face of the earth, except those he planned to save. Part of his omniscience is that he made sure that all organisms were created with exactly the DNA they needed to be able to get off the Ark and then re-populate the earth, resulting in the wonderful diversity we see in the past and today. HE KNEW.

> ***Then God said to Noah, "Go out from the ark, you and your wife, and your sons and your sons' wives with you. Bring out with you every living thing that is with you of all flesh – birds and animals and every creeping thing that creeps on the earth – that they may swarm on the earth, and be fruitful and multiply on the earth." So Noah went out, and his sons and his wife and his sons' wives with him. Every beast, every creeping thing, and every bird, everything that moves on the earth, went out by families from the ark.*** Genesis 8:15 – 18

17.7 CREATION AND THE AGE OF THE EARTH

Since the time of Christ, for at least 1,800 years, the age of the earth had been understood to be about 6,000 years old, with very little disagreement between scientists and clergy. This age was arrived at simply by reviewing the genealogies in Genesis 5 and 11, which include the life span of consecutive generations up to Abraham. Scholars agree that Abraham lived approximately 4,000 years ago and the covered time frame of the Genesis genealogies from Adam to Abraham is another approximately 2,000 years; hence, God created the earth about 6,000 years ago, about 4,000 years before Jesus was born. This was a well-accepted way of determining "when God did His creating" and up until the late 18th and early 19th centuries, religious leaders, scientists and lay people nearly universally believed the earth to be "young" because of this method of calculation ("young" is a relative concept - to you and me, 6,000 years into the past is a pretty long time but on the evolutionary time scale, 6,000 years is not long at all).

Figure 17.7.1

Archbishop James Ussher

James Ussher (1581 – 1656) held the highest rank in the Church of Ireland. He was a devout Bible reader and Hebrew scholar. He published *The Annals of the World*, a more-than-1,200 page historical review (in Latin) of the events of all of earth's history. In it, he used the genealogies provided in Genesis 5 and 11 to calculate how long ago God created everything, and arrived at a date of October 23, 4004 BC. It is interesting to note that the great scientists Johannes Kepler and Isaac Newton independently calculated the age of the earth using the same biblical method as Ussher and also arrived at dates right around 4000 BC. In *Annals*, Ussher meticulously correlated many historical events in the Bible with ancient writers who had written about them during or soon after they happened. Ussher even found independent descriptions of the earthquake and the darkness that occurred when Jesus was crucified.

But, why is this method of "age calculation" used? In other words, what would make a person believe that it is valid to "count time" using the generations and ages provided in Genesis such that an accurate age for the earth can be obtained? Since God's Word is inerrant and always true, and, as long as it is clear that God's intent is that He means something to be taken as literal fact, then it should be perfectly valid to "count time" using the genealogies. Is that the case with the age of the earth? Sometimes God uses literary techniques such as poetry, parables and allegories to make His points and so if one is not careful, it is possible to mistake literal and non-literal Bible passages. Fortunately, Hebrew was used to document this information and it is a language rich in literary techniques that often allow for pretty clear decisions about whether or not the meaning of the information is to be literal or figurative.

Therefore, the _only_ reason counting time using the genealogy method would be valid is if God _meant_ Genesis 5 and 11 to be historically accurate and not just "part of a poetic creation story." If God's intention was for Genesis to be historically accurate, then it would be entirely legitimate to calculate the age of the earth by such generational counting using the genealogies as historically accurate. If God meant for the genealogies to be allegorical, then treating them as historically accurate would be improper.

Well, how can we possibly know what God's intention was? By reading His Word. God knows the difference between Hebrew historical and figurative text and so it makes sense that he would have written the Genesis genealogies in the manner he intended they be understood. If God used Hebrew sentence structures and wording that is typical of the style meant to be interpreted as literal historical information, than that is how the genealogies should be interpreted. If he used figurative or "story telling" language, then they should not be taken literally.

Because _much_ scholarly research and commentary underlies the following reasons, we cannot get into them in great detail; however, I urge you to explore further if you are interested. _There are several clues that God fully intended the Genesis 5 and 11 genealogies to be understood as literal_ and, therefore, they are historically accurate as written. This means they contain no "gaps" and that when God says someone lived for a certain number of years, that is how long the person lived regardless of how "unbelievable" it may be to us.

These clues are:

1. The Hebrew language sentence structures and wording God used in Genesis is of the form of text meant to be taken as "literal history." The structure of Hebrew language, the specific words used and their relationships to one another in sentences are very important. God knows that. Hebrew historical text is written differently than non-historical text (such as poetry or prophecy) and Genesis is

clearly written using characteristics of Hebrew historical text. It is written to be taken literally (just as the information presented in a science book is) rather than figuratively (as poetic literature often is). Genesis is literal because the Hebrew context and wording God chose when he wrote it indicates it is supposed to be understood as literal history.

a. The way in which the Hebrew words "'ereb" ("evening"), "boqer" ("morning"), "yom" ("day") and "echad" (one or first) are used in Genesis is very meaningful.

> ***And God said, "Let there be light," and there was light. And God saw that the light was good. And God separated the light from the darkness. God called the light Day, and the darkness he called Night. And there was evening and there was morning, the first day.*** *Genesis 1: 3 - 5*

(Note: the pattern of word usage for the 2nd through 7th days is the same).

Some believe that the length of time communicated in Genesis by the word "yom" ("day") is not actually a literal 24 hour period, but instead is much longer - thousands or even millions of years. However, that is not how God wrote it using the Hebrew language that he created. Knowing how important word relationships are in Hebrew, God used the word "yom" in the way that means a literal 24 hour period of time.

As with yom, the use of ereb, boqer and echad is consistent _not_ with the figurative meaning of a "general and unspecified period of time" such as we convey when we say, "Back in the day..." or, "It was the morning of a new era..." Instead, when these specific words are used in the way in which they are in Genesis 5 and 11, _it is consistent with the intention of communicating a literal 24 hour period of time_. These same words are used together and in similar ways in other places in the Bible and in those instances, they are always interpreted as conveying literal time frames, rather than figurative. Most Old Testament Bible scholars, whether they personally believe that Genesis is historical, do agree that it is written as historical fact. Marcus Dods (1834 – 1909), liberal Scottish theologian, on the meaning of the word "yom" in Genesis:

> "If, for example, the word "day" in these chapters does not mean a period of twenty-four hours, the interpretation of scripture is hopeless."

Even this liberal scholar, who did not personally believe in the literal interpretation of Genesis, indicates it is clear that "yom" means a literal 24-hour period of time. In fact, he claims it is so foundational to scripture that, if it isn't accepted as meaning a true 24-hour period of time, then interpreting the rest of scripture is worthless. God meant Genesis 5 and 11 to be historical.

b. It is correct to note what appear at first glance to be inconsistencies between the Genesis 5 and 11 and Matthew genealogies since this could be a stumbling block; however, closer inspection identifies intent. There are two types of genealogies in the Bible – ones that are clearly intended to be accurate historically (called chronogenealogies) and those that are intended to establish someone's right to something. Biblical chronogenealogies are written to convey that there are no gaps in the genealogy – it is accurate as written – whereas genealogies written to establish inheritance or someone's right to something (like a kingship) often contain "gaps" in the list of names.

It is inadvisable to equate the intentions of the Matthew and Genesis genealogies. Matthew clearly states in 1:17 his intention is, through the presentation of three sets of 14 generational genealogies, to establish Jesus Christ's right to the throne of David and as Messiah. This is in sharp contrast to the genealogies of Genesis 5 and 11, which are written in the form of chronogenealogies. This, combined with the aforementioned historical intention of Genesis, indicates the Genesis genealogies should be read as accurate representations of "who begat who."

Interestingly, it was only in the 18th and 19th centuries when God's Word began to be discarded by scientists and some church leaders as THE source of truth that questions were raised regarding the age of the earth. Until then, scientists and theologians alike understood that the Genesis 5 and 11 genealogies were meant to be literal and were accepted as such. Most Biblical OT scholars, whether they personally believe the Genesis genealogies are true representations or not, do agree that God's intention is that they are to be understood literally and are historically accurate. James Barr (1924 – 2006), former Religious Professor of Hebrew at Oxford (who did not believe that the earth was "young"), in 1984 wrote in a letter,

> "...so far as I know, there is no professor of Hebrew or Old Testament at any world-class university who does not believe that the writer(s) of Genesis 1-11 intended to convey to their readers the ideas that
>
> (a) creation took place in a series of six days which were the same as the days/ of 24 hours we now experience
>
> (b) the figures contained in the Genesis genealogies provided by simple addition a chronology from the beginning of the world up to later stages in the biblical story...
>
> Or, to put it negatively, the apologetic arguments which suppose the 'days' of creation to be long eras of time, the figures of years not to be chronological, and the flood to be a merely local Mesopotamian flood, are not taken seriously by any such professors, as far as I know. The only thing I would say to qualify this is that most professors may avoid much involvement in that sort of argument and so may not say much explicitly about it one way or the other. But I think what I say would represent their position correctly. However, you might find one or two people who would take the contrary point of view and are competent in the languages, in Assyriology, and so on: it's really not so much a matter of technical linguistic competence, as of appreciation of the sort of text that Genesis is."

Figure 17.7.2

Charles Spurgeon

Throughout these three evolution and creation chapters, you will be seeing quotes from famous thought leaders from "both sides of the aisle." Sometimes, such as those from James Barr and Marcus Dods, the quote is provided by a person that does not believe the Bible is historically accurate but the quote shows clearly they understand the topic about which we are speaking. And, when scholarly persons who do not agree with a particular position provide information that clearly supports the position with which they ideologically disagree, that is an excellent point-making testament. I have taken great pains to not take anyone's words out of context or edit them such that the original meaning is different from the context in which the quotation is discussed in this textbook. Truthful argumentation flowing along the same context as the information content of the quote is far more powerful than a quotation that has been edited or taken out of context to the point that it amounts to little more than made-up words. Charles Spurgeon (1834 – 1892) is one of the greatest fundamentalist preachers and writers of modern day. Since he was alive before, during and after evolution became a scientific sensation, his words provide profound understanding regarding the implications of evolution, the "vain notion":

> *"In its bearing upon religion this vain notion is, however, no theme for mirth, for it is not only deceptive, but it threatens to be mischievous in a high degree. There is not a hair of truth upon this dog from its head to its tail, but it rends and tears the simple ones. In all its bearing upon scriptural truth, the evolution theory is in direct opposition to it. If God's Word be true, evolution is a lie. I will not mince the matter; this is not the time for soft speaking."*

2. The Fourth Commandment established the Sabbath:

> ***Remember the Sabbath day, to keep it holy. Six days you shall labor, and do all your work, but the seventh day is a Sabbath to the Lord your God. On it you shall not do any work, you, or your son, or your daughter, your male servant, or your female servant, or your livestock, or the sojourner who is within your gates. For in six days the Lord made heaven and earth, the sea, and all that is in them, and rested on the seventh day. Therefore the Lord blessed the Sabbath day and made it holy.*** *Exodus 20: 8 – 11*

This is another Scriptural passage that discusses the entire creation week in a manner salient to this discussion. As in the Genesis creation account, the Exodus description uses the same Hebrew sentence structuring with six consecutive, literal 24-hour days of creation followed by a seventh day when God rested. That, then, is used as the template for the human work week of six 24-hour periods in which humans are to work followed by a 24-hour day of rest. This is a very specific and direct relationship of the human work ethic to God's. It is fully irrational to conclude that God's work week was composed of different time frames for his days if we are to use his work week as the guide for ours. A literal meaning of the Genesis 5 and 11 genealogies is implicit.

3. There are many instances in which Jesus or a New Testament writer mentions creation. In all instances when context permits, it is clear that Jesus (who is, of course, God and the smartest human being who ever did or will live) or the writer (i.e. God) understood the creation events to be literal.

It is therefore quite reasonable to interpret the Genesis 5 and 11 genealogies as being accurate historical information, making this method accurate when used to "calculate the age of the earth."

17.8 HISTORY OF CREATION

Although their "creation belief status" is hard to definitively track in all cases, it is certain that many of the greatest scientists who ever lived wrote much (and in some cases more) about their belief in God, the Creator of the universe, as compared to their scientific endeavors.

> ***"After all, if the Bible is God's Word and it reveals Truth, then the closer we get to the Truth in our presuppositions, the faster we will discover the Truth in the details."*** *Sir Isaac Newton*

Figure 17.8.1

Sir Isaac Newton
Isaac Newton (1642 – 1727) is considered one of the greatest, if not the greatest, scientist who ever lived. A Christian and devout Bible reader, he spent much of his time writing about religious topics. He was a professor at Cambridge and made major contributions to calculus, mathematics, astronomy, optics and physics. *Philosophiae Naturalis Principia Mathematica* (*Mathematical Principles of Natural Philosophy*, often referred to as *Principia*) is considered one of the most important scientific works in existence. In it, Newton described the laws of motion, classical mechanics, the law of universal gravitation and commented upon Kepler's laws of planetary motions. Newton believed that it was his Godly focus and attending to the details in scripture that allowed him to elucidate the principles and laws of God's creation, which was a common belief for many of the pre-19th Century scientists.

For 1,800 years following the death of Jesus Christ, the discoveries that make up the foundations of modern biology, physics, chemistry, mathematics, medicine and astronomy happened as scientists knowingly and purposefully explored God's created, orderly universe. Also, for pretty much that same period of time, there were few *people* (not just scientists) who did not believe the earth to be about 6,000 years old. Therefore, the "modern" scientific belief that somehow a scientist is deficient and lacks credibility because he or she believes the earth is "young" (compared to evolutionary time frames) completely ignores the fact that virtually all of the most important scientists in history made their contributions *precisely because* they used the Bible as their source of truth, which caused them to approach their scientific endeavors with the mindset of understanding God's creation. And, as we will see time and again as we examine the scientific data, substituting man's truth (evolution) for God's continually leads scientists away from scientific discovery. Putting faith in God to reveal the secrets of his creation is what helped these scientists make their contributions.

> *Let no one deceive himself. If anyone among you thinks that he is wise in this age, let him become a fool that he may become wise. For the wisdom of this world is folly with God. For it is written, "He catches the wise in their craftiness," and again, "The Lord knows the thoughts of the wise, that they are futile."* 1 Corinthians 3: 18 - 21

Of course, this is one of those passages common to Paul's writings, in which he uses phrases that kind of confuse a person a little to make sure you are paying attention! In the passage, Paul uses the word "wise" to refer to people who are not really wise but think they are because they believe in the "wisdom of the world." That is why, then, that Paul says, "Let him become a fool again so that he may become wise." Basically, Paul is saying that the worldly must lose their faith in the world and become "a fool" (which, from the worldly perspective, means "to believe in God") so that he or she will then "become wise" (believe in God).

Creationists believe that "anyone among you who thinks that he is wise" would clearly refer to today's evolution-based scientists. They think they are wise because they don't believe in that "foolish" God of the Bible stuff, preferring to place their faith in God-less evolution. Paul says to be careful not to trust in the world – modern evolutionary-based science – because if you do, you will be the fool in God's eyes. The only way to be truly wise is to believe in God's Word, which conversely appears foolish to the world.

> *And he said to the man, "Behold, the fear of the Lord, that is wisdom, and to turn away from evil is understanding."* Job 28:28

Figure 17.8.2

Creation Scientists

Most of the greatest scientists of the past believed in a Creator, though not all shared the belief in the Trinitarian form of our Christian God. These scientists understood that the universe is too perfect and life forms too diverse and complicated to not have been created, and it was this belief that, in part or in whole, provided them insight into their areas of specialty that they would not have had otherwise. Because they fully recognized that the Creator is orderly and so would naturally create an orderly universe, they were able to discover this order in the universe and Laws he created to govern it. In so doing, they collectively made magnificent scientific advances, which would not have been possible if they had not believed in a created universe.

Scientist	Lived	Areas of Contribution
Francis Bacon	1561 – 1626	Developed the scientific method
Galileo Galilei	1564 – 1642	Physics and astronomy
Johann Kepler	1571 – 1630	Astronomy
Walter Charleton	1619 – 1707	President of the Royal College of Physicians
Robert Boyle	1627 – 1691	Chemistry
Isaac Newton	1642 – 1727	Physics, mathematics, astronomy, optics
John Hutchinson	1674 – 1737	Paleontology
Carolus Linnaeus	1707 – 1778	Taxonomy, modern classification system
William Herschel	1738 – 1822	Astronomy
John Dalton	1766 – 1844	Modern atomic theory
Georges Cuvier	1769 – 1832	Comparative anatomy, paleontology
Michael Faraday	1791 – 1867	Electromagnetics
James Joule	1818 – 1889	Thermodynamics
Rudolph Virchow	1821 – 1902	Pathology
Gregor Mendel	1822 – 1894	Genetics
Louis Pasteur	1822 – 1895	Bacteriology, biochemistry, sterilization, immunization
George Washington Carver	1864 – 1943	Inventor
Frank Marsh	1899 – 1992	Biology
Arthur Rendle Short	1885 – 1955	Surgery
Verna Wright	1928 – 1998	Rheumatology

Figure 17.8.3

Ben Carson

Ben Carson, MD (born 1951), Chief of Pediatric Neurosurgery at Johns Hopkins since he was 33 years old, seen here receiving the Presidential Medal of Freedom from President George Bush in 2008. He has performed countless life-saving operations, including the first surgery to separate twins conjoined at the head (so-called "Siamese" twins joined at the head) and the first surgery on a fetus to relieve pressure on the baby's brain. He is a Christian who believes in creation and has participated in debates against evolutionists, including Richard Dawkins.

White House archives

17.9 INTRODUCTION TO INTELLIGENT DESIGN

Intelligent design (abbreviated "ID") refers to the general concept that there must be an "intelligent designer" of life and the universe. Everything about living organisms is way too complicated and the physical laws of the universe that hold living things together are too "perfect" to have arisen by completely accidental and purposeless processes. Therefore, they must be the result of an intelligent being. Although there has been increasing coverage of the push to teach intelligent design in public schools the past few years, the concept that the "Why are we here?" question must be answered with a response that contains an intelligent agent as the cause is not that new. From Cicero's first century BC discussion of the apparent "purpose and reason" of the world around him to William Paley's 1802 (and still relevant) discussion of his logical conclusion that, just as a watch clearly implies the presence of the watchmaker (whether you see the watch being made, or not), the orderly functions of living organisms and the world around them clearly imply the presence of a designer is apparent.

However, one of the interesting things about the intelligent design concept is that there are actually *atheistic evolutionary scientists* who agree that it does appear that the universe and living organisms are designed because there are many scientific observations that support ID. Obviously, the atheist would not believe that the intelligent designer was God. Therefore, it is very important to understand that "believing in intelligent design" does not automatically mean "a belief in God." Believing in ID simply means that one believes there was some sort of intelligent cause that resulted in the appearance of living organisms.

Of course, for the Christian, God is the Intelligent Designer as he is the only thing that fulfills the requirements of a being capable of designing the universe and everything in it:

- It is true that scientific data do support a "life-is-way-too-complex-to-be-the-result-of-random-processes-and-so-there-must-be-an-intelligent-cause" conclusion; therefore, concluding that the scientific data points to an intelligent designer is rational. We will discuss this in detail.

- God is intelligent; in fact, he is omniscient. He knows everything there is to know and always has.

- God is powerful; in fact, he is omnipotent. He is powerful enough to do anything, which includes the ability to create the universe, life, the physical laws governing the universe, the genetic code, etc.

- The Bible states quite clearly that God – who meets the criteria required for an intelligent designer – created the universe and everything in it.

- The Lord Our God is therefore the Intelligent Designer.

> *Have you not known? Have you not heard? The Lord is the everlasting God, the Creator of the ends of the earth. He does not faint or grow weary; his understanding is unsearchable.* Isaiah 40:28

17.10 INTELLIGENT DESIGN AND THE INTELLIGENT DESIGN MOVEMENT

As we just noted, *technically,* a belief in ID doesn't automatically mean a belief that God is the intelligent designer. It really only indicates a person believes that the random and purposeless processes of evolution do not explain the origin of life; therefore, there must have been some intelligent agent that "started it all." This often creates confusion and I still remember the first time I heard a person speaking passionately about his belief in intelligent design because I knew this person was also an atheist! I thought, "How can it be that someone would believe in intelligent design and not believe in God?" It made no sense to me then (and it still doesn't now) because if a person doesn't believe that God is The Intelligent Designer, then there is nothing else left, really, to believe is the intelligent designer. Besides God, there is no other possibly describable entity in the universe that fulfills the criteria necessary to be able to "design" life. It *has to be God*.

Figure 17.10.1

Panspermia

Panspermia is the belief that "the seeds of life" exist throughout the universe and were brought to earth on meteors or asteroids. One of the most famous panspermists was atheist and ardent anti-Christian Francis Crick (1916 – 2004), the co-discoverer of the structure of DNA. Like many panspermists, he believed that life somehow originated elsewhere in the universe and was brought to earth when a meteor carrying "bacterial spores" landed on earth. Of course, the huge problem for panspermists and anyone who believes in ID but not God is evident in the question, "Where did life come from if it originated somewhere else in the universe?" No matter how far removed one tries to make the intelligent agent that designed life in the non-God scenario origin of life story, there is still the necessity to answer that question. Evolutionist Michael Denton says, in his best-selling book *Evolution: a Theory in Crisis*,

> *"Nothing illustrates clearly just how intractable a problem the origin of life has become than the fact that world authorities can seriously toy with the idea of panspermia."*

When one denies the truth of Scripture, there is no end to which one must go to answer the "How did we get here?" question. Of course, for creationists, God meets all the requirements of an intelligent designer. So He Is.

Photo by Marc Lieberman in Siegel RM, Callaway EM: Francis Crick's Legacy for Neuroscience: Between the α and the Ω. PLoS Biol 2/12/2004: e419

The foundation of believing in ID but not that God is The Designer is, of course, the fact that some people choose to deny God's existence and sovereignty over the universe and everything in it while at the same time they are able to clearly reason that something obviously has or had such control. Atheistic or agnostic ID'ers clearly understand that evolution cannot explain the origin or complexity of life but, since they don't believe in God, there is no way that something they don't believe in could be the designer. Some people believe that aliens were the intelligent designers and brought life to earth. Others believe that life originated elsewhere and was brought to earth by a meteor. Still others admit that they do not know what/who the intelligent designer is but they don't believe it is God. It seems an odd position to be in when one takes the position that a belief in God is unscientific because his existence cannot be proven while also believing that something intelligent created life while at the same time not having a "provable" explanation for what the intelligent something was!

In an attempt to clarify the "I-believe-in-ID-but-I-don't-believe-in-God" confusion, the "**intelligent design movement**" formed in the mid to late 1980's and has gained some steam over the past decade. The ID movement is a loosely organized scientific effort of proponents of intelligent design to publicize the multiple scientific problems with evolution. The goal of the ID movement is not to try to persuade that the Christian God is the Designer; instead, it is to educate the public about the general short-comings of evolution and its ability to explain the origin and diversity of life.

Some scientists in the "ID movement" are Christian creationists and some are agnostic or atheistic evolutionists. The common thread is the realization that life is too complex and organized to have arisen accidentally; therefore, evolution is not an acceptable origins explanation. Whether it is a "good thing" or not for Christian and atheist ID'ers to work in close association with a common goal is another issue.

> *My son, fear the Lord and the king, and do not join with those who do otherwise, for disaster will arise suddenly from them, and who knows the ruin that will come from them both?* Proverbs 24: 21-22

Figure 17.10.2

The ID Movement
Intelligent Design made international headlines in the middle to late part of the first decade of the 2000's due to extensive media coverage of prominent court cases and a national movie release. The Kitzmiller-Dover trial was a 2005 lawsuit brought against the Dover Area School District by 11 parents after the Dover Schools instituted a policy that intelligent design had to be discussed in science class along with evolution. In November of that year, after hearing pro and con intelligent design arguments, Judge John E. Jones decided that ID constituted religious education and decided against the school district, causing the removal of ID teaching from the curriculum. The Ben Stein documentary *Expelled: No Intelligence Allowed* opened in 2008, chronicling the intensely anti-ID approach that the scientific establishment takes. In the documentary, several ID scientists tell their story of the openly hostile environment they faced in their academic careers, resulting in the loss of their jobs and research positions. Science is superficially touted as an endeavor in which "truth" is sought and open debates are welcome.... unless, apparently, the one doing the questioning doesn't accept evolution.

17.11 INTELLIGENT DESIGN AND TELEOLOGY

Teleology is the study of design or purpose in nature and is a particularly powerful line of reasoning when endeavoring "to prove" the existence of a creator. Inherent in teleology is the concept that everywhere one looks, there is obvious purpose in nature and the only way that could happen is if something designed that purpose into nature. From the interdependence of bees and flowers to the intricate fit of enzymes to substrate, purpose is clearly seen. Nothing with purpose happens accidentally. Since purpose exists in virtually every aspect of all living organisms and associated systems, the logical conclusion is that there is a designer to that purpose.

Teleological arguments are ones that arise from teleology and have been used for centuries to prove that God is the Creator. After studying some property of living organisms or the physical universe and seeing that it fulfills every property of design, *the only reasonable conclusion is that it was designed*.

> **The Lord has made everything for its purpose, even the wicked for the day of trouble.** *Proverbs 16:4*

Figure 17.11.1

Chirality and Teleology

The chirality of the amino acids is one of the countless examples of design in nature. All amino acids are like hands – they come in two forms, "L" (left) and "D" (right) oriented forms, which is to say they exhibit the property of chirality (derived from the Greek word for "hand"). It is fascinating – and so far impossible for evolutionists to plausibly explain – why all 20 amino acids that are used to build proteins in all organisms are the L form instead of a close to 50-50 mix of L and D forms. One of the major foundational principles of evolution – random processes subject to the mathematical properties of probability – would predict that, when life was evolving in the "sea of chemicals" (often called the **primordial ooze**) evolutionists think existed billions of years ago, since both L and D forms of amino acids would have been randomly generated in the ooze (by an as-yet unknown naturalistic amino acid-forming mechanism), some of the amino acids that were incorporated into organisms as they evolved should be the L form and some the D. Statistically speaking, if both L and D forms of a given amino acid were just sitting there waiting to be incorporated into a protein, there is a 1 in 2 (50%) chance that the L form will be incorporated into the amino acid and a 1 in 2 chance that an R form would be incorporated. For two L forms to be successively taken into the amino acid is a 1 in 2 chance multiplied by a 1 in 2 chance, or 1 in 4 (25%). However, the likelihood that all 20 amino acid forms would be the L form (rather than a near 50-50 mix of L and R) is 1 in 1,048,576, or a 0.0000954% chance, a statistically highly improbable event (the same chance as flipping a quarter and getting "heads" 20 times in a row). The other way of looking at that probability is that there is a 99.9999046% likelihood that all L forms of amino acids did not become incorporated into proteins randomly. The fact that there are all L forms in proteins with essentially a 0% chance of arising randomly is completely inconsistent with the prediction of the evolutionary model. From the evolutionist's standpoint, since evolution obviously happened, then the statistical probabilities should favor it happening, or at least not indicate that it is nearly impossible to happen. The teleological argument seizes upon this because when something happens "against the odds," it is indication of an intelligent force being involved to counteract the highly improbably random happening. Intelligent design is the only logical way to explain a biological event that clearly "defies the odds" because it was designed not to! This is one way to apply a teleological argument for the involvement of a designer in the origin of life and, since God is the only known entity that fulfills the necessary criteria of an intelligent designer, the teleological argument leads to the conclusion that God is The Designer.

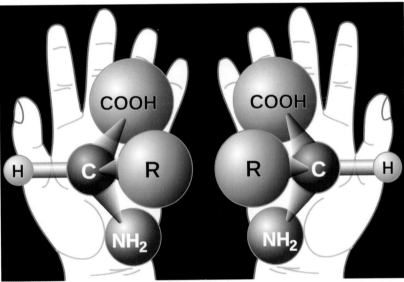

Christian intelligent design proponents very effectively use teleological arguments in support of God being the designer since even some atheists identify that the most reasonable and logical conclusion when one breaks down the properties of life is that there must be some sort of intelligent agent that caused life. Of course, in Genesis, the Bible describes how the Intelligent Designer created. Creationists simply put two and two together – the immaculate intricacies of life and the correspondingly high unlikelihood that they arose randomly demand an intelligent agent. The Bible describes an Intelligent Agent that is fully capable of fulfilling all of the requirements of an intelligent designer. The only logical conclusion is that the intelligent agent _is_ the God of the Bible because He is the only Entity that fulfills the "creator" requirements required by ID reasoning.

Figure 17.11.2

Enzymes and Teleology

The enzyme luciferase is made up of two separate protein subunits, the alpha unit (355 amino acids long) and the beta subunit (324 amino acids long). Since evolution is naturalistic and follows statistical principles, we can calculate the likelihood that even one of the subunits could form through the random assembly of the 20 amino acids. For the sake of argument, we will ignore the facts that: 1) amino acids cannot form by themselves (evolution requires it but not even cleverly designed laboratory experiments with carefully controlled conditions can cause stable amino acids to form by themselves); 2) the statistical impossibility that all of the 20 amino acids are L forms; and, 3) the fact that no randomly generated proteins have "biological activity" (enzymes are highly specific for their substrate and random sequences, as would have formed in the primordial ooze, don't "do anything"). The amino acid sequence of each subunit must be exactly correct or else the enzyme will not work. There are 324 amino acid positions in the beta subunit, each with 20 possible amino acids that could fill one of the 324 spots, which means there are 20^{324} possible beta subunit structures, or 10^{421} (that is 10 multiplied times itself 421 times) possible protein structures that could be made from the random linking of 1 of 20 amino acids in the 324 different positions. That is a lot of possible protein configurations, but just how many? To compare, there are about 10^{80} *atoms in the universe*, and so it is very unlikely that there are enough atoms in the universe to allow even one biologically active enzyme subunit to form through Darwinian "trial and error." The likelihood that proteins formed randomly in this fashion to give rise to the first functional cell goes even lower than it already is if we then consider that the most "primitive" type of cell has about 350 enzymes that would have had to form this way, each roughly having the same exceedingly improbable statistical likelihood of forming as luciferase does. In short, it is a statistical impossibility that life originated like evolutionists say it did; the evolutionary model fails on another prediction. When faced with scientific data such as these, the teleological argument would lead to the obvious conclusion that the only way to explain such statistical impossibilities is with input from an intelligent designer – there was no randomness involved at all. _I want to be very clear that I am not advocating that "God used evolution" to create life. He didn't. He created life just as the Bible said he did_. God is the intelligent designer because the Bible says he is. As we can see, applying statistics to God's creation underscores the fact that life had to be created the way the Bible says because any other way is impossible. By the way, despite intense research over the past three decades, it is still unknown exactly how the two luciferase subunits work together!

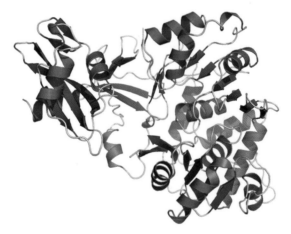

However valid and persuasive teleological arguments may be in concluding that God is the Intelligent Designer, there is actually an even better one to use to conclude God is the Creator – God's Holy and Inerrant Word. Life was designed by God (and for God) because God said it was.

> ***By faith we understand that the universe was created by the word of God, so that what is seen was not made out of things that are visible.*** *Hebrews 11:3*

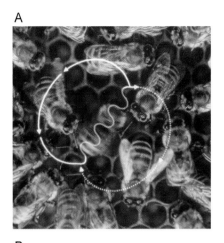

Figure 17.11.3

Honeybees and Intelligent Design

Another very clear example of design in nature that is not possible to explain via the naturalistic mechanisms of evolution is honeybee communication. Honeybees, which have brains roughly the size of a pin head, communicate the location of food sources to one another using very complex dances, called waggle dances. The top photo shows a bee doing the waggle dance, a figure-eight form in which the bee first turns to the right, returns through the center of the figure-eight waggling, then turns to the left and again walks through the center waggling (note that the bee in the center of the diagram under the squiggly line is blurry because it is waggling back and forth very quickly). The number of figure eight circuits can be from 1 to more than 100. In the bottom, we see that the angle at which the bee performs the dance in the hive in relationship to the location of the sun at the time of the dance provides the other bees the "direction" of the food source. The number of circuits and the length of time the bee waggles during the waggle phase provide further information to the other bees watching so that they can accurately find the food source. How this dance came to be, evolutionarily speaking, is a "chicken or egg" situation that cannot be explained via naturalistic mechanisms. Waggle dances are used by all varieties of honeybees, so it is a critical part of their communication system. If waggle dances evolved, how could bees have survived as the dance was "evolving" piece by piece, over time, since the entire dance is necessary to communicate where the food is? Also, there is no evidence that young bees learn the dances from older bees – they just know how to do it, which means it is hard wired into their genetics. Evolution cannot explain such genetic hard wiring (which is also found with direction-finding in migratory animals like birds and turtles). The only reasonable conclusion about in-born behaviors like the waggle dance is that they exist because it was designed into the organism. While evolution cannot explain such obvious design in nature, this scientific data perfectly supports the creation model. God built such mechanisms right into the DNA of organisms like bees, birds and turtles – that is the only explanation that makes sense and is just as expected when using the Bible as the source of truth.

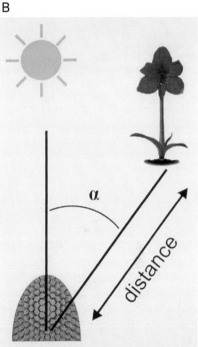

While I do think it important that you begin to understand the above nuances that exist with ID theory/ID movement, *from this point on, when I talk about intelligent design, I am specifically referring to the Christian God, the Almighty Biblical Creator of the Universe and everything in it, as being the "Intelligent Designer"* (rather than aliens). Even the panspermists evolutionist Francis Crick, said:

> *"An honest man, armed with all the knowledge available to us now, could only state that, in some sense, the origin of life appears at the moment to be almost a miracle so many are the conditions which would have had to have been satisfied to get it going."*

Figure 17.11.4

Piltdown Man

Portrait by John Cooke/Wikimedia Commons/{{PD-old}}

This photo of a famous 1910 painting shows several men, including Charles Dawson (1864 – 1916) standing 2nd from right, the "discoverer" of the partial skull and jaw bone of **Piltdown Man**. Also, Sir Arthur Keith (1866 – 1955), seated in the white coat, is examining the skull. Piltdown Man is a famous paleontological forgery in which an orangutan's jaw bone was placed with a human skull for the purposeful and deceptive intention of trying to make evolution look more plausible. It is not clear who fabricated the forgery, but both Dawson and Dr. Keith (among others) have been implicated. Perhaps the words of Dr. Keith himself can help us understand why some evolutionists have so strongly wanted to "prove evolution is true" that they are willing to compromise truth and their scientific credibility.

> ***"Evolution is unproved and unprovable but we believe it because the only alternative is special creation and that is unthinkable."***

Why is it "unthinkable?" Isn't everything supposed to be valid for honest scientific inquiry? As we will clearly see in the upcoming two chapters, it isn't "unthinkable" because the data doesn't support concepts of creation. No, the scientific data is perfectly compatible with a creation model. It is unthinkable because evolutionary world view is one that formed specifically to explain life in the absence of God. Dr. Keith, like most evolutionary thought leaders, was an atheist and if a person doesn't believe God exists, how could a God-based origins theory properly explain why we are here? Interesting note that the painting on the wall in back of the group is of Charles Darwin.

17.12 WHAT IS IT ABOUT DESIGN THAT WHEN YOU SEE IT, YOU KNOW IT?

The teleological argument is actually pretty simple – the intricacies of living organisms reveal their design. Living systems are so complex and yet work so well that they appear to have been designed just as any other intricately complex and interacting system was designed, leading one to the conclusion that they _were_ designed and so there must be a designer. But, what exactly is it about biological systems that causes even many atheists to believe that life was designed, or, at least, makes them state that life appears to have been designed? What is it that allows a person to fairly rapidly conclude, "This was designed" or, "This was not designed and is the result of randomness" almost as soon as it is seen? It is because there are objective "design properties" that all things that have been designed share, just as there are properties of randomness that all things that are the result of random forces share. Therefore, we should be able to apply design properties to biological systems and see if the biological systems reflect design or randomness.

Figure 17.12.1

A Brief History of Teleological Argumentation

Teleological argumentation dates at least as far back as ancient Greece, when arguments were made supporting a "universe designer" to counteract claims of naturalistic causes of the universe and life. Epicurus, (341 BC – 270 BC), left, argued for his version of evolution by explaining that the universe and everything in it formed as a result of particles colliding into one another. Marcus Tillius Cicero (106 BC – 43 BC), center, to counteract 200 years of "Epicureanism," argued for his version of intelligent design using the teleological argument that, since all art requires a designer and nature was more perfect than art, the universe is under the control of an intelligent designer (though Cicero's intelligent designer wasn't God). In the early 19th century, a still-pillar of teleological argumentation was written by British clergyman, philosopher and Christian apologist William Paley (1743 – 1805), right. He was born in Peterborough, England and used the teleological argument convincingly in his 1802 book, *Natural Theology; or, Evidences of the Existence and Attributes of the Deity*. In it, he forwarded what remains <u>the</u> classical argument for design – that as a watch is obvious evidence for its designer, so human anatomy and physiology are evidences of God The Designer. *Natural Theology* was required reading in England's universities for many decades and even Charles Darwin revered Paley's convincing logic leading to the conclusion that the universe was designed by God. In 1987, more than 175 years after *Natural Theology* was published, atheist philosopher Richard Dawkins published *The Blind Watchmaker*, an attempt to refute Paley's convincing design arguments. In it, Dawkins states that,

> **"(b)iology is the study of complicated things that give the appearance of having been designed for a purpose."**

So, even Richard Dawkins can see that biological systems are so complex that, if he wasn't looking at a living organism, he would say that the system was designed. Of course, as an atheist, Dr. Dawkins absolutely cannot believe the "complicated things" were designed because that would mean there was a Designer. Or, as the atheist geneticist Richard Lewontin said,

> **"We take the side of science in spite of the patent absurdity of some of its constructs, in spite of its failure to fulfill many of its extravagant promises of health and life, in spite of the tolerance of the scientific community for unsubstantiated just-so stories, because we have a prior commitment, a commitment to materialism."**

It is clear that evolutionary thought leaders *completely understand* that the creation/evolution debate is not about honestly discussing the scientific merits of creation and evolution as origins explanations, but ensuring that God cannot enter the origins discussion.

William Paley, (1789 – 1791) by George Romney. From National Portrait Gallery, London, in public domain.

Properties of design include:

- Specific, highly complex structure, known as "**specified complexity**."

- High degrees of order and regulation.

- Reproducible function and form.

- Irreducible complexity (more in the next section).

- Inexplicable existence by any mechanism other than design (i.e. when applying statistical methods to determine the probability of random formation, the mathematics indicate a random explanation is so unlikely that statisticians would consider it impossible).

- Purpose.

- A designer.

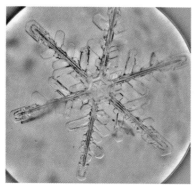

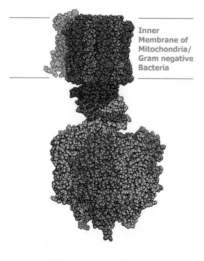

Inner Membrane of Mitochondria/ Gram negative Bacteria

Figure 17.12.2

Intelligent Design and Specified Complexity

We often hear it said that "no two snowflakes are the same." This is because snowflakes are made up of ice crystals that form when water freezes, and, while the crystals always form in one of 80 basic hexagonal shapes initially, as they grow larger they take on an infinite number of shapes as the crystals grow by randomly adding various arrangements of the 80 shapes to the growing crystals. So, while they are very complex, snowflakes form as a natural result of the physics and chemistry of frozen water and the surrounding environment, which interact in nonspecific ways, causing the water hexagons to build randomly as the flake grows bigger. Snowflakes are complex, but they are not specific since they can take on an infinite number of shapes. If snowflakes were specific and complex, they would always have the same shape. Contrast that to the structure of the enzyme ATP synthase, which is made up of multiple complex protein subunits and is found in all life forms. It is highly specific and performs the same specific function – making ATP – over and over. If the amino acid sequence of any of the 8 subunits (which are hundreds of amino acids long, except the C subunit, which is 71) is off, then the entire enzyme will not work and the organism will die. This enzyme, among many thousands of similarly specifically complex enzymes found in living systems, requires transcription and translation of very specific DNA segments done the same way, every time, which occurs billions of times per day in all organisms. Like the snowflake, ATP synthase is complex, but unlike the snowflake, it is also specific. ATP synthase is always built of the same complicated protein subunits and always catalyzes the same reaction. A system that is made via naturalistic processes (like snowflake formation and evolution) can at best be complex, but will never be specific because the combined properties of specificity and complexity are 100% design features. No scientific experiment has ever shown that structures or functions that are both specific and complex can arise as a result of random events or chemical interactions. Even a simple, designed system is always specific and complex. If it is ridiculous to conclude that a soda can, which holds soda while maintaining its carbonation and opens easily, arose as a result of random events, how much more nonsensical is it to conclude that the ATP synthase apparatus is the result of randomness? Biological systems, which are infinitely more complex than anything man can design, clearly reflect design because all known biologic molecules, enzymes, biochemical pathways, etc., demonstrate specified complexity, a design property.

Properties characteristic of randomness (purposelessness):

- May be complex or specific, but not both.

- Disorderly.

- Easily explainable by random events (i.e. when applying statistical methods to the "purposeless thing," the probability of it happening randomly is supported by the statistical calculations).

- Not reproducible.

- No identifiable structure.

- No identifiable purpose.

- Poor or no function of parts.

Figure 17.12.3

Randomness and Design Evidence
Whether or not a person can immediately articulate the "why" of design, it is obvious virtually from the second you look at the two pictures below that one is the result of a random process and one is the result of design. Tornado-related destruction is the epitome of a random process – although there is great complexity in that picture (look at all of the "stuff"), there is also a *high* amount of disorder with essentially nothing existing in an organized fashion. Contrast that to the inner workings of a watch. Very "simple" individual watch parts, yet each one sublimely designed with a specific intent, each with precise placement so that the entire watch mechanism fits perfectly inside the housing and lines up with the winding knob on top and the hands on the front. Further, inside, the gears and springs all have specific arrangements relative to one another such that the interaction of all the parts results in the designer's purpose – the precise keeping and display of time. The tornado is the definition of "*un*specified complexity" just as the watch is the epitome of "specified complexity." It is as unreasonable to look at the disorder of the tornado's path of destruction and conclude it is the result of design as it is to conclude that the complexity and order of the watch is the result of accidental and random processes. When the properties of design and of randomness are applied to biological systems, there is no logical line of reasoning that could lead one to the conclusion that things like highly ordered and strictly regulated chemical reactions and enzyme-substrate interactions, vastly more complex and specific than anything man ever will be able to design, are anything but the result of intelligent design by God.

US National Oceanic and Atmospheric Administration

© Jose Reynaldo da Fonseca/Wikimedia Commons/CC-BY-SA-3.0

In the next few sections, we will apply design and randomness properties to living systems to see which property is reflected in the scientific data.

17.13 INTELLIGENT DESIGN AND IRREDUCIBLE COMPLEXITY

Irreducible complexity is a term coined by Lehigh University PhD biochemist Michael Behe in his book *Darwin's Black Box*. Dr. Behe defines irreducible complexity as "a single system composed of several well-matched, interacting parts that contribute to the basic function, wherein the removal of any one of the parts causes the system to effectively cease functioning." That is, an irreducibly complex system does not function when any one of its parts are removed, and this provides the foundation of how irreducible complexity fits into the origins discussion. Although Dr. Behe does believe in intelligent design, he also believes in evolution and thinks that there are some things about living organisms that can be explained by evolution and some things that cannot (and so those things that cannot require a creator).

Regardless of his evolutionary beliefs, his clear elucidation of irreducible complexity is very pertinent because he effectively identifies a crucial property of designed systems. If you see "something" that cannot have any one of its "parts" (whether a man-made machine, a molecular machine or components of a chemical reaction) removed without ceasing to function, you know that "something" is an irreducibly complex system.

Figure 17.13.1

Reducibly and Irreducibly Complex Systems

The Willys Jeep is a great example of a complex system that was designed to be a reducibly complex one. Even though there are many moving parts that interact in very complicated and specific ways, it is possible to remove many of its components and still have it function perfectly well to get you from A to B. Further, you could remove a relatively large number of parts and not only would it still work, but it would still be recognizable as a Willys Jeep.

The mousetrap is an example of an irreducibly complex system. It has moving parts and so is complex; however, if any one of the parts are removed, the mousetrap ceases to fulfill its purpose of trapping a mouse. It cannot be reduced any further than the essential parts of platform, hammer, spring, holding bar and catch. All biochemical systems are irreducibly complex ones – remove any one of the parts of the system and it stops working. Such systems cannot be explained by step-wise evolution because there is no way that such a system can function unless it is complete and fully operational from the beginning. Fully functional systems from the beginning are what the creation model predicts.

Of course, creationists believe that 100% of the "well-matched parts" Dr. Behe uses in his definition are parts that have been precisely designed by God to be "well matched." God knew how he needed them to work and so that is how he designed them. Evolution is absolutely not necessary to explain anything about living systems and, in fact, evolution cannot explain the existence of irreducibly complex biological systems. So, it is with that clearly in mind that we examine irreducible complexity.

All individual biochemical pathways and the enzymes that catalyze them are irreducibly complex systems – if you remove one of the protein subunits, one of the enzymes, one of the substrates, etc., the product of that biochemical pathway will cease to exist. Therefore, whatever physiological effect the product was supposed to have never occurs. In other words, by removing one component of a biochemical pathway, that pathway will universally stop producing its product. And, of course, whatever that function is is a process critical to the living organism's survival.

Reaction 1 ⟶ A

Reaction 2 ⟶ B

Reaction 3 ⟶ C

Physiological effect

Figure 17.13.2

The Evolution Model and Biochemical Pathways

All of the many thousands of different types of biochemical reactions are ones in which the product of one reaction is necessary for the next step of the pathway, with the end product of the final reaction being the "thing" that exerts physiological change in the organism. In other words, the product of the final reaction in a biochemical pathway is what the organism needs. At left, generically we see that there are three reactions – 1, 2 and 3 – that make up a biochemical pathway. The product of Reaction 1 – "A" – is required for Reaction 2, which makes product "B." B, in turn, is required for Reaction 3 to make its product – "C." If A isn't made, then neither is B or C. If B isn't made, then neither is C. The only "thing" that A "does" is supply the necessary molecule for Reaction 2 and the only thing B "does" is provide the necessary molecule for reaction 3. Like all biochemical reactions, the only purpose of the series of reactions is to make C, the end product. The fully functional reaction system is necessary since it is the end product of the last reaction that the organism needs to live. Removing any one of the reactions or the products renders the entire series of reactions ineffective at "doing what they are supposed to do;" therefore, this is an irreducibly complex system. Irreducibly complex biochemical reactions like this cannot be explained by evolutionary mechanisms, which require step-by-step evolution of the individual parts. From the evolutionary perspective, you must start with Reaction 1 forming product A because B and C cannot be formed unless A first exists. So, evolutionarily, let's say that Reaction 1 somehow was able to form within an organism. It has no B or C, yet, because they haven't evolved. It is just making A. What does A do? Nothing. Its only purpose is to fuel Reaction 2 so that B can be made but there isn't any molecular machinery to make B yet since it hasn't evolved. The evolutionary model is very utilitarian – in order for a new trait, a chemical reaction or a new body part, for example, to be passed along from generation to generation, it must do something. If the chemical reaction or structure that arises doesn't do anything, it is removed from the population. Therefore, even if Reaction 1 could arise accidentally and make A, it would be removed from the population because it isn't doing anything since the enzymes for the reactions to make B and C don't yet exist. There would never be any "reason" for B and C to form. This is the simple beauty of the irreducibly complex design argument. In order for linked biochemical reactions to be explainable evolutionarily (and virtually all biochemical reactions are linked such as this example), they would need to be fully formed and operational from the outset, because if they weren't, they would be removed from subsequent generations of organisms. However, interestingly, fully functional systems from the beginning is the exact prediction of the creation model. Boom! There everything is, completely intact and operational. Irreducibly complex systems can only arise through creative powers and are not consistent with the evolutionary model.

One of the properties of evolutionary naturalistic process is that _in order for a new characteristic, structure or function to be "selected for" by nature, in order for it to "stick around" and be passed from generation to generation, it needs to have some beneficial function to the organism_. If a new trait, such as a new chemical reaction or enzyme, actually could arise but has no use to the organism, then nature would not "select for it" and that new trait would disappear. Because all biochemical pathways and enzymes exist only to make their product, unless they were fully functional from the very beginning, they would not be selected for since they would not be producing anything until becoming fully functional. This is why irreducibly complex systems cannot evolve in step-by-step fashion. According to evolution, such systems had to evolve step-by-step but, until they were fully functional they wouldn't have all of the parts or reactions necessary to produce their products and so, according to evolutionary concepts, the non-functioning system or enzyme would be eliminated.

Figure 17.13.3

The Evolution Model Cannot Explain Irreducible Complexity

This shows protein production. Starting in the nucleus, mRNA polymerase opens the DNA, transcribing mRNA. Then, the mRNA exits the nucleus and is translated into the protein (note that the ribosome is the little gray blob on the mRNA at the bottom). At all of these steps, enzymatic functions are heavily involved – opening the DNA, linking adenine (A), uracil (U), guanine (G) and cytosine (C) together to make the mRNA from the DNA template, linking the amino acids together inside the ribosome, etc. According to evolutionary concepts, these enzymes formed from step-wise appearance over hundreds of thousands and millions of years. However, this entire system is itself a tightly regulated, intricately linked step-by-step process, with the subsequent process 100% dependent upon the previous process being successfully completed. It is an irreducible and incredibly complex system and cannot be formed by stepwise evolutionary processes because if any one of the "sub-step" components is removed (or doesn't exist), the entire system doesn't work. For example, mRNA polymerase opens the DNA, reads it and then links together A, U, C and G to transcribe the mRNA from the DNA template. If mRNA polymerase is not fully functional and present from the nanosecond that DNA first existed, then the system would not work because no protein could be made. And, of course, the instructions to produce mRNA polymerase itself are encoded in the DNA and so, billions of years ago when this system was evolving, how could there even be any mRNA if mRNA polymerase didn't already exist from the very beginning so that it could open the DNA and make the mRNA that would be transcribed into mRNA polymerase? If this were the very first fully functional cell, why would the DNA contain instructions for mRNA when there is no way that the cell would know it needs mRNA since the DNA is just a random collection of nucleotides? Or, if RNA and DNA happened to have "evolved" independently in the primordial ooze and then got encapsulated together in the first cell, why would the DNA contain instructions to make mRNA when the two don't even "know" each other? Or, if the ribosome is removed from the system, the mRNA would not get transcribed and would then just sit there because the ribosome doesn't exist to translate it into a protein. Remove any one of the components of the DNA-to-protein process and the system doesn't work. This system absolutely had to exist, completely intact and fully functional, from the second the first cell formed in the evolutionary paradigm. However, there is absolutely no way to scientifically explain how the DNA-to-protein system evolved in the required step-by-step process since it cannot work unless all the steps are present. Highly specific, organized and irreducibly complex biological systems CANNOT be explained evolutionarily because they had to be fully functional from the beginning. This is not a property of the evolutionary model, but is of the creation model. As we will continue to learn, the predictions of the creation origins model fit much better with scientific observations and rational thought processes than the evolution model.

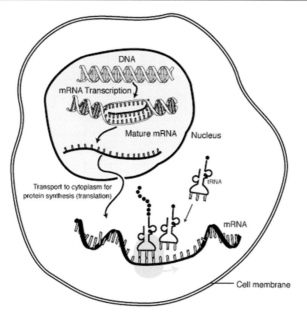

17.14 INTELLIGENT DESIGN - IS LIFE EXPLAINABLE IN ANY OTHER WAY?

A very powerful way, indeed, to determine design is if the answer to the question, "Is there any rational and objective way other than design to explain its existence?" is "No." We saw it when we discussed that a watch's existence clearly implied it had a designer – "Is the watch's existence explainable in any way other than it was designed?" No, of course there is a designer to the watch. Any other conclusion is ridiculous. That line of reasoning is one of the clear outcomes of the concepts of specified complexity and irreducible complexity. "Is there any way other than design to explain the existence of an irreducibly complex system that has specified complexity, such as a mousetrap or enzyme-substrate interaction?" No, there just is not. There is simply no reasonable argument to support a random origin explanation of biological irreducible and specified complexity. They scream "God designed me!"

Using this "Is it explainable any way other than design?" standard, we are going to break down the production of ATP to see if we can logically conclude "ATP production is _only explainable_ by creation because it clearly meets 'design criteria' and therefore _cannot be explained_ by random and purposeless evolutionary events."

Figure 17.14.1

Adenosine Triphosphate

Recall that ATP is the "energy currency" of the cell. Almost everything that happens in the cell requires energy provided by breaking the phosphate bonds of ATP in order to be able to fuel the endothermic reactions of life. DNA replication, DNA transcription, protein translation, all enzyme function, the movement of materials within the cell, etc., all require ATP. Indeed, if ATP did not exist, neither would life. Evolutionarily speaking, ATP production (which demonstrates both specific complexity and irreducible complexity) is unexplainable by step-wise processes. ATP cannot exist unless the enzyme that makes it – ATP synthase – first exists because ATP itself is required to make the ATP synthase. However, in that very first cell, where would the ATP have come from to make the first ATP synthase enzyme if ATP synthase didn't already exist? Without ATP, the DNA cannot be opened, mRNA cannot be made and the ribosome cannot function to build ATP synthase. Without ATP synthase, no ATP can be made. Without ATP to provide the energy needed for ATP synthase synthesis, ATP cannot be made. It is a conundrum that cannot be explained via the evolution model, which states that such series of linked biochemical reactions evolved over time. But, we can clearly see that it is impossible for them to do so since ATP cannot exist without ATP synthase and vice-versa. The intricate complexity of ATP synthase production and ATP synthesis are linked and the ability to synthesize both simultaneously had to have existed right from the beginning, which is not a prediction of the evolution model. Of course, this scientific necessity of fully operational, interlinked biochemical pathways from the beginning is predicted by the creation model.

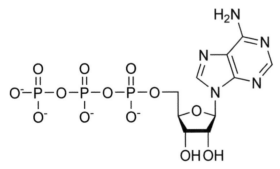

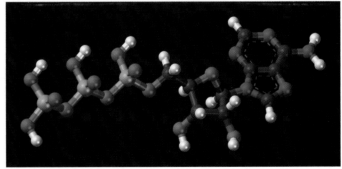

© cacycle/Wikimedia Commons/CC-BY-SA-3.0

Jynto (talk)/Wikimedia Commons/Public Domain

Almost all of the biochemical arguments against evolution are summed up as the "which came first, the chicken or the egg" dilemma. ATP production is one of them because _ATP production AND making the enzyme that makes ATP, ATP synthase, both require ATP_. The only way that a biochemical process that depends upon its own product to fuel itself can be explained is by the creation model. Further, such an interdependence specifically argues against evolution. When a biochemical pathway exists only to produce a certain molecule and that molecule is a component required for the biochemical pathway to proceed, there is no way that step-by-step evolutionary mechanisms can explain that pathway. If ATP is required to make itself, then it had to be present from the start, but, if for some reason it was, from where did it come since the biochemical reactions to make it could not have "evolved" without ATP? It is impossible to explain with any model other than creation.

Figure 17.14.2

ATP Synthase Revisited

Since the late 1980's, detailed studies of the mitochondrion's inner workings have more clearly identified how ATP synthase functions. High energy electrons (H^+) are produced inside the mitochondrial matrix during the Krebs cycle (citric acid cycle). These electrons are actively pumped out of the mitochondrial matrix, which causes them to accumulate in the intermembrane space. With more H^+ outside the matrix than inside, an electron gradient is established and the electrons then pass back across the inner mitochondrial membrane, doing so through the transmembrane enzyme ATP synthase, into the matrix. We now know that ATP synthase is one of many different "molecular motors" found in cells because, as the electrons pass through the ATP synthase into the matrix, their energy causes the head of the ATP synthase to rotate, up to 350 times per second! As the head rotates, it links a phosphate onto adenosine diphosphate (ADP), making ATP. Evolutionists and creationists both clearly understand the implications of this tiny 9 nm-sized enzyme motor – _there is no known motor that has ever come into existence accidentally_. All motors are specifically designed to be motors. In addition, the coupling of two irreducibly complex and unrelated processes – the Krebs cycle to make electrons to drive the ATP synthase motor and the synthesis of ATP – is further evidence of design! There is no reasonable way that one would depend upon the other if they had arisen randomly over hundreds of millions of years. Like all biochemical processes, the ATP-producing apparatus had to exist right away, fully intact and functional, from the beginning. The evolution model predicts step by step development of such systems, but it is clear that is impossible. This scientific data that leads to the logical conclusion that these two highly complicated, highly ordered, highly regulated and totally unrelated sets of interdependent biochemical reactions would have had to have been present and fully functional from the beginning is predicted by the creation model and is not supported by the evolution model.

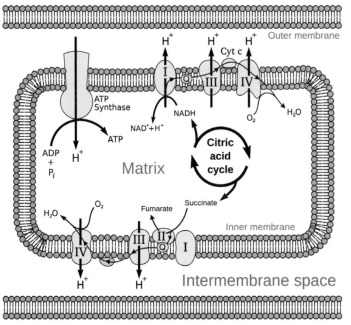

Fvasconcellos/Wikimedia Commons/{{PD}}

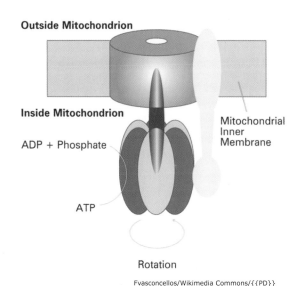

Fvasconcellos/Wikimedia Commons/{{PD}}

To look even a little deeper, when the cell needs more ATP synthase, it has to open up DNA, transcribe the mRNA encoding the ATP synthase production and then send it to the cytoplasm, which the ribosome translates into ATP synthase. All of these steps require ATP. But, back when things were very first evolving and ATP synthase didn't yet exist, from where did the ATP come that was necessary to provide the energy for the DNA-to-RNA-to-ribosome sequence? One cannot exist without the other.

Even more difficult for the evolution model to explain is the inter-dependence of the Krebs cycle and ATP production, which supposedly evolved separately over tens of millions of years. ATP synthase can't make ATP without the high energy electrons from the Krebs cycle, but the Krebs cycle needs ATP to make the high energy electrons. How could these two interdependent biochemical pathways have evolved stepwise when neither the completely intact Krebs cycle nor the completely intact ATP synthase-ATP can function without the product of the other?

Of course, there is no way to provide naturalistic, scientifically sound answers to these chicken-and-egg-type questions. Biochemical systems represent processes that are completely unexplainable using the evolution origin model. There is no way that the ATP biochemical pathway could "evolve" over time in a step-wise fashion when the product of the sets of reactions – ATP – is needed to fuel all of the reactions in the pathway! Replenish-able ATP synthase and ATP had to be immediately available as soon as life started or else life would not have lived on. The only reasonable explanation is that it was all created to work exactly as it does, faster than the blink of an eye, just like the Bible says.

> ***The fear of the Lord is the beginning of wisdom, and the knowledge of the Holy One is insight.*** *Proverbs 9:10*

Figure 17.14.3

ID, Specified and Irreducible Complexity and Rational Thought

The vertebrate (organisms with spines) coagulation cascade is an incredibly intricate inter-related network of "clotting factors" (molecules that make you stop bleeding) and "bleeding factors" (molecules that make you bleed) that are kept in just the right balance to prevent activation of the cascade unless it is necessary. It is highly specific - the clotting factors (the "Roman numerals" in the figure) only participate in a small step of the pathway (they don't "do" anything else). It is obviously highly complex – there is a tightly regulated balance of clotting and bleeding going on inside of every organism that allows the organism to continue to live but also aggressively respond to local tissue damage to limit bleeding when injured. With even minor disruption of the molecular structure of one of the clotting or bleeding factors and the entire system goes haywire, leading to many medical complications, including (commonly) death. One of the particular problems the coagulation cascade points out for Darwinian evolution regards the highly regulated nature of the system. All factors need to be present in exactly the proper amount with exactly the proper degree of biological activity for the system to be maintained. And, they cannot activate or deactivate too soon or too late or else bleeding goes on too long or clotting occurs too aggressively, leading to critical organism injury or death. These types of intricate and inter-related balances between physiological molecular forms and function are simply not explainable by a mechanism that would be formed in step-wise fashion because, if such a system were to "be in the step-by-step stages of development" predicted by the evolution model, there would never have been balance between "too much clotting" or "too much bleeding" because, by definition, a highly regulated system with multiple moving parts such as this one isn't "done" until the system is completely and intricately regulated. In its step-wise evolution before it worked right, the organism would either clot too much or bleed too much and die. No organisms would be able to live because the system isn't regulated until it is fully formed. Such a system must be fully operational and fine-tuned right from the beginning, which is not a prediction of the evolutionary model. It is irrational to conclude that such an irreducibly and specifically complex system like the coagulation cascade (or any of the other thousands of such series of linked, highly regulated biochemical reactions) could be formed over millions or billions of years by naturalistic and accidental changes; rather, such a sublime system necessitates a Designer and is a prediction of the creation model.

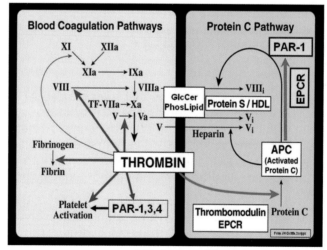

17.15 INFORMATION THEORY

Information theory, the scientific process of defining information based upon 5 different realms – statistics, **syntax**, **semantics**, **pragmatics** and **apobetics** (see Figure 17.15.4) is a newer branch of science. Initially applied to computer systems and linguistics (to crack codes during war time), concepts arising from information theory are now being increasingly applied to biological systems. Information theory often provides very powerful arguments in favor of intelligent design and in opposition of evolution because the deeper information theorists have examined the information found in all living organisms (contained in the genetic code of DNA), the stronger the argument becomes that there must be an intelligent designer as the originator of that information. As we see in all branches of science, the conclusion that, "All known sciences are perfectly compatible with God creating the universe and everything in it just as Genesis says" is further reinforced with information theory.

Figure 17.15.1

"Information"

Information is a lot like design – "we know it when we see (or hear) it." Also like design, the specific properties and implications of information can be elusive. The three images all provide glimpses of properties inherent to information. _All known information has a sender/originator, a receiver and a way to store the information_. There has _never_ been an occurrence of information that did not share those three characteristics. Although it may be that the originator of the information is more than one person (in the case of the Constitution) or is unknown (in the case of the writer of "Deep River"), none-the-less the presence of information _always_ means some intelligent source or sources produced the information. It is nonsensical to believe that information arises by itself as a result of random forces. For example, the suggestion that the Constitution could be written by randomly stringing together words is illogical. No evolutionist would argue with that concept, unless, of course, one were to apply that same reasoning to the massive amounts of biological information stored in the molecule deoxyribonucleic acid. The most vast quantities of information in existence are stored within the A-T-C-G structure of DNA (in humans, the equivalent of 1,000,000 pages or more of encyclopedic information). _DNA is the most efficient way to store information_, dwarfing the ability of the best computer storage devices, with a storage density that is _45 x 10^{12}_ (that's 45 trillion!) times more than the best man-made storage devices. If the total information presently stored in all of the world's libraries, estimated to be 10^{18} **bits** (a bit is a "storage unit"), was transferred into DNA, it would require all of 1% of the volume of a pinhead of DNA to accommodate that storage need. Despite these basic informational facts clearly implicating the presence of an information-of-life designer/creator who is infinitely creative and powerful, evolutionists instead believe that a molecular complex that contains more information than the summed total of information of the world's libraries and has its own built-in repair mechanisms is the result of random molecular interactions that occurred billions of years of years ago (in ways not able to be reproduced by even the most intelligently designed experiments) and that the information required to build self-replicating life forms then arose by chance. When viewed objectively, basic information-related scientific facts are far more compatible with the concept of God the Intelligent Designer than of an evolutionary explanation. It is beyond unreasonable to conclude that the information in, and the storage device of, DNA arose by chance.

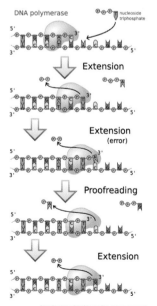

Constitutional Convention/Wikimedia Commons/Public Domain   Author Unknown/Wikimedia Commons/Public Domain   Madprime/Wikimedia Commons/ Public Domain

Claude Shannon (1916 – 2001) is the mathematician and engineer that created and developed information theory. He was the first to apply mathematics principles to study information content in order to quantify the amount of information present in anything that contained information. Advancements in computer sciences using Shannon's principles of information theory have been responsible for the massive increases seen in computer storage ability while at the same time reducing the physical size of the storage itself (we now carry more memory in our cell phones than the summed total of the world's computer memory that existed in the 1970s).

Although we will not be able to come close to doing justice for how important information theory concepts are to the study of DNA and the creation/evolution origins theories in this brief description, many have claimed that Claude Shannon's 1937 Massachusetts Institute of Technology (MIT) master's thesis that formed the foundation of information theory is the most important master's thesis of all time. The biological implications further underline its importance. More and more scientists are coming to regard information as a third "fundamental entity," along with matter and energy. This means that information is NOT of a physical or energy form and drives home the point that information theory is an extremely powerful scientific endeavor.

Historically, information theory was used in mathematics, computer science and electrical engineering. More recently, it has been used in language processing (linguistics), molecular decoding, detecting plagiarism, thermal physics and other types of data analysis. It is in information theory's application to the information content of DNA that we see powerful scientific support of the creation model and further active scientific argument against the evolution model.

Figure 17.15.2

Shannon's Information Theory

Claude Shannon's way of identifying information is very helpful in some ways but not in others. For example, if I asked you to tell me what the information content of the below sentence is, unless you are an information theorist, you would have a very hard time doing so. When you use your knowledge of the English language and how words and sentences are constructed, this sentence doesn't follow any rules, doesn't form any recognizable words and so doesn't convey any information to you. Shannon's approach to information theory would look at the information content of this sentence by assessing, based on the "rules of English," how likely or unlikely it is for the individual characters to appear in the sentence and assign each one a numerical probability value based upon statistical methods. Characters that are expected to appear less frequently have a higher information content than those that are expected to appear more frequently. While Shannon's statistical approach was groundbreaking and remains very important in many aspects of information theory, one of the great drawbacks of Shannon's approach is that it does not consider the _meaning_ of the message or the relative importance of the meaning contained in the message. His method is very helpful in some ways but obviously does not help you understand what information the sentence actually conveys.

Mxa qwfn wefia' qr[eif kduadfiuvn cjd d kkawpvlmv?

Since Shannon used purely statistical methods to identify information, it is referred to as a quantitative method of determining information. If the symbol is expected to show up very often in the language, its individual information content is lower than that of a symbol that is expected to show up far less often. While this may not make a lot of sense to those of us who don't understand the inner workings of computers, Dr. Shannon's way of applying quantitative methods to information analysis continues to lead to more effective ways to store larger quantities of information in ever smaller physical plants and write faster programs.

Figure 17.15.3

Information is More Than Its Mathematical Content

Claude Shannon's statistical-based information theory concepts have been applied very successfully to certain systems; however, it does not address all aspects of information content. There is much more to "information" than what is represented by statistical content. For example, if your friend said to you, "The sky is blue," you may reply, "Yes, it is blue because of the way that water molecules in the air scatter sunlight in the blue end of the spectrum differently than at the red end of the spectrum." Your friend – the information originator – communicated the message to you – the information receiver – and the "storage system" was, at first, the sound waves transmitting the sound from her voice box to your ear drums, with the ultimate storage system being electrical impulses in your brain generating the memory (by the way, there is no scientific explanation of how memory works). In this case, so far as it relates to the information content of your fiend's message to you, Shannon's methods of information theory do not really help you to understand the information contained in your friend's statement. To you, what meaningful information is found in the probability that a "b" or a "y" is going to appear in what she said to you? Viewing the information content of your friend's statement is meaningless using only Shannon's methods because there are rules inherent to the way in which information is formed and processed. In this case, these rules are what are considered "the rules of the English language" as well as "the meaning of words." Note that a given set of symbols used to convey information is called a **language**, which could be English, Russian, the computer languages C# or Fortran or the "biological language" of DNA. No matter the language, though, all have rules as to their construction. You automatically interpreted the information content from your friend based upon the rules of English and the meaning of words; therefore, you based your response upon the information you understood to be conveyed in her statement – that the sky is literally blue in color. And most certainly, you would be correct. Or, would you? Is that the *only* possible meaning of that sentence? What if that was not what she meant? What if your friend said, "The sky is blue" because it was raining outside and she was just messing with you by indicating that the sky was sad because it was "blue" (crying)? This example demonstrates the inherent problem of pigeon-holing information into a mathematical-only box. Besides the originator/receiver/storage properties, there are _many more_ components to information. If one of the components is not appropriately sent, received or stored, then the message is not clear.

Although we rarely think about it, "information" is an incredibly complicated subject because there are many components that make information meaningful. Because of this, further development of information theory has occurred over the decades. Werner Gitt, PhD (b. 1937) is a creationist and one of the world's leading information theorists. Until his retirement, he was the head of the Department of Information Technology at the German Federal Institute of Physics and Technology and has led the way in more recent advances in information theory.

After extensive study over many decades, it became clear that information not only has quantitative but also qualitative (meaning and importance) aspects. Dr. Gitt incorporated these two aspects into his work and identified five hierarchical levels of information (Figure 17.15.4). Qualitative approaches to information theory address the meaning and importance of the message of the information that the originator meant to convey to the receiver – issues of syntax, semantics, pragmatics and apobetics. This allows further dissection of information content in a way that is much more familiar to us – identifying whether or not the symbols are meaningful, meaningless, comprehensible, correct or incorrect and stimulate the originator's intended response.

Figure 17.15.4

The five hierarchical levels of information
Dr. Werner Gitt has pioneered ongoing elucidation of information theory to include another four levels – qualitative aspects of information – to Shannon's quantitative aspect.

Hierarchical Level	Definition	Detail
Statistics (quantitative)	This is Claude Shannon's foundation of information theory in which characteristics of information are based upon the expected frequencies of appearance of the symbols conveying information	The "meaningfulness" of a piece of information is not transmitted by "what a symbol means" but by how probable it is that the symbol would show up in the piece of information. As an example using the 26 letters of the English alphabet, purely from the statistical standpoint, the letter "x" has a higher information content than "e" because it is far less probable to show up in a given sentence than "e" is.
Syntax (qualitative)	The rule-based stringing together of symbols to form words and words to form sentences	In English, a general rule is "noun – verb – adjective" when making a sentence. "John ran fast" instead of "Fast John ran." The most effective way to transfer information is when using the expected syntax.
Semantics (qualitative)	The meaning of the information	All information is intended to transmit a meaningful message, which is independent of the way it is transmitted and stored. Syntax is the difference between information in the context of "data" (a computer determining values) versus "knowledge" (a person using creative thought to instill or derive meaning into information)
Pragmatics (qualitative)	The intended action the sender of the information had for the receiver	Sentences are not just strung together words – they are formulations of instructions, commands, questions, recommendations, etc. for the purpose of causing an action in the receiver.
Apobetics (qualitative)	The intended purpose the receiver identifies from the sender	This is the "fuzziest" information level because, like the "blue sky" example showed, it is not always possible to know with 100% certainty that the information the receiver identifies is the information the sender had in mind.

Dr. Gitt has incorporated the qualitative with the quantitative aspects of information and developed what he calls the Fundamental Laws for Information. These apply to every known information-applied system – biological, mathematic, computer, linguistic, sociology, psychology, medicine, etc.:

- It is impossible to set, store or transmit information without a code.

- It is impossible to have a code apart from free and deliberate convention.

- It is impossible to have information without a sender.

- It is impossible that information can exist without a mental source.

- It is impossible for information to exist without having been established voluntarily by a free will.

- It is impossible for information to exist without all five hierarchical levels: statistics, syntax, semantics, pragmatics and apobetics.

- It is impossible that information can originate in statistical processes.

Note the very strong word that Dr. Gitt uses – *impossible*. This is a word, especially in scientific endeavors, that is used with extreme caution because it seems like there is pretty much *always* an exception to "impossible," "always," and "never." However, despite many attempts, his "Information Laws" have _never_ been proven wrong and have been accepted in academic discussions and university conferences. This is quite remarkable because, since information theory has been applied _very effectively_ as an argument against evolution and for intelligent design, evolutionists are particularly interested in proving these laws wrong. Why are evolutionists so interested in proving them wrong? Perhaps the following quote from evolutionist Hubert Yockey, in _Information Theory and Molecular Biology_, helps identify the answer:

> **_"The belief that life on earth arose spontaneously from non-living matter, is simply a matter of faith in strict reductionism and is based entirely on ideology."_**

Dr. Yockey admits that evolution is based not upon scientific data but a belief system – a belief that life originated without God. Evolutionists are so ideologically committed to the absolute necessity of naturalistic explanations that even when faced with facts leading to the obvious conclusion that natural theories are insufficient to explain origins, they cannot acknowledge the truth because it forces them to then move in a direction (to God) they cannot go. Many evolutionists are very aware the evolution model is a widespread failure to predict and/or explain scientific data, but they cling to it because they must. It is the only "without God" model they have.

> **_I praise you, for I am fearfully and wonderfully made. Wonderful are your works; my soul knows it very well._** _Psalms 139:14_

Looking at the Information Laws, it is understood that information cannot exist without a mental source – in other words, there must be a designer, an "intelligent cause" of the information. _It is true that information has never arisen accidentally or without an intelligent cause_. Even the "simplest" organism contains in its DNA an information content that is larger and more compact than anything man can devise, containing all of the directions to make the organism. It is illogical to conclude that, in all instances in which information is present, it has an intelligent source except for the most intricate and powerful information conveyance and storage system in existence. Information theory is another scientific pursuit that aligns to predictions of the creation model and is not supported by the evolutionary model.

17.16 CONCLUSION

This chapter is only a small sampling of the enormous amount of information that has been uncovered showing that science clearly supports the Truth of God's Word. No "scientific discoveries" have provided objective facts that should be cause for anyone to question the sufficiency of the Bible to explain the world around us. There is no need to try to make God's Word "fit with modern science" when in so doing we are forced to accept a position that is counter to what God's Word says. Also, it is as true now as it has been since 1859 that the very large majority of evolutionary thought leaders are atheist or agnostic. Indeed, a 1998 survey of National Academy of Scientists (the "thought leaders" in their respective scientific fields) revealed that 93% of the members did not believe in God and so _must be_ ideologically dedicated to proving that origins are best explained _without_ God. As we will see in the next two chapters, objective assessment of the scientific data will continue to be consistent with the simultaneous conclusions that the creation model is supported and the evolution model is specifically argued against.

> **_Worthy are you, our Lord and God, to receive glory and honor and power, for you created all things, and by your will they existed and were created._** _Revelation 4:11_

17.17 PEOPLE OF SCIENCE

Jonathan Sarfati (b. 1964) was born in Australia and raised in New Zealand, ultimately receiving a PhD in physical chemistry from the Victoria University of Wellington. Early in his career, he led a dual life, publishing papers about high energy superconductors and spectroscopy (the study of the interaction between matter and radiated energy, such as light or acoustic energy) while serving as New Zealand's national chess champion in 1987 – 88. During this time, he played the former world chess champion Boris Spassky to a tie. In 1996, he joined Creation Ministries International and has been with them since that time, writing many books and articles and lecturing all over the world about the scientific evidence supporting creation and arguing against evolution.

17.18 KEY CHAPTER POINTS

- The creation origins theory (or model) is one that relies upon the Word of God to explain life's origins and diversity. In this model, the Bible provides the absolute truth and scientific concepts and data are interpreted based upon God creating the universe and everything in it. Organisms were created fully functional, about 6,000 years ago on days 3,5 and 6, exactly as the Bible states.

- The evolution origins theory (or model) is one that relies upon man's definition of truth to explain life's origins and diversity. In this model, all matter and life are the result of random and purposeless forces, having arisen billions of years ago. This model specifically excludes God and his activity in the universe and explains life as originating from non-living chemicals in the primordial ooze and, over time, ancestor organisms developed new, previously nonexistent traits to cause them to evolve into new and previously nonexistent organisms.

- Biblical kinds and varieties/types are more helpful descriptors of general classes of organisms, as opposed to the ill-defined term "species."

- Evolution is, literally, an ancestor kind acquiring new and previously nonexistent characteristics that, over time, cause it to lose its defining characteristics and gain those of new and previously nonexistent kind. Evolutionists recognize that there is dubious scientific data supporting this.

- There are copious amounts of scientific data showing that varieties form within kinds; however, despite evolutionists saying otherwise, this is not evolution.

- God created the universe and everything in it by speaking, forming and making.

- It is valid to use the genealogies in Genesis 5 and 11 to calculate the age of the earth because God's intention appears to have been to communicate actual historical information with them.

- Virtually all of the great scientists prior to 1859 were able to make their discoveries or contributions specifically because they were pursuing science with the intention of exploring God's Creation.

- Intelligent design and teleology are logical argument styles used to support God and the Creator.

- The intelligent design movement is a loosely organized effort between Christian and secular intelligent design proponents to present evidence against evolution.

- Specified complexity and irreducible complexity are design properties that living organisms have that cannot be explained by evolutionary mechanisms.

- Information theory is one of many scientific pursuits that actively argues for the creation model and against the evolution model.

17.19 DEFINITIONS

Apobetics
The intended purpose of a message the receiver identifies from the sender. The fifth level of Werner Gitt's hierarchical information levels.

Baramin
Another word for biblical kind.

Chronogenealogy
A genealogy that is written to be historically accurate in regards to the time covered.

Creationist
A person who believes that the creation model is the correct origins theory.

Creation theory (model)
An origins model that relies upon the Bible to provide the foundation for life origins. In this model, the universe and everything in it was created in 6 days by God, about 6,000 years ago.

Defining characteristics
A trait held by every member of a group of organisms such that when an organism has that trait, it is then identified to be a member of the group.

Empiric science
The type of science in which a hypothesis is tested under experimental conditions.

Evolutionist
A person who believes that the evolution model is the correct origins theory.

Evolution theory (model)
An origins model that discards the Bible as the source of truth and substitutes man's reasoning to explain the origin of life. In this model, life originated accidentally, more than a billion years ago, out of nonliving chemicals. Over time, all organisms arose directly from those before them.

Historical science
The type of science in which inferences or conclusions are drawn, based upon things that have happened in the past, in an effort to explain the data. There is no direct way to experimentally test historical science.

Information theory
The scientific endeavor of defining information based upon 5 realms – statistics, semantics, syntax, pragmatics and apobetics.

Intelligent design
The concept that, because life displays properties of a designed system, an intelligent designer is responsible for the origin of life.

Intelligent design movement
A loosely organized effort between Christians and secular scientists to promote the concept of intelligent design and present arguments against evolution origins theory.

Irreducible complexity
A single system composed of several well matched, interacting parts that contribute to the basic function, wherein the removal of any one of the parts causes the system to effectively cease functioning.

Kind
A group of organisms that share the same defining characteristics, originally created by God.

Language
A set of symbols and associated usage rules to convey information.

Naturalistic processes
Processes that occur in nature, which evolutionists believe to be entirely without purpose, random processes.

Omnipotent
All powerful; a property of God.

Omniscient
All knowing; a property of God.

On The Origin of Species by Means of Natural Selection, or the Preservation of Favoured Races in the Struggle for Life
The 1859 book by Charles Darwin, which evolutionists believe to be the seminal work that caused evolution to move into mainstream science.

Operational science
See empiric science.

Origin theory
A philosophy that explains the origin and diversity of life.

Paleontologist
A person who studies paleontology.

Paleontology
The study of life forms that existed in the past.

Panspermia
The theory that life started due to living organisms or biological molecules being brought to earth from other parts of the universe.

Philosophy
The investigation of the nature, causes or principles of reality, knowledge or values based upon logical reasoning rather than empirical methods.

Piltdown man
A famous scientific forgery in which an orangutan jaw bone and human skull were placed together in an apparent attempt to "prove" evolution is true.

Pragmatics
The intended action the sender of the information had for the receiver. The fourth level of Werner Gitt's hierarchical information levels.

Primordial ooze
The evolutionary "slang" term for the collection of biochemicals within salt water the evolution model predicts is where biomolecules naturalistically originated.

Semantics
The meaning of information. The third level of Werner Gitt's hierarchical information levels.

Speciation
The process of "species formation." Evolutionarily, this concept refers to two biologically separate processes "a less complex kind forming new traits and evolving into a previously nonexistent kind" (no scientific evidence to support this type) and varieties forming within kinds (ample scientific evidence to support this type). Creationists accept speciation as a process that causes varieties to form within a kind.

Species
The fundamental unit of evolution; a poorly defined/undefined term relating to grouping organisms.

Specified complexity
A design property in which both complexity and specific purpose of structure and/or function is displayed.

Syntax

The stringing together of symbols to form words and words to form sentences, based upon rules. The second level of Werner Gitt's hierarchical information levels.

Teleological arguments

Arguments of teleology used to advance the idea that God is the designer and creator of all.

Teleology

The study of design or purpose in nature.

Type

A group of organisms within a kind that share the same traits of the kind's defining characteristics. Variety is a synonym.

Variety

See Type.

STUDY QUESTIONS

1. What are the two main theories (or models) that address the origin and diversity of life?

2. True or False? Evolution is an attempt to explain how life originated in a way that specifically removes God from the picture.

3. Describe how the concept of "defining characteristics" pertains to differentiating one kind from another.

4. True or False? A group of organisms that share the same traits of a kind's defining characteristics would be called the same variety or type.

5. Evolutionists call the process in which "varieties form within a kind" evolution, just as they call the process in which "one kind develops new and previously nonexistent traits so that a new and previously nonexistent kind of organism" evolution. Are these biologically the same thing? If so, why? If not, why not?

6. True or False? Creationists strongly disagree with the evolutionary concept of how varieties form within kinds.

7. If someone says that evolution is an example of operational or empiric science, but creation is not, how would you respond?

8. Describe why it appears to be valid to use the genealogies in Genesis 5 and 11 as the foundation for calculating the age of the earth.

9. True or False? The word "yom" is almost never translated to mean an actual 24 hour period of time; instead, it usually refers to the figurative use of the word "day," as in, "back in the day..."

10. True or False? Prior to evolution being accepted by scientists, scientists like Sir Isaac Newton were severely handicapped by their views that God created the universe just as the Bible says.

11. How are intelligent design and the intelligent design movement different from one another?

12. True or False? All people who believe in intelligent design believe that God is the Intelligent Designer.

13. The curlew and the shearwater are types of migratory birds that have unusual social habits – the parents leave their offspring right before they are all due to leave their summer home and fly several thousand miles for the winter. This means that the juveniles, who have never migrated before, fly their migratory path on their own – and never get lost. Describe how this can be seen as a powerful argument for a designer and against evolution.

14. What type of argument did you just forward in the answer for number 13?

15. Why does there seem to be a fundamental disconnect between the randomness of naturalism leading to the formation and diversification of the intricacies of living organisms?

16. True or False? Natural forces cannot result in the formation of structures that are both complex and specific.

17. Describe how eye glasses – with a frame, hinges and a lens – represent an irreducibly complex system.

18. True or False? There are many examples of random forces generating systems or structures with specified complexity.

19. How do specified complexity and irreducible complexity fit into the intelligent design concept?

20. True or False? One can clearly see how an irreducibly complex system can be generated by concepts consistent with the evolution origins model.

21. Describe why you do or do not think it makes sense that information could arise through naturalistic processes like evolution.

Evolution: History and Present State

18

18.0 CHAPTER PREVIEW

In this chapter, we will:

- Explore further how Charles Darwin's evolutionary ideas specifically explain the existence of life without God.

- Review the history of naturalistic explanations of life origins and diversity in order to identify that evolution is a completely materialistic origins model.

- Learn about Charles Darwin's reluctance to publish his theory and how he overcame that with the political assistance of his scientific allies.

- Dissect natural selection and surprisingly learn that it is fully compatible with the creation model and is incapable of "doing" what evolution needs it to do.

- Learn that abiogenesis, a necessary event, is completely unable to be explained through naturalistic mechanisms.

- Properly define evolution not simply as "change" (as evolutionists do) but as the very specific type of change that it is.

- Point out that what evolutionists typically refer to as "evolution" is actually the result of the observable effects of natural selection, which is not "evolution" at all.

- Introduce "microevolution" and "macroevolution" and learn that "microevolution" is a terrible descriptor and "macroevolution" is not supported by scientific data.

18.1 INTRODUCTION

As we learned in the last chapter, up until the 19th century, creation was the overriding paradigm that fueled over 1,800 years years of scientific discoveries. However, by the 16th and 17th centuries, there was a shift in mankind from relying upon God's Providence as scientific inspiration to the man-made philosophy of naturalism. Hence, it is common to see the term "**naturalist**" interchanged with "evolutionist." A naturalist is a person who believes that nature, and nature alone, provides the explanations for the world around us. Evolutionists are naturalists.

To reinforce another subject from last chapter, using slightly different terminology, it is very important to recognize that _naturalism (and therefore evolution) is an origins philosophy that explains the origin and diversity of life specifically excluding God_. Evolution was never meant to be reconciled with creation. As that Chapter 17 quote from Charles Spurgeon indicates, evolution is an either-or proposition – either you believe in evolution or you believe in God. The two are not compatible. As originally presented by Charles Darwin and accepted by scientists today, the concepts of evolution (which Darwin at first called "descent with modification") specifically exclude the presence/activity of God in the life origins and diversity theory.

Modern day evolutionists commonly state that evolution is "change," which is not entirely true and not entirely false. Evolution is change, but it _is a very specific type of change and it is the specific type of change that evolution requires that is often lost in the discussion_. Let's review the essential components of evolution:

1. At first there was nothing besides the "raw materials" – carbon, hydrogen, oxygen, nitrogen, etc., on the Earth.

2. These non-living chemicals organized into the first living, self-replicating organism – a prokaryote.

3. Over time, that prokaryote ancestor organism was able to attain new and meaningful DNA that contained new, never-before-in-existence structural and physiological information, which caused it to transform into the first single cell eukaryote.

4. Over time, the single cell eukaryote ancestor organism acquired new and meaningful DNA that contained further new, never-before-in-existence structural and physiological information to give that ancestor organism traits it did not previously have, which caused it to transform into the first multicellular eukaryote.

5. Over more time, the ancestor multicellular organism acquired new and meaningful DNA that contained further new, never-before-in-existence structural and physiological information to give that ancestor organism traits it did not previously have, which caused it to transform into the first fish.

6. Over time, the fish ancestor organism acquired new and meaningful DNA that contained further new, never-before-in-existence structural and physiological information to give that ancestor organism traits it did not previously have, which caused it to transform into the first amphibian.

7. Over time, the amphibian ancestor organism acquired new and meaningful DNA that contained further new, never-before-in-existence structural and physiological information to give that ancestor organism traits that it did not previously have, which caused it to transform into the first reptile.

8. Over time, the reptile ancestor organism acquired new and meaningful DNA that contained further new, never-before-in-existence structural and physiological information to give that ancestor organism traits that it did not previously have, which caused it to transform not only into the first bird but also the first mammal (remember, according to evolutionists, human beings are nothing more than a thinking animal).

Figure 18.1.1

Evolutionary Change – a Preview to Keep in Mind

One of the main points of this chapter will be to continue to measure the scientific data with the creation and evolution yardsticks. We will clearly see that the scientific data does not conform to the predictions of the evolutionary model, misconceptions evolutionists present about the evolution model as related to the interpretation of the scientific data, or the lack of biochemical and genetic mechanisms that are necessary to effect the information changes necessary for evolution to occur. This graphic sums up all of the major problems that exist with evolutionary theory. On the left, we see a hypothetical representation of how sharks formed – starting with a "generic" ancestor shark like the lemon shark (top of the diagram), and over time, as that ancestor shark was exposed to different ocean environments, food sources, etc, it developed into other shark varieties like the blue shark, tiger shark and hammer head. Evolutionists think this is "evolution," but, as discussed last chapter, it is not. This is the process of varieties forming within a kind, the end result of which are organisms that are still the "starting" kind. There is nothing new – only different appearing and behaving sharks. In order for evolution to occur, an entirely new kind of organism with entirely new defining characteristics that never before existed needs to form. Clearly, the process of varieties forming within kinds only leads to organisms that look different from another, but they all continue to share the exact same defining characteristics. Creationists believe that the shark variety-forming process (or that of the dog from last chapter) is how the wonderful variety of organisms have formed, which was made possible by God creating organisms with great ability to vary, built right into their genetic information at creation. In order for Darwinian evolution to occur, shown on the right side where one kind develops into a new and previously nonexistent kind, the genetic information for the fish would have had to have been transformed into that of an amphibian (then that of the amphibian into the reptile and then the reptile's into the bird's). The fish ancestor would have had to have gained the DNA that codes for the amphibian traits so that it gained the defining traits of the amphibian kind, which never before existed. Not only is there no evidence that this happened, there is no genetic mechanism through which this can happen. Evolutionists postulate that genetic mutation is the genetic process that "creates" new and previously nonexistent genetic information, but there is absolutely no scientific data that supports such a claim. To reinforce, "evolution" is "one-kind-transforming-into-a-new-and-previously-nonexistent-kind," not varieties forming within kinds. Both of these processes obviously lead to "change," but they are genetically fundamentally very different processes.

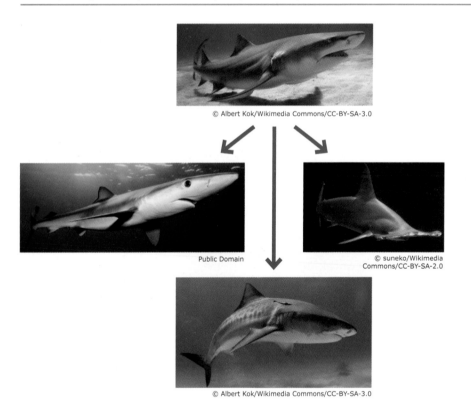

I know that evolution description was very redundant, but that was to reinforce the concept. It is critical to understand the type of change that evolution is, and the type it isn't. In order for evolution to occur, there must be a genetic mechanism that causes new and previously nonexistent DNA to arise so that the less complex organism can gain new traits and transform into a more complex organism. Unless there is such a mechanism with reasonable scientific data to support it, evolution cannot happen. The problem is that there is no biological process in which new and previously nonexistent DNA that provides new and previously nonexistent traits can arise, relegating evolution to "just a story" status. The evolutionist Richard Dickerson notes this:

> **"The evolution of the genetic machinery is the step for which there are no laboratory models; hence one can speculate endlessly, unfettered by inconvenient facts."**

The "inconvenient facts" he mentions are precisely the scientific data that continually arise arguing against the evolutionary model. The scientific data fits a creation origins model perfectly well, with much of the data specifically arguing against the evolutionary model.

18.2 CHARLES DARWIN – INTRODUCTION TO HIS "THEORY"

Charles Darwin was not the first scientist to postulate the concept of "evolution." He was the first person, though, to provide a scientifically accepted and completely God-less origins theory that contained a new concept – a proposed mechanism for "how naturalism works." That mechanism was (and is) natural selection (much more to come on this – for a brief refresher, see section 17.2). And, his timing was just right as there was mounting disbelief of God's Truth in Victorian England and Europe in general when he published this theory in *The Origin of Species by Means of Natural Selection or the Preservation of Favoured Races in the Struggle for Life* in 1859.

Figure 18.2.1

Charles Darwin
Charles Darwin, the "father of evolution," as he appeared in his early thirties (left) shortly after he returned to England from his around-the-world journey on the *HMS Beagle* and (right) as he appeared in his late sixties. He was raised Unitarian and in one of his many letters wrote that in his early years, "I did not then in the least doubt the strict and literal truth of every word in the Bible." He was also very fond of William Paley's *Natural Theology*, the seminal work about the design of nature reflecting the immenseness and brilliance of the Designer. However, that belief died and by the time he reached his early to middle 30's, he had lost faith in God so much so that in 1859, with the publication of *The Origin of Species*, he specifically provided a life origins and diversity explanation based on the entirely God-less story of "descent with modification."

Wikimedia Commons/
{{PD-art-old}}

Wikimedia Commons/
{{PD-art-old}}

Interestingly, although Charles Darwin is considered "the father of evolution," he actually did not use the word "evolution" to describe his theory until long after the 1st edition of *The Origin of Species* was published. Instead, in the first five editions of *Origin of Species*, Charles Darwin used the term **"descent with modification"** or **"transmutation of the species"** when he was referring to the concept that today is called "evolution" (and that we have described as "one kind transforming into a new and previously nonexistent kind"). Even though the term "evolution" had been used in the scientific literature for at least a century, Darwin very specifically avoided its use until his 1872 sixth edition of *The Origin of Species*.

But, why would he _not_ have used the term "evolution" right away? The answer underlines Darwin's intent to provide a completely God-less origins explanation. "Evolution" had a slightly different meaning prior to the 1859 publication of _The Origin of Species_. In Victorian England, "evolution" was understood to denote a process that was a "progressive" one; hence, with a purpose. If something has a purpose, then there must be someone directing that purpose – in the case of the origin and diversity of life, that would be God. However, the concept that the origin and diversity of life had any purpose was in direct opposition to _Darwin's idea that the process he intended to describe was one specifically with no purpose and so specifically excluded God_.

Darwin specifically did not use "evolution" because he wanted to make sure that no one misunderstood that _his descent with modification process was intended to be purposeless_; therefore, without God. He realized that if descent with modification/ transmutation had been understood to be equal to the early and mid-19th century understanding of the word "evolution," then the entire God-less and purposeless premise of the process he was describing would have been misunderstood to have had a purpose. Therefore, had Darwin intended that descent with modification be a process consistent with something God would do, _then he would have used the word "evolution"_ in the 1st edition of _The Origin of Species_ to describe his process. But Darwin knew that, had he done so, everyone in Victorian England would have understood that by "evolution" Darwin meant a "purposeful process," directly implicating God as the "purposeful agent." So, he specifically did not use the word "evolution." By the time he did use "evolution" 13 years after the first edition, the scientific community had started to apply the term in a manner consistent with Darwin's intent – the purposeless (God-less) descent with modification process. Some have attempted to meld evolution and Christianity, but the two concepts are mutually exclusive. The suppositions behind evolutionary thought only make sense if they are framed within the proper context – evolution was not and is not a process that is compatible with a life origins and diversity theory that includes God. Most atheist evolutionists completely understand that concept, as the following quotes attest:

> **"Oh but of course the story of Adam and Eve was only ever symbolic, wasn't it? Symbolic?! So Jesus had himself tortured and executed for a symbolic sin by a non-existent individual? Nobody not brought up in the faith could reach any verdict other than barking mad!"** _Richard Dawkins_

> **"The moderates' position seems to me to be fence –sitting. They half believe in the Bible but how do they decide which parts to believe literally and which parts are just allegorical?"** _William Provine, PhD, Cornell University_

18.3 EARLY HISTORY OF GOD-LESS ORIGINS THOUGHT

By the time Charles Darwin was born in 1809, origins philosophies contradicting the Genesis account of creation were known for more than two millennia. Concepts consistent with God not creating life, life originating from non-living substances and even what we consider today as fairly clear evolutionary processes can be dated at least as far back as 600 B.C. Despite the existence of these "alternative origins theories," though, for the 1,800 years following Jesus Christ's death and resurrection, the majority of scientists believed the Genesis account of creation and were amazingly productive in their exploration of God's Creation specifically because of their faith.

Figure 18.3.1

Ancient Naturalistic Explanations

Origins philosophies that life first originated in water, living organisms originated from non-living organisms or came from less complex life forms that transformed into more complex ones span the continents and date at least as far back as the ancient Greek and Mayan cultures. In 600 B.C., the Mayans believed that their "rain-god" made new organisms by building on those he already had made. Possibly drawing from the Hindus before them, the Greeks had well-developed God-less origins theories. Thales of Miletus (640 – 546 B.C.) thought that life started in the water and his student Anaximader developed the concept that humans came from fish-like organisms. Empedocles (493 – 435 B.C.), center, thought chance processes explained simple matter evolving into man and described concepts of natural selection 2,000 years before Charles Darwin. Aristotle (384 – 322 B.C.), right, also believed an evolution-like origins theory.

However, in the 16th and 17th centuries, philosophers, biologists, geologists and even scattered clergy were writing more often about the belief that the literal interpretation of the Bible was not correct. By the late 1700's and early 1800's, increasing numbers of scientists, a minority of the lay public and more clergy began to promote/accept the "scientific" idea that the earth was not 6,000 years old; in other words, they rejected not only the Biblical account of creation but the larger position in general that God is the source of all Truth. Thinking like this led to a "philosophical revolution" termed "the Age of the Enlightenment," a period spanning the late 16th through the 20th centuries characterized by many philosophical positions, generally all anti-establishment of the times:

- Anti-government as a reaction to the often tyrannical forms of government and monarchies
- Anti-church
- Pro-liberty
- Pro-democracy
- Pro-republicanism (the people govern themselves, not kings or dictators)
- Pro-private property rights
- Pro-free market economies/anti-mercantilism
- Anti-God through the emergence of literature, art and scientific study as the focus of importance

Certainly, not all of the new philosophies that emerged and were promoted as a result of the Age of Enlightenment ran counter to biblical principles. Some did, and some did not, but one of the core beliefs of the Enlightenment – God-doubting – definitely appealed to Charles Darwin and a growing number of people starting in the mid to late 1830's.

Figure 18.3.2

The Enlightenment
Rene Descartes (1596 – 1650, left, is considered the father of modern philosophy and his writings are generally attributed to be the start of the "Age of Enlightenment." Although he did not write on origins theories and his religious views have been described as anywhere from "devout Roman Catholic" to "atheist," he is certainly credited as a religious skeptic. His writings firmly set the stage for the development of rationalism that would be foundational for philosophers and scientists to the present. Georges Buffon (1707 – 1788), middle, was a French naturalist who wrote extensively about concepts that today are clearly evolutionary. He thought that apes and humans had a common ancestry and argued against God creating every kind of organism. Charles Darwin's grandfather, Erasmus (1731 – 1802), right, a famous physician, inventor, distant deist or atheist (depending upon whose Erasmus Darwin biography you read) and anti-Christian, was a prolific writer on the topic of evolution. Erasmus' 1794 *Zoonomia*, which Charles Darwin read at least twice, contained many of the same topics that appear in *The Origin of Species*.

Wikimedia Commons/{{PD-art-old}}   Wikimedia Commons/{{PD-art-old}}   Wikimedia Commons/{{PD-art-old}}

One of the common themes of the Age of Enlightenment was rejecting biblical truth in favor of using human reasoning as the source of all truth and knowledge. Rational thought processes were elevated above God's Word. The fear of the Lord as *the* path to knowledge and wisdom and – ultimately – truth, was increasingly rejected by Victorian society. This false philosophy that the exercise of man's reason, rather than God's word, provides the basis for knowledge and truth is called **rationalism**, and set the stage for *The Origin of Species* to be accepted by the mid-19th century scientific community.

Figure 18.3.3

Charles De Secondat Montesquieu
Montesquieu (1689 – 1755) was a French philosopher and political thinker. He is most notable as being a champion for the separation of the powers (executive, judicial and legislative), which forms the basis of our governmental structure. However, he also clearly advanced origins theories consistent with evolution since he wrote that in the beginning of time, there were relatively few types of animals and they have multiplied to their present state from those few starting types by "natural means."

Wikimedia Commons/{{PD-old}}

> *"I had gradually come by this time* (1836 to 1839) *to see that the Old Testament was no more to be trusted than the sacred books of the Hindoos* (sic) *or the beliefs of any other barbarian."* Charles Darwin

> *For the LORD gives wisdom; from his mouth come knowledge and understanding.* Proverbs 2:6

As a result, the rationalist false philosophy of discrediting the Bible led to the increasing acceptance of things that God's Word specifically says are wrong (and therefore are false belief systems):

- **Atheism** – the belief system that denies God's existence

- **Agnosticism** – the disbelief in, but not denial of the existence of, God (however, realize that to the "agnostic" God doesn't exist and so there is no practical difference between agnosticism and atheism)

- **Deism** – the belief that God created the universe and then has left it alone to do its own thing since

Although Charles Darwin was still a believer by the time he left for his 5 year around-the-world journey on the *HMS Beagle*, the increasingly accepted rationalist philosophy was in full force, to which he was exposed when he returned from his journey.

18.4 DARWIN'S TRAVELS

We will now explore a little further the social, scientific and philosophical scene in which Charles Darwin grew up and wrote *The Origin of Species,* beginning with an event in Darwin's experience that is often misconstrued as the "aha moment" for Darwin when he identified his theory of descent with modification. Contrary to what many think (and what many television shows document), Darwin did not have an "evolutionary epiphany" during his travels when he was on the Galapagos Islands. The five years he spent on the *HMS Beagle* observing life forms scattered across the globe were very instructive to his evolution roots while information he learned from a book he read on the *Beagle* provided the basis for the hundreds of millions of years his theory needed. Darwin's movement away from God and toward naturalism was well on its way.

Figure 18.4.1

The *Beagle* and its Captain

The *HMS Beagle*, as seen being hailed by Tierra del Fuegans in 1833, left, and its captain, Robert FitzRoy, right. Darwin's time on board, journaling extensively and making observations about the geology and biology of South America, New Zealand and Australia, was extremely formative for many reasons. One reason was that he read Charles Lyell's *Principles of Geology*, ironically a gift from Captain FitzRoy, while on board. The geological concepts in *Principles of Geology* were revolutionary to Darwin and provided him the extended time frames into the past within which his imagined slow processes of descent with modification could have occurred. Years after the *Beagle* returned, Captain FitzRoy, a fundamental Christian, at the very famous debate between Thomas Huxley and Samuel Wilberforce, spoke of his discontent that he had provided Darwin the book that gave Darwin the new thoughts that helped him to formulate his new theory.

The *Beagle* was built, originally, as an English brig and launched in 1820; however, the ship was refitted as an expedition barque-type ship in 1825 and, following that, went on three specimen collecting missions around the world. Charles Darwin was part of the second *HMS Beagle* expedition, which left England December, 1831 and returned October, 1836.

Figure 18.4.2

Charles Lyell

Charles Lyell (1797 – 1875) was a Scottish lawyer and geologist and, along with Thomas Malthus, probably had the greatest influence over Charles Darwin's thinking that ultimately led Darwin to discard his reliance upon biblical truth in order to rely on man's definition of truth. In his book *Principles of Geology*, Lyell strongly forwarded the concepts that the earth was "old" (hundreds of millions of years) and of **uniformitarianism** – the idea that forces seen to be operating today were the forces operating in the past and so the events of the past can be understood by applying that which is seen today. Lyell absolutely dismissed the idea that catastrophes such as the Great Flood occurred and instead stated that the Earth's rock layers were built up over millions of years. Interestingly, as a direct result, **catastrophism**, the belief that great catastrophic events shaped the earth in the past, a biblical idea, which had been a mainstay of geology, came to be considered a quaint belief system. Uniformitarian ideas drove evolutionary thinking for more than a century and a half, until relatively recently when even evolutionists have had to increasingly admit that the only way fossils can form is by being rapidly covered by sediments – basically, through the processes of catastrophic events. Evolutionists have had to modify their theory a bit, then, allowing for such catastrophic flood events – on a local level – to conform their theories with the scientific evidence. The catastrophic events are now interspersed with periods of thousands to millions of years where no catastrophes occur, giving the evolutionists the best of both worlds. They can keep their processes of millions of years _and_ explain how fossils form. Charles Darwin, though, was heavily influenced by the increasingly discredited and now revised uniformitarian concept.

Many people mistakenly believe that Charles Darwin was the ship's naturalist, but that is actually technically incorrect. After being carefully screened by FitzRoy, Charles Darwin originally was brought on as a personal aid and companion to the captain. Captain FitzRoy encouraged Darwin to take specimens and make geological surveys at every stop they made, so much so that the ship's naturalist (who was also the ship's surgeon), Robert McCormick, was upset that not only was Darwin well liked by the captain, he was also acting as a naturalist, which Dr. McCormick thought was his own job. In June 1832, he ended up resigning his position on the *Beagle*, leaving Darwin the lone naturalist.

Figure 18.4.3

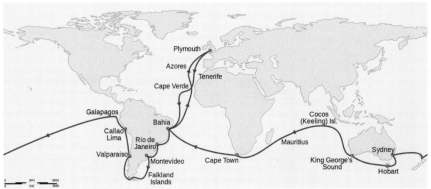

Journey of the *HMS Beagle*

Over the five year journey, Darwin took extensive specimens, made many drawings and recorded much about the geologic features of South America, the Galapagos Islands, New Zealand, and Australia. Notably, it was at the Galapagos Islands, where Darwin collected, among others, a number of bird specimens — commonly referred to as the "Galapagos finches" or "Darwin's finches" — that he took back with him to England to study and would later become "icons of evolution." As we will see, though, the finches are great examples of God's genetically endowed ability to vary, built into all kinds' genetic systems at creation.

Figure 18.4.4

Glyptodont

Many are surprised to learn that humans have been studying fossils for more than 2,000 years. Aristotle realized they were once living animals. The specimen to the right is Glyptodont, an extinct mammal, similar to an armadillo, but weighed up to 4,000 pounds. Darwin saw these fossils in South America and they played a role in his development of the theory of descent with modification as, like many paleontologists before him, he saw similarities between animals living and extinct. Whereas creationists see common body forms (such as "two arms and two legs" across a wide variety of animals) and similarities between animals as evidence of the Creator knowing the best way to design a structure, evolutionists see similarities as common ancestry. As Darwin lost faith in God and believed man's theories of a hundreds-of-millions-of-years old earth that was necessary to explain fossil formation from the uniformitarian position, he developed his theory of slow and purposeless natural selection driving descent with modification.

Darwin returned to England in 1836 with his specimens and journals and reviewed his findings with fellow scientists, during which time he thought about natural selection and "descent with modification" or "the transmutation of species." Darwin would write in his autobiography that, during the mid to late 1830's, he completely lost his faith in God. By 1839, he had developed essentially his entire theory of descent with modification through natural selection, but would not publish his ideas for another 20 years.

Figure 18.4.5

Thomas Malthus

Thomas Malthus (1766 – 1834) was a clergyman who was a famous economist in his day (he was also interestingly the model for Charles Dickens' Ebenezer Scrooge in *A Christmas Carol*) and provided the intellectual fuel for Darwin's development of the key element to his theory – natural selection. Though many of Malthus' economic ideas have not turned out to be true over time, his economic writings (dealing mainly with human populations growing at rates faster than food production could support) had a great impact upon both Charles Darwin and Russell Wallace, the two men who independently identified an almost identical "theory of evolution" (it isn't entirely clear why evolutionists almost completely ignore Wallace's contributions). Malthus' description of how populations rise and fall in response to various economic pressures provided Darwin and Wallace a good deal of inspiration regarding how natural selection could potentially work as a force to cause one type of organism to transform into a new and previously nonexistent organism purely through natural processes, without God the Creator. Recall that creationists understand that natural selection certainly exists and leads to changes in the traits of organisms of a population over time, but with clear limits on the type of change that is possible. The type of scientifically observable changes as a result of natural selection (and artificial selection in the cases of selective plant and domesticated animal breeding) simply cause changes within already-existing traits – no new and previously nonexistent traits have ever been observed to arise. There is no scientific data that supports the concept that natural selection can lead to the formation of entirely new traits and kinds of organisms.

18.5 20 YEARS?

You may have picked something up from the time line mentioned in the last section – it took Charles Darwin 20 years from the time he arrived home on the *Beagle* to publish *The Origin of Species*. Certainly, some of this time is accounted for by the necessary fact-checking and discussions with scientific experts so that Darwin could fully appreciate the depth of the observations he had made. After all, he did bring back about 5,500 specimens from the trip! Darwin realized that he was not an expert in all areas and appropriately sought scientific counsel as necessary. It would be unfair not to recognize the significant scientific contributions Darwin made simply as a result of his journaling and specimen collecting.

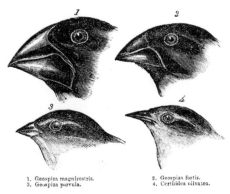

1. *Geospiza magnirostris.*
2. *Geospiza fortis.*
3. *Geospiza parvula.*
4. *Certhidea olivacea.*

Figure 18.5.1

"Darwin's Finches"
Four of the fifteen types of finch that Darwin found on the Galapagos Islands (actually, it is not entirely clear how many different finch varieties exist on the Galapagos – between 13 and 15 are documented in the literature). None of the Galapagos finch varieties are found anywhere else in the world besides the Galapagos. According to the late evolutionist Stephen Jay Gould, Darwin did not realize that the birds were all different kinds of finches until his colleague John Gould, the British ornithologist, studied the specimens in detail. Creationists and evolutionists agree that it is likely that all 15 types of finch on the islands today arose from the same ancestor finch population. Much more to come on this!

However, fact checking didn't take 20 years and so there must have been something else preventing Darwin from publishing his theory of descent with modification through the mechanism of natural selection. The main reason that Darwin did not finish *The Origin of Species* until 1859 – and hastily, at that, when he finally did – is because he knew full well that it was possible that Victorian England – scientists included – would roundly reject his descent with modification via natural selection theory because of the clearly intended implication inherent in the theory.

But, what "implication" could possibly be so severe that it would cause Darwin's contemporaries to reject his "scientific theory?" The implication is that Darwin's God-less theory amounted to the end-point of rationalism – **materialism**. Materialism in this sense is not the pursuit of material things (horses, carriages, houses, money, etc), but *the belief that physical matter is the only reality and everything (thought, feelings, will) is explainable by matter and physical phenomena only*. A **materialist** – one who believes in materialism – has no need for God or Biblical truth because the only recognizable truth is in the physical world, the "material" reality, man's reality. Materialism is a 100% out-and-out rejection of Jesus Christ as Lord and Savior. Further, it is rejection of the concept that man needs a Savior at all. Darwin knew full well that his theory, his "scientific" attempt to provide an origins theory, was anti-God. His evolutionary theory was never meant to be combined with Christian theology because it was specifically an attempt to explain life without God. As Charles Spurgeon so duly noted, there is nothing in evolution compatible with God.

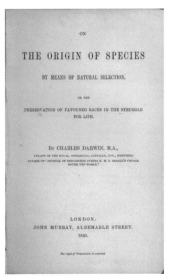

Figure 18.5.2

The Origin of Species and Materialism
Darwin and his scientific allies knew full well that his theory of evolution was equivalent to materialism. Richard Lewontin, atheist geneticist, confirms that evolution is 100%, absolute materialism:

> *"We take the side of science in spite of the patent absurdity of some of its constructs, in spite of its failure to fulfill many of its extravagant promises of health and life, in spite of the tolerance of the scientific community for unsubstantiated just-so stories, because we have a prior commitment, a commitment to materialism. It is not that the methods and institutions of science somehow compel us to accept a material explanation of the phenomenal world, but, on the contrary, that we are forced by our a priori adherence to material causes to create an apparatus of investigation and a set of concepts that produce material explanations, no matter how counter-intuitive, no matter how mystifying to the uninitiated. Moreover, that materialism is an absolute, for we cannot allow a Divine Foot in the door. The eminent Kant scholar Lewis Beck used to say that anyone who could believe in God could believe in anything. To appeal to an omnipotent deity is to allow that at any moment the regularities of nature may be ruptured, that Miracles may happen."*

Evolution is an origins philosophy committed to explaining life by excluding God. There is no reasonable way that the two can be reconciled.

It is abundantly clear from his personal writings that, by the 1840's and 1850's, Charles Darwin himself had progressed past the point of being a rationalist to being a full-fledged materialist.

> *"Oh you materialist! Why is thought, being a secretion of brain, more wonderful than gravity as a property of matter?"* Charles Darwin (referring to himself)

> *But false prophets also rose among the people; just as there will be false teachers among you, who will secretly bring in destructive heresies, even denying the Master who brought them, bringing upon themselves swift destruction.* 2 Peter 2:1

Darwin was concerned that when realization of the rank materialism of his theory, the utter purposelessness of evolution and the utter rejection of God's truths struck, his theory would face widespread rejection. Since Victorian society, was, after all, still a fairly Christian one, you may think that Charles Darwin was concerned that he would be ostracized from society and the church for "going counterculture" and suggesting materialistic life origins. Most do think that. However, that isn't the case. No, the main reason that he waited for twenty years was due to _fear of backlash from the scientific community_. He was concerned that his theory was too speculative, that it lacked sound scientific data and that, along with the materialism, would provide reason for rejection from his fellow scientists. This is perhaps best understood by Darwin's own words from an 1857 letter to George Bentham, in which Darwin lamented that The Origin of Species would be perceived as:

> *"(g)rievously too hypothetical. It will very likely be of no other service than collecting some facts; though I myself think I see my way approximately on the origin of species. But, alas, how frequent, how almost universal it is in an author to persuade himself of the truth of his own dogmas."*

According to Kevin Padian, evolutionary professor at U.C. Berkeley:

> *"(It is) a long disestablished myth that Darwin avoided publishing his theory for so long because he feared backlash from the religious establishment. In fact, he was much more concerned about criticism from the scientific community."*

Figure 18.5.3

Scientists Who Rejected Darwin's Theory
As this list of scientific powerhouses who disagreed with his theory demonstrates, Charles Darwin was correct to be concerned about scientists of his day rejecting descent with modification. These scientists and physicians, contemporaries of Darwin, all rejected Darwin's theory of evolution (some even wrote to him to tell him so), though not all are biblical creationists.

Scientist	Lived	Areas of Contribution
Adam Sedgwick	1785 – 1873	Geology
Michael Faraday	1791 – 1867	Electromagnetics
John Herschel	1792 – 1871	Mathematician, astronomer, chemist, inventor of photography
James Joule	1818 – 1889	Thermodynamics
Rudolph Virchow	1821 – 1902	Physician, pathologist
Gregor Mendel	1822 – 1894	Genetics
Louis Pasteur	1822 – 1895	Bacteriology, biochemistry, sterilization, immunization
William Thomson, Lord Kelvin	1824 – 1907	Mathematical physics
Joseph Lister	1827 – 1912	Physician and pioneer in antisepsis
James Clerk Maxwell	1831 – 1879	Mathematical physics

And, from the introduction to *The Origin of Species*, we see that Darwin was aware that his speculations arrived at dubious findings because they were not strictly supportable by the scientific data:

> *"I am well aware that scarcely a single point is discussed in this volume on which facts cannot be adduced, often leading to conclusions directly opposite to those which I have arrived."* *Darwin*

> *For the wrath of God is revealed from heaven against all ungodliness and unrighteousness of men, who by their unrighteousness suppress the truth. For what can be known about God is plain to them, because God has shown it to them. For his invisible attributes, namely, his eternal power and divine nature, have been clearly perceived, ever since the creation of the world, in the things that have been made, so they are without excuse. For although they knew God, they did not honor him as God or give thanks to him, but they became futile in their thinking, and their foolish hearts were darkened. Claiming to be wise, they became fools and exchanged the glory of the immortal God for images made to look like mortal human beings and birds and animals and reptiles.* *Romans 1:18 – 23*

18.6 DARWIN'S ALLIES

Because Darwin understood the difficulty of getting his theory accepted by the scientific community, he recruited assistance to get acceptance from other scientific allies who supported his God-less cause. Much of those post-*Beagle* twenty years were spent cobbling together scientific political support for his theory with the help of scientists that Darwin knew also desired to remove God from science and society. There needed to be a concerted effort to minimize and control the outrage he and his scientist allies expected evolution would generate.

Darwin spent a lot of time writing letters to close and distant scientists in order to recruit them as disciples, often sending letters to friends when he would convert someone. One such was the 1859 letter Darwin sent to Alfred Wallace when botanist Asa Gray finally converted:

> *"Our best British Botanist...is a full convert, and is now going immediately to publish his full confession of Faith..."*

Famous scientists of the day who were close to Darwin – Charles Lyell, Asa Gray, Joseph Hooker, Ernst Haeckel, T. H. Huxley – were not Christians and many were atheists or agnostics, so they all had reason to want to ensure that God was removed from *all* scientific endeavors. In addition, there was growing unrest as the rationalist movement grew, supplanting God's Word as truth and providing the social platform for widespread acceptance of the materialist theory, if it was presented just right. Evolutionary writer Peter Bowler, PhD, in his book *Charles Darwin* (p. 139), summarized Darwin's hesitancy about publishing his materialistic theory:

> *"...he must be very careful to minimize the materialistic aspects of his theory in any public pronouncement. He knew that, whatever the growing dissatisfaction with creationism, the vast majority of naturalists and ordinary people would only be willing to tolerate a process [of evolution] if they felt that the law expressed a divine purpose."*

Figure 18.6.1

Thomas Henry Huxley

Despite not completely agreeing with all of Darwin's concepts, Thomas Huxley, nicknamed "Darwin's bulldog," was none-the-less the most effective promoter of descent with modification. As Darwin was frequently ill and did not venture out of his country estate very often, Huxley was the key to helping to minimize the materialist message of evolution and growing the stable of Darwin-supporting scientists. Despite not having been formally schooled, Huxley was generally well-respected by the scientific community and had a long career. Not only was he the key figure in forwarding Darwin's theory but also in secularizing British society. In fact, Thomas Huxley coined the word "agnostic" in order to properly describe his own views in which he did not believe in God but also did not have the scientific or philosophical capacity to definitively state God doesn't exist. Vladimir Lenin, the communist leader of the Soviet Union from 1922 – 24, said of Huxley:

In Huxley's case...agnosticism serves as a fig-leaf for materialism.

One of Darwin's strongest contemporary scientific allies, Thomas Huxley, was the first to use the term "agnostic" to describe his own beliefs. He aggressively pursued the scientific acceptance of Darwin's theory even though he personally disagreed with some major elements of the theory, including whether or not natural selection even existed. Huxley was so dedicated to a concept that would wipe God of the map that he was willing to assist Darwin in gaining acceptance for descent with modification by natural selection even though he didn't completely agree with Darwin's tenets.

Figure 18.6.2

Alfred Russel Wallace

Alfred Russel Wallace (1823 – 1913) was a contemporary of Charles Darwin and, in 1858, while he was ill with intermittent high fevers and sweats in Indonesia, formulated the theory of evolution by natural selection independent of Darwin. He wrote a letter to Charles Darwin explaining his theory (and the circumstances surrounding his truly "aha moment"). When Darwin read it, he was down-trodden not only that Wallace had "scooped" him but that Wallace was able to do it, in Darwin's words:

"while in a fit of delirium, in the space of a couple of hours between the onset of chills and their subsidence in a pool of sweat."

However, the cadre of loyal followers that Darwin had accumulated over his 20 years of scientific politicking, most notably Charles Lyell and Joseph Hooker (1817 – 1911, a notable British botanist and explorer), had a plan. Since Wallace's letter was now on record with the date it was written, Darwin's disciples needed to find a way to publicize the evolutionary ideas of both at the same time so as not to allow Darwin to be publicly and scientifically scooped by Wallace. Certainly, Darwin had developed his evolutionary ideas over 20 years, but they were not very well organized into coherent thoughts, particularly as compared to those in Wallace's letter to Darwin. Lyell and Hooker therefore quickly arranged for Wallace's paper to be read at the Linnaean Society (Wallace was still out of the country and so he knew nothing of this) along with Darwin's descriptions of descent with modification from an unpublished paper Darwin wrote in 1844 and a letter to botanist Asa Gray in 1857. In so doing, they would be able to maintain Darwin's preeminence on the subject and point out how true descent with modification must be since Wallace also had independently thought of it. Even though Darwin later wrote that the 1844 paper and 1857 letter had not "been intended for publication and were badly written," with assistance of his loyal followers, this event solidified Darwin's place in evolutionary history such that he is considered the father of evolution and nary a thought is given to Alfred Russel Wallace, so powerful were Darwin's supporters.

Charles Darwin had another powerful ally, the pantheist (pantheism is an ill-defined term but is definitely not consistent with Christianity) Dr. Ernst Haeckel, a German physician and biologist. After reading *The Origin of Species* shortly after it was published, he left his medical practice and devoted himself to educating the European mainland of the wonders of Darwinism. Darwin expressed his admiration for Haeckel's efforts and Haeckel visited Darwin several times in his English countryside home.

Figure 18.6.3

Ernst Haeckel

Ernst Haeckel (1834 – 1919) was a powerful lobbyist for the acceptance of Darwinism. Haeckel was a prolific writer and illustrator. Unfortunately, his most famous drawing is probably this 1868 forgery, in which he took a drawing of a 25-day old dog embryo (drawn by T.L.W. Bischoff in 1845) and a 4-week old human embryo (drawn by A. Ecker in the 1850's) and purposely drew them so they would appear much more similar than they really are. The evolutionary thinking at the time, now disavowed by evolutionists, is that, since everything evolved from the same common ancestor organism, embryonic development in its very early stages causes all organisms that develop as embryos to look the same. These fraudulent drawings were uncovered by the great physician Dr. Wilhelm His. It is interesting to note the devotion that some evolutionists continue to have to their "leaders." Even though in 1909 Haeckel admitted that his drawings were "falsified," the Wikipedia entry for Ernst Haeckel says, "The pictures of the earliest embryonic stages are considered inaccurate" (this was as of September 25, 2012). Such misplaced political correctness is quite inappropriate in this instance. These are not "inaccurate" drawings. They are purposeful lies with only one intention –deception! These forged drawings still to this day show up in Biology text books as a "proof" of evolution, well over 130 years after Dr. His identified them as forgeries and more than 100 years after Dr. Haeckel admitted he faked them.

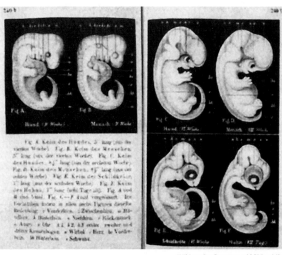

So, much of the twenty years Darwin spent prior to publishing his theory was spent garnering support from strategic members of the scientific community because he knew what a big bomb shell his materialistic "evolution by natural selection" theory would be. Still, as Darwin had foreseen, his theory was largely rejected by scientists of the time and, after more than 5 decades of promoting the theory, it finally began to take hold in the early 20th century.

> *"When Darwin deduced the theory of natural selection to explain the adaptations in which he had previously seen the handiwork of God, he knew he was committing cultural murder. He understood immediately that if natural selection explained adaptations and evolution by descent were true, then the argument from design was dead and all that went with it, namely, the existence of a personal god, free will, life after death, immutable moral laws, and the ultimate meaning of life."* Professor William Provine, evolutionary biologist

> *For the time is coming when people will not endure sound teaching, but having itching ears they will accumulate for themselves teachers to suit their own passions, and will turn away from listening to the truth and wander off into myths.* 2 Timothy 4:3-4

18.7 A DEEPER DIVE INTO NATURAL SELECTION

Natural selection is the Darwinian mechanism that evolutionists believe drives evolution. But, what exactly does it look like? It has often been described as "survival of the fittest" and, though some may argue that this description is overly simplistic, it does provide a pretty clear picture of natural selection. Although Darwin did not originate the term "survival of the fittest," he none-the-less thought that it fairly accurately described his concept of natural selection. Therefore, if the father of evolution thought that "survival of the fittest" wasn't a bad descriptor for natural selection, then we can certainly use it as a starting point to our discussion.

Figure 18.7.1

Edward Blyth

Edward Blyth (1810 – 1873), was a British ornithologist and zoologist and published one of the earliest known (perhaps the first) descriptions of natural selection. From 1835 – 1837, he published three separate articles describing natural selection (though he did not use the term "natural selection," he did accurately describe the concept). Unlike Charles Darwin and modern day evolutionists who believe that somehow natural selection is "creative" because it leads to the formation of new traits and ultimately new kinds of organisms that previously did not exist, Blyth's concept of natural selection was that it preserved populations of organisms by weeding out the weak, sick and the genetically different ones that stood out because of differences in color or behavior. In other words, Byth's concept was that natural selection is a destructive process because it results in the removal of unfit organisms, rather than being one that "makes new stuff." From the creationist perspective, natural selection is an observable scientific phenomenon and is one of the consequences of the Fall. Darwin was very aware of Blyth's descriptions of natural selection as there are copies of *The Magazine of Natural History* with Darwin's writing in the margins of Blyth's articles.

Just as the concept of an entirely naturalistic life origins theory had been around for a long time before Darwin, the idea of natural selection was also not new. Darwin knew of natural selection concepts from reading Blyth's papers in the mid to late 1830's. Therefore, Charles Darwin really did not contribute anything "novel" to science as far as patently new ideas are concerned when he published *Origin*. Since the teaching of "common descent" or "transmutation of the species" was not unknown in Darwin's time, he did not "reveal evolution to the world" in *The Origin of Species* as many think. He also didn't introduce the idea of natural selection in *Origin*. What Charles Darwin did do, though, was to provide a totally naturalistic mechanism – natural selection – as the way in which evolution occurred. He married natural selection to evolution in a way that was new and, in so doing, provided a unified God-less idea of how life originated. He provided what, at the time, appeared to be a scientifically plausible mechanism – natural selection – to fuel evolution.

Let's review natural selection. It means that those organisms that are most well-suited to their environment survive to have offspring and those that are not as fit die and do not leave any/as many offspring as the more fit organisms. When the "fittest" survive to reproduce more of their offspring (as opposed to fewer "less fit" organisms reproducing fewer offspring), they pass along to their offspring the "beneficial traits" that caused them to be more fit, which in turn pass their beneficial traits to their offspring, and so on. Over time, there will be an increase in the percentage of organisms that have the "more-beneficial" traits and a lower percentage of those with the "less-beneficial" traits. As a result, there can be observable changes in traits within organism populations.

However, and this is really important to keep in mind, we know that in organisms that have been subject to focused and heavy selection pressures – organisms like mountain lions (natural selection) and dogs (artificial selection) – there is actually a net loss of information. Yes, their beneficial traits become more pronounced as a result of the selection, but, overall, there is a net decrease in their ability to vary into the future.

Figure 18.7.2

Natural Selection is "Conservative"

The evolution model requires that natural selection provides new information that causes new and previously nonexistent traits to form in organisms; however, it actually does the opposite. We can see this probably the most clearly in dog breeding, which is actually artificial selection (however, one can think of artificial selection as "natural selection on steroids"). As we have noted, creationists and evolutionists believe that all dogs today are ancestors of a wolf-like animal, which obviously means that the dog-ancestor genome contained an incredible ability to vary since Great Danes and daschunds are both descendent from the wolf ancestor. However, now these specific varieties of pure-bred dogs have lost a large amount of their ability to vary at all. When dachunds breed with one another, they always make daschunds that look just like them – the same long body, short legs and small size. And, although this is an example taken from artificial selection, genetically the same process occurs as a result of natural selection – information is lost and with it so is the ability to vary. The more "specialized" an organism becomes as a result of natural selection, the less genetic variability they have, which is why successive generations increasingly look the same. There is some genetic variability preserved, for certain, but not nearly as much as their ancestor organisms had. This is yet another example of an erroneous prediction the evolution model makes, but is entirely consistent with the creation model.

Creationists do not deny the natural selection process. It is observable and does exactly what I just described; however, there is no scientific evidence that natural selection causes the formation of new traits and new kinds of organisms. Natural selection can certainly modify existing traits, and so cause varieties to form within already existing kinds, but it has never been observed to cause the formation of entirely new and previously nonexistent traits and kinds. As a brief example, creationists and evolutionists believe that an ancestor group of birds on the Galapagos Islands diversified into 15 different varieties, very likely starting from one group of ancestor finches. Even though there are now 15 varieties when initially there was only one variety only shows that birds beget birds. They are all still birds! None of the birds grew hair instead of feathers. There is nothing new genetically that didn't exist before. The single ancestor population were genetically all birds and the 15 different varieties are all still birds. In a few pages, we are going to break this down even more, but, for right now, it is enough to understand that natural selection definitely can lead to varieties of birds forming within a kind (varieties of finches from a finch ancestor) but that is very different than a reptile kind transforming into a bird kind.

Natural selection is very consistent with the creation model because it is the observable effects of the environment upon the built-in genetic ability to vary within the kind, a prediction of the creation model. Over time, what is scientifically observed is that natural selection leads to changes in the way organisms appear and/or behave, but _there is absolutely no evidence that varieties forming within kinds leads to the transformation into a new and previously nonexistent kind_. It is very important to clearly understand that evolution is specifically _not_ the kind of change that results in varieties forming within a kind and _is_ the kind of change that is "one kind transforming into a new and previously nonexistent kind."

> **_So Jesus said to the Jews who had believed him, "If you abide in my word, you are truly my disciples, and you will know the truth, and the truth will set you free."_** _John 8: 31-32_

Figure 18.7.3

Natural Selection and "Survival of the Fittest"

Conceptually, this is what evolutionists believe occurs as a result of natural selection. According to evolution, many hundreds of millions of years ago, there were no land animals, only fish and aquatic plants. Evolutionists believe that over tens of millions of years, an ancestor organism similar to a coelacanth-like ancestor fish acquired new DNA, providing the genetic information for the development of lungs, legs, smooth skin, a new structural form of the heart and an entirely new circulatory system such that the first amphibian was formed and life became land-based. This process would have been driven by natural selection, as the land-ancestor was exposed to new environments and gradually moved onto land, shaping the new traits the new DNA provided. As we move forward, we will closely explore whether or not there is any evidence that this can or did actually happen. We can do this by studying what we know about genetics to learn whether or not there is a genetic mechanism that can generate meaningful, new trait-forming genetic information. If there is no scientific data consistent with such a genetic process, then evolution lacks a mechanism, which would most certainly be a fatal flaw of the model. Further, one of the predictions of the evolutionary model is that, as ancestor organisms went through the slow process of gaining new traits, obviously organisms would have been formed in the past that have "dual" characteristics – those of the ancestor organism and the new kind of organism into which it is transforming (a so-called intermediate or transitional form). We will investigate that in Chapter 19.

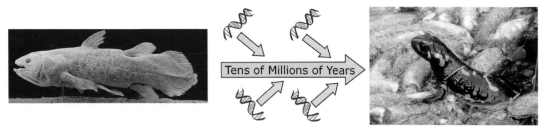

Tens of Millions of Years

Coelacanth © Alberto Fernandez Fernandez/Wikimedia Commons/CC-BY-SA-3.0 DNA © Squidonius/Wikimedia Commons/{{PD}} Spotted salamander © Aah-Yeah/Wikimedia Commons/CC-BY-SA-2.0

Evolutionists very clearly understand that in order for descent with modification to occur, an incredible amount of new information, providing many new traits that did not previously exist, must form (or "be created") in order for an entirely new kind of organism that never before existed to arise. Obviously, for a bacterium to transform into a man requires a significant amount of information added to the bacterial genome. The late, well known evolutionist Stephan J Gould talks about "natural selection as a creative force," which interestingly points out the primary and quite irresolvable problem of the evolution-by-natural-selection paradigm – it requires a source of intelligence because nothing that lacks intelligence can create. Evolutionists realize that in order for a less complex ancestor organism to gain new traits it didn't previously have and transform into an entirely new kind of organism, information needs to be added to, – or, literally, "created in" – the ancestor organism's genome to give it the new traits.

Figure 18.7.4

No Death Prior to the Fall

As we will discuss in more detail in Chapter 19, in Genesis, God makes a distinction between animals that have nephesh chayyah ("living souls" or "breathing creature") and those that don't. When applied to man, nephesh chayyah means "living soul" and when applied to animals with nephesh chayyah, means "breathing creature." There are organisms without nephesh chayyah, such as insects, bacteria and plants. Romans 8:19-23 says that before man ate of the Tree of Knowledge of Good and Evil, no creatures with nephesh chayyah (which includes man and vertebrates) died. This means man, mammals, birds, reptiles, amphibians and other animals with nephesh originally were all plant-eaters and didn't eat each other. Therefore, before the Fall there was no "natural selection" as we understand it today since there was no predation. Only after the Fall could natural selection have been a force that acted upon animals with nephesh. This is one of the strongest biblical arguments against compromising theology with science and taking a position that "God used evolution." If man did not appear on the scene until many hundreds of millions of years after life existed, that means there was death and dying as natural selection was working to shape life on earth. Such a belief is not consistent with scripture since it says that death and dying of nephesh animals was a result of the Fall (see 1 Cor 15: 21,22; Rom 5:12 and 8:19-23).

Wikimedia Commons/{{PD-old}}

Truly, then, we see that new information needs to be created to form new body plans, bigger brains, different structures like wings and beaks and feathers and scales, new sets of biochemical pathways, etc. As we learned last chapter, it is impossible for information to originate accidentally or without an intelligent cause, which obviously puts evolutionists in a corner from which one cannot get out. No matter how it is evolutionarily sliced and diced, information must be created to get from a single cell organism to a human being, a process that requires intelligence to originate the information. But, evolutionists cannot appeal to an intelligent source. All they have is the unintelligent and random process of natural selection to provide the stimulus to "create" the new information, which philosophically puts evolution in an indefensible position. There is just no way for evolutionists to get around that fact and so _evolutionists simply say that natural selection is "creative," not because there is any proof (there isn't), or even because it is logical (it's not), but because it must be creative in order for the evolution story to be true_.

Figure 18.7.5

What Does Evolution Need Natural Selection to Do? "Create!"

Darwin's concept of evolution, which stands today, is that of descent with modification; literally, bacteria evolved into birds. But, let's think about what that means had to have happened at the information level, because that forms the understanding of what natural selection must be able to do in order for evolution to occur. Creationists and evolutionists agree that the prototypical single cell organism – like the _Escherichia coli_, magnified 10,000x, on the left – contains far fewer traits and far less information than does the rainbow lorikeet. So if, over hundreds of millions and billions of years, that single cell organism really did evolve into a lorikeet, that means that the bacteria and all of the intermediate forms between the bacteria and the lorikeet that existed during the long line of evolution had to have continually gained new genetic information to provide new traits for the formation of each successive, more complex and previously nonexistent organism. According to evolution, as these new traits emerged, if they were beneficial and helped the organism survive, then as a result of natural selection, the trait would have been kept and passed along to successive generations. If the new trait didn't help the organism's survival, then that trait would have died out. As this happened, then, over time, new and previously nonexistent organisms would have formed, making evolution the only unintelligent cause of new information generation known to exist. There is only one drawback, though – there is no plausible and scientifically provable way for new information to arise via random processes. We will discuss this concept further in Chapter 19.

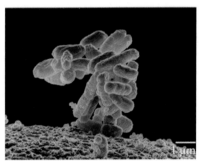
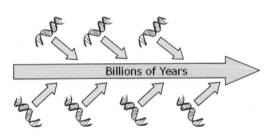

Billions of Years

The line of reasoning that evolutionists use to arrive at the natural-selection-is-creative destination is via the following:

- Without proof, it is accepted as "fact" that evolution properly explains origins.

- All organisms, then, evolved from those that existed before them.

- The first organism was a simple, single cell organism with relatively little information.

- Humans are extremely complex and "information rich" organisms.

- Evolution was able to generate this new information (it had to, it is the only "scientific" explanation of life origins in town).

- Since this information literally arose from nothing, evolution is a process that results in the creation of new information, the only known occurrence of unintelligent information origination.

• Since natural selection is what drives evolution, it has to be a "creative" process.

The problem with the above thinking is that the starting point – that all organisms evolved from those before them – is not true. It is scientifically unproven (and unprovable), but evolutionists believe it – by faith – because they must. It is essential to believe that the God-less process of evolution is true in order to believe in something – an unintelligent source of the most complex information in existence – that would otherwise be laughable. In any other setting, even the mere suggestion that a random process could generate the high degree of specified order and irreducible complexity of living organisms or could generate amounts of information equal to a million pages of precisely structured encyclopedic information would be (and absolutely should be) immediately discounted by a scientist. But, it is not because that is all the God-less process of evolution has.

"Hey, look at this 1,000 page book manuscript of mine that was just accepted for publication! You know what the crazy thing is? I sat down at my computer, blindfolded myself, randomly typed away and 3 hours later, I had this!" No one would believe that, and they shouldn't. It is ludicrous. Even though evolutionists seriously believing that the information of life is randomly generated is more ridiculous than believing that a 1,000 page book would emerge from random typing, they do…..they must. There is no

Figure 18.7.6

Creation Orchard, Tree of Life and Natural Selection
These two graphic depictions – the **evolutionary tree** (also referred to as the **phylogenetic tree**) on the left and the creation orchard on the right – explain the basic differences between evolutionist's and creationist's beliefs about the origin of life and what natural selection can and cannot do. According to evolutionists, starting at the base of the tree would be a single cell prokaryote. From there, over billions of years, everything evolved from that one common ancestor via the gradual, random acquisition of stunning amounts of biological information that were shaped through natural selection, leading to the formation of thousands of different kinds of organisms (in both models, the lines that do not make it to the present indicate varieties and/or kinds that have become extinct). Charles Darwin actually drew the first known tree in his notes. Creationists see biological diversity more as an orchard. God created the kinds with tremendous amounts of ability to vary built right into their information from the very start. Each "starting point" at the base of each tree is a created kind. Then, through natural selection, the genetic ability to vary, built into the kinds' genetics by God at creation, allowed organisms to diversify (or "speciate"), leading to the formation of wonderful variety within God's created kinds. In the evolutionary model, natural selection must be "creative" in order to generate new and meaningful traits from nothing. In the creation model, the genetic diversity is already there, brought out by natural selection. There is no evidence that random evolutionary forces can "create" new genetic information; however, there is excellent evidence that natural selection can alter already present traits. The creationist orchard fits much better with the observed scientific data.

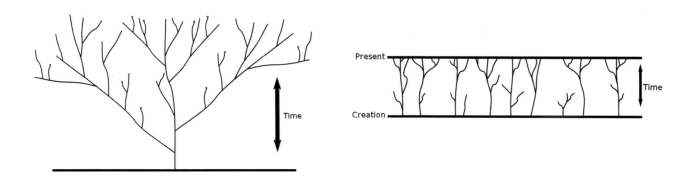

other explanation that merges with their God-less world view.

With that in mind, then, what does natural selection "do," if it can do anything at all? How is it even possible to observe what natural selection can "do?" Studying natural selection is best done when thinking about groups of organisms, often referred to as a **population**. A population is a group of the same kind of organism living in the same geographic location and interbreeding in order to make more of themselves. Since they are the same kinds of organism, they all share the same defining characteristics and so any changes can be observed over time. Although neither Blythe or Darwin directly observed changes due to natural selection, they correctly recognized that the collective characteristics of populations probably do change somewhat over time (body size gets bigger, fur changes color, fins get smaller, etc.) as a result of their field studies.

The Galapagos finches were (are) a great example of tremendous variety. Darwin identified that the various types of finches differed slightly in their beak size, body size, habitat, food sources, etc. Although he didn't recognize it immediately, after he analyzed his specimens and findings and spoke with other biologists, he came to the same conclusion over 150 years ago to which both evolutionists _and_ creationists have arrived today – the 15 different types of Galapagos finch originally came from one

Figure 18.7.7

The Birds and the Beaks

After returning to England and reviewing his notes and specimens, Charles Darwin realized that the finch populations that shared the same traits (i.e. physically looked the same, sang the same song, ate the same food) lived in the same habitat and bred with one another. Even though the 15 different types of finch varied somewhat, they are all, of course, members of the "bird kind." They all have the "finch body plan," with minor variations here and there. For example, the large ground finch tends to live in the arid parts of the Islands, has a larger body and beak size and eats seeds, while the slightly smaller common cactus finch has a smaller body and beak size, lives in the areas where cacti grow and eats the _Opuntia_ cactus for food. Darwin thought about that and came to the conclusion (with which creationists agree) that given the proper conditions, all of the 15 Galapagos finch varieties likely originated from one common ancestor finch population. Therefore, traits within the populations of different varieties of the same kind of organism must somehow change over time as a result of being "exposed to nature." Creationists and evolutionists alike endorse a scientific concept that these variations – such as the slightly bigger beak size of the large ground finch and the slightly smaller beak of the common cactus finch – are explained by natural selection. Remember, these 15 finch varieties are all finch birds – a bigger beak or a smaller beak is simply a variation of a trait that is already present in the bird kind. As we continue to learn, while there is ample scientific evidence that natural selection readily explains the presence of varieties within kinds, there is no clear scientific evidence that natural selection can explain origins and diversity (how a bacteria evolved into a person).

ancestor type of finch. To understand how is to see clearly what natural selection can and cannot do.

Now, don't incorrectly jump to any conclusions! Some read that "the 15 different types of Galapagos finch originally came from one ancestor type of finch" and think, "Hey, that's evolution!" _It is most definitely not evolution_ and it is extremely important to understand why since it underlines the foundational difference of what natural selection can do and what it can't do. Evolutionists constantly claim that the Galapagos finches are an example of "evolution in action;" however, they are a study of "natural selection in action." Remember, since evolution is specifically the origins theory that every type of organism is descended from one common ancestor via the hundreds-of-millions-of-years process of natural selection causing less complex organisms to transform into more complex ones, then "something more" needs to be seen with the finches if they are examples of "evolution in action." That is to say that if what is seen in the Galapagos finches truly is "evolution in action," the finches should be changing into a new and previously nonexistent organism with new and never before seen traits. They shouldn't still be all finch birds if they are in the process of changing into a more complex type of previously nonexistent organism, because that is what evolution is.

But, they aren't changing into anything. They all remain birds. _A process in which an ancestral finch species diversified over hundreds or perhaps several thousand years to form 15 different types is not evolution! Why? No new and previously nonexistent kind of organism has been formed._ The 15 different varieties of Galapagos finch are still all birds. _Not only that, they are all specifically finches_. There is no "new information."

There are no "new traits." They all still have beaks and wings and keels (breastbones) and lay eggs. They are all birds. The ancestral Galapagos finch didn't transform into a mammal. Had that happened, it, indeed, would be evolution! But that isn't what happened. The population started out birds and they are still birds. Natural selection can clearly lead to the formation of varieties within kinds but *natural selection cannot lead to the formation of new kinds (e.g. a bird from a reptile)*. There are no scientific data that shows that natural selection can cause entirely new and previously nonexistent traits to form. That is a made-up story that evolutionists desperately need to be true in order for their theory to be true.

Figure 18.7.8

What *Can* Natural Selection Do, or How Did the Finches Come to Be?

The Galapagos Islands (right) are in the Pacific Ocean about 500 miles west of the coast of Ecuador. The story of these four different kinds of Galapagos finch –1. Large ground finch; 2. Medium ground finch; 3. Small tree finch; 4. Green Warbler finch – demonstrates exactly what natural selection has been scientifically observed to "do." Creationists and evolutionists agree on the following concept, which is the scientific explanation of how the Galapagos finch population came to be made up of 15 different types. It is a story of natural selection, NOT of evolution. Sometime in the past – for creationists, many hundreds to no more than 4,500 years ago and for evolutionists, hundreds of thousands to millions of years – a small group of ancestral finches was blown off the mainland or perhaps floated on a natural land raft (this has been observed to occur fairly frequently) and landed on the Galapagos islands. There were no natural predators there and so this ancestral finch population thrived. As the birds reproduced over the years and the population grew, they naturally started to seek new areas on the islands in which to build their nests and find plentiful food. The Galapagos have a very wide variety of environmental conditions – lush forests, arid desert-like areas, coastal waters, beaches, etc. These areas have slightly different foliage and food sources, other animals that compete for food, etc. and so there are many different possible habitats the bird populations could have chosen. Over many generations, finches that survived better in the arid areas naturally began to preferentially live in those areas, just as finches that did better in the forests started to preferentially live there. This is the start of the natural selection process – organisms with slightly different traits that enable them to survive better in one area than another naturally begin to live in the habitat where they are better suited. Over many generations (these birds reproduce every year and so after only 300 years, there have been 300 generations!), the increasingly geographically-oriented populations were well on their way to developing **adaptations** owing to the many generations they have lived in their selected habitat. An adaptation is a trait that allows an organism to better survive in its given environment. Adaptations develop in response to **natural selection pressures** (the result of the interaction of the traits of a population with the environment such that it effects change in one or more traits of the population). As a result of continually living and reproducing with other finches that live in their same geographic area, the finches begin to develop similar traits (or adaptations) since they have all been living in the same area and have been subjected to the same natural pressures for many generations. Also, this same process is going on in different areas of the Islands, with populations of finches developing slightly different adaptations to their environments as compared to other populations. One population developed slightly larger beak and body sizes, another population developed slightly smaller beak and body sizes. Over time, as the populations begin to vary more and more in appearance and behavior from one another, they also largely stop interbreeding, which leads to a condition referred to as **reproductive isolation**. Once populations become reproductively isolated, they then usually breed only with those that have the same adaptations, which continues to cause the populations to further diverge from one another in appearance and behavior, forming the 15 different varieties. This process explains how the single ancestral finch population was able to diversify and form the 15 varieties of finch found on the Islands today. No matter how often evolutionists refer to this type of "speciation" as evolution, it isn't because no new and previously nonexistent trait or organism was formed. These all started out "birds" and they all remain "birds." No novel DNA. No novel traits. No novel organisms. This process is fully compatible with the creation model and does not "do" what evolution needs it to "do."

1. Geospiza magnirostris.
3. Geospiza parvula.
2. Geospiza fortis.
4. Certhidea olivaiea.

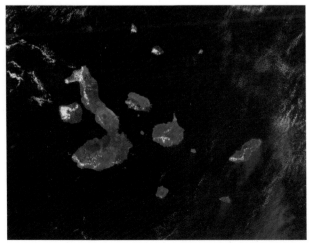

Like Blyth 20 years before him, what Darwin had recognized is the core concept of natural selection. That is, that the traits of a population of organisms can change over time as the conditions in their habitat change – food becomes more/less plentiful, food sources change in some way, predator-prey relationships change, etc. That's the essence of natural selection and it works on already-existing traits provided by already-existing genetic information. However, no new information has ever been scientifically observed to arise as a result of natural selection and no new and previously nonexistent organisms have ever been scientifically observed to have arisen. There have been observations that are consistent with varieties forming within a kind, as would be expected.

Figure 18.7.9

An Evolutionist's View of Natural Selection in Action

Princeton's evolutionary biologists Peter Grant and his wife Rosemary have been continuously studying the Galapagos finches for more than twenty-five years. Their team performs painstaking assessment of the numbers of birds that make up the fifteen species of Galapagos finch. They also routinely measure body size, weight, color, and beak size and you can see from the medium ground finch (left), the large ground finch (center) and the cactus finch (right), the different varieties have distinct features. They are all the bird kind, though each are different varieties because they have distinct traits to distinguish them from other finch varieties. It is important to also note that not only do the traits vary between varieties, but they also differ – to a lesser degree – between organisms of the same variety. That is to say that not all large ground finches have _exactly_ the same beak and body size, just like not all cactus finches have _exactly_ the same beak and body size and it is this variation within varieties upon which natural selection can act. In 1977, there was a severe drought on the islands and about 86% of the total finch population died off. As a result of their careful measurements, the Grants realized that after the drought, the surviving birds of all varieties had slightly larger beaks and body sizes than prior to the drought. The drought conditions had clearly selected for the trait of larger body and beak size since those were apparently beneficial traits for the birds to have to better survive the drought. The most fascinating scientific observation that Dr. Grant made was the speed at which these changes occurred within the finches. Remember that one of the hallmarks of evolution is "slow change" and previous to this study, evolutionists thought that it would take hundreds of thousands to perhaps a million years for finch varieties to form from ancestral populations. However, Dr. Grant's own calculations were that, had the drought conditions continued, based upon the changes in the finch traits he observed real-time, it would take only about 200 years for the medium ground finch to transform into the large ground finch and only 1,200 years to transform into the very different-appearing cactus finch. Such rapid speciation shocked evolutionists. And, remember, the only thing that happened during the drought was that already-present traits, encoded by already-present information, changed as a result of the changes in the natural conditions surrounding them (the natural selection pressures were different as a result of the drought as compared to prior to the drought). In other words, _existing traits_ were modified as a result of natural selection. They remained finches with beaks and feathers and wings and laying eggs after the drought just as before. And, what is even more sublime is that, once the drought condition ended, the bird populations all returned to their pre-drought measurements! This underlines the fact that what is happening is natural selection acting upon built-in variation from within already-present information. Nothing changed. All the information was already there, built right into their systems. They remain finches and, if the natural selection pressures change enough, their built-in ability to vary responds with corresponding changes in traits. Creationists are very comfortable with Dr. Grant's observations and the scientific implications because they are exactly what one expects to see as a result of natural selection. It works upon traits formed as a result of God-designed ability for organisms to vary, built right into their biological information. Dr. Grant's scientific observations clearly support a creation model and are decidedly not consistent with the evolutionary model.

To summarize up to this point, evolution:

- Is specifically an anti-creation, anti-God origins theory that all life forms in existence now or in the past are directly evolved from ones that came before them. There is nothing about evolution that is compatible with creation because it was *never* intended to explain origins through or by God.

- Is properly defined as the process in which a less complex ancestor organism acquires new genetic information, giving it new traits that it did not previously have, causing it to transform into a new and previously nonexistent organism.

- Is an oxymoron of a process since it requires that incredibly intricate information must be "created" from unintelligent sources through random and naturalistic processes, a concept that in any other context would be summarily dismissed by scientists.

- Is proposed to occur through the mechanism of natural selection, which in-and-of-itself is not possible since natural selection has only ever been proven to modify existing traits, not generate entirely new ones.

18.8 ABIOGENESIS – ANOTHER SCIENTIFICALLY UNPROVEN BUT NECESSARY CONDITION

Evolutionists believe that the universe is between 13 and 15 billion years old and the earth is about 4.5 billion +/- 500 million years old. Since theirs is an entirely naturalistic process, there cannot be any "help" from anyone or anything in order to "get life going" at the beginning and so, according to evolutionary theory, over billions of years, the precursor molecules of life – oxygen, hydrogen, nitrogen and carbon – were sitting around in the **primordial ooze**, the semi-liquid concoction in which abiogenesis occurred and life first formed. As they tell it, life started as a result of the random association of the non-living atoms and molecules, called **chemical precursors**, into the first living organism (about 3.5 billion years ago). **Chemical evolution**, or **abiogenesis** (which means, literally, "life from non-life"), is the process of chemicals randomly forming into the molecules of life and generating a living cell, the so-called **goo-to-you** or **particles-to-people evolution**. Abiogenesis is a necessity of evolutionary theory and is a process that is supported by not even a shred of scientific data.

Figure 18.8.1

Miller-Urey Experiment

For many years, the Miller Urey experiment was considered a triumph for evolutionary theory as it supposedly demonstrated that the biologically active macromolecules of life could be made under conditions that evolutionists believe existed early in the Earth's history. In 1953, Dr. Harold Urey (1893 – 1981) and his graduate student, Stanley Miller (1930 – 2007) intelligently designed this experiment for the purpose of testing whether or not organic molecules, necessary first steps to the formation of life, could be synthesized out of "chemical precursors". They set the experiment up as depicted, with the heat source constantly boiling the water in the flask, sending a continuous stream of heat into the closed system (which doesn't exist in nature, and neither did the strategically placed diverters to drain out the miniscule amounts of amino acids before they rapidly degraded in the surrounding "natural" conditions). As the steam passed into the spark chamber, it was subjected to 60,000-volt sparks in the presence of methane, ammonia and hydrogen gases. After several modifications to the experiment, Miller and Urey were able to isolate very small amounts of amino acids, mainly glycine and alanine. At the time, it was hailed as proof that abiogenesis was possible; however, today, despite the fact that this experiment continues to be proclaimed in evolutionary biology books as evidence that abiogenesis is true, even the most hearty evolutionist does not regard this experiment as anything other than an interesting experiment that was done more than 50 years ago. Interestingly, like the discredited embryos of Ernst Haeckel, according to a 2011 review by Dr. Jerry Bergman, the most recent editions of 19 of the most common 22 biology text books contained detailed descriptions of the Miller-Urey experiment and 18 contained frankly misleading information regarding the implications of the experiment. Repeated experiments attempting to demonstrate abiogenesis is possible have yielded results that reinforce the impossibility of abiogenesis rather than support it. Of course, it is really important to realize that, even if this experiment did produce copious amounts of many different kinds of amino acids, rather that the pathetically small amount of two different types of amino acids that were incredibly unstable and surrounded by toxic sludge, the only thing this experiment would prove is that intelligent human beings were able to design an experiment that synthesized amino acids. The entire construct of the apparatus creates ridiculously controlled and specific conditions that are entirely favorable to the formation of amino acids. It doesn't replicate the random conditions of "primitive earth."

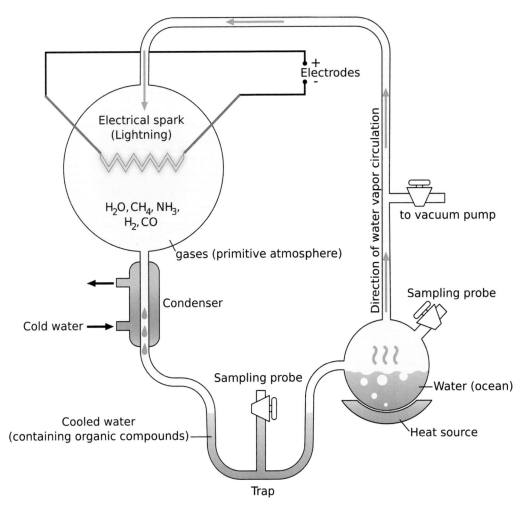

The idea here is that, somehow, the elements of carbon, hydrogen, nitrogen and oxygen were removed from the atmosphere to form complex molecules like proteins, enzymes, lipids and even RNA and information-containing DNA. Never mind that such a process has never been able to be reproduced in intelligently designed laboratory experiments. Never mind that evolutionists cannot decide on the conditions of the "primitive earth" that would have had to have been present in order for this to occur (in fact, a condition required for life – the presence of free oxygen – causes the rapid degradation of amino acids). Never mind the silliness that exists when the evolutionary scientific community does not seem to be able to identify how ridiculous it is that incredibly smart scientists are unable to design experiments to show that abiogenesis is possible when it supposedly occurred naturally and accidentally billions of years ago on an incredibly hostile earth with conditions that simply don't allow biochemicals to form or be stable. Never mind that, even if they could somehow have formed, when they were sitting unprotected in the goo of primitive earth, the highly reactive biomolecules would have rapidly degraded or reacted with one another, eliminating them from being available to be incorporated into a cell that was forming (the only reason biomolecules don't react with one another in living organisms is because of the highly controlled conditions organisms generate specifically to prevent that from happening). _There is not one shred of scientific evidence that abiogenesis could have occurred and there is overwhelming evidence against it and yet, evolutionists believe it occurred because there is nothing else if you remove God from his Creation._ Abiogenesis is all evolutionists have, so it must be true!

Despite being considered "fact" by evolutionists, there is no naturalistic mechanism accepted by evolutionists through which abiogenesis occurs. Further, many evolutionists believe it impossible for nonliving chemicals to form life; several reasons were already pointed out. Another is that, since this was a process subjected to naturalistic forces, it is possible to calculate the likelihood that abiogenesis actually happened. This is approached with statistical methods, which allows one to obtain the likelihood that various molecules were randomly formed and they all got together at the same time to form a cell. That chance is not one in a million (1,000,000, or 10^5). That chance is not even one in a quadrillion (1,000,000,000,000,000, or 10^{14}), but 1 in $10^{57,800}$ (a 10 with 57,800 zeros after it) of happening, which doesn't really make any sense it is so unlikely. It is roughly equal to the chance of winning the top prize in the lottery more than 8,000 times _in a row_. Statistically, it is an impossibility that abiogenesis occurred.

Once that first cell formed, it somehow contained information not only to perform all of the functions of life but also how to replicate itself (how did it even know it needed to do that when it was randomly forming from the ooze?). Then, a few hundreds of millions of years later, a new and previously nonexistent new kind of organism formed – a eukaryote. Evolution was on its way to providing all of the organisms that ever have or ever will live. These first single celled organisms were aquatic and gave rise to sponges, sea worms, star fish, clams, aquatic plants, and, eventually, fish. Then, fish evolved into amphibians, amphibians evolved into reptiles and reptiles into birds and mammals, etc.

Figure 18.8.2

Problems with Abiogenesis

The theory of abiogenesis, which is now the preferred term for "chemical evolution" (most evolutionists recognize that chemicals cannot "evolve" because they are not living), is becoming an increasingly difficult concept for evolutionists to scientifically defend. Below are some of the major problems with abiogenesis.

Scientific Condition or Implication of the Hypothesis that is Problematic for Abiogenesis	Why is it Problematic?
Initially, scientists thought earth's early atmosphere contained "reducing" gases such as methane, ammonia and/or hydrogen	This reducing atmosphere was required for chemical reactions necessary to make certain organic molecules, but the "sparking" – electrical impulses transmitted from lightning to the ground that provide the energy for atoms to join together to form larger molecules when they otherwise would not – will not occur in a reducing atmosphere. The concept of a reducing atmosphere has therefore been discarded from abiogenesis theory, but hasn't been replaced by anything else because the compounds that make a reducing atmosphere are required to provide a nitrogen and hydrogen source. The is no accepted scientific alternative to the reducing atmosphere yet.
Because all organic molecules contain oxygen, there must be a source for the oxygen, thought to be found in the early atmosphere that contained free oxygen	Free oxygen is toxic to unprotected organic compounds (they would have been sitting open to air in the primordial ooze), which (even if the molecules were able to be formed naturally) would rapidly degrade because of exposure to atmospheric oxygen. There is no accepted mechanism for how oxygen was incorporated into organic molecules while at the same time not breaking them down immediately after they formed.
Once formed via lightning in the primordial ooze, the new biomolecules would all be pooled with one another in the sludge	In order for a cell to form via natural mechanisms, the primordial ooze needs to contain all types of biomolecules so they are available to form a cell. Sugars, amino acids, nucleic acids, etc., would all be "naked" in the ooze, exposed to one another. Sugars and amino acids are highly reactive with one another and, when there is no organized cellular apparatus to protect them and keep it from happening, they would react with one another and degrade before they could be incorporated into a cell. There is no proposed mechanism that would have protected the biomolecules as they sat in the ooze.
Geological evidence for primordial ooze doesn't exist	Nowhere on earth is there any geological evidence of the primordial ooze, so it is just a made-up concept lacking provable scientific foundation.
All amino acids in living organisms are L-forms	All experiments trying to "naturally" form amino acids by reproducing suspected early conditions on Earth result in equal amounts of L and D forms (as expected based upon probabilities). If biomolecules had formed naturally as evolution requires, then both forms should be found in living cells. While evolutionists have proposed hypotheses to the "all L-form problem," none are universally accepted (and there are still the other problems mentioned in this table even if the "all L form" problem did have an adequate explanation).
Enzymes require amino acid sequences highly specific to only the substrate	The likelihood that even one enzyme could form naturally with the proper sequence of amino acids in the enzyme matching a particular substrate is a 1 in 10^{650}, which is as likely as winning the top lottery prize 90 times in a row. And, this would have had to have occurred many more times than once (in each case with the chance of happening as likely as winning the lottery 90 times in a row), since many enzymes are required in even the "simplest" cell. All experiments to synthesize biological molecules always yield randomly sequenced molecules, not ones that are highly specific and biologically active. There are no accepted proposed mechanisms for how enzyme specificity developed in the ooze.
Undirected energy is very harmful	All forms of uncontrolled energy – like lightning – are very harmful and quickly degrade any type of biological molecule that is synthesized. There is no proposed mechanism for biomolecules protection.

Scientific Condition or Implication of the Hypothesis that is Problematic for Abiogenesis	Why is it Problematic?
Polymerization and assembly disconnection	It is very difficult to explain how, even if the molecules could be produced, they would then spontaneously form into a protected cell with just the right concentrations of all of the chemicals necessary for the cell to live. For example, amino acids rapidly form bonds with chemicals other than other amino acids and can also form bonds other than peptide bonds with other amino acids. There is no proposed mechanism by which amino acids would have gone against all known chemical principles and remained un-bonded to anything other than amino acids only then to link only to other amino acids via a peptide bond in the ooze. Preventing normal chemical reactions such as this is only possible through already-highly regulated, enzyme driven systems, which is most definitely not a property of the primordial ooze.
The genetic code contains the instructions for its own existence and replication	It is not possible for information to arise through random, naturalistic processes and contain the necessary information to "make itself," which is what evolution demands be true. If all of the necessary biological molecules had been synthesized accidentally and not degraded and self-assembled into a cell, how could the DNA possibly have been formed randomly with the very specific information containing instructions necessary to replicate the cell that just formed from the random assembly of randomly made molecules? How could the code for the production and replication of the cell be built into the DNA that just randomly assembled inside of a cell for which it had no relationship to anything else in the cell other than happening to get trapped inside with it? It is not possible to explain why DNA would contain specific information encoding protein production when the DNA and proteins had already formed independent of one another. It would be like a human being sitting down with a paper and pencil and writing out random words and then when the random words were randomly strung together they happened to be detailed instructions for building something that previously did not exist but that had exquisite function and form and met an as-yet undefined need.

Let's take a brief detour. Recall our discussion of spontaneous generation from chapter 10, in which Louis Pasteur scientifically showed that life can arise only from life. Never has spontaneous generation been found to occur. In fact, it is a biological Law that "life begets life." It is inexplicable, then, that it is reasonable to believe that abiogenesis occurred when all "abiogenesis" really means is "spontaneous generation." Despite Pasteur disproving spontaneous generation, despite no experiment ever being able to be designed to show how abiogenesis could have occurred, despite all of the obvious and unanswered problems detailed in Figure 18.8.2, evolutionists believe that it happened none-the-less. _They have to believe abiogenesis occurred because it had to in order for life to have arisen without God_. It is their only option! They must believe that abiogenesis occurred despite total lack of supporting scientific evidence because if they don't, the only other option is God.

> **_"In order to have natural selection, you need to have self-reproduction or self replication and at least two distinct self-replicating units or entities...Probiological natural selection is a contradiction of terms."_** _Evolutionist Theodosius Dobzhansky, discussing abiogenesis (what he calls "Probiological natural selection")_

> **_The fear of the Lord is the beginning of wisdom; all those who practice it have a good understanding. His praise endures forever!_** _Psalm 111:10_

18.9 EVOLUTION IS NOT EQUIVALENT TO CHANGE

Recently, over the past perhaps 20 to 30 years, one of the emerging themes of teaching evolution is what amounts to an increasingly dumbed-down version; basically, teaching that evolution is equivalent to "change." While is it obvious that _if_ evolution did properly explain origins, and _if_ evolution had supportable scientific data, then it would certainly be characterized by "change." However, as we have already clearly identified, the type of "change" that evolution specifically is – particles to people or an ancestor organism gaining new and previously nonexistent traits and transforming into a previously nonexistent organism – doesn't happen. The only kind of "change" that we scientifically observe – varieties forming within kinds as a result of natural selection – is not evolution. _It is not true that "change" observed in the way kinds of organisms look or behave over time equals "evolution."_ More and more, though, evolutionists have altered the evolution narrative to simply describe it as "change," rather than the very specific "type of change" that it is.

> **"In fact, evolution can be precisely defined as any change in the frequency of alleles within a gene pool from one generation to the next."** _Helena Curtis and N. Sue Barnes in_ Biology _(a very popular secular biology text)_

> **"In the broadest sense, evolution is merely change, and so is all-pervasive; galaxies, languages, and political systems all evolve. Biological evolution ... is change in the properties of populations of organisms that transcend the lifetime of a single individual....Biological evolution may be slight or substantial; it embraces everything from slight changes in the proportion of different alleles within a population (such as those determining blood types) to the successive alterations that led from the earliest protoorganism to snails, bees, giraffes, and dandelions."** _Douglas Futuyma, evolutionary biologist, in_ Evolutionary Biology _(another very popular text)_

> **"Evolution is a change across successive generations in the inherited characteristics of biological populations."** _Wikipedia.org_

The problem with these definitions equating evolution to "change" is that evolution is not actually described anywhere in those definitions. A change in the "frequency of alleles" does not result in an organism acquiring new, never-before-in-existence characteristics to allow it to transform into an entirely new kind of organism. A change in the "frequency of alleles" involves _only_ already-existing DNA; no new information is created when the "frequency of alleles" changes. In order for evolution to occur, the frequency of alleles cannot "change;" _rather, entirely new alleles must arise_! If no new information is created via the formation of new alleles, neither would a new and previously nonexistent type of organism be formed. Any definition of evolution that does not contain a clear description of the process of the formation of entirely new alleles encoding novel traits, leading to the formation of new and previously nonexistent kinds of organisms, is not a definition of "evolution."

Figure 18.9.1

Evolutionary Sleight-of-Hand

Despite their very different appearance, both of these organisms are the moth kind and are the exact same variety – both are called the "peppered moth," *Biston betularia*. They demonstrate quite nicely what it means to express different alleles of the same trait; in this case the trait of coloring. There are two alleles – or "traits" – for color, melanic (black) and non-melanic (the lighter coloring). Although there is great debate about the veracity of the scientific studies that have monitored the predominance of one form over the other in the wild, what is reasonable to conclude is that the frequency of the allele for coloring has changed (likely more than once) over the past century. What that means is that, over time, sometimes there are more melanic varieties than non-melanic ones in the population –"the melanic allele is more frequent" – and sometimes there are more non-melanic varieties than melanic ones in the population –"the non-melanic allele is more frequent." The change in the frequency of the moth color allele is driven by natural selection and demonstrates why changes in frequency of alleles is NOT evolution. When environmental factors favor the melanic allele, then there are more black moths in the population. That is to say the melanic allele is more frequent than the non-melanic allele. Then, when environmental factors change and natural selection favors the non-melanic form, there are obviously more non-melanic moths than melanic ones and the allele frequency has changed again. But, how exactly is this change in allele frequency evolution? It isn't! These moths remain moths. The moths don't turn into birds or reptiles or monkeys. They remain moths. Not only that, they remain *Biston betularia* moths. In order for evolution to occur, entirely new traits need to form, leading to the formation of an entirely new and previously nonexistent kind of organism. However, the only thing that a change in allele frequency leads to is a change in the expression of already existing traits. Lighter colored moths predominate and, over time, give way to the darker colored ones. Finches with smaller beaks predominate and then give way to ones with slightly larger beaks. Moths remain moths. Birds remain birds. That is not evolution. It is natural selection and underlines why natural selection cannot drive evolution. The only thing natural selection can do is modify already existing traits, which is precisely another way to state, "change in allele frequency." Natural selection cannot generate entirely new alleles, which it must do in order for evolution to occur. Since natural selection cannot generate new alleles – new information – evolution is a false origins model.

For example, Dr. Futuyma says that slight changes in the proportion of different blood types in a population is "evolution." How is that? If, 1,000,000 years from now, the human allele frequency for blood types "changed" such that the percentage of people with blood type AB- (AB negative) went from its present 0.45% to 5%, that isn't evolution. Yes, the percentage of people with AB- blood would be roughly ten times larger a million years into the future, but so what? You still have human beings with AB- blood, just like there are now. There is no new information in that scenario because the alleles encoding the AB-blood type already exist in the human population. Human beings haven't changed. Their blood types haven't changed. They are still human beings with various blood types, one of them being AB-, just like now. The alleles encoding AB- blood type haven't changed. They still encode the AB- blood type. *That isn't evolution, Dr. Futuyma*, because there isn't the formation of a new and previously nonexistent trait or kind of organism and if no new and previously nonexistent traits or organisms have formed, then evolution hasn't happened. Those organisms in Dr. Futuyma's example are all still human beings with blood type AB-, exactly as there are now.

The fundamental problem we constantly experience with the evolution origins model is that evolutionists don't seems particularly interested in properly defining not only what a "species" is, but also exactly what "evolution" is. Equating "evolution" to "change" is scientific sleight-of-hand and should not be tolerated from the scientific community. Notice that none of the definitions of evolution contain the most essential element of the type of information-adding "change" that evolution requires. Unless the "change" of evolution results in the formation of new information that gives rise to new traits and eventually new and previously nonexistent organisms, then evolution will not happen. Consider that perhaps the reason that so many "evolution" definitions do not contain the prerequisite acquisition of new information so that a new and previously nonexistent kind of organism arises is because there is no scientific evidence that it has ever happened. Perhaps.

Let's take a brief digression and look at this in light of the "species problem" from Chapter 17. Would evolution have occurred if a "species" of amphibian evolved into the first ever-in-existence "species" of reptile (or, in creation terms, if the amphibian kind evolved into the reptile kind)? Yes, it would, because that would meet the definition of evolution – an ancestor organism – the amphibian – acquiring new information to provide new traits to cause it to transform into a previously nonexistent kind of organism – the reptile. _The problem is that there is absolutely no evidence that process ever occurred. Natural selection doesn't "do" that. Nothing like this has ever been scientifically observed and the data that evolutionists use (to be discussed in detail next chapter) is fully explainable by and is consistent with a creation model_.

18.10 "MICRO-" AND "MACROEVOLUTION"

Growing out of the already muddy scientific waters of the inability to clearly define "evolution" and the fundamental observable unit of evolution, "species," two terms have arisen. As scientific data has accumulated and the evolution model has been altered over the past three or four decades, it has been recognized that there is a very big difference between "the observable effects of natural selection" and "a less complex kind developing new information-containing DNA to provide new traits that previously did not exist such that it transforms into a new and previously nonexistent kind of organism." We will first deal with the term used to described the observable effects of natural selection, "microevolution," followed by the term used to describe "evolution" – "macroevolution."

Microevolution is a term that evolutionists (and, unfortunately, some creationists) use to describe the observable effects of natural selection and the associated random distribution of genes from parent to offspring within populations. For example, the 15 varieties of the Galapagos finch arising from one ancestor variety are cited as examples of "microevolution," as are the "changes in allele frequency" seen in the _Biston betularia_ populations. As we have discussed, these types of changes are not "less complex to more complex organism formation" and so they are NOT evolution. The evolution model needed a way to link the observable changes from natural selection to the unobserved changes of evolution; hence "microevolution" was coined to describe changes in traits due to natural selection. Now we will see how micro- and macro-evolution are used in the evolution model.

Microevolution is convenient since it describes a process that is observable. It gives the clear impression that evolution can and does occur. "Well, evolution must happen or else one would not add the prefix 'micro' to 'evolution,'" people figure. Creationists should very carefully consider whether this is a term we want to use, or not. _"Microevolution" is nothing more than the observational effects of natural selection/genetic variation due to genetic recombination on populations and has nothing to do with creating new and previously nonexistent types of information or kinds of organisms_. It would seem quite a bit more preferable to actually call "microevolution" what it really is – the observable effects of natural selection.

Macroevolution is a term for the process we have been describing as an ancestor organism acquiring new DNA (information) to give it new traits that it previously didn't have so that it transformed into a new and previously nonexistent kind of organism. "Macroevolution" is "evolution" (doesn't it seem odd to have to add a prefix onto a word describing a supposedly scientific concept when the addition of that prefix doesn't change the meaning, at all, of the prefixed word?). Macroevolution is summed up as microbes-to-man evolution and that graphic of the "tree of life" provides a nice picture of what it looks like. Particles-to-people evolution has never been shown to occur, and, as some of the quotes we have read from evolutionists themselves show us, it never could be shown to occur. Further, there is ample evidence that we have touched on this chapter and will discuss next chapter, that the scientific data not only supports God's Word, but also points directly against evolution. Finally, since evolutionists cannot even define "evolution" properly, it doesn't make sense to put a prefix on a word describing a scientifically unproven concept that has ample scientific evidence showing it doesn't exist.

Though it is important to not use "microevolution" as noted above, perhaps the main reason that its use is so dangerous is because the prevailing belief of many evolutionists (but not all) is that there is essentially no difference between microevolution and macroevolution. According to the evolution model, over long periods of time, the end effect of microevolution is macroevolution. That is to say that many evolutionists believe in a process that, through natural selection, results _only in_ modifications of already-existing traits – which is microevolution – can, over long periods of time, lead to the formation of entirely new traits that previously did not exist so that an entirely new kind of organism arises – which is macroevolution. There is no way that modifying existing information can lead to the formation of new and previously nonexistent information, traits and organisms. The things that occur to the DNA in "microevolution" do not result in an increase in information that "macroevolution" requires. The two are not related. Some evolutionists recognize this. Most don't (or, if they do, they aren't saying anything).

Now, therein lies the diabolical nature of using the term "microevolution." We can scientifically observe the effects of natural selection, which is, again, what evolutionists and some creationists call "microevolution." Referring to the effects of natural selection and the random distribution of genes in the population through sexual reproduction as "microevolution" is very misleading since those effects can scientifically be seen and if they can be seen, then a reasonable conclusion would be that microevolution does happen. If microevolution can happen, then that must mean that macroevolution can happen since evolutionists have conveniently defined macroevolution as "microevolution over long periods of time." "After all," evolutionists can then say, "since macroevolution is very difficult to see because it has taken billions of years to get here, take our word for it. It happens. No creationist would say that microevolution, as we have defined it, doesn't occur and since macroevolution is just the end-effects of microevolution, macroevolution obviously explains how we got here." That line of thinking is very wrong and is not supported by scientific data. It is critical to call the effects of natural selection and genes being distributed randomly in the population through sexual reproduction just that. "Microevolution" should be avoided.

Figure 18.10.1

Microevolution and Macroevolution, Conceptually

The prevailing evolutionary belief is that microevolution (which is nothing more than the modification of already-existent information that provides already-existent traits in already-existent kinds of organisms) can, over long periods of time, lead to macroevolution, which is the formation of new information providing new, previously nonexistent traits that result in the formation of a new and previously nonexistent kind of organism. For comparison, that would be exactly like taking the pages out of the children's reader, *New England Primer*, cutting out each individual word from every page, sitting there for a million years randomly rearranging all of the cut out words and thinking that when you are done you will have a complete Bible. Just like shuffling cut-out words from the *New England Primer*, microevolution does not involve an increase of information, it is just a modification of already existing information. In order to transform the *New England Primer* into the Bible, a ton of meaningful and specific information must be added to the *New England Primer*, just as a ton of new and meaningful genetic information must be added to the genome of a single cell organism to end up with a human being. Macroevolution, if it could occur, is a process that involves – ultimately – the formation of a far more complex organism with far more information content and evolutionists cannot get around the need for the creation of specifically meaningful genetic information for that to happen. Using our *Primer*-to-Bible analogy, macroevolution would be the equivalent of starting with the relatively information-poor *New England Primer*, randomly placing thousands and thousands of randomly generated words and expecting to end up with a fully complete, vastly more complex, information-rich Bible. That is silly.

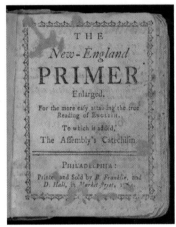

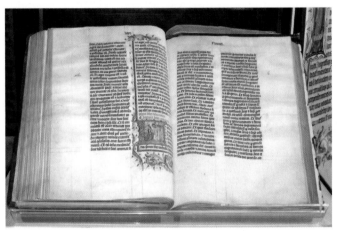

A final note, and a very important one, on microevolution leading to macroevolution. _Not all evolutionists believe that this can occur_! Wow! Here we have the "unifying theory" of evolution – microevolution over long periods of time leads to macroevolution – and not all evolutionists believe it! As stated, the processes behind microevolution and macroevolution are not related and some evolutionists are intellectually honest enough to identify that and so plainly refuse to state that it does. Ernst Mayr (1904 – 2005), one of the most revered evolutionists of the 20th century, credited with almost single handedly inventing the modern philosophy of biology, summed up the does-microevolution-cause-macroevolution-or-not question:

> ***"Among all the claims made during the evolutionary synthesis, perhaps the one that found least acceptance was the assertion that all phenomena of macroevolution can be 'reduced to,' that is, explained by, microevolutionary genetic processes. Not surprisingly, this claim was usually supported by geneticists but was widely rejected by the very biologists who dealt with macroevolution, the morphologists and paleontologists. Many of them insisted that there is more or less complete discontinuity between the processes at the two levels— that what happens at the species level is entirely different from what happens at the level of the higher categories. Now, 50 years later the controversy remains undecided."***

Dr. Mayr points out that the "one-kind-evolving-into-new-and-previously-nonexistent-kinds" of evolution is an entirely different process than "varieties-forming-within-kinds," just as we have been learning. In fact, he specifically said that the "microevolution-leading-to-macroevolution" has "found the least acceptance." Yet, the microevolution-leads-to-macroevolution is a pillar of the evolution model!

Knowing this first of all, that scoffers will come in the last days with scoffing, following their own sinful desires. They will say, Where is the promise of his coming? For ever since the fathers fell asleep, all things are continuing as they were from the beginning of creation. For they deliberately overlook this fact, that the heavens existed long ago, and the earth was formed out of water and through water by the word of God, and that by means of these the world that then existed was deluged with water and perished.   2 Peter 3: 3 – 6

Figure 18.10.2

Bats, Microevolution and Macroevolution

The supposed evolutionary history of bats provides great insight into the problems with the concepts of microevolution and macroevolution. Bats come in two kinds, the microbats (like the lesser false vampire bat, center) and the megabats (like the Livingstone's fruit bat, left). Evolutionists think that, over tens of thousands to tens of millions years or more, as a result of the kind of changes that occur as a result of natural selection (scientifically observed as existing traits of populations being modified over time) an ancestor organism can gain entirely new traits and transform into a new and previously nonexistent kind of organism. Evolutionists believe that bats evolved from an animal like a shrew, which is a kind of small, rat-like mammal. Bats possess one of the most complicated and exquisitely sensitive abilities of all organisms – echolocation, with a specialized larynx (voice box) that allows them to emit high frequency sounds that bounce off objects and return to the bat, hitting its specialized ear and being processed in highly sophisticated brain tissue. They can literally "see" in complete blackness using echolocation . They are able to discern sounds that are 2 millionths of a second apart, which is 3 to 4 times more sensitive than the most sophisticated man-made radar. They can also pick up only their own echolocation sounds even when surrounded by hundreds of other bats. And, of course, they are the only flying mammal. Certainly, the structures involved in echolocation and flying are "highly evolved" new and previously nonexistent traits, so surely evolutionists believe evolution accurately explains their existence because of overwhelming fossil evidence that shows their step-by-step progression as "microevolution" proceeded to change the "shrew ancestor species" into the bat through "macroevolution." One would think that, but it isn't true. The right photo is a fossil of *Palaeochiropteryx tupaiodon*, one of the "oldest" bat fossils, dated evolutionarily to be 48 million years old. This fossil shows a fully formed bat. It has wings and fully developed echolocation apparatus. There is no fossil that has ever been found to serve as "proof" of the "microevolution causes evolution" story. *Like all other organisms*, bats "just appear" in fossils fully formed and pretty much identical to their present day counterparts right from the very beginning of their documented existence, which is not at all consistent with the predictions of the evolutionary model (but is consistent with the creation model that states, as we will discuss further next chapter, that most fossils were formed in Noah's Flood). The evolution model would predict that as the shrew was transforming into the first bat, there should be many stages of organism captured in fossils demonstrating the step-wise change of the flightless and echolocation-less shrew into the bat. But, no such scientific data exists. Bats have always been bats, it seems, just appearing in fossils, just as fossil horses look like today's horses and fossil alligators and fish look like those alive today. This data fits much better with the creation model, of course. Creationists believe that God created the bat kind – it is not clear exactly "how many" of the microbat kinds and megabat kinds were created, but that isn't really important to the foundation of the model. The important thing is that the creation model states that God created microbat and megabat kinds with great genetic ability to vary within their kind. It was this great ability to vary that allowed bats to diversify into the more than 1,200 varieties we see today. Of course, Noah would have taken micro- and megabat kinds onto the Ark as directed by God (the Flood creating the fully formed fossils of them) and then, once off the Ark, their God-endowed ability to develop varieties would again be manifest as they moved out over the earth. And, remember Dr. Grant's study that demonstrated how rapidly varieties can form within kinds – a modest 1,500 years after disembarking the Ark would have given bats plenty of time to diversify! The scientific data clearly supports such a creation model.

18.11 THE BIG BANG

The **big bang theory** is a man-made story attempting to explain the origin of all of the physical matter in the universe. Although the big bang is not directly "an evolution concept," big bang time frames are on the order of billions of years, and so it provides the necessary time scales for evolution to occur. And, since it explains origins without the activity of God, it further appeals to evolutionists. According to the big bang, all of the matter in the universe rather spontaneously formed from nothing.

© Wikimedia Commons/Public Domain

Figure 18.11.1

The Big Bang

Today, the big bang is clearly a theory in crisis, though it has taken a while to get there and you wouldn't know it from the lack of mention in the media. The English astronomer, mathematician and Fellow of the Royal Society, Sir Fred Hoyle, mockingly first used the term in the 1950's. "[T]he big bang is an irrational process that cannot be described in scientific terms...[nor] challenged by an appeal to observation," he said. According to the theory, everything in the universe developed from a "**singularity**," which is an infinitely small point in the universe into which time, space and matter coexist. There are many problems with the big bang, of which secular and creation scientists are well aware, including its violation of the First Law of Thermodynamics (matter can neither be created nor destroyed) and its reliance on something that no one can see so that the math supporting the big bang works out. You see, in order to get the "physics" of the big bang to figure, not only "matter" (all the stuff we can see in the universe) but also "antimatter" would have been formed when the big bang occurred. The "antimatter," termed "dark energy" and "dark matter," are theoretical predictions of the big bang model and supposedly make up 95% of the "stuff" of the universe, with only 5% being made up of "stuff" we can see. Problem is, no one has ever seen dark matter and no one knows what dark energy actually is; both are simply the outcome of a bunch of very complicated astrophysics equations trying to show how the universe formed all by itself out of nothing. It seems decidedly unscientific to appeal to "stuff" that no one has ever seen and that may not even be able to be proven to exist in order to justify a God-less universe-origins theory. Of course, it is impossible for matter to originate from nothing unless there is a supernatural explanation for it, such as an all-powerful God that can create everything out of nothing, exactly like the Bible says. Only the Truth in the Word of Jesus Christ accurately explains origins of matter and life. The rest is smoke and mirrors, resorting to things that no one has ever seen to balance theoretical astrophysics equations.

Secular cosmologists continue to pursue the God-less big bang explanation to an almost embarrassing end. In order to explain how matter literally came from nowhere, some are turning to the concept of the "multiverse." According to the multiverse theory, there are many universes – maybe an infinite number – and if conditions are just right, matter and energy could be transferred through some sort of time-space-matter portal (a "singularity") from one universe into an entirely new universe. As mind blowing as that may sound, complete with really complicated physicist equations, _there is still the fundamental and totally insurmountable reality that matter has to have come from somewhere no matter how many universes are believed to exist._ If there are an infinite number of universes and our universe came from one of those, where did all of the matter come from to make up the infinite number of universes in the first place?

In fact, the mounting concerns, not from creation scientists but from the secular scientific community, became so great that, in 2004, 33 non-Christian, non-creation scientists went totally counter-culture (scientifically speaking) and published an open letter on the Internet (www.cosmologystatement.org). In it, they specifically dispute the validity of the big bang (among other reasons, because of the "something came from nothing reasoning"). To be sure, one of the goals of those 33 original signatories, now joined by another 547 scientists, was to encourage the "reallocation" of research funds so that alternate universe origins theories could be researched more completely. However, the fact that they have one agenda does not discount the credibility of their well thought concerns about the big bang.

They very clearly outline the multiple problems of the big bang theory, including:

- The reliance of big bang theory on, in their words, "hypothetical entities, things we have never observed..." When someone believes in something that has never been observed, then it is a faith-based belief, which is "against the rules" according to secular scientists. That is actually one of the main reasons evolutionists reject creation origins theory – invoking God (faith) isn't "scientific" – yet they think it is ok for the big bang.

- The big bang relies on "fudge factors," like dark energy and dark matter.

- _No_ predictions of big bang theory have ever been validated.

Interestingly, about a third of the big bang objection letter is devoted to fleshing out the true nature of the problem scientists face if they try to provide universe origins theories that aren't the big bang. As Ben Stein chronicled for intelligent design proponents in _Expelled_, these scientists identified that if they express doubt about the big bang, they suffer ostracism from the scientific community and potentially lose their funding. If a researcher loses funding, he or she loses his or her job. Teaching about evolution and the big bang is not about an honest scientific discourse. It is about preaching an anti-God agenda and drilling it into the head of every single person on this planet. As Charles Spurgeon wrote, evolution is anti-God and there is just no way around that.

As a final note on the nonsensical nature of the big bang, the letter states:

> **"In no other field of physics would this continual recourse to new hypothetical objects be accepted as a way of bridging the gap between theory and observation. It would, at the least, raise serious questions about the validity of the underlying theory."**

Obviously, the big bang is not accepted across the boards as the universe origins explanation as is commonly presented in the media and science.

> **Men, why are you doing these things? We are also men, of like nature with you, and we bring you good news, that you should turn from these vain things to a living God, who made the heaven and the earth and the sea and all that is in them.** Acts 14:15

18.12 A LOOK AHEAD

So far, we have learned that the evolution model proposes origins without God. Although even the basic concepts such as "evolution" and "species" are not clearly defined in the evolution model, we have properly defined "evolution" as a process that results in the successive formation of previously nonexistent traits in ancestor organism populations such that, over time, new and previously nonexistent organisms arise.

One thing we have not discussed yet, though, is precisely how, genetically speaking, evolutionists think bacteria evolved into basset hounds. The information theory section demonstrated, basically, that information cannot come from nowhere and that it cannot be generated from random processes because all known information has a sender (or creator). There has never been an instance in which information has "arisen spontaneously" – meaning, naturalistically – but that is precisely what evolutionists believe happened.

Surely, there must be some mechanism to which evolutionists turn to generate the necessary genetic information. There is - evolutionists believe that the information of life – the genetic code of every single organism that has ever or will ever exist – was generated out of nothing. The evolution model proposes that, somehow, the genetic information that codes for the production of living organisms literally was generated from nowhere, accidentally. We have already talked at length about the frank impossibility that life originated out of the primordial ooze in the manner in which evolutionists believe it did; as such, the "rest of the evolution story" is completely invalidated by the impossibility of their naturalistic origins model.

However, we have not discussed the biological process that evolutionists rely on to generate meaningful information. _The evolution model relies upon genetic mutation as the biological process that generates new and meaningful information_. It relies upon the random and nonspecific processes of genetic mutation as the "creative source" from where new information comes, giving rise to specific new and previously nonexistent traits and kinds of organisms. You may want to review Chapter 14 a little before moving onto Chapter 19 and re-familiarize yourself with the known effects of mutation. Next chapter, we are going to thoroughly discuss "beneficial mutations," to which evolutionists appeal as the necessary "creative force." We will also discuss Noah's Ark, the Flood, the creationist's view of adaptation and variety formation, genetic analysis and "common ancestry," and fossils.

Figure 18.12.1

Chapter 19 Preview
Next chapter, in addition to other concepts, we will discuss the abject failure of the evolutionary model on multiple levels, including genetically. Of course, lack of the genetic mechanism that must exist in order for evolution to be an accurate origins model should be reason to discard it from the scientific lexicon, yet it remains because evolution is all they have. Evolutionists believe that over billions of years, pond scum acquired new, specific, information-containing DNA, providing new and meaningful traits, that caused it to evolve into a fish, a reptile and a giraffe. While this may seem conceptually reasonable to think that "it wouldn't take much" for a fish to grow legs where the fins are and walk out of the water, the fact is that it just cannot occur unless there is some sort of plausible genetic mechanism capable of explaining exactly how an immense quantity of very specific information-containing DNA can be created when all of the scientific data specifically argues against such events. When mutations – the random genetic processes that lead to "changes" in DNA and, more exciting for evolutionists, sometimes even an "increase" in the amount of DNA – were discovered, evolutionists thought they had identified that critically necessary mechanism. We will see if they did next chapter.

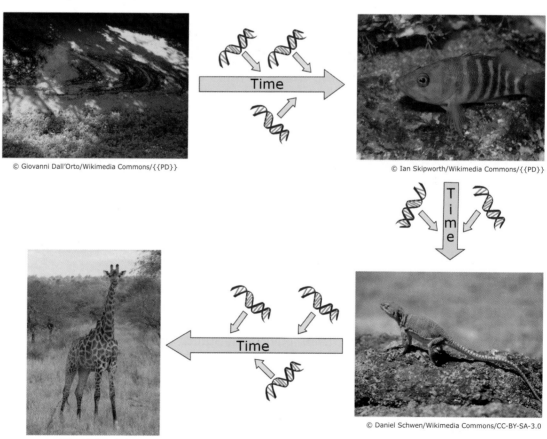

18.13 PEOPLE OF SCIENCE

Henry Morris (1918 – 2006), was born in Texas and was educated as a hydraulic engineer, obtaining his PhD from the University of Minnesota in 1950. He then spent the next two decades building very successful university engineering programs for the University of Louisiana-Lafayette, Southern Illinois University and Virginia Tech. In 1961, he and John C. Whitcomb wrote *The Genesis Flood*, an extremely comprehensive book that provided sound correlation of theologically sound creationism with the scientific data. Most creationists believe that this text was singly responsible for resurrecting creationism and "teaching" foundational Christians that science and the Bible were perfectly married, which was sorely needed after a hundred years of the malevolent confusion evolution had caused (and continues to cause). In 1972, he co-founded the Institute of Creation Research, a scientific organization dedicated to pursuing God-honoring scientific research and public education regarding creation, where he continued to work for four decades. Dr. Morris wrote more than 60 books and has hundreds, if not thousands, of articles posted on www.ICR.org that merge science with the Truth of the Living Word.

18.14 KEY CHAPTER POINTS

- Evolution is a naturalistic origins model, dedicated to explaining the origin and diversity of life specifically without God.

- Charles Darwin did not initially call his theory "evolution" because, in Victorian England, "evolution" was synonymous with a process that had a purpose, which required God and Darwin specifically intended to exclude God from his theory; therefore he used the terms "descent with modification" and "transmutation" to describe the process later called "evolution."

- Neither evolution nor natural selection were new concepts in 1859. What Darwin did when he wrote *The Origin of Species* was to provide the age-old concept of evolution with what appeared to be a scientifically explainable mechanism (at the time), natural selection.

- Charles Darwin was heavily influenced by Charles Lyell's *Principles of Geology* and Thomas Malthus' varied economic writings, which helped him to formulate his materialistic ideals.

- Although he had worked on them for twenty years, Charles Darwin hesitated to publish his evolutionary ideas not for fear of social backlash, but for fear of ostracism from the scientific community.

- Evolution relies upon natural selection as its "creative engine," but natural selection is incapable of "doing what needs to be done" in order to power evolution.

- Scientific observations reveal natural selection is capable of causing traits to vary within populations, but cannot cause entirely new and previously nonexistent traits to arise.

- Abiogenesis is the evolutionary process of nonliving chemicals forming into a living cell via random forces, a process that no scientific observations, experiments or chemical data supports.

- Evolutionists have taken to calling evolution "change" without being capable of accurately describing specifically what type of "change" evolution is.

- Micro- and macroevolution are ill-defined terms. Microevolution is simply the effects of natural selection upon populations' traits and macroevolution is evolution-speak for one kind evolving into a new and previously nonexistent kind, a process with no supporting scientific foundations.

- The big bang is a universe origins theory that provides the billions of years that evolution requires. Interestingly, the big bang literally states that, quite accidentally (and thus far inexplicably), everything in the universe just appeared from nothing.

18.15 DEFINITIONS

Abiogenesis
The naturalistic and completely-lacking-scientific-data-for-support explanation for the origin of life in which a living cell arose from the random formation and assembly of biomolecules.

Adaptation
A trait that allows an organism to survive better in its native environment as compared to an organism without the trait.

Agnosticism
Disbelief in, but not denial of the existence of, God.

Amoeba-to-man
See goo-to-you.

Atheism
The belief system that denies God's existence.

Big bang
The God-less story of how the universe was created out of nothing by an ill-defined and unprovable event in which a singularity produced all matter.

Catastrophism
The scientific belief that not slow and gradual processes but catastrophic events are responsible for shaping the earth and its life forms.

Chemical evolution
See abiogenesis.

Chemical precursors
Molecules such as nitrogen, hydrogen, carbon and oxygen that were present in the primordial ooze and are, without supporting scientific data, hypothesized to have served as the naturalistic building blocks of biomolecules

Deism
The belief that God created the universe and then has left it entirely alone to do its own thing since.

Descent with modification
The concept that all living organisms have descended from common ancestors over billions of years as a "less complex" organisms evolve into "more complex" ones. One of the terms Charles Darwin used to describe what we now know as "evolution."

Evolutionary tree
A schematic diagram showing supposed evolutionary relationships of all organisms to their ancestors.

Goo-to-you evolution
Creationist vernacular describing evolution.

Macroevolution
A term equivalent to "evolution," which is one kind tranforming into a new and previously nonexistent kind.

Materialism
The extreme of rationalism. The philosophy that the physical world is the only true reality, a belief system in direct opposition to biblical truth.

Materialist
A person who believes in materialism.

Microevolution

A term referring to the observable effects of natural selection and random gene distribution on populations. This leads to the modifications of already existing traits, not the formation of entirely new ones, and careful consideration should be given if this term is preferred over just saying "natural selection" (they both have the same number of syllables).

Natural selection pressures

The interaction between a population's traits and the environment such that one or more traits changes in some way over time in response to the environment.

Naturalist

A person who believes that nature alone explains the origin and diversity of life. An evolutionist is a naturalist.

Particle-to-people evolution

See goo-to-you.

Phylogenetic tree

See evolutionary tree.

Population

A group of the same type of interbreeding organisms living in the same geographic area.

Primordial ooze

The theoretical semi-liquid environment of "primitive earth" in which abiogenesis is believed to have occurred.

Rationalism

The philosophy that truth is defined by man's own thought, a philosophy in direct opposition to biblical truth.

Reproductive isolation

A condition thought to favor natural selection and the formation of varieties within kinds in which populations of the same kind of organisms become geographically isolated and begin reproducing only with other members of that geographically isolated population.

Singularity

A theoretical and unproven postulate of the big bang in which all time, space and matter coexist in an infinitely small space and, after exploding for an unknown reason via an unknown mechanism, all matter of the universe was generated.

Transmutation

See descent with modification.

Uniformitarianism

The scientific belief that processes of the past are exactly the same as those observed on earth today, an idea that is consistent with slow, gradual changes to the earh and living organisms.

STUDY QUESTIONS

1. Using creationist terms such as "kind" and "variety," describe what evolution is.

2. True or False? An "ancestor shark" kind diversifying into many different varieties of sharks is a great example of evolution.

3. Why didn't Charles Darwin use the term "evolution" until the 6th edition of *The Origin of Species*, instead choosing "descent with modification" or "transmutation" to describe what we know now as "evolution?"

4. True or False? Concepts that God did not create life and that it "evolved" had been around for more than 2,000 years by the time Charles Darwin published his ideas.

5. Describe how the Age of Enlightenment helped to set the stage for widespread acceptance of evolution.

6. True or False? Thomas Malthus' economic theories and Charles Lyell's geologic theories did not really influence Darwin's development of his ideas.

7. True or False? The main factor that caused Charles Darwin to wait 20 years to publish his ideas was fear of rejection from Victorian society in general since many people still believed that God did create life.

8. True or False? There was widespread and universal scientific acceptance of descent with modification soon after the first edition of *The Origin of Species*.

9. Describe how the scientific community's ignoring of Alfred Russel Wallace's contribution to evolutionary theory boldly underlines how successful Darwin was at garnering scientific political support for himself and, indeed, that getting evolution scientifically accepted was more on the basis of ideology and political maneuvers than on its scientific merit.

10. True or False? Natural selection was a new concept that Charles Darwin independently developed.

11. Provide a contrast of what natural selection has scientifically been observed to do and what evolutionists think it can do. Be sure to include concepts of kinds and varieties in your answer.

12. True or False? Creationists and evolutionists believe that natural selection properly explains how one variety of ancestor finch was able to diversify into the present-day 15 varieties on the islands today.

13. True or False? Scientific studies show that way more time than a few thousand years is necessary for varieties to form within kinds, which is one of the strongest arguments against the creation model.

14. Conceptually, for a less complex kind to transform into a more complex one, describe what needs to occur genetically for that to accurately describe origins.

15. Is there any scientific data that is consistent with such a process as described in the previous question?

16. True or False? When combining information theory with what absolutely needs to happen genetically for evolution to be true, we see that the two are incompatible.

17. Describe why evolutionists like to say that natural selection is a "creative process." Why is this a ridiculous statement?

18. True or False? Concepts like natural selection and reproductive isolation should make creationists uncomfortable because they are "not biblical."

19. Evolutionists like to say that Peter and Mary Grant's Galapagos finch study is evolution in action; however, creationists strongly argue against that concept. Why?

20. True or False? Natural selection has been observed to modify already existing traits, but not lead to the formation of entirely new and previously nonexistent ones.

21. What are at least three identified scientific observations that argue against abiogenesis?

22. What are at least three identified scientific observations that argue for abiogenesis?

23. True or False? Initially, the Miller-Urey experiment was hailed as proof that biomolecules could be synthesized from the supposed chemical precursors of life.

24. True or False? Abiogenesis is nothing more than an updated word for spontaneous generation, which Louis Pasteur disproved.

25. Why does the evolution model so desperately cling to the idea of abiogenesis?

26. True or False? Since both evolution and natural selection result in change, it is very reasonable for evolutionists to define "evolution" simply as "change."

27. Describe why the "change of evolution" and the "changes scientifically observed to occur as a result of natural selection" are not equivalent.

28. A hypothetical snake variety, *Sillius evolutionicus*, a pit viper, has been continuously observed over the past 500 years in its native habitat through a scientific observational study. During this time, it has been *scientifically documented* that *S. evolutionicus* has developed notably blacker coloration patterns, its tongue has grown both longer and wider by 10%, it lays an average of two fewer eggs per litter and its venom has been found to be 15% more concentrated. Evolutionists proclaim, "Look at this evolution in action!" What say you in response, and why?

29. True or False? Microevolution is a term that is a good, descriptive one and can be used confidently and ideologically by creationists.

30. Why is it scientifically unreasonable for evolutionists to believe that microevolution leads to macroevolution?

31. What is the most reasonable explanation as to why not all evolutionists believe that microevolution leads to macroevolution?

32. True or False? Although the big bang theory is not part of the evolution model, it does provide a naturalistic explanation for the origin of the universe and also the time frames required by the evolution model.

33. True or False? Because it is a scientifically sound and accepted universe origins theory, all non-creation scientists believe the big bang to be true.

34. This is a "think-way-outside-the-box" kind of a question. If evolution were true and you were present 5 billion years ago when the earth formed and you never died, describe what you would have seen as it relates to the origin of life, progressive formation of new and previously nonexistent organisms and their subsequent diversification.

From Fossils to neo-Darwinism

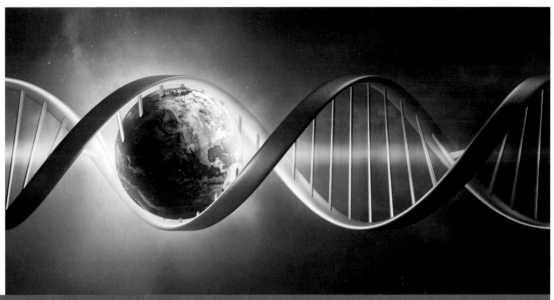

19

19.0 Chapter Preview

In this chapter we will:

- Explore neo-Darwinism, a.k.a. the modern evolutionary synthesis, and the problems it has explaining the origination of new, never-before-in-existence, trait-producing genetic information.

- Learn that beneficial mutations do exist, but they are not capable of "doing" what the evolution model needs them to "do."

- Differentiate the ways in which antibiotic resistance in bacteria develops to learn that they are not mechanisms that generate new and meaningful new DNA.

- Further explore nephesh chayyah and how it relates to creation, Noah's Flood and biological diversity.

- Through reviewing various scientific data in light of the Flood, learn that there is scientific support for such a catastrophic worldwide flood event and that the creation model states it was responsible for the majority of existent fossils.

- Apply concepts of comparative genomics to the creation and evolution models to learn that there is excellent scientific data that supports the creation model.

- Perform a review of the fossil record and find that the data provides support for the creation model, while there are several aspects of the fossil record that specifically argue against the evolution model.

- Explore radiometric dating in some depth to learn that there is convincing, relevant data rendering it a dubious scientific endeavor that at least requires further research.

19.1 INTRODUCTION

We will draw on the information learned in the past two chapters and, looking through creation glasses and evolution glasses, see how the respective models fare when measured against the observed scientific data. Since evolution receives extensive media coverage, one hardly ever hears how scientific discoveries relate to the creation model and when data arises that is directly contradictory to evolution (and such data exists), it is rarely discussed publicly. Often, when something is presented about some aspect of creation as related to science, it is negatively shown. Because the "common origins message" that is sent is so heavily inundated with the anti-God evolutionary theme, some creationists have come to the conclusion that creation is faith, rather than science. And, of course, it is:

> ***By faith we understand that the universe was created by the word of God, so that what is seen was not made out of things that are visible.*** *Hebrews 11:3*

But, that is where the creation and evolution models share some common ground. They are both faith based endeavors. With creation, that faith is anchored to God's Word being true, which is all we need. If we keep that in mind when assessing the scientific evidence, then there is scientific concordance. The problem is, though, that the integration of the evolution model into biology has changed the narrative such that, even though neither creation nor evolution are empiric science, the message has been received loud and clear that "evolution is science" and "creation is faith." This has been true even to the point that some creationists have stopped believing in the authority of the Bible and think that the creation model can't possibly be consistent with scientific evidence because "creation is faith but evolution is science," simply because of evolutionary teaching, rather than an objective assessment of the scientific data.

As we explored in the previous two chapters, the evolution and creation models are both faith-based endeavors, but that doesn't mean that we can't hold the principles of each up to the scientific data and learn which model measures up and which does not. As we have seen, the scientific evidence is certainly very compatible with the creation model and often incompatible with evolution.

Creationists believe that the incomprehensible power of God was responsible for creating everything. Materialists continue to struggle with explaining how everything came from nothing since they have no mechanism, yet, just like creationists, they have faith their model is true. Because of this dichotomy, however, many evolutionists clearly understand their belief in evolution is a faith-based one, as Hubert Yockey, a non-creationist information theorist, pointed out in 1977 in the *Journal of Theoretical Biology*:

> ***"Research on the origin of life seems to be unique in that the conclusion has already been authoritatively accepted ... . What remains to be done is to find the scenarios which describe the detailed mechanisms and processes by which this happened. One must conclude that, contrary to the established and current wisdom, a scenario describing the genesis of life on earth by chance and natural causes which can be accepted on the basis of fact and not faith has not yet been written."***

Dr. Yockey is not a creationist; however, he is intellectually honest when he identifies that not only has the conclusion that "evolution is true" already been accepted, it has been accepted without scientific data to support it. The bottom line is that belief in any origins theory is a faith-based belief system. With creationism, the faith is based in the inerrant Word of God; in Darwinism, the faith is based in materialism and man.

In this chapter, we are going to explore many "evidences" that are commonly presented as "facts supporting evolution" and put them under a critical microscope to see that observed scientific data supports creation as described in God's Word. And, sometimes, we will see that the data not only isn't consistent with evolution, it actively argues against evolution.

19.2 BRIEF REVIEW

As a brief review:

- Natural selection

  - is an observable scientific phenomena that creationists and evolutionists agree occurs.

  - through God-given (built-in) genetic information, coding for the ability to diversify through the process of adaptation as driven by natural selection, kinds are able to form into many different varieties (i.e. an "ancestor finch kind" population diversified into 15 types of finch kind).

  - is <u>incapable</u> of causing information-adding changes to an ancestor organism so that it forms new, previously nonexistent traits, leading to the formation of a previously nonexistent kind of organism (i.e. natural selection does not cause the type of change that causes a fish to transform into an amphibian).

- In order for a new and previously nonexistent, more complex kind of organism to arise through evolution, there must be some process that results in the generation of new genetic information within a less complex ancestor organism, giving rise to new and previously nonexistent traits, which lead to the formation of a new, more complex and previously nonexistent kind of organism.

- For "microbes to man" evolution to have occurred over billions of years, *an enormous amount of specifically meaningful information would have had to have been added* to the bacterial genome to result in the eventual formation of a human being.

- The generation of new information through the random process of naturalism violates several of Werner Gitt's Laws of Information (which, though perhaps not all geneticists or information theorists "like" them, have never been disproven):

  - It is impossible that information can exist without a mental source (DNA contains 42 trillion times more information per unit of volume than the next closest storage device and is the most complex type of information ever known).

  - It is impossible to have information without a sender (in the evolutionary model, there is no sender).

  - It is scientifically proven that it is impossible that information can originate via statistical (naturalistic) processes (in the evolutionary model, this is how it arises).

19.3 NEO-DARWINISM, OR THE MODERN EVOLUTIONARY SYNTHESIS

We have learned that natural selection "can't do what evolutionists need it to do," which means that evolution lacks the mechanism that it absolutely must have. As such, it is hard to conclude that evolution is an accurate origins model. Some may be wondering, "Well, if a lot of really smart scientists believe in evolution (and they do), from where do they think this enormous amount of information came that enabled a bacterium to transform into a man?" It is possible that 2 Peter 3:5 from last chapter may give some insight – perhaps the evolutionary model is formed in a way that "deliberately overlooks" the Truth. Another translation of that passage uses the words "willingly ignorant." The evolution model is the attempt to explain origins without God. It necessarily has to explain origins without God and so the attempt is made in the following way.

Evolutionists have spent a great amount of time and brain power trying to bring genetics into the evolution model. Without a plausible genetic mechanism for how information is created, for how meaningful genes are generated naturally and give rise to new and meaningful new traits, evolution is dead in the water. There *must* be a way for nature, and nature alone, to generate new and meaningful information – encoded in DNA, of course – such that new and previously nonexistent traits arise, giving rise to new and previously nonexistent kinds of organisms. If the evolution model did not include a way to explain the required creation of new-trait-generating DNA, then evolution would not be an acceptable origins and diversity explanation.

The materialist's answer for how a random, unintelligent process that can create vast amounts of specifically meaningful information is called **neo-Darwinism**, or the **modern evolutionary synthesis**. It is the naturalists' attempt to provide a genetic mechanism to drive evolution. Once evolutionists realized the very real implications of Mendelian genetics in the early 20th century, they clearly needed to provide an answer for "how evolution works" from the genetic standpoint. No longer was it reasonable for them to draw pictures of fish ancestor organisms progressively growing legs and walking out of the water. Neo-Darwinism melds genetics with natural selection to provide the proposed evolutionary mechanism.

But, from where, really, does this immense amount of new genetic information originate that allowed parasites to evolve into people? _Mutation_. Mutation is the only known "thing" – the only biological process – known to cause genetic change. Mutations have not ever been observed to create new and meaningful trait-giving information, though. But, after mutations were described and then shortly after in the mid 1930's to the mid 1940's when neo-Darwinism was being developed, scientists had very little knowledge of precisely the kind of change that mutation invoked in an organism's genes. They just knew that mutation "changed" the DNA. And that was _exactly_ what they needed... or so they thought.

Figure 19.3.1

Mutation – Evolution Model's Holy Grail?

When early to mid 20th century geneticists identified genetic mutation as a DNA-altering process that occurs all of the time, they thought they had the Holy Grail of a naturalistic explanation as to where new genetic information arises. In the evolution model, if there is no plausible naturalistic mechanism that can explain how new and meaningful information arises, then evolution simply cannot be an accurate origins model. Substitution, inversion, translocation (right), deletion and duplication mutations were quickly identified to alter the "normal" DNA sequences, which led to an observable change in the appearance and/or behavior of the organism. _Even though the vast majority of observable mutations either kill the organism or render it sterile_, the evolution model was formed relying on mutation, since it was the only process identified capable of "changing" DNA. The rest was just details and, as we will see, they are very important details. Does genetic mutation do what the evolution model needs it to do, cause new, specifically meaningful and previously nonexistent information to arise, leading to new and previously nonexistent traits and organisms? We shall find out.

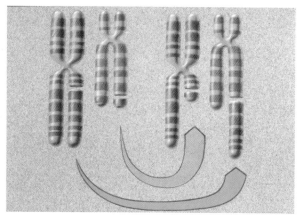

At first, it seemed like the evolution model was going to have all of the answers. "Genes control traits and mutation changes genes and we need a process that causes change to the DNA and mutation is it! The rest is elementary! As mutations change the DNA content and are passed from generation to generation, obviously new traits must arise, causing new organisms to form and over a couple hundred million years, bam! We got people! Woo hoo!" It seemed like the evolution model was complete now that there was the exact mechanism needed for organisms to generate new and meaningful information-encoding DNA, giving them new traits and leading to the formation of entirely new and never-before-existent organisms.

But, genetics isn't really that simple. As we learned in our genetics section, and to which no evolutionist can argue, _the overwhelming majority_ of mutations do not generate new and specifically meaningful information. They do not "increase information" and "cause new and previously nonexistent traits to arise." Instead, virtually all mutations either lead to a loss of life or information – meaning a decrease in function, form, life and ability to reproduce – or they are "neutral" – they don't appear to "do anything."

This is the real problem with the evolution origins model – it doesn't have a credible information-generating mechanism, which is as expected. It is impossible for information to arise without an intelligent sender. The neo-Darwinism/modern evolutionary synthesis appeals to mutation as the necessary information-creating event but, as has been our theme, the scientific data does not support this concept.

> *"The neo-Darwinist is now reaching the point of dignity in the history of science that the Ptolemaic system in astronomy, the epicycle system, reached long ago. We know that it does not work. And that is interesting. Because from the actual structure of a chromosome we can demonstrate that the human species did not come from a progressive humanization of a pre-human."* Jerome Lejune, pediatrician and Chair of Fundamental Genetics, University of Paris, France

19.4 "BENEFICIAL MUTATION" – EVIDENCE FOR EVOLUTION OR AN EXPECTED SCIENTIFIC FACT COMPATIBLE WITH THE CREATION MODEL?

Since, in the neo-Darwinian approach, mutation is what funds the formation of previously nonexistent traits and the majority of mutations kill or sterilize the organism with them, a concept of the "**beneficial mutation**" arose and has been embedded into the evolution model. A beneficial mutation is, by definition, one that benefits the organism in some way such that the mutation provides a "selective advantage" to the organism. This means that as a result of a gene mutation, the organism with it is somehow better able to live in its environment than it would be if it didn't have the mutation. Before we get too far along, let me state that _beneficial mutations do exist_ and are scientifically observable; however, a _beneficial mutation cannot be the "neo-Darwinian answer"_ to natural-selection-driving-evolution because they don't do what they need to do in order to cause particle-to-people evolution; we will see why.

A brief side track now. As we move into this deeper discussion of evolution in the context of mutation, it is very important to update our definition of "evolution." With respect to genetics, **evolution** is a biological process that occurs to cause a "less complex" ancestor organism to acquire new and meaningful DNA, through mutation, which leads to the formation of new genes, giving it new and previously nonexistent traits such that, over time, as it accumulates more novel genes and traits through mutation, it transforms into a "more complex" and previously nonexistent organism.

So, it is very important to reinforce some things about the nature of the mutations that drive the evolution model:

- They cannot kill or sterilize the organism (or else the mutations will never be passed along to subsequent generations).

- They cannot simply alter or rearrange already-existing information. _They must generate new, previously nonexistent and meaningful information that codes for the production of previously nonexistent traits_.

- If a mutation doesn't meet one of the two conditions above, then it cannot provide the necessary "increase in genetic information" that evolution requires.

- If no such "information adding" mutation process exists, the modern evolutionary synthesis piece of the evolution model is false.

- If the modern evolutionary synthesis is false, then evolution itself is false because evolution cannot occur without a genetic mechanism.

Figure 19.4.1

Beneficial Mutations are NOT Information-Adding Ones

This blind Mexican cavefish, Ástayanaz *mexicanus*, provides a great example of exactly what beneficial mutations are observed to be in nature. There are many kinds of blind cavefish in the world and they all share the same trait – they have no eyes as a result of a mutation in the part of their DNA that causes the eyes to form. This is the result of a loss of the information that codes for eye formation. But, how can it be "beneficial" to be blind? Cavefish live in absolute darkness and while swimming around, they bump into the cave walls. Hundreds to thousands of years ago, when the seeing cavefish ancestors swam into and stayed/got trapped in the caves, as they swam around and hit the walls of the cave, sometimes their eyes were scraped, became infected and they died. In every fish population, there are organisms that develop without eyes, which is normally not beneficial, but in a cave, that is very beneficial – no eyes, no infection, no death. The mutation that causes the eyes to "be lost" therefore is beneficial, a trait for which natural selection selects, even though genetically it resulted in a loss of information. Never-the-less, this information-losing mutation, allowed the organism to survive better. But, this is not evolution because it occurred as a result of loss of information, not a gain. And, this is still a fish. Evolution requires a net gain in information in order to happen. The evolution model relies heavily upon such beneficial mutations, even though they do not result in the required increase of trait-causing information required for evolution to occur.

And here is where the concept of a beneficial mutation, like a lot of concepts in evolution, seems to be a very powerful plus to the model. Consider the term "beneficial mutation." It seems very reasonable to attribute creative genetic powers to a "beneficial mutation." The problem is, though, that beneficial mutations don't do that, genetics proves that, but the evolution perspective on them is that, as a result of the beneficial mutations, new and meaningful information is added to the less complex organism's genome. That leads to fish growing lungs, thin skin permeable to oxygen, a new circulatory system, a new heart structure and legs and they walk out of the water.

More than 50 years of research, though, has failed to identify that a mutation event can result in the formation of new and previously nonexistent DNA, conferring new and previously nonexistent traits to arise. In short, observed science does not support the existence of the necessary genetic mechanism that supports neo-Darwinism. According to A. Lima-de Faria, evolutionary geneticist who believes the modern evolutionary synthesis is fatally flawed:

> **"Neo-Darwinism is a hindrance to the discovery of the mechanism of evolution."**

So, if beneficial mutations do exist but they don't add new and meaningful information, what do they do? Well, this is where we really need to stay on point or else it can get a bit confusing. _The fact that a mutation is beneficial does not stem from whether or not it adds new and meaningful information to an ancestor organism to give it a new and previously nonexistent trait; rather, it has to do with the effect that the mutation has on the organism with the mutation._ Remember that cavefish example. That fish benefitted from the mutation because it resulted in the fish not scraping its eyes on the cave walls, getting them infected and dying. So, a beneficial mutation is not defined by whether it adds new information to the organism's genome but by whether the effect of the mutation is beneficial to the organism's survival. Even though a beneficial mutation deletes information – meaning that it results in reduced or absent function of a normal process for the organism that has the mutation – it can still be a "beneficial" one if it actually helps the organism survive better than those without the mutation.

But here again is where the science causes problems for evolution. Remember from Chapter 14 that _the overwhelming majority of mutations result either in killing the organism or in the removal/alteration of information that codes for normal form or function of the organism such that it no longer looks or functions normally_. The scientific studies reveal that mutations can delete segments of genes or entire genes and that mutations can duplicate existing genetic information or cause it to shift location within a chromosome or even between other chromosomes. But, *mutations have never been observed to cause the formation of new and previously nonexistent genes giving rise to new and previously nonexistent traits and organisms*. Therefore, we cannot be confused by the term "beneficial mutation" and think that means "information adding." It doesn't and no such "information adding" mutation has ever been observed. The end effect of all identified beneficial mutations is the removal of genetic information.

There are many described and varying forms of beneficial mutations – they differ from

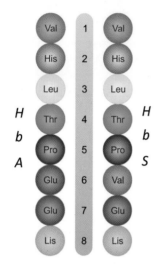

© Jsan92/Wikimedia Commons/SS-BY-SA-3.0

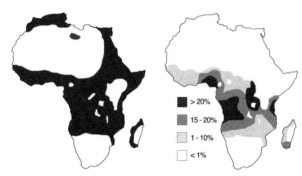

> 20%

15 - 20%

1 - 10%

< 1%

© Anthony Alison/Wikimedia Commons/CC0 1.0-UPD

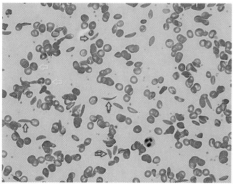

© Dr. Graham Beards/Wikimedia Commons/CC-BY-SA-3.0

Figure 19.4.2

The "Beneficial Mutation" of Sickle Cell Anemia

Recall we discussed sickle cell disease – an excellent example of a beneficial mutation – in Chapter 15. Sickle cell anemia also demonstrates why beneficial mutations have absolutely nothing to do with evolution. Recall that sickle cell mutation is a single substitution mutation that codes for the production of a beta-hemoglobin molecule that has valine, instead of glutamic acid, in the sixth position. Even though only one of the more than 500 amino acids in the hemoglobin complex are abnormal, the result is an abnormally shaped hemoglobin molecule that does not carry oxygen properly and causes red blood cells to be shaped like a sickle (bottom, yellow arrows are normal red blood cells and the blue arrows show sickled red cells in this peripheral smear). People that have sickle cell trait (one copy of the mutated gene and one normal gene, or heterozygous) have fewer sickled red blood cells than people with two copies of the sickle gene (homozygous for the condition). The reason that this mutation is considered beneficial is because it is "protective" against malaria, which is caused by a parasite that infects red blood cells. In areas where malaria occurs (left side of the Africa graphic), sickle cell-shaped red blood cells are not as easily infected by the malaria parasite as those that are normally shaped. The right side of the Africa graphic shows the distribution of the sickle cell gene (trait) in Africa, which overlaps prominently with the distribution of malaria. Those people homozygous or heterozygous for the sickle cell gene are better able to survive in areas where malaria is and so they are not killed by malaria as often as those without the gene, allowing them to pass the "beneficial" trait to their offspring. Note, though, that this is not "evolution" for three reasons. First, all organisms with the sickle trait are human beings. No new kind of organism is generated as result of this mutation. Second, this "beneficial" mutation causes life-long problems for the person with the sickle cell gene, including flares of very severe total body pain, organ damage and a significantly reduced life expectancy even in areas where there is no malaria. The evolution model is defined by "progress" toward more complex and better organisms, not ones that suffer as a result of the evolution process. Third, this mutation is not an information-adding one, which evolution requires in order to occur. This point mutation simply results in a change in the already present hemoglobin-coding information and results in a massively dysfunctional hemoglobin molecule that cannot perform its normal function. In other words, the mutation removes information that codes for a normally functioning hemoglobin molecule. It is interesting to note that in areas where malaria does not occur – like the United States – the sickle cell gene is slowly being eliminated from the population because it is otherwise detrimental.

one organism kind to another – *but their shared property is that they result in the loss of information*. The result of all known beneficial mutations is an organism that doesn't function "like it is supposed to" but the mutation none-the-less protects it in some way. Because of this, beneficial mutations cannot lead to the kind of step-wise progressive increase in genetic information necessary for evolution to occur. They have never, ever been observed to provide novel genetic information that gives rise to a previously nonexistent trait; they simply modify already-existing traits by deleting information that codes for a normal function.

Figure 19.4.3

Beneficial Mutations

This is not an exhaustive list of known "beneficial mutations," but these conditions, like all known beneficial mutation conditions, involve a loss of genetic information. That means that the organism with such a mutation has lost previously normal form and/or function and yet, as the "Benefit" column identifies, the mutation is protective to the organism with it. As we can see from this table, while the mutation does help the organism survive better in its environment, such a loss in associated form/function is not consistent with the type of information-adding genetic increases that need to occur in order to cause an ancestor organism to gain new genetic material and new traits so that it "evolves into" a previously nonexistent kind of organism.

Mutation Condition	Effect	Benefit
Sickle cell mutation, humans	Protect against malarial infection or severe infection	Occurs in peoples of African and Mediterranean descent, due to a single substitution mutation at the 6th position of the beta chain of hemoglobin (thymine is replaced by adenine in the DNA gene segment). The result is malformed hemoglobin and red blood cells that are not as effective at carrying oxygen but ARE more resistant to malarial infection.
Mutation causing non-formation of wings in some flightless beetles	Protect against being blown off of windy islands	Wingless beetles are commonly found on near-mainland islands (e.g. Madeira, Azores) and appear to be exactly the same as their mainland counterparts, except the island types have no wings. Creationists and evolutionists agree that winged beetles likely blew to the islands or were carried on debris rafts from the mainland and then, over time, wings were selected out of the population. All winged beetle populations normally produce organisms that have mutations that cause their wings not to form. In areas where wings are beneficial (like the mainland), wingless beetles are quickly caught and eaten and the wingless trait is not passed on. However, the islands are very windy and, after initially arriving on the island, beetles without the mutation develop normally with wings and were presumably blown off the island while flying, whereby they fall into the ocean and die. Beetles with the wingless mutation have a selective advantage because they cannot fly and would not be blown off of the island; therefore, over time, more wingless beetles survive to reproduce as the winged ones are blown off the island. Eventually, only wingless forms remain.
CCR5-delta 32 mutation, humans	Protective against HIV infection	This is a mutation that results in production of malformed and nonfunctional CCR5, a protein found on the surface of a variety of cells, including white blood cells. HIV (the AIDS virus) reproduces by attaching onto white blood cells via the CCR5 protein on the surface of the cell. A person with two copies of the CCR5-delta 32 mutated gene (homozygous for the condition) makes completely nonfunctional CCR5. As a result, HIV cannot attach to it and enter the white cells and infect the host.
Northern cavefish (*Ambylopsis spelaea*,) mutation resulting in loss of eyes	Protect against infection	These fish live in caves that are absolutely dark. In a completely dark environment, having eyes does not help survival and, in fact, may be a detriment. It is likely that a fish would bang into the walls, at times scratching the surface of the eyes, leading to infection and death. This mutation causing the eyes to not form (such mutations are observed in fish that live in light environments, too) would protect against this from happening, which would leave more and more fish without eyes available to reproduce and pass on their mutated eye genes to their offspring, while the fish with eyes were selected out of the population.

Seeing as how the science doesn't support this, it is, therefore, a leap of faith for the evolution model to be based upon beneficial mutations as the information-adding events that drive evolution. Without meaningful information-adding beneficial mutations to provide new and previously nonexistent traits so that new and previously nonexistent organisms arise, evolution lacks a necessary mechanism. Evolution simply cannot occur because mutations do not do what evolution requires they do.

So here we are, back at the faith clearing in the road of evolution and creation. Many evolutionary scientists bristle when they hear a creationist state evolution is as much a faith-based endeavor as Christianity and creation is, but there are <u>many</u> secular evolutionists who call it what it is:

"Evolution is promoted by its practitioners as more than mere science. Evolution is promulgated as an ideology, a secular religion—a full-fledged alternative to Christianity, with meaning and morality. I am an ardent evolutionist and an ex-Christian, but I must admit in this one complaint. . . the literalists (i.e., creationists) are absolutely right. Evolution is a religion. This was true of evolution in the beginning, and it is true of evolution still today." (Parenthesis in original). Michael Ruse, Professor of History and Philosophy at Florida State University

"After having chided the theologian on his reliance on myth and miracle, science found itself in the unenviable position of having to create a mythology of its own: namely, the assumption that what after long effort, could not be proved to take place today had, in truth, taken place in the primeval past". Dr. Loren Eiseley, evolutionary anthropologist, from his book *The Immense Journey,* on the evolutionist philosophy

To summarize:

- The evolution model <u>requires</u> gain of indescribable amounts of meaningful genetic material to provide new information, coding for new traits that previously did not exist, so that new kinds of organisms sequentially develop over time.

- Evolution <u>requires</u> this information gain to occur through mutation.

- Mutations most certainly do occur, though the overwhelming majority are either neutral or harmful to the organism (they result in no observable effect or reduce normal function, respectively, often to the point of death).

- No mutation has ever been scientifically shown to cause the addition of meaningful information or cause a new and previously nonexistent trait to arise. Neo-Darwinism lacks a scientifically proven genetic mechanism.

- In rare circumstances, mutations, though they delete information, do none-the-less benefit the organism and so are "beneficial mutations." More than 10,000 abnormal human conditions are caused by mutation and <u>very few</u> result in "benefit."

- "Beneficial mutation" does NOT equate to "information adding mutation" because all scientifically observed beneficial mutations delete, duplicate or exchange already-existing genetic information. Mutations never create new, meaningful, trait-giving information.

- No mutations ("beneficial" or not) can explain the necessary increase in new genetic information evolution requires.

- Evolutionary theory not only would predict, it requires, meaningful information-adding mutations exist. Their absence specifically argues against evolution as an origins and diversity model. There is nothing about beneficial mutations that are contrary to the creation model.

- Hence, evolution is a faith-based model because it lacks a genetic mechanism.

I am the LORD your God; walk in my statutes, and be careful to obey my rules. Ezekiel 20:19

In the creation model, mutations are the result of the Fall. There is nothing about the existence of beneficial mutations that is not consistent with the creation model.

19.5 MULTI-DRUG RESISTANT BACTERIA – EVIDENCE FOR EVOLUTION OR AN EXPECTED SCIENTIFIC FACT COMPATIBLE WITH THE CREATION MODEL?

Much has been made over the years of what the media like to call "superbugs," medically known as **multi-drug resistant bacteria** (MDRB). These are bacteria that are resistant to multiple antibiotics, which can make them very difficult to treat. When patients develop a MDRB infection, it leads to significantly longer and more expensive hospital stays and can even lead to overwhelming infection and death. There are three common mechanisms responsible for making bacteria resistant – built-in resistance, mutation and transfer of DNA-encoded resistance from one bacterium to another. When bacteria develop resistance, it is commonly described as "evolution in action;" however, nothing about the development of antibiotic resistance meets the "generation of new and previously nonexistent genetic information" criteria that is required for evolution to occur.

All organisms – even prokaryotic ones – have some degree or another of disease-fighting capabilities built right into their systems. You know the friend or family member that never seems to get sick and the one that always seems sick? That is due to their genetically-determined (i.e. built-in) disease-fighting ability. The one that never seems sick was blessed to have more genetically-determined disease fighting abilities than the person that is always sick.

Figure 19.5.1

Antibiotic Resistance Predates Antibiotics!

Penicillium notatum (now known as *Penicillium chrysogenum*), in a Petri dish (left), is the precise type of mold that, in 1928, Sir Alexander Fleming discovered produced a substance that killed bacteria. The story goes that one night Sir Alexander's assistant left the window open near an uncovered Petri dish that contained the bacterium *Staphylococcus*. Sir Alexander had perhaps plated them as shown in the middle picture, in which a small metal loop of bacteria is swiped across a nutritive medium, called agar, and allowed to grow. This results in colonies of the bacteria growing along the swipe path, as you can see especially in the right and bottom of the agar plate in the middle photo. As Sir Alexander picked up the bacterial plate the next morning, he noticed that scattered mold colonies had started to grow on the agar (mold spores are air-borne and no doubt some landed on the agar and started to grow). Further, where the mold had grown, there were no bacterial colonies growing. He correctly surmised that the *Penicillium* was producing a substance that killed the bacteria, which we now know is the antibiotic penicillin. What Sir Alexander saw would have looked very similar to the right half of the bottom right photo, which is a photo of antibiotic sensitivity testing. Discs containing the antibiotic colistin have been placed within a "lawn" of two different bacteria. On the left, you can see that the hazy lawn of bacteria grows right up to the edge of the antibiotic disc because the bacteria is not affected by colistin (it is resistant). Around the disc on the right, however, there is a clear zone (called a "zone of clearing") around the antibiotic disc because this bacteria is sensitive to it, and so is killed by the colistin. Sir Alexander would have seen such a zone of clearing around the mold growing in his Petri dishes because it secreted penicillin, which killed the bacteria in the Petri dish. When God created molds that produce natural antibiotics, like *Penicillin*, he provided them a built-in defense mechanism to fight off bacteria. Why? Mold and bacteria often compete for the same food sources and having an antibiotic to kill the bacteria gives the mold a slight advantage if it is trying to compete for the same food as some bacteria. However, not all bacteria are susceptible to the penicillins. Further, some bacteria have a built-in mechanism to inactivate some antibiotics to help them compete against molds! All scientific evidence indicates that some molds have <u>always</u> been able to produce antibiotics, just as some bacteria have always been able to resist antibiotics. That means that the antibiotic production did not arise slowly over time – it has always been there – as predicted by the creation model.

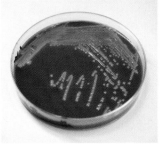

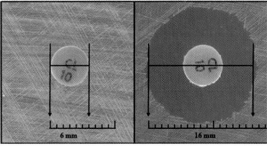

Bacteria are no different in that they have a built in ability to fight off diseases, too. For example, viruses not only infect humans, animals and plants, they also infect bacteria. It turns out bacteria have defenses against viral infection built into their DNA. Bacteria also spend time living around molds, and compete for many of the same food sources as molds do. Bacteria have built-in defense mechanisms to fight off molds, too. If the very first kind of organisms – prokaryotic cells – have an immune system to fight against infection, then it is not something that could have evolved in a step-by-step fashion as evolution predicts – it was there from the very beginning because if the resistance didn't exist right away, then all of the bacterial organisms would have died as soon as they were exposed to a virus or an antibiotic from a mold. Such an observation is consistent with the creation model since it predicts kinds – like the bacteria and mold kinds – were created intact and fully functional.

Figure 19.5.2

Vancomycin Resistance

Although vancomycin ("vanco") remains a powerful antibiotic, there are an increasing number of bacteria that are developing resistance to it. Like all other forms of antibiotic resistance, it does <u>not</u> develop from the formation of new and previously nonexistent DNA. In the case of vancomycin resistance, the resistance is caused by mutation leading to loss of information and loss of normal function. In the vancomycin sensitive bacteria (the normal bacteria), there is an enzyme that "caps off" the cell wall proteins with alanine as the final step of bacterial cell wall synthesis, seen in (1) in the vancomycin sensitive series. In the mutated bacteria, the vancomycin resistant ones, the gene that codes for that "capping enzyme" is mutated and makes a defective enzyme that caps the cell wall proteins with D-lactate, instead of the alanine (bottom 1). In (2), vanco binds tightly to the normal cell wall proteins, but cannot bind properly to the cell wall with the mutated protein made from the mutated enzyme. In (3), the cell wall cross-linking enzyme comes in to cross link the protein components and form the normal cell wall, but it cannot perform its normal function in the vanco-sensitive bacteria because the vanco is blocking the enzyme from engaging the proteins. However, in the vanco resistant organisms, since the vanco has not bound tightly to the abnormal cell wall proteins, the cross-linking enzyme is able to dislodge the vanco from the proteins and form the cross link between the cell wall proteins. It is an abnormal and weaker-than-normal cross link bond, but it does prevent the vanco from killing the bacteria. In (4), the vanco sensitive, un-cross linked cell wall is entirely defective, which causes the bacterial cell to break apart. Although not normal in strength and structure because of the abnormal cell wall proteins, the vanco resistant bacterial cell is still intact and able to continue to grow and cause infection. Note that like all bacteria that are resistant as a result of the effects of mutation, this resistant bacteria is only better at growing than the antibiotic sensitive bacteria in an environment in which the antibiotic is present. As soon as the antibiotic is gone, the bacteria that do not have the mutation – the normal antibiotic-sensitive ones – grow much better than the ones with the mutation – the abnormal-due-to-mutation antibiotic resistant ones. Notice that, like the other beneficial mutations we have described, one of the ways in which antibiotic resistance is conferred to bacteria is through a loss of information, not a gain. Gain of meaningful, new genetic information leading to new and previously nonexistent traits is required for evolution to occur. This is not that and so it is scientifically wrong to refer to antibiotic resistance as "evolution."

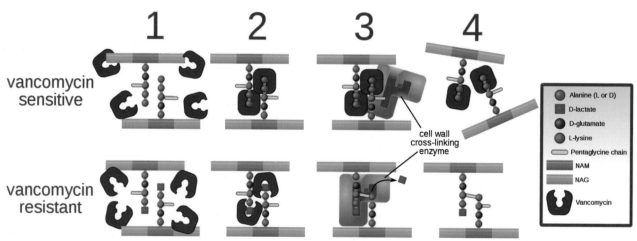

Antibiotics kill bacteria by disrupting some vital function of the bacteria; fortunately, since bacteria are prokaryotes and we are eukaryotes, our physiological processes are different enough that an antibiotic can safely alter an essential function of bacteria so as to kill them, generally without harming us. The same is true of the molds – the antibiotics they produce don't harm themselves but do kill the bacteria.

Figure 19.5.3

The Franklin Expedition and Antibiotic Resistance

This is a note authored by one of the members of Captain Sir John Franklin's lost expedition. In 1845, these men set out from England to navigate the last uncharted section of the Northwest Passage through the Arctic. Unfortunately, although an unknown number were able to survive until 1848, none ever made it back to England. This note documents some of the events of 1847 and 1848. Since these men died and were buried about a hundred years before Sir Alexander Fleming discovered antibiotics, you are probably wondering what could this possibly have to do with antibiotic resistance? Well, in the late 1980's, several of the men from this expedition were exhumed and had autopsies performed, which included taking bacterial cultures from their large intestines. The bodies were very well preserved because they had been frozen solid for the past almost-150 years. The cultures from their colons actually yielded results – bacteria grew, and they were not contaminants. Three of the six different types of bacteria that had been frozen 80 years before penicillin was discovered were resistant to the *synthetic* (man-made) antibiotics clindamycin and cefoxitin. Since the bacterial information for the resistance to these antibiotics, each of which was first made more than 100 years after the men died, was already present and encoded in the bacteria's DNA, that means that antibiotic resistance is a built-in feature. It is not something that has "evolved over time" as a result of increasing exposure to the man-made antibiotics (a prediction of the evolution model) because, prior to the existence of these antibiotics, there would have been no reason for the resistance to exist since synthetic antibiotics would not exist for over a century. An organism being resistant to an antibiotic more than 100 years prior to the antibiotic even existing is very difficult (actually, impossible) to explain from an evolutionary standpoint. However, it does fit the creation prediction that all information is "built in" by God. God provided built-in abilities for organisms to be "more fit" to survive in their environments, which included providing ways for bacterial organisms to fight off antibiotics via their God-designed genetic information.

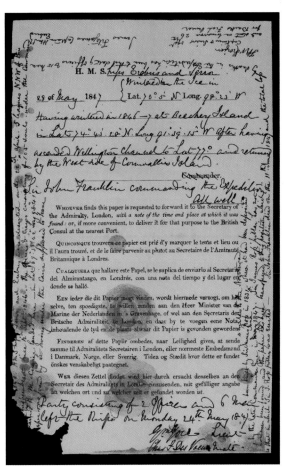

Wikimedia Commons/{{PD}}

Besides mutation-induced resistance, another way bacteria can become resistant to antibiotics is for the DNA encoding the resistant trait to be transferred from one bacterium to another. Usually, this type of resistance is due to a segment of DNA encoding the production of an enzyme that inactivates the antibiotic, which can be transferred between bacteria. Bacteria have the built-in ability to "swap" genetic material from one to another in a process called conjugation. If the DNA that is exchanged contains information that helps the bacterium resist the effects of an antibiotic when it previously did not have that ability, then that bacterium is now resistant to the antibiotic and that will be passed onto all future generations of that bacteria.

Figure 19.5.4

Antibiotic Resistance
Antibiotic resistance is rather specific to a certain type – or class – of antibiotic. Being resistant to one class does not make an organism resistant to all types because classes of antibiotics work differently from one another. For example, just because a certain bacteria type is resistant to beta-lactams (like penicillin) does not mean it is resistant to vancomycin (even though both classes kill sensitive bacteria by blocking cell wall formation, they do it in different ways).

Antibiotic Class/Type	Mode of Action in Sensitive Bacteria	Bacterial Resistance Mechanism(s)
Aminoglycosides (e.g. gentamycin)	Block protein synthesis	Inactivate antibiotic via enzyme
Beta-lactams (penicillins and cephalosporins)	Block cell wall formation	Inactivate antibiotic via enzyme; mutation of target structure so antibiotic can't bind
Glycopentides (vancomycin)	Block cell wall formation	Mutation of target structure so antibiotic can't bind
Macrolides (erythromycin)	Block protein synthesis	Ribosome protection
Quinolones (ciprofloxacin)	Inhibit bacterial DNA replication	Mutate target structure so antibiotic can't bind
Rifampin	Inhibit bacterial RNA polymerase	Mutate target structure so antibiotic can't bind
Tetracyclines	Block protein synthesis	Inactivate antibiotic via enzyme
Trimethoprim sulfonamides	Block formation of nucleic acids	Mutate target structure so antibiotic can't bind

"Now, wait a minute," you may say, "that conjugation thing sounds an awful lot like an organism acquiring new DNA to give it a trait it didn't previously have!" True enough; however, if a bacteria picks up the genetic material in this way, then all that has happened is _that the genetic material has simply moved from one bacterium to another_. There has been no new formation of genetic material – it already existed in the bacterial realm; it was only transferred from one place to another. The bacterium with its newly acquired "antibiotic-inactivating gene" is still a bacterium – it hasn't turned into a eukaryote, which is "the next step up," evolutionarily speaking. There has been no new development of a trait in the bacterial kind that didn't already exist. No new genetic material has formed. No new organism has formed – all the offspring are all still bacteria of the same type that existed before the swap of DNA. Do not let development of this type of resistance fool you into thinking that evolution can occur. This is not evolution because no new trait has come into existence that didn't already exist in the bacteria world. And, no new previously nonexistent organism has been formed no matter the number of antibiotics the organism can resist! Bacteria remain bacteria!

Figure 19.5.5

Types of Antibiotic Resistance

This is a listing of the many different ways in which bacteria can become resistant to antibiotics. Note, though, that the critically important fact is that _no new genetic information is generated when a bacteria becomes resistant to an antibiotic_. And, even when a bacterial type becomes resistant to an antibiotic, it is still classified as the same bacterial type that it was before it became resistant. By that I mean that if an _Escherichia coli_ bacteria type becomes resistant to the antibiotic ciprofloxacin, it is still an _Escherichia coli_ bacteria type. It doesn't become a new and previously nonexistent organism. Evolution can only occur if previously nonexistent DNA develops to give rise to a previously nonexistent trait so that a previously nonexistent kind of organism is formed. Evolutionists obviously realize that no new information is generated in the bacterial realm because they do not give a new scientific name to a bacterial type that develops antibiotic resistance even though the evolution model looks at the development of antibiotic resistance as "evolution in action." Antibiotic resistant _E. coli_ is still _E. coli._

Mode of Resistance	How Resistance is Conferred
Produce inactivating enzyme (e.g. beta-lactamase production)	Genetic material encoding the production of the enzyme beta-lactamase, usually carried on a plasmid, can be transferred between bacteria via conjugation. This is a simple "swapping" of already existing genetic material. Nothing new is formed when bacteria become resistant through plasmid-mediated genetic exchange.
Increase metabolism	Some bacteria have the pre-programmed ability, when stressed by antibiotics, to significantly increase their metabolism so that the previous levels of antibiotics can no longer kill them. There is no evidence to indicate that this property is a unique prediction of the evolution model and is completely explainable by the creation model.
Production of a compound via a secondary pathway when an antibiotic blocks the primary way the bacteria produces the compound	Some antibiotics inhibit bacteria's ability to make a specific product through a specific pathway. If a bacterium picks up DNA that codes for production of the product through a biochemical pathway that is different than the blocked pathway, then the bacterium can make the product again since the antibiotic specifically blocks only the one pathway. Like beta-lactamase production, this process is mediated by the exchange of already existing information. No new information arises in the bacterial realm.
Antibiotic pumps	Conjugation can transfer already existing genes encoding the production of proteins that pump antibiotics out from the interior of the bacterium so the antibiotic cannot exert its action and kill the organism. As with many other mechanisms, this is not a "new" trait to the bacterial world since the DNA encoding the information for the pump already exists.
Mutations to bacterial DNA	Mutations in the bacterial DNA can alter the intracellular target site of certain antibiotics so that when they get inside the bacterial cell, they can't find their target and so don't work. For example, tetracycline, which targets a specific bacterial ribosomal protein, can be rendered inactive if the bacteria has a mutation that codes for a slightly different ribosomal amino acid sequence than normal. This causes the tetracycline to not be able to bind the bacterial ribosome and inhibit protein synthesis and so if a person is infected with a tetracycline-resistant bacterial type, it will not be killed by the tetracycline. This is not the formation of a trait caused by new genetic material, but loss of function due to the mutation deleting the information that codes for the production of the normal ribosome.

In summary, looking at bacterial antibiotic resistance through evolution glasses, on the surface it looks like it might be evolution. As we continue to see, though, it really is nothing more than the effects of bacteria picking up DNA/traits that already exist in the bacterial world or the information-losing effects of mutation. If this is what evolution is, then there would never be the formation of new and previously nonexistent organisms because no new DNA arises to provide new traits. Loss of function is a loss of information and swapping DNA does nothing other than result in the exchange of already-existing DNA. Nothing new results. Bacteria remain bacteria.

Creationists view the development of antibiotic resistance within the creation framework inherent in God's Creation. He gave bacteria the built-in ability to compete for survival, which included the ability to develop immunity to antibiotics through information-losing mutation and the exchange of already-existent genetic material. But, the creation model does not allow for a naturalistic process to create new information, and no new information is what is observed scientifically as a result of mutation. Mutations don't "do" what the evolution model needs them to do. The evidence is consistent with the creation model and is not possible to explain with the evolutionary model.

19.6 NEPHESH CHAYYAH

Are the following specifics in the Bible? No, and so we cannot approach this dogmatically and aggressively take a position that "This is how it is, and that is that. End of discussion." Rather, the following information is meant to provide well-thought out linkages between science and biblical concepts as a continued demonstration that scientific data supports the creation model. Even though the Bible doesn't specifically address "natural selection" and "genetic diversity," and even though it isn't a geological textbook, none-the-less reasonable and scientifically sound conclusions can be drawn when using the Bible as _THE_ authoritarian frame of reference.

A widely held Christian view concerning the implications of the specific words God used to describe His Creation is that _before_ Adam sinned, there literally was no physical death of human beings and _some_ animals. That means that some animals did die and some didn't before sin. Only those animals that have the property of **nephesh chayyah**, which means "living soul" (when applied to humans) or "living creature" (when applied to animals) are the ones that the Bible says were created to not die. Genesis 2:17, Romans 5:12 and 8:20 indicate that Adam's sin caused the entrance of death into creation for all organisms that were nephesh chayyah. This is a complex exegesis and details can certainly be researched if you are interested. It is the property of being a nephesh chayyah organism that made an organism perfect before the Fall and subject to the consequences of Adam's sin after the Fall.

> **And the Lord God commanded the man, saying, "You may surely eat of every tree of the garden, but of the tree of knowledge of good and evil you shall not eat, for in the day that you eat of it you shall surely die."** Genesis 2:16-17

> **Therefore, just as sin came into the world through one man, and death through sin, and so death spread to all men because all sinned.** Romans 5:12

> **For the creation was subject to futility, not willingly, but because of him who subjected it...** Romans 8:20

Figure 19.6.1

Nephesh Chayyah Conferred Immortality to Those Organisms With It

Although the Bible does not specifically list the kinds of organisms (besides humans) that have *nephesh chayyah* and those that don't, it is very clear that *nephesh chayyah* is a distinctive identifying property that makes some living organisms elementally "different" than others. For example, while they are certainly "living" organisms, according to the Bible, insects and plants <u>do not</u> have the property of *nephesh chayyah*. It is clear that most vertebrates (animals with "back bones") like fish, amphibians, reptiles, birds and mammals are *nephesh chayyah*, just as human beings are (but in a fundamentally different way than animals). Genesis 1:29, 30 establishes that, prior to the Fall, animals and people were vegetarian; hence, there was no death as a result of them eating each other. And, creationists believe that because God described His Creation as "very good," it is unlikely that for *nephesh* organisms there was death due to disease, accident or natural causes or else God would not have described His creation as "very good." Further in support of *nephesh* organisms not dying before the Fall, Paul writes that Adam's sin not only caused death to enter the world for humans, but also for *nephesh* organisms (Romans 8:20, 21). It is absolutely critical to understand that *nephesh* organisms and all of creation are subject to the Fall directly because of Adam's sin and <u>not</u> because of any transgression of non-human organisms. It was through the sin of the fallen man, Adam, that humanity was cursed and through the death and resurrection of the sinless man, Jesus Christ, that we are redeemed. These narratives are intertwined and the historicity of one cannot be removed from the other.

© Wikimedia Commons/{{PD}}

© Michael Gabler/Wikimedia Commons/CC-BY-SA-3.0

© Magnus Manske/Wikimedia Commons/CC-BY-SA-2.0

© Wikimedia Commons/{{PD}}

© Wikimedia Commons/{{PD}}

© Wikimedia Commons/{{PD-art}}

So, let's consider what that means – biologically/genetically – if neither man nor nephesh animals died prior to the Fall. It is a reasonable scientific inference, in order to never die, that the God-created nephesh genetics must have been perfect. In order for an organism to never die, that would mean that all organs had to remain in perfect working order – forever. Since everything about the body's function is caused and maintained by an organism's genetic make-up, it makes sense that the only way something could never die would be for it to have perfect genetics to maintain the organism in perfect working order.

Figure 19.6.2

Drosophila melanogaster

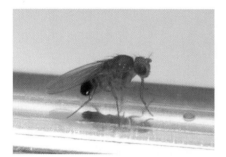

Sanja565658/Wikimedia Commons/CC-BY-SA-3.0

Although insects are definitely not nephesh organisms, *Drosophila melanogaster* is a classic animal that has long been used in genetics studies. One of the interesting things learned through study of its 1G5 gene is that some mutations may be "preprogrammed." Many mutations are truly random – they occur unpredictably. But, by studying the 1G5 gene, it is becoming increasingly evident that some segments of genes or DNA undergo many more mutation events than would be predicted by a truly random process. Not only that, after close enough study, although it isn't possible to predict when a mutation will occur, it is often possible to predict where, leading to the clear conclusion that some mutations are an algorithmic event, which is not a prediction of the evolution model. It appears likely that all organisms have these mutational "hot spots" that follow fairly precise algorithms. Such mathematical predictability would not be expected if these "hot spots" had arisen from the random forces of evolution; rather, they clearly implicate the intelligence of the Creator. Although the reason for this "hot spot" phenomenon cannot be accurately known, of course, maybe God designed the genetic system with the ability to mutate at predictable locations, perhaps as a way to safely generate and maintain genetic variation within kinds. Such genetic variation is a healthy thing for populations. So, it is possible mutations existed prior to the Fall but, if they did, they would have been the pre-programmed type that God used perhaps as a means of maintaining healthy variation within kinds and would not have been harmful to the organism or deleted information like the overwhelming majority of mutations observed today do. Predictability of some mutations is absolutely not a hypothesis of the evolution model and is *only* explainable by the creation model.

Conversely, if God did not create pre-Fall genetics to be perfect, then organisms would have died from the same causes of death that we see today as a result of imperfect genetics – aging, cancer, high blood pressure, various genetic disease (muscular dystrophy, cystic fibrosis, etc). It is highly unlikely that God would have described His Creation as "very good" if there was death, disease, cancer, bad mutation, etc., prior to the Fall. It is therefore very reasonable that creationists take the view that pre-Fall genetics were perfect and that any mutations that did occur were specifically designed into the system by God, likely as a mechanism to maintain a healthy amount of genetic diversity. After the Fall, harmful mutations began and have been slowly building over time.

Figure 19.6.3

Biblical Patriarchs and Perfect Pre-Fall Genetics

Some find it hard to believe that the ages of many of the patriarchs mentioned in the Bible are "real ages" because they lived so long – more than 900 years is a long time! But, if we approach Scripture as the True Word of the Living God and look at the ages through that lens, what might we see? In that case, we would see that people _really did_ live as long as the Bible says. If so, what could possibly be the scientific foundation of a more-than-900-year-old person? Creationists believe that harmful and information-deleting mutations started with the Fall. The Bible says that as a result of man's sin, all of creation was subject to various "curses," such as women being pained during child birth, snakes being changed in function (and likely in form) so that they would slither on their bellies, and death literally entered into the world. Mutations are entirely consistent with the curse described as a result of the Fall – the opposite of a "very good" creation. Perfection was lost and along with that, genetics would have started to decay, meaning the perfectly functioning genetics no longer were so. Mutations would have then started to happen, slowly accumulating over time, leading to organ and, eventually, organism failure. Adam's cause of death, then, ultimately, would have been from the mutations slowly building up in his originally perfect genome, leading to his organs failing at extreme old age. In addition, mutations would be passed from generation to generation, just as they are now, with mutations additively accumulating from one generation to the next. As a result of an ever increasing "load" or "build up" of mutations from generation to generation, we would naturally expect to see that the life expectancy would decrease over the generations – and that is indeed what we see. The early patriarchs lived very long lives since their DNA was more pristine with less mutations than subsequent generations, allowing their cells and organs to function better for longer periods of time as compared to the following generations that carried with them a higher load of genetic mutation. Life expectancies would be expected to decrease, which is exactly what the Bible documents! So, these long life spans are entirely consistent with expectations of the "genetic state" pre- and post-Fall, making the more-than-900-year-old lifespan seem very reasonable.

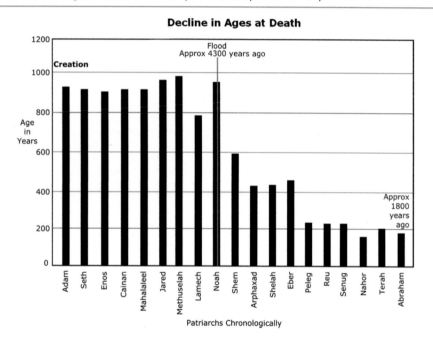

Decline in Ages at Death

19.7 NOAH AND THE FLOOD – DOES THE SCIENTIFIC DATA SUPPORT IT?

Detailed analysis of the wording used to describe the Flood and associated events and concepts throughout the Bible make it clear that the scope of the flood was not local/regional but worldwide. This resulted in the death of all land dwelling/air breathing creatures except those God commanded Noah to bring on the Ark. The idea that Noah's Flood was an actual event that occurred worldwide, just as the Bible says, often leads to many thoughtful questions and discussions! Let's review a couple of them – using the Bible as the authority – and see if science provides reasonable support for an actual worldwide flood, or not.

One of the very common objections to the "Noah story" is that there would not have been enough room on the Ark for all of the animals. This is, though, driven by the misunderstanding of the potential numbers of animals God put on the Ark. _Many people incorrectly believe that two of each type of animal got on the Ark_. By that I mean, using dogs as an example, two Great Danes, two Labradors, two basset hounds, two Chihuahuas, two collies, two poodles, two dachshunds, etc. But, that isn't what Genesis 6:20 says. Rather, it says,

> **_Of the birds_ <u>_according to their kinds_</u>_, and of the animals_ <u>_according to their kinds_</u>_, of every creeping thing of the ground,_ <u>_according to its kind_</u>_, two of every sort shall come in to you to keep them alive._**

And Genesis 7:14 reiterates that,

> **They and every beast, <u>according to its kind</u>, and all the livestock <u>according to their kinds</u>, and every creeping thing that creeps on the earth <u>according to its kind</u>, and every bird, <u>according to its kind</u>, every winged creature.**

Again, sticking to God's Word, we see that he used the concept "according to its/their kinds" seven times in those two verses. *<u>God's Word very clearly says the he did NOT place two of every type of animal on the Ark</u>*. Instead, *<u>God brought two of every animal kind to the Ark</u>*. So, God would have had to place only two of the "dog kind," two of the "cat kind," two of the "elephant kind," two of the "cattle kind," etc., on the Ark, which substantially decreases the numbers of animals to a much more manageable number.

Figure 19.7.1

© Wikimedia Commons/{{PD-Art-Old}}

Noah's Ark – How Did All Those Animals Fit?
God told Noah to build the Ark to exact specifications, which were recorded for us. From that, we can calculate that the volume of the Ark was 1.54 million cubic feet, the equivalent of approximately 325 double-deck 48-foot long cattle trailers, each of which can hold 80 head of 450 pound cattle. This is the equivalent of a line of cattle trailers end to nose – no tractor cabs, just trailers filled with 80 cattle each – over 3 miles long. That gives a total holding space in the Ark equal to over 30,000 head of 450 pound cattle. It has been estimated (information readily available online) that the volume of the Ark is more than enough to accommodate the animals, Noah's family and food for a year for all life forms on board. Further, estimates are that the number of animals that Noah would have had on the Ark was around 16,000 (total), with the large majority of them being smaller than a medium-sized dog. There is nothing that requires that the animals we think of as "very big" necessarily were full grown when aboard the Ark. As with the old patriarch's ages, when critically assessing what God says and assuming His Word is absolutely true, we see that what may seem "unbelievable" at first is actually scientifically very supportable.

One thing to keep in mind is that it is not entirely clear what a "kind" is. For some kinds of animals – such as dogs – it is relatively easy to understand that all organisms that belong to the "dog kind" – wolves, coyotes and domestic dogs. All these could reasonably be descended from the same dog kind ancestor pair that stepped off the Ark, filled with God-given ability to form lots of varieties built right into their genes. It isn't so clear, though, for every animal and plant kind as to what the boundaries of their "kind" are. There is intense scientific work presently being undertaken to identify, as best as possible, how organisms are related to one another within the "created kind" framework. The authority for this "kind identification" that creation researchers are using is, of course, the Bible, supplemented with scientific data (like fossil study, anatomy and genetics) and common sense.

Once a person understands that God said that he put 2 of every "kind" and not two of every "type" onto the Ark, the next thought often is that "only" 4,500 years isn't long enough for the kinds to form the diverse varieties that we see today. This really reveals how much evolutionary dogmatism has crept into our thinking! Remember Dr. Grant's Galapagos finch study- the classic example of "rapid speciation" – that showed that varieties can form very quickly. Dr. Grant himself was surprised to estimate that one variety would have morphed into another variety in "only" 200 to 1,200 years. The hundreds of thousands of years required by the evolution model are not necessary – scientific observations made by evolutionists tell us varieties form much faster, which is far more consistent with the creation model.

> **Then God said to Noah, "Go out from the Ark, you and your wife, and your sons and your sons' wives with you. Bring out with you every living thing that is with you of all flesh – birds and animals and every creeping thing that creeps on the earth – that they may swarm the earth, and be fruitful and multiply on the earth.** *Genesis 8:15 – 18*

Figure 19.7.2

Rapid Adaptation Supports Creationist "Built-in Genetic Variability"

Creationists assume God's Word to be true and look to His Creation as a scientific reflection. There are many examples of what is termed "**rapid speciation**," which is what evolutionist's call "rapid" changes that occur within one "species" and transform it into another "species." Remember that the evolutionary model predicts that speciation – or the changes in the traits between different populations of organisms that results in them developing into different "species" (or kinds) – occur very slowly, over tens to hundreds of thousands of years. Therefore, any "speciation process" that occurs faster than that evolutionists refer to as "rapid speciation." Remember, though, to firmly keep the observational science firmly in hand – rapid speciation is nothing more than different varieties forming within a kind, which is not an event that has been scientifically observed to be "slow." Scientific observations are that "rapid" adaptations (changes in appearance and/or behavior) readily occur as organisms within a population respond to changes in their environment. Remember that adaptation is a process driven by natural selection to modify already existing traits (genes); therefore, no new genetic information is required. The evolution model incorrectly views modifications of existing traits/genes – which is adaptation – as "evolution" even though no new traits/genes arise; only existing ones are modified. According to evolutionists, the adaptations described below can be seen at rates up to 10 million times faster than "average rates," which are rates that are predicted by the evolutionary model not based upon scientific data but upon the assumption that life is more than 3 billion years old. *There is no objective evidence adaptations require millions and billions of years to form, that is just what the evolutionary model requires.* And, data from Dr. Grant's study show that adaptations clearly can form in hundreds of years. From the creationist perspective, the time available for organism diversification is a total of about 4,500 years (starting from Noah's Flood). The Grant's Galapagos finch study – viewed in light of the 4,500 years – shows the speed of the changes described below are completely consistent with predictions made by the creation model! There is no need to appeal to unknown mechanisms of the evolution model that would lead to a concept of "rapid speciation" occurring 10 million times the "usual" assumed rate because the creation model rate actually occurs at the rate that is scientifically observed. This "rapid speciation" is entirely consistent with and predicted by the creation model and, as evolutionists themselves have noted, is not at all predicted by an evolutionary model.

Condition	Scientific Observation and Implication
Galapagos finch population traits change in response to drought conditions	Rapid changes in various bird traits caused evolutionary researcher Peter Grant to estimate that it would take approximately 200 years for one finch "species" to transform into another, much faster than the 1,000,000 – 5,000,000 years evolutionists had predicted prior to the scientific observational studies. This is not "evolution" because no new traits (DNA) arose; only modification of existing traits.
Saltwater stickleback fish lose armor plating when isolated in fresh water	There are two different stickleback types – freshwater and saltwater – differentiated by the saltwater type having thickened side scales, or armor plates. Sometimes the saltwater variety gets trapped in freshwater bodies, in which they can survive. Within about 15 years of this happening, the once-saltwater fish descendants lose their thick side scales and become freshwater sticklebacks. This is not evolution because this is a loss of genetic information/traits and they are all still stickleback fish and always will be. Also, this happens far more rapidly than predicted by the evolutionary fossil record. The end result is the transformation of the saltwater into the freshwater type in only 15 years through loss of information combined with the effects of natural selection!
Guppies in Trinidad relocated to a new pond, with different predator-prey conditions	The guppies rapidly adapted to their new environment by becoming larger, maturing slower and having less offspring. This occurred at a rate of 10,000 to 10,000,000 times that predicted by the evolution model. Clearly, novel genetic information could not be generated this quickly and, besides, these are still guppies! No new traits, only modification of existing ones built into the DNA through natural selection.
Lizards moved from forest habitat to one with smaller bushes	Over only several generations, the lizards' legs became shorter, at a rate many thousands of times faster than that predicted by the evolution model. This is not evolution since no new traits developed, the lizards' existing legs only became shorter. The only thing that occurred was loss of information coding for longer legs, through natural selection, obviously favored by the change in habitat.
Mosquitoes become entrapped in the London subway tunnel system during digging	Prior to becoming trapped in the tunnels, the mosquitoes, *Culex pipiens*, exclusively fed on birds. After becoming entrapped, with subsequent generations, the population of tunnel *C. pipiens* developed the ability to feed on humans and rats, bred year round and became cold intolerant, all of which are traits that the above-ground type does not share. However, this is still a mosquito and no new genetic information has been created to account for these changes. Further, these mosquitoes do not appear capable of interbreeding with their above-ground relatives. "Speciation" has occurred far more rapidly than evolution predicts; however, this type of rapid diversification fits right in with the expected ability of all organisms to rapidly diversify due to built-in genetic variability endowed by God at creation. Like all of the examples discussed in this table, that ability to vary was built right into the DNA of the organisms by God.

God gave Noah, his family and all of the animals a mandate – he told them to be fruitful and multiply. He most certainly would not have said that if there was no way for all of them to do it! Also, with God knowing and being in control of everything from the very beginning, he would have known that he was going to send the Flood, that he would have only two of every kind plus Noah and his family to fulfill His mandate to "swarm the earth, be fruitful and multiply." Therefore, it is a very reasonable conclusion that God would have given all of the organisms He intended to save, as well as man, exactly the genetic content and genetic variability necessary for them to accomplish the "swarm the earth, be fruitful and multiply" task. The only way that man and the animal kinds coming off the Ark could have done that and formed into the extensive, diverse life forms we see today is if:

- Genetic content was in "very good shape" when the Flood hit. If it was heavily mutated and not in good shape, man's lifespan would not have been in excess of 900 years prior to the Flood, nor would it have been more than 200 years for several generations after the Flood. It is very reasonable to conclude that nephesh genetics were in much better shape than we see them in today.

- God created "built-in" potential for great genetic diversity within kinds. God pre-ordained man and all organisms at creation with the genetic potential they would need to fulfill His plan for the extensive biological diversity we see today and have seen throughout the past.

- When man and animals got off the Ark, they naturally started to spread out geographically from the Middle East, in search of food and habitat.

- As they spread geographically, they were subject to the type of natural selection pressures we discussed extensively in Chapter 18.

- The further out from the Ark life moved chronologically, the more and more natural selection had a chance to work on the animals and their traits. Since the animals had a large amount of genetic diversity built in, they had great potential to vary, which they did. Over time, natural selection made different population types of the same kind of animals look and behave a little differently from other types because of the adaptations that developed in response to natural selection. In short, varieties "rapidly" formed within kinds after dispersing from the Ark.

- However, at no time did natural selection make one kind evolve into another kind – a reptile never evolved into a bird. The variation that developed occurred entirely within the same kind – a lizard ancestor kind diversified into the many different lizard types we see today.

- Hence, there is a "limit" to what natural selection was able to do after life dispersed from the Ark. Existing traits within kinds can be modified, but new, never-before-in-existence traits or organisms cannot be formed by natural selection. That is truly a God function.

Another common question is, "Where did all of the water come from and where did it go when the Flood was over?" In order to answer that, we need to explore a concept that we don't usually think about, but is very important – that concept is the appearance of the earth prior to the Flood. Most naturally think that the pre-Flood earth looked pretty much like the post-Flood earth; however, while there is debate among creation geologists about specifics, it is true that nothing in the Bible excludes the possibility that the earth physically looked very different before the Flood as compared to after, and we will discuss one possible Flood model.

Many creation geologists believe that the pre-Flood earth indeed looked very different from the earth of today – mountains weren't as high and ocean floors weren't as deep and perhaps, also, the land masses were arranged differently so that the global map prior to the Flood looked a lot different than it does now.

> **And God said, 'Let the waters under the heavens be gathered together into one place, and let the dry land appear.' And it was so.** *Genesis 1:9*

Conceptually, if the waters were gathered into one place, that would indicate that as the waters gathered, the dry land appeared as one land mass or else the water wouldn't be in "one place." So, it is possible that there was one big, pre-Flood land mass. There must, then, have been some way that God used to separate the land mass sometime during the Flood so that he ended up with the continents looking like they do today.

Figure 19.7.3

Pangaea
The evolution model and some creationist's creation model propose that there was likely one massive land mass "in the beginning," though the time frames are obviously very different. Evolutionists think Pangaea existed 300 hundred million years ago, while creationists think that Pangaea could have perhaps been the way the earth looked in the beginning after God gathered the waters, or perhaps Pangaea was formed during the Flood and then pulled apart rapidly as part of the violent Flood conditions. Even though the name "Pangaea" is an evolutionary term, creationists tend to use it, too, because it provides a common way to refer to the concept of a single land mass that formed when God gathered the waters in one place under the heavens .

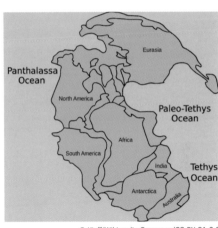

How did the land mass separate, then, if it was one big one right around or during the Flood? We know that continental land masses move today on massive slabs called **tectonic plates**, with all of the plates contacting one another where they come together. During the incredibly violent 1 year period of the Flood, creation geophysicist John Baumgardner, PhD proposes that God used the tectonic plates to pull the land masses apart through what he calls **catastrophic plate tectonics**. He postulates that at some point, the individual tectonic plates making up the single land mass were rapidly pulled apart into the continental anatomy as we know it today, not at the present day, evolutionary rate of two inches a year but five miles per hour!

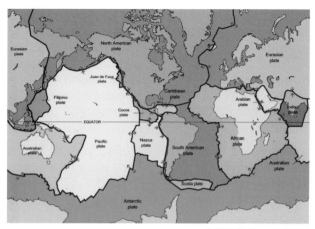

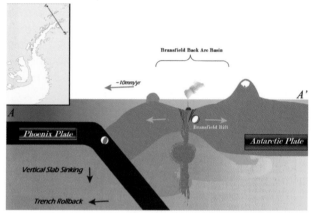

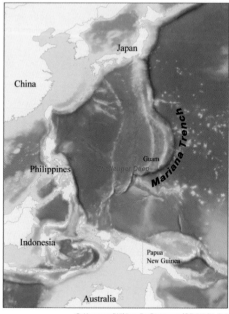

Figure 19.7.4

Tectonic Plates – How God Could Have Changed the Face of the Earth

All "hard earth" structures – whether above-the-water continents or under-the-water ocean floor – sit upon massively huge slabs of rock, the tectonic plates (top left). These plates are mobile and "float" on top of rock that is under so much pressure and is so hot that it is in liquid form, called "**molten**" rock. Presently, the rate of movement of most of the plates is about 0 – 2 inches per year and the evolution model predicts this rate has always been pretty much the same. The areas where the tectonic plates come together and contact one another is under high stress (middle), since the plates tend to move in different directions – moving away from one another, sliding past one another or even directly into one another. When the plates move suddenly, earthquakes occur. Because tectonic plates move today, there is every reason to believe that they have moved in the past; however, there is no definitive objective scientific data that would indicate that the plates absolutely moved at the same rates in the past they do today. Since the plates move, it is reasonable to conclude that how the earth looks presently may not necessarily be the way it looked when God created it. For example, in addition to the possibility of one large land mass, many creationists believe that the pre-Flood earth was much "flatter" than it is today, meaning that the mountains weren't as high and oceans not as deep. The bottom left shows the deepest place on earth, the Challenger Deep, more than 8 miles below the ocean's surface. There are many places on the ocean floors that are more than 5 miles deep. Obviously, it takes a lot of water to fill in these deep ocean depths. Some creation geologists believe that before the Flood, ocean trenches were not nearly as deep and were created as the Flood receded. The end result of lower mountains and shallower oceans would be that there would have been less "total water need" to cover the entire earth during the Flood since not so much was needed to "fill in the deeper deeps" and "cover the higher highs" of the present-day earth. Also, we often don't realize this, but there is an unknown amount of water _under_ the Earth's surface, and _University of Hawaii oceanographer Mike Mottl believes that there may be as much as two more global oceans-worth of water inside the earth_.

> ***In the six-hundredth year of Noah's life, in the second month, on the seventeenth day of the month, on that day all the fountains of the great deep burst forth, and the windows of the heavens were opened.*** *Genesis 7:11*

Scientific data indicates there is plenty of water present on/in Earth to cover the planet, globally, just as God's Word says.

The only real argument that billions-of-years geologists have with catastrophic plate tectonics is the time frame within which Dr. Baumgardner has postulated the continental plates are said to have moved in a single year, even though they have no reason to object to it since Dr. Baumgardner has identified geological data that indicates it could have occurred as he suggests. One of the implications of the very rapid and violent tectonic plate movements during the Flood would have been to create the very deep ocean trenches and high mountains in areas where the plate edges contact or moved away from one another very rapidly, leaving a deep cleft in the ocean floor. Psalms 104:7,8 seems very consistent with the postulates of catastrophic tectonic plate theory:

> ***At your rebuke they fled; at the sound of your thunder they took to flight. The mountains rose, the valleys sank down to the place that you appointed for them.***

Toward the end of the Flood, the plates began their rapid movements toward their present-day positions. As they moved, trenches were opened, deepening the ocean and allowing it to accommodate more water. As the tectonic plates moved into one another, mountains developed. The flow of water from the deep ceased, ocean trenches deepened, the wind blew and the rain stopped, allowing the new form of the earth to easily accommodate the water supply.

Although the catastrophic tectonic plate theory is by no means a "perfect" one and continues to be refined by Dr. Baumgardner and others, it is consistent with observed scientific data and also seems to be supported by biblical descriptions.

Figure 19.7.5

Post-Flood Earth
In the evolutionary paradigm, over the past 300 million years, as a result of tectonic plate activity, the continents broke apart and continued to move about 2 inches per year until assuming the position we see today. Some creationists have another postulate – that through catastrophic plate tectonics God pulled the singular land mass apart at speeds up to 5 miles per hour, creating the conditions for the water to recede and the continents to assume their familiar positions.

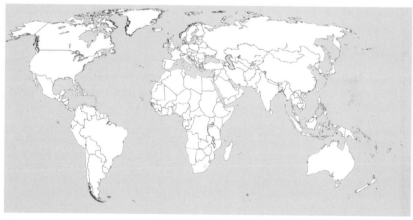

19.8 BASIC POPULATION ECOLOGY – EVIDENCE FOR EVOLUTION OR AN EXPECTED SCIENTIFIC FACT COMPATIBLE WITH THE CREATION MODEL?

Ecology is the study of the relationships organisms have with their environment and each other. **Population ecology** is a field of study within ecology that studies the changes of population sizes over time, and what the factors may be that influence the changes. We will use some simple concepts of population ecology to study an often asked question, "If the Flood was only about 4000 years ago, how can there be almost 7 billion people on earth already?" This question is actually answerable by applying principles of how human populations grow by taking into account the things that influence increases, decreases and stable population numbers.

Relevant facts and calculations:

- Although no one was keeping accurate population records until the past 150 years or so, through observation over that time frame and making rational inferences of human population numbers in the past, it is possible to come up with a reasonable number of average years it takes for the human population to double. There are some factors (wars, famines and plagues) that keep the human population from growing at a precisely steady rate and so the doubling time is not exact. But it is scientifically accepted that the length of time it takes the human population to double is – on the slow side – about every 135 years. For example, it took about 500 years to go from 500 million to 1 billion (from about the year 1300 to 1800), 127 years to go from 1 billion to 2 billion (1800 – 1927), 47 years to go from 2 billion to 4 billion (1927 – 1974) and 39 years to go from 3 billion to 6 billion (1960 – 1999) and, per United Nations data, a projected 96 years to go from 5 billion to 10 billion (1987 – 2083).

- The Flood was about 4300 years ago (there are differing calculations, but the one I am going with is available online, presented by Dr. John Osgood, and places the Flood at 2304 BC +/- 11 years), which, with a doubling time of 135 years, means <u>*there have been about 33 doublings of the population since the Flood*</u>. [*Note: As man continues to try to remove God from the world, it is becoming increasingly common to see years referred to not with BC (before Christ) or AD (Anno Domini), but with BCE (before common era) and CE (common era). For example, you may see 2500 BC written as 2500 BCE and 515 AD written as 515 CE.*].

- There was a population of 8 after the Flood, but let's start with only 6 (assuming the reproductive population was Shem, Japheth and Ham and their wives since it isn't entirely clear if Noah and his wife had any children after the Flood).

- In 33 doublings, starting from a population of 6 and using a doubling time of 135 years, there would be 25.76 billion people on earth today.

- Therefore, it is definitely possible for a human population to grow from "8" post-Flood to over "7 billion" in "only" 4300 years.

Figure 19.8.1

Human Population Growth – Consistent With Scripture
This secular-produced human population growth curve makes it very clear that after a relatively "short" period of time, evolutionarily speaking, human population growth accelerates well beyond any limits that would allow objective conclusion that humans have been on the earth for longer than 10,000 years. If "modern humans," as evolutionists call us, had been on earth for more than 200,000 years as the evolution model claims, then that would give enough time for about 1,481 doublings of the human population. However, after "only" 36,450 years – the time it would take for the population to double only 270 times – there would be more than 4.74×10^{80} people on earth, which is more than the estimated number of *electrons in the universe* (estimated to be 1×10^{80}). After 200,000 years there would be so many people that they couldn't fit onto all of the planets in the universe. The scientific pursuit of human population studies confirms that a biblical approach is a reasoned approach.

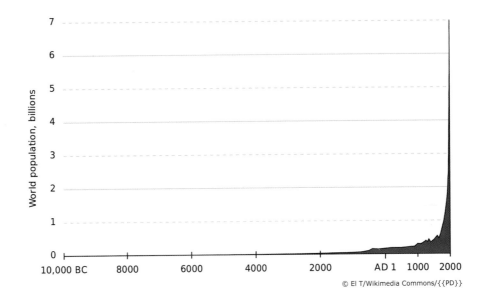

© El T/Wikimedia Commons/{{PD}}

19.9 COMPARATIVE GENOMICS – EVIDENCE FOR EVOLUTION OR AN EXPECTED SCIENTIFIC FACT COMPATIBLE WITH THE CREATION MODEL?

A related neat genetics fact that further confirms biblical truth is reflected in various applications of evidence learned from **comparative genomics**, which is the study of relationships of DNA between different kinds of organisms. In 2007, John Hawks and his team of evolutionary scientists published a study in the journal *PNAS*, which compared the genomes of four genetically different people groups – Han Chinese, Japanese, African Yoruba and Northern Europeans. By knowing the mutation rate of humans, his team used the known differences in DNA sequences between the four people groups to calculate backwards in time how long ago these four people groups started to become different genetically. In other words, they worked backwards to identify about when in the past these four people groups' DNA was essentially the same. Of course, the evolutionary model predicts that these populations diverged well over 200,000 years ago.

Interestingly, their result was shocking (at least, to those viewing the data through evolution glasses, it was shocking) – *these people groups had essentially the same DNA content "only" 10,000 years ago*! The evolution model predicts that these people groups would have been genetically identical more than 200,000 years ago. With their evolution glasses on, they do not even consider the possibility that the reason the number of years ago into the past that the people groups' DNA was essentially the same is because that *is* about how long ago they were the same.

Biblical truth is completely discounted and the evolutionary model must explain this finding in a different way, which is to go against their uniformitarianism beliefs and state that the mutation rate in humans was much slower in the past and has "sped up" the last 10,000 years. However, if we let the observed science speak for itself, it is obvious that the Hawks' study closely supports the creation model and is yet another piece of evidence arguing against the evolution model. That 10,000 years ago time frame is not a "hard" date, though. That simply provides the upper limit of how long ago into the past it could have been, no more than 10,000 years. The creation model predicts it was slightly less at about 6,000 years ago.

Another abject failure of the evolutionary model is seen in the concept of **junk DNA**. It is true that only a relatively small portion of DNA is genes. Early on in genetics (quite frankly, when we didn't know very much), for more than three decades the evolution model relied heavily upon the concept that the DNA that "didn't do anything" – the non-gene encoding DNA – was "junk DNA." With evolution glasses on, this DNA was considered a remnant of "left-over stuff" from billions of years of "information-adding" mutations causing new and previously nonexistent organisms to arise, one after the other.

Enter comparative genomics, which seeks to identify how "evolutionarily close" organisms are based upon the similarity of their DNA content. Since junk DNA was just a remnant and "didn't do anything," when early studies were done comparing the similarities between the genomes of different kinds of organisms, these huge segments of DNA that "didn't do anything" were excluded from the similarity analyses. Further, it was common that only areas that were already highly similar between chimps and humans actually made it into the formal analyses of the similarity studies. Therefore, when these studies were first done in the 1970's and 80's, the reports came out that the DNA sequence similarity was over 98% between chimps and humans.

Figure 19.9.1

Human-Chimp DNA Similarities?

Now that the myth of junk DNA has been completely debunked, with refinements in analysis techniques, greater care being taken to prevent external human DNA contamination during the analysis processes and taking the full human and nearly the full chimp genomes into account, more recent genome comparison studies identify that the human and chimp genomes are _very dissimilar_. Now we know that human-chimp sequences differ not by 2% that is still commonly reported in evolutionary texts, _but by at least 23%_ . Some geneticists like Dr. Richard Buggs even suggest that the dissimilarity may be as high as 30%. Another way of looking at it is that the similarity is only 70%, nowhere close to the 98% that continues to be incorrectly listed in many evolutionary text books. One of the conclusions of the more-recently identified vast dissimilarity in human and chimp genomes was published in the peer-reviewed journal _Molecular Biology and Evolution_ with a summary statement, "...a genealogy results in which humans and chimpanzees are not each other's closest relatives." This is a total "do-over" in the evolutionary paradigm. From a creationist perspective, since humans and chimps share the same "body plans" – they are about the same size, have two arms and two legs, five digits on the hands and feet, mammal characteristics, etc – it is valid to conclude that God knew how to genetically build things and so he used similar gene content with similar chromosome structures and gene segments (when appropriate) to build similar body structures, so of course there is genetic similarity. It is the same concept of why all road vehicles (cars, trucks, motorcycles, tractors, etc.) look pretty much the same – wheels attached to axels and frames, engines, rubber tires, brakes, exhaust systems, etc.). They look like that because the designers know that is how to make a vehicle that needs to move over the ground. Creation provides a very reasonable alternative explanation that is supported by the scientific data, while postulates of the evolution model frequently lead to erroneous conclusions.

The science has been updated considerably since these studies decades ago. The junk DNA predictions of the evolution model have been shown to be absolutely wrong. Now we know that virtually every single sequence in DNA "does something" – _there is no such thing as junk DNA_. That was a completely invalid scientific conclusion driven only by evolutionary beliefs that blinded many scientists for decades as to the important function that non-gene encoding segments of DNA have. The realization that no DNA can be excluded from similarity analyses made it necessary to "redo" the DNA comparison studies to include all the regions of DNA – the gene- _and_ non-gene-encoding ones. When this was done, the previously identified "similarities" between the genomes plummeted, which has caused significant "rethinking" on the evolutionary side as to how exactly comparative genomics fits into the modern evolutionary synthesis.

Figure 19.9.2

Y Chromosome Analysis Does NOT Support "Common Ancestry"

This is a human karyotype, and the very small chromosome at the bottom right is the Y chromosome, which, recall, confers maleness. It doesn't contain that many genes, and the ones it does contain tend to code for similar traits across many different kinds of animals as well as humans. This allows for further analysis to see if the evolutionary paradigm stands up to scientific rigor. Because the evolution model states that everything came from a "common ancestor," that means that the human Y chromosome is descended from the chimp's Y chromosome, and so any difference between the two must be solely explained by mutation. Since both the human and chimp Y chromosomes are entirely sequenced, we know by how many base-pairs they differ. As in other comparative genomic endeavors, it is possible to calculate how long into the past it would have been for the two to have shared a "common ancestor" by using the known mutation rates of the two kinds. We can calculate how long it would take for the chimp Y and human Y chromosomes to become as dissimilar as they are now, assuming they started with essentially the same genetic sequence when they were still in the form of the shared common ancestor. Using this method, it appears that humans and chimps split from the common ancestor not 6 million years ago _but 320 million years ago_. The scientifically observed human and chimp mutation rate is not fast enough – not by a long shot – to explain the difference that exists between the human and chimp Y chromosomes. This difference of 314 million years (about a 50,000% error, which is pretty bad) between observed and expected time into the past is another example of the failure of the evolutionary model to accurately predict scientific observations. As we continue to learn more and more about genetics, the underlying principles of neo-Darwinism are increasingly not supported by the scientific data, while at the same time the argument for the creation model are strengthened.

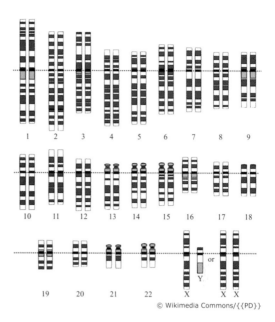

© Wikimedia Commons/{{PD}}

Now that junk DNA is known to be "junk science," one of the persistent problems that comparative geneticists face is known as **Haldane's dilemma**. This condition was described in a 1957 paper by one of the most revered evolutionary geneticists, J.B.S. Haldane. In it, he identified that "there isn't enough time" for mutations to have accumulated in the human genome to make it as different from the chimp genome as it is observed to be. Despite his preeminent status in the population genetics field at the time (he was one of the founders), his idea did not really receive much attention, so much so that in 1992 the influential evolutionist George C Williams (1926 – 2010), professor of biology at SUNY-Stony Brook, gave a call for the evolutionary community to address Haldane's dilemma with scientific rigor. That call was ignored by the evolutionary community, but Walter ReMine, a creationist electrical engineer, wrote 1993's *The Biotic Message*, which is an excellent and detailed study of the evolution model, including how critically relevant Haldane's dilemma is in the debate.

With the creationist model, Haldane's dilemma is, of course, not a problematic issue precisely because Haldane's dilemma argues so strongly against the evolution model and provides another link in the chain of evidence that is consistent with creation origins. That time frame identified in the John Hawks study fits quite nicely with humans being created about 6,000 years ago. Principles of basic population ecology and genetics are inconsistent with evolution and support scientific observations and the predictions of a biblical creation model. Haldane's dilemma confirms that even 300 million years isn't enough time for evolution to account for the differences in DNA between the chimp and human.

"We have no acceptable theory of evolution at this time. There is none; I cannot accept the theory that I teach to my students each year...I teach the synthetic theory known as the neo-Darwinian one, for one reason only; not because it's good, we know it is bad, but because there isn't any other." Jerome Lejune

Beware of false prophets, who come to you in sheep's clothing but inwardly are ravenous wolves. You will recognize them by their fruits. Are grapes gathered from thornbushes, or figs from thistles? Matthew 7:15-16

19.10 FOSSIL DOGMA

Fossils are the remains of previously living life forms, or, per the definition of the American Geological Institute, "The remains or traces of animals or plants which have been preserved by natural causes in the earth's crust." (I suppose it is semantics whether Noah's Flood was a "natural cause" or a "supernatural cause"). A fossil may be the actual organism or part of the organism—such as a bone, shell, woody stem, pollen, or tooth. A fossil may also be the mineralized remains of the organism or part of the organism. The **fossil record** is the collective of all known fossils, along with the scientific interpretations made related to the fossilized organism's habitat, diet, size, social habits and relationships to other fossilized and presently living organisms.

Taken by J.D. Griggs, US Geological Survey, Public Domain

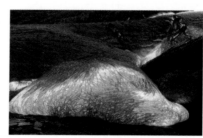

© Wikimedia Commons/{{PD}}

© Luis Fernandez Garcia/Wikimedia Commons/CC-BY-SA-2.5

© Siim Sepp/Wikimedia Commons/CC-BY-SA-3.0

Figure 19.10.1

Igneous Rock

Igneous rock forms when lava or magma cools. **Lava** (top left) is molten rock that is forcefully ejected from underneath the earth. **Magma** (top right) is molten rock that oozes, or "**extrudes**," onto the earth's surface. There are more than 700 types of igneous rock; granite (bottom left) and diabase (bottom right) are typical examples. Fossils are not found in igneous rock because the extremely hot, molten nature destroys the fossil. Until very recently, geological dogma was that igneous rock forms very slowly, perhaps over millions of years. However, because of scientific observations into the formation of granite crystals, according to granite expert John Clemens, its formation is catastrophic and rapid, _perhaps being completely formed in months_. Increasingly, scientific data shows that deep time evolution is not necessary. Creation time frames are entirely supported.

Figure 19.10.2

Sedimentary Rock

Sedimentary rock is formed when small particulates of organic and mineral matter (called **detritus**) fall to the bottom of bodies of water, accumulating in layers, a process called **sedimentation**. Over relatively short periods of time, the detritus cements together and becomes hard. These layers pile up on top of one another and are called **strata** or **beds.** They are found on every continent, not uncommonly stretching for thousands of square miles as a contiguous unit. The very large majority of fossils are found in layers of sedimentary rock (you can see the fossil shells in the sedimentary rock on the right). Up until recently, evolutionary dogma regarding how sedimentary layers formed was that each layer formed slowly, as the sediments slowly trickled to the bottom of the ocean or lake, eon after eon. However, over the past couple of decades, evolutionists have identified what creationists have been saying for 50 years – that, if sedimentary beds did deposit slowly like this, then fossils never would form because the organism would have decomposed to nothing long before it was completely covered by sediments. Therefore, the evolution model has been amended to one that sounds very similar to the creationist view – the majority of fossils are indeed formed in catastrophic conditions, where massive amounts of sediments are moved at one time, completely entombing organisms. To creationists, that event accurately describes the Great Flood. To evolutionists, that describes local and regional floods only.

© MeanStreets/Wikimedia Commons/{{PD}}

© Simeon87/Wikimedia Commons/CC-BY-SA-3.0

© Brocken Inaglory/Wikimedia Commons/CC-BY-SA-3.0

Figure 19.10.3

Metamorphic Rock

Metamorphic rock is formed from the transformation of other rock types as a result of being subjected to intense heat and high pressures after the original rock has already formed. This results in physical and/or chemical changes of the original rock. Looking at the gneiss-textured rock, right, you can get a sense of the intense pressure that must have existed to cause the formation of the curved banding patterns. Because of the high heat and pressure, fossils are rarely found in metamorphic rock and when they are, they are usually deformed and hazily recognizable as a fossil.

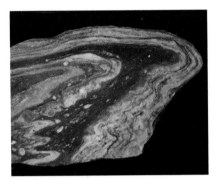

Interestingly, Darwin's evolutionary views were heavily influenced by Charles Lyell's uniformitarian approach to geology, about which Darwin read on his *Beagle* voyage. Specifically, Lyell's view was that there were no catastrophes like Noah's Flood to explain sedimentary layers; rather, he believed that slow and steady sedimentation explained the presence of sedimentary layers and the fossil found in them. He envisioned a process where sediments slowly fell to the bottom of bodies of water endlessly, over hundreds of thousands and millions of years and, if something died and fell to the bottom, it was slowly covered. This idea, which dominated evolutionary geology for more than 100 years, is now discredited and evolutionists have adopted a catastrophic fossil forming model, just like creationists.

What is so fascinating about this is that a completely incorrect scientific viewpoint such as this – that it takes hundreds of thousands and millions of years for sedimentary rock and the fossils in them to form – is what so forcefully moved Darwin to formulate a theory to fit Lyell's strata forming theory. Darwin's misunderstanding of the fossil record, based upon a humanistic world view instead of a Biblical one, continues to dominate paleontology even though it is clear that fossils cannot form via uniformitarian processes.

Figure 19.10.4

Fossils

A **mold** (top left) is a type of fossil that looks like an imprint of the organism and is formed when the organism is covered by sediments and then the body totally dissolves, leaving a "hole" in the rock shaped like the organism. When molds get filled in with minerals and harden, a hard fossil is made – called a **cast** (top right) – that looks like the original organism. Common fossils in the form of molds and casts are fern leaves, trilobites (an extinct shelled life form found in the seas) and most boney fossils. Other times, organisms (especially insects) can be trapped by and fossilized in sap. Sap which traps organisms in it is called **amber** (bottom right). Amber deposits were sensationalized in the movie *Jurassic Park* in which mosquitoes were found entombed in amber. In the movie, the blood in the fossilized mosquito was removed, then the DNA was extracted to use to make dinosaurs. There have been a few finds of fossilized tracks (bottom left), or footprints, of animals and humans found in preserved, dried out mud. Occasionally, teeth, bones, or even entire organisms (mummies and frozen wooly mammoths in Siberia) are unearthed. According to the evolution model, fossils have formed for the past 3 billion (or so) years. Per the creation model, since no nephesh organisms died before the Fall, there are obviously no nephesh fossils created before the Fall. And, since God described His creation as "very good," it isn't likely that there were catastrophic floods before the Fall and so it is highly unlikely that many fossils formed at all before the Fall. It is possible that some fossils formed after the Fall. Most of the fossils, though, formed during the Flood, with widespread death of many different organisms during a time when massive amounts of sediments were moved worldwide. Perfect fossil forming conditions.

3 mm

© Wilson 44691/Wikimedia Commons/{{PD}}

© Tim Evanson/Wikimedia Commons/CC-BY-SA-2.0

© jynus/Wikimedia Commons/CC-BY-SA-3.0

© Brocken Inaglory/Wikimedia Commons/CC-BY-SA-2.5

Now that it is obvious that fossils cannot form in anything other than catastrophic conditions, the evolution model has been amended to include fossil formation as a result of local/regional catastrophic events that would entomb much of the local plant and animal life. However, the evolution model is wed to the long ages; therefore, the hundreds of millions of years must come from somewhere, and it does – very long periods of time of slow sedimentation situated in between the massive regional sedimentation events. This gives the evolutionists the "best of both worlds," so to speak – the catastrophic fossil-forming events and the millions of years of sedimentation.

Creationists point out a real problem with that concept. If the large majority of sedimentary layers were formed slowly, over thousands of years (or more) each, there should be widespread evidence of erosion of the layers since they would have been exposed to the elements over the thousands of years in which each layer slowly formed. The problem is, there is precious little evidence of that.

Figure 19.10.5

Fossilized Squid

There are many fossilized "soft" animals (many aquatic), such as this squid, as well as the soft parts of plants. Obviously, in order for a soft aquatic organism to form into a fossil, it would have to have been buried very rapidly. Likewise, fossil plants would need to be completely covered rapidly. Otherwise, the organism would rapidly be broken down and never fossilize. Such findings challenged the part of the evolutionary dogma that stated "fossils form slowly over long periods of time as they are slowly covered by silt at the bottom of the ocean or lake" that for many years pervaded evolutionary viewpoints on fossil formation. Conceptually, if fossils were covered slowly by sedimentation as they sat on the bottom of a lake or ocean, by the time the sediments built up enough to completely encase the organism, it would have long been completely destroyed by being degraded into nothing by scavengers and bacteria such that no fossils would ever form. The only way for sedimentary fossils to form is via very rapid deposition of enormous amounts of sediments, completely entombing organisms and protecting them from biodegradation that normally begins almost immediately upon death. It is true that the majority of fossils of all kinds are of high quality, with preservation of intricate details, including colors, which supports very rapid sedimentation. As more and more such fossils have been found, evolutionists have had to amend the "fossil formation position" a bit to allow that most fossils were, indeed, formed as a result of very rapid and massive sedimentation events such as that observed during a flood. Of course, though, the evolution model excludes a worldwide flood and so only "regional" flooding is considered as an evolutionary explanation for such sedimentation events. For creationists, the Great Flood explains the existence of most, but certainly not all, fossils since it is perfectly possible that some have been formed in the ensuing 4,500 years.

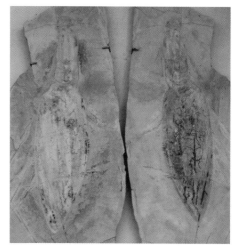

We will call this persistent clinging to uniformitarian principles, to millions and billions of years of fossil and rock formation despite faltering evidence, "**fossil dogma**." It is deeply entrenched in the evolution model and has four key parts with resultant predictions:

- Strata generally form slowly – with layer deposition taking thousands of years, and more. The total evolutionary time period the fossil record represents is about 3 billion years. This is the foundation of fossil dogma and cannot be amended because evolution requires the hundreds of millions and billions of years this part of fossil dogma supports.

- Fossils form as a result of localized massive sedimentation events, preceded and followed by eons of slow sedimentary layer formation.

- Because evolutionists believe that "less complex life forms evolved into more complex ones," these "primitive" (or "older") fossil organisms are found in lower strata and the more "complex" ("newer") fossils are found in the higher strata. That is the implication of fossil dogma in a sentence! "Old on bottom, new on top." Also, note that this tenet of fossil dogma is not always true. Fossils are frequently found "out of place," requiring re-working of the fossil record or alternative explanations as to why.

- Since less complex organisms directly evolved into more complex ones, an absolute prediction of fossil dogma is that the fossil record should be rich in the presence of so-called **transitional** (or **intermediate**) **forms**. Transitional or intermediate fossils are the remains of organisms that share characteristics of the ancestor organism that is being "evolved from" and characteristics of the organism that is being "evolved into."

Figure 19.10.6

Fossils as Filtered Through Evolution and Creation Models

The creation and evolution models treat the fossil record very differently. Evolution dogma dictates that organisms that are lower in the strata be older and less complex, with progressive increases in "complexity," from fish to amphibian to reptile to bird to mammal. This is _generally_ what is observed, true enough. Aquatic organisms (less complex evolutionarily) are in the lower sedimentary layers while the mammals (more complex) tend to be found in greater amounts in the higher layers. However, it is very important to note it is not like this is an "absolute pattern" so that this diagram means there is a clear progression of aquatic animals to amphibians to reptiles to mammals and birds. That isn't the case. The progression shown below is general but, for example, fully formed mammals looking every bit the "modern mammal" as those we see today – more than 430 different kinds – have been found in the same layers as the dinosaurs. They clearly lived together. The creation models views the fossil record as having been formed through a couple of different generic processes, with the stratification of fossils reflecting the order in which organisms would be expected to be buried in a world wide cataclysm. When God opened the fountains of the deep, that would have moved massive amounts of ocean sediments, trapping aquatic organisms first; hence, aquatic life is found in the lower strata. As the waters rose, less intelligent and/or slow organisms that live near the coasts would have been buried next, typically amphibians. As the waters continued to rise, the next slowest organisms in general – reptiles – would have been buried, while the smarter and more mobile mammals and birds temporarily found refuge on higher ground. Lastly, the majority of humans would have been buried as they would have been able to elude the Flood waters the longest. The creation model describes the observed fossil record somewhat better than the evolutionary one because it leaves room for finds that, evolutionarily, "don't fit." For example, if a mammal fossil is found "too low" in the strata from the evolutionist point of view, it can severely dusrupt evolutionary relationships because the mammals "aren't supposed to be there yet." In the creation model it is certainly possible (and, actually, expected) that some mammals would have been buried "earlier" in the Flood (and so appear "lower" in the strata) if they weren't fast enough or didn't realize they needed to run away from the water fast enough. This is a very active area of evolution-creation debate. Also, differing opinions are held evolutionist to evolutionst and creationist to creationist, but the predictive ability of the creation model seems more accurate than that of the evolutionary one.

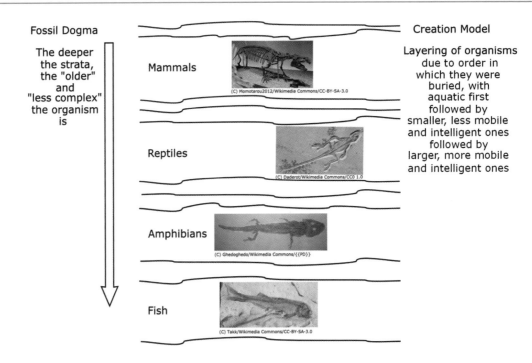

If one does not discard the many facts that argue against fossil dogma (some of which we are about to review), and instead considers that they may be leading to an explanation other than the naturalistic one of evolution, it is apparent that God has provided many clues that fossil dogma does not adequately explain the age of fossils or their relationships to one another over time. Using the Bible as the framework to build our interpretation of the fossil record, creation "fossil dogma" looks like:

- All life forms were created very close to one another in time, days 4 – 6 of creation.

- Since God said His Creation was "very good," there was no death of nephesh animals and man before the Fall; hence, no such fossils exist from before the Fall.

- Nephesh animals and man were vegetarian before the Flood, but Adam's sin introduced death to them and so post-Fall, pre-Flood fossils are not excluded from the creation model (but their existence is unlikely).

- Due to their superior genetic content and the fact that all nephesh animals and man were vegetarians for the entire time prior to the Flood, there would have been a _lot_ of animal and people mass that developed over about 1,500 years from creation to the Flood.

- There were, therefore, a lot of people, animals and plants present on earth on the day of the Flood. The vast majority of all fossils were formed when they were covered by very rapidly-deposited sedimentation in the global catastrophic conditions created by Noah's Flood.

- Because of the catastrophic conditions, one would expect that fossils "got jumbled" to some extent, but, certainly, a prediction of the creation model is that it is possible for fossils to be "preferentially located" in the sedimentary layers. Aquatic organisms and ones that live near the oceans would be expected to be found first (they are), followed by the smaller sized animal fossils (they aren't as fast or as smart, usually), then the larger ones (they are faster and tend to be smarter). Also, plants are expected throughout the sedimentary layers. These patterns are largely what is found. The creation model provides very reasoned predictions as to the appearance of the fossil record.

- Formation of some fossils since the Flood is not excluded from the creation model but the majority of fossils are believed to be from the Flood.

We are going to look carefully at the scientific observations relating to fossils and see if predictions of the evolutionary model or the creation model are supported.

Figure 19.10.7

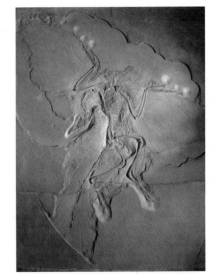

Archaeopteryx – Transitional Form or Bird?

Evolutionary dogma has it that a branch from within the dinosaur line evolved into birds. Many evolutionists view birds as dinosaurs with feathers. Even though new fossil finds make the "birds-are-dinosaurs" story harder and harder to make, almost all evolutionary texts call **Archaeopteryx** (two such fossils are shown at left) a transitional form – basically a dino-bird morph. However, what makes the argument more confusing is that, _according to other evolutionists, there is no better example of a fully functional and 100% bird than_ Archaeopteryx. It has fully formed bird feathers made for flying (not "inbetween feathers"), a foot made for perching (which shows that it had full flying capabilities), a keel (breastbone) for the attachment of the powerful flight muscles, a bird skull and brain, and hinged upper and lower jaws, all anatomical features of today's birds. Depending upon one's perspective, then, _Archaeopteryx_ is an intermediate form (some evolutionists) or 100% bird (some evolutionists and all creationists). The "it-is-an-intermediate-form" evolutionists say, "_Archaeopteryx_ has three little claws on each wing, just like the 3-fingered reptile claws." The "_Archaeopteryx_-is-a-bird" evolutionists and all creationists counter that comparative **embryology** (the scientific study of embryo development) clearly shows that the three reptile digits are the "thumb" (1st), "index" (2nd), and "middle" (3rd) digits but birds retain digits 2, 3 and 4. _If birds were "living dinosaurs," they should be the same digits._ In addition, creationists would point out even more problems with the _Archaeopteryx_-is-a-transitional-form argument – there is absolutely no proposed biochemical, physiological or genetic mechanisms for how the reptile lung evolved into the bird lung (they are very different), specifically how folds in reptile skin turned into the intricately structured feather and how cold-blooded dinosaurs became warm blooded birds. _These drastic changes in anatomy and physiology are impossible to explain evolutionarily._ Finally, even if all evolutionists agreed that it was an intermediate form (and if there was even a little possibility that _Archaeopteryx_ was an intermediate, it would seem that there would be no disagreement), there is the continued problem that "there isn't anything between a dinosaur and _Archaeopteryx_." By that I mean even the _Archaeopteryx_-is-a-transitional-form believers say that _Archaeopteryx_ is as close to a bird as one can get. Where are all the transitional forms between it and whatever it evolved from? The only one possible intermediate between dinosaurs and _Archaeopteryx_ that some evolutionists point to is 20 million years _younger_ than _Archaeopteryx_. Does it make sense to propose that a transitional form (the "parent," so to speak) between dinosaurs and _Archaeopteryx_ (the child) is 20 million years younger than its own child? It doesn't compute to have a dinosaur-_Archaeopteryx_ intermediate exist at the same time a fully functional and developed bird does. Perhaps the world's leading evolutionary bird paleontologist, recently retired professor Alan Feduccia, can sum _Archaeopteryx_ up for us:

> **"Paleontologists have tried to turn Archaeopteryx into an earthbound, feathered dinosaur. But it's not. It is a bird, a perching bird. And no amount of 'paleobabble' is going to change that."**

Despite thousands and thousands of known fossils, and the estimation that, if evolution were true then there would have been thousands of transitional forms in the pond-scum-to-person evolution story, there is not one indisputable example of a transitional form fossil. This strongly argues against the evolution model. Even Darwin himself stated that if no transitional forms were ever to be found, his theory would be invalid because transitional forms are such a strong prediction.

Darwin was deeply committed to fossil dogma. All evolutionists today believe some form of it, even to the point that if some very meaningful data or observation is made that contradicts that belief, rather than being more closely examined, it is discarded (we will be reviewing much of these data) and there is never any true scientific discourse to understand it. As long as new fossil data fits fossil dogma, everything is fine. If a scientist attempts to question fossil dogma, he or she risks losing funding for his or her work because the scientific establishment will not tolerate deviance from evolution ideology. Non-biblical thinking fueling fossil dogma has confused a lot of people and has led to very erroneous interpretation of the meaning of fossils and their relationships to one another and to us.

> **Beloved, do not believe every spirit, but test the spirits to see whether they are from God, for many false prophets have gone out into the world. By this you know the Spirit of God: every spirit that confesses that Jesus Christ has come in the flesh is from God, and every spirit that does not confess Jesus is not from God. This is the spirit of the**

> ***antichrist, which you heard was coming and now is in the world already.
> Little children, you are from God and have overcome them, for he who
> is in you is greater than he who is in the world. They are from the
> world; therefore they speak from the world, and the world listens to
> them. We are from God. Whoever knows God listens to us; whoever is
> not from God does not listen to us. By this we know the Spirit of truth
> and the spirit of error.*** *1 John 4:1 – 6*

Figure 19.10.8

The Evolutionary "Geologic Time Scale" – Deep Time

The concept of the **geologic time scale** – that the time-history of earth is reflected in rock strata and could be counted if one knew how strata accumulation related to time – likely dates, perhaps surprisingly, way back to the 17th century, to the catholic bishop Nicolas Steno (1638 – 1686). Evolutionists commonly teach that Steno did not accept the truth of scripture, but reading Steno's own words in his book *Prodromus*, it is clear that he believed the creation account because he actually correlated geological features with the Genesis creation and Flood passages in his scientific writings. He formulated the basic concept that rock layers are formed in succession and represent slices of time, but not the millions-of-years of time evolutionists today claim. Since then, the geologic time scale has been amended by evolutionists as new discoveries are made. Rather than being based upon objective data, the strata are assigned "geologic ages" based upon the specific type of fossils that are found in them. The so-called **index fossils** are ones that are so commonly found in a certain layer that when you find a certain index fossil, you automatically know you are in a certain layer and the evolutionary time frame to which it is supposed to correspond. By that I mean that "how far back in time a certain layer should be dated" is determined not by some sort of reproducible measurement or other objective data but, ultimately, by which fossils a layer contains. Based upon the billions-of-years-old-earth assumptions, strata are assigned "dates" based upon supposed evolutionary relationships between the fossilized organisms they contain. Because evolution requires that "fish are older than birds" and "amphibians are older than mammals," combined with fossil dogma that "less complex, older organisms" should be found in deeper layers as compared to more modern forms, the earliest fossil remains of each are excluded from appearing in the same strata based not upon identifiable scientific fact but simply upon assumed evolutionary relationships. Practically, what that means is let's say evolutionists believe that a rock layer is thought to be a certain age because it contains a specific index fossil, but then a different fossil is found in the same strata that doesn't "belong there" because this new fossil is evolutionarily expected to be "older" than the index fossil. This causes a problem for evolutionists, requiring constant re-arranging of the "dates" that organisms were said to have lived because they must preserve the "evolutionary relationship" between the organisms. For example, in 1999 the evolution story-age for the origination of the eukaryotic cell was changed from 1.7 to 2.7 billion years ago, despite there not being any solid evidence of eukaryotic organisms in the fossil record for that entire newly created 1 billion year gap. The "evidence" used to push the date back are molecules called steranes found in some partially metamorphosed rock in Australia. Prokaryotes do not produce steranes, eukaryotes do and so, if these truly are steranes, then eukaryotes did produce them. One problem here is that steranes require oxygen to be synthesized and oxygen was not supposed to have been present in the atmosphere 2.7 billion years ago. Therefore, the entire atmospheric evolutionary history needs to be rewritten. The main problem that evolutionists have in relation to the geologic time scale is that evolution is assumed to be true; as such, it is unbending and this unproven and unprovable conclusion is used to provide the logic behind dating the strata as they are. Note that while creationists obviously disagree with the time frames, they do refer to the strata using the terminology based upon the era, period and epoch names as shown below because the naming system allows a common frame of reference as to which layers are being referred. The naming system is valid regardless of how "old" they are purported to be.

Millions of years	Eon	Era	Period	Epoch	Organisms
				Holocene (Recent)	"modern" humans arise
0.01			Quaternary	Pleistocene	humans arise
1.8				Pliocene	large carnivores arise
5.3			Neogene	Miocene	mammals diversify
23.8				Oligocene	diverse grazing animals arise
33.7				Eocene	early horses arise
54.8		Cenozoic	Paleogene	Paleocene	more modern mammals arise
65			Cretaceous		mass extinctions, including dinosaurs
144			Jurassic		dinosaurs diversify; birds arise
208		Mesozoic	Triassic		primitive mammals arise; mass extinction; dinosaurs arise
245			Permian		seed plants arise; reptiles diversify; mass extinction
290			Carboniferous		reptiles arise
354			Devonian		amphibians arise; mass extinction
417			Silurian		land plants arise
443			Ordovician		fish arise; mass extinction
490	Phanerozoic	Paleozoic	Cambrian		marine invertebrates arise
540					
4,600	Precambrian (a "supereon") with its own eons, eras and periods				prokaryotes, then eukaryotes arise

Formation   of   the   Earth

Since evolutionists operate under fossil dogma, that should mean that they do so because scientific observations about fossils always (or nearly always) fit the "strata form over hundreds of thousands to millions of years and fossils-are-millions-of-years-old" concept. However, the scientific data often do not, and this is why creationists continue to question fossil dogma and conduct their own scientific studies on the subject. Based upon fossil dogma assumptions, there are many predictions about the fossil record that should be true if the dogma is true. Let's look at some of the predictions of fossil dogma, what the scientific observations actually are and how the creation model explains the same fact.

Figure 19.10.9

Polystrate Fossils
This picture shows a fossilized tree trunk that spans dozens of strata, called a **polystrate fossil** (evolutionists refer to these as "**upright fossil trees**"). Note that it is at 90 degree angles to the surrounding strata. Evolutionarily, the only explanation for such fossils is that the tree remained upright while it was covered with sediments and was somehow prevented from rotting for thousands or tens of thousands of years as the strata slowly piled up and formed around it. The evolutionary hypothesis is that the trees continued living as they were covered by sediments near the bottom of the trunk, eventually being once and for all covered by a massive "sediment event." There are many hundreds, if not thousands, of these fossils, with some finds being so numerous they are described as "forests." There are, though, several problems with the evolutionary explanation of polystrate trees, including the rarity of an intact system of fossil roots being attached to the polystrate tree trunks and the fact that it is common that polystrate tree trunks span one or more coal strata, which supposedly take hundreds of thousands of years – or longer – to form (the polystrate tree could not remain unrotted for hundreds of thousands of years). In addition, there are no animal fossils preserved in areas where "forests" of such polystrate fossils exist. A "sedimentation event" massive enough to entomb forests of trees 15 or more feet deep in sediments in a matter of seconds would have also included a lot of animal life since all known forests are teeming with animals. In the creation model, polystrate tree fossils/forests are not made by trees that were fossilized "as they grew;" instead, they are formed when trees are dislodged by a flood, float in the water vertically until becoming water logged and then sink to the bottom, where they impale many feet through the soft bottom, upright. Polystrate forests are explained by observed scientific phenomenon, such as what was observed when Mt. St. Helens erupted in 1980. Thousands of trees were uprooted and left floating together in Spirit Lake, eventually sinking, roots down, to the bottom and lodging vertically many feet into the layering muck. Not only are polystrate fossils unable to adequately be explained by the evolutionary model, the apparent first steps in their formation has even been observed and is very consistent with the polystrate fossil formation process prediction of the creation model.

Henry Morris' and John Whitcomb's 1961 **The Genesis Flood** provided a firm scientific geological basis for interpreting the Bible exactly as God wrote it, which was – and is – in direct contrast to fossil dogma. Since that time, creationists have been forwarding the argument that neither fossils nor strata form slowly. Over the past 50 years, the creationist model has built onto that of Drs. Morris and Whitcomb as new discoveries are made. One of the most interesting has been that geological experiments and observation from natural floods show that strata can form extremely quickly, on the order of twenty or more strata 25 feet in depth. Time and again, scientific observations support the creation model and teach us that evolutionary deep time is not the only way to explain things. However, evolutionists can't ideologically budge from their millions-of-years position, or else their theory is lost. Evolutionary geologist Derek Ager PhD knows this:

> "*...we cannot escape the conclusion that sedimentation was at times very rapid indeed and at other times there were long breaks in sedimentation, though it looks both uniform and continuous.*"

Dr. Ager acknowledges two important scientific findings regarding fossilization that all evolutionists know – sedimentation rates must be very rapid in order for fossils to form but at the same time the sedimentation rate cannot *always* be so fast because, if it was, there are presently not enough strata on earth to support the age of 4 or 5 billion years old that fossil dogma requires. The evolutionary billions-of-years-old viewpoint therefore requires an "offset" to allow for the necessary rapid strata formation for fossils to form *and* evolutionary time scales. So, the necessary rapid fossil-forming strata deposition needs to be interspersed with "long breaks" in strata formation *even though strata formation looks "uniform,"* or always the same. In essence, Dr. Ager is saying that the strata appear to have been formed the same way – uniform – but the evolution model relies upon two very different processes (i.e. non-uniform) to explain strata that appear to have been formed through the same process.

And this is kind of a big deal. If the uniformitarian evolution concepts are correct, then there must be a way to distinguish between strata that are formed from two entirely different processes. Either the uniform process of slow strata formation or the uniform process of rapid strata formation has to explain the geological picture. This is an irreconcilable condition for the evolution model. It cannot be both ways – if uniform slow strata formation is the process, then fossils never would have formed and if uniform rapid strata formation is the uniform process, then there aren't enough strata on the planet as would be seen for billions-of-years of rapid strata formation. Finally, if strata form due to a combination of the two processes, then the strata can't physically look the same. If different processes caused them to form then that difference needs to be reflected in the way the strata appear. But is isn't – "it looks both uniform and continuous."

Evolutionists are in a doctrinal pickle, but ideology, not science, is what is relied upon to support the model. Recall the atheist geneticist Richard Lewontin's quote:

> **"We take the side of science in spite of the patent absurdity of some of its constructs, in spite of its failure to fulfill many of its extravagant promises of health and life, in spite of the tolerance of the scientific community for unsubstantiated just-so stories, *because we have a prior commitment, a commitment to materialism*."** *(emphasis mine)*

> ***For the wrath of God is revealed from heaven against all ungodliness and unrighteousness of men, who by their unrighteousness suppress the truth. For what can be known about God is plain to them, because God has shown it to them. For his invisible attributes, namely, his eternal power and divine nature, have been clearly perceived, ever since the creation of the world, in the things that have been made. So they are without excuse. For although they knew God, they did not honor him as God or give thanks to him, but they became futile in their thinking, and their foolish hearts were darkened. Claiming to be wise, they became fools, and exchanged the glory of the immortal God for images resembling mortal man and birds and animals and creeping things.*** *Romans 1:18 – 23*

Creationists agree that the strata reflect a uniform deposition process, from a certain point of view – the point of view that the "uniform process" is that the only way that fossil containing strata could have been formed is through the extremely violent conditions of Noah's Flood. Such an event caused massive sediment movement and deposition and eventually thousands of layers formed, with the entombment of billions of organisms – some in the act of eating or giving birth – that led to them becoming fossils. Geological observations and more recent experimentation on sediment layering are compatible with the creation model, while at the same time are very difficult to interpret with consistency in the evolutionary model.

The *Scipionyx samniticus* fossil, seen in Figure 19.10.10, points out another incidence of fossil dogma and millions-of-years thinking blinding scientists from the truth and leading toward conclusions that are not supported by the data. Evolutionists Cristiano

Dal Sasso and Marco Signore, the paleontologists who have extensively studied the *Scipionyx* fossil, have postulated that it likely had feathers of some sort. Now, that is confusing because one would think such a statement would most certainly be based upon the finding that this highly preserved specimen, *perhaps the best preserved specimen ever found relative to "soft parts"* (feathers are "soft parts"), has evidence of primitive feather imprints around it. Recall the feather imprints around *Archaeopteryx*. Such imprints are practically universally found on bird fossils. However, such is not at all the case. *Despite that fact that Scipionyx shows absolutely no evidence of anything even resembling a feather*, Dal Sasso and Signore believe it probably did have them (along with some other evolutionists, but not all).

Figure 19.10.10

Fossilized Soft Tissues
These are images of a fossilized dinosaur, *Scipionyx samniticus*, supposedly 100 million evolution years old. It was found in Italy in the early 1980's. This fossil demonstrates another scientific fact that is very consistent with rapid fossilization thousands of years ago and not consistent with fossilization millions of years ago – it has very well preserved soft tissues. If you look closely in the right image, you can see that this fossil is three dimensional and that there are actually well-defined soft tissues. That "curl" of lighter-colored tissue in the middle just above the forelegs is intestine! Detailed microscopic analysis of this fossil has identifiable liver, intestinal and skeletal muscle tissue and even individual cells! If this organism were truly encased 100 million years ago, it is very difficult to scientifically explain the presence of *identifiable cells* in a specimen that is supposedly that old. No evolutionist would have predicted such a finding as evidenced by how stunned the evolutionary establishment was at such a finding. However, from the creation model perspective, soft tissue being present in fossils that are only several thousand years old would fully be expected. It is *not possible* to explain identifiable soft parts in the evolution model but is not surprising in the creation model. Holding the evolution and creation model up to the scientific data, we continue to see that the creation model is fully supported while the evolutionary model not only is not supported, but some scientific data, such as fossilized soft parts, specifically argues against it.

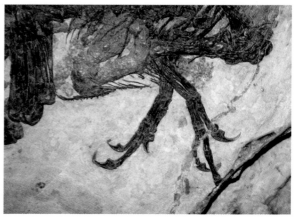

© Givanni Dall'Orto/Wikimedia Commons/{{PD}}   © Givanni Dall'Orto/Wikimedia Commons/{{PD}}

So, the question is, "Why would they make that statement if there is no scientific data that supports it when it is clear that, if this animal did have feathers, they would have been as well preserved as all of the rest of the soft parts in the fossil?" *Because fossil dogma requires it*. If birds evolved from dinosaurs, then it is critical that somewhere along the way an intermediate form is found. If *Archaeopteryx* were, indeed, a bird-reptile transitional form, then there would be universal agreement among evolutionists that it is a transitional form. But, there isn't, and so the effort is to find another candidate. Even though *Scipionyx* is fully a reptile and there is absolutely no evidence of feathers, some evolutionists still postulate that the animal *could have* had them. That conclusion flows from fossil dogma, not objective science.

Fossils like *Scipionyx* reveal another fact about fossil dogma – just as the dogma blinded evolutionists for many decades about *how* fossil-containing strata form, it also has kept them from making the revolutionary discovery that there are lots of fossils with soft tissues! Why did fossil dogma prevent this? *Because there being soft tissues in fossils is absolutely not a prediction of the evolution model; therefore, no one looked*! Why would someone look for soft tissue in tens-of-millions-of-years-old fossils when everyone knows soft tissues don't last that long? But, preserved soft tissue in fossils of all kinds abound! It is becoming increasingly more common to find soft tissues in fossils – muscle, intestine and other organs, cartilage and even cells, proteins and DNA! According to a 2005 article in *Science*:

> ***It has long been assumed that the process of fossilization results in the destruction of virtually all original organic components of an organism, and it has been hypothesized that original molecules will either be lost or altered to the point of nonrecognition over relatively short time spans.***

Pretty much every single evolutionist, including Mary Schweitzer, the first person to look for and find "ancient" soft tissues, was taken by surprise that these supposedly tens of millions of years old fossils still had original organic matter in them. There just shouldn't be any, having been replaced by minerals many, many millions of years ago. At first, the evolutionary explanation centered around an unusual phenomenon affecting the individual fossils with the soft tissues that somehow allowed its soft tissues to be preserved; however, as more and more fossils are found to have soft tissues, cells, proteins and DNA, that explanation no longer is sufficient. _It seems to increasingly be the norm that fossils have soft tissues, not the exception_ – the *Scipionyx* fossil, mastodon teeth, *T rex* fossils, mosasaur fossils – all found to have soft tissues. Evolutionists still have no unifying answer to this statement from a 2006 *Discover* magazine article:

> ***By all the rules of paleontology, such traces of life should have long since drained from the bones. It is a matter of faith among scientists that soft tissues can survive at most for a few tens of thousands of years.***

The "rules of paleontology" are the same false belief system that drives the assumption that fossils are millions and millions of years old – fossil dogma. As soon as evolutionists started to find soft tissues in these specimens, a re-thinking of how old they really are _should have been mandated_ by the evolutionary community because we know that soft tissues should _not_ last for more than several thousand years after the organism dies.

Scientific studies have shown that biomolecules are very reactive with their surrounding environments and degrade quickly – this is universally true. For example, collagen, one of the major components of cartilage, was identified in a supposedly-75-million-year-old mosasaur fossil. Scientific studies have demonstrated that the half life of collagen is fairly limited, on the order of 1,000 years. The **half life** of something is the length of time it takes for the original amount to decay or degrade such that only one-half of the original amount is left. With collagen having a half life of 1,000 years, that means that 1,000 years after an organism dies, one half of the collagen it had when it died will be left in the sample; 2,000 years after the organism dies there will be one-quarter the amount it had when it died (which is one-half the amount that was present at 1,000 years after death); 3,000 years after the organism dies there will be one-eighth the amount (one-half of the amount that was present at 2,000 years), and so on. Eventually, after so many half lives, there will be such a small amount of the original substance left that it would not be possible to identify the tissue as cartilage because the molecules that make up the majority of the cartilage – collagen – would be gone.

Figure 19.10.11

Fossil Dogma Prevented Significant Scientific Discovery for Decades

Early on in our discussion of creation and evolution, we discussed that it was the belief that the great scientists of the past have had that they were exploring for answers within God's created framework that allowed them to make the discoveries they did. The presence of soft tissues in fossils shows the opposite of that – evolutionary dogma _prevented_ scientists from finding soft tissues in fossils for 150 years. Why? Because since they believe fossils are tens of millions of years old, of course there aren't any soft tissues left! However, Dr. Mary Schweitzer, the first scientist to find soft tissue (in a _Tyrannosaurus rex_, left and center, the actual leg bone Dr. Schweitzer's team used, along with microscopic slides showing branching blood vessels) started a revolution since first going against that evolutionary dogma and looking for soft tissue when it shouldn't exist. But it did, and that revolution has led to the discovery of soft tissue, proteins and DNA in multiple other specimens. The prediction of the evolution model is that soft tissues specifically should _not be found_ since fossils are many millions of years old. Since that prediction is false, it would seem to be a reasonable next step to reconsider how old fossils really are. Fossil soft tissues are not a surprising finding in the creation model.

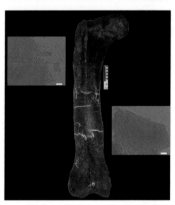

Just how long is that? How many half lives must pass before the original substance is "gone" (i.e. non-detectable)? Certainly, it must be many thousands, _if not hundreds of thousands_, of half lives since this fossil that is supposedly 75 million years old (75,000 half lives of collagen) still has collagen in it. Well, actually, evolutionists and creationists agree that, generally, _it is assumed that after 10 half lives (for any substance), the original substance is, practically speaking, entirely gone_. That means that for cartilage, after only about 10,000 years, the collagen should be gone. There is no way that it should last tens of millions of years, and evolutionists have not proposed any mechanism through which any tissue or molecules could be preserved tens of thousands of times longer than its scientifically-studied half live would estimate it could last. Why? Because there is no plausible mechanism! You would think that such scientific observations – such facts – would lead to serious reconsideration of evolution as an origins and diversity model, but so far it hasn't. Evolutionary ideology in the form of fossil dogma, not scientific fact and reason, must rule in the evolution model.

Let's look a little more closely at this because it is important to understand where the evolutionary argument goes wrong. It doesn't falter in the "soft-tissues-shouldn't-last-millions-of-years." The science supports that it is very reasonable for evolutionists to have assumed this because that is what the scientific observations support. _The mistake they have made, and continue to make, is to ignore the very clear scientific evidence that their fossils-are-millions-of-years-old theory is false._ They are willingly ignorant, as 2:Peter 3:3-6 tells us. _Scientific study supports the conclusion that soft tissues, cells and biomolecules degrade in thousands of years; therefore they absolutely should not exist in millions of years old fossils. Since there are soft tissues in fossils, they OBVIOUSLY ARE NOT MORE THAN SEVERAL THOUSAND YEARS OLD_. It is not a complicated logic trail one takes in order to arrive at this conclusion.

The data that very specifically contradicts fossil dogma is perfectly compatible with the creation model. If most fossils are the result of the Flood 4,300 years ago, it is perfectly reasonable – _and fully expected and predictable_ – that there would be some identifiable soft tissues. The scientific predictions of the creation model, which fully contradict many aspects of fossil dogma, are what is scientifically observed.

19.11 RADIOMETRIC DATING – EVIDENCE FOR EVOLUTION OR AN EXPECTED SCIENTIFIC FACT COMPATIBLE WITH THE CREATION MODEL?

There is probably no single area that has created so much origins confusion as the subject of **radiometric dating**, which is the pursuit of providing the "age" of materials by measuring the amount of a specific radioactive element (or elements) in the matter and then using the measured amounts to calculate time into the past the matter was formed (if the matter being dated is rock) or the organism died (if the matter being dated is organic). Evolutionists like to tell us, and those in the media love to promote, that radiometric dating provides independent verification of how old something is. Radiometric dates are presented as "objective fact" corroborating the billions of years old earth. There is perhaps no one lie as powerful as this that has caused Christians to abandon their faith in absolute biblical truth.

After all, if radiometric dating is "objective scientific data that independently verifies how old a fossil is" or that dates human remains to more than 200,000 years ago, then how can using the generations listed in the Bible to arrive at an age of "only" about 6,000 years old be true? The implications of the Truth of the Bible and radiometric dating are in direct contradiction to one another, every bit as much as evolution and creation are. Many a young person, fully invested in understanding the Bible and the True Word of God, upon learning that radiometric dating seems "so scientific" and tells us the earth is billions of years old, decides that the creation model is wrong. Well, let's see if that stacks up.

Figure 19.11.1

How Radiometric Dating Works

All radiometric dating methods rely on the same generic principles in order to obtain the "age" of a sample. Some of the principles are based in objective science, such as the fact that "radioactive" (unstable) isotopes do exist and do degenerate into more stable element forms. Some of the principles, though, are based on assumptions that are scientifically unprovable, rendering radiometric dating as nothing more than sophisticated guessing. The provable science is that in any given sample, whether rock or organic matter, there are mixtures of both stable and unstable isotopes. Also true is that, over time, the unstable isotope, called the **parent isotope**, decays into the more stable form, called the **daughter isotope** and the amounts of parent and daughter in any given sample can be measured. This is where the provable science ends and the unprovable assumptions begin for radiometric dating. Evolutionists believe that, by measuring the relative amounts of parent-daughter isotopes in a sample, it is then possible to calculate how far into the past the rock formed or the organism died. In this example, we see the potassium-argon decay cycle. Potassium-40 (K-40), the parent, is an unstable form of potassium that decays into argon-40 (Ar-40), the daughter. Evolutionists believe the half life of K-40 is 1.25 billion years, which means that after 1.25 billion years, the amount of K-40 is half of what it was when it started. Conversely, the daughter isotope, Ar-40, should have increased in the same relative amount that the K-40 decreased. This is the basic concept that evolutionists follow when they perform radiometric dating and we are going to look deeper into why this simply does not work.

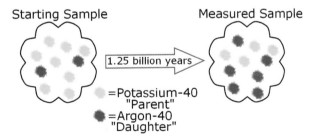

Starting Sample   Measured Sample

1.25 billion years

= Potassium-40 "Parent"
= Argon-40 "Daughter"

If we dig a little more into radiometric dating, we find serious reasons to question the objectiveness of the principles that underlie it as a "scientific pursuit" because, ultimately, _all dating methods are based upon assumptions that cannot be proven_. Once we know how the methods work, we realize that no radiometric dating method provides "accurate" or "independently verified" ages. The end of the story here is that all the radiometric dating techniques do is confirm that man can build radiometric dating techniques that confirm how old he already thinks a sample is to begin with. It is absolutely impossible to prove that an object is a certain age unless you know unequivocally that it is that age. Let's see what I mean.

There are a number of different radiometric dating methods, all of which are based upon provable scientific concepts, but that isn't all upon which they are based. Many people do not understand how radiometric dating works, and erroneously believe that the age of a sample is the byproduct of the process used to date it, meaning the dating methods provide a direct "measurement" of how old the sample is. That isn't the case. All radiometric dates are calculated dates, not directly measured, and the only way the dates can be calculated is if several assumptions are made, assumptions that cannot be proven.

Figure 19.11.2

Radiometric Dating Methods are Based on Assumptions

There are many different radiometric dating methods, all of which are based upon some sound scientific principles while at the same time they are based on other, unprovable assumptions. This table describes three of the most common radiometric dating methods, as well as the "evolutionary age range" of the method. The age range is determined by the half life of the unstable parent isotope – the shorter the half life, the shorter into the past the evolutionists believe the method is reliable to date materials.

Dating Method	Science of the Method and Associated Unprovable Assumptions	Dating Method "Age Range"
Carbon-14	Can only be used to date organic matter, so this method dates once-living things, not rocks themselves. Most atmospheric carbon is the "normal" form of carbon 12 (C^{12}, the daughter, with 6 protons and 6 neutrons) and just a very little is carbon 14 (C^{14}, the unstable parent, with 6 protons and 8 neutrons). C^{14} is formed when high energy cosmic energy from the sun enters our upper atmosphere and hits elements, displacing neutrons from their nuclei. These neutrons then bash into nitrogen (N^{14} with 7 protons and 7 neutrons), which causes N^{14} to lose a proton and gain a neutron, forming C^{14}. Plants incorporate both C^{12} and C^{14} into their structures during photosynthesis in the same relative amounts they are present in the atmosphere. Animals then eat plants, transferring both forms from the plant to the animal that ate it. When plants and animals die, evolutionists believe they no longer incorporate C^{14} into their bodies and the unstable C^{14} starts to degrade. By measuring the relative amounts of C^{12} and C^{14} in a previously living sample, evolutionists believe they can determine how long ago into the past the organism died. _One unprovable evolutionary assumption_ is that it is possible to know how much C^{14} was in the atmosphere in the past. Evolutionists believe that the amount of C^{14} has reached a steady state such that no more is being added to or removed from the atmosphere, but measurements indicate that the amount of C^{14} presently is increasing – it _hasn't_ reached steady state. That means that the evolutionary assumption that C^{14} has been in a steady state for billions of years may not be true, which cripples one of the evolutionary assumptions underlying C^{14} dating. This makes it _impossible_ to know the "starting amount" of the C^{14} in the sample. Without knowing that, there is no way to accurately calculate how much parent has degraded, which makes it impossible to know how many half lives have passed, which makes it impossible to calculate the age of the sample. Not being able to know how much "starting parent amount" was in the sample is an unprovable assumption that all radiometric dating methods share.	Evolutionists believe the half life of C^{14} is 5730 years, so this method is used to date materials suspected to be <60,000 years old

It is therefore important to consider the implications of a process that doesn't directly measure the age of the material being dated. Although sometimes we don't consider this, probably the most important thing to realize is that radiometric dating methods didn't just appear out of nowhere. It isn't like a machine grows on a tree and you go out and pick one, turn it on, set it to "radiocarbon dating" or "thorium-uranium dating" and start dating rocks and organic matter, obtaining the "correct age" of the material every time. Of course, these dating methods all had to be painstakingly developed.

But, how does one develop a way to measure how old something is when there is no way to know if the result the method is giving you is the "right answer?" When calibrating your dating method – or how you ensure that it gives you the right result – how would you _know_ beyond a shadow of a doubt that some rock you are dating _really is_ how old the method is telling you it is? Objectivity tells you that, when looking at a rock or a fossil or dead organic matter, _the only way to know for sure how old it is would be to have been there when it was formed or when it died_. There is no other way to know with 100% certainty that a rock or dead organic matter is a given age unless you were there when the rock formed or the living thing died.

Figure 19.11.2, Continued

Dating Method	Science of the Method and Associated Unprovable Assumptions	Dating Method "Age Range"
Potassium-Argon (K-Ar)	Used to date igneous rocks. The radioactive potassium isotope (parent) degrades into argon (daughter), an inert gas. Once the molten rock solidifies, the potassium starts to degrade into argon and is trapped in the rock. Theoretically, the more argon the sample contains, the longer the time the potassium parent has been degrading into argon; hence, the older it is. By measuring how much argon a rock contains, evolutionists use that to calculate how long ago into the past the rock formed. _Another unprovable evolutionary assumption_ is that no process other than radioactive decay can change the amounts of the parent or daughter in the sample. Evolutionists recognize that there are processes besides the decay cycle that can change the parent-daughter amounts, but they think that they are somehow able to tell when a process other than radioactive decay has occurred to alter the parent-daughter amounts, and when such process hasn't. Creationists object to this since evolutionists do not use any scientific fact to identify when such a process has occurred; instead, they rely on their opinion of whether or not such a process contaminated the sample. This is not scientific. Since there are known processes other than radioactive decay that cause parent-daughter amounts to change, then that invalidates "the objectivity" of all radiometric dating processes.	Evolutionists believe the half life of K-40 is 1.25 billion years, so this method is used to date materials suspected to be >100,000 years old
Uranium-238 (U-238)	Uranium-238 (parent), a naturally occurring and radioactive element, very slowly decays into lead (daughter). _Another unprovable evolutionary assumption_ of radiometric dating is that radioactive decay has always occurred at the same rate at which it occurs today. That is to say that evolutionists believe that nothing can change how fast an isotope decays; the rate _is always and has always been the same_. There is evidence from creationist and evolutionist researchers that the "decay rates are stable" dogma isn't entirely supported by emerging scientific data. If decay rates are not stable, then calculating a sample's age based upon the assumption that it is obviously isn't accurate.	The half life of U-238 is 4.47 billion years, so this method is used to date materials suspected to be more than several million years old

Figure 19.11.3

Creation's Eye Witness to Everything

Evolutionists have no ability to prove any of the assumptions upon which dating methods are built, and the ultimate one that undoes radiometric dating is the fact that there is no way to prove that something that is supposedly millions or billions of years old is really that old. In essence, that means that the radiometric dating techniques are nothing more than a technological fallacy. No one was there to see a rock formed millions of years ago. No one documented when in time a tree was alive 300 million years ago. Evolutionists refuse to acknowledge this is _the_ Achilles' heel of radiometric dating. The creation model does not suffer from such lack of provability. God has been there from before "in the beginning" and, as such, there is an eyewitness to everything that has ever happened. Fortunately, God wrote a lot of things down for us and His Word is absolutely true! Whenever anyone says something is true that specifically goes against God's Word, then we know it is automatically false. Such is the entire nature of evolution, which has been an anti-God explanation of the origin of life from its very inception.

Of course, evolutionarily speaking, when dating fossils, it is not possible to know when the rock formed or the once living thing died. Therefore, the answer to the critical question of, "How does one know how to calibrate a method to provide the age of something no one can prove is a certain age" is _the_ critically important radiometric dating-related answer. Since, then, being able to compare the result of the dating method to the _known_ age of the sample cannot be used for calibration purposes, what is used? What is the surrogate information used to determine if the age of a sample the dating method is giving is "accurate?" That is to say that, when a researcher radiometrically dates something, how does he know he is getting the "right age?"

Quite interestingly – _and not objectively_ – _the surrogate used for calibrating all radiometric dating processes is the evolutionary assumption of how old the material is already suspected to be_! Yes, that is correct. The "objective" data that is used to determine whether or not the radiometrically-obtained age is "accurate" is the already-suspected age of the object! The ultimate attestation as to "how old something is" isn't any objective and scientific process used to date it or any known fact about the age of the material; rather, it is the evolutionist's subjective and completely unsubstantiated assessment of "how old we already think this is." "I found this fossil in a layer that in 1906 was dated at 55 million years old. If my radiometrically obtained date doesn't fit with that, then I need to calibrate my dating method until it does." The evolution model uses the assumption that the model itself is true in order to calibrate the radiometric dating methods. As evolutionary paleontologist Ronald West, PhD puts it:

> **"Contrary to what most scientists write, the fossil record does not support the Darwinian theory of evolution because it is this theory which we use to interpret the fossil record. By doing so, we are guilty of circular reasoning if we say the fossil record supports this theory."**

Figure 19.11.4

"Calibrating" the Radiometric Dating Process

All radiometric dating techniques are calibrated to provide ages based upon the already-determined evolutionary-ages of rock layers. For example, the potassium-argon dating method is used to date rocks that are suspected to be more than 100,000 years old. At right is an area of the geologic column from the Grand Canyon, containing the Redwall Limestone, Temple Butte Formation and Muav Limestone. If I were working on calibrating the potassium-argon method and I tested a sample of rock from the Muav Limestone layer and obtained parent-daughter measurements so that I calculated a date of 200 million years into the past, how would I "know" whether or not that was "right?" The only way I would know would be to consult the agreed-upon geologic strata table and see that evolutionists, with their pre-supposed and completely "un-provable" billions-of-years-old philosophy had long ago (way before radiometric dating was perfected) determined that the Muav layer was approximately 500 million years old. If I was an evolutionist I would then need to re-work my dating method so that it came up with the "right" result or identify an explanation as to why I was getting the "wrong" date. There is no absolute way to "double check" the dating method calibration. The ultimate date of the layer/fossil is determined by the already long-ago-agreed-upon age of the layer, not by any objective result spit out by the machine. These dating methods are not infallible and, in reality, the only thing that the radiometric dating techniques end up doing is "confirming" the already agreed-upon rock layer ages by being calibrated specifically to do just that. As the geological guidebook *Rocks and Landscapes of the Townsville District* (for an area of Queensland, Australia) puts it,

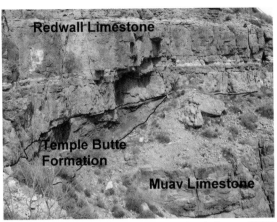

© Wikimedia Commons/{{PD}}

> **"Also, the relative ages (radiometric dating results) must always be consistent with the geological evidence....if a contradiction occurs, then the cause of the error needs to be established or the radiometric results are unacceptable."**

This reinforces what we have been learning – the ultimate authority is not the radiometric dating analysis but the pre-established dates of the geologic strata. If the radiometric date doesn't agree with the pre-supposed age of the rock layer or fossil, then evolutionary geologists throw the date age out and stick with the already-determined age. That is really not the definition of objective science providing absolutely true "ages."

Since the ages of the rock layers have already been determined by people who think the earth is billions of years old, of course the dating methods will be calibrated to give long ages. They have to if evolution is to be considered valid. If the radiometric dating method gets an age close to how old the evolutionists have already determined it is, great. If not, *they recalibrate the method until it does* or they throw the dating result out and stick with their already-determined strata age, anyway. Radiometric dating "confirms" that the earth and fossils are old because the methods have specifically been calibrated to give the evolutionists old dates. That is not "objective and unbiased science."

It is this invalid circular logic path described by Dr. West that evolutionists use to show that radiometric dating is giving them the true age of the material":

Q – "How do you know that the radiometrically obtained age of this fossil is 300 million years old?"

A – "Because it was found in a layer that is 300 million years old."

Q – "How do you know the layer is 300 million years old?"

A – "Because the fossil dated at 300 million years old."

That is not valid, logical thought. The "radiometrically obtained age" *is not* a scientific absolute of "how old the material really is" but instead reflects how well the radiometric dating process has been designed/calibrated to arrive at the long-ago agreed-upon ages of the rock layers that they are supposed to be independently dating. It is a self-fulfilling prophecy. Whatever tweaking that needed to be done to the radiometric dating techniques in order to give the "expected dates" was done in order to obtain these dates, which ultimately are based upon the suspected age of the rock layer being dated or in which the fossil was found, not based upon strict rules of nuclear decay physics. The earth always "dates" as being "old" (even though it isn't) because all of the radiometric dating methods have been specifically calibrated to measure it old!

This is not to say that radiometric dating is purposely a dishonest process or that radiometric dating is of no use at all. Evolutionists truly believe they are practicing "good science." What I am saying, though, is that radiometric dating, like all man-designed systems, is perfectly designed to get the results it gets. The methods are all calibrated specifically to provide dates that have already been identified as being "correct" based upon the assumption that the earth is billions of years old. Nothing more, nothing less. It is clear that we need to approach radiometric dating with skepticism, not with unquestioned awe and universal acceptance.

Figure 19.11.5

Radiocarbon Dating "Really Old Stuff" – Major Blind Spot for Fossil Dogma

Radiometric dating exposes many evolutionary blind spots caused by fossil dogma. Usually, when scientific data directly contradict the predictions of a hypothesis, that hypothesis is thrown out. In radiometric dating, we see contradictions occur frequently, yet no real re-think of the process ever occurs. For example, nuclear decay physics predicts that, when 9 or 10 half lives have passed, then the amount of the radioactive element is non-detectable. Therefore, that _absolutely means_ that, when dating the age of something that is expected to be old enough that more than 10 half lives have passed for a given parent, then there should not be any detectable parent in the sample being measured. What do I mean? The half life of C^{14} is 5730 years, and so, 10 half-lives later (about 60,000 years after something is dead), _there shouldn't be any C^{14} left in the sample_. Period. Suspected to be more than 60,000 years old, no C^{14}. However, that is not the case. In the 1990's, fossil organic matter started to be tested for C^{14}, led mainly through the efforts of the Institute for Creation Research, _and in virtually every instance when organic matter expected to be well older than 60,000 years has been C^{14} dated, there has been C^{14} found in the sample_. This should automatically result in evolutionists reconsidering the radiocarbon dating methods or at the very least the assumptions upon which it is based. If something expected to be over 60,000 years has detectable C^{14} in it, then either your assumption about how old stuff is is way off, or your radiocarbon dating method doesn't work. Below is a partial listing of specific finds, the expected age of the material (based upon the long-ago identified evolutionary ages of the rock layers in which the material was found) and the age the material gave when it was radiocarbon dated. _None of these samples should have had any C^{14} in them since they are all supposedly millions of years old, but they all do_. Note that the "radiocarbon dated age" does not mean that the sample really is as old as that date because the radiocarbon dating method was specifically calibrated to give ages of up to 60,000 years. The main point here is that C^{14} is found in virtually all organic matter, even if it is supposedly hundreds-of-millions-of-years-old gasoline, oil, coal and diamond. This is, frankly, unexplainable from an evolutionary standpoint, but very explainable if the earth is about 6,000 years old since everything would be expected to have C^{14} in it. Again, we see a picture in which observable scientific facts are neither predicted by nor explainable with the evolutionary model, but fit very well with a creation model.

Material and Location of Find	Evolutionist-suspected Age Based Upon Layer in Which It Was Found	Radiocarbon Dated "Age" (this doesn't mean this is how "old" it is – the point here is that the material contains C^{14} and it should not if it was really as old as evolutionists say it is)
Wood found in Marlstone Rock Bed, Jurassic period	140 – 201 Ma (Million years)	20,700 – 28,820 years
Coal from 10 US coal beds, Eocene Epoch to Pennsylvanian Period	40 – 320 Ma	48,000 – 50,000 years
Ammonite shells, Cretaceous Period	65 – 145 Ma	36, 400 – 48, 710 years
Tree stump, Permian	252 – 298 Ma	33,700 years
Wood, Tertiary basalt lava flow	47.5 Ma	37,500 years
Diamonds (made of pure carbon)	Tens of millions to billions of years old	55,000 years

Let's look a little further into three of the radiometric assumptions and see that there are valid scientific concerns that these assumptions are not accurate and so radiometric dating should not be dogmatically accepted as "truth." If these assumptions upon which radiometric dating techniques are based are not provable or end up being false, then the dating results as presently interpreted provide data that is completely invalid. And, *it is entirely impossible to prove that these assumptions are true*. As with all that we have discussed in Chapters 17, 18 and 19, there is abundant and high quality information on the Web and I urge you not to trust me. Research it for yourself!

Unprovable assumption #1 – Radioactive decay rates do not change. For 50+ years, it has been considered a proven and unquestioned "fact" that the rate in which parent decays into daughter – the **radioactive decay rate** – has been the same over the past 5 billion years. Why? Because evolutionists assumed it was as a result of their uniformitarian approach. The rates needed to be constant in order to fit the evolutionary dogma, not because it is proven that they are constant. Therefore, creationists challenge that "fact" and, if it isn't true, then radiometric dating techniques are all providing invalid results since they are all calibrated based upon decay rates being constant.

Decades of creationist objections to the "decay rates are stable" theory have largely been dismissed until fairly recently. Joining data published a decade ago by creation scientists, now evolutionists have published papers showing that decay rates can be affected to different degrees by various physical and chemical conditions – *they indeed do not appear to be constant*. Some of the changes in the decay rates that have been measured have been small, less than a 2% change, but anything that changes decay rates to *any* amount means that decay rates are not constant and should then automatically lead to the conclusion that "we need to study this more because our radiometric dating methods appear to be based upon this invalid assumption."

Figure 19.11.6

Unprovable Assumption #1 – Effects of Inconstant Decay Rates
One of the unprovable assumptions upon which radiometric dating is based is that decay rates don't change. However, there is emerging evidence that they can change. Creationists point out that just because radioactive isotopes decay at a certain rate today does not mean that they have always decayed at that rate. Creationists think it is probable that decay rates were much faster in the past, spiking during the Flood. From an objective standpoint, when radiometrically dating a sample, the only thing that you know for sure is how much parent and daughter is in the sample you are measuring. There is *no way* to know if the decay process that resulted in a sample containing a certain amount of parent and daughter got there via evolutionary slow and constant decay rates over millions of years or creation-based variable and faster decay rates over a couple thousand years. It would be scientifically equally as valid to develop a radiometric dating process based upon the "variable-and-faster-decay-rates-over-shorter-periods-of-time" as it would be to use the "slower-and-constant-decay-rates-over-long-periods-of-time." However, we actually do know which model is correct – the one that is based upon the absolute truth of the Bible, which means that the "faster-decay-rates-over-shorter-periods-of-time" is absolutely true.

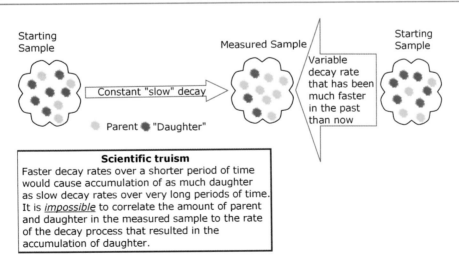

Starting Sample

Constant "slow" decay

Measured Sample

Variable decay rate that has been much faster in the past than now

Starting Sample

Parent ● "Daughter"

Scientific truism
Faster decay rates over a shorter period of time would cause accumulation of as much daughter as slow decay rates over very long periods of time. It is *impossible* to correlate the amount of parent and daughter in the measured sample to the rate of the decay process that resulted in the accumulation of daughter.

As examples, one study experimentally identified different factors capable of accelerating the decay rate up to one billion times faster than presently measured rates. Another identified increasing evidence that electromagnetic radiation from the sun affects nuclear decay (and we clearly do not understand to what degree). Note that if something speeds up radioactive decay of parent into daughter the end result is more daughter and less parent than you think should be there as compared to if the decay is constant, which will make the sample erroneously give a date that is older than it should be. If decay-accelerating processes have acted in the past as the creation model predicts, then the result would be that rocks and fossils date older than they should be.

The bottom line is _there is scientific data indicating that decay rates are not constant_. This means that the scientific community should have strong interest in exploring this topic further. The effects of inconstant decay rates should be identified. Dating processes need to be reconsidered and, if appropriate, refined and re-calibrated. It is possible that the conditions that have been experimentally proven to affect decay rates may have been present in the past. Perhaps decay rates may be found to vary so much that it is impossible to accurately predict what they actually are, making radiometric dating an invalid pursuit.

However, I would be neglect if I didn't point out that there are unresolved problems with the creation model, one of which is reflected in the decay-rates-were-possibly-much-faster-in-the-past hypothesis. This problem is one of heat. There are lots of radioactive isotopes in the earth and the atmosphere and if they decayed a lot faster in the past than they do now, there is a decay rate acceleration factor beyond which the decay would be so fast that an enormous amount of energy would be released. The creation model cannot account for how this energy was dissipated – where did it go and how did it not destroy the earth? Perhaps God performed a miracle and protected the earth somehow. Or, perhaps the decay rate wasn't accelerated very much and there are there other answers as to how the inconstant decay rate affects radiometric dating. There is ongoing research on this topic.

Unprovable assumption #2 – "Knowing" how much parent and daughter were present in the sample when it was formed (in the case of dating rocks) or when it died (in the case of C^{14} dating). Evolutionists believe that, somehow, it is possible to know for certain how much parent and daughter started out in the sample. It is clearly acknowledged in the evolution model that this is an important thing to know and that it cannot be known for certain, but it is in essence brushed off by evolutionists as a minor annoyance of radiometric dating techniques. But, there is no disputing that it is critically important to know, and totally impossible to prove, that whatever assumption that has been made as to the starting amount of parent-daughter is actually correct. Since there is no way to be sure how much parent and daughter isotopes "started out" in the sample, the "date" that is arrived at is nothing but a guess. It is far from scientific. The only way to know for certain would be to measure the parent/daughter amounts at the point in time the organism died or the rock formed to _know without a doubt_ how much was in it.

Figure 19.11.7

Unprovable Assumption #2 – "Starting" Isotope Estimation

Unprovable assumption number 2 is largely a theoretical one, but it is very important none-the-less. The top diagram represents the scenario in which the "true" starting amount of the parent-daughter isotope amounts could actually be known. The only way that would be possible is if someone went back in time and directly measured it. In this theoretical example, someone did just that and measured "4 units" of C^{14} in the starting sample. The measured sample has "2 units" of C^{14}. That means that the starting amount of C^{14} has degraded to one-half its original amount, or one half life. This results in a sample age of about 5,730 years old. In the bottom example, the evolutionary researcher measuring the exact same sample has erroneously assumed there was more C^{14} in the starting sample than it actually contained. Even though he obtains the correct <u>measured</u> amount in the sample, because he overestimated how much C^{14} was in the organism when it died, he thinks that more C^{14} has decayed into C^{12} than really did. Therefore, instead of correctly identifying that one half life has passed, he thinks that slightly under two half lives have passed – the more half lives that have passed, the older the sample "dates." He then "dates" the sample more than 3,000 years too old because of his erroneous assumption on the starting amount of C^{14}. Evolutionists refuse to acknowledge that there is no way to know <u>for sure</u> how much parent-daughter isotope was in a given sample when the sample formed, which means that all they are doing is guessing at the amount, hardly an objective and "scientific" dating method. Creationists could object to radiometric dating based only upon this unprovable assumption and their objection should stand because it is an indisputable fact.

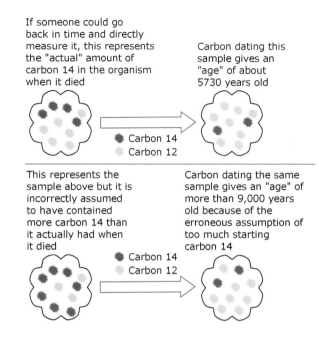

If someone could go back in time and directly measure it, this represents the "actual" amount of carbon 14 in the organism when it died

Carbon dating this sample gives an "age" of about 5730 years old

● Carbon 14
○ Carbon 12

This represents the sample above but it is incorrectly assumed to have contained more carbon 14 than it actually had when it died

Carbon dating the same sample gives an "age" of more than 9,000 years old because of the erroneous assumption of too much starting carbon 14

● Carbon 14
○ Carbon 12

All of the radiometric dating techniques suffer from this same problem of not being able to know how much parent and daughter was in the sample to begin with, relying rather upon an unprovable estimate. If you cannot accurately know the starting amount, it is not possible to state factually that a sample is a certain age because that is a calculation that depends entirely on the relative and "guessed-at starting amounts" of parent and daughter in the sample when it was formed.

Unprovable assumption #3 – The only process that changes the amount of parent or daughter in the sample is radioactive decay. Another way of looking at this is in order for the dating method to be valid, the decay process has to be a closed system – nothing external to the decay process in the fossil or rock can affect the amount of parent or daughter in it. The evolutionary mantra about dating rocks is that nothing changes the normal parent-daughter amounts except the natural radioactive decay process….except, that is, unless evolutionists say something else has changed it.

It is well known in the evolutionary geological literature that there are processes – such as ground water flowing around underground rock layers, excessive heating events, contamination with external parent or daughter in layers above from lava below or a daughter isotope leeching into the rock after being released from other rock layers underneath it – that can alter the parent-daughter amounts in a sample. In other words, it is accepted that the decay process is not a closed system in all instances. If some external process affects the parent-daughter in some way, the date will not be accurate.

For example, it is known that underground sources release argon gas and that diffuses up and into the strata above. This externally increases the amount of argon – the daughter in the potassium-argon decay cycle – that is present in a sample. When that sample is dated with the K-Ar method, because of the externally added argon, there will be more daughter in the sample than that which came from the decay process alone, which results in the appearance of more radioactive decay having occurred than really did. This causes the calculation that more half lives have passed than really did; ergo, the sample dates older than it really should. Not all radioactive decay is a closed system!

The confusion enters because evolutionists seem to think they are uniquely capable of determining if a process other than radioactive decay has changed parent-daughter amounts...that it is possible to accurately determine in each and every case whether or not the rock/fossil remained in a closed system for hundreds of millions or billions of years. That just doesn't seem possible. Usually, when radiometric dates are "way off," they appeal to such external parent-daughter altering conditions as having occurred. If the date "matches" to what they are already expecting, then it is assumed the radioactive decay system remain closed. It seems somewhat intellectually disingenuous for evolutionists to believe that they are the only ones capable of identifying when the decay system has not remain closed while they exclude all reasonable creationist objections to radiometric dating based on the known fact that not all fossil decay systems are closed!

Figure 19.11.8

When Radiometric Dating Methods Don't Agree

There are extensive anomalies in radiometric dating – so many, in fact, that there are a number of very intelligent creation scientists rigorously testing all forms of radiometric dating. The RATE (Radioactivity and the Age of The Earth) group is the source of some of the data below, as are evolutionists themselves. Discrepancies just like these provide reasonable scientific foundation for questioning the validity of radiometric dating. If these techniques were as accurate as claimed, then such discrepancies should be very rare. Creationists are researching with great intensity the physics behind nuclear decay and, specifically, what can influence the rapidity at which it occurs. In addition, there is a growing body of evidence that evolutionary uniformitarian beliefs about how radioactive isotopes form, particularly C^{14}, are wrong (in part because of the reduced C^{14} that is formed when the earth's magnetic field is stronger, and we know it has been two to four times stronger in the past than it is now). *Also, to reinforce the concept, remember that just because radiocarbon dating gives an "evolutionary age" of more than 6,000 years old does not mean that it is more than 6,000 years old*. Creationists simply use the radiocarbon dating result as the evolutionary "upper limit" of how old something can be, to show just how absurd it is when a sample contains a radioactive element that is many thousands of half lives past its "expiration date" (see the diamond Figure at the end of this section) or when two different dating techniques do not arrive at the same date (which they always should if radiometric dating is as scientific and accurate as they want us to believe).

Dating Event	Results and Implications
Wood embedded in an Australian lava flow radiocarbon dated at 45,000 years old while the lava itself K/Ar dated to 45 million years old	These radiometric dates that differ by more than 44 million years clearly cannot both be correct since the wood obviously embedded into the lava when the lava formed – either the wood and the encasing lava flow are 45 million years old or they are no more than 45,000 evolution years old. Since the half life of C^{14} is 5,730 years, and the tree embedded in the lava still has C^{14} in it, the absolute oldest that this lava flow should be is about 60,000 years old, anyway. If it was 45 million years old, there should not be any C^{14} left in the wood. Evolutionists can only resolve radiometric problems such as this by appealing to a process that inherently changes the parent-daughter amounts after the rock is formed or the wood dies. Creationists ask, "How is it possible that parent-daughter altering processes occur only in certain samples?" Such explanations cannot be objective scientific explanations when they are only selectively applied.
Skull 1470, found in KBS Tuff Africa	Based upon the strata in which it was found, Richard Leaky dated this skull at 2.9 million years old. Because the KBS Tuff layer contains a lot of fossils of many important animals, its date is critical to evolutionists. Over the next decade after the skull find, multiple different dating methods (potassium-argon, argon-argon, paleomagnetism) obtained skull ages between 1.6 to 231 million years old. Finally, "agreement" was reached that the KBS Tuff layer dated to about 1.8 million years ago (why does "agreement" need to be reached if radiometric dating is the end-all be-all of determining the age of something?). Evolutionists blamed the different dating results on processes that alter the assumed parent-daughter amounts. Again, why is it that such parent-daughter altering processes can only occur in rocks whose dating is under dispute and not in others whose ages just happen to agree with the expected result? Radiometric dating techniques clearly are not independent confirmation of dates (otherwise they would agree) – they are totally dependent upon the already agreed-upon strata dating.

Dating Event	Results and Implications
Study done comparing dating results of K-Ar, Rb-Sr (rubidium-strontium), Sm-Nd (samarium-neodynium) and Pb-Pb (lead-lead) of rock samples from Beartooth formation in Wyoming and Bass Rapids diabase in Arizona	The intent of this study was to identify if, when dating the same samples with four different methods, concordant (the same) dates were obtained. The four methods gave dates for the Beartooth formation that varied 500 million years between them. Since the maximum age of this formation is supposedly 1.3 billion years old (at the oldest), that represents a variance of more than 30%! That is a huge discordance between the four dating techniques. Similar discordances were found for the four methods when dating the Bass Rapids formation, too. Such discordant ages when dating rocks from the same strata with different radiometric dating methods is common, being reported in dating rock from the Zimbabwean Great Dyke, Australian Stuart dyke swarm and Uruguayan dyke swarm, where ages have differed by as much as 400 million years. If these methods were as accurate as commonly reported, then they should give very similar dates when they are employed to date the same materials.

Figure 19.11.9

Radiometric Dating Techniques Often Give Unexpected Results

Lava flows of known ages often provide further evidence that the assumptions made in radiometric dating are highly questionable and likely not accurate. Hardened lava is often tested with the potassium-argon dating method and frequently gives dates that are very, very wrong. A lava flow from the Mt. St. Helens eruption, known to be less than 30 years old at the time it was dated, gave an age of 350,000 years old. Evolutionists believe that more of the daughter – argon – was incorporated into the lava than they would assume based upon present geologic conditions and so it dated older than expected. But, creationists ask the evolutionists, "Why is it that more argon than expected was incorporated into the Mount St. Helens flow but it isn't possible that this exact same thing happened in other lava flows?" Generally, as long as the material dates to when they think it should, evolutionists trust the dating method; when it doesn't, they throw the radiometric date out and go with how old they think it is. To explain the dating inaccuracies, they rely upon a process that altered the expected parent-daughter concentrations at formation or a process that contaminated the material after formation. It seems like the evolution model endorses a "radiometric dating is only reliably accurate when we say it is" concept.

It is instructive to learn how evolutionists ultimately determine if the rock sample is unaltered, or "pure," so to speak – from the date that the radiometric dating provides! If the material dates to about when they think it should, the date must be correct. If the rock dates "older" or "younger" than they think it should, then the date is usually thrown out as being incorrect, more rock samples from the area are obtained and they give it another go until they obtain the age they are expecting. The critical point here is to understand that the radiometric dating is not the "end all, be all" of determining how old something is. No, that honor is given to the century-old determination of rock layer ages. This should really reinforce that the ultimate determinant of sample age is the rock layer itself, which is not objective fact but man's subjective opinion.

Presently, creationists find some use for radiometric dating, mainly to point out the great problems that exist with the concept that the earth is old. Creationists utilize the great discrepancies between the dating methods and the evolutionary practice of "selective explanation" when radiometric dates don't match strata ages as obvious reasons why these methods should be questioned. Creationists say, "See, these radiometric dating methods are obviously based upon flawed assumptions or else they would reliably provide accurate and concordant results!"

Figure 19.11.10

Diamonds

© Parent Gery/Wikimedia Commons/{{PD}}

Diamonds provide a solid argument against the evolutionary beliefs that go into radiometric dating. They are made entirely of carbon atoms and are the hardest substance known. Diamonds require very high pressures to form, making it likely that they are formed 50 or more miles under the earth's surface and have been brought upward via volcanic eruptions. Evolutionists believe that diamonds were made between 1 and 3 billion years ago. Since they "are so old," they should not have any C^{14} in them, but all diamonds known to be tested for C^{14} do, indeed, contain it. Because they are so hard, evolutionists and creationists agree that they are truly closed systems and so external contamination cannot be the evolutionist's explanation as to why there is C^{14} in diamonds. Also, they cannot rely upon the "incorrect assumption as to how much C^{14} was present when the diamond was formed" excuse since it is impossible for any C^{14} to be left in a 1 billion year old diamond when the half life is "only" 5,730 years. After a billion years, there shouldn't be any left no matter how much it had to start. There really is no reasonable way to explain the presence of C^{14} in diamonds, except, of course, that they weren't actually formed billions of years ago but about 6,000 years ago. If they were formed around the time of creation, then they would fully be expected to have C^{14} in them. It should also be noted that virtually all forms of organic carbon – coal, gasoline, oil, natural gas, etc. – have C^{14} in them and these carbon sources are all supposedly tens of millions, if not hundreds of millions of years old. If radiometric dating were as "scientific" and "authoritative" as evolutionists and the media say it is, then radiometric carbon dating, quite simply, should never, ever identify any C^{14} in diamonds, oil, natural gas, coal, etc. However, the creation model would predict that there would be C^{14} in diamonds because they are no more than a little over 6,000 years old. Scientific observations are very consistent with the creation model and specifically argue against evolution origins theory.

19.12 SUMMARY

The main objective of the material we have reviewed in this and the previous two chapters is to show that scientific data are not only consistent with creation, they also frequently and specifically argue against evolution. What we have studied represents an incredibly small amount of the extensive material that shows there is no need to bend theology to meet science; indeed, I hope that you have learned that evolution was never even compatible with 2,000 years of Christian creation doctrine in the first place. Naturalism's inability to provide a proven genetic vehicle capable of causing meaningful information-adding mutations to cause new and previously nonexistent traits to arise, leading to the formation of new and previously nonexistent kinds of organisms is the main failure point of the modern evolutionary synthesis. Time and again, scientific data is _not consistent with_ predictions of the evolutionary model, always being very consistent with predictions of the creation model. Further, it is evident that evolutionary biases among scientists often prevent revolutionary scientific discoveries, as we learned with the soft tissue preservation in fossils.

God's Word is entirely sufficient and has been facilitative to scientists throughout the centuries. There is no reason to "forget about God" when pursuing scientific endeavors. He's the inventor of the universe, the designer of life, and created all biologic processes – searching for scientific truth within his Kingdom is the only way to completely understand "how we got here" and "where we are going."

> **But false prophets also arose among the people, just as there will be false teachers among you, who will secretly bring in destructive heresies, even denying the Master who brought them, bringing upon themselves swift destruction. And many will follow their sensuality, and because of them the way of truth will be blasphemed. And in their greed they will exploit you with their false words. Their condemnation from long ago is not idle, and their destruction is not asleep.** _2 Peter 2:1 – 3_

> **So Jesus said to the Jews who had believed in him, "If you abide in my word, you are truly my disciples, and you will know the truth and the truth will set you free."** _John 8:31_

19.13 PEOPLE OF SCIENCE

Over a period of 15 years, John Baumgardner obtained his bachelor's degree in electrical engineering, two masters degrees (electrical engineering and geophysics and space physics) and his PhD (geophysics and space physics). Prior to obtaining his degrees in physics, he worked on laser weapons development for the United States Air Force and Rocketdyne. After obtaining his PhD, he became the thought and research leader in geophysics, even garnering a four page article on his work from *US News and World Report* in which he was described as "the world's pre-eminent expert in the design of computer models for geophysical convection." He is presently vice president and senior research associate for Logos Research Associates, where he continues his work on refining his theory of catastrophic plate tectonics, among other endeavors.

19.14 KEY CHAPTER POINTS

- Neo-Darwinism (the modern evolutionary synthesis) is not a reasonable naturalistic explanation for how new, trait-giving genetic information arises because there is no scientific data that supports the ability of random mutations' ability to generate such "creative" information.

- While beneficial mutations do exist, they have never been demonstrated to cause new and previously nonexistent traits to arise; instead, their universal effect is to remove information from the organism. Therefore, they cannot explain the emergence of new and previously nonexistent trait-giving genetic material.

- Bacterial antibiotic resistance is not "evidence of evolution" because it is not caused by the generation of new trait-giving genetic information.

- The implications of the biblical descriptions of nephesh chayyah and how organisms with it were affected by Adam's sin leads to the reasonable conclusion that the human genome was created perfect. Within this context, many biblical descriptions – such as life expectancies more than 900 years – make scientific sense.

- The scientific data supports the concept that Noah's Ark was a real ship, it had more than enough room to fit the kinds on it and they had more than enough time to diversify into the wide organism variation we see today, just as the Bible describes.

- The vast majority of fossils were created during the 1 year global Flood.

- Population ecology and comparative genomics do not provide support for the evolution model, but do for the creation model.

- Fossil dogma is an extension of the necessity for the earth to be billions of years old and can cause the fossil record to be misinterpreted or discarded altogether if it doesn't fit into the ideology of the evolution model.

- The evolution model makes many predictions of the fossil record – such as the existence of transitional forms and absence of identifiable biological material in tens-of-millions-of-years-old-fossils – that the fossil record itself proves false time and again.

- Radiometric dating is based upon many assumptions that not only cannot be proven, but have also been shown to possibly be false (such as decay rates are constant, that it is possible to accurately estimate the "starting amount" of daughter in a sample and the decay system is closed); therefore, further research needs to go into the dating methods. The results need to be interpreted within that light because they do not provide the "end-all, be-all" age of a specimen.

- Discordant fossil ages obtained by dating the same samples with different dating methods and getting wildly incorrect dates for samples of known ages provide measurable scientific proof that radiometric dating is not a highly reliable technology.

19.15 DEFINITIONS

Amber
Tree sap that captures and preserves organisms.

Archaeopteryx
A bird fossil that some evolutionists call a transitional form while other evolutionists and all creationists call a bird.

Beneficial mutation
A mutation that "benefits" the organism with it such that, even though it reduces or removes "normal" function, it assists the organism to survive better in some way as compared to if it didn't have the mutation.

Beds
See strata.

Cast
A fossil that is formed when the hard parts of an organism are covered by sediments, the organism breaks down and as it does, it is replaced by minerals, resulting in a hard fossil impression that looks like the organism.

Catastrophic plate tectonics
A creationist concept describing very rapid and violent movement of the tectonic plates during the Flood.

Comparative genomics
A field of study within genetics that compares DNA of different kinds with the intent of assigning evolutionary relationships.

Daughter isotope
A stable form of an element into which the parent decays.

Detritus
Small particulates of organic matter and minerals that fall to the bottom of bodies of water.

Embryology
The study of embryo development.

Evolution
The biological process that occurs through mutation, in which a "less complex" ancestor organism acquires new and meaningful DNA that leads to the formation of new genes, giving it new and previously nonexistent traits such that, over time, as it accumulates more novel genes and traits through mutation, it transforms into a "more complex" and previously nonexistent organism.

Extrude
The process of magma "oozing" onto the earth's surface.

Fossil
A remain or trace of humans, animals or plants that has been preserved by natural causes in the earth's crust.

Fossil dogma
The evolutionary approach to the fossil record, based entirely on the supposition that the earth is 4.5-ish billion years old and life 3-ish billion years old, resulting in an ideological approach to the data that can sometimes lead to difficult-to-support conclusions about the fossil record or refusal to consider alternative explanations that fall outside the dogma because so doing may threaten evolution's acceptance.

Fossil record
The collective of all known fossils, along with the scientific interpretations made related to the fossilized organism's habitat, diet, size, social habits and relationships to other fossilized and presently living organisms.

Geologic time scale
Assigning ages to strata based upon the fossils they contain inside the framework that the strata span more than 3 or 4 billion years.

Haldane's dilemma
The evolutionary conundrum that "there isn't enough time" for observed mutation rates to explain the observed differences seen in the genomes of "evolutionarily closely related organisms."

Half life
The length of time it takes something to decay to one-half its original amount.

Igneous rock
Rock that forms when lava or magma cools.

Index fossils
Fossils so commonly found in certain layers that they serve as the identifier to being in that specific layer – "When you see that fossil, you know you are in such-and-such layer."

Intermediate form
See transitional form.

Junk DNA
A direct product of the evolutionary model, the now totally discredited concept that the very large segments of non-trait coding DNA "don't do anything" and are therefore "junk."

Lava
Forcefully ejected molten rock.

Magma
Extruded molten rock.

Metamorphic rock
Rock that is formed from the transformation of already-formed rocks when they are subjected to high heat and intense pressure.

Modern evolutionary synthesis
See neo-Darwinism.

Mold
A fossil type that looks like the imprint of the organism.

Molten
Rock that is so hot and under so much pressure that it is in liquid form.

Multi-drug resistant bacteria
Bacteria that are resistant to a large number of antibiotics, such that they are very difficult to treat because they are sensitive to only a few (or no) antibiotics.

Neo-Darwinism
The scientifically unproven explanation for "how evolution works" on a genetic level.

Nephesh chayyah
The biblical description of organisms, including humans, which confers the special property of "living soul" (humans) or "living creature" (animals). Only organisms with nephesh chayyah were exempt from pre-curse death and subject to the effects of the curse for Adam's sin.

Parent isotope
An unstable form of an element that degenerates into a more stable form.

Polystrate fossil
A fossil that traverses more than one strata.

Population ecology
A field of study looking at the changes of population size over time and what the factors are that influence the changes.

Radioactive decay rate
The rate in which a parent isotope decays into the daughter.

Radiometric dating
A process in which provable science is mixed with several assumptions in order to attempt to calculate the evolutionary ages of rocks or once living matter.

Rapid speciation
An evolutionary concept of rapid changes in a group of the same organisms ("species") that cause them to form new characteristics as compared to their ancestors. The creation perspective is that such rapid speciation is not, in fact, "rapid"; rather, the evolutionary concept of a "rapid" time frame over which organism groups become different from one another is "how speciation always happens" because that is what is scientifically observed to happen.

Sedimentary rock
Rock that is formed as a result of sedimentation.

Sedimentation
The process of detritus falling to the bottom of bodies of water.

Strata
Layers of rock.

Tectonic plates
Massive slabs of moving earth the make up the continents and ocean floors.

The Genesis Flood
The hallmark book by Henry Morris and John Whitcomb that provided extensive scientific support for the literal Noah Flood, bringing creationism back into the scientific age.

Transitional form
An "in between" fossil form that shares characteristics of the "less complex" organism it is evolving from and the "more complex" organism it is evolving into. Such fossils are predicted by the evolutionary model but so far not one undisputed transitional form has been accepted.

Uniformitarianism
The belief that the processes responsible for forming the earth and life observed to occur on the earth today are the only processes that occurred in the past.

Upright fossil trees
See polystrate fossil.

STUDY QESTIONS

1. Dr. Yockey's quote in the introduction contains an interesting message regarding the scientific basis of evolution. What do you think that message is?

2. True or False? In order for an origins model to be accepted as accurate, it should, in part, make accurate predictions about future scientific observations.

3. If the predictions of a scientific model (hypothesis) are frequently incorrect or new scientific data arises that directly contradicts the predictions of the model, what is usually done with that model?

4. True or False? Creationists should reject the concept of natural selection altogether because it goes against the Word of God.

5. Describe what neo-Darwinism (or the modern evolutionary synthesis) is.

6. True or False? Mutations have scientifically been proven to generate new and meaningful DNA, causing many documented instances of new and previously nonexistent traits and organisms to arise.

7. Describe why mutations cannot be the source of novel genetic information that ultimately leads to the formation of an entirely new kind of organism.

8. Discuss where the following statement goes wrong: Beneficial mutations are ones that cause an organism to be able to better survive in its environment, which, over time, gives it a selective advantage over those organisms without the mutation and ultimately leads to the formation of an entirely new and previously nonexistent kind of organism.

9. True or False? All known beneficial mutations, such as the sickle cell mutation, cause a loss of genetic information and therefore cannot be the evolutionary source of new and meaningful information to drive evolution.

10. True or False? The lack of genetic data that demonstrates that meaningful, trait-giving mutations occur and give rise to new and previously nonexistent traits is a major flaw of neo-Darwinism.

11. Describe why, contrary to what proponents of the evolution model state, the development of multi-drug resistant bacteria is not an example of "evolution in action."

12. True or False? When DNA that codes for the ability to inactivate an antibiotic is transferred from one bacterium to another via conjugation, evolution has occurred because now the receiving bacterium possesses a trait that it previously did not have.

13. How do creationists view what appear to be "built-in" abilities, such as antibiotic resistance and some mutations occurring according to an algorithm?

14. True or False? The creation model predicts the fossil record contains fossils of organisms that died and started the fossilization process prior to the Fall.

15. True or False? Adam's sin affected only humans.

16. Although most certainly if you answered, "Because the Bible says so," you would be correct, please provide plausible biological/genetic reasoning as to how people could possibly have lived over 900 years "in the beginning."

17. It is true that the fossil record documents the presence of a variety of different organisms with cancer and even organisms in the act of eating one another. According to the evolution model, these organisms died long before man "arrived on the scene." Why is it a problem for Christians if animals had cancer or ate each other prior to the Fall? (This is a tough one!).

18. True or False? There is overwhelming scientific evidence arguing against the creation model position that the 4,500 post-Flood years is not enough time for animals to diversify after getting off the Ark.

19. What is wrong with the very common evolutionary response to Noah's Ark of, "There is no way that 2 of every animal variety could have possibly fit onto the Ark. There are way too many species for that"?

20. How does natural selection play into the post-Flood development of many varieties within kinds?

21. True or False? Scientific studies have clearly shown that there is not enough water on/in earth to be able to cause a world-wide flood as described in the Bible.

22. Do you think it is problematic that there is not universal agreement between creationists about such things as catastrophic plate tectonics or that the creation model is not fully able to explain how excess heat was dissipated if nuclear decay was very accelerated in the past?

23. True or False? Human population growth studies demonstrate that there is not enough time for the human population to have reached its present level if mankind started with only 6 – 8 individuals 4,500 years ago after the Flood.

24. Why is it not valid to perform comparative genomics studies only on genes and ignore the non-gene encoding regions?

25. True or False? When comparative genomics studies are performed on the entire genomes of two kinds, the amount of similarity goes way up as compared to when the studies are done when excluding junk DNA.

26. Apply Haldane's dilemma as it pertains to the evolution model prediction that humans and chimps shared a common ancestor about 6 million years ago.

27. True or False? The evolution model hypothesizes fossils found in lower strata are more complex than those in the higher strata.

28. Why aren't any fossils found in igneous rock?

29. When does the creation model propose that most fossils formed?

30. True or False? No processes consistent with the formation of polystrate tree fossils have been observed in modern day and so the evolution model's portrayal of them forming as they grow in place, slowly being covered by sediments for a long time before once and for all being covered by a massive sedimentation event, is very reasonable because it is supported by other scientific data.

31. What is a transitional form?

32. Are there any universally accepted transitional forms in the evolutionary model?

33. Describe the creation model's explanation as to why there is layering of fossils in the fossil record, following the general plan of aquatic organisms lowest, followed by amphibians, reptiles, mammals and birds as one moves up the strata.

34. True or False? In the evolution model, *Archaeopteryx* is a very good example of a transition form.

35. A paleontologist makes two different finds in the exact same strata – one is the partial skeleton of a small dinosaur and the other is clearly an arrowhead that is embedded in the femur (thigh bone) of the small dinosaur. How would the researcher interpret this if she were an evolutionist? How would she interpret this if she was a creationist?

36. True or False? An index fossil is a fossil that is found so commonly in a certain strata that when you find that type of fossil, you know that you are in the strata of a certain geological time period.

37. Why is there potentially a problem with the evolution model's prediction that strata formation are not uniform over time?

38. Why are the researchers who postulated that *Scipionyx* had "primitive feathers," and so may be an early reptile-bird transitional form, on somewhat shaky ground?

39. True or False? Identifiable soft tissues, cells and even biomolecules found in fossils are reasonable predictions of the evolution model.

40. What is a half life?

41. Why is it a problem for the evolution model when carbon 14 is found in a fossil that is supposed to be 125 million years old?

42. A researcher radiometrically dates a fossilized specimen and calculates it to be 74.4+/- 0.1 million years old. Answer the following:
    • True or False? This radiometric dating technique is based in part upon sound scientific principles.
    • True or False? Any assumptions upon which this method may be based are entirely objective and scientific because they are provable.
    • True or False? The radiometric dating method directly measures the age of the specimen.
    • True or False? The radiometric dating method provides an objective and unbiased assessment of the specimen's age.

43. List at least three assumptions upon which radiometric dating is based. Why is it a problem that this supposedly scientific method is based upon unprovable assumptions?

44. Why is it a problem that the evolution model relies upon the suspected date of a sample in order to calibrate a given radiometric dating method?

45. True or False? Identifying a parent with a half life of 12,500 years in a sample that is supposedly 370 million years old should lead to serious questioning if the assumptions underlying the dating method are valid.

46. List three possible sources of "contamination" that scientifically are suspected of altering parent-daughter isotope concentrations.

47. If decay rates were significantly faster in the past, say immediately surrounding the Flood, what effect would that have on radiometrically dating samples based upon the assumption that decay rates are constant?

48. If I was radiometrically dating a sample and I assumed that there was four times more starting parent isotope in the sample than there really was, would my calculated date for the sample be inappropriately too old or too young?

49. True or False? When radiometrically dating the same samples with different methods, there is never discordance (disagreement) between the different methods because they always provide nearly the same ages.

PLEASE TAKE TEST #7 IN TEST BOOKLET

Biological Classification and Viruses

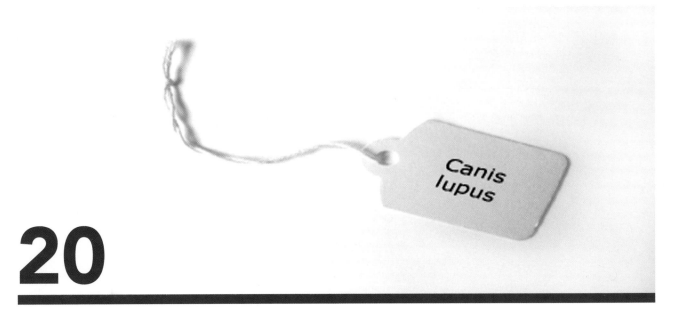

20

20.0 CHAPTER PREVIEW

In this chapter we will:

- Review a brief history of classification schemes.

- Discuss the classification devised by Linnaeus, which is still in use today, called the binomial system.

- Introduce the six classification kingdoms of Archaebacteria, Eubacteria, Protista, Fungi, Plantae, and Animalia.

- Investigate the structure and function of the non-living particles called viruses.

20.1 OVERVIEW

Previously, we briefly touched on the subject of the classification of all life forms encountered on earth. We discussed that organisms can be classified a number of ways, using herbivore/carnivore/omnivore or producer/consumer/decomposer. However, these methods do not allow for much specification. In this and forthcoming chapters we will spend more time learning how species are classified. Because of the great biological diversity present, this is actually quite a dynamic subject.

The process of classifying life forms had been performed for two thousand years, starting with Aristotle. He used a simple, but effective, method of classifying everything as either a plant or an animal. He then further broke the plants down into three groups based on their stem structures; the animals were broken down into air-, land-, or water-dwelling animals. This system was used for approximately sixteen hundred years. Once more species were encountered, it became difficult to classify them.

One of the main reasons for the difficulty classifying species with Aristotle's method was that the local names of the organisms were used. Quite often, the common names did not adequately describe the organism, or were confusing. For example, a jellyfish is not a fish at all, and there are many more than one species of jellyfish. Therefore, a new method of classification was needed in order to:

1. improve communication among biologists who spoke different languages

2. avoid confusion based on inadequate common names

3. make the information gathering, reporting, and storing process more accurate

Common names were not specific enough to meet the scientific needs.

Figure 20.1.1

The Problem with Common Names
Common names are not specific enough for science. In America, we all know the organism on the left as the panda bear. However, there are actually two types of pandas; this one is properly called the giant panda. In China, though, this animal is also known as the "mottled bear" and by many other different local names. Naming the organism scientifically with the current naming system avoids all confusion. It is classified scientifically as *Ailuropoda melanoleuca*. There is only one organism with that particular name. The organism on the right probably has more common names than any other on the planet. It is known as the mountain lion, cougar, puma, panther, and others. It is scientifically named *Felis concolor*. No other organism shares this name.

20.2 LINNAEUS

As the classification problem grew through the fifteenth and sixteenth centuries, a Swedish biologist named Carolus Linnaeus (1707-1778) began to formulate the foundation for the modern classification system. He recognized the huge biological diversity and felt that many more levels than the two provided by Aristotle's method would be needed. Although he came up with his seven-level system arbitrarily, it is still used today because it works well.

Initially, Linnaeus developed a seven-level system with only two Kingdoms: plants and animals. Later, once microscopic organisms were identified and "plants" like the fungi underwent further study, a five-level Kingdom system was developed. In the latter part of the twentieth century, bacteria were split into two Kingdoms, so now there are six Kingdoms, total.

20.3 TAXONOMY

Taxonomy is the science of classifying organisms. Today's modification of Linnaeus' system uses what is called a **hierarchical**, or multi-level, method of classification. Biological life forms are placed into categories, called **taxa** (singular **taxon**). The highest level of order, which is the least specific, is the Kingdom. There are six Kingdoms: **Archaebacteria**, **Eubacteria**, **Protista**, **Fungi**, **Plantae**, and **Animalia**. (Just so you are aware, in some slightly older biology text books, you will find the Archaebacteria and Eubacteria grouped together in the same Kingdom called **Monera**). Organisms are then grouped further into (in order from least to most specificity):

Kingdom

Phylum (plural phyla non-plants) or **Division** (Plantae and Fungi)

Class

Order

Family

Genus (plural genera)

Species

There is a good mnemonic to help you remember the order of the seven taxa: "**K**ing **P**hillip **C**ried **O**ut, **F**or **G**oodness **S**ake!" The first letter of each word corresponds to the first letter of a taxa. Again, as one moves from the top of the taxa to the bottom, one is moving from a more broad description of the organism to a more narrow (i.e., least specific to more specific). Occasionally, the taxa are split into subgroups, so do not be confused if you see that. For example, there are many "sub-phyla" and "sub-species" that you may see listed. This is simply a further level of specification within particular taxa.

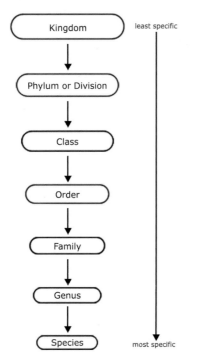

Figure 20.3.1

Classification specificity
The seven levels of classification are shown from the least specific to most specific from the top to the bottom.

20.4 BINOMIAL NAMES

Taxonomists say that the current system is a **binomial system**. This is because when an organism is classified, once the genus and species are assigned, the organism then will have a binomial name. A binomial name is a two-part name. All organisms are then known by their binomial names because only one specific organism has a given binomial name. The first part of a binomial name is the genus and the second part is the species.

Binomial names are written a specific way. The binomial name is always in Latin so that no matter what language a scientist speaks, the binomial name is always the same. Binomial names are either underlined or written in italics. The genus is always capitalized while the species is not. Occasionally, the genus is abbreviated with the first letter only. Each species is a certain type of organism so that it is the only one with its particular binomial name. This system does not allow for any confusion.

For example, the bacterium *Escherichia coli* can also be written Escherichia coli, *E. coli*, or E. coli. From this information, you know the genus for this bacterium is *Escherichia* and the species is *coli*. There is only one species with this name. As an example of a sub-classification, take a look at the name for modern humans, *Homo sapiens sapiens*. The genus is *Homo* and the species is *sapiens*. The subspecies is *sapiens* because there is another type of organism classified as *Homo sapiens* (as you may recall)—*Homo sapiens neanderthalensis*. From this you then know there are two sub-species of *H. sapiens*—*sapiens* and *neanderthalensis*.

Although there are several million bacteria, fungi, plants, and animals already classified using this system, each year several thousand more are discovered and need to be classified. Sometimes, as more information is learned about a particular species it is found that it properly belongs in a different taxonomic class and its classification changes.

20.5 METHOD OF CLASSIFICATION

Classifying an organism is based on many things. Keep in mind that since the majority of scientists performing the classifications are evolutionists, they tell you that taxonomy is now based on evolutionary relationships between organisms. However, since evolution is not fact, as stated in the previous three chapters, taxonomy will not be presented here as such. It is something you should keep in mind for the college entrance exams, though.

The basic philosophy of the classification scheme is based on similarities. Organisms can be classified appropriately regardless of the supposed evolutionary relationships. Similarities exist among organisms to varying degrees regardless of evolution. The fact is that some organisms are more similar to one another than others. A flower and a tree, for example, are more similar to one another than a flower and a duck-billed platypus are. Mammals are more similar to one another than they are similar to birds. Taxonomists simply rely on many different characteristics of organisms as the basis of the seven-level taxonomy system.

There are two basic characteristics taxonomists rely on to divide organisms into the proper groups: structural and physiological/biochemical. Similarities in appearance are called **structural similarities**. Similarities in how organisms function are called **physiological** or **biochemical similarities**. Occasionally, as more is learned about a particular organism's biochemistry, its particular classification may change a bit.

For example, it has long been thought that horseshoe crabs (*Limulus polyphemus*) are true crabs. However, as their physiology and biochemistry has been more completely understood, they are found to be much more similar to fellow-arthropods, spiders, than they are to crabs. Their sub-phylum was changed from *Crustacea* (where crabs are classified) to *Chelicerata* (where spiders and sea spiders are).

The first basic difference that is identified is whether or not the organism is a prokaryote (no nucleus and no membrane-bound organelles) or eukaryote (membrane-bound nucleus and organelles). If it is a prokaryote, it is placed in the Archaebacteria or

Eubacteria Kingdoms. If it is a eukaryote, then it will be placed in the appropriate one of the other four Kingdoms based on a number of characteristics of the organism. As the organism is then further studied, the appropriate phylum (or division if a plant or fungi) is determined, followed by the class, order, family, genus, and species. The individual who discovered the organism is given the first opportunity to name it.

Figure 20.5.1

Taxonomical Hierarchy

Notice that the grizzly bear has two names listed for its species name. This gives it three binomial names. This automatically tells you that it is a sub-species. There are some organisms that are close to one another in traits and behaviors. They are so similar that they share the same genus and same species name. The only way these similar species are separated is by adding a second name to the species name—the subspecies. There are several sub-species of *Ursos arctos – U. arctos horribilis* (Grizzly Bear), *U. arctos middendorffi* (Kodiak Bear), *U. arctos nelsoni* (Mexican Grizzly, possibly extinct), and *U. arctos californicus* (Golden Bear, extinct).

	Grizzly bear	Horseshoe crab	Ginkgo tree	Diarrhea-causing "E. coli"
Kingdom	Animalia	Animalia	Plantae	Eubacteria
Phylum/Division	Chordata	Arthropodia	Ginkgophyta	Proteobacteria
Class	Mammalia	Merostomata	Ginkgoopsida	Gamma Proteobacteria
Order	Carnivora	Xiphosura	Ginkgoales	Enterobacteriales
Family	Ursidae	Limulidae	Ginkgaceae	Enterobacteriacaea
Genus	Ursus	Limulus	Ginkgo	Escherichia
Species	arctos horribilis	polyphemus	biloba	coli
Binomial Name	*Ursus arctos*	*Limulus polyphemus*	*Ginkgo biloba*	*Escherichia coli*

  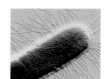

20.6 PROKARYOTE KINGDOMS

All prokaryotes are classified into either the **Archaebacteria** or **Eubacteria**. Although they are microscopic in size, together they make up the largest number of living things on earth. Archaebacteria have a distinctly different cell membrane than the Eubacteria. Archaebacteria often live in hostile environments like hot sulfur springs and salty lakes. They often are chemoautotrophs and produce flammable gasses. Eubacteria are the "bacteria" we commonly picture. This is the Kingdom of bacteria that causes human and animal bacterial illnesses. They are usually **aerobic** (aerobic means they require oxygen to live), but there are some that are **anaerobic** (anaerobic means they cannot survive in oxygen). Oftentimes, the anaerobes are the ones that cause the most difficult to treat diseases.

Figure 20.6.1

Archaebacteria and Eubacteria
The photo on the left is taken from a hot sulfur spring in Yellowstone National Park. Archaebacteria thrive in extreme conditions. The yellow-orange film on the water is from heavy growths of Archaebacteria. The bacterium on the right is a type of Eubacteria. It has a single flagellum to propel the organism. Many eubacterial species have flagella.

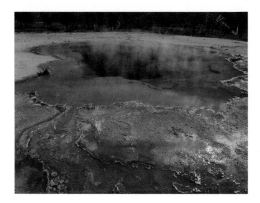 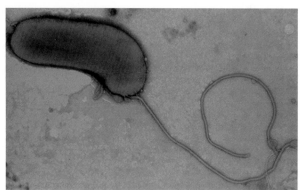

20.7 EUKARYOTE KINGDOMS: PROTISTA

The defining features of organisms from the Kingdom **Protista** are that they are single-celled or grouped eukaryotic organisms. Some protists are autotrophs, while others are heterotrophs. The red and brown algae are the only true multi-cellular protists. A "group" means that many single cell organisms have come together and are all doing the same thing, but they are not working together. They generally live in aqueous environments and require a microscope to see. There are plant-like forms that contain chlorophyll (red and brown algae), fungus-like forms (such as the slime molds), and animal-like forms (such as *euglena, paramecium* and *amoeba*).

Figure 20.7.1

Protists
Organisms from the *Amoeba* (left), *Spirogyra* (center), and *Paramecium* (right) genera are all examples of protists.

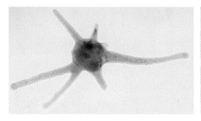 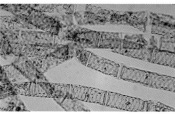 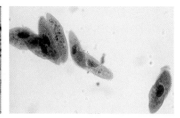

20.8 KINGDOMS: EUKARYOTE – FUNGI

Fungi are primarily decomposers. They are mainly multi-cellular, but there are some unicellular forms. They include mushrooms, puff balls, and bread molds. There are over 100,000 species classified in the Kingdom Fungi. Their defining characteristics are that they are all decomposers and their cell walls are made of a carbohydrate polymer called chitin.

Figure 20.8.1

Fungi
All of the organisms below are classified in Fungi. Mushrooms and toadstools are commonly seen throughout the world. The photo on the right is a micrograph of a species from the *Mucor* genus, which is capable of causing infections in humans.

  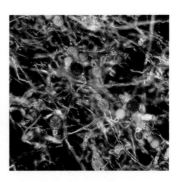

20.9 KINGDOMS: EUKARYOTE – PLANTAE

The next structurally and physiologically more complex Kingdom is **Plantae**. It is made up primarily of autotrophs, although there are a few parasitic forms. These organisms are commonly known as "plants" and include trees, shrubs, flowers, grasses, mosses, and ferns. It includes over 350,000 species. Their defining characteristics are multicellularity, photosynthesis, and cell walls made up of cellulose.

Figure 20.9.1

Plantae
Organisms in the Kingdom Plantae are adapted to all environments and soil conditions.

20.10 KINGDOMS: EUKARYOTE – ANIMALIA

The final of the six Kingdoms is **Animaia**. Defining characteristics of almost all organisms in Animalia are multicellularity, heterotrophic, lack of cell walls, sexual reproduction, ability to move, and a symmetric body plan. A symmetric body plan means the right half of the organism looks similar to the left half, or the top half looks similar to the bottom half. Some species of Animalia asexually reproduce but most organisms in Animalia sexually reproduce. When most of us think about an animal, we automatically think of their property of **locomotion** (moving). This Kingdom includes insects, fish, amphibians, birds, reptiles, and mammals.

Figure 20.10.1

Animalia

The organisms from Animalia are also adapted to a wide range of habitats (living environments) and modes of locomotion (movement).

20.11 VIRUSES

Some of you may have heard of something called a virus. Scientists have known about the probable existence of the virus since the mid 1800s. Louis Pasteur first suggested in 1884 that something smaller than bacteria was the causative agent in rabies. At the time, the unknown agents were called a virus, which is derived from the Latin for "poison." The name has stuck for these infectious agents.

Viruses are microscopic (25 nm to 250 nm). The largest virus is about the same size as the smallest bacterium. Because of this, they were too small to see with the available microscopes in the late 1800s and early 1900s. A common technique for isolating bacteria was to run fluid containing bacteria through a filter; this would "catch" the bacteria. Viruses, though, were too small to be caught by the filter. It wasn't until 1935 with the advent of more high power imaging, that the first virus, from a tobacco plant, was isolated. Since then, hundreds of viruses have been isolated from animals and plants.

Figure 20.11.1

Viruses

Viruses do not meet the criteria for "life, and so they are not properly called organisms. They are referred to as particles. Even though they are much smaller than bacteria, they can be seen through an electron microscope. The electron micrograph on the left is of a cell nucleus filled with viruses. All of the small black dots are individual virus particles, which have replicated inside of the cell nucleus. The photo on the right is an enlarged image of the particles in the nucleus. This is a type of pox virus that causes warts.

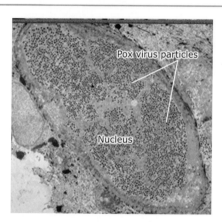
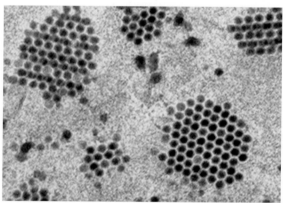

Viruses are not included in the six Kingdom classification system because they are technically not "life." Recall from Chapter 1 that life has several defining properties. Note from the table that there are multiple characteristics that define life that viruses do not exhibit.

Figure 20.11.2

Properties of Life: Do Viruses Have What it Takes?

Note that viruses, at best, contain only one true marker of "being alive"—DNA. However, not all viruses contain DNA, some only contain RNA. Also, note that viruses are an **obligate intracellular parasite**. This means that they are incapable of reproducing unless they have infected a host's cell to direct the cell to reproduce the virus.

Characteristic of life	Virus	Prokaryotic/Eukaryotic cell
Growth	No	Yes
Homeostasis	No	Yes
Metabolism	No	Yes
Nucleic acid	DNA or RNA (not both)	DNA and RNA
Reproduction	No, obligate intracellular parasite	Yes
Structure	Nucleic acid core, protein covering, sometimes an envelope	Cytoplasm, cell membrane, cytoskeleton, organelles

A virus is properly characterized by biologists as a **particle**. All viruses have a common structure and content. All viruses are composed of an outer protein coat called a **capsid**. Inside of the capsid is the nucleic acid of the virus, either DNA or RNA, but never both. There are no organelles or cytoplasm. If the virus contains DNA it is called a **DNA virus**, and if it contains RNA it is called a **RNA virus**. Some viruses have a lipid layer around them called an **envelope**, which is derived from the lipids of the host cell when the virus particle forms. Unlike true organisms, viruses do not have a cellular structure, but they do take on many different shapes, depending on the type of the virus.

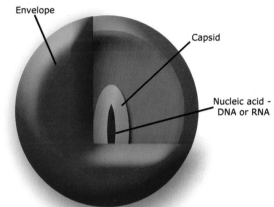

Figure 20.11.3

General Virus Structure
The generic viral structure is shown here. The envelope is a lipid bilayer that is derived from the host membrane when the virus is formed. The capsid is a protein coat that protects the nucleic acid. Viruses contain either RNA or DNA in their capsids, but not both. RNA viruses also contain reverse transcriptase in the capsid.

The interesting thing about a virus is it is completely incapable of reproducing itself without help. Since the virus contains incomplete machinery for replication inside the capsid, it needs to find another way to reproduce itself. A virus needs a **host** cell. It then hijacks the cellular machinery of its host to make more of itself.

Figure 20.11.4

The Four General Virus Particle Shapes

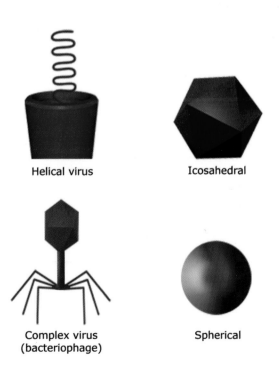

Helical virus

Icosahedral

Complex virus
(bacteriophage)

Spherical

Whether the virus is DNA or RNA, it needs to infect the host cell in order to make more viruses. The process of infection is basically the same for the DNA or RNA virus. Viruses can infect only certain types of cells. For example, the virus that causes AIDS (acquired immunodeficiency syndrome), HIV (human immunodeficiency virus) only infects human white blood cells. It does not infect muscle cells, skin cells, bone cells, or lung cells, only white blood cells. The influenza viruses (viruses that cause the "flu") only infect cells of the respiratory system; they will not and cannot infect cells of the urinary bladder or intestines, for example.

In order for the virus to be able to have such specificity for the cell it infects, the virus has proteins on the capsid that recognize the appropriate cell and then attach the virus to the cell. The virus is then either engulfed by the host cell, or it injects its RNA or DNA into the cell. Once the viral nucleic acid is in the cytoplasm of the host cell, it will do one of several things depending on what type of virus it is. The virus can either enter the lytic cycle or the lysogenic cycle, as explained below.

Lytic Cycle for DNA Virus

Some DNA viruses enter the lytic cycle right away. Once DNA gets into the host cytoplasm, it immediately starts to tell the host cell to start making and assembling virus particles. (**Lytic** means to burst or destroy.) It does this by taking over the chemicals and ribosomes in the host and directing them to start making capsid proteins and replicate viral DNA. The host's DNA is often broken down to supply the nucleic acids for the new viral DNA. Many new viruses are made in one host cell. As more and more of the viruses are made, eventually the cell becomes full and bursts open, allowing the newly-made virus particles to be released and infect other surrounding cells. It can take as little as twenty minutes for a lytic cycle to be completed once the virus infects the cell. When a virus is in the lytic cycle, it is said to be **virulent**, or "disease causing."

Figure 20.11.5

Lytic Viral Cycle
The lytic viral cycle is seen with DNA viruses. The virus injects its DNA into the cell and takes over the protein making machinery of the cell. More and more viral components are made and assembled in the host cell. When the cell gets filled with viral particles, it bursts open and releases more viruses to infect other cells.

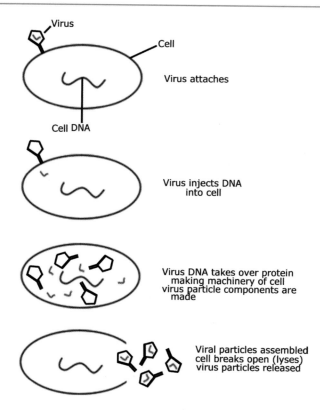

Virus
Cell
Virus attaches
Cell DNA

Virus injects DNA into cell

Virus DNA takes over protein making machinery of cell virus particle components are made

Viral particles assembled cell breaks open (lyses) virus particles released

Lysogenic Cycle for DNA Virus

Some viruses do not immediately become virulent, but enter the lysogenic cycle. Once the viral DNA enters the host cell, rather than immediately directing the host to start making more virus particles, instead the DNA **integrates**—or becomes a part of— the DNA of the host. An integrated virus is called a **provirus** or **prophage**. It stays integrated for a period of time. Every time the host cell divides, the viral DNA is replicated along with the host DNA. Then something triggers the viral DNA to activate, perhaps exposure to UV light, x-rays, environmental changes or even stress. Once the viral DNA activates, it then enters the lytic cycle.

Figure 20.11.6

Lysogenic Viral Cycle
The key feature of the lysogenic viral cycle is the integration of the viral DNA into the host DNA. While the viral DNA is integrated, it is protected from being destroyed by the host. Integrated viral DNA is called a prophage. Every time the host cell divides, the viral DNA is replicated and passed onto the daughter cells. At some point, the virus activates and it enters the lytic cycle.

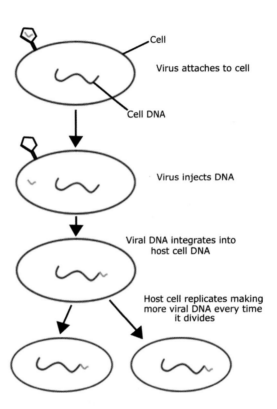

Cell

Virus attaches to cell

Cell DNA

Virus injects DNA

Viral DNA integrates into host cell DNA

Host cell replicates making more viral DNA every time it divides

Lytic cycle RNA virus

This is similar to the lytic cycle for a DNA virus, with only slight modification. Since RNA viruses contain only RNA, they can serve as the template for the ribosomes to directly attach to and start making more capsid proteins right away. New viruses are made by the host and assembled. Once the host cell becomes "full," the cell bursts and new viruses are released.

Lysogenic cycle RNA virus

These types of viruses are very unusual. These viruses contain RNA and one other thing, an enzyme called reverse transcriptase. This is a specialized enzyme that makes DNA from RNA (we did discuss this a bit in the genetic chapters). In order to enter the lysogenic cycle, the information from the virus must be in the form of DNA. Reverse transcriptase is used in the host cell to make viral DNA from the RNA. Once the DNA is made through reverse transcriptase, the viral DNA then integrates, and becomes a prophage. Then, after the proper stimulus, the viral DNA activates, starts to make more viruses, and enters the lytic stage. Due to the backward nature of these viruses (making DNA from RNA), they are called **retroviruses**. HIV is a retrovirus.

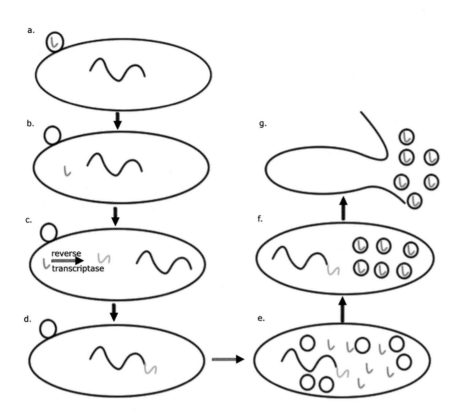

Figure 20.11.7

Lysogenic RNA Viral Cycles
Lysogenic RNA viruses use reverse transcriptase to accomplish their goal of infecting the host and making more viral particles. Figure (a) shows the virus, which contains RNA, infecting the cell. In figure (b), the RNA is injected into the cell, along with reverse transcriptase contained in the viral particle. In figure (c), the viral RNA is made into DNA by reverse transcriptase. In figure (d), the viral DNA integrates into the host DNA. In figure (e), the viral DNA seizes control of the cell's machinery. This results in the cell producing large amounts of viral particles and reverse transcriptase. Also, the viral coat particles and anything else the virus needs are made. In figure (f), the RNA is packaged into the viral particles along with reverse transcriptase. In figure (g), the cell bursts open, releasing the viral particles.

Various diseases in humans are caused by viruses. The majority of "colds," "sore throats," and infectious diarrhea are caused by viruses. Many cases of pneumonia (a lung infection) are viral induced. Also, the human T lymphotropic virus is implicated in causing leukemia, the hepatitis B virus (infection of the liver) is implicated in causing liver cancer, and the Epstein-Barr virus can cause Burkitt's lymphoma (cancer of the lymph tissue). See the accompanying tables for human diseases caused by viruses.

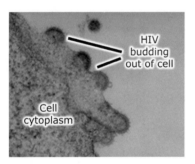

Figure 20.11.8

HIV
The human immunodeficiency virus—HIV—is a retrovirus that is responsible for causing AIDS (acquired immunodeficiency syndrome). HIV infects the infection fighting cells called T-cells. HIV infects the T-cells and slowly buds out of them, releasing more viral particles into the blood stream, which can then go and infect other T-cells. Each T-cell that is infected eventually dies. One of the problems with HIV/AIDS is that after years of infection with HIV, enough infection-fighting T-cells are lost that the person gets an infection they cannot fight off.

Figure 20.11.9

Human Disease Caused by Viruses

Virus type	Nucleic acid	Shape	Envelope	Diseases
Retroviruses	RNA	icosahedral	yes	AIDS, cancer
Rhabdoviruses	RNA	helical	yes	rabies
Myxoviruses	RNA	helical	yes	influenza
Picornaviruses	RNA	icosahedral	no	polio, hepatitis, cancer
Poxviruses	DNA	brick shaped	yes	small pox
Herpes viruses	DNA	icosahedral	yes	chicken pox, herpes, shingles, mononucleosis
Adenoviruses	DNA	icosahedral	no	respiratory and intestinal infections
Papovaviruses	DNA	icosahedral	no	warts, cancer

20.12 VIROIDS AND PRIONS

These are also not considered life forms, but their importance in causing human and animal disease is becoming more understood. **Viroids** are simpler than viruses and are the smallest particles known to replicate. They are bare, short strands of RNA without a capsid or envelope. They infect only plants by altering the cell metabolism. They have been known to damage entire crops of potatoes, cucumbers, and oranges.

Prions are even simpler than viroids. Prion stands for proteinaceous infectious particle. They are abnormal forms of proteins, about 250 amino acids in length. Almost all animals and plant probably contain prions; not all prions are harmful. However, the disease-causing agent of mad cow disease (called bovine spongiform encephalopathy) is a prion. This prion clumps inside of cells and kills them. The way they actually function is not known, but they are able to somehow reproduce themselves. This is interesting because prions are the only molecules which are able to reproduce themselves other than nucleic acids.

Prions generally infect brain cells and take a long time to cause disease. Mad cow disease can also affect humans. The slow degeneration of the nervous system of sheep, called scrapie, is caused by a prion. In humans, the prion-induced brain degeneration called **Creutzfeldt-Jakob** disease is beginning to be better understood. It causes progressive memory loss and death. Kuru is one of the first prion-induced diseases. It was prevalent among a tribe in Papua New Guinea. The members of this tribe were cannibals and ate the brains of their dead tribesman. Now that this tribe no longer practices cannibalism, kuru is gone from their population.

20.13 PEOPLE OF SCIENCE

Carl (Carolus) Linnaeus (1707–1778) was a Swedish scientist who developed the modern system of classification. He was educated as a physician and had great interest in botany, also. He was the chairman of medicine at the Uppsala University for two years and then exchanged the chairmanship of that department for that of the department of botany. Through his work in the field as a botanist, he is also considered one of the fathers of modern ecology.

20.14 KEY CHAPTER POINTS

- Biological classification is the systematic placement of all living organisms into categories based on their anatomy (the way they look) and their biochemistry (the way they function).

- The modern classification system is a seven-level system in which all organisms are first placed into an appropriate Kingdom. They are then placed into a phylum, class, order, family, genus, and species.

- All organisms are referred to by scientists using their binomial name (*Genus species*). This avoids confusion since only one organism has a given binomial name.

- The six Kingdoms are Archaebacteria, Eubacteria, Protista, Fungi, Plantae, and Animalia.

- Viruses, viroids, and prions are not technically considered "life" because they are unable to reproduce themselves independently.

- Viruses have been studied well due to their ability to cause disease in plants, animals, and humans. They have well defined life cycles.

20.15 DEFINITIONS

Animalia
Organisms classified in this Kingdom are all multi-cellular and heterotrophic.

Archaebacteria
Organisms classified in this Kingdom are prokaryotic organisms that tend to live in hostile environments.

binomial system
The name that the modern classification system is commonly known as. In it, all organisms receive a name consisting of the Genus and species.

capsid
The outer protein coat of all viruses.

class
The taxonomic level, which is more specific than the phylum, but less specific than the order.

Creutzfeldt-Jakob disease
A disease caused by a prion.

division
The plant taxonomic level equivalent to phylum.

DNA Virus
A virus containing DNA.

envelope
Lipid layer around some viruses.

Eubacteria
Organisms classified in this Kingdom are prokaryotic and typically referred to as bacteria.

family
The taxonomic level, which is more specific than order, but less specific than genus.

Fungi
Organisms classified in this Kingdom are multicellular decomposers with cell walls composed of chitin.

genus
The taxonomic level, which is more specific than family, but less specific than species.

hierarchical system
Refers to the fact that taxonomy is a multi-level method of classification.

host
A cell which a virus infects. A host is necessary for a virus to reproduce itself.

integrate
To become a part of.

kingdom
The least specific taxonomic level.

locomotion
Capable of motion.

lytic (lyse)
To burst or destroy.

Monera
Refers to the classification system Kingdom, which has now been broken into Archaebacteria and Eubacteria.

order
The taxonomic level, which is more specific than phylum, but less specific than family.

particle
Characterization of a virus.

phylum
The taxonomic level, which is more specific than Kingdom, but less specific than order.

Plantae
Organisms classified in this Kingdom are multicellular autotrophs with cell walls made of cellulose.

prions
Abnormal forms of proteins, which can infect cells, clump inside and kill them.

prophage
A virus that has integrated into the host DNA.

Protista
Organisms classified in this Kingdom are mainly unicellular (though some are multicellular) organisms and are heterotrophic, autotrophic, or decomposers.

provirus
See prophage.

retroviruses
Viruses that are composed of RNA and contain reverse transcriptase to make DNA from the RNA.

RNA Virus
A virus containing RNA.

taxa
Categories of biological life forms; levels of classification.

viroids
The smallest particles known to replicate.

virulent
Disease causing.

STUDY QUESTIONS

1. Why is a systematic classification system important?

2. What were some of the problems associated with classification systems prior to the current system?

3. How many levels of classification are in the modern classification system?

4. True or False? Using the binomial name in science significantly reduces, but does not completely eliminate, confusion regarding the organism(s) being studied. Why did you answer as you did?

5. Name at least two criteria biologists use when classifying species.

6. Please circle the correctly written binomial name (more than one may be correct). *Escherichia* coli. Escherichia coli. <u>Escherichia coli.</u> *Escherichia coli*. <u>E. coli</u>. *E. coli*.

7. True or False? The Kingdom level of classification is more specific than the species level.

8. How many Kingdoms are the prokaryotic organisms classified into?

9. How many Kingdoms are the eukaryotic organisms grouped into?

10. Why are viruses not considered "living organisms"?

11. Draw a typical virus and label the parts.

12. What is a DNA virus?

13. What is the difference between the lytic and the lysogenic virus cycle for DNA viruses?

14. Why are retroviruses important to DNA technology?

15. True or False? Unlike viruses, viroids and prions are living organisms.

Kingdom Eubacteria and Archaebacteria

21

21.0 CHAPTER PREVIEW

In this chapter we will:

- Understand the main differences between the organisms of Eubacteria and Archaebacteria.

- Discuss common bacterial cell shapes and review bacterial cell structure.

- Investigate Eubacterial cell wall structure and how it relates to the Gram-staining procedure.

- Discuss the mechanism of action of antibiotics.

- Review bacterial modes of obtaining energy and manufacturing organic molecules.

Figure 21.1.1

Eubacteria and Archaebacteria
The top left photo shows a small round dish filled with blood agar. Agar is a substance which is obtained from algae and provides nutrition for bacteria to grow on it. Blood agar is made by adding blood to the agar. This is a common way of growing bacteria, called culturing. The bacteria on the top right is our old friend *E. coli*, a member of the Eubacteria. Below, on the left, is another member of the Eubacteria, *Staphylococcus aureus*. Note the difference in shape between the two bacteria. Archaebacteria species are shown in the bottom right photo. The different colors are huge growths of Archaebacteria in a hot spring. Archaebacteria are also called extremophiles because they love to live in extreme environments—very hot, poor nutritional conditions, etc. If you have ever been to a marsh or a swamp, the stinky air is due to methane produced by Archaebacteria that live under the surface of the muddy, rotten water.

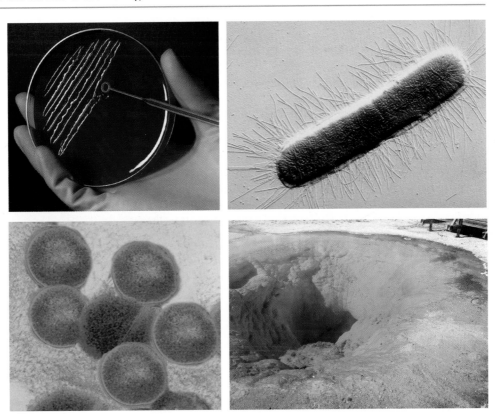

21.1 OVERVIEW

We have learned about some of the small DNA, RNA and protein-containing particles that exhibit some characteristics of life but are not living. The organisms with the simplest physical structure to carry out the functions of life are the prokaryotes, or bacteria (singular bacterium). **Eubacteria** and **Archaebacteria** are all prokaryotic organisms and all prokaryotic organisms are called "bacteria". One of things to remember about the classification system is that there is considerable debate, especially with some of the less structurally complex organisms such as the prokaryotes, about how they should be classified. Therefore, in some of the older schemes of classification, all bacteria are placed in the Kingdom **Monera**. However, due to significant differences in cell structure and physiology, most of the newer classification systems discard Monera and instead break the bacteria into two Kingdoms, Archaebacteria and Eubacteria. We will continue to use the Archaebacteria and Eubacteria system.

21.2 GENERAL BACTERIAL PROPERTIES

Bacteria are microscopic prokaryotes whose sizes range from 1-5 μm. This compares to the typical eukaryotic cell size of 10-100 μm. However, there is one prokaryotic organism whose size is 500 μm. Bacteria are ubiquitous (found everywhere). They live in air, soil, water, and ice. They are found six miles under the ocean and in the Arctic and Antarctic. They are found in locations that no other organisms can survive, such as at the openings of deep sea **hydrothermal vents** (areas under the ocean surface where heat from the earth's interior superheats the water) where the temperatures are well in excess of 100° Celsius (212° Fahrenheit). More bacteria live in the human mouth than the number of human beings who have ever inhabited the earth.

Without bacteria, life would cease to exist. Bacteria are the final pathway for returning dead organic matter to a form that is again usable by plants and animals, due to their primary role in decomposing matter. Bacteria are useful in sewage systems to safely break down sewage material so it can be returned to the environment without any harmful effects. They are useful in the economy in the form of making yogurt, cheese, and buttermilk. They are a useful organism in the intestines of many eukaryotes (including humans) to help digest food and repel infectious organisms. Unfortunately, many bacteria are able to cause minor and serious disease in animals and plants. Some infections like **meningitis** (a bacterial infection of the tissues surrounding the brain and spinal cord) and **endocarditis** (a bacterial infection of the heart valves) can be fatal unless treated quickly.

21.3 BACTERIAL SHAPES

Bacteria take three basic shapes: **bacilli** (singular bacillus), also called **rod-shaped**; **cocci** (singular **coccus**), also called **spherical shaped**; and **spiral**, also called **spirochete**. Often, cocci are found in pairs, called **diplococci**, in clusters like grapes (common in the genus *Staphylococcus*) or on long chains (common in the genus *Streptococcus*). Rod-shaped bacteria usually are solitary. Many of them have adaptations that cause them to be especially hardy.

Figure 21.3.1

Bacterial Shapes

The three basic bacterial shapes are shown below. The bottom left is a graphical representation of an electron micrographic appearance of a Gram-positive bacterium called *Streptococcus pneumoniae*. It is an organism which causes pneumonia (a lung infection) and meningitis (an infection of the tissue around the brain and spinal cord). It is a coccus shape. The center graphic is a representation of a bacillus, or rod. The bacterial species *Clostridium botulinum* is an example of a Gram-negative rod. This bacteria causes botulism, a disease which paralyzes animals and humans infected with the bacteria. The right is an electron micrograph of the spiral-shaped bacteria, *Campylobacter jejuni*. This spirochete causes bacterial diarrhea.

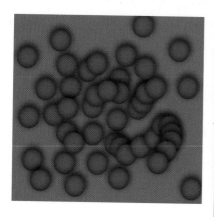 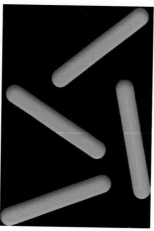 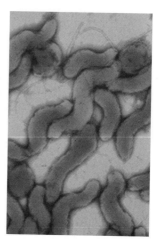

21.4 BACTERIAL STRUCTURE

All bacteria are prokaryotes. Although we have already covered the basic prokaryote cell structure, we will review and expand on this a bit more. Recall that prokaryotes do not have a nucleus, nor do they have membrane-bound organelles. They do have a lipid bilayer membrane similar to eukaryotes with an inner cytoplasm. The single circular chromosome is housed in an irregularly-shaped area of the cytoplasm called the nucleoid.

Figure 21.4.1

General Bacterial Structure

The general structure of a prokaryote is seen below. The center of the prokaryote is similar to that of the eukaryote cell. It is filled with a jelly-like substance called cytoplasm. Within the cytoplasm are numerous ribosomes. DNA is not housed in a nucleus, but it does congregate in an area called the nucleoid. Since the DNA is exposed to the cytoplasm, mRNA production and protein synthesis often occur simultaneously. Many bacteria also have plasmids inside of them, which we discussed in genetics. The cytoplasm is bound by the cell membrane. Like the eukaryotic cell membrane, it is also a double layer of phospholipids. All bacteria have a cell wall which serves as added protection to the cell. Many bacteria also have a second layer outside of them called a capsule. The capsule serves as another protective barrier. It also makes certain bacteria able to infect other organisms. Recall our discussion about transformation in the genetics chapter and that the bacteria which did not have the capsule (the rough cells) were not able to infect the mice. When the rough cells were exposed to the DNA which coded for the capsule, they started to make the capsular molecules and express a capsule. At that point they were able to infect the mice.

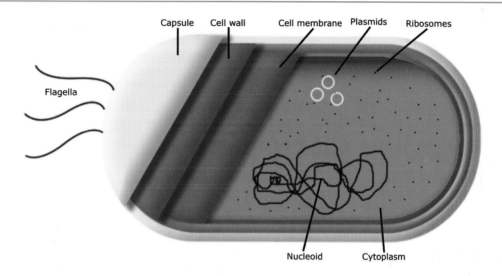

The prokaryotic cytoplasm is similar to the eukaryotic cytoplasm in consistency, but it only contains ribosomes and proteins, including enzymes to catalyze the reactions of cellular respiration. Also, there may be one or more plasmids in the cytoplasm. Photosynthetic and chemosynthetic bacteria have inner folds of membranes (**not** chloroplasts or mitochondria) that are called thylakoid (like plants). Also, like plants, bacterial thylakoid contain the photosynthetic pigments, such as chlorophyll a.

21.5 ENDOSPORES

Some rod-shaped species, like those in the *Clostridium* and *Bacillus* genera, form an **endospore**. An endospore forms in times of environmental stress, which creates unfavorable living conditions. In these cases, a protective covering forms around the nucleoid, and includes a little cytoplasm and RNA. This is a highly resistant and inactive (**dormant**) structure. Endospores do not perform any metabolism. They can remain dormant for years. Once the conditions are favorable for bacterial growth, the DNA housed inside of the endospore activates. The endospore opens and a bacterium emerges to begin life again. Bacteria that have the capacity to do this have proven particularly infectious and hard to get rid of over the years.

Figure 21.5.1

Endospore

This is a graphic of the relationship of endospores and the bacteria which produce them. The green bacillus is *Bacillus anthrasis*. It is a spore-producing bacteria that causes the disease anthrax. The round structure next to it is one of its spores. The graphic to the right shows the spore structure in detail. Spores can sit dormant for many years. When conditions are favorable, the nuclear material activates, and a new bacterium emerges from inside the spore.

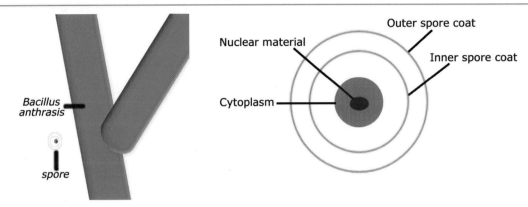

21.6 BACTERIAL CELL WALLS

All bacteria have cell walls. The cell wall is an additional layer of protection outside of the outer cell membrane. Although plants also have cell walls, the walls of bacteria and plants are not at all similar. The cell wall of the Eubacteria is composed of **peptidoglycan**. This is made up of short chains of peptides ("peptido") and carbohydrates ("glycan") linked together (recall that plant cell walls are composed of cellulose). The cell walls of the Archaebacteria are not made up of peptidoglycan, but of other types of polysaccharides and proteins.

Figure 21.6.1

Cell Wall

Eubacterial cell walls have two distinct structures. One type of cell wall is simpler than the other. The simpler cell wall has a thick outer peptidoglycan layer. The more complex cell wall has a thin peptidoglycan layer sandwiched between two lipid bi-layer membranes. The thicker peptidoglycan cell wall is found in Gram-positive bacteria. The thinner peptidoglycan layer cell wall structure is found in Gram-negative bacteria. When bacteria are stained using the Gram-stain technique, the thicker peptidoglycan layer retains the first stain, crystal violet. The bacteria which retain the crystal violet stain are said to be Gram-positive bacteria. They look dark blue or purple after the Gram-stain. The bacteria with the thinner peptidoglycan layer do not retain the crystal violet stain. They are called Gram-negative bacteria. After being stained with the crystal violet, they are then stained with a reddish stain called safranin. They look reddish or pink after the Gram-stain.

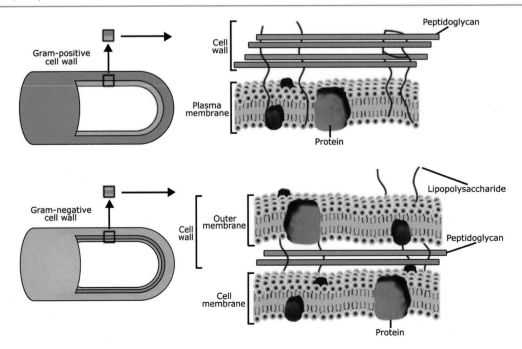

21.7 GRAM-STAIN

Although there is great debate on exactly how to classify the Eubacteria taxonomically, there is universal acceptance that the lab procedure of the **Gram-stain** is helpful to group them. Gram-staining is a way to stain bacterial cells by adding dyes to them and then looking at them under the microscope. It is helpful in the classification of the Eubacteria. Archaebacteria usually are not Gram-stained or classified with the assistance of the Gram-Stain. Whenever a bacterium is encountered in a laboratory or medical situation, the first thing that is done to identify it is a Gram-stain. Then the bacteria can be classified as either Gram-positive or Gram-negative. Further, the shape of the bacteria is also noted. The bacteria are commonly referred to by microbiologists and doctors as "Gram-positive cocci," "Gram-negative rods," etc. For example, *E. coli* is a common bacteria that causes infections in the urinary bladder, commonly called "bladder infections." *E. coli* is a Gram-negative rod. When someone in the hospital gets a fever, their urine is sent to the lab and it is tested in several ways. One of the urine evaluations is to see if there are any bacteria in it, and what type they are. If we find out there are Gram-negative rods, it is likely the bacteria will be *E coli*. That information helps us start appropriate antibiotics if they are needed until the bacteria is completely identified by the lab.

Figure 21.7.1

Gram-Staining

This staining technique provides the first step of identifying and classifying bacteria. The Gram-stain takes advantage of the fact that there are two types of cell walls—a thick and thin. Let's say we had a sample that we knew contained both Gram-positive and Gram-negative bacteria in it. This sample is placed on a microscope slide and passed through a Bunsen burner flame several times. This makes the bacteria stick to the slide. Then some crystal violet dye is applied to the microscope slide. After the dye sits for a minute, it is washed off with a little water. Iodine is then applied, which makes the crystal violet that is stuck to the cell walls stick even better. Next, the slide is washed with alcohol. This removes all the crystal violet that is not bound to any bacteria. At this point, if the slide were viewed, only the bacteria with the thicker cell walls would be able to be seen. Bacteria with a thicker peptidoglycan layer of the cell wall retain the purple color of the crystal violet are said to be **Gram-positive**. They would look dark blue or purplish if you looked at the microscope slide after rinsing with the alcohol. The bacteria with a thinner peptidoglycan layer of the cell wall do not retain the crystal violet during the water and alcohol rinses. You would not be able to see the Gram-negative bacteria because all of the crystal violet coloring would have been washed out. However, they are still there. The last step is the application of a reddish colored dye called safranin. Safranin binds to both the Gram-positive and the Gram-negative bacteria, but does not change the way the Gram-positive bacteria look because they are already stained a dark blue or purple. Safranin binds to the Gram-negative bacteria and makes them look red-pink in color. A bacterium which does not retain the crystal violet stains pink from the safranin is said to be **Gram-negative**. So when you are all done with the Gram-stain, you would see the Gram-positive bacteria as dark blue or purple and the Gram-negative bacteria as light red or pinkish in color.

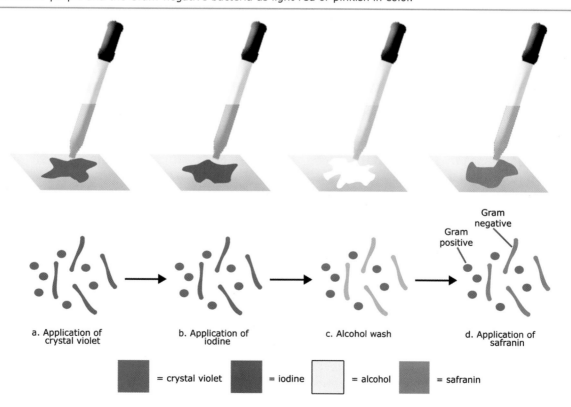

a. Application of crystal violet   b. Application of iodine   c. Alcohol wash   d. Application of safranin

Gram positive   Gram negative

= crystal violet   = iodine   = alcohol   = safranin

Gram-positive bacteria have a thicker, but simpler cell wall structure than Gram-negative bacteria. Gram-negative bacteria have a thinner, but more complex cell wall structure. Gram-negative bacterial cell walls are located between two membranes, the inner cell membrane and another, outer membrane. This additional membrane layer often makes the Gram-negative bacteria more resistant to antibiotics.

Key points to remember:

- Gram-staining is applied to the Eubacteria only.

- Gram-positive bacteria have thicker peptidoglycan layer and cell walls.

- Gram-negative bacteria have a thinner peptidoglycan layer that is sandwiched between two membranes.

Figure 21.7.2

Gram-Positive and Negative Stains
Below are graphics of two samples stained using the Gram-stain. The sample on the left depicts Gram-positive cocci. A typical presentation for a person who is infected with this bacteria would be a patient who had a high fever and headache caused by bacterial meningitis. Meningitis is an infection of the tissues surrounding the brain and spinal cord. These bacteria would be found in fluid surrounding the brain, called the cerebral spinal fluid. The small, round bluish cells are consistent with Gram-positive cocci of the species *Streptococcus pneumoniae*. This is an organism which commonly causes meningitis. The larger cell in the bottom right is an infection fighting cell called a polymorphonuclear cell. It is found in the blood, fluids, and tissues of the host. The graphic on the right is a depiction of a Gram-stain of a Gram-negative rod. This bacteria commonly causes infection of the urinary tract ("bladder infections"). This could be an example of the Gram-negative rod *Serratia marcescens*.

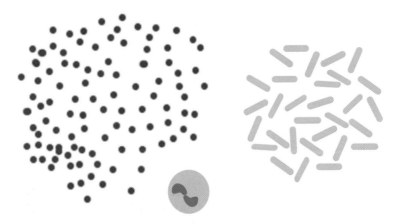

21.8 OTHER BACTERIAL STRUCTURES: CAPSULE, PILLI, AND FLAGELLA

As an added layer of protection, some Eubacteria have an outer-most layer called the **capsule**. This is a polysaccharide coating to the bacteria and helps to prevent it from drying out. Also, the capsule can make some bacteria more **pathogenic** (more able to cause disease) by protecting the bacteria from the body's immune system. Recall our discussion earlier in the course about the two strains of *Streptococcus*, one of which had a capsule and caused the disease, the other of which did not have a capsule and did not cause disease.

Sometimes, there is a fuzzy coating of sugars on the capsule called the **glycocalyx**. This helps the bacteria stick to the host cells so it can infect them easier. Another structure called the **pilli** also helps the bacteria stick to host cells. These are small projections from the bacterial cell and are found only on some Eubacterial species. Pilli also help to transfer genetic material from one bacterium to another in rare cases.

About half the known bacterial species are able to move in a directional way. This is accomplished in a variety of ways. Bacteria contain flagella, as some eukaryotes do. These propel the bacteria in different directions. Although eukaryotic and prokaryotic flagella are made of proteins, the flagella structure of bacteria and eukaryotes is different. Bacterial flagella are about one-tenth the diameter of eukaryote's flagella.

Other bacteria move by producing a layer of slime around them and then moving their cell membranes in a wave. Spiral-shaped bacteria move by contracting their membranes and twisting through their environment.

All bacteria reproduce by the asexual process of binary fission. This is a relatively simple process that we covered in chapter eleven.

21.9 EUBACTERIA

The Eubacteria comprise most of the prokaryotic species on earth. Although there is debate among taxonomists about how to classify the Eubacteria within phyla, these bacteria are initially classified by their shape (coccus, bacillus or spiral) and their reaction to the Gram-staining procedure. There are Gram-negative cocci, Gram-positive cocci, Gram-negative bacilli, Gram-negative cocci, Gram-positive spiral, and Gram-negative spiral bacteria.

We will not go through an exhaustive description of the various species and phyla of Eukaryotes. Instead, we will cover a few of the more common bacteria that affect humans, and some that are well known through the media or movies. The majority of bacteria on the planet do not cause any harm to humans or animals. Many of them are symbionts, in fact. However, all of the disease-causing bacteria are members of the Eubacteria Kingdom.

Gram-negative bacilli (rods) are some of the most feared organisms in hospitals. They cause severe disease and sometimes even the most powerful antibiotics do not work against them. *Helicobacter pylori* is found in the human small intestine and often infect ulcers, making them hard to treat. *Haemophilus influenzae* and *Legionella pneumophila* both cause pneumonia and *H. influenzae* causes many cases of meningitis (infection of the tissues surrounding the brain). However, *H. influenzae* is preventable with a vaccination. *L .pneumophila* causes Legionnaire's Disease (pneumonia). *Acinetobacter baumannii* is a bad actor in hospital-acquired infections and is often resistant to many antibiotics. Some Gram-negative bacteria produce **endotoxins**. An endotoxin is part of the outer membrane of the Gram-negative bacterial cell wall. When the bacteria are killed by the host's immune system, they break apart, and some of the lipid and carbohydrate molecules of the membrane enter the blood stream. This causes fever, body aches, and weakness; it can also damage blood vessel walls.

Gram-positive bacilli are responsible for some well known, but rare, infectious diseases. *Bacillus anthrasis* causes anthrax which is transmitted from infected livestock to man. It is fatal unless treated with antibiotics. *Clostridium tetani* and *Clostridium botulinum* cause tetanus (lock jaw) and botulism, respectively, and are both caused by the release of exotoxins by the bacteria. **Exotoxins** are protein-based chemicals produced by some Gram-positive bacteria. They are secreted by the bacteria and are harmful to the host tissues. These bacteria all form endospores and can exist for long periods of time in the soil.

Gram-negative cocci are fairly unusual but are important human pathogens. *Neisseria ghonorrhoeae* and *Neisseria meningitidis* both have pilli on their surfaces to increase their ability to infect their host (humans). *N. ghonorrhea* causes the second most commonly reported sexually transmitted disease, gonorrhea. *N. meningiditis* causes many cases of bacterial meningitis.

Gram-positive cocci are common, and many different species of *Staphylococcus* and *Streptococcus* live on human skin without causing any infectious problems (they are considered "normal flora"). However, *Staphylococcus aureus* causes many infections in the hospital that are difficult to treat, and *Streptococcus pneumoniae* causes many cases of pneumonia in the community. There is an immunization against *Strep pneumo*. Both *S. aureus* and *Streptococcus pyogenes* can release endotoxins and cause toxic shock syndrome.

Spirochetes (the spiral-shaped bacteria) often do not Gram-stain well. *Treponema pallidum* causes the disease of syphilis. It is easily treated with antibiotics. The gangster Al Capone died in what is called "syphilitic madness." As the disease progresses, it begins to infect nerve tissue such as the brain and spinal cord. When this happens, people forget things and cannot walk due to imbalance. *Spirillum minus* causes rat-bite fever, so named because it is often contracted through a rat bite. It is pretty rare in the US, but common in underdeveloped countries. *Borrelia burgdorferi* is the spirochete that causes Lyme disease. This is a disease that is transmitted from deer to humans through the bite of a tick.

There are a few bacteria that are neither bacilli nor cocci, but are called **coccobacilli**. They are kind of like short rods or slightly elongated cocci. The bubonic plague, or Black Death, is caused by the coccobacillus *Yersinia pestis*. This was responsible for killing almost 30% of the population of Europe in the 1300s. *Bordetella pertussis* is the bacterium that causes the whooping cough (called pertussis). This is preventable with immunization.

Because of their ability to cause diseases that spread rapidly, some bacteria are employed as biological weapons. These are usually designed to explode and release a vapor of bacteria or their spores, which are then inhaled by many people causing serious illnesses.

21.10 HOW DO ANTIBIOTICS WORK?

By the late 1800s, it was understood that bacteria caused fatal infections. In 1928, Sir Alexander Fleming, a British **microbiologist** (one who studied bacteria) made the observation that a type of mold, which had contaminated a bacterial culture, was killing the bacterial colonies adjacent to it. He purified the substance and named it penicillin. Testing showed that, as long as one was not allergic to the penicillin, it was not harmful to humans but effective at eradicating bacterial diseases such as pneumonia and skin infections. This was the first antibiotic known to man, but it was not until the early 1940s that it was mass produced. From that point on, there has been intensive research by pharmaceutical companies to produce more powerful and safer antibiotics.

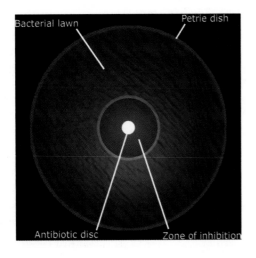

Figure 21.10.1

Antibiotics

Here is a culture, or Petrie, dish filled with agar. Bacteria have been placed on the surface of the agar and are allowed to grow and cover the surface of the dish like a lawn. Then a disc containing an antibiotic is placed in the center of the lawn. As you can see, there is a clear ring around the antibiotic disc. This is because the antibiotic kills the bacteria around it. This is a common method used by microbiologists to test how well an antibiotic kills a particular bacterial species. The larger the zone of inhibition, the more susceptible the bacteria is to the antibiotic.

What is it about antibiotics that make them effective at killing bacteria and not the host (people or animals)? Fortunately, there are properties and functions that bacteria exhibit which humans do not. For example, bacteria have cell walls, and humans do not. Also, there are some differences in how bacteria synthesize their DNA and proteins. Antibiotics are designed to inhibit some critical function of bacteria so it cannot grow, reproduce, or protect itself.

For example, penicillin-type drugs, cephalosporins, and vancomycin all inhibit the bacteria's ability to make the cell wall. Without the cell wall, the bacteria cannot maintain homeostasis and dies. Because synthesis of bacterial DNA is a little bit different than that of a human, some antibiotics are made to interfere with the bacteria's ability to reproduce its DNA, and it cannot divide and grow, so it dies. Other antibiotics disrupt protein synthesis of the bacteria, but not humans. So antibiotics are selectively toxic to bacteria because of differences in the physiology of bacteria and animals.

Some bacterial organisms can become resistant to antibiotics that previously killed them. As the use of antibiotics escalated through the 1970s, 80s, and 90s, bacteria were repeatedly exposed to them. Due to genetic variability, some of the bacteria were less susceptible to the antibiotics than others. The bacteria which were more resistant were continually exposed to the antibiotics and developed resistance through natural selection. They passed their DNA to many generations. Over time, these bacteria became resistant to more and more antibiotics.

Also, there are plasmids that are known to give antibiotic resistance to bacteria. Plasmids can be transferred from one bacterium to another through pilli. Now, there are some bacteria that are resistant to so many antibiotics that there are only one or two antibiotics that they are sensitive to. Antibiotic resistance is a major problem in hospitals around the country, and steps are being taken to slow the emergence of resistant organisms.

21.11 MODES OF OBTAINING ENERGY AND CARBON

Archaebacteria and Eubacteria have the most diverse adaptations of any Kingdom for obtaining their energy and carbon. Bacteria can obtain their energy (a.k.a. generate ATP) from the sun—photosynthesis; or from chemicals—**chemosynthesis**. They can be heterotrophs, obtaining their carbon from organic sources, or they can be **autotrophs**, obtaining their carbon from inorganic sources (usually CO_2).

The **photoautotrophs** obtain their energy from the sun and their carbon from CO_2. These photosynthetic bacteria have thylakoid membranes (not chloroplasts), which house the photosynthetic pigments. As in plants, the light-absorbing pigments are different colors, including green chlorophyll. The Red Sea gets its name because of the large mass of red-pigmented bacteria that cover the surface. Sometimes, in favorable conditions, these bacteria grow explosively in water environments and form a **bloom**.

The **photoheterotrophs** obtain their energy from the sun and their carbon from organic matter. This is an unusual way for bacteria to function, but a few species do this. These species have chlorophyll, as plants do. However, the chlorophyll is not contained in chloroplasts as it is in plants. Instead, chlorophyll in bacteria is attached to the cell membrane. Photoheterotrophic bacteria are also called the blue-green algae, but they are not algae. They are bacteria.

The **chemoautotrophs** obtain their energy from inorganic substances such as hydrogen sulfide (H_2S), ammonia (NH_3), and iron-containing material. This is a unique mode of generating ATP that is found only in a few prokaryotes. They obtain their carbon from CO_2.

The **chemoheterotrophs** obtain their energy and carbon from organic sources. This is a common form of obtaining carbon and energy. Chemoheterotrophs are found in many species, including many bacterial, plant, animal, fungi, and protist species.

Bacteria are specialized to obtain their cell mass and organic molecules in a number of different ways. As stated, the majority of the prokaryotes are chemoheterotrophs. They can exist as **saprophytes**. A saprophyte is an organism that feeds off dead and decaying matter. A saprophyte is a decomposer. Or, they can be **parasites**, which obtain their nutrients from the body fluids of living hosts. A parasitical relationship is always bad for the host and good for the parasite. When bacteria become parasitic to a human or animal host, we call it an infection. Finally, bacteria may obtain their nutrients in a **symbiotic relationship**. A symbiotic relationship is usually defined as a relationship between two organisms in which the presence of each organism benefits the other, and no harm is done to either one. Bacteria which normally live in the guts of grazing animals and humans are **symbionts**.

Bacteria also have different adaptations for requiring oxygen. Some bacteria are unable to grow in the presence of oxygen; it is actually fatal to them. These types of bacteria are called **obligate anaerobes** (obligate = "have to," and anaerobe = "no oxygen"). Some require oxygen and die without it; these are called **obligate aerobes**. Still others can live with or without oxygen and are called **facultative anaerobes**.

21.12 ARCHAEBACTERIA

Evolutionary biologists think Archaebacteria are the likely candidates for the first life forms on earth several billion years ago. As stated, for a long time the Archaebacteria and Eubacteria were classified in the same Kingdom, Monera, and many text books and classification systems continue to use this scheme. However, as mentioned earlier, the cell walls of the Archaebacteria and Eubacteria are structurally different. The Archaebacteria react differently to antibiotics than Eubacteria do.

With the advancement in technology in the field of cellular biology, it has been found that the sequence of the bases in the Archaebacteria tRNA's and rRNA's is different. These three differences are felt to warrant placement of the Archaebacteria into their own Kingdom. The minority of bacteria are classified as Archaebacteria. Sometimes these bacteria are called cyanobacteria or blue-green algae.

Archaebacteria are known for their ability to thrive in extremely inhospitable environments. Often, the only known organism to live in a particularly hostile environment is a species of Archaebacteria.

The **methanogens** are a class of chemosynthetic Archaebacteria that produce methane during carbon fixation. They are facultative anaerobes and are often found living in dead and decaying matter, such as that found at the bottom of swamps and marshes, or in sewage treatment plants. These are critical organisms in returning dead and decaying matter back to the energy cycle.

The **extreme halophiles** are named due to their ability to survive in extremely salty environments. They are the only prokaryotes that live in the Great Salt Lake and the Dead Sea. They utilize salt—NaCl—to generate their ATP. **Thermoacidophiles** live in extremely hot temperatures—typically 60° to 80° Celsius (140° to 176° Fahrenheit). They also thrive in acidic environments such as hot sulfur springs. There is even one species that has been found living near a hydrothermal vent in temperatures of 105° Celsius (221° Fahrenheit).

Figure 21.12.1

Archaebacteria
This photo is from a hot spring area in New Zealand. The brown and green colored areas are all blooms of Archaebacteria.

21.13 PEOPLE OF SCIENCE

Sir Alexander Fleming (1881-1955) was born at Lochfield, Scotland. He moved to London where he attended the Polytechnic. He spent four years in a shipping office before entering St. Mary's Medical School, London University. He researched at St. Mary's under Sir Almroth Wright, a pioneer in vaccine therapy. He became a lecturer at St. Mary's until 1914. He served throughout World War I as a captain in the Army Medical Corps. He returned to St. Mary's after the War and was elected Professor of the School in 1928 and Emeritus Professor of Bacteriology at the University of London in 1948.

During his research, in 1921, he discovered an important **bacteriolytic** (bacteria killing) substance in tissues, which he named lysozyme. In 1928, while working on influenza virus, he observed that mold had developed accidentally on a staphylococcus culture plate and had created a bacteria-free circle around itself. He named the active substance penicillin.

Sir Alexander wrote numerous papers on bacteriology, immunology, and chemotherapy, including original descriptions of lysozyme and penicillin. They have been published in medical and scientific journals. He was a member of many prestigious societies. In 1945 he was awarded the Nobel Prize in Medicine and Physiology for his work on penicillin.

21.14 KEY CHAPTER POINTS

- Prokaryotes are mainly bacteria and are classified into the Kingdoms of Archaebacteria or Eubacteria.
- Bacteria are the most numerous organisms on earth and live in a wide variety of locations and environmental conditions.
- Bacteria have three common shapes: bacillus (rod shaped), coccus (spherical), and spiral.
- Bacteria have a cell wall surrounding the cell membrane as an added layer of protection.
- Some bacteria have an additional layer outside the cell wall called the capsule.
- There are two types of cell walls which stain differently during the Gram-stain procedure.
- Many Eubacterial species infect and cause disease in humans and animals.
- Antibiotics work against bacteria, because bacteria perform certain biochemical processes which humans and animals do not. Antibiotics prevent bacteria from performing some critical process which kills the bacteria.
- Bacteria have the most diverse means of obtaining their energy molecules.
- Archaebacteria are adapted to live in harsh environments and are called "extremophiles."

21.15 DEFINITIONS

bacilli
    A rod-shaped bacterial cell structure.

bacteriolytic
    Bacteria killing.

bloom
    A rapid and large growth of bacteria or algae on the water surface.

capsule
    An outer most layer of some Eubacteria species.

chemoautotrophs (bacteria)
    Bacteria that obtain their energy from inorganic substances.

chemosynthesis
>   To generate ATP from chemicals.

cocci
>   A spherical bacterial cell structure.

coccobacilli
>   A bacterial cell shape which is not elongated enough to be a bacillus but not spherical enough to be a coccus.

diplococci
>   Pairs of cocci.

dormant
>   Inactive.

endospore
>   A bacterial structure that forms in times of environmental stress. The endospore has the ability to develop into a new bacterial organism when conditions are favorable for growth.

endotoxins
>   Part of the outer membrane of the Gram-negative bacterial cell wall.

exotoxins
>   Protein chemicals secreted by Gram-positive bacteria that are harmful to host tissues.

extreme halophiles
>   Bacteria able to survive in extremely salty environments.

facultative anaerobes
>   Bacteria that can live with or without oxygen.

glycocalyx
>   Fuzzy coating of sugars on the capsule of some Eubacteria species.

gram-negative bacilli
>   Rod-shaped bacteria that do not retain the crystal violet stain during the Gram-stain procedure.

gram-negative cocci
>   Coccus shaped bacteria which do not retain the crystal violet stain during the Gram-stain procedure.

gram-positive bacilli
>   Rod-shaped bacteria that retain the crystal violet during the gram-stain procedure.

gram-positive cocci
>   Coccus-shaped bacteria that retain the crystal violet during the gram-stain procedure.

gram-stain
>   A way to stain bacterial cells.

hydrothermal vents
>   Areas under the ocean surface where heat from the earth's interior superheats the water.

methanogens
>   A class of chemosynthetic Archaebacteria that produces methane as part of obtaining their carbon.

microbiologist
>   One who studies bacteria.

obligate aerobes
Bacteria that require oxygen and die without it.

obligate anaerobes
Bacteria that die in the presence of oxygen.

parasites
Species which obtain their nutrients from the body fluids or tissues of living hosts.

pathogenic
Able to cause disease.

peptidoglycan
Short chains of peptides and carbohydrates that make up the cell wall of the Eubacteria.

photoautotrophs
Bacteria that obtain their energy from the sun, and their carbon from CO_2; photosynthetic bacteria.

photoheterotrophs
Bacteria that obtain their energy from the sun and their carbon from organic matter.

pilli
Structure that helps bacteria stick to host cells.

rod-shaped
See bacillus.

saprophytes
Species that absorb their nutrients from dead and decaying matter.

spherical shaped
See coccus.

spirochetes
Spiral-shaped bacteria.

symbionts
In this chapter, this term refers to bacteria that normally live in the guts of grazing animals and humans. However, symbionts in general means that two or more organisms live together for the mutual benefit of the other.

symbiotic relationship
Bacteria and host co-exist with no harmful effects to either one.

thermoacidophiles
Bacteria that live in extremely hot temperatures.

STUDY QUESTIONS

1. What is the Kingdom Monera? Into which Kingdom(s) are the organisms that used to be classified in Monera now classified?

2. What are the three most common bacterial shapes?

3. Draw a prototypical bacterial cell and label the cytoplasm, capsule, cell wall, DNA, nucleoid, cell membrane, plasmids, ribosomes, and flagella.

4. True or False? Only a few bacteria contain cell walls.

5. True or False? Gram-staining is a common procedure used to identify Archaebacteria organisms.

6. Why do Gram-positive bacteria stain the way they do when Gram-stained? What color are they? Why do Gram-negative bacteria stain negative? What color are they?

7. Why do antibiotics kill bacteria and not their human hosts?

8. True or False? Archaebacteria and Eubacteria are the most diverse organisms in relation to how they obtain their energy and carbon.

9. For which general property are Archaebacteria known?

10. Discuss the difference between obligate and facultative anaerobe.

11. True or False? Photosynthetic bacteria contain chloroplasts.

12. What is an endospore?

13. What is the difference between an endotoxin and an exotoxin?

14. List at least two differences that have caused microbiologists to separate prokaryotes into the two kingdoms of Eubacteria and Archaebacteria.

PLEASE TAKE TEST #8 IN TEST BOOKLET

Kingdom Protista

22

22.0 CHAPTER PREVIEW

In this chapter we will:

- Discuss how the organisms in Protista acquire their energy source.

- Describe the common body structures of algae.

- Discuss the reproductive cycle of algae, protozoa and slime molds/water molds.

- Introduce the concept of the reproductive cycle of alternation of generations, which will also be a common mode of reproduction for many Fungi and Plantae species.

- Discuss the attributes of organisms in Protista.

22.1 OVERVIEW

The organisms that make up the Kingdom of Protista are commonly referred to as **protists**. They are the least complex eukaryotes, from a structural and functional standpoint, but are certainly more complex than the prokaryotes we just discussed. They are the most diverse Kingdom in terms of size of organisms, from microscopic forms to organisms that are over three hundred feet long. Unfortunately, this great diversity causes quite a bit of disagreement between taxonomists regarding the proper way to classify the organisms that comprise the Protista Kingdom. Therefore, we need to briefly discuss the current state of classification of the protists. It is important to understand that, like the Eubacteria/Archaebacteria vs. Monera schemes, there are differing opinions regarding the proper placement of many protist organisms. You should be aware that evolutionists believe the Protists evolved from the Archaebacteria/Eubacteria Kingdom a couple billion years ago.

There are many "older" classification schemes that are still widely taught that divide Protista into two "sub-Kingdoms," the Protozoa and the Algae. However, more recently this two-level breakdown has been slightly modified to a three-level scheme. Therefore, we will be using the three-level breakdown of Protista into: **protozoa**, the "animal-like protists," **algae**, the "plant-like protists," and **slime molds** and **water molds**, the "fungus-like protists."

We can understand the division of the protists in a slightly different, and perhaps more common-sense way. This way is to divide them based on their mode of obtaining their carbon source. You can think of the protozoa as **heterotrophic protists**, algae as **autotrophic protists**, and the fungus-like protists as **absorptive protists**. During the upcoming discussion on protists, if you get confused about the **nomenclature** (names) used, return to this section for a review. In addition, remember that there are now between thirty and forty phyla recognized in the Protist Kingdom, but we are only going to cover a few of these. We are mainly covering Protista to gain a better appreciation of the great biodiversity.

Figure 22.1.1

Classification Schemes of Protista
The two classification schemes for Protista are shown here. We will be using letter (b).

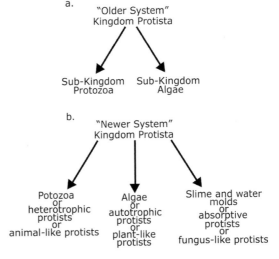

Protists are generally unicellular, though there are many different multi-cellular forms. Like many of the bacteria, most protists have cilia or flagella at some point in their life cycles. However, recall that prokaryotic and eukaryotic flagella are quite different. Prokaryotic flagella are attached to the cell surface, while eukaryotic flagella are an extension of the cytoplasm and are formed by microtubules in a 9 + 2 arrangement.

In rivers, lakes, and oceanic environments, both the algae and the protozoa are part of the **plankton** population. Plankton is the collection of microscopic and small macroscopic life forms floating in the water that serve as the starting point in the food chain. Plankton synthesizes about 50% of the carbohydrate sources available on earth, as well as a large majority of the oxygen in the atmosphere. Algae are referred to as **phytoplankton**, and protozoans and bacteria are called **zooplankton**.

22.2 ALGAE: GENERAL

The algae make up the most diverse phyla of Protista. They can be microscopic in size or several hundred feet long. Some classification systems you may see have the algae grouped with plants. However, algae lack the tissue differentiation seen in plants and as such the algae do not have stems, leaves, or roots. Also, the reproductive structures are different in algae than they are in the plants. Algae form their gametes (eggs and sperm) in single-celled chambers (called **gametangia**). The gametangia of plants are multi-cellular. For these reasons, algae are most often placed in Protista rather than Plantae.

Algae are autotrophic and contain chlorophyll a. Most algae also contain chlorophyll b, c, and/or d; occasionally they contain other pigments such as the carotenoids as well. Most species are aquatic. Most of the greenish things you may see growing in rivers, lakes, oceans, or aquariums are algae. "Seaweed" is algae. There are commonly seven phyla of algae recognized; these will be listed at the end of this section.

Figure 22.2.1

Algae

Algae can take many forms. The green film that grows on the tops of slow-moving water, ponds, and lakes is algae. Beds of giant kelp, which can grow to more than three hundred feet in length, are also a type of algae. Most of the aquatic growth referred to as "seaweed" is algae.

22.3 ALGAE: STRUCTURE

Algae can take on various forms, or structures. Many species of algae are unicellular. Multi-cellular algae are commonly referred to as seaweed and include kelp. Kelp has a well-described structure system. The body of plant-like algae is called the **thallus**. Because algae do not have true tissue differentiation, they do not have roots, stems, and leaves; however, there are specialized portions of the thallus that take on these plant functions. Usually the thallus has a root-like portion that anchors it called a **holdfast**, a stem-like portion called a **stipe** and a leaf-like portion called a **blade**.

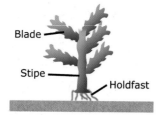

Blade

Stipe

Holdfast

Figure 22.3.1

Algae Structure

The entire algal structure is called the thallus. The three components are the blade, stipe and holdfast. This is a common structural plan for multicellular algae commonly referred to as "seaweed".

Four types of algae have been identified based on their cell structure and associations with other algal organisms. **Unicellular algae** are unicellular; most are phytoplankton. Most algae are unicellular. The genus *Chlamydomonas* is an example of unicellular algae. **Colonial algae** consist of groups of individual algal cells that function together in a coordinated way. *Volvox*, a colonial alga, consists of thousands of algal cells in a single layer contained in a hollow, membrane-like- sphere. **Filamentous algae**, like *Spirogyra*, have a thallus that consists of rows of algal cells linked together on end. Some of the filamentous algae have a holdfast. **Multicellular algae**, like *Ulva* and *Macrocystis*, have a large, complex thallus with a holdfast, stipe, and blades.

Figure 22.3.2

The Seven Phyla of Algae

Phyla	Thallus Format	Photosynthetic Pigments	Form of Food Storage	Cell Wall	Species
Chlorophyta (green algae)	U, C, F, and M	Chlorophylls a and b, and carotenoids	starch	polysaccharides, mainly cellulose	7,000
Phaeophyta (brown algae)	M, often large	Chlorophylls a and c, carotenoids, fucoxanthin	laminarin (oily carbohydrate)	cellulose and alginic acid	1,500
Rhodophyta (red algae)	M	chlorophyll a, phycobillins, carotenoids	starch	cellulose or pectin	4,000
Bacilliariophyta (diatoms)	U, some C	Chlorophylls a and c, carotenoids, xanthophyll	leucosin (oily carbohydrate)	pectin and silicone dioxide	11,500
Dinoflagellata (dinoflagellates)	U	chlorophylls a and c, carotenoids	starch	cellulose	1,100
Chrysophyta (golden algae)	U, some C	chlorophylls a and c, xanthophyll, carotenoids	laminarin (oily carbohydrate)	cellulose	850
Euglenophyta (euglenoids)	U	chlorophylls a and c, xanthophyll, carotenoids	paramylon (a starch)	no cell wall, pellicle	1,000

U = Unicellular, C = colony forming, F = filamentous, M = multicellular

22.4 ALGAE: PHYLA

The organisms categorized in **Chlorophyta**, of the green algae, are diverse. They exhibit all four cellular types. **Phaeophyta**, or the brown algae, are commonly called seaweed or kelp. These organisms can adequately absorb light up to depths of over three hundred feet. They are the source of **alginate**, an additive for cosmetics and food. **Rhodophyta**, or red algae, are also commonly called seaweed and kelp. Most are marine, and some can absorb light over six hundred feet underwater. The depth at which they live determines their color, so not all of the "red algae" are red. **Agar**, used for culturing bacteria and other microbes, is obtained from the cell walls of the rhodophytes.

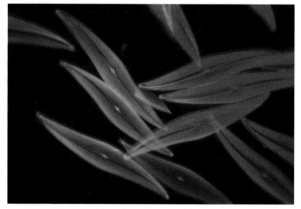

Figure 22.4.1

Diatoms
Diatoms are microscopic unicellular algae. Their bodies have two halves, which fit together like a gift box. Diatoms make up a large part of the phytoplankton in marine and fresh water environments.

Species in **Bacilliariophyta** are also called **diatoms**. Their cell walls are often rather firm and are commonly called shells. The shells have two halves, called valves, and fit together like a shoe box and lid. They are the most abundant of the algae. The organisms of **Dinoflagellata** are all small and usually autotrophic. Some species are able to emit their own light, called **bioluminescence**. Most of the dinoflagellates have two flagella of unequal length, which causes them to spin around when they swim through the water. **Chrysophyta** are common in fresh water and also have two flagella of unequal length.

Figure 22.4.2

Euglenophyta
Euglena is a unicellular alga species. It has a single flagella.

The organisms of **Euglenophyta** are abundant in fresh water. The prototypical organism of this phylum is from the genus *Euglena*. *Euglena* has a single flagella at one end of the cell and a large contractile vacuole to help rid it of excess water and maintain homeostasis. It does not have a cell wall and is fairly flexible and able to change its shape. However, for extra support, there is a proteinaceous layer under the plasma membrane called a **pellicle**. *Euglena* is usually photosynthetic, but if exposed to darkness for a period of time, it will lose its chloroplasts and chlorophyll, becoming heterotrophic. Once this happens, it will remain heterotrophic for the remainder of its life.

22.5 ALGAE: REPRODUCTIVE

Algae have a diverse reproductive cycle. Some of these protists reproduce asexually while others are able to reproduce both sexually and asexually. Sexual reproduction is often triggered by harsh environmental conditions, at which time the algae forms a protected reproductive structure called a **zygospore**. Most adult algae are haploid, but the zygospore is diploid. There are two different, common reproductive cycles in multicellular algae that are illustrative.

Figure 22.5.1

Reproductive Cycle of Unicellular Algae
This shows a typical reproductive cycle of unicellular algae. Many algae are able to reproduce either sexually or asexually, depending on environmental conditions. Sexual reproduction is usually triggered by harsh conditions. The zygospore is a hearty structure which is resistant to unfavorable conditions. The important thing to remember here is that the sexual reproductive cycle contains a meiosis event, as do all sexual reproductive cycles.

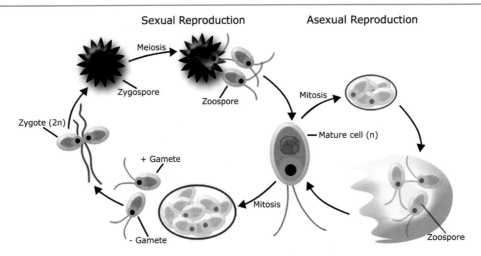

The species *Oedogonium* is a multicellular filamentous alga. The male unicellular gametangium, called the **antheridium** and, underneath it, a separate female gametangium, called the **oogonium**. These are both located on the stipe. The flagellated sperm from the antheridium swim down to the oogonium and fertilize the egg. The zygote is released as a zoospore and falls to the floor of the body of water. It undergoes meiosis to form four haploid cells. The cells are released from the zoospore and form a new filament.

Figure 22.5.2

Reproductive Cycle of Multicellular Algae
This is a common reproductive cycle for multicellular algae. The alga fertilizes itself when sperm moves from the antheridium to the oogonium of the same stipe. Their DNA fuses and a new single cell organism is formed, called a zygote. The algal zygote is referred to as a zoospore. Zoospores can grow into new algae if they land in a nice growing area.

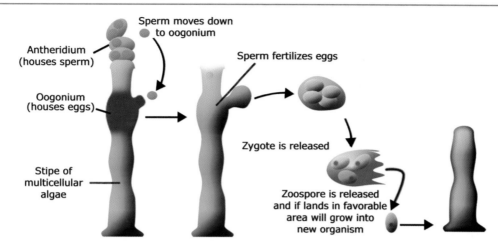

A more complicated process is demonstrated by the algae *Ulva*. It is a multicellular algae that reproduces via **alternation of generations**. In this process, the alga exists in one generation in the haploid state. When the organism is haploid, it is called a **gametophyte**. During the next generation, the organism exists in the diploid state. When the organism is diploid, it is called a **sporophyte**. Please see the diagram for further details. Also, please remember the concept of alteration of generations as this property is displayed by many Kingdoms, including Fungi and Plantae.

Figure 22.5.3

Ulva Reproductive cycle
Ulva is a multicellular alga that is also called sea lettuce. It grows in coastal areas and is eaten by many people groups. It has a complicated reproductive cycle called alternation of generations. This is a very common cycle that most Fungi and Plantae organisms also display (so remember it!). *Ulva* lives as a gamete producing, haploid gametophyte in one generation. It produces haploid plus and minus gametes (not male and female). The gametes fuse with one another (as all gametes do) to form a zygote. The zygote grows in size by mitosis into a spore-producing, diploid sporophyte. The sporophyte then produces haploid spores by meiosis and these grow into the haploid gametophyte.

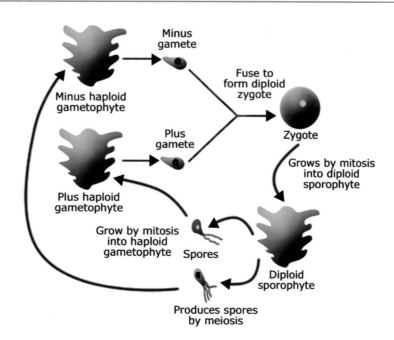

22.6 PROTOZOA

The protozoa, also called the "animal-like" or heterotrophic protists, are all single celled. There are over 65,000 species in the four phyla that include protozoa. They are found in fresh and salt water and make up a large part of the zooplankton population. They are found also in soil and on plants. They can be independently living, or can be parasites or symbionts. All protozoa are able to move independently, and the phyla are divided based on the mode of locomotion.

Most of the species of protozoa are heterotrophs and break down their nutrients in **food vacuoles**, which are membrane-bound chambers filled with digestive enzymes. Some of the parasitic forms need to reproduce inside their hosts while others reproduce asexually or sexually. Most protozoa do not have a cell wall and are only separated from their environments by the plasma membrane.

Figure 22.10

Four Phyla of Protozoans

Phylum	Common Name	Locomotion	Nutrition	Example Genera
Sarcodina	sarcodines	pseudopodia	H, some P	*Amoeba*
Ciliophora	ciliates	cilia	H, some P	*Paramecium*
Zoomastigina	zooflagellates	flagella	H, some P	*Leishmania, Giardia*
Sporozoa	sporozoans	none (as adults)	H, some P	*Plasmodium, Toxoplasmosis*

H = heterotrophic   P = parasitic

22.7 PROTOZOA: PHYLUM SARCODINA

Organisms in the phylum **Sarcodina** mostly have their plasma membranes exposed to the external world, but a few have a protective shell, called a **test**, to protect them. Sarcodines are characterized by the organisms from the genus *Amoeba*. There are over 40,000 species of sarcodines; most live in and around ponds and streams. They have characteristic, flexible membranes, which function both for locomotion and for obtaining nutrition. Their cell membranes are able to move and stretch out through the process of **cytoplasmic streaming**. As this occurs, finger-like extensions of the cell membrane, called **pseudopods**, reach out and propel the organism (called **amoeboid movement**) or engulf food via phagocytosis. The sarcodines also have a contractile vacuole that expel water in order to maintain homeostasis. Several species are able to cause infection in the intestines, called **amoebic dysentery**, leading to fever and diarrhea.

Figure 22.7.1

Amoeboid Movement
A light micrograph of an amoeba is shown left. Its pseudopodia are easy to see. The way it is able to move is shown on the right.

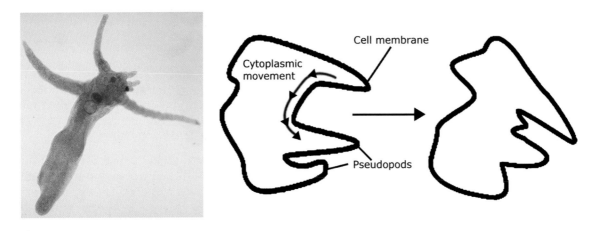

22.8 PROTOZOA: PHYLUM CILIOPHORA

There are eight thousand species in the **Ciliophora** phylum. They are typified by organisms from the genus *Paramecium*. Ciliates are found in ponds and streams. Their mode of locomotion is through the use of cilia, small hair-like extensions of the cytoplasm surrounding the cell that move in a wave-like manner through the actions of microtubules. Ciliates also have the most elaborate structures of any protozoan organelles and a pellicle.

Figure 22.8.1

Paramecium
The top photo is a light micrograph of a *Paramecium*. Notice the structures on the inside of the organism, which are labeled on the diagram on the bottom. Also note the *Paramecium* is covered with cilia.

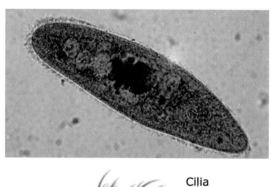

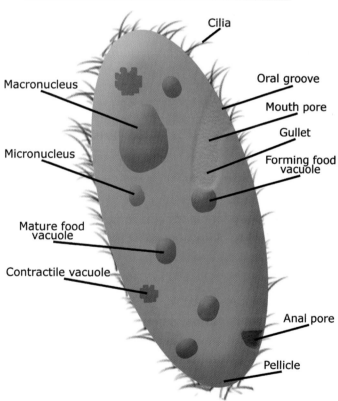

Ciliates have at least two nuclei, a **macronucleus** that participates in the regulation of the cell's metabolism, and at least one **micronucleus** which participates in cellular reproduction. Asexual reproduction is through binary fission, in which the micronucleus divides by mitosis, and the macronucleus elongates and splits in two.

Sexual reproduction is through the process of **conjugation**. Two organisms line up next to each other and their membranes join. Each organism's macronucleus disintegrates, and the diploid micronuclei undergo meiosis to form four haploid micronuclei in each organism. Three of each organism's micronuclei disintegrate, and the remaining micronucleus undergoes mitosis. There are now two haploid micronuclei in each organism.

One micronuclei from each organism is exchanged between the cells and fuses with the micronucleus that stayed behind. There is now one diploid micronucleus in each organism with 50% different genetic material than it had before conjugation started. The organisms then separate and the macronucleus reforms using the genetic material from the three disintegrated micronuclei. Each organism then divides to form four organisms that are genetically identical to one another, but genetically dissimilar to the parent organism.

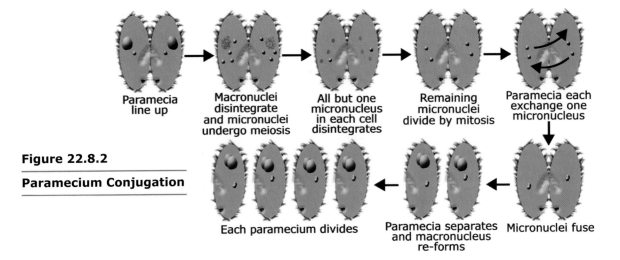

Paramecia line up → Macronuclei disintegrate and micronuclei undergo meiosis → All but one micronucleus in each cell disintegrates → Remaining micronuclei divide by mitosis → Paramecia each exchange one micronucleus

Each paramecium divides ← Paramecia separates and macronucleus re-forms ← Micronuclei fuse

Figure 22.8.2

Paramecium Conjugation

22.9 PROTOZOA: PHYLUM ZOOMASTIGINA

Zoomastigina includes some 2,500 species. They are found mainly in lakes and ponds. These organisms move through one or more flagella. The whipping motion of the flagella pushes or pulls the organism through the water. Some species from this phylum cause human disease, including those from the *Trypanosoma* (causing African sleeping sickness, with fever, sleepiness, and coma), *Giardia* (diarrhea), and *Leishmania* (causing leishmaniasis, a blood disease with skin sores which affects millions in Africa).

22.10 PROTOZOA: PHYLUM SPOROZOA

The organisms from the phylum **Sporozoa** cause the most human disease of any organisms on earth. There are six thousand species, and most are parasitic. The adult forms cannot move. In order for most of the sporozoans to move they need to be transported by another organism. The organism which transports them is called a **vector**. The organism which is infected is called the **host**. They have complex life cycles, as typified by the organisms from the genus *Plasmodium* (which cause several different forms of malaria).

Malaria is a disease that affects over 500 million people annually in Africa, Asia, and the Mediterranean Sea region. It causes symptoms of fever, tiredness, anemia (low blood count), kidney failure, and death. The vector is the *Anopheles* mosquito, and it serves both to carry the parasitic *Plasmodium* species to and from humans and as a site for the part of the reproductive cycle of *Plasmodium*.

The *Anopheles* mosquito bites a person and injects the immature form of the parasite, called a **sporozoite**, into the human. The sporozoite travels to the liver through the blood stream, where it divides and emerges as another form called a **merozoite**. Merozoites infect red blood cells and, at fairly regular intervals, the red blood cells burst open, releasing toxins that cause the illness as well as more merozoites. The merozoites then develop into another form a **gametocyte**. The gametocyte is taken up by the mosquito when it bites an infected person. Inside the mosquito, the gametocyte then develops into a sporozoite, and the cycle begins again.

Figure 22.10.1

Plasmodium Life Cycle

There are several species of *Plasmodium* that can cause infection in humans. The typical life cycle for this protozoan is shown below. The vector is the *Anopheles* mosquito. *Plasmodium* cannot mate and form zygotes in the stomach of any other mosquito species. When a mosquito that has the zygotes in the stomach bites a human, the sporozoites are introduced into the host's blood. They immediately infect the liver and mature into merozoites. Merozoites then infect red blood cells. At regular intervals, the red blood cells break open causing fevers, anemia and other symptoms. Some of the merozoites mature into gametocytes in the red blood cells. When the infected person is bitten by a mosquito, the gametocytes are taken into the stomach and combine to form sporozoites and the whole cycle starts over.

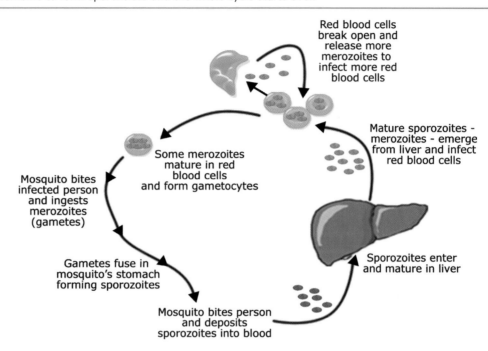

Fortunately, there are antibiotics to treat malaria if it is contracted, as well as to prevent the sporozoite from infecting a person if they are bitten. However, forms of malaria that are resistant to the standard anti-malarial antibiotics have been developing, just as is happening in the case of bacterial resistance. There are newer antibiotics being developed to account for this situation, as science tries to stay one step ahead of the parasite.

22.11 SLIME MOLDS AND WATER MOLDS: THE FUNGUS-LIKE PROTISTS

These organisms include the slime molds and water molds. Because they have some characteristics in common with the Fungi Kingdom, they have often been classified as Fungi. However, they have life phases that set them apart from the Fungi, as well as other Protista organisms. Despite this, they are usually classified as protists.

The slime molds and water molds are eukaryotic and are either multicellular or large unicellular organisms. They all have a two-phase life cycle, a mobile **feeding stage** and a stationary **reproductive stage**. While in the feeding stage, they resemble colonial protists; in the reproductive stage they resemble fungi. Environmental conditions largely dictate what phase the molds are in as harsh environmental conditions usually trigger the organism to move from the feeding to the reproductive stage. All fungus-like protists produce **fruiting bodies** during the reproductive phase. Fruiting bodies contain reproductive spores and are released into and dispersed by the wind.

There are two phyla in the slime mold category, **Acrasiomycota**, or the **cellular slime molds**, and **Myxomycota**, or the **plasmodial slime molds**. Water molds are classified in the **Heterokontophyta** phylum.

22.12 SLIME MOLDS: ACRASIOMYCOTA AND MYXOMYCOTA

The phylum Acrasiomycota constitutes sixty-five species. They are found in moist places where there is a lot of decomposing matter for them to eat since they are decomposers. They are typically found in forests on rotting logs and damp soil and look like shiny, white, slimy masses—like a snail without its shell. When conditions are moist, they are in the feeding stage and exist as single cells. When conditions begin to dry, they release a chemical that causes hundreds or thousands of individual cells to merge and form one big, blobby mass of cells, called a **pseudoplasmodium**. Although the cells remain individual, they function and move together as a unit. This is the reason they are referred to as the cellular slime molds. When it is time to reproduce, the pseudoplasmodium moves to a warm and dry place. It then produces one or more reproductive fruiting bodies.

The phylum Myxomycota constitutes about 450 species. They are yellow or orange in color. These are masses of cytoplasm with several hundreds of nuclei that can be several centimeters in size. They are not true multicellular organisms, because there is no division of the cytoplasm by cell walls or membranes. In the feeding phase, they are mobile, like the organisms in Acrasiomycota. When conditions get too dry, they go into the reproductive phase and form fruiting bodies.

22.13 WATER MOLDS: HETEROKONTOPHYTA

The water molds consist of the water molds, white rusts, and downy mildews. They are important decomposers in fresh water and some are pathogenic (remember this means disease-causing) to plants. They consist of branching filaments of cells and appear as cottony masses on dead algae and fish. They can reproduce via sexual and asexual reproduction. Potato blight kills potatoes and is in the phylum Oomycota. It caused the Irish famine in the mid 1800s.

22.14 PEOPLE OF SCIENCE

Christian Gottfried Ehrenberg (1795-1876), German naturalist, zoologist, comparative anatomist, and microscopist, was one of the most famous and productive scientists of his time. He was born in Germany, near Leipzig. He studied medicine, theology, and natural sciences in Berlin. He became a friend of the famous explorer Alexander von Humboldt. He traveled several times with von Humboldt in the early to mid 1800s, collected thousands of plant and animal specimens and published extensively on his findings. Starting in the early 1930s, he began to concentrate his studies on microscopic organisms which, until then, had not been systematically studied. For nearly thirty years, Ehrenberg examined samples of water, soil, sediment, and rock, describing thousands of new species. Among these were now well-known flagellates, such as Euglena, and ciliates such as *Paramecium aurelia,* and *Paramecium caudatum*. He was particularly interested in diatoms. He also demonstrated that the phosphorescence of the sea was due to micro-organisms. He continued until late in life to investigate the microscopic organisms of the deep sea and of various geological formations. He died in Berlin on June 27, 1876. Dr. Ehrenberg was professor of medicine at Berlin University in 1827. He was a foreign member of the Royal Society of London since 1837. In 1839, he won the Wollaston Medal, the highest award granted by the Geological Society of London. He was also the first winner of the Leeuwenhoek Medal in 1877. After his death in 1876, his collections of microscopic organisms were deposited in the *Museum für Naturkunde* at the Humboldt University, Berlin. The "Ehrenberg Collection" includes forty thousand microscope preparations, five thousand raw samples, three thousand pencil and ink drawings, and nearly one thousand letters of correspondence.

22.15 KEY CHAPTER POINTS

- Organisms from the Kingdom Protista are mostly unicellular, but there are some multicellular species.

- Protozoa are the "animal-like protists." They are the heterotrophic protists.

- Algae are the "plant-like protists." They are autotrophic protists.

- Slime molds and water molds are the "fungus-like protists." They are the absorptive protists.

- Most all protists are able to reproduce sexually and asexually.

- Algae are photosynthetic. The species are very diverse—some being microscopic while others are quite large.

- The protozoa are mainly heterotrophic. Amoeba and paramecium are the prototypical protozoans.

- Species from the protozoa phyla of Zoomastigina and Sporozoa commonly cause human disease. Malaria is caused by a Sporozoan.

- Slime molds and water molds are absorptive organisms. They are important decomposers in wet environments. Most are multicellular or large, unicellular organisms.

22.16 DEFINITIONS

absorptive protists
Protists which obtain their energy by absorbing dead matter; also called the fungus-like protists.

Acrasiomycota
A protist phylum that includes slime molds

agar
Used for culturing bacteria and other microbes; obtained from the cell walls of some algae.

algae
Protists that obtain their energy through photosynthesis; also called the "plant-like" protists.

alginate
An additive for cosmetics and food obtained from algae.

alternation of generations
The biological property of a species living one generation as a haploid organism, then the next generation as a diploid organism.

amoebic dysentery
Infection of the intestines caused by an amoeba.

amoeboid movement
Refers to the way in which amoeba move by sending out pseudopods.

antheridium
Algae's male unicellular gametangium.

autotrophic protists
See Algae.

Bacilliariophyta
A protist phylum commonly called diatoms.

bioluminescence
Species that are able to emit their own light.

blade
The leaf-like portion of the algal thallus.

cellular slime molds
A type of protist.

Chrysophyta
A protist phyla commonly called golden algae.

Ciliophora
A protist phylum commonly called paramecia.

Chlorophyta
A protist phylum commonly called green algae.

colonial algae
Groups of individual algae cells that function together in a coordinated way.

conjugation
The process of sexual reproduction, which occurs in some bacterial and protist organisms.

cytoplasmic streaming
The process of cell membranes moving and stretching out due to movement of the cytoplasm underneath.

diatoms
See Bacilliariophyta.

Dinoflagellata
A protist phylum commonly called the dinoflagellates.

Euglenophyta
A protist phylum commonly called euglena.

filamentous algae
Algae that have a thallus consisting of rows of algal cells linked together end on end, forming a long "string" or filament.

food vacuoles
Membrane-bound chambers filled with digestive enzymes.

fruiting bodies
The spore-producing structure of a protist or fungus.

gametangia
Single-celled chambers in which algae form their gametes.

gametocyte
A cell produced by meiosis. A cell for the purpose of sexual reproduction.

gametophyte
An organism which exists in the haploid state. The gametophyte stage produces gametes.

heterotrophic protists
Protists which obtain their energy by eating other protists or bacteria. Commonly referred to as the animal-like protists or protozoa.

holdfast
The root-like portion that anchors the thallus.

macronucleus
Participates in the regulation of the cell's metabolism.

merozoite
The daughter cell of protozoan parasites.

micronucleus
Participates in conjugation.

multicellular algae
Commonly known as seaweed.

Myxomycota
A protist phylum commonly called a slime mold.

nomenclature
Name.

oogonium
Algae's female gametangium.

pellicle
Proteinaceous layer under the plasma membrane of euglenoids and some other protozoa that helps them maintain their shape.

Phaeophyta
A protist phylum commonly called brown algae.

phytoplankton
The algal component of plankton.

plankton
The collection of microscopic and small macroscopic life forms floating in the water that serve as the starting point in the food chain.

protists
The organisms that make up the kingdom of Protista.

protozoa
See heterotrophic protists.

pseudoplasmodium
A mass of cells formed by hundreds or thousands of individual cells slime mold cells.

pseudopods
Finger-like extensions of the cell membrane.

Rhodophyta
The protists phylum commonly called seaweed and kelp.

Sarcodina
The protist phylum commonly called the sarcodines or amoeba.

sporophyte
An organism which exists in the diploid state. Sporophytes produce spores.

sporozoite
Immature form of a parasite.

sporozoa
Parasitic protozoans; includes the organism that causes malaria.

stipe
The stem-like portion of the thallus.

test
Protective shell of some of the sarcodines.

thallus
The body of plant-like algae.

unicellular algae
Algae that are made up of one cell.

vector
> An organism that transports a parasite from one host to another.

water molds
> See absorptive protist.

Zoomastigina
> The protist phylum commonly called zooflagellates.

zooplankton
> Plankton that consists of animals, including the corals, rotifers, sea anemones, and jellyfish.

zygospore
> Protected reproductive structure formed in algae.

STUDY QUESTIONS

1. What are the three classes of protists?

2. Why is plankton important? Why are the protists important in relation to plankton?

3. True or False? Most protists can reproduce sexually and asexually.

4. True or False? Algae form their gametes in single celled chambers called gametangia.

5. Draw the common structure of a multicellular alga and label the structures.

6. What does "alternation of generations" mean? Draw the reproductive cycle of *Ulva* and label the major events.

7. True or False? Algae are all unicellular organisms.

8. True or False? *Euglena* and diatoms are common forms of Algae.

9. What is a common trigger for sexual reproductive cycles to begin in the protists?

10. Describe or draw amoeboid movement. How does it occur?

11. What is conjugation?

12. Why are some of the organisms in the phylum Sporozoa studied so intensely?

13. How do the slime molds and water molds obtain their source of energy?

Kingdom Fungi

23

23.0 CHAPTER PREVIEW

In this chapter we will:

- Discuss the common characteristics Fungi share.

- Define the general structure plan of Fungi.

- Investigate the modes of sexual and asexual reproduction of the fungal divisions of Basidiomycota, Ascomycota, Zygomycota and Deuteromycota.

- Define the specific structural plans for the four Fungi divisions.

- Investigate the structure and function of lichens.

- Learn the beneficial and harmful features of Fungi.

23.1 OVERVIEW

The organisms of the Kingdom Fungi are not as diverse as Protista, but are more complex organisms in regard to their function and form. The majority of the organisms in Fungi are multi-cellular, and they are all heterotrophic. There are over 100,000 species in this Kingdom, and about 1,000 new species per year are added. Fungi includes some common organisms such as yeast, mushrooms, molds, and mildews. Fungal organisms can be very small or very large. There is reported to be one single, fungal organism in Washington State that covers an area of fifteen hundred acres. There are also fungi which are important disease-causing organisms in humans and plants.

23.2 FUNGI CHARACTERISTICS

Initially, fungi were placed in the same Kingdom as plants. However, there are several important differences between plants and fungi that warrant their own Kingdom. First, there are no photosynthetic fungi; they are all saprophytes (decomposers). Second, their physical structure is significantly different from plants. Third, although fungi do have cell walls like plants, their cell walls are made from the glucose polymer **chitin**, rather than the glucose polymer cellulose. (Chitin is also found in the skeletons of insects.) Finally, all fungi reproduce by the formation of spores. Most plants reproduce using spores and seeds.

Like plants, fungi are stationary and are unable to move in their environment. However, they are able to grow toward their food source at a rapid rate. The growing part of the nutrient-obtaining structures, called hyphae (discussed in a bit), grows at a combined rate of up to 1 km/day. Fungi grow in and on their food, which is dead and rotting organic matter.

Figure 23.2.1

Types of Fungi
The organisms classified in the Kingdom Fungi have a wide range of appearances and growth habits. Most of us know the organism in Fungi as mushrooms and toadstools, but there are many other types of organisms we will learn about.

As stated, fungi are all generally decomposers, although there are some important parasitic species. The species which are parasitic cause diseases in humans, animals, and plants. Combined with saprophytic bacteria, their function as decomposers releases the majority of organic nitrogen and carbon back into the circle of life. Once the elemental carbon and nitrogen is released, it is then re-incorporated into plants and bacteria, and recycled back into organisms. Many fungi have developed symbiotic relationships with plants and algae, as will be discussed.

All fungi obtain their nutrients the same way: they digest their food before they absorb it. This is called **extracellular digestion** and is accomplished by the secretion of digesting enzymes outside of the fungus. This breaks down the dead and rotting material on which fungi feed and allows it to be absorbed for nutrients. Often, when a fungus is harmful to another species living near it, it is because of the secreted digestive enzymes.

23.3 STRUCTURE

All fungi have a common structure. The basic building block of fungi is called the **hypha** (plural **hyphae**). This is a small tubular structure created by individual fungal cells lining up. Each hypha can be made up of millions of cells, and each fungus can have thousands, or more, of hyphae per fungus organism. The cell contains cytoplasm and typical eukaryotic organelles. It is surrounded by a cell membrane with an outer cell wall made of chitin.

Figure 23.3.1

Basic Fungal Structure
This is the basic structure of a fungus. It may look a little like a mushroom. That is because mushrooms are a type of fungus. The basic unit of Fungi is called a hyphus (plural hyphae). Hyphae are made up of individual cells that are linked together end to end. The cells of most species of Fungi retain their individual cell borders, as shown in (a). These are called septated hyphae. Some hyphae lose their borders and form one large cell mass. This is shown in (b). These are called non-septated hyphae. All hyphae form into long filaments and group together to form the structure of the fungus. All fungi have a reproductive structure which produces spores. This is sometimes referred to as the **fruiting body**, because this is where the spores are produced (or the "fruits" of the fungus). The familiar structure of a mushroom cap is a type of fruiting body. The mycelium is the network of hyphae which digest, absorb, and transport nutrients for the rest of the fungus.

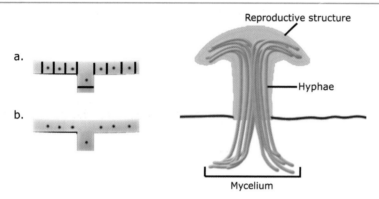

Hyphae can take on two different appearances. They can be separated into individual cells by cross walls, or **septa** (singular **septum**), and are then called **septated hyphae**. Some species do not have septa at all. These are called **non-septated**, or **coenocytic** (SEE'-no-si-tic), hyphae and appear as one continuous cytoplasmic mass with multiple nuclei. These form by the process of nuclear division without cellular division. During mitosis, the nuclear envelope does not disintegrate. Rather, it stays intact during the four phases of mitosis, then pinches in two parts following anaphase.

Hyphae of the fungus form an intricate lattice-work that serves as the nutrition network. The growing part of a fungus is called the **mycelia**. The portion of the mycelia underground or in the organism the fungus is obtaining its nutrients from and decomposing functions to digest and absorb the food. The portion of the mycelia that is above the ground or food source transports the nutrients to where they are needed by the fungus. In order to obtain enough nutrients, the hyphae grow in length, not width. When the fungus is in the growth state, most of the nutrients are transported by the mycelium to the tips of the hyphae, where the growth takes place. When the fungus enters the reproductive stage, the nutrients are transported to the area of the mycelium, where the reproductive structures are forming and active.

23.4 REPRODUCTION

Most fungi exist in the haploid state during their life cycles. They can reproduce sexually or asexually. Like the protists, whether the fungus enters into the sexual reproductive cycle depends on the environmental conditions. During times of favorable growing conditions, fungi reproduce asexually. This is performed via cellular mitosis, creating gamete clones of the parents, called **spores**. When environmental conditions become unfavorable, they enter into sexual reproduction. This is because the structure formed from sexual reproduction is hardy and can withstand harsh conditions. Once the conditions become favorable again, the sexually-produced gametes are released and germinate to form haploid organisms.

You should know that fungi do not come in male and female forms; rather, they are termed **plus** and **minus**. When a plus species encounters a minus species, if the environmental conditions are right, they will participate in sexual reproduction. A hypha from the minus comes in contact with a hypha from the plus organism. The hypha fuse; inside, a specialized reproductive structure forms with gametes inside. The gametes then grow into new organisms. This is the general description of sexual fungal reproduction. We will cover it more specifically when we talk about the divisions of Fungi. But the ways in which Fungi reproduce sexually serves as the basis for classifying them into different divisions.

Fungi normally reproduce asexually. However, the details of the asexual reproductive cycles are slightly different for different phyla of Fungi and we will individually discuss them below. The general pattern, though, is for the organism to form a stalk which holds the reproductive cells, called **spores**. Spores are tiny haploid reproductive cells that have the ability to grow into a new fungal organism. Other fungi do not form stalk-like structures. Some, like *Tinea pedis* (the organisms that causes athlete's foot), use a method called **fragmentation**. In fragmentation, a hyphal cell becomes brittle and shatters, releasing spores. **Budding** is a common asexual reproductive mode for yeast. This is performed by the yeast cell splitting into two asymmetrical cells.

23.5 DIVISIONS OF THE KINGDOM FUNGI

There are commonly three well-accepted divisions of the Kingdom Fungi (sometimes referred to as phyla) and usually a fourth. The three well-accepted divisions are **Basidiomycota**, **Zygomycota**, and **Ascomycota**. Most of the classification systems also use a fourth division, but for some reason they don't include it in the beginning of the chapter, and throw it in at the end, which is confusing. We will include the fourth division, **Deuteromycota**, up front, with the other three.

As already stated, the divisions are decided by the form of sexual reproduction the fungus carries out. However, the form of asexual reproduction does not figure into the classification of the divisions (it does figure into the classification further into the classification system). Therefore, within the kingdom of Ascomycota, for example, there are species that asexually reproduce by sporangiophores, conidiophores, fragmentation, or budding. However, all species in Ascomycota sexually reproduce the same way.

Figure 23.5.1

Four Divisions (Phyla) of Fungi

Division	Structure	Asexual Structures	Sexual Structures	Example
Basidiomycota	septated	rare	basidia produce basidiospores	mushrooms
Zygomycota	coenocytic	spores	conjugation with zygospores	*Rhizopus Penicillium*
Ascomycota	septated or unicellular	conidia	asci produce ascospores	yeasts
Deuteromycota	varies	conidia	none	*Arthrobotrys*

23.6 DIVISIONS OF THE KINGDOM FUNGI: BASIDIOMYCOTA

There are approximately 25,000 species classified in the division of Basidiomycota. They are often referred to as the **club fungi** due to the club-like appearance of their sexual reproductive structure. Mushrooms are the prototypical basidiomycete.

Mushrooms have an underground network of the mycelium. When the mushroom enters into the sexual reproductive cycle, a plus and minus mating strain come together. They form an above-ground extension that is the sexual reproductive structure. This is what we can see that looks like a mushroom. The stem of the mushroom is called the **stalk** which is formed by the hyphae of the mycelium. The top of the mushroom is called the **cap**. The undersurface of the cap contains many small slits, called **gills**. The inside wall of the gill is called a **basidia** (singular **basidium**) and, on the basidia, the **basidiospores**, or sexually-produced gametes, form. Each basidium produces four basidiospores. The entire structure of the stalk, cap, and gills is referred to as a **basidiocarp**.

Figure 23.6.1

Basidiomycete Structure

This is the typical structure of a mushroom. The gills are on the underside of the cap. This is where the spores are formed. Basidia are structures on the surface of the gills. Basidiospores form on the basidia. If you take a freshly-picked mushroom, remove the cap, and place it gills down on a sheet of paper, a thin black film will slowly develop on the paper. These are the spores which have fallen out of the gills. Spores can be spread by the wind or by water. Fungi produce so many spores because spores are fragile. Unlike most plant seeds, spores are small and not protected from the environment.

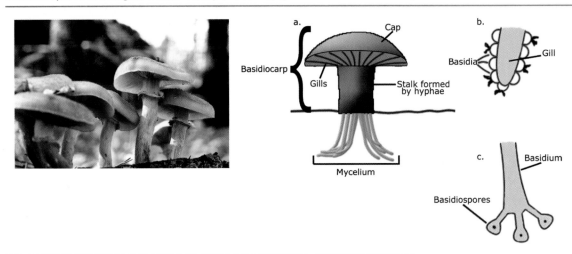

23.7 DIVISIONS OF THE KINGDOM FUNGI: ZYGOMYCOTA

There are approximately 600 species of zygomycetes. Most are terrestrial and live in moist places. The black bread mold *Rhizopus stolonifer* is a common example from this division.

Rhizopus grows on bread by sending hyphae into the bread. These are called **rhizoids**. Rhizoids are hyphae that grow into the surface of whatever the fungus is living on. It also sends some hyphae over the surface of the bread, called **stolons**. Stolons are hyphae which grow over the surface of whatever the fungus is living on. In times of harsh conditions, sexual reproduction is undertaken through the process of conjugation. When a hypha from a minus strain meets a hypha from a plus strain, they align side by side and fuse. A large multinucleate cell forms at the site of fusion, and spores are made inside of it. This is called a **zygospore** and is a resistant-reproductive structure. When conditions become favorable for growth, the zygospore undergoes meiosis. A sporangiophore grows out of the zygospore and haploid spores are released.

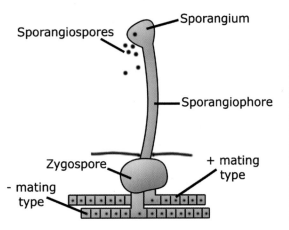

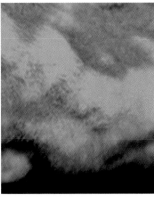

Figure 23.7.1

Zygomycete Structure

Bread mold, *Rhizopus* species, (left) is a typical organism from the Zygomycota division. Far left, a plus and minus mating type of *Rhizopus* have joined their hyphae for sexual reproduction. A zygosporangium has formed, and a sporangiophore has grown out of it. The reproductive structure, called the sporangium, is at the top of the sporangiophore. The sporangium is the fruiting body of the zygomycete and produces many spores.

23.8 DIVISIONS OF THE KINGDOM FUNGI: ASCOMYCOTA

There are between thirty thousand and sixty thousand species in this division. When the four-division system is abandoned for a three-division system, most of the organisms from Deuteromycota are placed in this division; hence the large discrepancy between number of species. The ascomycetes are also called the **sac fungi**. These forms are often parasitic and are found in salt and fresh water, as well as on land.

Sexual reproduction begins when a plus and minus strain come together. Even though fungi do not have male and female organisms, the reproductive structures are still referred to as a male and female reproductive structure. (I believe this is an attempt by evolutionary botanists to make you think they are related to plants from an evolutionary point of view, because the names of the fungal male and female reproductive organs are similar to those of the male and female plant reproductive organs.) The hyphae align and meet. At the site where they join, a female reproductive structure called an **acsogonium**, and a male reproductive structure called an antheridium, form. The two fuse together, and nuclei from the antheridium cross over to the ascogonium. New hyphae then grow out of the ascogonium to form an **ascocarp**. The ascocarp is the visible sexual reproductive structure. The ascocarp produces millions of spores.

There are many examples of ascomycetes that you are probably familiar with: brewer's yeast (to make beer and wine), baker's yeast to make bread, Dutch elm disease, red bread mold, and truffles. These will be discussed a bit later, though.

Figure 23.8.1

Ascomycete Structure
Left is a typical ascomycete. The structure that you can see is the ascocarp. This is the fruiting body. At the top of the figure on the right, the asexual reproductive structure is shown. It is called the conidia. Ascomycete fungi, like the *Penicillium* species from which we obtain the antibiotic penicillin, reproduce asexually using a **conidiophore**. The conidiophore is a stalk like hyphae. Conidia develop on top of the conidiophore. **Conidiospores** are produced by the conidia. Note the antheridium and ascogonium growing from the minus-mating type and the plus-mating type hyphae, respectively. They join together for sexual reproduction and form an ascogonium. The ascocarp grows out of the ascogonium. Inside of the ascocarp are thousands or millions of spore producing asci. Note that each ascus produces eight spores, called ascospores.

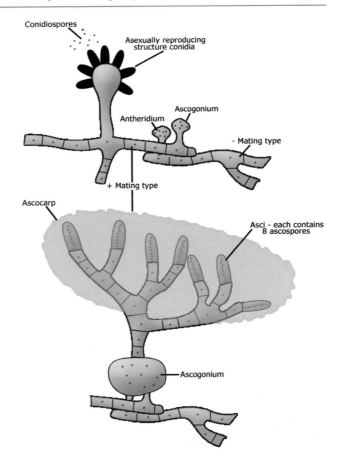

23.9 DIVISIONS OF THE KINGDOM FUNGI: DEUTEROMYCOTA

As already noted, this is a debatable division, but we should discuss why organisms are classified into it. Sometimes the deuteromycetes are grouped into the Ascomycota division, but often they are left in Deuteromycota. They are often referred to as *Fungi imperfecti*, which is Latin for imperfect fungi. The reason for classifying a fungus into this division is that we have not yet discovered what sexual reproductive cycle they use, if any. However, as research goes on, species which were classified as *Fungi imperfecti* are often found to have a sexual reproductive cycle and are then placed in the appropriate Fungi division.

The most common example of organisms from this division are the molds. A mold is simply a rapidly growing and asexually reproducing fungus. Sometimes, fungi from the other divisions will initially grow as a mold, then turn to whatever sexual structure they may use to sexually reproduce. For example, *Rhizopus* often begins its life as a mold then, when it moves into the sexual reproductive cycle, it is obvious that it is *Rhizopus*. If that were the case, the mold would be classified as a *Rhizopus* mold. Other times, though, there is no observable sexual cycle, so the organism is kept in Deuteromycota.

Some of the organisms in this division are parasitic, and others are heterotrophic. However, there are a few forms that are predatory, like the *Arthrobotrys* species, which traps live round worms in its mycelia and digests them for nutrition.

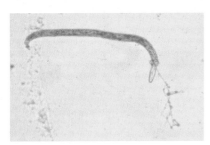

Figure 23.9.1

The Atypical Fungi *Arthrobotrys*
On the left is a picture of the fungus *Arthrobotrys* and a worm that is a species of nematode. The worm is the larger tubular structure, and the fungus is the stringy looking structure at the bottom right of the picture. Notice the fungus is wrapped around the nematode. *Arthrobotrys* is one of the predatory Fungi. It wraps around nematode species, then digests them. Image is courtesy of K.H. Wang, University of Florida, Department of Entomology and Nematology. More images like this can be seen at http://agroecology.ifas.ufl.edu.

23.10 YEASTS

These are unicellular fungi in aquatic or moist environments. "Yeast" is not a true division. Some fungi can live as a unicellular organism or a multicellular organism. When a fungus is in the unicellular state, it is said to be a yeast. However, when the conditions are right, the yeast will begin to grow and become truly multi-cellular. At that stage, it can be classified into one of the three divisions.

Yeast reproduce asexually by **budding**. This is a process similar to mitosis, except that two asymmetrical cells are formed. One cell is larger than the other, but they are both fully functional. Once the yeast buds, the smaller cell grows slightly to become as large as the parent cell. When environmental conditions are favorable, yeast reproduces in this way. When the conditions are not favorable, yeast undergoes the budding process, but the two cells remain attached instead of separating. After the yeast has budded many times and remains attached to one another, it forms a **filamentous mycelium**.

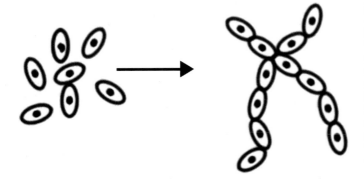

Figure 23.10.1

Budding Yeast
Yeast cells reproduce rapidly by the process of budding, which we have discussed previously. Under certain conditions, yeast will form into a filament. In the figure on the left, there are many yeast cells which have formed by budding. On the right, the yeast cells have formed into a filament. Although the yeast cells are all attached to one another, they all function independently of one another, so this is not a multicellular organism. They are simply "stuck" together.

23.11 LICHENS

Lichens are fascinating organisms in life. They are neither plant nor fungus. Rather, **lichens** are a symbiotic association of millions of photosynthetic organisms living in the mycelium of a fungus. The fungus is either from the Ascomycota (usually) or Basidiomycota (seldom) divisions. The photosynthetic organisms are either unicellular, or filamentous algae, or photosynthetic bacteria. The cells of the fungus and the photosynthetic organism that inhabit it reproduce independently of one another.

Lichens are actually given their own genus and species within the Kingdom Fungus, with the genus and species name being that of the fungus component of the lichen. There are about 25,000 different lichens classified.

The external structure of the lichen is that of the fungus. The fungus supplies the physical structure for the photosynthetic organism to grow. The photosynthetic organism supplies nutrients to the fungus that would not otherwise be present for the fungus to grow. Because of their symbiotic relationship, lichens are often able to grow where no other vegetation is found. They can grow on solid rock and in both the arctic and desert regions. It is interesting to note that the fungus cannot live independently of the photosynthetic organisms.

Figure 23.11.1

Lichens

Fungi, usually from the Ascomycota division, form the framework of the lichen. A photosynthetic organism, such as an alga species or a photosynthetic bacteria, colonize the mycelium of the fungus. Both species benefit from one another in this symbiotic relationship. The two pictures below are both lichens. The color of the lichen depends on the photosynthetic pigments of the algal or bacterial species which colonize the fungus.

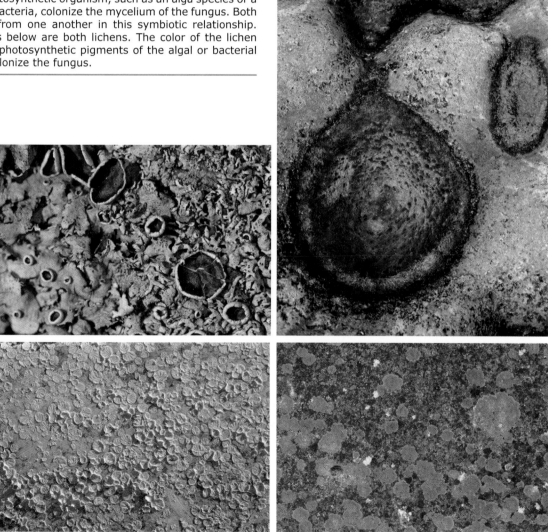

23.12 MYCORRHIZAE

The term "mycorrhizae" does not refer to another division within Fungi, but to the relationship that many fungi have with plants. All three Fungi divisions have species that fall under the category of mycorrhizae. **Mycorrhizae** describe the symbiotic relationships that many fungi have with plant roots. Fungi are often found living in and near the roots of many vascular plants (trees, bushes, woody flowers). It is beneficial to plants and fungi to have fungi living around and near a plant's roots, because the hyphae of the fungi help provide added nutrients to the plant. Up to 95% of all vascular plants have mycorrhizae. You will notice this relationship often near the base of an oak, birch, or pine tree where mushrooms commonly grow. The presence of the basidiocarp above ground indicates the relationship between the tree and fungus going on under the soil.

23.13 PRACTICAL ASPECTS REGARDING FUNGI

Fungi and bacteria are the primary decomposers in the world. This has been stated many times, but it is an important concept to understand. Without these decomposers, virtually nothing would ever decompose, and all of the nitrogen and carbon contained in the skeletons of plants and animals would never be available for organic use again. The fungal hyphae invade the dead material and release enzymes to break it down, making the nutrients available to the fungus and to anything else in the area that can benefit from the fungus's actions. This organic matter is then taken up by plants and animals back into the circle of life.

Unfortunately, the parasitic fungal species are also present and good at what they do. Mostly, these fungal parasites attack plants, but they can infect animals and humans. It is estimated that 10-50% of the world's fruit harvest is lost each year to parasitic fungi. Dutch elm disease, imported to the US from Europe in the early 1900s, is a fungal infection that has nearly wiped out the entire population of American elm trees. Another fungus has similarly attacked American chestnut trees.

Ergot, a parasitic fungal infection of the rye plant, causes disease in humans. Usually, when infected with the fungus *Claviceps purpurea*, the grain looks purple, but it is not always noted prior to processing. When ingested, the disease ergotism develops and is characterized by vomiting, intense feelings of heat or cold, and constriction of the arteries to the hands and feet—sometimes causing gangrene and hallucinations. It is commonly fatal. The last outbreak of this occurred in France in 1951 when 150 people became hysterical and four died. It is commonly thought that ergotism was the cause of the unusual behavior in Massachusetts of the 1600s, which led to many accusations of witchcraft.

Fungi have many helpful properties, however. The first antibiotic, penicillin, was found to be produced by a fungus. Now, many fungi are commonly assessed for their ability to produce antibiotics. Several species—from *Penicillium* and *Cephaloaporium*—are known to produce antibiotics. The yeast *Saccharomyces cerevisiae* is used to make bread rise and to ferment beer and wine. Also, the ethanol (alcohol) that is added to gasoline is made by yeast.

Fungi are commonly eaten, especially the basidiocarps (mushrooms). Truffles, the sexual reproductive structure of underground ascocarps, are popular for their taste. Unfortunately, many mushroom species look similar. This can lead to deadly mishaps if the wrong mushroom is picked and eaten. No wive's tales can accurately predict whether a mushroom is toxic or not; you need to know how to be able to accurately identify them to be safe. A popular mushroom picked and eaten in Asian countries, *Volvariella volvacea*, looks very similar to a mushroom in the US called *Amanita phalloides*. *A. phalloides* is also called the death cap. This mushroom is responsible for 90% of mushroom related deaths in the world. It has toxins that inhibit the synthesis of RNA by inhibiting RNA polymerase. Victims die from kidney and liver failure. The only known cure is liver and/or kidney transplant.

23.14 PEOPLE OF SCIENCE

George Washington Carver (1864-1943) was born a slave in Missouri. While working the fields following emancipation, he was able to obtain a high school education and was admitted to Simpson College in Iowa. He transferred to what is now Iowa State and received a Bachelor's and Master's Degree in 1894 and 1896, respectively. He was then appointed Department Head of Agricultural and Dairy Science at the Tuskegee Institute by Booker T. Washington. Although he is commonly remembered for his contributions to the many uses of the peanut, potato, and soy bean, he also made important contributions into the world of **mycology**, or the study of fungus. He regularly corresponded with and sent specimens to the pre-eminent mycologist of his time, Job Bicknell Ellis. Mr. Carver was particularly adept at collecting rare and new species, and Dr. Ellis would study them further and classify them. Two of these, Dr. Ellis named in honor of Mr. Carver.

23.15 KEY CHAPTER POINTS

- Fungi are more complex structurally than Protists.
- Fungi are all saprophytes, and their cell walls are made of chitin.
- The basic building block of a fungus is the hypha.
- Most fungi are haploid and produce reproductive structures called spores.
- There are four Divisions (Phyla) of Fungi—Basidiomycota, Zygomycota, Ascomycota, and Deuteromycota.
- Basidiomycota are called the club fungi. The typical basidiomycete is the mushroom.
- The typical zygomycete is common bread mold.
- Ascomycetes are also called the sac fungi. Bread yeast is a typical ascomycete.
- Deuteromycetes are also called the fungi imperfecti.
- Lichens are a symbiotic relationship between a fungus and an alga or photosynthetic bacteria.
- Mycorrhizae is the term used to describe the association of a fungus growing in and around plant roots.
- Many fungi cause human and plant diseases.

23.16 DEFINITIONS

ascocarp
   The visible sexual reproductive structure of the organisms from the phylum Ascomycota.

ascogonium
   Female reproductive structure of organisms from Ascomycota.

Ascomycota
   The division of Fungi that uses the ascocarp as the visible sexual reproductive structure.

basidia
   Small outpouchings on the gills that produce basidiospores.

basidiocarp
   The entire structure of the stalk, cap, and gills of a mushroom from the phylum Basidiomycota.

Basidiomycota
   The division of Fungi that uses the basidiocarp as the sexual reproductive structure.

basidiospores
  Sexually-produced gametes formed on the basidia of basidiomycetes.

cap
  The top of a mushroom.

chitin
  The glucose polymer that makes up the cell walls of fungi.

coenocytic
  Hyphae that are one continuous mass with multiple nuclei.

conidiophore
  A specialized hyphae that produces conidia.

conidiospores
  Spores produced by organisms in Ascomycetes.

Deuteromycota
  The division of Fungi commonly known as the "atypical fungi," or Fungi imperfecti.

ergot
  A parasitic fungal infection of the rye plant.

extracellular digestion
  The process of fungi digesting their food before absorbing it.

filamentous mycelium
  The name given to the filamentous structure formed when yeast cells stick to one another.

fragmentation
  When a hyphal cell becomes brittle and shatters, releasing spores.

gills
  Slits in the undersurface of a mushroom cap.

hypha
  A small tubular structure created by individual fungal cells lining up. Hyphae are the basic structural units of Fungi.

lichens
  A symbiotic association of millions of photosynthetic organisms entangled in the mycelium of a fungus.

minus
  A fungal mating type.

mycelia
  The intricate lattice-work that serves as the nutrition network of fungus.

mycology
  The study of Fungi.

mycorrhizae
  The symbiotic relationship that many fungi have with plant roots.

non-septated hyphae
  Hyphae that are one continuous mass with multiple nuclei.

plus
  A fungal mating type.

rhizoids
  Structures that anchor nonvascular plants to the ground and absorb water and nutrients.

sac fungi
Species from the division Ascomycetes.

septa
Cross walls that separate hyphae into individual cells.

septated hyphae
Hyphae that are separated into individual cells by septa.

sporangiophore
The stalk that grows as a result of sexual reproduction between a plus and minus mating type in the Zygomycetes division.

sporangiospores
Haploid spores produced by the sporangium.

sporangium
Sac at the top of a sporangiophore.

spores
Gamete clones of parent fungi.

stalk
The stem of a mushroom.

stolons
"Runners" that extend out from the main plant, and run on top of the ground, from which new organisms grow.

Zygomycota
A division of Fungi which sexually reproduces using a zygospore.

zygospore
The site of fusion where a gametangium forms; spores are made inside of it.

STUDY QUESTIONS

1. True or False? Like plants, all organisms in Fungi are photosynthetic (autotrophs).

2. All fungi have cell walls made up of the _____ polymer _____.

3. How do fungi obtain their nutrients?

4. What is the basic building block of the fungi?

5. What forms mycelia? What function do mycelia perform?

6. True or False? Most fungi exist in the diploid state during their life cycles.

7. True or False? Fungi only reproduce asexually.

8. What are the three commonly-accepted divisions of Fungi?

9. What general criteria is used to classify Fungi into divisions?

10. Draw a picture of a typical organism from Basidiomycota and label the major structures.

11. You are looking at a fungus growing on your bread. It looks kind of blue and black in color and has tiny "roots" growing into and on the surface of the bread. It appears to have zygospores. Which division would this organism be classified into?

12. True or False? Species in Deuteromycota are known to reproduce asexually but not sexually.

13. If you were out in the forest and saw a fungus with antheridia, which division would you assign the species to?

14. What is a lichen?

15. How are lichens classified?

16. What are mycorrhizae?

17. True or False? Fungi are relatively harmless because they do not cause disease in humans, animals, or plants and so there is no problem eating any type of mushroom you may find in the forest.

PLEASE TAKE TEST #9 IN TEST BOOKLET

Plants: Introduction, Structure and Function

24

24.0 CHAPTER PREVIEW

In this chapter we will:

- Review plant cell structure.

- Discuss the structure of plant cell walls.

- Define the difference between vascular and nonvascular plants.

- Introduce the basic concepts of plant reproduction with special attention to monocots and dicots.

- Investigate the specialized structure and function of the tissues that form the roots, stems, and leaves of plants.

- Discuss the important place that water has in maintaining the structure and function of plants.

24.1 INTRODUCTION TO PLANTS

Plants are a vitally important part of the food and energy chain on the planet. Although phytoplankton produces the majority of the oxygen on earth, plants do contribute to the world's oxygen content to a significant degree. Plants are also the main source of carbon fixation for all terrestrial organisms. This means plants are the primary producers on earth. The organisms classified as plants include trees, grasses, flowers, ferns, and mosses. There are over 250,000 species classified in the Kingdom Plantae, divided into twelve divisions (or phyla).

We will be learning more about the taxonomy of plants, but first we need to learn the structure of plants. This is because both the internal and external structure of plants dictates how they are classified within the Kingdom. **Botany** is the study of plants; scientists who study botany are called **botanists**.

Figure 24.1.1

Characteristics of Plants

Multicellular
Cells form into specialized tissues
Contain photosynthetic pigments of chlorophylls a and b, and carotenoids
Cell walls made out of cellulose
Reserve energy stored as starch
Gametangia are protected by layers of cells to prevent drying of gametes
Developing embryo protected inside the female reproductive structure
Life cycle exhibits alternation of generations

You should be aware the evolutionists believe plants evolved from algae, because plants and algae have some common characteristics. They both contain chlorophyll a and b and similar carotenoids. They both have cell walls made of cellulose and store their sugar in the form of starch. This "fact" may come up on college entrance tests. Recall that one of the major differences between plants and algae is that plants have multi-chambered gametangia while algae have single-chambered gametangia. In addition, recall that the gametes of both algae and fungi are fertilized outside of the organism but plant gametes are fertilized within the female gametangium (we will learn about that soon).

All plants are autotrophic, which means, of course, that they are photosynthetic. They are all true multicellular eukaryotes with well-developed tissues and have adapted to a wide range of habitats. A few, true plants are aquatic, while others are found in the frozen tundra of Siberia or in deserts. The rain forests contain the largest number of different plant organisms, though. There are some that are only a few centimeters in height, while others are over one hundred feet tall.

24.2 PLANT CELL STRUCTURE

We discussed cell structure in Chapter 4 and spent time discussing the internal workings and structure of plant cells in Chapter 7. Please review these chapters as needed.

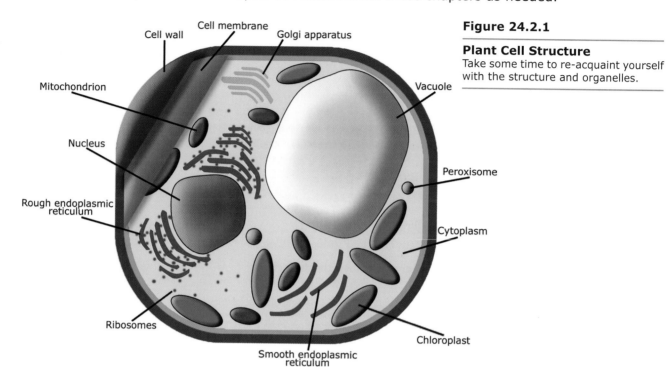

Cell wall · Cell membrane · Golgi apparatus · Mitochondrion · Nucleus · Rough endoplasmic reticulum · Ribosomes · Smooth endoplasmic reticulum · Vacuole · Peroxisome · Cytoplasm · Chloroplast

Figure 24.2.1

Plant Cell Structure
Take some time to re-acquaint yourself with the structure and organelles.

Since plants are eukaryotic, they have the expected organelles within their cell membranes. The methods of transport across the cell membrane are the same as those described in Chapter 4. Plant organelles function the same whether the cell is plant or animal or human. Plant cells perform mitosis and meiosis as described in Chapters 10 and 11.

Figure 24.2.2

Review of Organelles in Eukaryotic Cells

Organelle/Structure	Plant	Animal
Nucleus	yes	yes
Nucleolus	yes	yes
Nuclear envelope	yes	yes
DNA structure	chromosomes	chromosomes
Mitochondria	yes	yes
Chloroplasts	yes	no
Endoplasmic reticulum	yes	yes
Ribosomes	yes	yes
Golgi apparatus	yes	yes
Lysosome	yes	yes
Vacuole	Yes, large	yes, but small
Cytoskeleton	yes	yes
Centrioles	no	yes
9+2 cilia/flagella	yes in ferns, cycads, and bryophytes only	yes
Plasma membrane	yes	yes
Cell wall	yes	no

24.3 PLANT CELL WALL: GENERAL

One major area where plant and animal cells differ is that plants have a cell wall and animal cells do not. The cell wall is a modification of the cell surface and lies outside the plasma membrane. The cell wall of plants is made up of the polymer glucose called **cellulose**. Because plants lack the support of the animal's extracellular matrix, the cell wall functions to provide added support and stability. The cell wall is porous to allow the exchange of gasses, water, and nutrients from the plant cell to the rest of the plant. The cell wall varies in thickness, depending on the function of the cell and the type of plant species.

24.4 PRIMARY CELL WALL

As a plant cells grows, it first secretes a thinner cell wall outside the plasma membrane, called the **primary cell wall**. This is surrounded by sticky molecules called **pectins**. The layer of pectins combines with other sticky, strong molecules to form the middle lamella. This functions to hold adjacent cell walls together. The primary wall is thin and flexible so it can stretch, while the cell is growing. Once the cell is finished growing, non-cellulose polysaccharides harden the primary wall.

24.5 SECONDARY CELL WALL

The cells of woody plants have a second cell wall that forms between the plasma membrane and the primary cell wall called a **secondary cell wall**. This wall is thicker than the primary cell wall and adds more structural support. The secondary cell wall is made up of more cellulose than the primary wall: it also contains **lignin**. Lignin is a chemical compound that is rigid and constitutes almost 30% of the dry weight of wood. Sometimes plants that are woody are referred to as "**lignified**."

Figure 24.5.1

Cell Wall Structure
This is an electron micrograph of the cell wall structure of a plant that forms a secondary cell wall. Note the secondary cell walls form inside the primary cell walls of each cell. The secondary cell wall becomes hard when lignin is deposited in it. This is more commonly known as "wood."

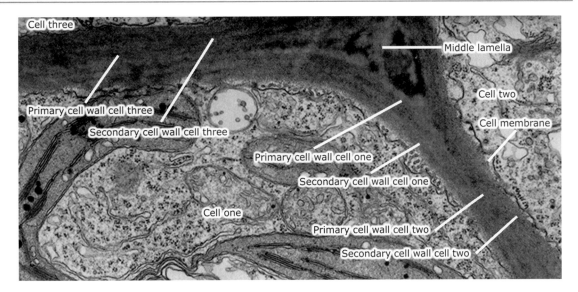

24.6 PLASMODESMATA

Plant cells connect to one another so they can exchange nutrients, water, and chemicals. This is accomplished through small, thin channels that form through the cell walls, called **plasmodesmata**. Cell membranes of adjacent cells extend through the plasmodesmata and communicate with one another. Materials such as water and nutrients can be passed from cell to another through the plasmodesmata. This allows for highly coordinated cellular activities.

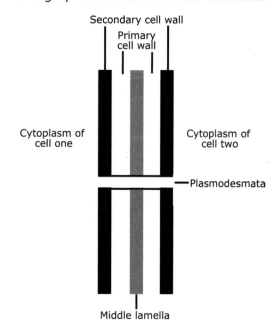

Figure 24.6.1

Plasmodesmata
Plant cell walls have small tracts in them, called plasmodesmata. They run from one plant cell to another, through the cell walls. Cell membranes extend through the plasmodesmata so plant cells can communicate with one another and share nutrients and water.

24.7 VASCULAR AND NONVASCULAR PLANTS

Plants can transport water and nutrients through the plant in two different ways. One way is to use a series of interconnected tubes; these form a continuous network from the roots through the stems and branches to the leaves. These tube systems are similar to blood vessels in animals. Plants that use such a system of interconnected tubes are called **vascular plants**. Most plants are vascular. The trees, flowers, grasses, bushes, etc., are all vascular plants.

However, there are some plants—the mosses, liverworts, and hornworts—that are not vascular. These plants make up the three phyla of **nonvascular plants**. Nonvascular plants all grow in moist environments. Nonvascular plants cannot move large amounts of water and nutrients through them, so they are not large. Nutrients and water are transported through nonvascular plants by diffusion. We will be discussing these in a little while.

Vascular tissues are an adaptation that has allowed plants to grow large and effectively transport material within the plant. Because plants are fairly large, they need an effective way of transporting the water and nutrients absorbed from the roots to the rest of the plant tissues. Also, because the plant manufactures most of its food in the leaves and green stems, there needs to be a way to transport this food to the rest of the plant. The vascular tissue meets this need. It is a continuous system of tubes that move water, nutrients, and minerals "up" the plant from the roots and food "down" the plant from the leaves.

The vascular, or transport, tissues are made up of **xylem** and **phloem**. Xylem tissue is composed of tube-shaped cells. Xylem carries water and minerals from the roots to the rest of the plant. Xylem is actually composed of dead cells. Since the cells are dead, the interior of the cell dries up. However, the cell walls remain. Material flows up from the roots through the hollow, dead cells connected by their cell walls. The cell walls of xylem are lignified and function to support the plant. In trees, xylem is the wood.

Phloem functions to carry the food (glucose) manufactured in the leaves and green stems during photosynthesis to the other plant structures. Unlike, xylem, it is living tissue, but arranged in tubes. Xylem and phloem form a continuous network from the tips of the roots, through the stem, all the way to the leaves.

24.8 GENERAL PLANT REPRODUCTION

Usually when we think of how a new plant grows, we think of a seed. However, there are a number of different structures plants use for reproduction. Some plants use seeds and spores, other plants use only spores. Some plants do not use seeds or spores. Those plants have sperm which swim to an egg. Most of the nonvascular plants reproduce by a method in which sperm swim to an egg. That is another reason the nonvascular plants tend to be small and grow in wet places. The bottom line is that the method by which the plant reproduces is one way botanists classify plants.

A **seed** and a **spore** are different structures. Both seeds and spores can grow into new plants if they are planted where it is favorable for them to grow. A spore contains only one cell, which has the ability to grow into a new plant. Spores also do not have any type of protective coating, as seeds do. Spores are small, and plants that reproduce with spores usually make millions of them. Seeds are much larger than spores. A seed is a structure with a protective coating which contains more in its inside than a single cell. A seed contains a plant embryo surrounded by a protective coating. An embryo is a multicellular "mini plant" which will grow into a new plant. Along with the embryo is **endosperm**. Endosperm functions to feed the newly sprouted plant until it can start photosynthesizing. Plants that form seeds are all vascular plants.

Figure 24.8.1

Seeds and Spores

Spores are small reproductive structures. They are nothing more than a single cell. The spore on the right has been enlarged many times its normal size. A seed is more durable, and has a protective coat. Inside is a plant embryo which looks like a mini plant. There is also a supply of food, called endosperm, which the embryo uses when it begins to grow. Since seeds are hardier than spores, seed plants usually produce far fewer seeds than spore-producing plants produce spores. The added durability of the seed means it is more likely to grow into a new plant than a spore. To be sure that an adequate number of new plants grow, spore-producing plants often make millions of them.

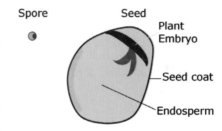

24.9 GENERAL CLASSIFICATION SCHEME OF PLANTAE: ATTENTION TO THE MONOCOTS AND DICOTS

One of the important things to notice in the table is the last two lines. You can see there are two classes of angiosperms listed there. Angiosperms are flowering plants. Any plant with a flower on it is an angiosperm, and all plants which form a flower are angiosperms. It turns out there are two types of seeds that angiosperms form. They form seeds with one cotyledon and seeds with two cotyledons. **Cotyledons** are also called "seed leaves," because they often become the first leaves of the new seedling. They are literally "cup-shaped spaces," which store and provide nourishment to the embryo when the endosperm runs out, before the new seedling begins to photosynthesize. Until the seedling is able to produce more leaves, the cotyledon functions as the only nourishment source available to the plant.

The reason this discussion about cotyledons is important is that flowering plants either produce seeds that form one cotyledon or two. Plants that produce seeds with two cotyledons are called **dicotyledons**, or **dicots**, and plants that produce seeds with one cotyledon are called **monocotyledons**, or **monocots**. This distinction of monocot and dicot serves to further classify the flowering plants. The spore-producing plants are not described by the terms monocot and dicot since they do not form seeds. These terms only apply to the seed-producing flowering plants, or angiosperms. Of note, gymnosperms produce seeds with a variable number of cotyledons. Some gymnosperm seeds have as many as ten or more cotyledons.

Figure 24.9.1

Breakdown of Plantae
This table will give you some idea of the overall way the plants are organized within the Kingdom. You will be seeing this information again, but try to get the general flavor now.

Plant Type	Division (Phylum)	Common Name	# of Species
Nonvascular			
	Bryophyta	moss	10,000
	Hepatophyta	liverwort	6,500
	Anthocerotophyta	hornwort	100
Vascular/seedless			
	Psilotophyta	whisk fern	10
	Lycophyta	club moss	1,000
	Sphenophyta	horsetail	15
	Pterophyta	ferns	12,000
Vascular/seed			
Gymnosperms			
	Cycadophyta	cycads	100
	Ginkgophyta	ginkgoes	1
	Coniferophyta	conifers	550
	Gnetophyta	gnetophytes	70
Angiosperms			
	Phylum Anthophyta	flowering plants	240,000
	Class Monocotyledones	monocots	70,000
	Class Dicotyledones	dicots	170,000

Another interesting thing about monocots and dicots is that there are other characteristics—such as stem, root, and leaf structure—which the monocots show and dicots do not, and vice-versa. These differences are used to further divide the monocots and dicots.

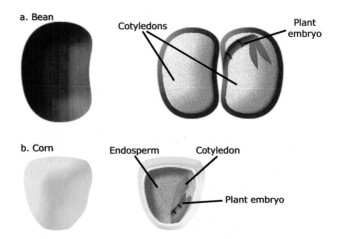

a. Bean
Cotyledons
Plant embryo

b. Corn
Endosperm   Cotyledon
Plant embryo

Figure 24.9.2

Seed Structure of Monocots and Dicots.
Figure (a) shows the structure of a dicotyledons seed, or dicot seed. There are two cotyledons, or seed leaves, which serve as nutrition for the growing embryo. Figure(b) shows a monocotyledon seed, or monocot seed. There is only one cotyledon. In dicots, as the seed is forming, the two cotyledons absorb the endosperm tissue and store the food. During initial growth of the dicot, the embryo receives nutrition directly from the cotyledons. Monocots have well-defined endosperm tissue and a well-defined single cotyledon. During growth of a monocot embryo, the cotyledon absorbs nutrition from the endosperm and passes it to the embryo. The plumule is another name for the plant embryo.

24.10 PLANT BODY

By definition, roots, stems, and leaves need to contain vascular tissue to be called "roots," "stems," and "leaves." Since the nonvascular plants do not have vascular tissue, they do not have true roots, stems, and leaves. The nonvascular plants are said to have **root-like structures**, **stem-like structures**, and **leaf-like structures**. Often, the body of a nonvascular plant is referred to as the **thallus**. The "roots" of the nonvascular plants are called rhizoids. Rhizoids are thin, hair-like structures; they are not as large as true roots.

Figure 24.10.1

The Three General Plant Tissue Types

All plants contain three basic types of tissue: parenchyma, collenchyma, and sclerenchyma. Parenchyma is unspecialized tissue and is found in all structures of the plant. Tissue that performs photosynthesis is made up of parenchymal cells which contain chloroplasts. Collenchyma cells have thicker primary cell walls than parenchyma cells. Collenchyma cells provide structural support for immature areas of the plant. Celery is made up mainly of collenchyma cells. Sclerenchyma cells have thick secondary cell walls. Their secondary cell walls fill with lignin and become wood.

a. Parenchyma   b. Collenchyma   c. Sclerenchyma

  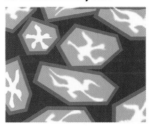

All of the tissues of the plant are formed from three basic types of generalized tissues: parenchyma, sclerenchyma, and collenchyma. These three tissue types differentiate into specialized tissues. The entire structure of the plant, or **body**, is broken into two functions: vegetative and reproductive. The vegetative structures are those that contribute to the plant's growth. Reproductive structures contribute to making seeds or spores. The **vegetative organs** consist of the roots, the stem, and the leaves. **Reproductive organs** vary depending on the type of plant. The reproductive organs of the flowering plants are contained in the flower. The reproductive organs of gymnosperms are cones. In this chapter, we will discuss vegetative organs; the next chapter reproductive organs.

The tissues and organs of a plant function in the same way as in an animal or human; they all work together for the good of the entire organism. They each have a specific function, and specialized tissues and cells to perform whatever task they need to in order for the plant to grow and reproduce properly.

Figure 24.10.2

Vegetative and Reproductive Structures

The basic structure of a plant is shown on the left. The entire plant structure is called the body. The body is made up of roots, stem, and leaves. Everything you see on the tree below is a vegetative structure. An orchid is shown on the right. It is a reproductive structure. The reproductive organs of flowering plants are flowers. Reproductive organs of gymnosperms (pine trees) are pine cones. Flowers are responsible for producing the male and female gametes. When the male and female gametes fuse together, the resulting embryo grows inside the female plant and matures into a seed.

24.11 MERISTEM TISSUE

Regardless of the area where growth takes place—stem, roots, leaves, flowers, etc.—all growth occurs in specialized tissue called **meristem tissue**. Meristem tissue is located in the tips of roots and stems. This is called the **apical meristem**. Roots and stems grow in length due to growth of cells in the apical meristem. The meristem cells are able to undergo mitosis rapidly. As the cells divide, the stem and root grows in length. Behind the apical meristem tissue is the **elongation region**. This is where most of the growth occurs. The **maturation region** is behind the elongation region. Cells mature into their tissue-specific cells in this area.

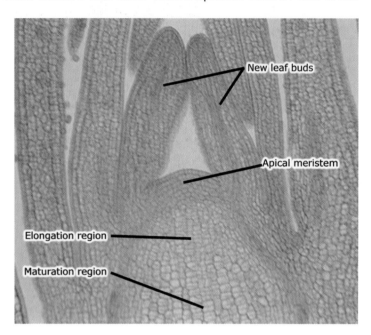

New leaf buds

Apical meristem

Elongation region

Maturation region

Figure 24.11.1

Apical Meristem
This is a cross-section of the tip of a growing tree branch. Meristematic tissue has the ability to grow rapidly. All plant growth occurs in meristem tissue. When plant structures grow in length, the growth occurs from apical meristem tissue, shown below. When plant structures grow in girth, or circumference, the growth occurs in lateral meristem tissue. The maturation region is found behind the meristem tissue.

24.12 ROOTS

The **roots** are the structures of the plant that serve to anchor it into its surroundings and to absorb water and minerals from the soil. Some plants also store food in their root systems. A carrot is such a plant; when you eat a carrot, you are eating the root where the carrot plant stores its nutrients. Since most plants have roots that grow below the ground, when we discuss roots, we are referring to the ones that do grow under ground. However, some plants are parasitic, and their roots sink directly into other plants. Also, some plants grow within the structures of other plants. In those cases, the roots of the plant wrap around branches and leaves of the plant it grows into and collects water and nutrients accumulating on the surface of the plant.

A special side note on **insectivorous plants** (plants that digest insects) like the pitcher plant or Venus flytrap. These plants obtain their water from the roots and their glucose from photosynthesis like other plants. However, they grow in nutrient-poor soil and digest insects to obtain the minerals and other nutrients, especially nitrogen.

Roots are found in two forms, or systems: **fibrous** and **taproot**. When a seed germinates, it forms a **primary root**. This is the first root to shoot out of the seed. If the primary root remains as the main and largest root and has smaller offshoots, or branches, then it is a taproot system. If the primary root begins to branch out and form many other roots with no "main" root, then it is a fibrous root system. There are some plant species that are able to grow roots from their stems or leaves. This type of root is called an **adventitious root**.

Figure 24.12.1

Root Systems

Fibrous roots from grass are shown on the left. There is no single main root. A dandelion's taproot is shown in the middle. There is a large central root with smaller roots growing from it. An adventitious root system is shown on the right. Most monocots have a fibrous system. Most dicots have a taproot system. Prop roots are found in monocots and are a type adventitious root since they grow directly from the stem into the ground.

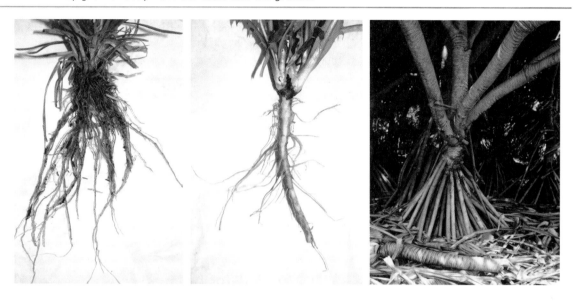

Figure 24.12.2

Carnivorous Plants

Carnivorous plants like the pitcher plant (left) and the Venus fly trap (right) grow in nutrient-poor soil. Their roots absorb water, but they trap and digest insects to obtain needed nutrients that are not found in the soil.

24.13 ROOT TISSUES

The mature root forms an outer layer called the **epidermis**. This is usually several layers thick and protects the root. Just inside the epidermis is the **cortex**, which is used as a site for storage. The next layer in is the **endodermis**, which is one cell-layer thick. The endodermis protects the inner-most **vascular cambium**, or **chamber**, which is the structure that runs throughout the roots, stems, and leaves to transport nutrients and water. The vascular cambium is where the xylem and phloem are located. Between the vascular tissues and the endoderm is a layer called the **pericycle**. If the root needs to send out a branch, it will form from the pericycle.

In monocot roots, the xylem and phloem are organized like spokes on a wheel. In dicot roots, the xylem is oriented like an X. Phloem is in between the arms of the X.

Figure 24.13.1

Monocot and Dicot Root Structure
Not only do monocots and dicots differ in their root systems, but also in the internal structure of their root, as seen below. Monocots have the vascular bundles arranged in a ring around the center of the root. Dicot vascular bundles are grouped in the center of the root tissue.

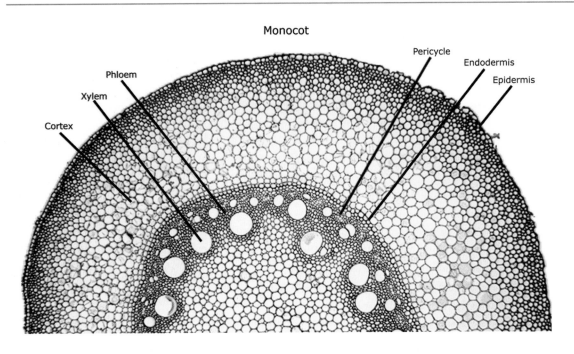

Monocot

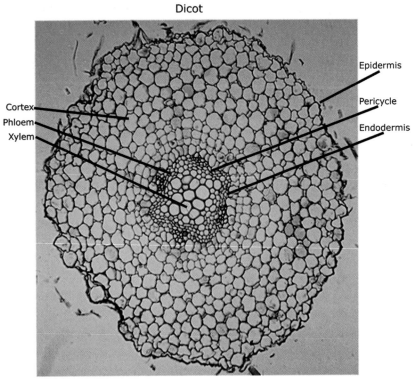

Dicot

24.14 STEM

The stem functions to support the leaves and branches of a plant. It also serves as the structure that allows the flow of nutrients and water to occur. Like the roots, stems only grow at the tips through the apical meristem structure.

Once again, a stem is considered a stem because of the presence of vascular tissues. Nonvascular plants have structures which resemble stems. Since they do not have vascular tissues, they are not called stems, but **stalks**.

The stem is divided into sections called **nodes** and **internodes**. The node is where the leaf or branch is attached to the stem, and the internode is the space between the nodes. At each node is a **lateral bud**, which is capable of growth, but usually only grows under certain conditions. When the lateral bud grows, it creates more branches or leaves. At the tip of the stem is a **terminal bud**, which is where the stem grows in length when the apical meristem cells undergo mitosis. When the terminal bud grows, the stem gets longer.

There are two types of stems: **herbaceous** and **woody**. Herbaceous stems are soft and fleshy, while woody stems are hard. Monocots and dicots each contain species in their groups that have woody or herbaceous stems. Even though there are differences between the structures of the monocot and dicot stems, they do have some similarities: the outer layer of a monocot and dicot stem is called the epidermis; each type of stem contains fibrovascular bundles of xylem and phloem; and each stem contains a region called the **pith** to conduct substances to and from the vascular bundles and plant cells.

However, there are differences, too. The dicot's fibrovascular bundles of xylem and phloem form a ring near the outer part of the stem. In the monocot stem, the fibrovascular bundles are arranged throughout the stem. Also, in a dicot there is a region of **cortex tissue** between the fibrovascular bundle and the epidermis, while the monocot lacks cortex tissue.

A final difference between a monocot and dicot stem is the presence of vascular cambium in the dicot. Monocots do not have a vascular cambium. A vascular cambium is a region within the fibrovascular bundle that is capable of forming new, but limited, amounts of xylem and phloem if the plant's needs dictate that it needs more.

Figure 24.14.1

Monocot and Dicot Stem Structure
Monocot stems contain the vascular bundles scattered throughout the stem. The vascular bundles of dicots are located in a ring around the center of the stem.

Monocot

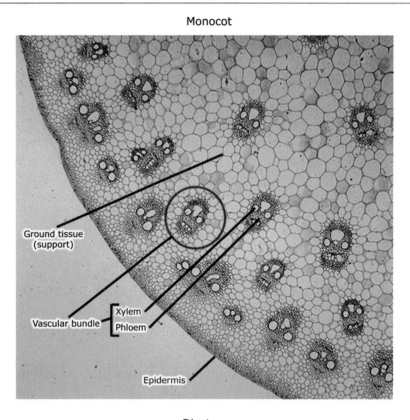

Dicot

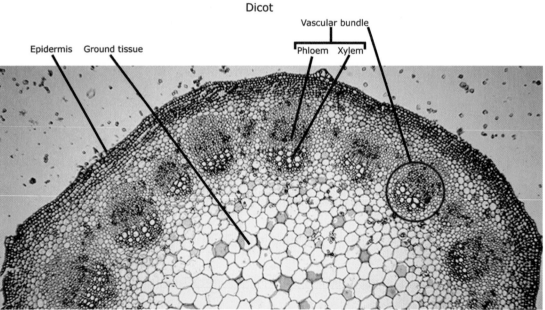

Not all stems form above ground and look the way we would normally think stems should look. There are some specialized stems, such as those of onions and potatoes. Onions are actually a collection of specialized leaves growing from underground stems. Potatoes are underground stems (called **tubers**) specialized to store food in the form of starch.

24.15 BARK

Woody stems have further structure that requires discussion due to the presence of **bark**. Bark is the outermost layer of a woody stem. Bark consists of the **inner bark** and the **outer bark**. In between the inner and outer bark is the **cork cambium**. The cork cambium—cork for short—continually produces cork cells. As the cork cells are made, they soon die and form the outer bark. The outer bark, therefore, is the outermost protective layer of a woody stem made up of dead cork cells. The inner bark is made up of the phloem and cortex tissue.

Figure 24.15.1

Bark Structure
Bark is not only for protection of the tree. The inner layer of bark actually contains the phloem. Since this is a woody stem, the xylem would be hard due to lignin deposits.

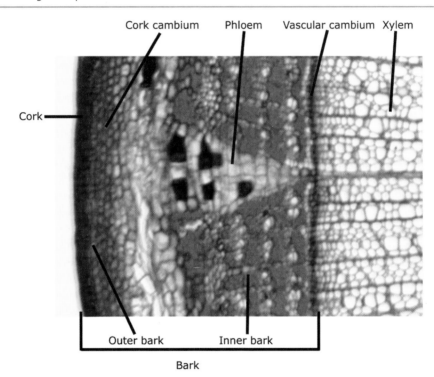

The way the bark forms is what allows a woody stem to continually grow throughout the life of a woody plant. As the stem grows in circumference, the outer bark cracks. The cork cambium simply fills in the cracks with new cork cells, which die and form new outer bark in the crack. This is the reason bark on trees is cracked and rough.

Xylem and phloem in woody stems is continually being made by the vascular cambium as the stem grows. Because the phloem is living tissue, it is able to restructure itself to accommodate for stem growth. However, since the xylem is dead tissue, the vascular cambium continually needs to make new xylem. As the stem grows in circumference, older xylem dies and more is made. This is the process of the formation of tree rings.

24.16 GROWTH RINGS

Tree rings (also called growth rings) are rings of xylem. In the springtime, when water is plentiful, a lot of xylem is needed to transport water, so more xylem is made in the spring than in the late summer, fall, and winter. Therefore, the spring xylem is larger and not as densely packed as the later xylem. When a tree is cut down, the spring xylem is lighter in color and the later xylem is darker in color. During the winter, when no xylem is made, a dark line forms between the late xylem of one season and the spring xylem of the new growing season. The number of rings present indicates how old the tree is, and the thickness of the rings gives an idea of how harsh the climate was for any particular growing season (year).

Figure 24.16.1

Growth rings

Growth rings form every year in woody-stemmed plants. A growth ring is made up of two separate rings. The first ring of a growth ring is the lighter-colored and usually thicker ring. It is formed during the rapid spring growth. The second part of the growth ring is the darker and thinner ring. That ring is formed during the later summer and fall when trees do not grow as quickly.

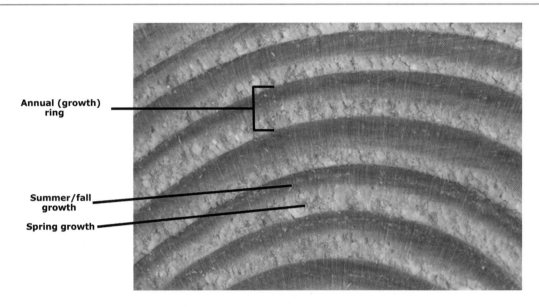

Annual (growth) ring

Summer/fall growth

Spring growth

24.17 LEAVES

Leaves are the main photosynthetic organ of the plant. They also function to exchange gas and absorb sunlight in order to perform photosynthesis. Also, many leaves have a layer of wax over them, called a **cuticle**, to minimize water loss. Leaves vary significantly in structure, as can be seen from the figure. All leaves consist of a flattened blade, which can be one of many forms. Within the blade run extensions of the vascular bundle called **veins**. The blade is attached to the stem at the node by a stalk called the **petiole**. Grasses and other monocots do not have a petiole, but have a sheath at the base of the leaf that envelops the stem.

Leaves of monocots and dicots differ in their structures. The **venation** (or vein structure) of monocots shows the major veins that run the length of the leaf. Grass is a monocot. If you look at a blade of grass, you will see the veins run up and down the length of the blade of grass. Dicot veins form a branched network. Maple, oak, and birch trees are dicots. The veins on a maple, oak, or birch tree form a network that branches out across the leaf.

Figure 24.17.1

External Leaf Structure

Leaf veins are the visible pathways that the vascular bundles take through the leaf. The veins of monocot leaves run parallel with one another and do not criss-cross (left). Dicot leaves have one, large central vein from which other smaller veins branch out (middle). Ferns (right) are vascular non-flowering plants. Most ferns have easy-to-recognize leaves because they are numerous and small.

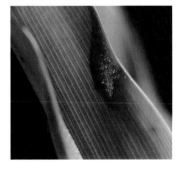  

The top and bottom of the leaf is covered by a single layer of cells called the epidermis. The epidermal cells secrete the waxy cuticle. Sometimes, if a leaf does not have a cuticle, it will have small hairs growing on it. On the underside of most leaves are many tiny little openings called **stomata** (singular stoma). These allow for the exchange of gasses into and out of the leaf. Each stoma is surrounded by two cells called **guard cells**. Guard cells close the stoma when there is poor water supply, but keep them open when the water is plentiful. Because photosynthesis requires a lot of water to perform, the plant cannot afford to have photosynthesis occurring when there is little water. When the stoma are closed, no CO_2 can enter the leaf, and no O_2 or H_2O can exit the leaf, thereby effectively shutting down photosynthesis until the water supply becomes more plentiful.

Under the epidermis, on both sides of the leaf are **parenchyma tissues**, where photosynthesis occurs. The parenchymal tissue is made up of two tissue subtypes: the **palisade mesophyll** and the **spongy mesophyll**. The palisade mesophyll is a densely-packed layer directly underneath the upper epidermis (on the "top" of the leaf) where photosynthesis occurs. Beneath the palisade layer (on the "bottom" of the leaf) is the loosely packed spongy mesophyll, which allows gasses and water to move in and out of the leaf.

Figure 24.17.2

Microscopic Leaf Structure
The top photo is a light micrograph of leaf stoma. These are closed, so water must have been scarce. Leaf veins are formed because of the xylem and phloem running in the area. The palisade layer is where most of the photosynthesis occurs.

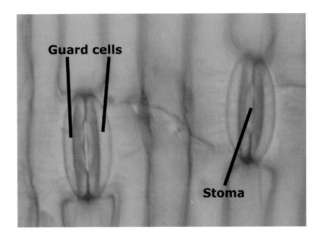

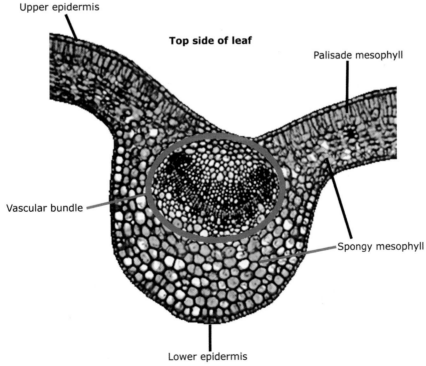

24.18 IMPORTANCE OF WATER FOR PHOTOSYNTHESIS

Water is an extremely important component of a plant's inner workings. Without proper water supply, and a way to maintain the water supply, the plant will not be able to function and will die. Some plants are able to function on little water, such as desert cacti (singular cactus) which often only get watered two or three times per year. Other plants, such as house plants and ornamental flowers, need to be watered two or three times per week to maximally grow. Water is critical in four plant processes: photosynthesis, turgor pressure, hydrolysis, and transport.

We have already discussed photosynthesis at length, but recall that during photosynthesis, the plant uses water and carbon dioxide to make glucose. Without water, photosynthesis cannot occur. We also discussed **hydrolysis** (Chapters 3 and 6). Hydrolysis is the use of water to break larger molecules into smaller ones through the actions of enzymes. It is something that all eukaryotes perform, not plants. Water is essential for the hydrolysis of large molecules into smaller ones.

24.19 IMPORTANCE OF WATER FOR TURGOR PRESSURE

Turgor pressure is the pressure that keeps herbaceous stems upright and leaves full. Plant cells have large central vacuoles, which contain high concentrations of solutes. Water is drawn into the vacuole by osmosis, causing the vacuole to swell to a large size. This pushes the cytoplasm and organelles up against the plasma membrane, making the cell "stiff" or "tight" with the pressure from the large vacuole. When the turgor pressure in all the plant cells is high, the cells push against one another and maintain the shape of the fleshy parts of the plant.

To help picture this, think about what happens when a plant is not watered for a long time. As the soil and the plant dries out, the leaves and stems lose water and start to wilt. The turgor pressure is low. As soon as the plant is watered, the turgor pressure returns to normal, and the plant returns to its usual shape.

24.20 WATER AND NASTIC MOVEMENTS

Turgor pressure is also responsible for **nastic movements** in plants. Nastic movements are simply physical movements of the plants due to changes in the plant's environment. They occur as the result of changes in turgor pressure. The response of the plant occurs independently of the direction of the stimulus. **Thigmonastic movements** are nastic movements in response to touching or shaking a plant. This results in rapid changes in turgor pressure to move some part of the plant. Closing of the Venus flytrap around its prey is an example of thigmonastic movements.

Nyctinastic movements occur in response to changes in light. These are slower changes in turgor pressure that occur in response to day and night changes. Many species of plants have flowers that fold their petals "closed" at night, then "open" them during the day. The same thing is seen in certain plants with the orientation of their leaves to the sun; at night the leaves are folded vertically and when the sun comes out, the leaves move to a horizontal position.

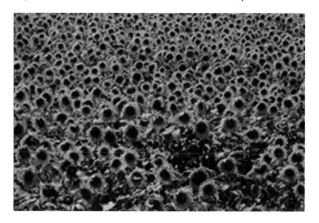

Figure 24.20.1

Nyctinastic Movements
If you have ever seen a sunflower field, you may have wondered why all of the sunflowers were facing the same way. Sunflowers do this because they show strong nyctinastic movements and always have their flowers facing the sun. Nyctinastic movements are possible because of changes in turgor pressure.

24.21 WATER AND TRANSPORTATION

The use of water for **transportation** within the plant is of critical importance. The roots absorb both water and mineral nutrients from the soil. These nutrients are then transported from the roots to the rest of the plant through the xylem (contrary to what many think, leaves do not absorb water). The photosynthetic products are transported from the leaves and green stems to the rest of the plant through the phloem. How does this occur? There is no pump to move it through the plant vasculature as there is in animals.

The answer, it is thought, is due to water. Scientists have suggested the following theory to explain plant transport. It has been tested to some degree and seems to explain transport of substances from roots to the rest of the plant. The theory is called **cohesion-tension theory**. To set the stage for understanding this theory, recall from Chapter 3 that water has many special properties making it uniquely suited to perform many functions in life processes. Hydrogen bonding, which causes enhanced attraction from one water molecule to another, is important in the cohesion-tension theory. The effect of the hydrogen bonding is that water wants to "stick together." This is called cohesion of water.

The cohesion-tension theory starts with water loss in the leaves of the plant. During the daytime, when water is plentiful, the guard cells keep the stoma open so leaves can exchange gas and maximally perform photosynthesis. Photosynthesis causes the plant to lose water. Also, there is evaporation of the water directly from the leaves, called **transpiration**. Both photosynthesis and transpiration lead to significant water loss in the plant occurring at the leaves, meaning there is an overall deficit of water in the leaves.

As water exits the plant from the leaves, the remaining water in the xylem of the branches, trunk and stem want to stick to the water that is being lost in the leaves. This causes tension to develop because the amount of water in the leaves is less than the amount in the rest of the plant. As the water exits the leaves, the rest of the water in the plant wants to stick to that water. This creates tension due to the hydrogen bonds between the water molecules. This tension "pulls" the rest of the water molecules up toward the leaves from further down the plant. Since the nutrients absorbed in the roots are dissolved in the water, they go along for the ride, and there is a continual transport of water and nutrients up the plant from the roots.

This theory also is proposed for the movement of water and nutrients in nonvascular plants. Although there is no xylem or phloem in nonvascular plants, they still lose water through the leaves in the same way the vascular plants do. This causes the flow of water through the plant tissues from the roots to the leaves. It is thought by scientists that this rather inefficient transport of water and nutrients in nonvascular plants is why they are small.

The movement of glucose or other carbohydrates from the leaves to the rest of the plants through the phloem does not occur by the cohesion-tension method. Movement through phloem occurs by **translocation**. Whereas movement of water via the cohesion-tension theory is passive (it occurs without any effort or work on the plant's part), translocation is an active process. That is why the phloem tissue is living tissue. It needs to be able to actively control the flow of glucose through the phloem.

Translocation occurs in a similar way as water movement. Leaves perform photosynthesis and therefore have high concentrations of carbohydrates. Non-photosynthetic areas of the plant constantly use carbohydrates to stay alive. Therefore, non-photosynthetic areas are lower in carbohydrate concentrations than leaves. The carbohydrate moves from the leaf into the phloem, then flows toward areas of lower carbohydrate concentration. In this way, glucose and other carbohydrates are "pushed" from areas of high concentration to areas of lower concentration. The sugar molecules are used for energy or to make **cellulose**. Cellulose is a carbohydrate polymer and is the main structural molecule of a plant.

24.22 PEOPLE OF SCIENCE

Joel Roberts Poinsett (1779-1851) was born in South Carolina. He became a physician and an accomplished amateur botanist. He served as a member of the U.S. House of Representatives, was the first U.S. Ambassador to Mexico, and was the U.S. Secretary of War under Martin Van Buren. While he was serving as a special agent to the U.S. in South America, he discovered and sent samples back of a flower that would later be known as the poinsettia. He was one of the organizers of the National Institute for the Promotion of Science and the Useful Arts, which would later become the Smithsonian Institution.

24.23 KEY CHAPTER POINTS

- Plants are the primary organisms performing carbon fixation for terrestrial organisms.

- The study of plants is called botany.

- Plant cells are eukaryotic. All plant cells have a cell wall, and some have two.

- Plasmodesmata are small tubes which connect plant cells to one another.

- There are two types of plants—vascular and nonvascular.

- Plants can reproduce with seeds and spores, spores only, or neither seeds nor spores.

- There are two types of vascular seed plants—gymnosperms and angiosperms.

- Plants are composed of roots, a stem, and leaves.

- Water is critical for photosynthesis to occur.

- Water is needed for plants to maintain the proper turgor pressure.

- Nastic movements are physical movements of plants which are performed due to changes in their environment.

- Water is critical for the transport of nutrients and glucose in plants.

24.24 DEFINITIONS

adventitious root
　　A root which forms from the stem.

angiosperms
　　Flowering plants that house their seeds in fruit.

apical meristem
　　Rapidly dividing tissue where all length-wise plant growth occurs.

bark
　　The outermost layer of a woody stem.

body
　　The roots, stem, and leaves of a plant.

botanists
　　Scientists who study plants.

botany
　　The study of plants.

cellulose
　　The polymer glucose that makes up the cell wall of plants.

cohesion-tension theory
　　The theory which attempts to explain how water and nutrients are transported from the roots to the rest of the plant.

cork cambium
Layer between the inner and outer bark that produces cork cells.

cortex
A site for storage inside the epidermis.

cortex tissue
The tissue between the epidermis and the endodermis of a plant.

cotyledons
Cup-shaped spaces in seeds that store and provide nourishment to the embryo when the endosperm runs out and before the new seedling begins to photosynthesize.

cuticle
Layer of wax on leaves to minimize water loss.

dicots
Plants that produce seeds with two cotyledons.

dicotyledons
Seeds with two cotyledons.

elongation region
Region behind the apical meristem.

embryo
The organism formed when two gametes fuse.

endodermis
The one cell layer thick structure that protects the inner-most vascular cambium.

endosperm
Food/nutrition source for a newly sprouted monocot or dicot plant.

epidermis
The outer layer of the plant.

guard cells
Cells that surround leaf stoma.

gymnosperms
Plants that form seeds that are not housed in fruits.

herbaceous
Refers to stems which are soft and fleshy.

hydrolysis
The use of water to break larger molecules into smaller ones through the actions of enzymes.

inner bark
Inner layer of a woody stem, made up of phloem and cortex tissue.

insectivorous plants
Plants that digest insects.

internodes
The space between the nodes.

lateral bud
Node which is capable of growth but usually does not grow except under certain conditions.

lignified
Plants that are woody.

lignin
A chemical compound that is rigid and constitutes about 30% of the dry weight of wood.

maturation region
 The mature root behind the elongation region.

monocots
 Plants that produce seeds with one cotyledon.

monocotyledons
 Seeds with one cotyledon.

nastic movements
 Physical movements of plants due to changes in the plants environment and occur as the result of changes in turgor pressure.

nodes
 Location where the leaf or branch is attached to the stem.

nonvascular plants
 Plants which do not contain vascular tissue.

nyctinastic movements
 Nastic movements in response to changes in light.

outer bark
 Outermost protective layer of a woody stem made up of dead cork cells.

palisade mesophyll
 Densely packed layer directly underneath the upper epidermis on the top of the leaf, where photosynthesis occurs.

parenchyma tissues
 Structure beneath the epidermis where photosynthesis occurs.

pectins
 Sticky molecules that surround the primary cell wall.

pericycle
 Layer between the vascular tissues and the endoderm, that forms when the root needs to send out a branch.

petiole
 The stalk that attaches the blade to the stem at the node.

phloem
 Vascular tissue that carries the food manufactured in the leaves and green stems to the other plant structures.

pith
 Region of a stem that conducts substances to and from the vascular bundles and plant cells.

plasmodesmata
 Small, thin channels that form through the cell walls to allow plant cells to exchange nutrition and water.

primary cell wall
 The thinner and first to form plant cell wall.

root cap
 Structure at the tip of the root that secretes a slimy chemical to help the root pass more easily through the soil.

roots
 The structures of the plant which serve to anchor it into its surroundings and to absorb water and minerals from the soil.

secondary cell wall
 A second cell wall that forms between the plasma membrane and the primary cell wall in the cells of woody plants.

seed
A plant embryo surrounded by a protective coating.

spongy mesophyll
Layer beneath the palisade layer on the bottom of the leaf, which allows gasses and water to move in and out of the leaf.

stalks
Structures that resemble stems in nonvascular plants.

stomata (singular stoma)
Tiny little openings on the underside of most leaves.

taproot
A root which forms as one dominant root with smaller branches coming off of it.

terminal bud
Structure at the tip of the stem where the new stem growth occurs each spring.

thigmonastic movements
Nastic movements in response to touching or shaking a plant.

translocation
The process of transporting sugar in the phloem.

transpiration
Evaporation of water directly from the leaves.

tree rings (growth rings)
Rings of xylem in the stem of a tree.

tubers
Underground stems.

turgor pressure
Water pressure that keeps herbaceous stems upright and leaves full.

vascular cambium (chamber)
The structure that runs throughout the roots, stems and leaves to transport nutrients and water.

vascular plants
Plants which use a system of interconnected tubes to transport water and nutrition.

vegetative organs
The roots, stem, and leaves of a plant.

veins
Vascular bundles within leaves.

venation
Vein structure.

woody
Hard stems.

xylem
Tissue composed of tube-shaped cells, that carries water and minerals from the roots to the rest of the plant.

STUDY QUESTIONS

1. What is a scientist who studies plants called?

2. True or False? All plants perform photosynthesis.

3. True or False? Some plants have a cell wall made from cellulose while other

plants have cell walls made from chitin.

4. True or False? Like animal cells, plants perform mitosis and meiosis. However, plant cells do not contain centrioles to form the spindle.

5. Let's say you were small enough to stand inside of a mature plant cell. As you walked from the inside of the nucleus to the outside of the cell, list the following structures in the order in which you would pass through them: primary cell wall, cytoplasm, cell membrane, nucleoplasm, secondary cell wall, and nuclear membrane.

6. What is lignin? Why is it beneficial to some plants?

7. If you were again standing inside of a plant cell, what would be the easiest way to move from one cell to another?

8. What is xylem and phloem? Where are they found? Why are they important? What are plants called that contain xylem and phloem?

9. What are seeds? Do all plants form them? What are the two groups of plants called that do form seeds?

10. What is the difference between a monocot and a dicot plant? Which larger group of plants is formed by the monocots and dicots?

11. What are nonvascular plants?

12. Are rhizoids roots? Why or why not?

13. If you pulled a dandelion out of the ground and were actually able to not break the roots, you would see that there is a long central root with small branches on it. What type of root system is that?

14. All plant growth occurs at the _____ _____.

15. True or False? Plants do not show much organization in their root, stem and leaf structures.

16. How do tree rings form? If there was a wet year in an area with good nutrition, would the growth ring be thick or thin?

17. What do guard cells do? Where are they located? What is the main stimulus for them to perform their function?

18. In what tissue of the leaf does photosynthesis occur?

19. What is turgor pressure? Why is it important?

20. True or False? Water is important in the nastic movements of plants.

21. Describe the cohesion-tension theory.

22. What is transpiration? Is it important in the movement of substances in plants?

Plants: Physiology, Reproduction, and Classification

25

25.0 CHAPTER PREVIEW

In this chapter we will:

- Discuss plant hormones and their effects on plant tissues.

- Discuss asexual means of plant reproduction.

- Study the sexual reproductive cycle of mosses, ferns, conifers, and angiosperms.

- Investigate the structure and function of the flower.

- Discuss the process of pollination and germination.

- Discuss general features of organisms in the Plantae divisions as a wrap up of our study of plants.

25.1 OVERVIEW

We will continue the physiology of the plant in this chapter. In addition, we will discuss plant reproduction more thoroughly, and end with a wrap-up of the twelve Phyla of the plant Kingdom.

25.2 PLANT HORMONES

Hormones are chemicals used by plants and animals to control certain aspects of the physiology of the organism. Generally, hormones are made by one tissue type and affect functions of other tissue types that may be far from the site the hormone was synthesized. Because the meristematic tissue is very effective at growing, there needs to be a way to regulate various aspects of cell growth within the plant. Plants use five groups (and probably a sixth) of hormones for growth control. They are auxins, gibberellins, cytokinins, abscisic acid, and ethylene. The sixth possible group is called florigen, but it has not been definitely identified as a plant hormone as of yet.

25.3 TROPISM

Tropism is the directional movement of a plant in response to an environmental stimulus. Do not confuse tropism with nastic movements. Nastic movements occur independent of the stimulus direction, but tropism occurs in direct response to a specific stimulus. **Auxin** was the first plant hormone to be identified, in the 1920s. It is normally produced in the apical meristem tissue. Auxin is responsible for regulating the amount of elongation that plant cells undergo. The presence of auxin causes cells to elongate. The absence of auxin causes cells not to elongate. When auxin is present, stems and other plant tissues grow. When auxin is absent, the plant does not grow. Auxins are mainly responsible for the different types of tropisms.

Phototropism is the directional growth of a plant toward a light source. The stem cells exposed to the light do not make auxin. Auxin accumulates in the dark side of the stem. This causes the cells on the dark side of the stem to elongate. As these cells selectively get longer, the stem bends toward the light source. **Thigmotropism** is the plant's growth response to touching a solid object. This is responsible for vines wrapping around poles and other objects. Auxin accumulates in the stem opposite the site being touched, which causes the stem to grow toward the object and wrap around it.

Gravitropism is the directional growth of plants directly against gravity. For example, if a potted plant is laid on its side and allowed to grow like that for a while, auxin will accumulate in the part of the stem closest to the ground and cause the cells in that part of the stem to elongate. This has the effect of bending the top of the stem back up so that the plant is growing straight up against gravity. The final tropism that auxin is responsible for is **chemotropism**, or the directional growth of the plant toward a positive chemical stimulus and away from a negative chemical stimulus. An example of this that occurs when a plant is pollinated will be discussed later in the chapter.

Figure 25.3.1

Gravitropism

Tropisms are plant movements controlled by auxins. Although tropisms and nastic movements both cause the plant to move, what separates them is the reason the plants move. Tropisms are caused by cell growth but nastic movements are caused by changes in turgor pressure. Nastic movements occur more rapidly than tropisms. Gravitropism is the plant property of growing upward against gravity. These bean plants have been growing on their side for about 10 days. Auxin is present in higher concentrations on the bottom of the stem than on the top. This causes the cells on the bottom of the stem to grow faster than the ones on the top, and the stem bends upward against gravity. The way that plants are able to sense which way is up is unknown.

Gibberellin also affects stem elongation, but does so by affecting mitosis rates. **Cytokinins** promote cell division in plants and affect growth of all plant tissues. **Abscisic acid** causes the guard cells to close the stomata and retards growth when conditions are not favorable to sustain growth. **Ethylene** ripens fruit and causes tree leaves to detach and fall. Ethylene is used commercially all of the time. Fruits are often shipped unripened because they tolerate the shipping better. When they get where they need to go, they are exposed to ethylene, which immediately ripens the fruit. **Florigen** is not understood well; its presence has not been definitely identified yet. However, botanists believe it controls bud and flower formation.

25.4 REPRODUCTION: ASEXUAL

Most of the organisms in Plantae are able to reproduce asexually. All can reproduce sexually. Recall that asexual reproduction results in an exact genetic copy of the parent. In plants, this can be achieved in several ways. In sexual reproduction, the reproductive organs of the plant are used to generate new plants. **Vegetative reproduction** is the term used to describe the formation of a new plant asexually. In vegetative reproduction, a new plant is grown from a normally non-reproductive part of the plant. Almost any part of a plant—stem, roots, or leaves— is able to form a fully functional new plant under the correct conditions.

For example, stems are often able to produce new plants. The eyes of potatoes (a tuber, or underground stem) are able to be cut off the potato, planted, and grown into a new potato plant. The practice of **stem cutting** takes advantage of the ability of some plants to form a new plant from a cut stem. Leaves from the African violet plant often sprout and grow into a new African violet after falling onto the jungle floor. Finally, plants such as strawberries have above-ground stems called **stolons**. Stolons run along the top of the ground some distance away from the parent plant. A new strawberry plant grows at the end of the stolon. As soon as the newly formed strawberry plant at the end of the stolon grows roots, the stolon dies, and the plant is on its own.

Grafting is a procedure many plant growers and orchard owners use to increase the yield of their woody flowers or fruit trees. A stem or branch is cut from a woody donor plant; this is called a **scion**. A hole is then made in the bark of a woody receiving plant, called the **stock**. Care is taken to be sure the vascular bundles of the scion and stock match properly, so nutrition and water flow to and from the scion. The scion then becomes a working part of the stock, but retains all properties of the tree it was taken from. Grafting works best when the scion and stock are members of the same genus. It would be more effective to graft a scion from an apple tree onto an apple tree than to graft a scion from an apple tree onto an orange tree.

For example, let's say a farmer had some trees that were particularly good at producing large and tasty apples, but these trees were susceptible to disease. The farmer has other trees that are not good at producing apples, but are resistant to disease. The farmer can cut some of the branches off of the disease-resistant trees and graft some scions from the apple-producing trees onto the disease resistant stock. In that way, the scions still produce large and tasty apples, but are now resistant to disease. This is a common practice among farmers and plant growers.

25.5 REPRODUCTION: SEXUAL, GENERAL

All plants exhibit the **alternation of generations**. This means that plants have one generation which is lived as a haploid **gametophyte**, and then the next generation is lived as a diploid sporophyte. A gametophyte is a haploid plant. This means it has n chromosomes. A sporophyte plant is diploid. This means it has 2n chromosomes.

In the nonvascular plants, the gametophyte stage dominates. This means the gametophyte plant is larger than the sporophyte plant. In other words, when you look at a liverwort plant or a moss, you are looking at a gametophyte. In vascular plants, the sporophyte is dominant to the gametophyte; so when you look at a vascular plant such as grass, a tree, or a flower, you are looking at a sporophyte. In seedless vascular plants, the gametophyte is a small organism that usually grows separately from the sporophyte. In the seed plants, the gametophyte usually grows as a tiny parasite plant living off the sporophyte.

Figure 25.5.1

Plant Life Cycle
Like many of the organisms we have already discussed, plants follow the "alternation of generation" life cycle. One generation of the plant is spent as a gamete-producing gametophyte. Gametophytes are haploid and make haploid gametes. Plants do have male (sperm) and female (eggs) gametes. A sperm fuses with an egg (or a sperm fertilizes an egg) to produce a sporophyte embryo. The sporophyte grows into a mature sporophyte plant through mitosis. The sporophyte produces haploid spores by meiosis. A haploid spore then grows into a gametophyte plant by mitosis and the cycle starts over.

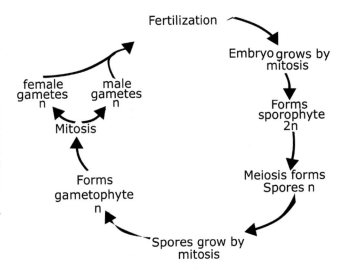

Figure 25.5.2

The 12 Divisions (Phyla) of Plantae

Plant Type	Division (Phylum)	Common Name	# of Species
Nonvascular			
spores	Bryophyta	moss	10,000
seedless/spore-less	Hepatophyta	liverwort	6,500
seedless/spore-less	Anthocerotophyta	hornwort	100
Vascular/seedless			
	Psilotophyta	whisk fern	10
	Lycophyta	club moss	1,000
	Sphenophyta	horsetail	15
	Pterophyta	ferns	12,000
Vascular/seed			
Gymnosperms	Cycadophyta	cycads	100
	Ginkgophyta	ginkgoes	1
	Coniferophyta	conifers	550
	Gnetophyta	gnetophytes	70
Angiosperms	**Phylum** Anthophyta	flowering plants	240,000
	Class Monocotyledones	monocots	70,000
	Class Dicotyledones	dicots	170,000

25.6 REPRODUCTION: SEXUAL, MOSSES

Mosses, which are nonvascular, have a dominant gametophyte phase of their sexual reproductive cycle. The haploid gametophyte produces male and female gametes in two different structures. However, each individual gametophyte produces male and female gametes. The male gametophyte (sperm) develops in the **antheridium** (plural antheridia), and the female gametophyte (the egg) in the **archegonium** (plural archegonia). When it is moist, the flagellated sperm swim out of the antheridium to the archegonium and fertilize the egg. The sporophyte (2n) then grows directly out of the gametophyte on a long stalk and produces haploid spores. The spores are then released and dispersed by the wind.

Figure 25.6.1

Moss Reproductive Cycle
The gametophyte phase of the moss plant is dominant. That means the gametophyte plant is larger in size than the sporophyte plant. The gametophyte produces male and female gametes—sperm and eggs. A sperm fertilizes an egg and a diploid zygote is formed. The zygote grows by mitosis into a diploid sporophyte plant. Haploid spores are produced by mitosis and they grow into a haploid gametophyte plant.

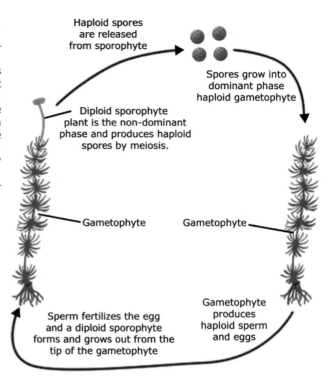

Haploid spores are released from sporophyte

Diploid sporophyte plant is the non-dominant phase and produces haploid spores by meiosis.

Spores grow into dominant phase haploid gametophyte

Gametophyte

Gametophyte

Sperm fertilizes the egg and a diploid sporophyte forms and grows out from the tip of the gametophyte

Gametophyte produces haploid sperm and eggs

25.7 REPRODUCTION: SEXUAL, FERNS

Fern sporophytes grow directly out of the gametophyte. Since ferns are vascular, the sporophyte is dominant. Some fern sporophytes are as large as a tree. A fern gametophyte is rarely larger then 0.5 inches (10 mm) in diameter. Each individual fern gametophyte plant produces male and female gametes.

Fern archegonia and antheridia form on the under surface of the gametophyte. When the conditions are moist, the flagellated sperm swim from the antheridium to the archegonium and fertilize the egg. A diploid sporophyte then begins to grow right out of the haploid gametophyte, crushing the gametophyte as it gets larger.

Once the fern sporophyte matures, it usually has leaves called **fronds**. The spore producing cells, called **sporangia**, form on the under surface of the fronds and cluster together to form **sori**. Inside of the sporangia, millions of haploid spores are formed by meiosis. The spores are released and dispersed by the wind.

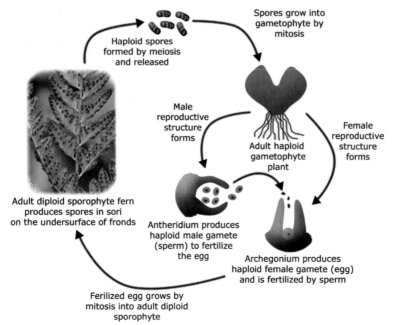

Haploid spores formed by meiosis and released

Spores grow into gametophyte by mitosis

Male reproductive structure forms

Adult haploid gametophyte plant

Female reproductive structure forms

Adult diploid sporophyte fern produces spores in sori on the undersurface of fronds

Antheridium produces haploid male gamete (sperm) to fertilize the egg

Archegonium produces haploid female gamete (egg) and is fertilized by sperm

Ferilized egg grows by mitosis into adult diploid sporophyte

Figure 25.7.1

Fern Life Cycle
Ferns display alternation of generations. The sporophyte phase dominates. The gametophyte is rarely larger than a dime in size. It produces haploid eggs and sperm that fuse to form a diploid sporophyte plant. Mature sporophytes produce spores on the undersurface of their leaves. The spores are released and spread by the wind. They grow into haploid gametophyte plants.

25.8 REPRODUCTION: SEXUAL, GYMNOSPERMS

In the **conifers**, or gymnosperms, the diploid sporophyte is the dominant form. In fact, the gametophyte phase is often microscopic, while the sporophyte phase produces the largest trees in the world (redwoods). Conifers are unlike mosses and ferns because they produce male and female spores. The male spores are called **microspores** and grow into male gametophytes. The female spores are called **megaspores** and grow into female gametophytes. We will use the example of the pine tree, since it is a familiar conifer.

Pine trees often do not reach **sexual maturity** until they are at least three years old, and sometimes not until they are more than thirty. Once sexual maturity is reached, the organism can reproduce sexually. The mature 2n sporophyte produces two separate types of cones on the same tree, male and female. The male cone makes microspores and the female cone make megaspores. These spores never leave the cone to mature, but do so while still on the tree. Within the cone, the male spore develops into a haploid male gametophyte while the female spore develops into a haploid female gametophyte. The male gametophyte is released by the tree and spread by the wind, landing on the female cone to fertilize the female gametophyte. A diploid zygote is formed and develops into an embryo in the form of a seed. When the seed is mature, the embryo is released from the cone and lands on the ground. If conditions are right, the seed with the embryo will then grow into a diploid sporophyte.

Figure 25.8.1

Conifer Life Cycle
The sporophyte phase of the conifer is the "pine tree" we are familiar with. When you look at a pine tree, you are looking at a diploid sporophyte plant. It produces haploid spores, which grow into male and female gametophyte plants. Conifer gametophytes are microscopic and live in the cone of the sporophyte. The gametophyte is haploid and produces male and female gametes. The gametes fuse in the cone and form an embryo, which is covered by a seed. The seed is dispersed by the wind and can grow into a new sporophyte plant.

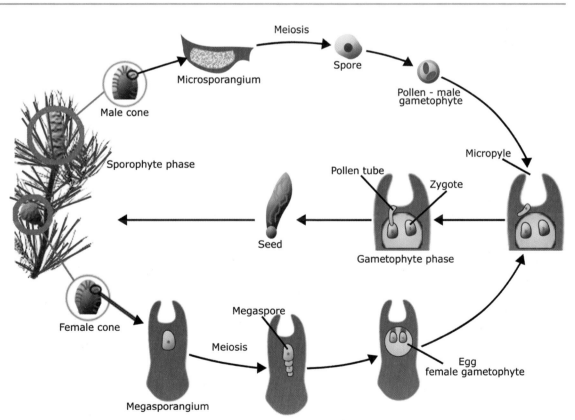

Figure 25.8.2

Pine Cones

Female pine cones (left) tend to be on the higher branches than male cones (right). They stay on the trees much longer, as the male cones fall off after they release their pollen. Male cones tend to form in bunches on the lower branches, near the trunk. Male cones are usually smaller than female cones.

25.9 REPRODUCTION: SEXUAL, ANGIOSPERMS

The **flowering plants**, or **angiosperms**, are the final plants to discuss. The 2n sporophyte is the dominant phase over the n gametophyte. Like the conifers, the sporophyte produces separate male and female spores. Like the conifers, the male and female spores are not released from the sporophyte. They develop into gametophytes right in the sporophyte. The male gametophyte (in the form of **pollen**) is released to fertilize the female gametophyte, while the female gametophyte is still housed in the sporophyte. Don't skip over the fact that the male gametophyte plant is what is contained in pollen.

Figure 25.9.1

Flowers

Flowers are the reproductive organs of angiosperms. They are specialized to get the pollen from one flower to another. Pollen contains the male gametophyte plant, so the gametophyte phase of angiosperms is very small. The pollen must be transferred from one flower to another so the sperm can fertilize the egg, which remains in the flower. The process of moving pollen from one flower to another is called pollination. Flowers that are pollinated by animals and insects are usually brightly colored, fragrant, and nectar-producing. All of these specializations help the flower attract the organisms that pollinate them. Not all flowers are brightly colored, though. Most flowers whose pollen is spread by the wind are not colorful and are open to the air, so the wind can spread the seeds effectively. This design is seen in the far right photo, which shows the flower of a grass species.

As their name implies, their sexual reproductive structure is the **flower**. The flower actually has a fairly complex structure, which we will spend a little time getting to know. The flower is made up of a **flower base**, to which four different types of appendages attach. These appendages, or "things that stick off" the flower base are sepals, petals, stamens, and carpels. Flowers may contain more or less of these appendages, but they are almost always located in the same order. The outer layer of the flower is made up of the **sepals**. Sepals protect the flower until it opens. The next layer in from the sepal is the **petal**. Petals are often brightly colored to attract the insects and birds that help them spread pollen. Petals of plants that use the wind to spread the pollen are often small or absent. The layer inside of the petals is where the reproductive structures are located. The male structure is called a **stamen**. Flowers usually have more than one stamen. The stamen consists of a long stalk, called a **filament**, with a cap on the top, called the **anther**. The anther is the site where the male gametophyte (pollen) is made.

The female reproductive structure is called the **pistil**. The pistil is made up of the **ovary**, which is attached to the flower base. Inside of the ovary **ovules** are formed that house the female gametophytes. A stalk called a **style**, rises from the ovary and has a cap, called a **stigma**, on top of it. The stigma is often sticky, or has hairs that will help capture the pollen as it comes in contact with the stigma. Some plants produce only male or female flowers. If the plant only produced male flowers, there would be no pistils; if the plant only produced female flowers, there would be no stamens.

Figure 25.9.2

A Generic Flower Structure
Not all flowers contain all flower parts as shown below, but most do. The pistil is the female reproductive organ, and the stamen is the male reproductive organ. Some plants have separate flowers that are female-only and male-only, with both on the same plant. This type of plant is called monoecious. The female gametophyte is formed and "grows" right inside the ovary of the sporophyte plant. The male gametophyte is formed and "grows" in the anther of the sporophyte.

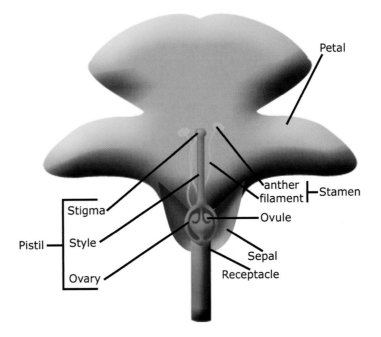

Female gametophytes are produced and developed inside the ovary. Each ovule contains a **megaspore mother cell** enclosed in a tissue covering. The 2n megaspore mother cell undergoes meiosis to form four haploid megaspores. Only one of the four haploid megaspores survives; it then undergoes mitosis to form eight haploid nuclei. The haploid nuclei migrate within the ovule as indicated in the figure. At this stage, the female gametophyte is mature and is called an **embryo sac**. Inside the embryo sac is the egg, which will fuse with the sperm from a grain of pollen to form an embryo. Also in the embryo sac are other cells left over from the megaspore division. Some of these cells will fuse with other sperm cells to form the endosperm in the seed.

Figure 25.9.3

Production of the Egg

Since angiosperms exhibit alternation of generations, the sporophyte plant (the phase with the flower) produces spores. The female spore is called the megaspore and the male spore is the microspore. A megaspore mother cell undergoes meiosis in the ovary of the sporophyte and forms four haploid cells, called megaspores. Three of the megaspores degenerate and disappear but one gets larger. This one undergoes mitosis and forms a large cell with eight nuclei. This is the gametophyte plant and it is housed in the ovary. Inside, a single egg cell is formed, along with several other "supporting" cells. The two nuclei in the middle are called polar nuclei. They will fuse with one sperm and form the endosperm during fertilization. The egg fuses with another sperm to form the embryo. The embryo sac is the female gametophyte "plant," contained in the ovary, waiting for a pollen grain (the male gametophyte) to come along. Inside of the embryo sac is the haploid female gamete, the egg.

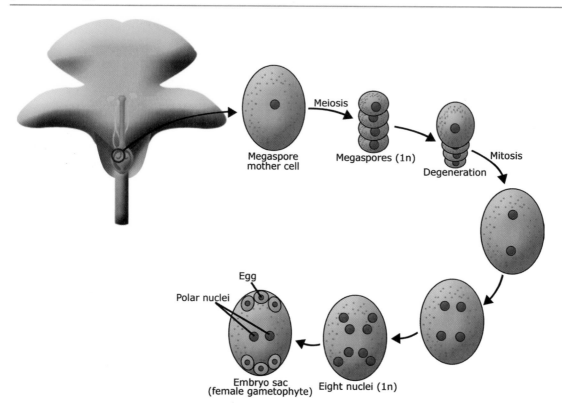

The male gametophyte forms and develops inside the anther. Each anther contains four **pollen sacs** with 2n **microspore mother cells** inside. The microspore mother cells undergo meiosis to form four haploid male gametophytes called microspores. Each of the four haploid microspores undergoes mitosis to form four sets of two haploid microspores. A wall forms around each two-celled microspore set. This is the male gametophyte and is called pollen. Within each pollen grain are two cells—a larger **tube cell** and a smaller **generative cell**. When the pollen lands on the stigma of the pistil, the tube cell grows a tube down the style to the ovary. The generative cell divides by mitosis to form 2 sperm, which swim down the tube to the ovary.

Figure 25.9.4

Production of Pollen

The sporophyte plant produces microspores in the anther. The cell that forms male spores is called the microspore mother cell. It meiosis to form four haploid spores. The haploid spores develop into the male gametophyte "plant," called pollen, right in the anther. Pollen contains two haploid gametes, called sperm. Pollen are small granules that are carried from the anther to the stigma either by the wind or by animals, a process called pollination.

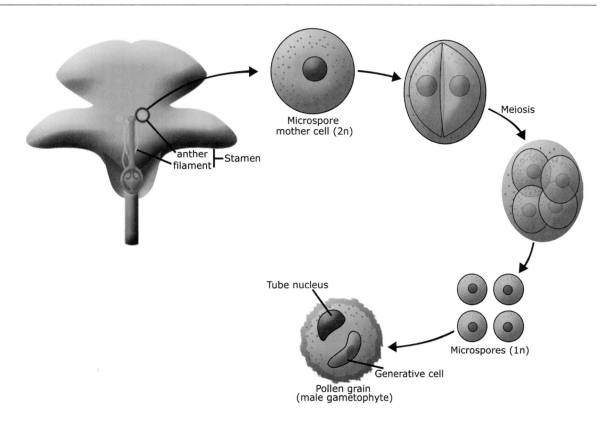

25.10 POLLINATION

Pollination is the process of transferring pollen from the anther to the stigma. If the pollination occurs within the flowers of the same plant, or with a genetically identical plant, this is called **self-pollination**. If pollination occurs with flowers of genetically different plants, this is called **hybridization**. Hopefully this sounds familiar, as this is what Gregor Mendel did with pea plants. Pollen can be transferred from flower to flower mechanically by an insect or animal that comes to feed on the **nectar** of the flower. Nectar is a sweet, sugar solution. When the insect feeds on it, some pollen sticks to it and is carried from one plant to another. Pollen can also be transferred purposefully, as Mendel did, or by the wind.

Once the pollen grain lands on a stigma, the tube cell starts to grow down the style towards the ovary. This occurs due to chemotropism. The tube cells are attracted to chemicals secreted by the ovary, which stimulates the tube cells to grow the correct direction.

At the same time, one of the two original sperm cells divides by mitosis, forming two haploid sperm cells. These then travel down the style, through the tube, to fertilize the ovary. The other original sperm cell fuses with two of the polar bodies to form a **triploid** (3n) nucleus that develops into endosperm. The endosperm serves as nourishment for the two sperm that travel down the tube. This process of two individual sperm cells fusing (one with the polar bodies and the other with the female gametophyte) is called **double fertilization**.

Figure 25.10.1

Fertilization

A pollen grain lands on the stigma, and the pollination/fertilization process begins. The tube cell in the pollen grain grows a tube, called a pollen tube, down the style to the ovary. This process takes a day or two and is controlled by plant hormones. When the pollen tube reaches the ovule it enters the micropyle (the small opening in the ovule which allows the sperm to enter and fertilize the egg and polar nuclei). Two sperm travel down the pollen tube. One fertilizes the egg, and the other fuses with the two polar nuclei, forming a triploid cell. A triploid cell has three copies of chromosomes. The sperm and egg combination form the embryo, or zygote. The triploid cell mass grows into the endosperm. As time passes, the ovary matures into a fruit and contains the seed in some way.

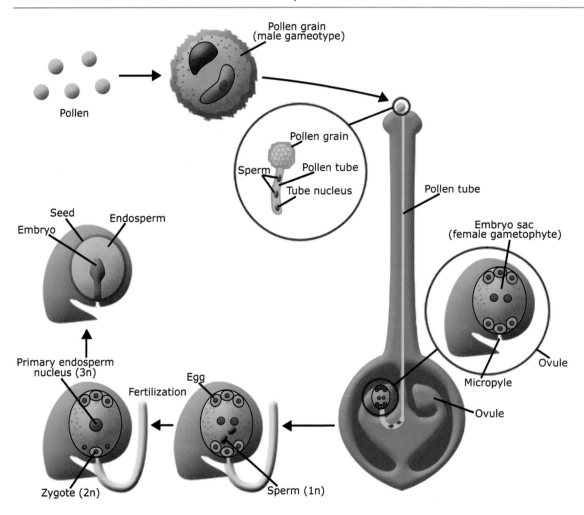

The product of the fertilization of the sperm and the egg is a zygote, which is initially housed in the ovary of the pistil. The zygote differentiates into an embryo, is encased in a tough protective covering, and is called a seed. The protective covering is called a **seed coat**. Along with the embryo is a supply of endosperm to serve as nutrition in the early stages of the embryo's growth. The seed is packaged in a structure called a fruit. Botanists define a **fruit** as a **matured ovary**. There are many different kinds of fruits as seen in the table.

The purpose of a fruit is to help spread seeds. Generally, it is not advantageous for a plant to drop its seed right next to itself and have another, new plant competing for the same resources as the parent plant. Therefore, plants have many ways to spread their seeds far away. Spreading of seeds by the wind accomplishes this, as does packaging seeds in fruits. Fruits are usually picked and carried away from the parent plant, then eaten. Eating the fruit exposes the seeds to the outside world and makes it possible for the seed to grow into a new plant. Fruits are effective devices to spread the seeds from the parent plant to avoid competition.

25.11 GERMINATION

Once the seed has been dispersed, it needs to have favorable conditions in order to break out of the seed coat and sprout. This is a process called **germination**. Appropriate conditions, especially those regarding water presence and temperature, are needed for a seed to germinate. Seeds from different species require different conditions in order to germinate. For example, some seed will not germinate unless they have passed through the digestive tract of an animal. Other seeds, like apple seeds, need to be exposed to cold temperatures for many weeks before they will germinate.

Figure 25.11.1

Germination
Monocot (a) and dicot (b) germination is shown below. Unlike the monocot, the dicot's cotyledons usually emerge from the seed and the ground upon germination.

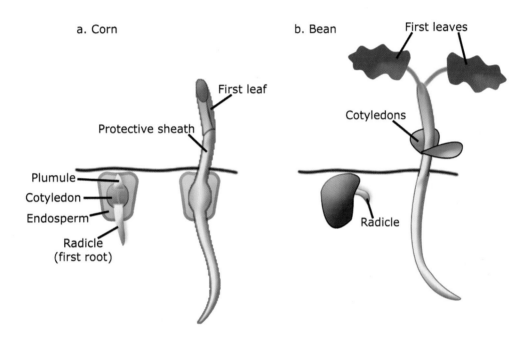

The basic components of germination remain the same, assuming that the proper environmental conditions have been met. Since the seed coat is firm and dry, water must soften the seed coat and penetrate into the seed. Once water hydrates the embryo, enzymes are activated that make the nutrition in the endosperm available to the growing embryo. The seed leaves (cotyledons) emerge from the seed and begin to photosynthesize. (Remember, if there are two cotyledons the plant is a dicot; if there is only one cotyledon, the plant is a monocot.) Roots will soon begin to grow into the ground, signalling that a new plant has been formed.

Figure 25.11.2

Classification of Fruits and Examples

Fruit Category	Fruit Type	Examples
Dry at maturity, splits open	**Legume**; splits along two sides	pea, peanut
	Follicle; splits along one side	milkweed
	Capsule; splits in variety of ways	poppy, tulip
Dry at maturity, does not split open	**Grain**; thin ovary wall fused to seed coat	corn, wheat
	Nut; thick ovary wall not fused to single seed	oak, chestnut
	Achene; thin ovary wall not fused to single seed	sunflower, dandelion
	Samara; thin ovary wall not fused to single seed; has thin, flat wing	ash, maple
Fleshy at maturity, does not open	**Drupe**; stony inner layer around seed	cherry, coconut, pecan
	Pome; core with seed surrounded by thin ovary walls; outer part formed by sepals	apple, pear
	Typical berry; thin skin	grape, tomato, banana
	Pepo; berry with a thick, hard rind	watermelon, cucumber
	Hesperidium; berry with leathery, easily removed skin	orange, grapefruit
Aggregate Fruit - formed from several pistils of a single flower	dry at maturity	tulip tree, magnolia
	fleshy at maturity	raspberry, strawberry
Multiple fruit - formed from several flowers growing together	dry at maturity	sycamore
	fleshy at maturity	pineapple, fig

Figure 25.11.3

A pea is a legume, a cherry is a drupe. A tomato is actually a fruit (a berry). Strawberries are not berries at all, but aggregate fruits. Watermelons and cucumbers are fruits called pepos.

25.12 SPECIFIC DIVISIONS (PHYLA) OF PLANTAE

We will now spend some time discussing the specific Divisions of Plantae. It is becoming more common for biologists to refer to the "Divisions" in Fungi and Plantae Kingdoms as "Phyla." We have already discussed many particulars regarding reproductive cycles. This section will serve to pull everything together.

25.13 NONVASCULAR PLANTS

Note that "nonvascular" is not actually part of the classification scheme, but serves as a useful clarifying term. The approximately 17,000 species of nonvascular plants are classified into the Divisions of **Hepatophyta** (liverworts), **Anthocerotophyta** (hornworts), and **Bryophyta** (mosses). They do not have xylem and phloem and are therefore quite small, usually less than one inch high. They grow in moist environments. They do not form seeds, but reproduce through spores. Their reproductive cycle includes the dominant gametophyte stage with the sporophyte growing directly out of the gametophyte.

Figure 25.13.1

Mosses
Mosses are familiar types of nonvascular plants. They grow in moist areas such as forest floors.

25.14 VASCULAR PLANTS

Since there are over 255,000 species of vascular plants, it is unlikely that we are going to cover all of them. We will briefly go over the nine remaining Divisions of Plantae. The species in these divisions all have xylem and phloem, but botanists generally categorize them as **seedless vascular** and **seed vascular plants**. The seedless vascular species reproduce with spores and include the Divisions of **Psilotophyta**, **Lycophyta**, **Sphenophyta**, and **Pterophyta**. The seed vascular plants include the Divisions **Cycadophyta**, **Ginkgophyta**, **Coniferophyta**, **Gnetophyta**, and **Anthophyta**.

Figure 25.14.1

Grouping of Vascular Seedless and Vascular Seed Plants
This is part of the same table presented at the beginning of the chapter. I just have it here again to help to keep things clear.

Plant Type	Division (Phylum)	Common Name	# of Species
Vascular/Seedless Plants			
	Psilotophyta	whisk fern	10
	Lycophyta	club moss	1,000
	Sphenophyta	horsetail	15
	Pterophyta	ferns	12,000
Vascular/seed plants			
Gymnosperms	Cycadophyta	cycads	100
	Ginkgophyta	ginkgoes	1
	Coniferophyta	conifers	550
	Gnetophyta	gnetophytes	70
Angiosperms	**Phylum** Anthophyta	flowering plants	240,000
	Class Monocotyledones	monocots	70,000
	Class Dicotyledones	dicots	170,000

Psilotophyta comprise species that are called **epiphytes**. Epiphytes grow on other plants, but not as parasites. They do not have roots or leaves. They produce their spores on the ends of short branches. Species in **Lycophyta** include the prototypical club mosses, which look like mini pine trees. **Sphenophyta** species are also called horse tails. They have photosynthetic stems with joints in them. **Pterophyta**, or the ferns, are the most diverse avascular seedless plants. They are found in the tropics, deserts, moderate climates, and arctic regions. Some ferns are aquatic, while others look like palm trees and can grow up to twenty-five feet tall.

Figure 25.14.2

Horse tails are on the left. A typical fern is seen in the middle and on the right. The curved structure in the middle picture is called a fiddlehead. Fiddle heads are the immature stems and leaves of ferns. As the fiddlehead grows, it unrolls to form leaves and a stem, called fronds.

Vascular seed plants constitute the largest number of species with over 240,000. The plants in this group are broken into the gymnosperms and angiosperms. Angiosperms are also called the flowering plants and produce seeds that are protected in fruit. The gymnosperms do not produce fruit, and the seed is an exposed structure. Most of the gymnosperms are "evergreens" and produce cones for their reproductive structures. Note that there is only one phylum of angiosperms, but they are further divided into monocots and dicots based on the internal structure of their seeds.

Cycadophyta, or the cycads, are mainly tropical plants that grow slowly. They have leaves resembling fern leaves that sit on top of short, thick trunks. They produce large cones and are often mistaken for palm trees. Some species can live for more than a thousand years. **Ginkgophyta** include only one species, a tree called *Ginkgo biloba*. Unlike most of the other species of gymnosperms, *Ginkgo* loses its leaves at the end of the growing season. This property of losing leaves at the end of the growing season is called **deciduous**. **Gnetophyta** species are mainly tropical and arid (desert) species. They include the genus (*Ephedra*) that a popular nasal decongestant (ephedrine) is derived from.

Figure 25.14.3

The leaves of the ginkgo tree have a very distinct shape.

Coniferophyta is the largest Division of gymnosperms, with over 550 species. It includes species often called "evergreens" or "pines." These produce cones to house their gametes and have needle-like or very slender leaves. They are not deciduous, keeping their leaves all year round. Earlier in the course we discussed amber, and species from Coniferophyta are responsible for producing the sap that hardens into amber. They are also valuable sources for paper and wood.

Figure 25.14.4

Conifers or "evergreens" are found almost every where. They are used for ornamental shrubs and are also the largest trees in the world. They keep their leaves—the needles—all year round.

The vascular seed plants, also called angiosperms or the **flowering plants**, include over 240,000 species and are classified in the Division **Anthophyta**. (There have been some recent published opinions from a group of botanists called the Angiosperm Phylogeny Group who have proposed that the division name be changed from Anthophyta to Magnoliophyta, but we will continue to use Anthophyta until there is more agreement about whether this should be done.)   Angiosperms are the most diverse group, with plants growing in all environments on the planet. They produce seeds that are surrounded by fruit. Not only are there photosynthetic forms, but also aquatic, parasitic, and epiphytic environments. Recall that the species in Anthophyta are further divided into monocots and dicots based on their seed structure and other characteristics as outlined in the table. Monocots are grouped into the class **Liliopsida** and the dicots are placed in the class **Magnoliopsida**.

Figure 25.14.5

The lily is the prototypical monocot organism and is the namesake for the class Liliopsida and is shown in the top two photos. The magnolia is a large tree and is shown in the bottom two photos. It is the prototypical dicot, the namesake for the class Magnoliopsida.

25.15 PEOPLE OF SCIENCE

Sir Francis Darwin (1848-1925) was born in England, the son of Charles Darwin. He was a botanist. He graduated from undergraduate school from Trinity College, then went on to earn a medical degree, but never practiced medicine. He pioneered the studies of phototropism with his father, and their work was the basis for the discovery of auxin.

25.16 KEY CHAPTER POINTS

- Plant hormones are chemicals used by plants to control aspects of their physiology, mainly growth and fruit ripening.

- Auxins, gibberellins, cytokinins, abscisic acid, ethylene, and florigen are all plant hormones.

- All plants are capable of reproducing asexually.

- Plants exhibit alternation of generations in their reproductive cycles.

- Nonvascular plants reproduce sexually with sperm and eggs.

- Ferns reproduce with spores.

- Gymnosperms reproduce with seeds.

- The reproductive structures of angiosperms are contained in flowers.

- Pollination occurs when pollen lands on a stigma.

- Fertilization occurs when the pollen tube grows through the style to the ovary, then the sperm from the pollen fertilizes the egg in the ovary.

- The embryo develops inside the ovary and forms into a seed.

- The ovary matures into a fruit, and the seed is housed inside.

- When a seed begins to grow, it is called germination.

- Nonvascular plant phyla discussed: Hepatophyta (liverworts), Anthocerotophyta (hornworts), and Bryophyta (mosses).

- Vascular plant phyla discussed: the seedless vascular species which reproduce with spores and include the Divisions of Psilotophyta (whisk ferns), Lycophyta (club mosses), Sphenophyta (horsetails), and Pterophyta (ferns); the seed vascular plants including Divisions Cycadophyta (cycads), Ginkgophyta (gingkoes), Coniferophyta (conifers), Gnetophyta (gnetophytes), and Anthophyta (angiosperms).

25.17 DEFINITIONS

abscisic acid
   A plant hormone which causes stoma to close and retards growth.

anther
   The cap on top of the filament, where the pollen is made.

archegonium
   The structure that houses the female gamete in certain plants, especially the nonvascular plants.

auxin
   The plant hormone responsible for regulating a variety of plant related growth.

chemotropism
   The directional growth of the plant in response to a chemical stimulus.

conifers
   Plant species classified in Coniferophyta.

cytokinins
   A plant hormone which promotes cell division.

deciduous
   The property of losing leaves at the end of the growing season.

double fertilization
   The process of two individual sperm cells fusing, one to the egg and one to the two polar nuclei.

embryo sac
The mature female gametophyte.

epiphytes
Plants that grow on other plants, but not as parasites.

ethylene
The plant hormone that ripens fruit and causes tree leaves to detach and fall.

ferns
Plant species that are vascular and seedless and are classified in Pterophyta.

filament
The long stalk of the stamen.

florinogen
A plant hormone.

flowering plants
Plants that are classified as monocots or dicots and are placed in the Anthophyta division.

fronds
Leaves of a fern.

fruit
A matured ovary.

gametophyte
The phase of a plant which produces gametes. Gametophytes are haploid.

germination
The process of a seed breaking out of the seed coat and sprouting.

gibberellin
A plant hormone responsible for stem growth.

grafting
The practice of removing a stem from one tree and placing it onto the trunk of another tree.

gravitropism
The directional growth of plants directly against gravity.

hormones
Chemicals used by plants and animals to control certain aspects of the physiology of the organism. Hormones are manufactured in one tissue and released into the organism to cause effects in tissues far from where the hormone was made.

hybridization
Pollination that occurs with flowers of genetically different plants.

matured ovary
A fruit.

megaspore mother cell
The structure that produces the egg inside of a plant ovary.

megaspores
Female spores.

microspores
Male spores.

mosses
A type of nonvascular plant group.

nectar
A sweet, sugar solution made by plants to attract pollinators.

ovary
The base of the pistil; houses the egg.

ovules
Structure that houses the female gametophytes.

petal
A layer of flower that is often brightly colored.

phototropism
The directional growth of a plant toward a light source.

pistil
The female reproductive structure.

pollen
Male gametophyte released to fertilize the female gametophyte; pollen contains sperm.

pollen sac
The anther structure, which contains the microspore mother cell.

pollination
The process of transferring pollen from the anther to the stigma.

scion
A stem or branch cut from a woody donor plant and grafted onto another plant.

seed coat
The protective covering of a seed.

seed vascular plants
Plants which have vessels and reproduce with seeds.

seedless vascular
Plant species that reproduces with spores and have vessels.

self-pollination
Pollination that occurs within the flowers of the same plant, or with a genetically identical plant.

sepals
The outer layer of a flower.

sexual maturity
The point at which a sexually-reproducing organism can sexually reproduce.

sori
Clusters of sporangia that form on the under surface of fern fronds.

sporangia
Spore producing cells.

stamen
The male structure of a flower.

stem cutting
A type of artificial, asexual reproductive technique.

stigma
The top of the pistil.

stock
Woody "receiving" plant in the grafting process.

stolons
An above-ground stem.

style
The upright portion of the pistil.

thigmotropism
A plant's growth response to touching a solid object.

triploid
A cell with three copies of all chromosomes.

tropism
The directional movement of a plant in response to an environmental stimulus.

tube cell
The cell that forms the tube down the style, allowing sperm to travel to the ovary.

vegetative reproduction
Term used to describe the formation of a new plant from a normally non-reproductive part of the plant.

STUDY QUESTIONS

1. What are plant hormones? List the six hormones we learned about.

2. True or False? Gravitropism is the plant's response to grow directly opposing gravity.

3. What is the difference between tropisms and nastic movements?

4. What does ethylene do? Can you think of one way it could be used commercially?

5. What is vegetative reproduction? Can any plant perform vegetative reproduction?

6. What is alternation of generations?

7. True or False? The dominant phase of most vascular plants is the sporophyte form.

8. What is the dominant phase of most of the nonvascular plants?

9. If you were looking at a small plant growing under a decaying log in the forest and identified an antheridium and archegonium, what general type of plant would you be looking at? (The general name or phylum is okay.)

10. What are contained in sori of ferns?

11. What is in a pine cone? How can you tell the difference between a male and a female cone?

12. Draw a flower, include all of the parts and label them.

13. Why are some flowers brightly colored and contain nectar?

14. What is made in the anther?

15. What is formed as the outcome of pollination in angiosperms?

16. What is germination?

17. Draw the reproductive cycle of an angiosperm and label the events that occur at each step.

18. What is the largest group of plants—the angiosperms, gymnosperms, or nonvascular plants?

19. What type of reproductive structure is formed by a gametophyte plant? Is a gametophyte haploid or diploid? Is its reproductive cell haploid or diploid?

20. What type of reproductive cell is formed by a sporophyte plant? Is a sporophyte haploid or diploid? Is its reproductive cell haploid or diploid?

PLEASE TAKE TEST #10 IN TEST BOOKLET

Kingdom Animalia I

26

26.0 CHAPTER PREVIEW

In this chapter we will:

- Introduce the phyla of animals we will be discussing.

- Differentiate vertebrates from invertebrates.

- Define body structure and symmetry terms.

- Discuss the following properties of animals:
    - germ layer/tissue development
    - embryonic tissue differentiation
    - segmentation
    - embryonic development
    - development patterns
    - tissue and organ systems

- Investigate the organisms of the Placozoa and Porifera phyla.

26.1 OVERVIEW

In discussing the bacterial Kingdoms, Protista, Fungi, and Plantae, we have already covered the majority of species on earth in terms of numbers. However, those species are also the least well known. The last Kingdom, Animalia, makes up the vast majority of species that we are familiar with. Further, when most of us think of an animal, we instinctively think of a mammal, such as a horse, or maybe a bird or fish. All of these animals are **vertebrates**. Vertebrates are animals with backbones. All vertebrate animals are species of Animalia. Most organisms in Animalia do not have backbones, though. They are called **invertebrates**. Invertebrates either have a soft body (like jellyfish and squid) or have an outside skeleton (like insects). Of the more than 1,000,000 species in Animalia, only about 5%, or around 50,000, are vertebrate species. The remaining 950,000 are invertebrates.

Figure 26.1.1

Burgess Shale Sponge
This may look more like an organism from the Kingdom Plantae than Animalia, but this Burgess shale sponge is indeed an animal

If I were to show you pictures of various organisms and ask you whether or not they were animals, you would probably be able to accurately identify an animal the majority of the time. However, there might be some confusion—as in the case of sponges. They do not look like an animal at all, yet they are. You need to know about both animals with backbones and animals without backbones in order to include all of the species in the animal Kingdom. Therefore, we need to work out a definition of "animal."

In general, while not all animal life forms have all of the following characteristics, the majority of animal species do. Animals exhibit the following: eukaryotic cell structure; ability to reproduce sexually; multicellularity with specialization of the cells into tissues that have distinct functions; heterotrophic through ingestion and digestion; storage of carbohydrates in the form of **glycogen** rather than starch; no cell walls with special adhesive network outside of the cells called the extra-cellular matrix; ability to move through the environment by specialized muscle and nervous tissue; and need for oxygen.

Figure 26.1.2

Phyla of the Animal Kingdom
The phyla in bold are the ones we will be discussing at some length in the upcoming chapters.

Phylum	Common Name/Miscellaneous
Invertebrates no "backbone"	
Placozoa	only one species, simplest animal
Porifera	sponges; 10,000 species
Orthonectida	
Rhombozoa	adults have about thirty cells
Cnidaria	jelly fish, corals, sea anemones; 10,000 species
Ctenophora	comb jellies; 100 species
Acoelomorpha	similar to flat worms
Platyhelminthes	flat worms; 18,000 species
Nemertea	ribbon worms, 800 species
Gastroctricha	
Gnathostomulida	jaw worms
Micrognathozoa	
Rotifera	rotifers; 1,800 species
Acanthocephala	thorny-headed, parasitic worms
Priapulida	
Kinorhyncha	mud dragons
Loricifera	
Entoprocta	
Nematoda	round worms; 80,000 species
Cycliophora	
Mollusca	clams, oysters, squid, octopus, snails; 110,000 species
Sipuncula	peanut worms
Annelida	segmented worms; 15,000 species
Nematomorpha	horsehair worms
Tardigrada	water bears
Onychophora	velvet worms
Arthropoda	insects, spiders, centipedes, millipedes, lobster, crab, shrimp; more than 1,000,000 species
Phoronida	
Ectoprocta	moss animals
Brachiopoda	
Echinodermata	star fish, sea urchins, sand dollars; 7,000 species
Chaetognatha	arrow worms
Hemichordata	acorn worms
Vertebrates "backbone"	
Chordata	mammals, birds, reptiles, fish, amphibians; 45,000 species

Figure 26.1.3

Characteristics Almost All Species in Animalia Have in Common
All animals possess the following characteristics but a note should be made about mobility. Not all animals are mobile at all times, but they are all mobile at some point in their lifetime.

Eukaryotes
No cell walls
Multicellular
Cells held together by specialized network called extra-cellular matrix
Cells organized into tissues
Sexually reproduce
Mobile
Heterotrophic
Store excess energy as glycogen
Aerobic (require oxygen)

Some of the terms above may be new to you. Recall that early on in the course, we discussed "tissue." A tissue is a group of cells that all function in a similar way. Recall that plants have tissues (vascular tissue of xylem and phloem, for example) so the presence of tissue in an organism is not unique to Animalia. **Ingestion** is the intake of nutrients specifically through a mouth. Digestion is the breaking down of ingested nutrients in a specialized structure called the **gut**. Glycogen is a polymer of glucose that animals use to store their energy. You should also know that evolutionists believe animals first evolved as aquatic life forms, then moved from the water to land.

26.2 CLASSIFICATION CRITERIA

In order to help with taxonomic listings, many features of the animal are evaluated. As with all other Kingdoms, evolutionists believe they classify the species based on their evolutionary relationships. However, as with all other Kingdoms, the species in Animalia are able to be placed into taxonomic categories based on their observable physical appearances, patterns of embryonic development, and biochemistry. The characteristics of animals that are evaluated when classifying them include: symmetry; tissues; embryonic development; segmentation; and body cavities.

26.3 BODY STRUCTURE AND SYMMETRY

Body structure is one of the features used to classify animals. The body structure is the observable appearance of the animal. A key feature almost all animals exhibit is **symmetry**. Symmetry is the property of one half of an animal looking like the other half of the animal. For example, if we split your body down the middle, leaving a right and left half, the left and right sides would look similar. The type of symmetry where the right half looks like the left half is called **bilateral symmetry**. All vertebrates are bilaterally symmetric. Most invertebrates are also bilaterally symmetric, although some are not (see below). Some animal species, especially many sponges (Porifera), are not symmetrical at all. Species which are not symmetrical are called **asymmetric**.

Figure 26.3.1

Asymmetry
Animals such as the sponge in Figure 26.1.1, corals left, and sea anemones right, are all asymmetrical. No one half of the animal looks like the other half. Only aquatic animals display asymmetry.

Figure 26.3.2

Bilateral Symmetry
Organisms which have right and left halves are bilaterally symmetric. If a line is drawn down the middle from the head to the tail, the right half of a bilaterally symmetric animal looks like the left half. Most animals are bilaterally symmetric.

Animals that are bilaterally symmetric have a left and right half and a top/back side (called the **dorsal** side) and a bottom/front side (**ventral** side). They have a head region (**anterior** region) and a tail region (**posterior** region). In addition, most animals that are bilaterally symmetric tend to lead with their heads when they move through the environment (think of how any vertebrate moves, its head is always the first structure of its body to get to where it is going). Another interesting feature about bilaterally symmetrical animals is the high concentration of sensory tissues (eyes, ears, nose, and mouth) and the brain in the anterior region. This is called **cephalization**.

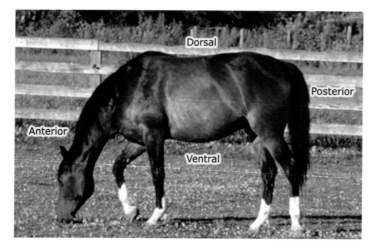

Figure 26.3.3

Anterior, Posterior, Ventral and Dorsal
All animals with heads have anterior (front or head portion), posterior (tail or rear end portion), ventral (belly portion), and dorsal (back portion) parts.

Another type of symmetry that animals display is called **radial symmetry**. This is the type of symmetry that occurs mainly in the aquatic species that do not have a "right/left halves," or a "front/back" side, but have a top and bottom. This is typical of the symmetry that jellyfish and hydras display. No land-living animals display radial symmetry; it is only a property of aquatic animal species.

Figure 26.3.4

Radial Symmetry

Aquatic organisms that are round are often radially symmetric. They have a top half and a bottom half, but not a right and left half. You can draw a line down the middle of the organism along any plane and each half looks like the other. The hallmark feature of an animal that has radial symmetry is that you can draw more than one line down the animal and still have it symmetric. Bilaterally symmetric animals only are symmetric across one line of symmetry. Starfish have a special type of radial symmetry called pentaradial symmetry. This refers to the fact that they have five arms (usually) and a line drawn through the animal starting in the middle of one of the arms results in one half looking like the other half. The two examples shown below are of a line of symmetry drawn for a jelly fish and another for the hydra.

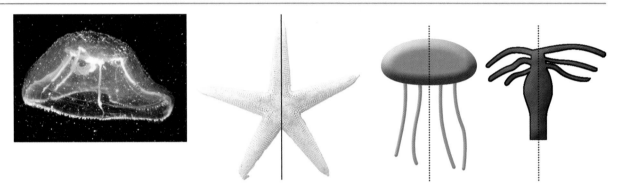

26.4 TISSUES

Tissues are groups of cells that all function in a similar way. Recall that plants also have tissues, so tissues are not unique to animals. The basic tissue types in animals are **connective** ("hold together"), **epithelium** (for covering and protection), **muscle** (for locomotion and responding to the environment), and **nervous tissues** (for communicating to other tissues, sensing the environment and directing movements). Not all animals have all these types of tissue, but all animals, except sponges (Porifera) and Placozoans, have some type of true tissue.

26.5 GERM LAYERS: ENDODERM, MESODERM, AND ECTODERM

Cells **differentiate**—or "turn into"—tissues during **gestation**. During gestation, organisms develop from one cell to a multicellular organism. Development begins after the haploid female egg fuses with the haploid male sperm. This is called **fertilization**. Once this happens, a single-celled diploid **zygote** is formed. A zygote is the cell formed from the union of a sperm and an egg. The single-celled zygote divides repeatedly by mitosis, forming two cells, and those two cells then divide by mitosis to form four cells, and so on. This process occurs hundreds, thousands, millions and billions of times following fertilization. As the zygote divides, different tissue layers begin to form. As the zygote gets larger, it is called an **embryo**. As the cells begin to build up in the embryo, they form into layers, called **germ layers**. As the embryo continues to develop, the germ layers further **differentiate** into tissues and organs of the fully developed animal. For example, ectoderm develops into skin, teeth, and nails.

Figure 26.5.1

Germ Layers

Germ layers are tissues which form in the developing animal (embryo). They are generic tissue which at first has no specific function or structure, but as the embryo develops more, the germ layers develop into specific tissue. For example, all of our muscle cells are derived from mesoderm. As the embryo develops, cells throughout the mesoderm begin to differentiate into muscle cells. Nerve cells differentiate from ectoderm. We will discuss this more in the next few pages. Cnidarians and ctenophores develop from only two germ layers – endoderm and ectoderm. All other animal species develop from endoderm, mesoderm, and ectoderm. The graphic to the right shows the germ layers early on in the development of animal embryos. At the stages shown here, the organism is a hollow ball of rapidly dividing cells called a blastula.

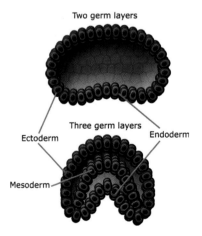

Figure 26.5.2

Sperm and Egg
As in plants, the male gamete is called sperm and the female gamete the egg. Sperm are physically much smaller than eggs. In the diagram below, the sperm has been enlarged many hundreds of times to show its structure. Sperm have a flagella so the sperm can swim to the egg. When the sperm cell membrane contacts the egg cell membrane, they "melt" together, and the haploid chromosomes of the sperm are injected into the egg. Then the chromosomes of the sperm (from the male parent) fuse with the chromosomes of the egg (from the female parent) and a single-celled organism called a zygote is formed. The zygote then begins to undergo rapid mitotic divisions to grow into a new organism.

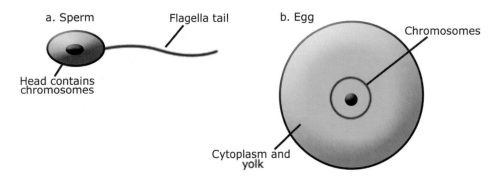

Different animal species have a different number of germ layers in the embryonic stage. There are two germ layers in the **embryonic development** of cnidarians and ctenophores. These two layers are called **ectoderm** and **endoderm**. All other animal species have three germ layers during their embryonic development. These three germ layers are called the ectoderm, **mesoderm**, and endoderm. Germ layers are important because all of the tissues in the mature animal form from these layers. We will learn more about germ layers and embryonic development in a few pages.

26.6 SEGMENTS

Most animals are **segmented**, or are said to display the characteristic of **segmentation**. This refers to the fact that the body is broken down into a series of repeated units. Sometimes the units are easy to see, other times the segments may be more obvious when examining the skeleton or the embryonic development of the animal.

Figure 26.6.1

Segments are typical in animals
Animal segmentation is sometimes very obvious, such as in the caterpillar. Other times, the segments are not as obvious, but are present nonetheless. Almost all land animals are segmented, even humans. Our segments can be seen in the repeating units of the ribs and vertebrae (bones of the spine).

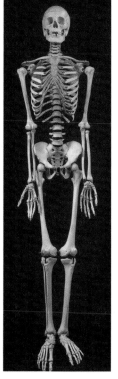

26.7 COELEM

Another characteristic used to classify animals is the presence of a body cavity, or **coelem**. Almost all animals (except Placozoans, sponges, and flat worms) have a cavity that separates the digestive tract, or gut, from the outer wall of the animal. There are different types of coelems and **zoologists** (biologists who study animals) use these to help classify animals. Some animals use their coelem to help with swimming, or for buoyancy. The exact classification of coelem types is a bit beyond the scope of this class, but you need to be aware, in general, of what a coelem is.

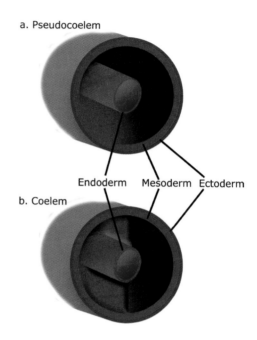

a. Pseudocoelem

b. Coelem

Endoderm   Mesoderm   Ectoderm

Figure 26.7.1

Coelem Types
There are basically two coelem types—a true coelem and a pseudocoelem. A pseudocoelem is lined with mesoderm, but the gut, which is derived from endoderm, is suspended in fluid surrounding it. A true coelem is also lined with mesoderm, but the mesoderm connects to the endoderm, anchoring it to the body wall.

The way that many zoologists use the above information breaks down like this:

- Multicellular adult with limited tissues in two layers = Placozoa and Porifera

- Multicellular adult with true tissues in two layers and radial symmetry = Cnidaria and Ctenophora.

- Multicellular adult with true tissues in three layers and bilateral symmetry = all other phyla.

Within the last grouping, the presence or absence of a coelem, type of coelem, and pattern of development are used to further divide and classify animal species.

26.8 EMBRYONIC DEVELOPMENT: GENERAL

Because embryonic development is an important property of animal taxonomy, we will spend more time discussing this process. Although there are some animal species that are capable of asexual reproduction, it is the product of sexual reproduction (a zygote) and the subsequent development that is used by taxonomists to help classify animal species. Embryonic development includes the time of egg fertilization through the time a fully-developed organism has formed. Embryonic development has also been termed **morphogenesis**.

As noted above, all animal cells initially begin as a single cell, called a zygote. A zygote is created when the haploid sperm of the male fertilizes the haploid egg of a female. In almost all species, the sperm is small when compared to the egg. It also has a flagellum, so it can swim. Fertilization occurs when the membrane of the sperm fuses with the membrane of the egg. The sperm then injects its nucleus into the egg, and the egg and sperm nuclei fuse together. This union of the haploid chromosomes from the sperm and the haploid chromosomes from the egg creates the diploid zygote. The zygote then begins to grow through successive mitotic divisions, with one cell giving rise to two cells, two cells to four cells, four cells to eight cells, eight cells to sixteen cells, and so on. In embryology (the study of embryonic development) the mitotic cell divisions are called **cleavages**.

26.9 EMBRYONIC DEVELOPMENT: BLASTULA

Initially, the cells of the developing embryo do not grow in size; they simply undergo mitosis and split into two cells. The cleavage process is a highly regulated process, as is the development of the embryonic germ tissues. After five cleavages, the embryo is made up of sixty-four cells and is called a **blastula**. The blastula is a ball of tissue with a cavity on the inside, so it is hollow. The cavity inside the blastula is called a **blastocele**.

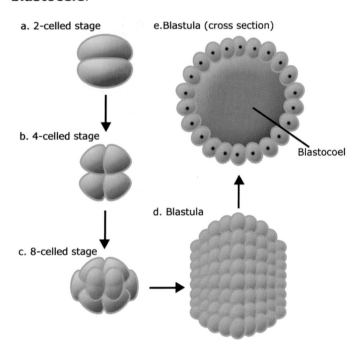

a. 2-celled stage

e. Blastula (cross section)

Blastocoel

b. 4-celled stage

d. Blastula

c. 8-celled stage

Figure 26.9.1

Early Embryonic Development
After fertilization, the single cell zygote begins to undergo mitosis, growing in size. Each time a mitotic division occurs, the zygote doubles the number of cells it contains. Each cell division is called a cleavage. After five cleavages, the embryo contains sixty-four cells and is called a blastula. It is a hollow ball of cells. The cavity inside is called a blastocele.

26.10 EMBRYONIC DEVELOPMENT: GASTRULA

Once the embryo reaches the blastula stage, it begins to fold in on itself, or **invaginate**. During this process, some of the cells of the blastula elongate, while others do not grow at all. As one side of the membrane of the blastula begins to invaginate, a process called **gastrulation**, it resembles a filled water balloon with someone pushing the side of their hand into one side of it. The "groove" that is formed when the gastrula invaginates develops into a cavity called the **archenteron**. The archenteron will later become lined with mesoderm and form the gut.

When the embryo completes gastrulation, it is called a **gastrula**. As the gastrula grows in size, there are many changes in the sizes of the cells and cell adhesions. The gastrula begins to develop two distinct tissue layers, or germ layers, called the ectoderm and the endoderm. Later, in the animals that have three germ layers, the mesoderm forms between the ectoderm and the endoderm. As the embryo grows larger, the germ layers differentiate into different types of tissues.

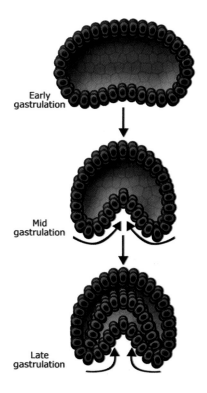

Figure 26.10.1

Gastrulation

As the blastula continues to grow in cell number and physical size, it bends, or invaginates. The process of the bending is called gastrulation and when the invagination is complete, the developing embryo is called a gastrula.

Figure 26.10.2

Structures or Tissues Produced by the Three Embryonic Germ Layers

This table shows the three embryonic germ layers and which tissues they give rise to in the adult animal.

Endoderm	Mesoderm	Ectoderm
pancreas	skeleton (bones)	brain and spinal cord
liver	muscles	nerves
lungs	gonads	outer (top) layer of skin, nails
lining of digestive system	excretory system (like sweat glands)	eyes and lens
	inner (bottom) layer of skin	nose and ears

26.11 EMBRYONIC DEVELOPMENT: NEURAL TUBE

As the gastrula develops, adjacent to the archenteron, an inner body cavity forms and becomes completely lined with mesoderm; at this point, it is called a coelem. In addition, in vertebrate species, on the dorsal surface of the gastrula, a rapidly dividing fold of tissue forms from the ectoderm. These folds rise up and pinch together, forming a tube. This tube is called the **neural tube**, and the process by which it is formed is called **neurulation**. The neural tube will become the brain and spinal cord in the fully-developed organism. Just underneath, or ventral to, the neural tube, another tube structure forms from mesoderm. This mesoderm-derived tube is called the **notochord** and will become the bones of the spine—also called "back bones," vertebrae, or the spinal column.

Figure 26.11.1

Formation of the Neural Tube

Neurulation is the process of the embryo forming the dorsal groove, which becomes the neural tube. The neural tube is better known as the spinal cord and brain. The spinal cord and brain tissue forms when layers of ectoderm fold in on themselves and form a hollow tube on the dorsal surface of the embryo. Just ventral to (or in front of) the neural tube, the notochord forms from mesoderm. In vertebrates (animals with spinal columns or spinal bones) the notochord develops into the bones.

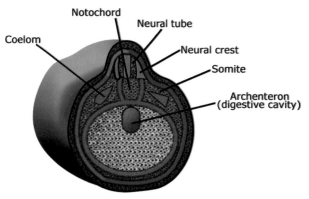

26.12 DEVELOPMENT PATTERNS

There are two basic types of development patterns. They are called direct and indirect development. Once they are out of the embryonic stage (i.e., once they are born or hatched), some organisms in Animalia exhibit **direct development**. This means the organism that emerges from the embryonic stage looks like a smaller version of the adult organism. Most of the "animals" you are familiar with have this kind of pattern. For example, birds, mammals, humans, reptiles, etc., all have direct development.

Indirect development is exhibited in most invertebrate species. The organism that emerges after the embryonic stage does not look like the mature adult. In these species, the immature organism undergoes further **metamorphosis**, or changes in body structure, after it emerges from the embryonic state.

These species have an **intermediate stage**, then change later to the adult form. Often, the intermediate form is referred to as a **larva** (plural larvae). You will be reading a lot about larvae in the upcoming chapters. Whenever you see that an organism has a larval stage, you should realize it means they exhibit an intermediate stage in their development. This development pattern is typified by the development of butterflies, moths, and frogs, which most of us are familiar with. The butterfly and moth emerge from their embryonic stage in the intermediate form of a larva, called a caterpillar. They exist as caterpillars for a time, then enter a cocoon (moth) or chrysalis (butterfly). Inside the cocoon or chrysalis, the caterpillar changes into a moth or butterfly, then emerges in the mature form. A frog starts life in the intermediate stage of a tadpole, with no legs and a tail. The intermediate form later metamorphs, or transforms, into a frog.

Figure 26.12.1

Indirect Development
Although there are many examples of indirect development, the best known is probably the metamorphosis of the frog. Below left is the frog egg. It is the little speck on the left of the photo. When the egg hatches, the larval form of the frog, the tadpole, emerges. The tadpole gradually undergoes a metamorphosis in which it loses its gills and tail, then grows legs and develops lungs. When it is done, it looks like a frog.

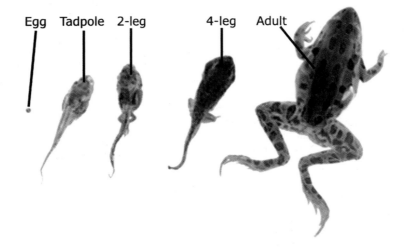

Egg   Tadpole   2-leg   4-leg   Adult

26.13 VERTEBRATES AND INVERTEBRATES

As noted in the beginning of the chapter, there are more than 1,000,000 animal species, but only about 50,000 of them have a "backbone," or are vertebrates. The backbone is also referred to as the spinal column or vertebrae. The remaining 950,000 animal species do not have a spinal column. This means the majority of species classified as animals are invertebrates. Organisms like sponges, jellyfish, insects, crustaceans, spiders, and worms are invertebrates.

Why do we focus so much on vertebrates, then? Probably because we are vertebrates, and the other vertebrate species are important to human nutrition and companionship.

The main difference between vertebrates and invertebrates is the presence of the neural tube and notochord. All vertebrates, at some point in their existence, have a notochord. Invertebrates do not. Sometimes the notochord persists throughout the organism's life, and other times the notochord is only present for a short time during embryonic development. Please see the table for a summary of the differences between vertebrate and invertebrate species. The other difference between vertebrates and invertebrates is the presence of the dorsal neural tube, which is surrounded by a spinal column. Vertebrates have a dorsal nerve tube surrounded by vertebrae (spinal column) but invertebrates do not.

Figure 26.13.1

Differences Between Vertebrate and Invertebrate Species

Invertebrate	Vertebrate
Symmetry	
radial and bilateral	bilateral
Segmentation	
most	all
Digestive	
sponges absorb nutrients from environment through tissues; most others have gut	gut
Excretory	
rid wastes (ammonia) directly or have membranes to convert ammonia to less toxic substance and then excrete	kidneys filter blood and remove ammonia then break it into less toxic substances and excrete
Nervous System	
sponges have no neurons or nerve cells, but do have cells to respond to environment; cnidarians have neurons in a loose association; mollusks have a slightly more complex nervous system	highly regulated and developed nervous system including brain and spinal cord; large brain to body volume
Reproduction/Development	
sexual and asexual; some are **hermaphrodites** (the same organism has both male and female reproductive parts); many also exhibit indirect development	sexual reproduction largely via **direct development**, although some amphibian and fish species exhibit indirect development; fertilization is usually **internal** (the sperm enters the female and fertilizes the egg), although some species show **external** fertilization (the eggs are ejected from the female, and the male sperm is ejected onto the eggs)
Support of Organism's Body	
many aquatic species have no formal structural support, but maintain their shape through the buoyancy of water and the coelem; other aquatic species and insects have an external skeleton (**exoskeleton**) formed by chitin	internal skeleton (**endoskeleton**) formed by bones, or cartilage in the case of sharks and related species
Circulatory System	
most move blood or similar fluid through body to bring oxygen and nutrients to cells and carbon dioxide and waste from cells; cnidarians and sponges do not have a circulatory system, so the individual cells absorb and excrete directly; arthropods and some mollusks have an **open circulatory system** in which blood is pumped from the vessels into the body cavity and back into the vessels; annelids and some mollusks have a **closed circulatory system** in which the blood is pumped through and stays in vessels	closed circulatory system with a multi-chambered heart to pump blood from the heart to the lungs and all other tissues through blood vessels
Gas Exchange	
sponges and cnidarians take oxygen up and release carbon dioxide directly by/from the individual cell into the environment; other species have gills	gills in fish and sharks; lungs in other vertebrates

We have covered the main characteristics that zoologists use to classify the species. We will now briefly discuss thirteen phyla of Animalia, starting with the simplest invertebrates in this chapter and proceeding through the more complex invertebrates to, finally, the vertebrates in the upcoming chapters. Discussion of each of the phyla will include discussions about general properties of characteristic organisms of each phyla, so when we are done with the next few chapters, we will have discussed the circulatory, respiratory, digestive, excretory, nervous, reproductive, locomotion, support, and connective systems in some depth.

26.14 INVERTEBRATES: PHYLUM PLACOZOA

This is the smallest phylum in Animalia. It contains only one species: *Trichoplax adhaerens*. It is an organism that is similar to an amoeba, but it is multi-cellular. It contains several thousand cells in three layers. The innermost cell layer has a single cilium for locomotion. It absorbs its nutrition (rather than ingesting) and is capable of sexual and asexual reproduction. It produces sperm and eggs, even though it does not have discreet reproductive tissue. It was first described in 1880 after being discovered on the walls of a marine tank. Its native habitat is unknown since it has never been observed in the wild.

26.15 INVERTEBRATES: PHYLUM PORIFERA

There are over ten thousand species in Porifera. They are commonly called sponges. They are entirely aquatic and most are marine, although there are some that are fresh water. Sponges do not have a gastrula stage during embryonic development, since they have no true tissues or organs. Adult sponges are **sessile,** which means they do not move. They anchor themselves to the water bottom, or to a rock, and are often mistaken for a plant. Their size ranges from half an inch to over six feet in diameter. In general, the sponge does not display a pattern of symmetry.

Figure 26.15.1

Sponges
Sponges are sessile filter feeders.

The sponge's body is a hollow cylinder which is two cell-layers thick. The body is filled with openings, called **pores**. The presence of pores is what gives the name of the phylum. It does have some internal structural support from proteins and tiny hard particles made of calcium carbonate. When you use a real sponge, you are actually holding the skeleton of a sponge. The cylinder is closed at the bottom and open at the top. At the top of the body, the opening is lined with flagellated cells. The flagella beat and draw water into the sponge through the opening at the top and through the many pores in the body. In this way, sponge cells obtain their nutrition directly from the water by filtering out and absorbing bacteria and algae. For this reason, sponges are called **filter feeders**. Also, sponges perform gas exchange when the water moves through the pores.

Figure 26.15.2

Sponge Structure

The interior of the sponge is lined with special cells called collar cells. Collar cells have a single flagellum on their surface. The flagella beat back and forth and draw water in and out of the sponge through the pores in the body. Support for the sponge's structure is through a network of proteins called spongin or a structure called a spicule. Spicules are small, hard spikes that support the structure of some sponges.

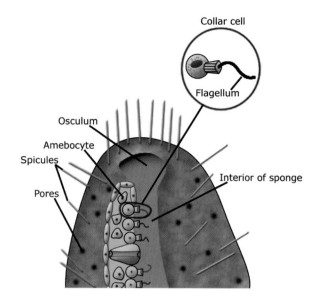

Sponges are hermaphrodites and are able to reproduce asexually and sexually. Asexual reproduction is through budding. The sponge produces a structure called a **gemmule**, which is a bud of sponge tissue containing sponge cells. During harsh conditions, gemmules are released and are able to form into new sponges when conditions are favorable. Sponges also release sperm into the water; the sperm then floats to another sponge and is absorbed by the pores. The sperm is transported to the eggs. After fertilization, a **larva** is formed. A larva is an immature form of the adult organism. It swims out of the parent sponge using flagella and then settles on a rock or water bottom. It then reorganizes its cells and grows into an adult sponge.

Figure 26.15.3

Sponge Reproduction

Sponges can reproduce sexually and asexually. Asexual reproduction is through the production of a gemmule. A gemmule is a small bud of sponge tissue which falls off the parent sponge and then can grow into a new sponge. Sponges are also able to regenerate lost parts. Some sponge species can form a completely new organism from a piece of the animal smaller than a dime. Sexual reproduction is shown on the right. Sponges release sperm into the water that then swim to another sponge and fertilize the egg. When the egg is fertilized, the embryo grows into a larva. Therefore, sponges have indirect development. When the larva matures, it grows into an adult sponge.

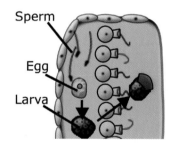

Placozoa and Porifera represent the structurally simplest animal species. We will move on in the next chapter to increasingly more complex organisms.

26.16 PEOPLE OF SCIENCE

Aristotle (384 BC–322 BC) was a Greek philosopher, biologist, physicist, and poet. He wrote many books on these subjects (and more). Through his study of biology, he founded the basic principles for classifying all species. His classification system of plants and animals was used by all scientists until the modern system was devised by Linnaeus almost 2,000 years later.

26.17 KEY CHAPTER POINTS

- Although the number of organisms in Animalia is much less than the numbers in the Kingdoms we have already discussed, "animals" are the most well known.

- The organisms of Animalia are divided into invertebrates and vertebrates.

- The organisms of Animalia are classified based upon similarities and differences in their structures and function.

- The organisms in Animalia:
    - are symmetric
    - have tissues
    - are segmented
    - sexually reproduce
    - develop as embryos before emerging as independently functioning organisms
    - store excess energy as glycogen
    - do not have cell walls
    - have cells held together by the extracellular matrix
    - are mobile
    - are heterotrophic
    - are aerobic

- Vertebrates have a "backbone"; invertebrates do not.

- Phylum Placozoa is the most structurally simple phylum in Animalia.

- The phylum Porifera is made up of sponges.

26.18 DEFINITIONS

Annelida
Segmented worms; fifteen thousand species.

anterior
The head region.

archenteron
The cavity formed when the gastrula invaginates.

Arthropoda
Animalia phylum which includes insects and spiders; one million species.

asymmetric
Species which are not symmetric.

bilateral symmetry
The type of symmetry occurring in animals with a head and a tail end. This results in the right half of the animal looking like the left half.

blastocele
The cavity inside the blastula.

blastula
An embryo that is made up of sixty-four cells.

body structure
The organization of an animal's body; used to classify animals.

cephalization
The high concentration of sensory tissues, including a brain, in the anterior (head) region.

Chordata
Animalia phylum, which includes: mammals, birds, reptiles, fish, amphibians; 45,000 species.

cleavages
Mitotic cell divisions occurring during embryonic development.

closed circulatory system
A circulatory system in which blood is pumped through and stays in vessels.

Cnidaria
Animalia phylum, including jelly fish, corals, sea anemones; ten thousand species.

coelem
> A body cavity.

differentiate
> Refers to the process of unspecialized cells "transforming into" specialized tissue cells.

direct development
> Pattern of development where an organism emerges from the embryonic stage looking like a smaller version of the adult organism, then simply grows larger in size.

dorsal
> The top or back side.

Echinodermata
> Animalia phylum including sea urchins, sand dollars; 7,000 species.

ectoderm
> The outer germ tissue layer.

embryo
> A larger zygote.

embryonic Development
> The pattern of changes in tissues and size during an embryo's growth period.

endoderm
> The inner germ tissue layer.

endoskeleton
> Internal structural system formed by bones or cartilage.

epithelium
> Tissue for covering and protection.

exoskeleton
> External structural system.

external
> Outside.

filter feeders
> Animals that obtain their nutrition from the water moving through their structure.

gastrula
> An embryo that has completed gastrulation.

gastrulation
> The process of one side of the blastula beginning to invaginate.

gemmule
> A bud of sponge tissue that contains sponge cells.

germ layers
> Layers that form as the cells begin to build up in the embryo.

gestation
> The time in an organism's development after the haploid female egg has been fertilized by the haploid male sperm.

glycogen
> A polymer of glucose that animals use to store their energy.

gut
> The part of an animal that houses the digestive organs.

hermaphrodites
> An organism that has both male and female reproductive parts.

indirect development
> Pattern of development where an organism emerges from the embryonic stage, then goes through an intermediate stage before changing to the adult form.

ingestion
> The intake of nutrients specifically through the mouth.

intermediate stage
> The stage of a species between the embryonic and adult form.

internal
> Inside.

invaginate
> The process of an embryo folding in on itself after it reaches the blastula stage.

invertebrates
> Animals without backbones.

larva
> The intermediate form of a species.

mesoderm
> The middle germ tissue layer

metamorphosis
> Changes in body structure that occur when a larva changes into an adult.

Mollusca
> Animalia phylum; includes lobsters, squid, octopus, shrimp; 110,000 species.

morphogenesis
> Embryonic development.

muscle
> Contractile tissue for locomotion and responding to the environment.

Nematoda
> Animalia phylum, including round worms; 80,000 species.

Nemertea
> Animalia phylum including ribbon worms; 800 species.

nervous tissues
> Tissues for communicating to other tissues, sensing the environment and directing movements.

neural tube
> The structure that forms from ectoderm and develops into the spinal cord and brain.

neuralation
> The process of the embryo forming the neural tube.

notochord
> The mesoderm-derived tube.

open circulatory system
> Circulatory system in which blood is pumped from the vessels into the body cavity and back into the vessels.

Placozoa
> Animalia phylum with only one species: *Trichoplax adhaerens*

Platyhelminthes
> Animalia phylum which includes flat worms; 18,000 species.

pores
> Openings in a sponge's body.

Porifera
Animalia phylum which includes sponges; 10,000 species.

posterior
Tail region.

radial symmetry
The type of symmetry that occurs only in aquatic species that do not have "right/ left" halves, or a "front/back" side, but have a top and bottom.

segmented/segmentation
Refers to the fact that the body is broken down into a series of repeated units.

sessile
Does not move.

symmetry
The property of one half of an animal looking like the other half.

ventral
The bottom or front side.

vertebrates
Animals with backbones.

zoologists
Biologists who study animals.

zygote
A single-celled diploid organism which is formed when a sperm fertilizes an egg.

STUDY QUESTIONS

1. Into which two general groups are animals usually classified?

2. What common characteristics do animals share?

3. What criteria are usually used to classify organisms in Animalia?

4. What type of symmetry does a jelly fish exhibit? A giraffe? A snake? A starfish (seastar)?

5. What side of a horse do you sit on, the ventral or dorsal? What side does a snake crawl on?

6. What is cephalization?

7. True or False? Almost all animals have true tissues.

8. If you were looking at an embryo of an animal which had two embryonic tissue layers (ectoderm and endoderm), which of two possible phyla would you be studying?

9. What is morphogenesis?

10. Which comes first, the blastula or gastrula?

11. True or False? The brain, skeleton, and muscles all are derived from (come from) mesoderm.

12. True or False? The notochord develops into the brain and spinal cord.

13. How is direct development different from indirect development?

14. True or False? All vertebrates exhibit bilateral symmetry.

15. What is the support structure of an invertebrate called? Of a vertebrate?

16. Contrast the systems (i.e., circulatory, nervous, skeletal, etc.) in vertebrates and invertebrates.

17. True or False? Sponges are filter feeders.

18. What is a gemmule and what is its function?

Kingdom Animalia II

27

27.0 CHAPTER PREVIEW

In this chapter we will:

- Resume our discussion of the Animalia phyla of:
  - Cnidaria
  - Platyhelminthes
  - Nemertea
  - Nematoda
  - Mollusca
  - Annelida
  - Arthropoda
  - Echinodermata
  - Chordata
- Discuss the differences between the vertebrate and invertebrate organisms of Chordata.

27.1 OVERVIEW

The last chapter ended with discussions about the first two phyla listed in Figure 27.1. They represent organisms that are structurally and biochemically simple animal life forms. As we proceed through this chapter, we will be discussing progressively more complex organisms, from an organizational and functional standpoint.

Figure 27.1.1

Review of Certain Phyla of Animalia

I have tried to avoid calling organisms simple and complex because any life form is complex. However, it is an unavoidable fact that some body plans of organisms in Animalia are more complex than others. This table lists the organisms from top to bottom, starting with less complex life forms and moving toward those that are more complex body plans. The next few chapters will discuss these in the same order and follow the least complex to more complex body plan. Pay particular attention to when new features arise. For example, note that a complete, one way digestive tract (like yours and mine) first arises in Nemertea (Nemertina).

Phyla	Species	Common Names
Invertebrate		
Placozoa	1	*Trichoplex adherens*
Porifera	10,000	sponges
Cnidaria	10,000	hydras, jellyfishes, corals, sea anemones
Platyhelminthes	18,000	flatworms
Nemertea	800	ribbon worms
Nematoda	80,000	pinworms, roundworms, hookworms
Mollusca	110,000	clams, snails, octopi, squids, mussels, slugs
Annelida	15,000	sandworms, earthworms, leeches
Arthropoda	1,000,000	insects, spiders, horseshoe crabs, scorpions, ticks, crayfish, lobsters, shrimp
Echinodermata	7,000	sea stars, sea urchins, sea cucumbers, sand dollars
Chordata	2,000	"tunicates"
Vertebrate		
Chordata	45,000	fish, amphibians, reptiles, birds, mammals, humans

27.2 INVERTEBRATES: PHYLUM CNIDARIA

The cnidarians include both fresh water and marine species. The phylum is broken into three classes, Hydrazoa (hydras), Scyphozoa (jellyfish), and Anthozoa (sea anemones and corals). They demonstrate radial symmetry and exhibit two basic body shapes, the **medusa** and **polyp** forms. Animals with the medusa shape are mobile. Those with the polyp shape are sessile. Most cnidarians are polyps.

Cnidaria are composed of ectoderm and endoderm germ tissue. Some species exist only as a medusa or a polyp, but some have both forms during their life cycle. The medusa is mobile while the polyp form is sessile. Cnidarians are hermaphrodites and can reproduce asexually or sexually. A hermaphrodite is an animal that contains both male and female reproductive tissue. Usually hermaphrodites cannot self-fertilize. Asexual reproduction is accomplished by producing **buds**. We talked about budding in the mitosis and meiosis chapters. Recall budding is reproduction through small outgrowths that form from the main animal, then pinch off to form new animals after they land on the water bottom. Sexual reproduction is accomplished by the release of eggs and sperm into the water. The sperm fertilizes the egg and the embryo lands on the water floor and grows into a new organism.

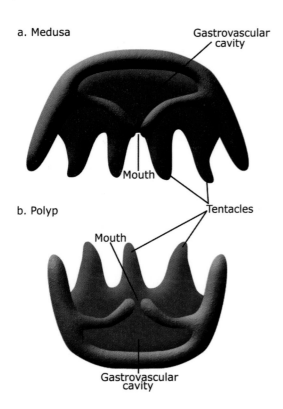

a. Medusa

Gastrovascular cavity

Mouth

Tentacles

b. Polyp

Mouth

Gastrovascular cavity

Figure 27.2.1

Body Forms of Cnidarians
Cnidarians have two body forms. The medusa is mobile and the polyp is sessile.

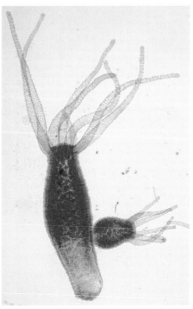

Figure 27.2.2

Cnidarian Asexual Reproduction
Hydra can reproduce asexually through budding. A small version of the adult animal grows from its side, then falls off. It is capable of living independently as soon as it comes off the parent. Hydras are sessile; this is the polyp form.

There is much more cell and tissue specialization in cnidarians and all "higher" species. There are specialized nerve cells, which form a nervous system that consists of interconnected nerve cells. This is called a **nerve net**. Although there is no brain or centralized controlling nerve organ, it does function in a coordinated way due to the interconnectivity of the cells. Besides catching food, one of the major movements the medusa forms need is swimming. The nerve net coordinates movements of muscles around the gastrovascular cavity. Cnidarians swim by sucking water into the cavity, then pushing it out again.

A distinguishing feature of cnidarians is a specialized cell called a **cnidocyte** which gives them the ability to "sting." These are cells specialized to capture prey and protect the animal. Cnidocytes contain a unique organelle called a **nematocyst**. The nematocyst is a thread-like filament that ejects out of the cnidocyte. Nematocysts are triggered when the organism is touched, causing the cnidocyte to eject the nematocyst. The nematocyst sticks into whatever it hits. The filament then injects poison or sticks tight in order to assist bringing the prey in through the mouth. Once it enters the mouth, the food goes into the **gastrovascular cavity** where it is enzymatically digested and absorbed. The digestive tract of cnidarians has only one opening; it is called **two-way** because food goes in and waste goes out of the animal through the same opening.

Cnidarians do not have specialized respiratory or vascular tissue. Instead, the cells perform exchange of CO_2 and O_2 across the membranes of the individual cells.

We will be discussing **gas exchange** quite a bit in the next few chapters. Gas exchange is the name given to the process of moving oxygen into the organism and carbon dioxide out of the organism. Recall that oxygen is required during aerobic cellular respiration to make ATP and carbon dioxide is a product of cellular respiration. Therefore, gas exchange is the process of exchanging oxygen across a membrane to get oxygen into the cell and organism and get carbon dioxide out.

Figure 27.2.3

Cnidarians

Some common cnidarians. The two jellyfish (left and middle) are medusas. *Obelia* (right) exists both as a polyp and a medusa in its life. The polyp form is shown. Polyps are typically sessile.

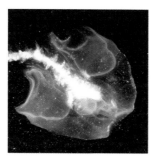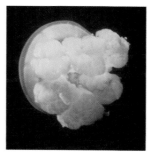

27.3 INVERTEBRATES: PHYLUM PLATYHELMINTHES

Platyhelminths are also called flatworms. This phylum includes three classes: **Trematoda** and **Cestoda** are parasitic species; **Turbellaria** are free living species. This phylum is also the first in which the organisms are composed of all three germ cell layers—ectoderm, mesoderm, and endoderm. In fact, from this phylum on, all species are composed of tissues from all three germ layers. They are bilaterally symmetric, but do not have a coelem, which is the reason they are flat. They are mobile through the actions of cilia or muscular contractions to swim.

The platyhelminths are hermaphroditic and capable of sexual and asexual reproduction. Asexual reproduction is accomplished by the animal breaking apart. Each piece then forms a genetically identical and fully functional organism. Sexual reproduction is through sperm fertilizing an egg. Many of the flatworms are parasitic; this makes their life cycle complex and we will not extensively discuss it in this course.

Planarians are from the class Turbellaria. They are free living in fresh and marine water and are considered the prototypical free-living flatworm. Free living means an organism is able to obtain food without being a parasite. We will use the flatworm as an example. From a body-complexity standpoint, the flat worms are considered the most primitive phylum to demonstrate cephalization. They have a high concentration of nerve and sensory tissue at their anterior end (their "heads"). Their bodies function as a unit through integration of sensory input and muscular output. Information about environmental changes is sensed by the longitudinal nerves. The longitudinal nerves carry sensory information to the brain. The brain takes in the sensory information and processes it. Then the brain sends signals to the muscles through the longitudinal nerves that cause the animal to respond to its environment. They have two eye spots on their head. These cannot "see," but can sense light and dark.

Figure 27.3.1

Turbellaria
Turbellarians (planarians) are free-living species. They are carnivorous, eating mainly dead organisms.

Like the cnidarians, they have a two-way gastrovascular cavity. Food enters through the mouth which is located on the undersurface of the animal. Food enters the gastrovascular cavity and then is digested and absorbed by the cells within the cavity. There are extensions of the gastrovascular cavity into all areas of the worm's body. Cells receive their nourishment and exchange gasses through these extensions. Cells also deposit their wastes into the cavity. Waste products and undigested/unabsorbed food exits back out through the mouth. They have no specialized respiratory or circulatory tissue/system, therefore, the individual cells perform gas exchange.

There are several species of flatworms that are parasitic to humans. *Schistosoma mansoni*, class Trematoda, also called the blood fluke, infects nearly 200 million people world wide. The adult blood flukes live in the intestines of human hosts and feed off blood. Sometimes, blood flukes can parasitize so much blood that the infected person becomes anemic (to be anemic is to not have enough red blood cells).

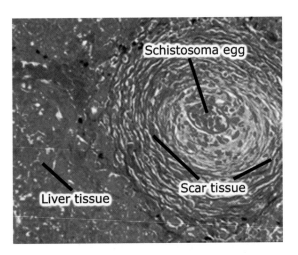

Figure 27.3.2

***Schistosoma* Infection**
Schistosoma parasitizes blood of its host. It often eats enough blood that the host becomes anemic. In addition, the eggs deposit in a number of different tissues. Here, an egg is seen in the liver. There is a lot of dead tissue and scar around the egg with normal liver tissue seen far from the egg mass.

Another flatworm, the tapeworm, also lives in the intestines of humans, as well as pigs and cattle. It has a specialized head, called a **scolex**, which has a strong sucker and barbs to anchor the worm to the intestine. Once in the intestine, it lives off the digested food of its host, absorbing it directly through its cells, and so does not need a digestive tract. As it grows, it forms many repeating units of **proglottids**, which are basically egg forming units that constantly release eggs into the feces of the host. Tapeworms can grow in the intestines to sixty feet long or more and are capable of absorbing enough nutritive components that their hosts become malnourished.

Figure 27.3.3

Tapeworm Structure
Tapeworms are members of the *Taenia* genus of Platyhelminthes. They are parasites and live in the intestines of their hosts. The generalized body plan is seen in the top graphic. The head of the tapeworm is called a scolex. It has hooks and suckers to anchor the animal to the interior of the intestine of the host which it parasitizes. A micrograph of an actual scolex is shown below on the right. The animal grows in length by adding proglottids. Each proglottid is a section which is capable of forming and releasing countless numbers of eggs into the feces of the host. A couple of proglottids sections are shown below on the left. A large tapeworm can be many hundred proglottids long.

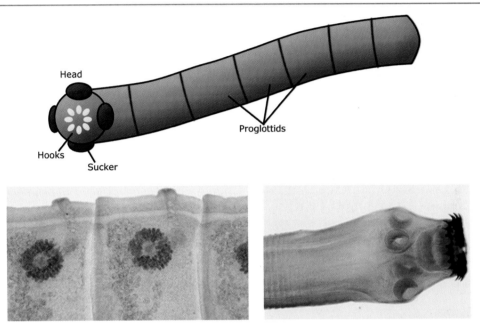

27.4 INVERTEBRATES: PHYLUM NEMERTEA (A.K.A. NEMERTINA)

Commonly called ribbon worms or proboscis worms, these are species that live in marine or fresh water environments. Some species live in damp soil. They are composed of ectoderm, mesoderm, and endoderm and have a small fluid-filled cavity that operates an extendable nose, which is used to capture prey.

Nemertines have features that are commonly seen in all phyla from this point on. They are the simplest organisms to demonstrate a formed circulatory/vascular system. The circulatory system carries nutrients absorbed in the gut to the tissues. It consists of separate tubes, called **vessels**, which carry nutrients and oxygen to the tissues. The vessels also carry carbon dioxide and waste from tissues to be eliminated. There is no heart but muscles throughout the organism that squeeze the blood through the vessels. Nemertines have a simple, but complete, digestive tract. This means that it is a one-way, rather than two-way, digestive system. Nutrients are taken in through the mouth, and specialized cells in the digestive tract break down and absorb the ingested material. Waste is then expelled through the anus.

27.5 INVERTEBRATES: PHYLUM NEMATODA

Nematodes are also known as roundworms and hookworms. They are often parasitic (in the intestines) to humans and livestock, but some are free living in marine, fresh water, and damp soil environments. They are bilaterally symmetric organisms that are between 1mm and 4 ft. in length. They have a pseudocoelem (see Figure 26.7.1). Reproduction is always sexual, and there are separate male and female organisms.

This phylum includes the parasitic genus *Ascaris*. The species in *Ascaris* are parasitic to humans, cattle, and pigs. They are hookworms that infect more than 1 billion people world wide. Another genus is *Enterobius*, which are pinworms that infect 16% of adults and 30% of children in the United States.

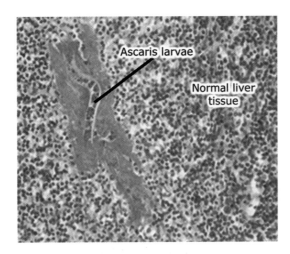

Figure 27.5.1

Ascaris lumbricoides

Ascaris is one of the most successful human parasites. It has a rather disgusting way of infecting the host. It is acquired by eating the eggs. The eggs hatch in the intestine and the larvae enter the blood stream and travel to the lungs. Once in the lungs, they burrow through the lung tissue and into the airway. They crawl up the windpipe to the back of the throat and are re-swallowed. They mature in the intestine and attach onto the lining of the intestine where they live and continually lay eggs into the feces of the host. Often, the larvae infect tissues other than the lungs, such as is seen in the photomicrograph on the left. A larva has taken up residence on the liver.

27.6 INVERTEBRATES: PHYLUM MOLLUSCA

This phylum includes clams, squids, octopi, snails, oysters, and slugs. This is the second largest phylum in Animalia to Arthropoda. Like Arthropoda, because it is such a large phylum, there is no one particular organism that typifies the phylum, so we will be discussing generalities that will be descriptive of the organisms for the most part. Mollusca is further subdivided into classes.

Figure 27.6.1

Selected Classes of the Phylum Mollusca

Class	Common Name
Bivalvia; 80,000 species	Bivalves, clams, mussels
Gastropoda; 40,000 to 150,000 species	snails, slugs
Cephalopoda; 786 species	squids, octopi (a squid has 10 tentacles, an octopus 8)

Mollusks are bilaterally symmetric animals with a true coelem. A coelem offers several advantages as compared to organisms that don't have one. A coelem allows the muscle of the body wall to contract without inhibiting the function of the gut so food can pass through without restriction. Also, a coelem provides space for the circulatory system to transport blood without hindrance from the other internal organs.

Mollusks generally have an identifiable and enlarged head, with the exception of the **bivalves**. Bivalves are mollusks with shells; a common type is a clam. The body plan of a mollusk is broken down into the **head-foot** and **visceral mass**. The head portion consists of the mouth and sensory organs, and the foot consists of a large muscular organ utilized for locomotion. Most bivalves move through the action of the foot, but bivalves are sessile. The visceral mass is made up by the heart and organs of digestion, reproduction, and excretion. The bodies of some mollusks are protected by shells (notably the bivalves) and others are not.

Figure 27.6.2

Mollusks

All mollusks have a soft and fleshy body, but some are protected by shells. Bivalves like clams (left), snails (middle), and the octopus (right) are all common examples of mollusks.

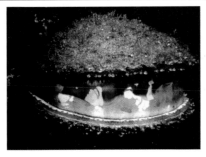

They have some hermaphroditic forms, but most mollusk species have separate female and male organisms. Most mollusks exhibit an indirect development with an intermediate larval stage. Mollusks that are still in the larval stage are called **trochophores**.

Figure 27.6.3

Trochophore

Trochophores are the larval stage of mollusks and annelids (the next phylum we will discuss). Not all mollusks have a larval stage but most do. Trochophores are mobile through the action of cilia, which cover their bodies.

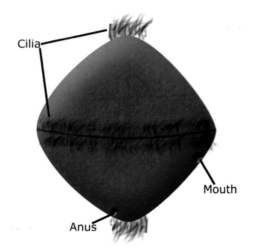

The nervous system of mollusks consists of a small grouping of nerve cells called **ganglia**. The ganglia are found throughout the body, and are interconnected so the organism can function in a coordinated way. In the Cephalopod class, the nervous system is extremely developed into a rather large brain with good eyesight and the ability to sense changes in the chemical make up of the water through nerves in the tentacles.

Mollusks have a complete one-way digestive tract with a mouth, stomach, intestine, and anus. Some mollusks are filter feeders and others, like the squid and octopus, are predatory. Gas exchange is not through individual cells, but through the use of gills or lungs. **Gills** are a specialized respiratory tissue that extract oxygen from the water and absorbs it into the blood stream. Gills also extract carbon dioxide from the blood and release it into the water.

Figure 27.6.4

Mollusk Body Plan

Despite looking different, mollusks all have a common body plan. They are divided into two parts—the head-foot and visceral mass. The head-foot contains the head and its sensory structures and the foot, which is basically a large mass of muscles to move the animal. The visceral mass is above the head-foot. The visceral mass contains the digestive, reproductive, excretory, and circulatory organs. The visceral mass is covered by a layer of tissue called the mantle. The coelem is a small space formed only around the heart.

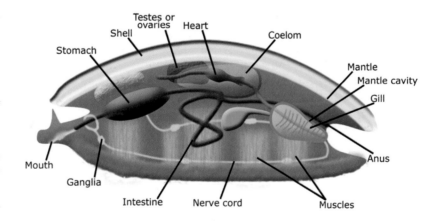

The circulatory/vascular system is mainly an open one. Squids and octopi have a closed system, all others have an open system. In an open circulatory system, the blood fluid is pumped through vessels, dumping into the body cavity. After supplying the tissues with oxygen and nutrients, and picking up the carbon dioxide and wastes, blood then moves from the body cavity back into the vessels. In a closed system, the blood fluid never leaves the vessels. Since blood carries oxygen and carbon dioxide, in a closed system, gas exchange occurs across the walls of the blood vessels.

27.7 INVERTEBRATES: PHYLUM ANNELIDA

We all know what annelids are, but we don't know them by that name. Annelids are earthworms and leeches, for the most part. They are bilaterally symmetric animals with a true coelem; they generally have well-developed organ systems. Most annelids have external bristles called **setae** and some have fleshy protrusions called **parapodia**. Because the earthworm is the prototypical species of Annelida, and because we are going to examine it in some detail in the lab for this week, we will spend some time getting to know its structure and function better.

Figure 27.7.1

Lumbricus terrestris
This is an annelid most people are familiar with. Its segments are easily seen.

The earthworm is a highly segmented animal, having up to one hundred segments or more. It is composed of muscle fibers that wrap around the animal, called **circular muscles**; and muscles that run the length of the animal, called **longitudinal muscles**. Movement of the earthworm is a function of the longitudinal and circular muscles contracting while the setae anchor the middle of the worm to the ground. This has the effect of the front end of the worm pulling the back end forward.

Earthworms are hermaphrodites, but an individual worm is incapable of fertilizing its own eggs. Therefore, earthworms must reproduce sexually. Sperm from one organism is transferred to the other mate, and vice versa, during the mating process. The sperm is stored in the earthworm for a short time, then the eggs are fertilized. About two weeks later new earthworms hatch.

The nervous system is made up of chains of ganglia connected to one another by a nerve cord. Usually, each segment has its own pair of ganglia. Even earthworms demonstrate cephalization as the anterior of the worm (the "head") has a concentration of many ganglia, which form into a **cerebral ganglion**, or kind of a "worm brain." A **ganglion** is a group of nerve cells. The cerebral ganglion is located in the third segment. It functions to coordinate the earthworm's movement and process the sensory information that is received from the many sensory nerves of the earthworm.

The digestive system is a one-way system with soil entering the earthworm's mouth at the anterior end of the worm and passing into the **crop**. The crop stores the soil, then passes it into the **gizzard**, which functions to grind the soil down. The food then passes from the gizzard into the intestine, where the nutrients are absorbed. Waste then passes out the anus at the posterior end of the worm.

Earthworms have a closed circulatory system. The blood is pumped from the anterior end by five pairs of tubes called the **aortic arches** into the **ventral vessel**. The ventral vessel carries the blood from the anterior end of the worm to the middle and posterior parts of the worm, where the exchange of oxygen/carbon dioxide and nutrients/wastes occurs in the cells. The blood returns to the anterior end of the worm by the **dorsal vessel**.

The earthworm does not contain specialized tissue for gas exchange. Rather, oxygen and carbon dioxide exchanges occur across the skin of the worm. This is why worms are always moist and slimy, as this facilitates the gas exchange. However, they do have specialized excretory structures, called **nephridia**, which function to remove harmful waste products, such as ammonia, from the organism. Each segment in an Annelid contains a pair of nephridia.

Figure 27.7.2

Lumbricus terrestris
Earthworms do have a head (anterior) and a tail (posterior) end. Their internal structural design is shown below.

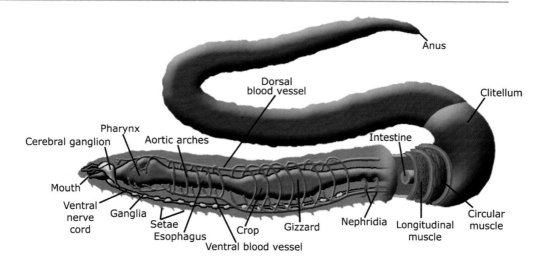

27.8 INVERTEBRATES: PHYLUM ARTHROPODA

This is the largest phylum with over 1,000,000 species. This phylum includes insects, spiders, millipedes, centipedes, crabs, lobsters, and horseshoe crabs. This is such a large phylum that it is first divided into sub-phyla before dividing it into classes. The subphyla are divided based on differences in developmental patterns and the structure of mouth parts.

Figure 27.8.1

Sub-phyla (classes) of Arthropoda

Sub-phyla	Common Name/Miscellaneous
Trilobitomorpha	trilobites, an extinct arthropod species
Chelicerata	spiders, scorpions, and horseshoe crabs
Myriapoda	centipedes (one pair of legs per segment) and millipedes (two pairs of legs per segment)
Hexapoda	insects; Hexapoda means "six legs"
Crustacea	lobsters, crabs, shrimp, crayfish, barnacles

There is no prototypical arthropod organism in a phylum that has over one million species in it. Therefore, we will focus on the general characteristics of arthropods.

Figure 27.8.2

Body Plan of Arthropods
Generally, arthropods are divided into three segments—head, thorax (middle), and abdomen (behind) sections. Some arthropods have fusion of the first two segments, such as lobsters and crayfish.

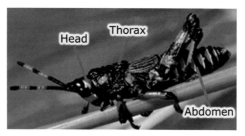

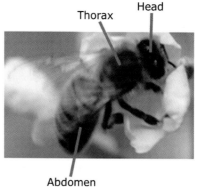

An arthropods' body structure is segmented, though at first they may be difficult to see. Arthropods have pairs of jointed **appendages**. An appendage is an arm or leg. All arthropods have an **external skeleton**, called an exoskeleton, made of chitin. This means their skeleton is on the outside of their body. It gives support and protection to the organism. This is opposed to the type of skeleton you and all mammals have, called an endoskeleton. An endoskeleton is an internal structural system, usually made of bones.

Figure 27.8.3

Arthropoda
Although the majority of arthropods fly, there are species which are aquatic (crabs, top middle and shrimp, top right), and some that do not fly at all. In addition, the most frequent fossil find, the extinct *Trilobite* organisms (top left), were also arthropods. Most arthropods have six legs, but arachnids (spiders and scorpions) have eight. Some species, like the millipedes and centipedes, can have a hundred or more legs. By the way, there is a difference between centipedes and millipedes. Centipedes have one pair of legs per body segment, millipedes have two. Also, many centipedes are poisonous but millipedes are not. Beetles are the most numerous animal species on earth. More than 30% of all animals are beetles.

Since the exoskeleton is rigid and external, it does not allow for much growth of the organism. However, the organism does grow. As it does, the exoskeleton begins to get "stretched." Eventually, the rigid exoskeleton is shed, and the arthropod emerges from the exoskeleton with a soft outer body, which soon hardens into a mature exoskeleton. This process is called **molting**.

Figure 27.8.4

Molting

Being covered by an exoskeleton is protective, but it is hard to grow when covered in rigid chitin. To accommodate growth, the exoskeleton is shed many times during an arthropod's life, a process called molting. Below left, a species of cicada is seen emerging from its shed exoskeleton. On the right, a grasshopper is seen next to its old skeleton.

Reproduction is generally sexual, and all species in Hexapoda have a male and female organism. Most arthropods exhibit indirect development with a larval stage. However, there are two types of metamorphosis patterns which insects display, **complete** and **incomplete metamorphosis**. In incomplete metamorphosis, the egg hatches and the organism looks similar to—but not exactly like—the adult form. This type of metamorphosis pattern is typified by the grasshopper. The immature form in incomplete metamorphosis is called a **nymph**. A grasshopper nymph looks like a small version of a grasshopper, but is smaller and sexually immature. A grasshopper nymph also does not have any wings. As the nymph grows, it molts several times. Each time it molts, it begins to look more and more like the adult grasshopper. It gets physically larger and its wings grow. Eventually, with the last molt, the nymph transforms into the mature adult.

Complete metamorphosis occurs when there are two stages of development between the egg hatching and the appearance of the mature adult. The initial appearance of the animal after hatching (when the animal is a larva) looks nothing like the appearance of the animal following metamorphosis. This is typified by the development of a monarch butterfly. When a monarch larva emerges from the egg, it is a caterpillar. The caterpillar undergoes several moltings. At the last molting, its exoskeleton falls off, revealing a form of the butterfly called a **pupa**. The pupa is enclosed in a protective casing called a **chrysalis**. Inside the chrysalis, the pupa turns into a butterfly. The two forms of the monarch are, therefore, the larva (caterpillar), and the pupa.

Figure 27.8.5

Complete Metamorphosis

A typical segment of complete metamorphosis is seen here. The caterpillar is the larval form of a butterfly. When the caterpillar spins a cocoon, it is called a pupa. The process of becoming encased in the chrysalis (cocoon), and changing into the butterfly, is called pupating. After a time in the chrysalis, the caterpillar has transformed into a butterfly.

The arthropods are fully mobile, with muscles attaching onto the exoskeleton to move the appendages and wings. Arthropods are capable of walking, running, flying, swimming, crawling, and skittering over the surface of water. A few adult arthropods, such as barnacles, are sessile, although their larval stages are mobile.

The arthropods exhibit a high degree of cephalization and have a brain to coordinate the functions of the animal. Nerve signals travel to and from the brain through the **ventral nerve cord**. They have **compound eyes**, which are individual light-sensing cells, each with their own lens, for sight. They also have segmented antennae that sense environmental and chemical changes. Small sensory hairs project off the body and appendages, sending signals to the brain. They have a one way digestive system with a mouth anteriorly and an anus posteriorly.

The circulatory system of all arthropods is open, and the blood is pumped by a formal heart. It is used to carry nutrients to and from cells, but not for gas exchange. In some arthropods, exchange of CO_2 and O_2 is performed directly by the cells through the use of a system of complex air tubes called **trachea**. Aquatic arthropods have gills for gas exchange. Spiders and scorpions use a system of folded tissues, called **book lungs**, which exchange gas as it passes past the folded membranes. These are not true lungs, though, and the name refers only to the fact that the folded tissue looks like the pages of a book.

Figure 27.8.6

Internal Structure of the Lobster
Lobsters are one of the arthropod species that have a fused anterior and middle segment, called a cephalothorax. This is a female—note the ovary, which produces the egg.

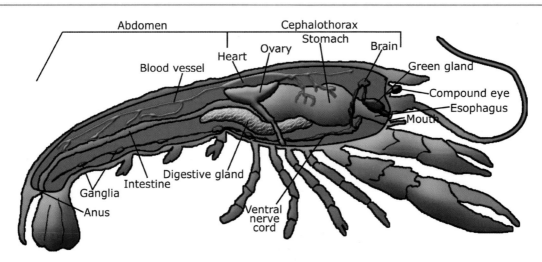

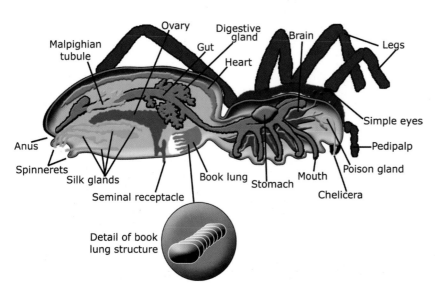

Figure 27.8.7

Internal Structure of the Spider
Spiders have a special organ, called a book lung, which enhances their ability to exchange gasses. Note the detail of the book lung. It is named for its appearance—like books stacked next to one another. Most spider species can spin webs, but not all. Each web is an intricate network of silk, with a structure that is unique to the species. It is fascinating that the web is spun perfectly on the first try every time. (This poses an interesting question for the evolution debate: how did each species of spider independently evolve their own unique web style?)

Most arthropods have a developed excretory system to rid them of cellular waste products, again mainly ammonia. The structures are called **Malpighian tubules**, and they collect water and waste. The tubules concentrate the waste products by removing the water, returning it to the organism, and excreting the waste products.

Figure 27.8.8

Internal Structure of the Grasshopper
In all these diagrams, note the similarities and differences in structure between the species. For example, they all have areas where the food is taken in and processed—basically a mouth, stomach, intestine, with the individual names being slightly different depending on the insect species. Also note that even these "primitive" animals have a centralized grouping of nerve tissue—a brain—to coordinate their activities and respond to their environments.

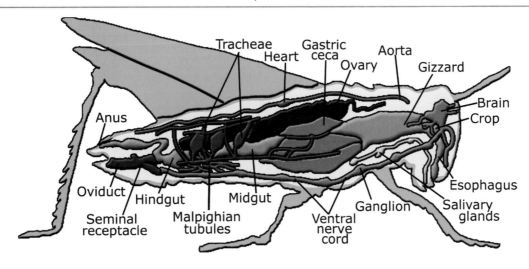

27.9 INVERTEBRATES: PHYLUM ECHINODERMATA

This phylum includes the sea stars (star fish), sand dollars, sea urchins, and sea cucumbers. All species of echinoderms are marine. They exhibit radial symmetry, and sea stars have a special type called **pentaradial symmetry**. This is the type of symmetry that exists when there is a central body with five appendages (hence the prefix "penta" which is Greek for "five") extending off the central body. Echinoderms have an endoskeleton made of calcium carbonate plates called **ossicles**. Echinoderms do not have discreet reproductive, circulatory, or respiratory organ systems. They have all three germ cell layers and a true coelem.

Figure 27.9.1

Sand Dollars and Sea Stars
Sand dollars (left photo) are actually animals, as are starfish, or sea stars. They are filter feeders and exchange gasses directly with the water around them.

Figure 27.9.2

Sea Urchin
All echinoderms have a larval stage. Interestingly, the larvae of all echinoderms are bilaterally symmetric and develop into radially symmetric adult forms. Most of the echinoderms do move, albeit slowly, over the floor of the ocean. There are a few sessile forms.

Sea urchin larva

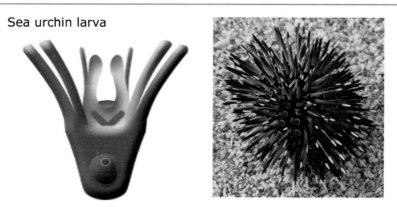

Most echinoderms have separate male and female organisms. They exhibit indirect development. Interestingly, echinoderms develop from bilaterally symmetrical larvae into radially symmetrical adult forms. Sea stars are able to reproduce asexually by splitting their bodies, then growing the "lost" parts generated by the split. Also, sea stars can regenerate lost parts as long as the remaining parts are still connected to part of the central region.

Many echinoderms are sessile, but some are mobile. They contract their muscles and slowly crawl along the bottom. Gas exchange is performed directly across the membranes of the cells. Nutrition is obtained by ingesting food through the mouth, passing it into a complete one-way digestive system and eliminating the waste through the anus. Also, the **water vascular system**, a system of canals within the body of echinoderms, functions to move water through the organism, which facilitates movement, respiration, and digestion.

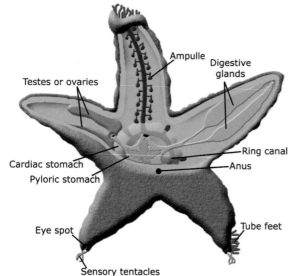

Figure 27.9.3

Internal Anatomy of a Sea Star
Sea stars have a true coelem, so their internal organs are attached to the body wall by tissue derived from mesoderm. Most species of starfish have separate male and female organisms. There is a pair of ovaries (to make eggs) or testes (to make sperm) inside each arm of a starfish. One of the favorite foods of starfish is bivalves, such as clams and oysters. The starfish is able to grip the shell of the bivalve with the suction action of its legs and pry it open with muscular contractions. Then the starfish pushes its stomach out through its mouth and the opening of the shell. Stomach juices secreted into the body of the bivalve digest it, and the starfish sucks out its meal.

27.10 INVERTEBRATES: PHYLUM CHORDATA

This is the last of the invertebrate phyla we will cover. Note that the phylum Chordata contains both vertebrates and invertebrates. That is because Chordata is not defined by the presence of a "backbone," but by the presence of a notochord. All species in Chordata have a notochord at some point in their life, but not all species in Chordata have a "backbone." Also note "backbone" is in quotation marks; this is because there is no "backbone." The term "backbone" implies there is only one bone in the back. In fact, the bones of the back are made up of a series of bones, called **vertebrae**, which for some reason or another have come to be known as the "backbone." From this point on, the terms "vertebrae" or "spinal column" will be used instead of "backbone."

Although it is not in the taxonomic system, it is convenient to use the presence of vertebrae to further divide the animals in Chordata. If you do that, you will see there are two sub-phyla which we will discuss—Urochordata and Cephalochordata—which do not have vertebrae. There is one sub-phylum—Vertebrata—which does have a vertebral column.

Figure 27.10.1

Subdivision of Chordata
Trying to put the animals in Chordata into further groups is easier when using the presence or absence of vertebrae. Animals in Urochordata and Cephalochordata have notochords, but do not have vertebrae. All animals in Vertebrata have both a notochord at some point in their lives as well as a boney spinal column to protect the spinal cord.

Phylum Chordata			
Subphylum	Urochordata	Cephalochordata	Vertebrata
Characteristics	notochord as larvae, no vertebrae	notochord, no vertebrae	notochord, vertebrae
Examples	tunicates, sea squirts	lancelets	fish, amphibians, reptiles, mammals

Chordates are distinguished from the other Animalia phyla for two main reasons.

- First, they are the only organisms which have a notochord at some point in their life time. Recall the notochord is a flexible tube of cells that develops from mesoderm between the gut and the dorsal nerve cord. Most chordates have a notochord only during their embryonic development.

- Secondly, all chordates have a dorsal, hollow nerve tube (spinal cord) that develops during neurulation.

If this is confusing, please review the last chapter.

Interestingly, there are both vertebrate and invertebrate members of Chordata. The vertebrate members are in the sub-phylum Vertebrata and are represented by many animals which you are already familiar with (fish, amphibians, reptiles, mammals, birds). The invertebrate chordates are represented by two subphyla, **Cephalochordata** (the lancelets) and **Urochordata** (the tunicates). Most adult lancelets are mobile, although they prefer to live almost completely in the sand. Tunicates (called sea squirts) are largely marine, sessile, filter feeders.

Figure 27.10.2

Tunicate
The tunicates are called sea squirts because they suck water in through one hole, the incurrent siphon, and squirt it out through the outcurrent siphon. This brings food into this filter-feeder organism. Adult tunicates do not have a notochord or a dorsal nerve cord, but their larval stages do, so they are considered chordates.

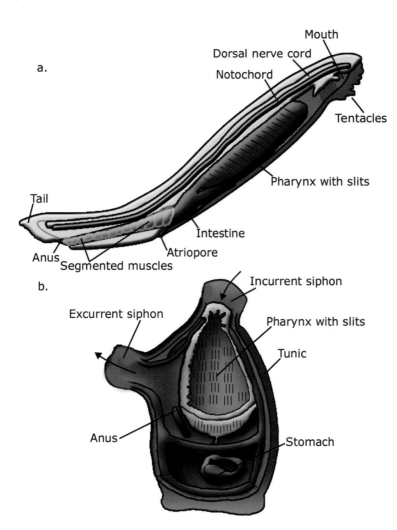

a.

b.

Figure 27.10.3

Anatomy of a Lancelet (a) and Tunicate (b).
Note the adult lancelet has a notochord and a dorsal nerve tube, but the tunicate does not. Tunicates are sessile. Although lancelets can move, they usually choose to be sessile. They tend to stay buried in the sand at the bottom of the ocean with only their head sticking out. Most lancelets are filter feeders. They draw water into their mouths and filter food out through the pharyngeal slits.

27.11 PEOPLE OF SCIENCE

Thomas Say (1787–1843) was an American biologist who specialized in studying insects (called entomology) and mollusks (called malacology). He was trained as a pharmacist but abandoned that and became a self-taught naturalist. He founded the Academy of Natural Sciences and is known for describing over one thousand new beetle species and more than four hundred insects in other orders. He wrote two large volumes about American entomology and American conchology before he died early of typhoid fever.

27.12 KEY CHAPTER POINTS

- Cnidaria includes hydras, jelly fish, sea anemones, and corals.

- The organisms of Platyhelminthes are called the flatworms.

- The organisms of Nemertea are called the ribbon worms.

- The organisms of Nematoda are called the roundworms.

- Mollusca includes squids, octopi, snails, oysters, slugs, and clams.

- Annelida includes earthworms and leeches.

- Arthropoda includes insects, trilobites, centipedes, millipedes, spiders, scorpions, crabs, lobsters, shrimp, and barnacles.

- Echinodermata includes sea stars, sand dollars, sea urchins, and sea cucumbers.

- Chordata includes tunicates, lancelets, sharks, fish, amphibians, reptiles, birds, mammals, and humans.

• The presence of a dorsal nerve tube and a notochord separate Chordata from all other phyla in Animalia.

27.13 DEFINITIONS

aortic arches
Tubes that pump blood from the anterior end of an earthworm into the ventral vessel.

appendages
Anything that sticks off of an organism's body, such as an arm, leg, wing, or antenna.

bivalves
Mollusks with two shells, such as a clam.

book lungs
System of folded tissues in spiders and scorpions to exchange gas.

Cephalochordata
Sub-phyla of Animalia including the lancelets.

cerebral ganglion
A "worm brain"; the formation of ganglia in the anterior of an earthworm.

Cestoda
Parasitic species of the platyhelminth phylum.

circular muscles
Muscle fibers that wrap around an earthworm.

cnidocyte
A specialized cell contained in cnidarians, giving them the ability to sting.

complete metamorphosis
A type of metamorphosis that occurs when the larva looks nothing like the mature form of the animal.

compound eyes
Individual light sensing cells, each with their own lens.

crop
Part of an earthworm's digestive system that stores the soil.

dorsal vessel
The blood vessel that returns blood to the anterior end of an earthworm.

external skeleton
An external structural/support skeleton.

ganglia
Groupings of nerve cells into a common location. This forms a "bulge" of nerve tissue.

gastrovascular cavity
Location where food is enzymatically digested and absorbed.

gills
Respiratory tissue in aquatic animals that extracts oxygen from the water and absorbs it into the blood stream.

gizzard
The part of an earthworm's digestive system which functions to grind the soil down.

head-foot
Head and foot section of a bivalve.

incomplete metamorphosis
Type of metamorphosis which occurs when an immature form of the adult, called the nymph, looks similar to the adult form it morphs into.

longitudinal muscles
Muscles that run the length of an earthworm.

malpighian tubules
Structures that collect and remove wastes in arthropods.

medusa
Mobile body form of cnidarians.

molting
The process of an arthropod shedding its rigid exoskeleton.

nephridia
Excretory structure of an earthworm.

nerve net
Nervous system consisting of interconnected nerve cells.

nymph
The immature form of an organism, which undergoes incomplete metamorphosis.

ossicles
Calcium carbonate plates making up the endoskeleton of echinoderms.

parapodia
Fleshy protrusions present on annelids.

pentaradial symmetry
The type of symmetry that exists when there is a central body with five appendages extending off the central body.

polyp
Sessile body form of cnidarians.

proglottids
Egg-forming units of some platyhelminths that constantly release eggs into the feces of the host.

pupa
The form of a butterfly during the last molting stage.

scolex
Head of a tapeworm with a strong sucker and barbs to anchor the worm to the intestine.

setae
External bristles present on annelids.

trachea
Structure that carries air from the neck into the chest.

Trematoda
A parasitic species of the Platyhelminthes phylum.

trochophores
Mollusks that are still in the larval stage.

Turbellaria
Free-living species of the Platyhelminthes phylum.

two-way gut
A digestive system in which the food enters and waste exits through the same opening.

Urochordata
A sub-phylum of Animalia which includes tunicates.

ventral nerve cord
Structure that carries nerve impulses to and from the brain.

ventral vessel
Carries the blood from the anterior end of an earthworm to the middle and posterior parts of the worm.

vertebrae
Series of bones that make up the back of vertebrates and protect the spinal cord.

vessels
Tubes that carry nutrients and oxygen to and from the tissues.

visceral mass
The heart and organs of digestion, reproduction, and excretion of a bivalve.

water vascular system
A system of canals within the body of echinoderms, which moves water through the organism to facilitate movement, respiration, and digestion.

STUDY QUESTIONS

1. What type of symmetry do the cnidarians demonstrate?

2. Draw the medusa and polyp form of a typical cnidarian.

3. What is a cnidocyte?

4. What is considered to be the "most primitive" phyla to show cephalization?

5. Which two phyla have two-way digestive systems?

6. In which phylum does a complete digestive tract first appear?

7. In which phylum does a simple, but complete, circulatory system first appear?

8. Animals from which phyla discussed in this chapter are common parasites to humans?

9. What are ganglia and what function do they perform for the mollusks?

10. True or False? Most mollusks exhibit indirect development.

11. Do mollusks have an open or closed circulatory system?

12. What is a cerebral ganglion? What phylum has this structure?

13. True or False? Annelids are the first phylum in which lungs are found.

14. What is a scolex? What phylum is this structure commonly found? What purpose does it serve?

15. What function do nephridia perform?

16. What is the first phylum in which the body plan includes appendages (arms, legs, etc.)?

17. What type of skeleton do the arthropods have? What particular problem does this type of skeleton cause for an arthropod and how does it overcome it?

18. Explain the difference between complete and incomplete metamorphosis. Be sure to include the stages of development for each.

19. What methods do the arthropods use for gas (air) exchange?

20. What sub-phylum (or class) has book lungs?

21. What is the first phylum to have an endoskeleton?

22. True or False? All sea stars and sand dollars are sessile.

23. What is a convenient way to sub-divide the animals classified in the phylum Chordata?

24. What common features do all chordates have?

PLEASE TAKE TEST #11 IN TEST BOOKLET

Kingdom Animalia III

28

28.0 CHAPTER PREVIEW

In this chapter we will:

- Discuss the features of vertebrates.

- Discuss vertebrate organ systems.

- Review the features of the organisms classified into:
  - Agnatha
  - Chondrichthyes
  - Osteichthyes
  - Amphibia
  - Reptilia

- Introduce the concept of the one-loop and two-loop circulatory systems.

- Discuss the function of capillaries.

- Investigate the structure and function of the amniotic egg.

- Discuss endothermia and ectothermia.

28.1 OVERVIEW

In this chapter, we will begin discussion on the sub-phylum of the vertebrate species from the Chordata phylum. The defining characteristic of a vertebrate is an animal which has its **dorsal spinal cord** protected (or surrounded) by a spinal column made of bone or cartilage. The dorsal spinal cord is the structure which carries the nerve impulses from the brain to the body and from the body to the brain. All chordates also have a notochord at some time during their lives. For the vast majority of chordates, the notochord is present only for a short time during embryonic development. All together, there are over 45,000 species of vertebrates, with the large majority of them—23,000—boney fish species.

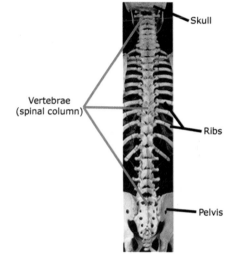

Figure 28.1.1

Vertebral Column
The difference between vertebrates and invertebrates is the spinal column. Vertebrates have a protective support structure—the spinal column or "backbone"—surrounding their dorsal nerve tube—the spinal cord. Each bone of the spinal column is called a vertebrae; hence the name vertebrates. The spinal column is human.

To review, all chordates have a notochord present at some point in their life, and all have a hollow spinal cord. Because there are many species involved in Chordata, we will continue to follow the same general way of discussing the organisms as we have the past two chapters, with more or less time spent discussing specific features or organ systems as indicated. Most of the time, information will be summarized in table form; particularly important information will be expounded upon in the text. Please see Figure 28.1.2 for details on the phyla we will be discussing.

Figure 28.1.2

Overview of Seven Vertebrate Classes in the Phylum Chordata of the Kingdom Animalia
Note that "terrestrial" means "lives on land." You will become familiar with all the terms below over the next two chapters.

Class & Number of Species	Common Names	Basic Structure
Agnatha 80	lampreys, hagfishes	aquatic, no jaw, cartilage skeleton, gills, no fins
Chondrichthyes 800	sharks, skates, rays	aquatic, cartilage skeleton, jawed mouth, gills, fins
Osteichthyes 23,000	boney fish (blue gill, bass, tuna, sail fish, aquarium fish)	aquatic, jaw, bony skeleton, gills, fins
Amphibia 3,000	Amphibians—frogs, toads, salamanders	aquatic and terrestrial, jaws, boney skeleton, lungs, four appendages ("legs")
Reptilia 6,000	Reptiles—turtles, snakes, lizards, crocodiles, alligators	terrestrial, jaws, boney skeleton, lungs, amniotic egg, tough skin
Aves 10,000	birds	air, terrestrial, jaws, boney skeleton, lungs, feathers for flight, amniotic eggs
Mammalia 4,400	mammals	terrestrial and aquatic, jaws, boney skeleton, mostly placental and nurse young, hair on skin

28.2 EVOLUTION OF LAND ANIMALS?

This is an area in which you should be aware of current evolutionary thought. As has been the case throughout the course, I will not be presenting evolutionary views as truth, because I think there is ample evidence to put evolution into question. I will present enough information so you will understand the current thoughts regarding evolutionary beliefs in case it comes up on college testing. In addition, I think it can stimulate good thought and discussion on the evolution-creation issue. Where appropriate, I will also offer the creationist's viewpoint. However, we have discussed what the creationist view is in the evolutionary chapters. I would like you to note that evolutionists have never been able to explain *how* all of these supposed evolutionary changes took place from a biochemical and genetic level. There is a whole lot of information about this subject easily accessible on the Internet and in books that I encourage you to explore.

Evolutionists believe that the first vertebrate species were likely aquatic, like fish, and appeared about 550 million years ago. The earliest dated fossils of vertebrates are of sharks and jawless fishes that are presumably about 400 million years old. It is interesting to note that both fish and sharks appear in the fossil record **completely formed** and appearing as fish and sharks do today. There are certainly many species which have become extinct. However, there are no "pre-sharks" or "pre-fish" fossils. The sharks of today look almost exactly the same as their ancestors. Does that sound like what should happen if evolution were a fact? It does not to me. If evolution were true, then one would certainly think that in a half billion years the species of today would have evolved. They should appear different. Creationists point to that fact as evidence that everything was created, since most fossil species "appear" out of nowhere *and* the species which are supposed to be ancient do not change. Creationists believe this is strong evidence that everything was created. We have all probably heard that alligators and crocodiles are "living fossils." Why? If evolution occurs, they should not look like they did 300 million years ago.

Land-based vertebrates were supposedly present in the form of amphibians about 370 million years ago. Egg-laying reptiles came next, supposedly evolving directly from egg-laying amphibians, about 350 million years ago. Mammals were able to evolve from reptiles about 300 million years ago. Interestingly, birds, which are the organisms most closely related to the reptiles they supposedly evolved from, took **another 150 million** years before they were able to grow feathers and fly. It took birds 150 million years longer than mammals to evolve from their supposed ancestors. This thought process does not appear logical. According to evolutionary thought, it took birds longer to evolve from the reptiles than mammals, even though birds are more closely related to reptiles according to evolutionists. Birds did not need to gain as many gene causing mutations as mammals did to evolve from the dinosaurs, therefore it should not have taken them 150 million more years than mammals to do so. Since evolution is purely by chance, the mutation rates that bird and mammal ancestors experienced would have been the same. Accordingly, birds should have evolved much sooner from their reptile ancestors than mammals since birds had to gain much less genetic material to do so.

28.3 ORGAN SYSTEMS

Recall that life is highly ordered. One of the areas we see a high degree of order is in how cells are organized. Cells which share a common function are grouped together and are called a tissue. Tissues which share a common function are grouped together into an organ. Therefore, an organ is a group of tissues which perform a common function. For example, the heart is an organ. It is made up of muscle tissue, connective tissue and nerve tissue. These tissues all function together to cause the heart to pump blood through the body.

As we discuss different phyla, we will also be spending a good deal of time learning more about different organ systems, and how they differ between phyla. I would like you to study the following table, which explains the various tissue systems and what they do for the organism. Also, you need to be familiar with the components of the systems. For example, you should know that a fully developed excretory system in mammals consists of kidneys to filter wastes from the blood, ureters to carry the urine from the kidneys to the bladder, and a urethra to carry the urine from the bladder out of the body. These will be listed during the discussion of each class below. The names are all similar, so please refer back to this table if you become confused.

Figure 28.3.1

Animal Organ Systems and Functions

System	Function and Components
Reproductive	functions to generate gametes; female ovary makes eggs and male teste makes sperm
Neurologic	brain to coordinate the activity, movement and responses of the animal to its environment; brain is connected to the hollow dorsal spinal cord, which carries signals to/from the brain from/to the rest of the organism; spinal nerves carry impulses to/from the spinal cord; from/to the tissues and cells
Digestive	functions to obtain and process food; mouth is the opening and food passes through the pharynx ("throat") and the esophagus to the stomach; stomach enzymatically digests and physically breaks food down (by squeezing), then passes it to the small intestine; small intestine is specialized for absorbing nutrients; last part of the pathway is the large intestine which completes absorption and packages waste for elimination
Circulatory	functions to carry oxygen and nutrients in the blood to the tissues and carbon dioxide and waste from the tissues for removal from the body; consists of heart to pump and vessels to carry the blood; heart is made up of one or two chambers to receive the blood called atria (singular atrium), and one or two muscular chambers called ventricles to pump blood to the body and lungs; vessels include arteries (carry blood away from the heart), capillaries (tiny vessels, and the site of gas and nutrient/waste exchange in the tissues and lungs) and veins (carry blood to the heart)
Respiratory	functions to bring oxygen into the blood and remove carbon dioxide from the blood; this can be done with gills or lungs; no matter what the organ, gas exchange occurs in the smallest blood vessels, the capillaries
Excretory	functions to remove metabolic wastes (usually ammonia) from the tissues; consists of kidney to filter waste from the blood and a system to store/eliminate the waste
Musculoskeletal	muscular system functions to move the organism; skeletal system is an endoskeletal design which supports the body of the vertebrate; skeleton also functions to protect vital parts of the organism such as brain, spinal cord, heart, and lungs
Connective	composed of blood, ligaments, tendons, cartilage, extracellular matrix, and fat; functions to hold the organism together and provide connections of bone to muscle (tendon) and bone to bone (ligament)
Endocrine	composed of chemical messengers, which are released into the blood to allow one tissue or organ to communicate with another tissue or organ which is far away
Immune	composed of tissues which protect the organism from foreign invaders and provide ways to heal injuries

28.4 PHYLUM CHORDATA, CLASS AGNATHA

Organisms classified in Phylum Chordata, Class Agnatha are also called the **jawless fishes,** as that is their defining feature. They are the only vertebrate in which the notochord remains throughout the organism's life. They are entirely aquatic, with the **hagfishes** being only marine organisms and **lampreys** living in marine or fresh water environments. (Again, marine means living in salt water). An interesting note about lampreys is that they only mate in fresh water, so organisms that live in the sea return to fresh water for mating purposes. They exhibit indirect development with a larval and adult stage.

Lampreys and hagfishes have a fairly well-developed neurological system and demonstrate cephalization. They have a structure called the **lateral line,** which many fish and shark species have, too. The lateral line is a group of nerve cells that run down both sides of the organism and collect information from the environment such as vibration and electrical currents. This information is carried to the brain through the dorsal spinal cord. This is a sensitive part of the nervous system and allows the organism to sense and respond to changes in its environment.

Figure 28.4.1

Summary of Characteristics of Agnatha

Characteristic	
Developmental/ Reproductive	bilateral symmetry; notochord present throughout life; lay eggs with **indirect development**; **external fertilization** (female lays eggs and male ejects sperm onto them after they are laid)
Neurological	cephalization with coordinating brain; **lateral line system**
Mobility	swim through actions of muscles
Nutrition/Digestion	no jaw; specialized mouth to burrow into food or attach to surface to parasitize body fluids
Circulatory	tubular type of heart; closed circulatory system
Respiratory	**gills** (we will discuss gills in the fish section as they work essentially the same)
Excretory	kidneys and gills both excrete cellular waste products (ammonia)
Skeleton	cartilage

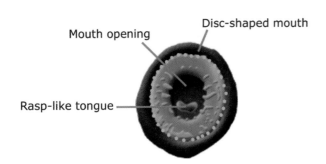

Mouth opening

Disc-shaped mouth

Rasp-like tongue

Figure 28.4.2

Lamprey
The hallmark feature of the jawless fish is the round mouth. The mouth of the lamprey is specialized so the animal can latch onto its host. The lamprey is a parasite and uses its rasp-like tongue to scrape away flesh. It also secretes chemicals to keep its host's blood from clotting. Unfortunately, usually the animal which the lamprey parasitizes is not killed. The lamprey stops feeding and comes off the host. Sometimes the host recovers, other times it dies of infection or loss of blood. This has resulted in population reductions of many types of game fish in the Great Lakes. The hagfish has a similar mouth structure but eats dead animals after burrowing into their insides.

28.5 PHYLUM CHORDATA, CLASS CHONDRICHTHYES

The name of this order literally means "cartilage fish," so named because they have skeletons made from cartilage. Cartilage is softer and more pliable than bone. This order includes **sharks**, **rays**, and **skates**; almost all the organisms are marine. They are exclusively carnivores, although not all hunt their prey; sometimes they eat it after it is dead. Sharks usually hunt their prey as it swims in the water. Rays are adapted to bottom-dwelling and feed on the mollusks and crustaceans on the bottom. The two largest species of this class in terms of size, the whale shark and the basking shark, feed exclusively on the smallest organisms in the sea—plankton. The animals of Chondrichthyes have multiple rows of teeth, between six and twenty, which are constantly replaced as they fall out. Some species of sharks may produce twenty thousand teeth in their lifetime.

Organisms in this order exhibit cephalization with a large brain, well developed eye sight, and smell, as well as a lateral line system.

Figure 28.5.1

Summary of Characteristics of Chondrichthyes

Characteristic	
Developmental/ Reproductive	bilaterally symmetric; paired fins on the ventral ("bottom") surface; internal fertilization of eggs; **internal fertilization**; direct development after live birth from the mother (eggs hatch inside female) or after eggs are ejected ("laid") from the female
Neurological	cephalization with coordinating brain; spinal cord to carry signals from/to brain to/from rest of organism; lateral line system; excellent sense of smell and sight; able to sense vibration and weak electrical fields
Mobility	swim through actions of muscles; skin covered with rough **placoid scales** (oriented with the tips of the scale facing the tail of the animal) to help reduce drag of water
Nutrition/Digestion	jaw; complete one way digestive system with esophagus; stomach, liver, small intestine, and anus
Circulatory	heart pumps blood past gills and to rest of organism through closed circulatory system (all blood is contained in blood vessels and heart and does not leave the vessels or heart)
Respiratory	gills; the fish needs to be in constant motion, or needs to pump water past gills by opening/closing mouth for respiration to occur effectively
Excretory	rectal gland near anus helps remove ions from blood and maintain homeostasis
Skeleton	cartilage

Figure 28.5.2

Sharks, Rays, and Skates
Sharks are the most numerous members of Chondrichthyes. Rays and skates are similar in appearance. There are differences between the two, though. Skates (middle) have shorter and fleshier tails than rays (right). Also, skates lay eggs, whereas rays give birth to live young. Rays also grow much larger than skates. The Manta ray can grow to more than twenty-two feet from wing to wing and weigh several tons.

28.6 PHYLUM CHORDATA, CLASS OSTEICHTHYES

These organisms are called the "**boney fish**," or simply **fish**. Their skeleton is made of bone, rather than cartilage, and so is more rigid. There are two general categories of boney fish, the "lobe-finned" fish (class Sarcopterygii) and the "ray-finned" fish (class Actinopterygii). The lobe-finned fish have fleshy appendages for a fin, while the ray-finned fish have fins supported by boney elements, called rays that extend from the body of the fish. When we think of what a fish looks like, we usually picture a ray-finned fish.

Figure 28.6.1

Osteichthyes
There are many different species of fish. The marine (living in salt water) fish (top left and top middle) are usually more colorful than freshwater fish (top right). Fish are diverse structurally, too. The Moray eel, below left, and the seahorse (below right) are a species of fish.

An interesting property of many species, particularly as we move from the fish to the reptiles, birds, and mammals, is **parental care**. Parental care is when one or both parents care for their young in some way. Some fish species show parental care in guarding the eggs while they are developing prior to hatching. Also, some species, like the ring-tailed cardinal fish, *Apogon aureus*, carries the fertilized eggs in its mouth until they hatch. There are no species of Chondrichthyes which display parental care. There is increasing parental care as we move from fish to reptiles to birds to mammals.

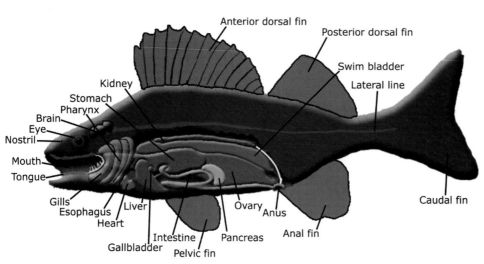

Figure 28.6.2

General Fish Anatomy
Fish display cephalization and have a small brain for an animal of their size. The lateral line extends from the head down each side of the fish body. It is an added sensory organ and brings information from the outside world to the brain. The heart is located close to the gills. Gills are specialized gas-exchange tissue loaded with capillary beds. When blood passes through the gill capillaries, carbon dioxide is released from the blood and oxygen is picked up. The blood then travels to the rest of the organism to supply needed oxygen and remove carbon dioxide. Note this is a female fish due to the presence of ovaries.

Fish have a well-developed nervous system, with specific areas of the brain developed to control specific functions of the fish. For example, there are enlarged areas of the brain that process vision and muscle movements while swimming and chasing prey. They have a two-chambered heart to pump blood through their closed vascular system. The chamber that receives the blood returning to the heart is called the **atrium**. Once the atrium fills with blood, it squeezes, or contracts, and pumps the blood to the **ventricle**. When the ventricle fills with blood, it contracts and sends the blood to the gills, where the blood releases carbon dioxide and absorbs oxygen. The blood—now full of oxygen—flows from the gills to the tissues. Oxygen is absorbed by the tissues. Blood absorbs carbon dioxide from the tissues. The blood then returns to the atrium.

Figure 28.6.3

Summary of Characteristics of Osteichthyes

Characteristic	
Developmental/ Reproductive	bilaterally symmetric; paired fins on the ventral ("bottom") surface; separate male and female organisms with testes to make sperm and ovaries to produce eggs; most species have external fertilization with direct development; species that have internal fertilization also have some parental care
Neurological	cephalization with coordinating brain and specialized areas of brain function; spinal cord carries information from/to brain to/from rest of the fish
Mobility	swim through actions of muscles; skin covered with rough scales for protection and to help reduce drag of water
Nutrition/Digestion	complete one way digestive system with esophagus, stomach, liver, small intestine, and anus
Circulatory	**Two-chambered heart** pumps blood past gills and to rest of organism through closed, "one loop" circulatory system
Respiratory	gills; the fish needs to be in constant motion or needs to pump water past gills by opening/ closing mouth for respiration to occur effectively; fish also have a swim bladder, which is a small membrane-bound bag that fills with gas to help the fish float, or deflates so the fish can sink
Excretory	fish have kidneys which remove ammonia from the blood and maintain proper ion balance; gills also are effective at removing some ammonia and exchanging ions; fish kidneys convert the ammonia to urea before excreting the nitrogenous wastes, which takes energy, but spares water— this is a common pattern of excreting wastes in vertebrate species
Skeleton	bone in almost all species

This occurs in beds of **capillaries** contained in the gills. Capillaries are very small blood vessels, often only large enough to let one cell pass through them at one time. Because they are so small, and their walls are thin, they are perfect for gas, nutrient, and waste exchange between the blood and tissues. From the gills, the pressure provided by the ventricle continually pumping blood toward the gills sends the blood out of the gills to the rest of the organism. The gills of Agnatha, Chondrichthyes, and Osteichthyes require that water move past the gills in order for gas exchange to happen normally. This is why many people think that sharks need to keep swimming or else they will die. That is partially true, but there is another way to move water past the gills—by the mouth opening and closing. Either way, the water has to keep moving past the gills to carry away the carbon dioxide and bring in more oxygen.

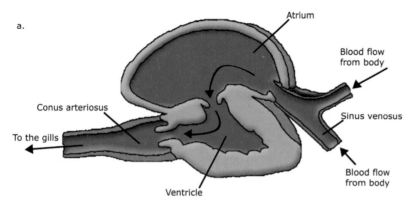

a.

Atrium

Blood flow from body

Conus arteriosus

Sinus venosus

To the gills

Blood flow from body

Ventricle

Figure 28.6.4

Fish Heart and One-Loop Circulation
Deoxygenated blood from the fish's body returns via veins to the two-chambered heart and enters the atrium. It passes into the ventricle and the ventricle pumps it into the gills. Gas exchange occurs, then the oxygenated blood continues through the arteries, on its way to the rest of the tissues.

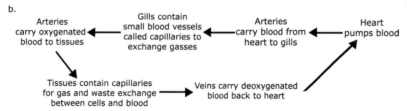

b.

Arteries carry oxygenated blood to tissues

Gills contain small blood vessels called capillaries to exchange gasses

Arteries carry blood from heart to gills

Heart pumps blood

Tissues contain capillaries for gas and waste exchange between cells and blood

Veins carry deoxygenated blood back to heart

28.7 PHYLUM CHORDATA, CLASS AMPHIBIA

The organisms of Amphibia have adaptations that allow them to live on land (legs and lungs), but also have needs that require them to be close to water. They do not have scales, but have a thin skin that needs to be kept moist. This is because most amphibians use their skin in addition to their lungs for respiration. If the skin becomes too dry, amphibians cannot perform gas exchange properly, and they will die. Most amphibians have internal fertilization, although many (such as frogs) do not. Once the eggs are fertilized, they need a moist environment to mature, so most amphibian eggs are laid in or near water. If there is not moisture, the eggs will dry out and the embryos will die. Some amphibians have indirect development with a fully aquatic larval stage, while others display direct development. Because of their heavy reliance on water, combined with the fact they have legs to walk on land, most evolutionists believe amphibians evolved from the lobe-finned fishes.

Figure 28.7.1

Three Orders of Amphibia

Order	Examples	Characteristics
Anura	frogs, toads	four legs; no tail; external fertilization; indirect development with larval stage referred to as a **tadpole**; larvae respire through gills and adults have lungs; tadpole undergoes metamorphosis into a frog
Urodela	salamanders	four legs; tail; adults do not have lungs and respire through skin; most have internal fertilization
Apoda	caecilians	no legs; "wormlike"; tropical; not much is known about them

However, this requires some thought regarding the genetic changes that would need to occur to cause a water living creature to permanently move onto land. Note the two well-understood orders of Amphibia—Anura and Urodela—exchange gasses in completely different ways. One order has lungs, while the other exchanges gasses through the skin. How would natural selection select for the two groups of amphibians to develop the same traits with the exception of how they perform gas exchange? Also, on a genetic basis, how did gills behind the eyes turn into internal lungs? Even harder to comprehend is how gills turned into gas-exchanging structures found throughout the skin. Remember, for these changes to have taken place, there would need to be countless information-gaining mutations to the DNA that would lead to the development of these amphibian traits. Apparently, these information-gaining mutations no longer occur, as there has never been an information-gaining mutation which has resulted in the change in a useful trait.

Figure 28.7.2

Amphibians
Frogs (order Anura, left), toads (order Anura, middle), and salamanders (order Urodela, right) are all types of amphibians. Caecilians (order Apoda, not shown) are the third type of amphibian. They look like a salamander without legs—almost the amphibian version of a snake.

Figure 28.7.3

Frog Reproduction
Below left are fertilized frog eggs. Frogs have external fertilization. The female lays the eggs and, as they are being laid, the male releases sperm on them. The eggs remain suspended in the water until they hatch into tadpoles (right).

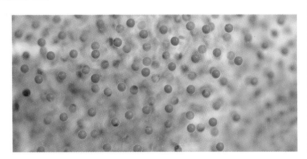

With the presence of lungs, an entirely new pattern of blood circulation develops. In the species with gills, the heart simply pumped the blood to the gills, then the blood moved from the gills to the rest of the organism's tissues, and back to the heart. It was a one-loop circuit. In vertebrates with lungs, there is a **two-loop system**. One loop is for pumping the de-oxygenated blood from the heart to the lungs, then back to the heart. The second loop is for pumping the blood from the heart to the rest of the tissues and back to the heart again. Here is how it works.

Amphibians have a **three-chambered heart**. There are two atria and one ventricle. The **right atrium** receives blood returning from the tissues and passes it into the single ventricle. The ventricle then pumps it to the lungs. The **left atrium** receives the oxygenated blood returning from the lungs, then passes it into the same single ventricle. Here, the ventricle pumps it to the rest of the body. The loop to the lungs is called the **pulmonary circulation**, and the loop to the tissues is called the **systemic circulation**.

Let's use blood in the right atrium as the starting point. Blood in the right atrium has just returned from the tissues. It carries a lot of carbon dioxide and little oxygen. This is called **deoxygenated blood**. The heart pumps the deoxygenated blood into the ventricle, and the ventricle pumps the blood to the lungs. In the lungs, carbon dioxide is released from the blood and oxygen is absorbed into the blood. The blood now has a lot of oxygen and no carbon dioxide; it is called **oxygenated blood**. Oxygenated blood returns to the heart. That completes the pulmonary loop.

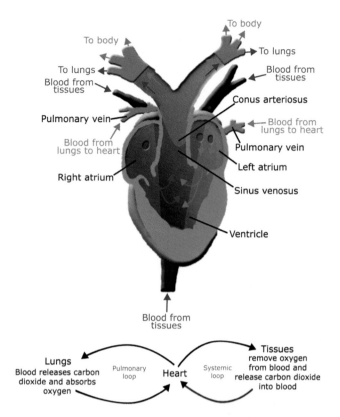

Figure 28.7.4

Adult frog circulation
As tadpoles, frogs have a one-loop system and a two-chambered heart. Adult frogs gave a two-loop system and a three-chambered heart. De-oxygenated blood returns from the tissues through veins and enters the heart through the right atrium. The blood then enters the single ventricle and is pumped through the pulmonary loop. The blood enters the pulmonary artery and is oxygenated in the lungs. It then returns to the left atrium of the heart, and the pulmonary loop is completed. The blood moves into the ventricle, and the systemic loop. It is pumped from the ventricle into the arteries and the rest of the systemic tissues. When the blood gets to the capillaries, gas and nutrient exchange occurs, then the blood is carried back to the right atrium through veins. The systemic loop is completed.

Upon arriving at the heart, the oxygenated blood first passes through the left atrium, then into the ventricle. The heart pumps and the ventricle squeezes the oxygenated blood from the heart to the tissues. In the tissues, oxygen is taken from the blood into the tissues, and carbon dioxide is released from the tissues into the blood. The blood then flows back to the heart, arriving in the right atrium. This completes the second loop. That completes the pulmonary loop. **The way this two-loop system works is consistent for all vertebrate species with lungs (amphibians, reptiles, birds, and mammals), so be sure to be familiar with it**.

Hopefully, you are thinking, "Wait a minute! If there is only one ventricle and it has to pump both oxygenated and deoxygenated blood, why don't the two mix together? How does the blood know where to go?" That is an excellent question. The inside surface of the ventricle is irregularly shaped, which helps to direct the blood in the proper direction. Also, the atria contract in such a way as to prevent significant mixing of the oxygenated blood from the lungs with the deoxygenated blood from the tissues.

Figure 28.7.5

Summary of Characteristics of Amphibia

Characteristic	
Developmental/ Reproductive	bilaterally symmetric; some species have four legs and a tail, some four legs, and some no legs at all; both direct and indirect development exhibited; eggs generally hatch several days after fertilization
Neurological	cephalization with coordinating brain and specialized areas of brain function; spinal cord carries information from/to brain; good eye sight with **nictitating membrane** (a clear eyelid to close and cover the eye so organism can see under water)
Mobility	swim via the tail in the larval stage; adults with legs can walk, hop, or swim well
Nutrition/Digestion	all amphibians are carnivores eating insects, worms, other small amphibians, etc.; complete one-way digestive system with esophagus, stomach, liver, small intestine, and **vent** (common opening that cloaca uses to eject products of reproductive system and waste from digestive and excretory systems
Circulatory	Three-chambered heart pumps blood through closed circulatory system with "Two loops"
Respiratory	either through the skin or lungs and skin depending on the species
Excretory	kidneys convert ammonia to urea before excreting to conserve water
Skeleton	bone in all species

Another interesting thing to note about amphibians is that they are the only vertebrate species which displays incomplete development. Where did all of those genes come from if fish evolved into amphibians? Where did the genes go if amphibians evolved into reptiles? No reptiles display indirect development. What possible explanation could there be for only one "in between" phylum to display indirect development? Also, since indirect development is a feature of most of the "more primitive" animals (according to evolutionists) then amphibians acquiring the trait of indirect development is backwards evolution.

Most of us know what tadpoles are. We commonly think of **tadpoles** as the immature forms of frogs. However, the larval stage of any amphibian is referred to as a tadpole. Tadpoles live in the water. They have gills and a one-loop circulatory system. As the tadpole undergoes metamorphosis, it loses its tail, grows legs, develops a three-chambered heart from a two-chambered one and a two-loop circulatory system from a one-loop one. How could all of the genetic information which codes for those complicated changes possibly have been added to fish DNA as a result of random mutations?

Figure 28.7.6

Frog Anatomy

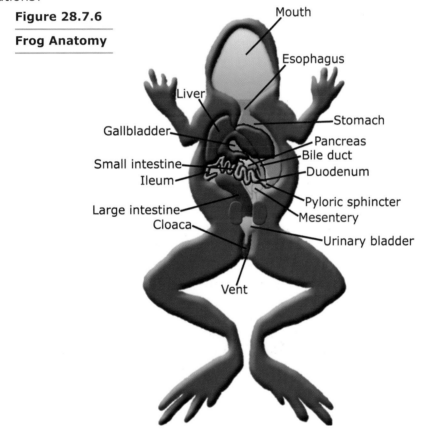

28.8 PHYLUM CHORDATA, CLASS REPTILIA

The reptiles are adapted to nearly any type of environment on earth, including water. They are on all continents except Antarctica. Their tough and watertight skin allows them to be completely independent of the water, unlike all the species we have discussed so far. Recall that water plays a big part in reproduction by providing a moist environment for amphibian eggs to properly develop and hatch. Reptiles do not need to rely on water this way, but they do need to have a moist environment for their embryos to safely develop until they hatch. Amphibian embryos are kept moist by environmental water. Reptile embryos are kept safe by encasing the embryo in a watery environment surrounded by a protective shell. This is called an egg. Inside the egg, the embryo is surrounded by water and all the nutrients it needs before it hatches. This safe environment is provided by the **amniotic egg**.

Figure 28.8.1

Four Orders of Reptilia

Order	Examples	Characteristics
Testudines 250 species	turtle, tortoise	hard shell for protection, which consists of fused boney plates; often aquatic; no teeth, but sharp beak
Crocodilia 21 species	crocodile, alligator, caiman, gavial	large and heavy bodied; aquatic; all are carnivorous
Squamata 5,500 species	snakes, lizards (chameleon, gecko, iguana)	loosely jointed upper jaw allows them to eat prey that are much larger than their head; prominent Jacobsen's organ
Rhynchocephalia 2 species	tuataras	found only in New Zealand

Figure 28.8.2

Reptiles
Lizards (top left) and snakes (bottom left) are in the order Squamata. Turtles (top right) are in the order Testudines, and crocodiles (bottom right) are in the order Crocodilia.

In addition to providing the embryo with water and nutrients, the membranes of the amniotic egg help exchange gasses through the porous surface of the shell with the outside air. The amniotic egg basically provides a protective aquatic environment for the embryo to develop until it is ready to hatch.

Immediately surrounding the embryo is the **amniotic membrane**, or **amnion**, which encloses the embryo in fluid. The embryo is attached to a **yolk sac** from which the embryo gets nutrition as its cells undergo rapid mitosis. The **allantois** is another membrane inside the egg, which stores nitrogenous wastes and exchanges gasses from the embryo to the outer air and back. The **chorion** is the outer-most membrane and surrounds all other membranes. There is also a layer of **albumin** ("egg white") the embryo uses as a source of protein and water for hydration. This amniotic egg is found in all reptiles, birds and egg-laying mammals. However, some of the reptiles and nearly all egg-laying mammals do not have a hard shell surrounding the egg, but one that is soft and flexible.

Figure 28.8.3

Amniotic Egg

A graphic of the amniotic egg is shown below on the left. The embryo is surrounded by the amnion. It receives nutrition from the yolk sac and albumen and waste is stored in the allantois. Air exchange occurs through small pores in the egg shell. These can be seen on the ostrich egg on the right. Reptiles, birds, and egg-laying mammals lay amniotic eggs.

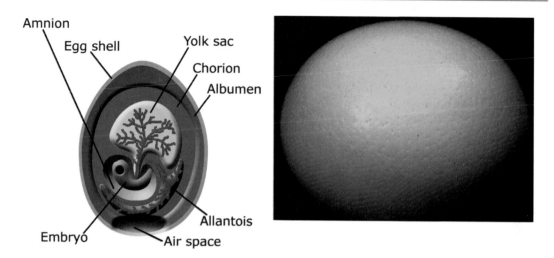

Figure 28.8.4

Summary of Characteristics of Reptilia

Characteristic	
Developmental/ Reproductive	bilaterally symmetric; some species have four legs and a tail, some no legs at all; no indirect development exhibited; internal fertilization; **amniotic egg**; crocodilians display fierce parental care and protection of eggs and young
Neurological	cephalization with coordinating brain and specialized areas of brain function; spinal cord carries information from/to brain; good eyesight; **Jacobsen's organ** (located on the roof of the mouth) is found in snakes, lizards, and some turtles; good hearing (except snakes)
Mobility	swim, walk, or crawl
Nutrition/Digestion	complete one-way digestive system; reptiles can be carnivores, herbivores, or omnivores
Circulatory	crocodilians have a four-chambered heart while all other reptiles have a three-chambered heart; closed circulatory system with pulmonary and systemic loops; blood does not mix in organisms with three-chambered hearts due to the way the atria contract and the presence of one-way valves to prevent blood from back-flowing
Respiratory	lungs
Excretory	kidneys convert ammonia to urea before excreting to conserve water
Skeleton	bone in all species

There are a couple of noteworthy changes in the body structures and physiology of reptiles as compared to the previous phyla. The **Jacobsen's organ** is tissue specialized to sense chemical changes in the environment. It is found in snakes, lizards, and some turtles. It is located on the roof of the mouth and is activated when the flicking tongue brings chemicals from the air into the mouth. The chemicals activate the cells of Jacobsen's organ and allow the animal to sense minute changes in the chemistry of the environment.

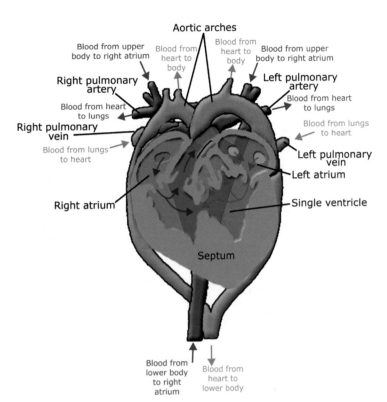

Aortic arches

Blood from upper body to right atrium

Blood from heart to body

Blood from heart to body

Blood from upper body to right atrium

Right pulmonary artery

Left pulmonary artery

Blood from heart to lungs

Blood from heart to lungs

Right pulmonary vein

Blood from lungs to heart

Blood from lungs to heart

Left pulmonary vein

Left atrium

Right atrium

Single ventricle

Septum

Blood from lower body to right atrium

Blood from heart to lower body

Figure 28.8.5

Reptile Heart
The reptile heart is similar to the amphibian heart. All reptiles have a three-chambered heart, except for the crocodilians, which have a four-chambered heart. There is a two-loop system as we have described previously.

In addition, reptiles have fairly good hearing and a system to activate their sense of sound that is similar to that of mammals and birds. Their sound organ consists of a thin, mobile outer membrane called the **tympanum**, or "ear drum." Sound waves move the tympanum when they strike it. The tympanum then moves a single inner "ear bone," called an **ossicle** (humans have three ossicles), which causes movement of fluid in the inner ear. As the fluid moves, it makes small hair cells that are resting in the fluid wave back and forth. The movement of the hair cells triggers the perception and reception of sound in the brain. Snakes also have an ossicle, but they do not have a tympanum. The ossicle is activated by vibration in the ground, which then is transmitted from the snake's jaw to the ossicle. This is a handy system for sensing approaching prey (or a predator) when you do not have any legs.

28.9 PARITY

In the developmental world, there are three different types of egg/embryo development. **Oviparity** describes the process of a shell forming around an embryo, which is internally fertilized, then the female immediately (or nearly immediately) depositing it somewhere (i.e., laying it) to complete embryo development and hatch. **Ovoviviparity** is the process of a shell forming around the embryo after it is internally fertilized, then retaining in the female until it hatches, or just before it hatches. **Viviparity** is the process most of us are familiar with, since this is how we develop. A shell does not form around the embryo. The embryo receives its nourishment and performs gas exchange directly from the mother through a structure called the **placenta**. Once fully developed, the embryo is then born. This is the process by which almost all mammals and a few lizards and snakes develop.

28.10 ECTOTHERMS AND ENDOTHERMS

You may know that reptiles are "cold-blooded." Amphibians and fish are also cold blooded. The biological term for this is **ectothermia**; therefore, fish, amphibians, and reptiles are **ectotherms**. Ectotherms do not have a high metabolism rate and are unable to generate their own body heat. They need to rely on their environment in order to maintain proper temperature regulation. This is the reason reptiles "sun" themselves on cooler days or retreat to the shade on hot days.

Mammals and birds, on the other hand, are "warm-blooded." They are **endothermic** and are called **endotherms**. Endotherms have a high metabolic rate. The metabolism of endotherms is so high, in fact, that they generate enough heat to keep themselves warm no matter what the outside temperature (within obvious limits, of course). The main drawback of being endothermic is that it requires a lot of fuel to generate the heat. The fuel comes from the food the organism eats. Endotherms require much more food than ectotherms.

28.11 PEOPLE OF SCIENCE

Archie Carr (1909–1987) was an American Professor of Zoology at the University of Florida. He grew up the son of a Presbyterian minister in Alabama, Texas, and Georgia. He wrote both technical/research papers as well as lay books, such as several books for the *Time-Life* series on reptiles. He was one of the foremost experts on sea turtles.

28.12 KEY CHAPTER POINTS

- A vertebrate is an animal with a dorsal spinal cord protected by a spinal column.

- Evolutionists believe that land-based animals evolved from aquatic animals. Creationists believe all animals were created to occupy whatever environment they currently occupy.

- Vertebrates have tissues which are highly developed into organ systems.

- Agnatha include hagfishes and lampreys.

- Chordata includes many classes with which we are all familiar—Chondrichthyes includes the sharks, rays, and skates; Osteichthyes includes the boney fish; Amphibia includes the amphibians; and Reptilia includes the reptiles.

- There are three different types of embryo development among vertebrates—oviparity, ovoviviparity, and viviparity.

- Ectotherms have a low metabolic rate and do not produce body heat. They are dependent upon their environment to maintain a homeostatic temperature.

- Endotherms have a high metabolic rate and produce their own body heat. They are not dependent upon their environment to maintain a homeostatic temperature.

28.13 DEFINITIONS

albumin (egg white)
Protein and water source for the embryo in an amniotic egg.

allantois
Amniotic egg membrane which stores nitrogenous wastes and exchanges gas from the embryo to the outer air and back.

amniotic egg
The safe environment inside the shell of reptiles and birds, where the embryo is surrounded by water and all of the nutrients it needs before it hatches.

amniotic membrane (amnion)
Structure which encloses the embryo in fluid.

atrium
The chamber that receives the blood returning to the heart.

boney fish
Organisms in the class Osteichthyes.

capillaries
Small blood vessels, often only large enough to let one cell pass through them at one time. The location where gas and nutrient exchange takes place.

chorion
The outer-most membrane of an amniotic egg; it surrounds all other membranes.

deoxygenated blood
Blood returning from the tissues to the heart that contains low concentrations of oxygen and high concentrations of carbon dioxide.

ectothermic
Cold-blooded.

ectotherms
Organisms that are cold-blooded.

endothermic
Warm-blooded.

endotherms
Organisms that are warm-blooded.

hagfishes
A species of jawless fish

internal fertilization
Fertilization that occurs while the egg is still in the female.

Jacobsen's organ
Specialized reptile tissue to sense chemical changes in the environment.

jawless fishes
Organisms in the class Agnatha.

lampreys
A species of jawless fish.

lateral line
A group of nerve cells running down both sides of fish species to collect information from the environment, such as vibration and electrical currents.

left atrium
Receives oxygenated blood returning from the lungs.

nictitating membrane
A clear eyelid that many aquatic species have; it closes when the organism is in the water and protects the eye, but still allows the organism to see.

ossicle
Inner "ear bone."

oviparity
The reproductive condition in which a shell forms around an embryo after it is internally fertilized, then the female immediately deposits the egg containing the embryo to complete development before hatching.

ovoviviparity
The reproductive condition in which a shell forms around the embryo after it is internally fertilized, then is retained in the female until it hatches, or just before it hatches.

oxygenated blood
Blood that has high concentration of oxygen and low concentration of carbon dioxide.

parental care
When one or both parents care for their young in some way.

placenta
Structure through which an embryo receives its nourishment and performs gas exchange directly from the mother.

placoid scales
Special type of scales found on Chondrichthyes organisms.

pulmonary circulation
The circulatory loop to the lungs.

rays
A type of cartilaginous fish.

right atrium
Receives de-oxygenated blood returning from the tissues.

sharks
A type of cartilaginous fish.

skates
A type of cartilaginous fish.

systemic circulation
The circulatory loop to the tissues.

three-chambered heart
Heart that has two atria and one ventricle.

two-chambered heart
Heart with one atrium and one ventricle that is part of a one-loop system.

two-loop system
The type of circulatory system that is present in organisms with lungs.

tympanum (ear drum)
Thin and mobile membrane on the sound organ.

vent
Common opening to eject products of reproductive system and waste from digestive and excretory systems.

ventricle
The muscled chamber that pumps blood out of the heart.

viviparity
The reproductive condition in which a shell does not form around an embryo and live birth is given.

yolk sac
Structure that an embryo is attached to from which the embryo gets nutrition as its cells undergo rapid mitosis.

STUDY QUESTIONS

1. What is the key feature of all of the organisms in Vertebrata?

2. What are some of the problems associated with believing that land animals evolved from water animals? You can also think of some for yourself and bring in some discussion from the earlier chapters on evolution.

3. What is an organ?

4. What is a lateral line? Why is it important?

5. What is the main difference between the classes Chondrichthyes and Osteichthyes?

6. How do the aquatic, non-mammalian vertebrates exchange gasses?

7. What is an atrium in the heart? What is a ventricle?

8. Draw a circulatory system of a boney fish. Be sure to label the structures. Is this a one-loop or two-loop system?

9. What are capillaries specialized to do?

10. What do amphibians have that aquatic species do not have, allowing them to live on land? If evolution were true, can you think of some of the genes which the animals would have had to gain in order to allow them to live on land? Does this seem likely, knowing what we do about mutations?

11. What is a tadpole?

12. Draw the circulatory pattern of a frog. Label the structures. Is this a one-loop or two-loop system?

13. True or False? Some land vertebrates have a one-loop system as adults.

14. Which class has more heart chambers, amphibians or birds?

15. Why does the oxygenated and deoxygenated blood not mix together very much in amphibians?

16. What is a nictitating membrane?

17. Why are amphibians dependent on water, while reptiles are not?

18. Draw a picture and label the structures of an amniotic egg. Why is this an important structure to land-based animals?

19. What is Jacobsen's organ?

20. What does it mean to be oviparous? Ovoviviparous? Viviparous?

21. What is the difference between an endotherm and an ectotherm?

Kingdom Animalia IV

29

29.0 CHAPTER PREVIEW

In this chapter we will:

- Discuss the classification of birds into the phylum Aves.

- Review the evolutionary paradigm that birds evolved from reptiles and the evidence against that occurring.

- Investigate the bird structure and function of feathers and air sacs.

- Discuss the classification of mammals into three classes—Monotremata, Marsupialia, and Placentalia.

- Discuss common mammalian traits.

- Investigate mammalian specializations of:
  - flight
  - aquatic life
  - echolocation
  - brain enlargement

- Introduce human organ systems.

29.1 OVERVIEW

This chapter will focus on the two classes of endotherms, **Aves** (birds) and **Mammalia** (mammals). These are the only two classes made up of endothermic animals. We will cover the basic characteristics of the birds and mammals, as well as explore some of their systems and physiology in depth. It is important to remember there is an awful lot of information concerning these two classes, as there has been with the already discussed mammalian classes. Out of necessity, we cannot go into great detail. However, in the upcoming sections on human anatomy and physiology, we will cover the organ systems in more detail. It is remarkable how similar the functions are of similar organ systems in all multi-cellular organisms.

29.2 PHYLUM CHORDATA: CLASS AVES

Birds comprise over 9,700 species and are the largest single class of Chordata. They live in all environments and are found on every continent. While most birds live life in the air, there are species that are specially adapted to the water (like penguins), and others that cannot fly at all (like ostriches). The study of birds is called **ornithology** and the biologists who study them are called **ornithologists**.

Figure 29.2.1

Aves

Birds are found on every continent and in every environment. Some birds, like the Victoria crowned pigeon (top left) have ornamental feathers. Some make unusual sounds, like the laughing kookaburra (top middle). Penguins do not fly, but are excellent swimmers. Their wings are for steering underwater. Ducks, like the white faced whistling duck (below left) are adapted to water and air. The Waldrap ibis (below middle) is a wading bird that walks through the mud eating buried crustaceans. Many bird species, such as the fairy bluebird, display wide variation in coloration between the male and female birds. The female is shown below. The male is mainly black with a blue tail. However, all birds share the same characteristics of laying amniotic eggs, feathers, a beak, and a light-weight skeleton.

Figure 29.2.2

Characteristics of Birds
All birds have the following characteristics in common

Characteristics	Function
Endothermic	able to maintain constant body temperature of 104°-106°F (40°- 41° C)
Feathers	formed from the protein keratin; specialized for flight, and to conserve body heat (insulation)
Wings	the front limbs are specially adapted for flight
Beak	a toothless beak, although some extinct birds had small teeth
Oviparity	all birds lay hard-shelled, amniotic eggs
Specialized Respiratory System	to meet the high-oxygen requiring demands of flight demands
Light-weight Skeleton	to make flight possible

Figure 29.3.2

Selected Orders of the Twenty-nine of Aves

Order	Example
Anseriformes 160 species	swan, goose, duck
Apodiformes 420 species	hummingbird
Ciconiiformes 120 species	heron, stork, egret
Columbiformes 310 species	dove, pigeon
Falconiformes 310 species	falcon, eagle, vulture
Galliformes 260 species	pheasant, chicken, turkey
Passeriformes 5,700 species	blue jay, wren, cardinal, robin
Piciformes 350 species	woodpecker, toucan
Psittaformes 360 species	parrot, parakeet, cockatoo
Sphenisciformes 17 species	penguin
Strigiformes 180 species	owl
Struthioniformes 13 species	ostrich, emu, kiwi

29.3 BIRD EVOLUTION? ARCHAEOPTERYX AND BIRDS

Evolutionists believe that birds evolved from dinosaurs about 150 million years ago. Because birds evolving from dinosaurs is commonly accepted as "truth," I would like to spend a little time reviewing the information from our evolution and creation chapters specifically concerning this subject. A common misconception that is taught by evolution-based texts is that *Archaeopteryx*, the oldest known bird fossil (supposedly 150 million years old) is a "link" between birds and dinosaurs. It is certainly not. It has no features that are intermediate between dinosaurs and birds. It has entirely bird characteristics.

Archaeopteryx was for many years thought to be a hoax because it *looked* like the perfect intermediate form between dinosaurs and birds. However, it is absolutely not a hoax. It is a real fossil—a real bird fossil. Although it did have teeth, like lizards, that does not make it a dinosaur. Many fossilized birds had teeth, and none of them are proposed by evolutionists to be transitional forms. Also, it has completely developed feathers. As you will see, feathers are an extremely complicated structure and would take a long time to evolve, even in evolutionary time frames. But the feathers of *Archaeopteryx* are **identical** to the feathers of modern day birds. When *Archaeopteryx* appears in the fossil record, it is already completely a bird.

Recall the quote from Dr. Alan Feducia, says of *Archaeopteryx*:

> **"Paleontologists have tried to turn Archaeopteryx into an earth-bound, feathered dinosaur. But it's not. It is a bird, a perching bird. And no amount of 'paleobabble' is going to change that."**

And do not forget the conclusions of the evolutionist society of the *International Archaeopteryx Conference* that *Archaeopteryx* is a bird, not an intermediate form between lizards and birds. Please do not be mislead by evolutionary texts and the media. The leading evolutionary proponent, the late Steven J. Gould, did not believe it was a transitional form. Even in the minds of leading evolutionary advocates, *Archaeopteryx* is not a transitional form. As such, *Archaeopteryx* does not lend any weight to the idea that *Archaeopteryx* evolved from dinosaurs, yet the leading Biology text books continue to teach, and the media continues to state, this as fact. *Archaeopteryx* is a bird, plain and simple, not a link between dinosaurs and birds.

Figure 29.3.3

Archaeopteryx
This is a graphic of one of the known specimens of *Archaeopteryx*. It has fully formed bird feathers, including modern appearing flight feathers. Evolutionists point out that it had teeth, like dinosaurs, and relate that to being evidence that it is an intermediate form between birds and lizards. However, many extinct bird species had teeth; none of them are supposed to be transitional forms between birds and dinosaurs. It seems the only fair conclusion regarding *Archaeopteryx* is what the *International Archaeopteryx Conference* concluded—it is a bird.

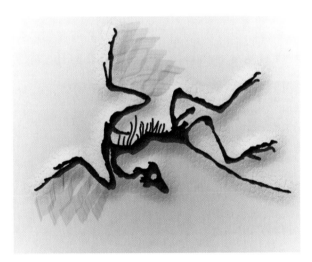

29.4 BIRD EVOLUTION? FEATHERS

Another statement that is pervasive regarding bird evolution is that "a feather is a modified (reptile) scale." But this statement does great disservice to the intricate workings and structure of a feather. Not only are feathers and scales structurally nothing alike, but they are also developmentally nothing alike. The only thing they have in common is they both are made from the protein **keratin**. Hair and fingernails are also made from keratin. Keratin is a useful protein in nature. However, the actual isomer (form) of keratin protein in skin and scales (a-keratins) is not the same isomer in feather proteins (f-keratins). A reptile scale is a little fold in the skin. A bird feather grows from the skin out of a specialized cell called a **follicle**, just like mammal hair does. No evolutionist would consider mammal hair to be a "modified scale," yet evolutionists do state that feathers are a modified scale. Hair and feathers are more structurally similar than scales and feather *and* develop from the same structure (a follicle) but evolutionists do not believe that birds and humans are directly related. Finally, the feather receives its nutrition (blood supply) completely differently than a scale does.

Usually in the evolutionary world, in order to say that a structure on one organism evolved into a structure on another organism, there needs to be some similarity between the two structures. Sometimes the structures are derived from the same embryonic layer, while other times the structures have common blood supplies, or similar overall structures. The problem with the "scale to feather" theory is that there are absolutely no similarities between a reptile scale and a feather. Scales and feathers are nothing alike, but if your belief system dictates that birds did evolve from dinosaurs, then some degree of similarity must be found.

Figure 29.4.1

Feathers
There are several different types of feathers. Some feathers are soft and fluffy; these are called down (upper left). Other feathers are strictly for show and called ornamental, such as the peacock's display. A flight feather is shown below on the left. Note the asymmetrical design, with the leading edge of the feather being shorter than the trailing edge. This is one of the design features of the feather that gives it lift so the bird can fly. Airplane wings are designed in a similar way. On a smaller level, the design of the feather is even more intricate, as shown below right. Barbs extend from the center feather shaft. Each barb has barbules and hooks, which interlink with the barbs and barbules adjacent to them. This allows the feather to be very light but very strong.

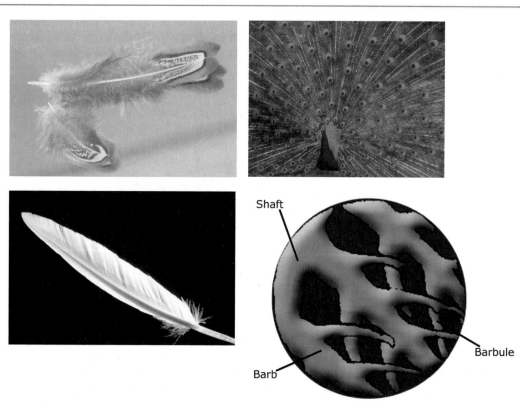

29.5 AVES: CHARACTERISTICS

Now we will move from the highly speculative field of evolution to the facts regarding birds. Birds reproduce sexually through internal fertilization. Once the sperm from the male enters the female, it fertilizes the egg. As the fertilized egg begins to move out of the female, a hard shell is formed around the embryo and other egg tissues. Birds have an amniotic egg, like reptiles. All birds are oviparous.

Once the eggs are laid, the parents begin to show a high degree of parental involvement. A nest is built prior to mating. Birds have a high degree of parental care. All bird species incubate (or keep warm) their eggs continuously until they hatch. Once they hatch, the baby birds are completely dependent on the parents for their nutrition until they are able to fly or walk well enough to get food for themselves.

Because birds are endothermic, they require more food for their body weight than reptiles, amphibians, or fish do. In fact, most endotherms need a fairly continuous supply of energy to continually fuel their metabolism, which is what is responsible for generating constant body heat. Mammals usually store vast quantities of fuel in the form of fat, so even when there are times when there is not a continuous supply of food, mammals are still able to provide a continuous power supply. However, birds do not store much fat, so they are constantly eating to provide more fuel for their endothermic reactions.

An interesting feature of birds that is not found in any other animal species is the presence of **air sacs**. Air sacs are part of the respiratory system of birds and are continuous with the lungs through tube-like connections. They are found in the chest and abdominal cavity. Usually, most bird species have nine air sacs.

Figure 29.5.1

Air Sacs
Most bird species have nine different air sacs in their body. Gas exchange is not performed in the air sacs, though. Air sacs serve two purposes. First, they make the bird lighter, so they can fly with less effort. Second, they provide for a continuous flow of air into the lungs, so the bird can perform gas exchange on inhalation and exhalation. This is necessary to provide enough fresh air to rid the bird's body of CO_2, and supply enough O_2 for the flight muscles.

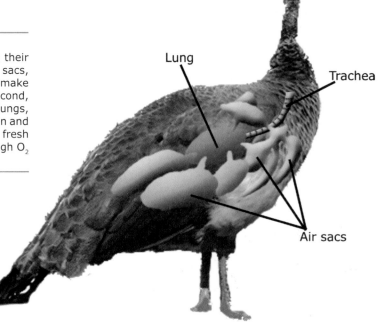

Because birds use a lot of oxygen to fuel their big flight muscles, they need an effective way to obtain the oxygen. This means they breathe in a special way. Air enters into the bird through the nostrils and goes not only into the lungs, but also into the air sacs, filling them. During **inspiration** (breathing in), the lungs extract oxygen and release carbon dioxide while the air sacs are filled with air (**no** gas exchange occurs in the air sacs, as they simply store the air during inspiration). During **exhalation** (breathing out), the air in lungs, now containing carbon dioxide, rushes out of the lungs and is replaced with the air from the air sacs, which still has oxygen in it. This allows the lungs of birds to continually exchange gas, because the lungs are always filled with oxygen-containing air. In addition, air sacs help to significantly reduce the weight of the bird.

Many bird species **migrate** every year. This means they spend part of the year in one location, then move to another location during another time of the year. Typically, species spend the summer in northern climates and the winter in southern climates to exploit the favorable food producing times of the year. There has been a lot of study on the mechanisms used by birds to get where they are going without getting lost. Different bird species use different methods to find their way during migration. Birds have been found to use the stars, the position of the sun, and the earth's magnetic field to help them navigate the route.

Figure 29.5.2

Summary of Characteristics of Aves

Characteristic	
Developmental/ Reproductive	bilaterally symmetric; all species have **wings**, but not all fly; internal fertilization with hard-shelled amniotic egg; significant parental care before the young hatch and after
Neurological	cephalization with coordinating brain and specialized areas of brain function; well-developed brain parts, especially the **cerebellum**, which coordinates flight; spinal cord carries information from/to brain; good vision and hearing
Mobility	fly, swim, or run/walk depending on species
Nutrition/Digestion	complete one-way digestive system; waste exits out through cloaca
Circulatory	complete four-chambered heart (two atria and two ventricles) to prevent mixing of oxygenated and de-oxygenated blood; closed circulatory system; two-loop circulatory system
Respiratory	highly efficient lungs with air sacs
Excretory	kidneys convert ammonia to urea before excreting to conserve water; urea waste exits out cloaca mixed with feces
Skeleton	hollow and light weight bone in all species; many bones are fused together to provide a rigid frame for powerful flight muscles; **keel** is modified breast bone for attachment of the powerful flight muscles

As a note to the above table, wings are a special feature that all species of Aves have. Although all birds have wings, not all birds fly. The wings of birds that do not fly—penguins, ostriches, and emus—are smaller. However, penguin wings are specialized for swimming.

The cerebellum is a specialized part of the brain that is especially large in birds and many mammals (humans included). The cerebellum is the part of the brain which coordinates movements and balance. Flight requires a lot of finely coordinated movements and the bird's cerebellum is specially designed to provide the balance they need while flying.

29.6 PHYLUM CHORDATA: CLASS MAMMALIA

There are over 4,400 species of mammals classified into twenty orders. They are found on every continent as well as in every ocean. Some species are even designed for life in the air. Mammals are divided into three categories, or Sub-classes: **Monotremata**, "the egg laying mammals"; **Marsupialia**, "the pouched mammals"; **Placentalia**, "the placental mammals", which contains over 95% of the mammal species.

Figure 29.6.1

Three Sub-classes of Mammalia with Selected Orders

Sub-class	Orders	Examples
Monotremata Three species	Only one, Monotremata	duck-billed platypus, echidna
Marsupialia 280 species	Seven Orders	kangaroo, wallaby, koala
Placentalia 4,200 species	Twenty Orders, including:	
	Edentata, thirty species	armadillo, sloth
	Primates, 235 species	human, monkey, ape, gorilla, chimpanzee
	Rodentia, two thousand species	rat, mouse, beaver, hamsters, guinea pig
	Lagomorpha, seventy species	rabbit, hare
	Chiroptera, nine hundred species	bat
	Carnivora, 260 species	dog, cat, bear, raccoon, seal
	Perissodactyla, seventeen species	zebra, horse, rhinoceros, tapir
	Artiodactyla, 210 species	deer, goat, sheep, pig, cow, moose, giraffe
	Cetacea, ninety species	whale, dolphin, porpoise
	Hyracoidea, eleven species	hyrax
	Poboscidea, three species	elephant

Figure 29.6.2

Three Orders of Mammals
Monotremes (left) are egg-laying mammals. Marsupials (middle) are pouched mammals. Placental mammals are typified by the American bison. The marsupials and placental mammals are viviparous and monotremes are oviparous.

29.7 MAMMALIA: CHARACTERISTICS

Mammals have characteristics that are common to the class. The functions of specific organ systems will be covered in the human anatomy and physiology section that is coming up, because the functions of the organ systems and the anatomy are similar to all mammals. Notable exceptions will be identified where appropriate. Like birds, mammals are endothermic. Unlike birds, mammals store extra energy in the form of **fat**, which acts as **insulation** (to keep the animal warm) as well as a constant source of energy if food is not plentiful. All mammals have **hair**. Most mammals except humans, aquatic mammals (dolphins, porpoises, whales, dugongs, and manatees) and certain land mammals (rhinos, elephants, and hippos) are covered with a thick coat of hair to further insulate against heat loss. The presence of hair is a defining characteristic of mammals, since all mammals have at least some hair.

Another defining characteristic of mammals is the presence of **mammary glands**. Female mammals provide milk to feed their young through mammary glands. Mammal milk is highly nutritious and contains fats, protein and carbohydrate. Mammals exhibit a high degree of parental care, more so than any other class in Animalia. In the wild, some mammals provide parental care for years before the young go out on their own. The most parental care is seen in humans. Mammals also tend to stay together in family groups.

Figure 29.7.1

Mammary Glands
All mammal mothers have mammary glands to feed their young. The glands produce nutritious milk, which is often the only source of nourishment for the young for two years or more.

All mammals have a completely divided four-chamber heart (two atria and two ventricles) that circulates blood in a two-loop system. In addition, all mammals have a single, lower jaw bone. In reptiles and other vertebrates, the lower jaw bone (the **mandible**) is made of several fused bones. In mammals, the mandible is one single bone that hinges with the skull. In all other vertebrate species, the mandible is formed by the fusion of two or more bones.

Figure 29.7.2

Jaw
Mammal jaws, below right, are formed from one bone. Other species like the shark, below left, are formed from the fusion of one or more bones. If you look in the middle of the lower jaw, you can see a line where the two bones fuse together.

 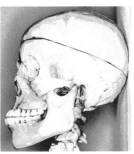

As part of both jaws, mammals have specialized teeth. This means teeth in certain areas of the upper and lower jaw perform certain specific functions. The front teeth (**incisors** and **canines**) are specialized for biting, cutting, and seizing prey. These teeth tend to be thin, or sharp and pointed so they can penetrate food. The teeth toward the side and the back of the jaws are specialized for crushing, grinding, and chewing. These teeth are usually large and flat to provide a surface for smashing the food up. Other animals such as reptiles and fish do not have specialized teeth. Their teeth all look the same.

Figure 29.7.3

Teeth
All mammals have specialized teeth. This means the teeth are shaped differently in different parts of the mouth to reflect their function. Cats have sharp teeth in front and somewhat pointed teeth in the back to help them cut through their meal. Hippos have large, dull teeth to help grab and crush vegetation. Humans have sharp front teeth for cutting and flat back teeth for grinding. Other non-mammal animal species, like crocodiles and the shark from the jaw graphic, have teeth which all look the same and reflect their diets. For example, sharks and crocodiles are meat-eaters that swallow their food nearly whole. They have pointed, sharp teeth to cut through their meal and no flat teeth for chewing.

 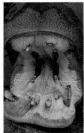 

Notable exceptions to the presence of teeth are the **baleen whales** (blue whales, humpback whales, grey whales, and others). Even though baleen whales are the largest living species on earth, they feed off of microscopic plankton. Since plankton do not really need to be chewed or bitten, the baleen whale does not need teeth to do this.

However, plankton is very small. The baleen functions as a giant filter, extending from the top of the whale's mouth. The whale takes in large mouthfuls of sea water, which contains plankton, then closes its mouth. The water is forced out of the mouth through the porous baleen, but all of the plankton remains trapped in the mouth and is swallowed.

29.8 MAMMALIA: SUB-CLASS MONOTREMATA

Monotremes are the egg-laying mammals; there is one species of platypus and two surviving species of echidnas. Monotremes only live in Australia, New Guinea, and Tasmania. They lay one or two large amniotic eggs with soft, leathery shells and guard the eggs until they hatch. Once they hatch, the young are fed by the mother through the milk from the mammary glands.

Figure 29.8.1

Echidna
The echidna is sometimes called the spiny anteater, as seen in the wild in Australia. Recently the name of spiny anteater has been abandoned to avoid confusion between this animal and the anteater, which is a placental mammal.

29.9 MAMMALIA: SUB-CLASS MARSUPIALIA

The majority of marsupials live in Australia. Kangaroos, bandicoots, wombats, and Tasmanian devils are all marsupials. There are a few species of marsupials in South America, and one which lives in North America (the Virginia opossum). Marsupials and placental mammals do not lay eggs. The female has an organ called the **uterus**, which is where the developing embryo(s) form until they are born. In marsupial species, once internal fertilization occurs, the embryo remains in the uterus and receives nutrition from a type of yolk sac. It emerges from the uterus at an immature stage—baby kangaroos are only about one inch long when they emerge from the uterus—then crawl into the mother's pouch and attach to a nipple, where it will remain for several weeks before moving again.

Figure 29.9.1

Marsupials
All marsupials are born at an immature stage and need to crawl up into the pouch of the mother immediately after they are born. When they are born, baby kangaroos, called joeys, are little more than red blobs of tissue about one centimeter long. They stay in the mother's pouch for nine months before coming out for short periods. A female kangaroo is almost always in a constant state of pregnancy, except for the day she gives birth.

29.10 MAMMALIA: SUB-CLASS PLACENTALIA

The defining characteristic of placental mammals is the way in which their embryos develop. Rather than develop in eggs, or partially develop in the uterus, placental mammals develop entirely in the female uterus. Once internal fertilization occurs in placental mammals, the embryo attaches to the lining of the female uterus. Once attached, a specialized organ called the placenta begins to grow from tissue of both the mother and the embryo(s). The placenta functions to supply the developing baby mammal with nutrients from the mother's blood and exchange gas and wastes for the embryo. When mature, the baby mammal is born first; shortly thereafter, the placenta is discharged from the uterus (called the **afterbirth**). All species of mammals show a high degree of parental care, sometimes lasting many years.

Figure 29.10.1

Placental Mammals
Humpback whales, elephants, camels, grizzly bears, and humans are placental mammals.

29.11 PLACENTALIA: SPECIALIZATIONS, AIR

Many species exhibit specialized adaptations to their environments. We will explore some of the specific adaptations not covered above.

Bats, order Chiroptera, are the only mammals that can fly, but they are extremely successful at it. They are placental mammals. There are over nine hundred species of bats, and they are found everywhere except in polar environments. They have a specialized forelimb with elongated wrist and finger bones. Between the elongated bones is a membrane that attaches to the body. The elongated membrane allows the bat to fly, and they are exceptional fliers. Generally, bats are further subdivided into the large bats, macrobats; and the small bats, microbats. The macrobats, like the fruit bat, eat fruit; the microbats are carnivorous (insects or small animals) or feed on blood (vampire bats).

Figure 29.11.1

Micro and Macro Bats
The vampire bat, left, is an example of a micro bat. The fruit bat, right, is an example of a macro bat. Bats are the only mammal species that can fly.

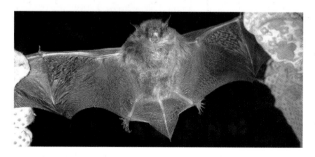

29.12 SPECIALIZATIONS: WATER

There are several different orders of mammals that live in the water. Some, such as seals, sea lions, beavers, and otters, are part aquatic and part terrestrial. These types of animals rely heavily on water for food and protection, but they are able to move around on land. They have modifications of the feet that include membranes between their toes. This fashions the feet into a paddle, improves their ability to swim more effectively, and does not hinder them too much on land. Some, like the otter, walk and run quite effectively on land. Others, like the beaver, lumber slowly, but effectively, and get where they need to go. The walruses, seals, and sea lions, however, move poorly on the land, but use the land for breeding purposes. Seals, sea lions, and walruses do not move well on land because they have flippers for all four appendages, rather than legs. This adaptation makes them effective swimmers, but poor walkers. Some aquatic mammals, like the dolphins and whales, cannot leave the water at all.

It is interesting to note at this point that evolutionists believe aquatic mammals evolved from the land mammals. This notion does not hold with the theory of evolution, as we discussed earlier. A major move in evolutionary thinking was the move from water to land. If evolution is a continual process in which the drive is to improve the species, then the move back to the water is considered de-evolution. Moving back into water would require that the traits these organisms had spent millions of years acquiring to move onto land be lost so they can return to the water. This would be similar to birds losing their wings. That type of "backward evolution" is not consistent with evolutionary theory.

Figure 29.12.1

Water Designs for Land Mammals
Some mammals spend a lot of time in the water, but do not live there full time. Mammals like the beaver, left, and the sea lion, right, exhibit special features for aquatic life. They have streamlined bodies to move easily in the water. They have special features to help them navigate the water more effectively, like the beaver's large paddle-like tail and the flippers of the sea lion.

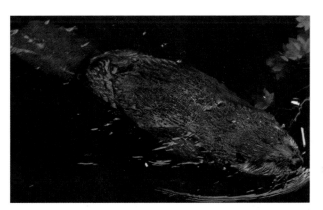

We will now focus on those species that are exclusively aquatic—**Cetacea** (whales, dolphins, porpoises) and **Sirenia** (manatees, dugongs)—and examine the adaptations that have allowed them to remain exclusively in the water (meaning they never come up on land). There are several similarities in the body structure between cetaceans and sirens that have made aquatic life possible.

Remember that aquatic mammals do not perform respiration through gills (they don't have gills) but through lungs. All mammals have lungs, so all aquatic mammals have lungs. That means they need to surface from time to time to breathe air. Cetaceans and sirens have extremely large lungs to hold a large quantity of air. Their tissues are specialized to extract the maximum amount of oxygen. This allows some aquatic mammals to remain underwater for several hours at a time.

One of the first structural differences that is noted between terrestrial and aquatic mammals is the appendages, or "arms and legs." The front legs of all aquatic mammals are modified into a paddle, called a flipper. This retains the same basic structure of bones that is almost always found in all mammal species: one upper arm bone (the **humerus**), two forearm bones (**radius** and **ulna**), several wrist and hand bones (**carpals** and **metacarpals**, respectively) and, usually, five "finger" bones (the **phalanges**). However, they have skin covering the entire area, which allows the appendage to function effectively as a paddle.

The "legs" of aquatic mammals are noticeably absent. They do have legs, but they are small structures that are contained in the pelvis of the animal, around the urinary bladder and sex organs. Evolutionists like to state that the "legs" of cetaceans and sirens are vestigial and have no function. However, further research has found the legs do have function—they support the sexual organs during mating and birth.

It is a common misconception that the legs of aquatic mammals make up the tail; they do not. The tail of cetaceans and sirens does not contain any bone at all, but rather tough, fibrous tissue and muscles. Generally, the term "tail" refers to a structure that has bones in it, so the "tail" of aquatic mammals is properly called a **fluke**. The movement of a mammal's flukes is distinctly different than that of a fish. The fluke moves up and down, while fish tails move left and right.

Figure 29.12.2

Tails and Flukes
It is a common misconception that the tails of aquatic mammals are the legs. Tails of aquatic mammals are properly called flukes. Flukes do not have any bones in them; tails do. Also, note a big difference between a tail of a fish and the fluke of a mammal. The fluke—seen on a humpback on the left and a manatee in the middle—is oriented horizontally. The tail of a shark and all other fishes is oriented vertically.

The cetaceans have a further adaptation to life in the water. The sirens breathe through nostrils, but the opening of the cetacean's airway to the outside world is through the **blow hole** on top of the head. Again, from a genetic standpoint, think of the genetic information which needed to be gained to change the position of the nose from the face to the back of the head.

Figure 29.12.3

Blow Hole
All cetaceans have a blowhole on the top of their head through which they breathe. Sirens breathe through their noses.

29.13 SPECIALIZATIONS: ECHOLOCATION

Echolocation is the use of sound waves to detect or locate objects in their environment. The only mammal species to use this are the organisms in Cetacean and Chiroptera Orders. Specifically, whales, dolphins, porpoises, and microbats use echolocation. The sirens and the larger bat species do not. There are also two bird species that use echolocation. Although the process of echolocation is rather simple to understand, the animal's ability to detect objects is unbelievable. The animal emits a sound or series of sounds, which strike any object in the path of the emitted sounds. The sounds then bounce off the object(s) and return to the animal. The returning sounds are picked up and processed in the brain. This allows the animal to form images of what is in front of them before they get there. Some bat species are able to detect a wire 0.08 mm in diameter (about the size of human hair).

29.14 SPECIALIZATIONS: BRAIN

A final adaptation is more of a general one, that being the physical size and thinking ability of the mammalian brain. A mammal's brain is about fifteen times larger than a comparative non-mammal organism of the same size. The area of the brain that is expanded most in size in mammals is the **cerebrum**. The cerebrum has many functions, but one of the most important is that it is that part of the brain that thinks and solves problems. All mammals have a great ability to solve problems, with humans being superior in that regard. Humans have the largest brain for their body size than any other organism in Animalia.

Figure 29.14.1

Summary of Characteristics of Mammalia

Characteristic	
Developmental/ Reproductive	bilaterally symmetric; adapted to all environments (sea, land, and air); significant parental care before the young are born and after; three types of reproductive patterns—eggs (monotremes), viviparous with immature birth and further development in pouches (marsupials), and viviparous with full term birth (placental mammals); marsupials and placental female mammals have a special organ called the uterus for embryo development
Neurological	cephalization with coordinating brain and specialized areas of brain function; well-developed brain parts; spinal cord carries information from/to brain; good vision and hearing; some species have echolocation
Mobility	fly, swim, run, walk
Nutrition/Digestion	complete one-way digestive system; waste exits through anus; many grazing animals (the **ungulates**, or hoofed mammals, like cows, horses, deer, goats) and others, like the rabbit, are able to break down cellulose because of symbiotic bacteria that live in the gut that are able to break the cell walls of the cellulose down; once broken down, the energy in the cellulose is available to the organism; carnivores and omnivores are unable to break cellulose down
Circulatory	complete four-chambered heart (two atria and two ventricles) to prevent mixing of oxygenated and de-oxygenated blood; closed circulatory system
Respiratory	highly efficient lungs with large surface area due to the presence of microscopic air pockets in the lungs called **alveoli**
Excretory	kidneys convert ammonia to urea before excreting to conserve water; urea waste exits out separate excretory opening usually called **urethra**
Skeleton	bone

29.15 INTRODUCTION TO HUMAN SYSTEMS

We have now completed the overview of Animalia with a brief look at specialized adaptations of the organisms that constitute the majority of all classified animal species. We have also looked in some minor detail at the tissue and organ systems of animals. In the next chapters, we will be focusing in more detail on the human organ systems listed in the following table. Although we are specifically discussing humans, the function (**physiology**) and structure (**anatomy**) of the organ systems is remarkably similar across the mammalian species.

Figure 29.15.1

Human Organ Systems, Basic Anatomy and Physiology Discussed in the Upcoming Chapters

System	Function and Components
Excretory	**functions** to remove metabolic wastes from the tissues, usually ammonia; **components**: kidney, ureters, urinary bladder, urethra
Neurologic	**functions** to think and coordinate the activity, movement, and responses; **components**: brain is connected to the hollow dorsal spinal cord, which carries signals to/from the brain from/to the rest of the organism; spinal nerves carry impulses to/from the spinal cord from/to the tissues and cells
Endocrine	**functions** as a chemical communicator (through the actions of hormones) from one tissue to another, usually far away; **components**: brain, adrenal glands, thyroid gland, testes/ovaries, parathyroid glands, pancreas
Immune	**functions** to protect from infections; **components**: lymph tissue, antibodies, immune cells, thymus gland
Circulatory	**functions** to carry oxygen and nutrients in the blood to the tissues and carbon dioxide and waste from the tissues for removal from the body; **components**: heart and blood vessels to carry the blood; vessels include arteries (carry blood away from the heart), capillaries (tiny vessels; the site of gas and nutrient/waste exchange in the tissues and lungs) and veins (carry blood to the heart)
Respiratory	**functions** to bring oxygen into the blood and remove carbon dioxide from the blood; **components**: nose, trachea, bronchi, lungs
Digestive	**functions** to obtain, process, and absorb nutrients as well as eliminate waste; **components**: mouth, pharynx ("throat"), esophagus, stomach, small intestine, large intestine, anus, liver, and pancreas
Musculoskeletal and Connective Tissue	**functions** for support, attaching bones to bones/muscle to bone and movement; **components**: blood, bone, ligament, cartilage, tendons, muscles

29.16 PEOPLE OF SCIENCE

John Audubon (1785–1851) was an American biologist and painter born in Haiti and raised in France. He came to the United States in 1803. He became especially fond of birds and was the foremost American ornithologist of his time. He was the first person to band birds and found that the first species of bird he banded, the Eastern Phoebes, returned to the same place year after year. He was the first person to shoot a bird with fine shot, then stuff and mount it so it could be accurately painted and set true to life in their natural habitat. He published several large books, notably *Birds of America*. In 1896, a nature conservancy society was founded and named in his honor, the National Audubon Society. It is one of the oldest societies of its kind. It continues to publish an illustrated magazine, *Audubon*.

29.17 KEY CHAPTER POINTS

- This chapter focuses on the classes Aves (birds) and Mammalia (mammals).

- The study of birds is called ornithology.

- Archaeopteryx is not a transitional form between birds and dinosaurs. It is a bird.

- Feathers could not possibly have evolved from scales because there is nothing similar about scales and feathers.

- Birds have: amniotic eggs; high parental behavior; light-weight skeleton designs; wings; large cerebellum to coordinate flight. They are also all endothermic.

- Mammals are divided into egg-laying mammals (Order Monotremata), pouched mammals (Order Marsupialia), and placental mammals (Order Placentalia).

- Mammals have: mammary glands; hair; extra energy stored as fat; a single lower jaw bone; specialized teeth; high degree of parental care.

- Many mammal species have specialized adaptations: wings, fins, blow holes, echolocation, and large brains.

29.18 DEFINITIONS

afterbirth
   The placenta after it is discharged from the uterus.

air sacs
   Part of the respiratory system of birds that are continuous with the lungs through tube-like connections and provide a constant supply of fresh air to the lungs.

alveoli
   Microscopic air pockets in the lungs where gas exchange occurs.

anatomy
   Structure of the organ systems.

Aves
   Order of Animalia that includes birds.

baleen whales
   Whales that do not have teeth.

blow hole
   The opening of a cetacean's airway.

carpals
   Wrist bones.

cerebellum
   The part of the brain that coordinates movements.

cerebrum
   The area of the brain that thinks and solves problems.

exhalation
   Breathing out.

fluke
   The tail of aquatic mammals.

follicle
   Specialized cell from which a bird feather and mammal hair grows.

hair
   Specialized structure made of keratin which grows from a follicle in mammals.

humerus
   Upper arm bone.

inspiration
   Breathing in.

insulation
   A structure that keeps heat in, such as downy feathers on a bird, or fat and hair on a mammal.

keel
   Modified breast bone for attachment of the powerful flight muscles.

keratin
   Protein that makes up hair, fingernails, feathers, and reptile scales.

Mammalia
   Animalia class which includes animals that are covered with hair and have mammary glands.

mammary glands
Glands whose function is to provide milk to feed the young.

mandible
Lower jaw bone.

Marsupialia
Animalia sub-class that includes the pouched mammals.

metacarpals
Hand bones.

migrate
Spend part of the year in one location, then move to another location during another time of the year.

Monotremata
Mammalian sub-class that includes egg-laying mammals.

ornithologists
Biologists who study birds.

ornithology
The study of birds.

phalanges
Finger bones.

physiology
Function of the organ systems.

Placentalia
Animalia sub-class that placental mammals.

radius
One of the two forearm bones.

ulna
One of the two forearm bone.

ungulates
Hoofed mammals.

urethra
Excretory opening which urea waste exits.

uterus
Mammalian female organ where the developing embryo forms until birth.

wings
A specialized structured for flight.

STUDY QUESTIONS

1. What is an ornithologist?

2. What are two characteristics of the organisms of Aves that no other species on earth has?

3. Why do you think evolutionists have persisted to state birds evolved from reptiles (dinosaurs), even though the evidence does not support it?

4. What are air sacs and why are they important to birds? How do air sacs function?

5. True or False? Birds, reptiles and some mammals lay amniotic eggs.

6. What mechanisms do birds use to find their way during migration?

7. True or False? Birds show a high degree of cephalization with a large cerebellum.

8. What is a keel?

9. List at least two bird features that make them light.

10. What is the main difference between the organisms of Monotremata, Marsupialia, and Placentalia?

11. True or False? All mammals have a four-chambered heart with a two-loop circulatory system.

12. True or False? Some mammals do not have a vertebral column but most do.

13. True of False? All mammals feed their young through mammary glands.

14. True or False? Most mammals have a single, lower jaw bone called a mandible, but not all.

15. True or False? Aquatic mammals use gills to exchange gasses.

16. True or False? The tails of aquatic mammals contain bones for the muscles to attach.

17. Why do aquatic mammals represent a potential problem for evolutionists?

18. True or False? Legs of aquatic mammals have been reduced to vestigial structures with no function as a result of evolution.

19. What is echolocation? What mammalian orders are capable of echolocation?

20. What is the area of the brain that has expanded the most in mammals as compared to other species? What is the function of this area of the brain?

21. What is an ungulate?

22. True or False? All mammals are viviparous.

23. True or False? Human organ systems function significantly different than those of other mammals.

PLEASE TAKE TEST #12 IN TEST BOOKLET

Human Anatomy and Physiology I

Nervous System & Special Senses

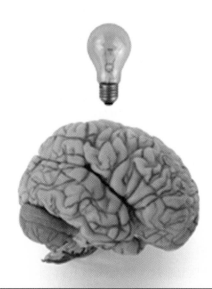

30

30.0 CHAPTER PREVIEW

In this chapter we will:

- Describe the anatomy and physiology of the nervous system, with attention to:
  - the individual nerve cell (neuron)
  - the neuron's ability to generate and conduct an electrical impulse
  - neurotransmitters
  - the central nervous system
  - the peripheral nervous system
  - the autonomic nervous system

- Describe the anatomy and physiology of vision, hearing, taste and smell.

30.1 OVERVIEW

We will begin the discussion of human biology realizing that humans are unique among the species of Animalia. We are the only species wired to walk on two legs instead of four. We are also the only species to exhibit fully developed functions of an enlarged brain. High level problem solving, intricate forms of language, the ability to think into the future, and complex social structures are all made possible by our enlarged brains. However, humans are eukaryotic organisms, so our cells contain many of the same organelles as a rabbit or yeast. The way our organ systems function is similar to other mammals, so we can use the human structure and form as a template for how most mammalian systems operate.

In this and upcoming chapters, we will be discussing human anatomy and physiology. Anatomy is the structure of living things; physiology is how the anatomy works. However, the basic concepts of how the systems work and what their structures are hold true whether we are discussing people, rabbits, monkeys, or elephants. For example, when any animal ingests food, the pancreas is stimulated to release a hormone called insulin. The insulin tells the cells what to do with the glucose that is being absorbed from the intestines. This happens whether the animal is a human or a pig. The same is true for many of the topics we are going to discuss. Although we are discussing human anatomy and physiology, the structures and processes are similar across all mammalian species.

30.2 NERVOUS SYSTEM: GENERAL

The nervous system is a complicated network of cells functioning to sense changes in the environment and transmit the information to the brain. Once the information is received by the brain, the nervous system coordinates how the organism responds to the information. All nervous systems are highly complex systems, even those found in the "simple" jellyfish. However, no nervous system is as complex as the human brain, spinal cord, and peripheral nerves.

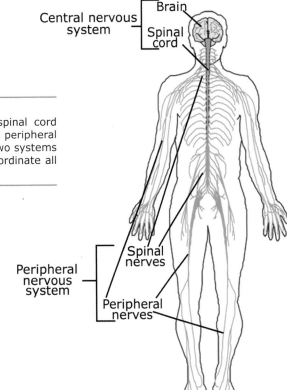

Figure 30.2.1

Nervous System Anatomy
The components of the nervous system are the brain and spinal cord (referred to as the central nervous system); and the spinal and peripheral nerves (referred to as the peripheral nervous system). These two systems interact with one another thousands of times per second to coordinate all bodily activities, actions, thoughts, etc..

Figure 30.2.2

Function of the Nervous System Components

Component	Function
Brain	"super controller"—controls every aspect of the body—homeostasis, movements, thought, behavior, etc.
Spinal cord	brings signals to the brain from the body and carries signals from the brain to the rest of the body
Peripheral nerves	carry signals from the spinal cord to the body and from the body to the spinal cord
Eyes	receive visual information, which is transmitted to the brain for processing by the optic nerve
Ears	receives auditory information (sound) which is transmitted to the brain for processing by the acoustic nerve
Nose	receives olfactory (smell) information which is transmitted to the brain for processing by the olfactory nerve
Tongue	receives gustatory (taste) information which is transmitted to the brain by the facial and glossopharyngeal nerves

30.3 NERVOUS SYSTEM: NERVE CELLS AND TISSUES

Electricity can be generated in two generic ways—flow of electrons and flow of ions. The electricity we use every day is generated by flowing electrons. The nervous system uses electricity generated by the flow of ions to communicate to other nerves and other parts of the body. Nervous tissue contains cells that receive and send messages, called **impulses**, to one another by using "chemical" electricity. These cells are called **neurons**. Neurons make up all of the transmitting tissue in the brain, spinal cord, and peripheral nerves. **Glial cells** (called **astrocytes**) are also part of the nervous system. They are the supporting cells that hold the neurons and neural tissue together.

Figure 30.3.1

Cells of the Nervous System

Cell	Function
Neuron	transmits electrical impulses
Glial cell	provide support for neurons and hold them together

There are more than 100 billion neurons in the human brain. They are highly specialized cells, as can be seen from the figure. The neuron is composed of a central portion, called the **cell body**, which has many projections extending out from it. The cell body is where the nucleus is located and where all the proteins are made for the cell. As can be seen from the figure, there are numerous projections from the cell body. The one largest projection is called the **axon**. It is responsible for carrying all impulses and information away from (or out of) the nerve cell. Axons of some neurons are coated with a layer, or **sheath**, of fat called **myelin**. Not all axons have myelin, but many do. Myelin provides insulation to the nerve, not to keep it warm, but to increase the speed that the axon can transmit impulses. Myelin is formed along the length of the nerve in units. The coat of myelin is not continuous, but occurs with small gaps from one unit of myelin to the next. These small gaps are called **nodes of Ranvier** and are important to the upcoming discussion on nerve conductance. The other and more numerous projections on the cell body are called **dendrites**. Dendrites are responsible for bringing electrical impulses and information toward (or into) the neuron.

Figure 30.3.2

General Neuron Structure

An individual nerve cell is called a neuron. A neuron is made up of the cell body, which houses the nucleus and organelles. Dendrites are extensions of the cell body that bring information into the neuron. Each neuron has many, sometimes hundreds, of dendrites. Dendrites collect information from other neurons and from sensory organs, such as the skin, and transmit this information to the cell body. There is only one extension that carries information away from the neuron. This is called the axon. Many neurons have axons that are covered in a coating of fat called myelin, or myelin sheath. Myelin greatly increases the speed at which nerve impulses travel. Myelin forms in organized blobs over the length of the axon. There is a small space, called a node of Ranvier, in between each blob. The axon ends in many little endings called the brush. The brush allows the axon of one neuron to communicate with dendrites of many other axons.

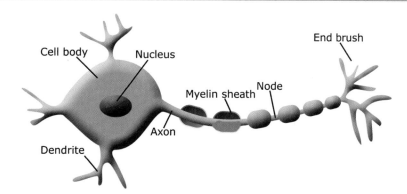

Inside of the cell body are the nucleus and the other organelles responsible for generating the ATP and proteins the neuron needs. The cell body makes all of the proteins, ATP, and other substances the neuron needs to function properly. Once the substances are made in the cell body, they are transported wherever they are needed on the cell.

There are three basic types of nerves: **sensory neurons** (they make you "feel, taste, see, smell, or hear" something), **motor neurons** (they make you move, or contract your muscles), and **interneurons** (they transmit impulses from one nerve to another, kind of a neurological go-between). Sensory neurons are responsible for transmitting impulses from the body and environment to the brain. The body and the environment are called the **periphery**. The spinal cord and brain are considered **central**. The brain and spinal cord are referred to as the **central nervous system** (CNS). The sensory and motor nerves in the body and arms and legs are referred to as the **peripheral nervous system** (PNS).

Sensory impulses originate in the periphery—the eyes for sight, the nose for smell, the ears for hearing, the tongue for taste, and the skin for touch, temperature, and pain—then are transmitted by the sensory nerve to the brain. For sensations that come from the head and face structures—skin, eyes, ears, and tongue—the sensory nerves generally bring the information directly to the brain. For sensory information that comes from structures below the head—neck, arms, legs, and body—the information is first brought to the spinal cord through the sensory nerve, then transmitted to the brain via the spinal cord.

In order for a sensory nerve to generate an impulse, the dendrites of the sensory nerve need to be stimulated. The event that causes a sensory nerve to generate an impulse is called the **stimulus**. If a sensory nerve is one that senses pain, then a painful stimulus will generate an impulse. If the sensory nerve is one that senses smell, then the nerve will generate an impulse when it is exposed to smells. If the nerve is one that senses cold, then cold will stimulate the nerve to generate an impulse. You get the picture. The stimulus is sensed, or "picked up," by the dendrites of the sensory nerve. Once the dendrites are stimulated, the impulse is carried to the cell body, then into the axon. It is then taken by the sensory axon to the brain or spinal cord. Remember sensory dendrites receive information from the periphery (skin, eyes, ears, etc.) and sensory axons carry the information to the brain through the spinal cord.

While the impulses for the sensory nerves originate in the periphery of the body, the impulses for motor nerves originate in the brain, or centrally. Let's say you are holding a ball and want to throw it. The signal telling your arm to throw the ball originates in the brain. From the brain, the impulse travels down the axon of the motor neuron and ends up at the proper muscles. Once the impulse reaches the proper muscles, they contract in a coordinated fashion and the ball is thrown. Remember motor dendrites receive information from the brain and motor axons carry information to the muscles through the spinal cord.

A "nerve" as we think of it, is actually not one neuron, but groups of neurons contained in a common bundle of motor and sensory nerves, all held together by connective tissue. Your "funny bone," or "crazy bone," at the elbow is actually the ulnar nerve. This nerve typifies all of the other nerves in the body in that it is made up of many sensory nerves (as evidenced by the pain, numbness, and tingling that shoots down your arm into your hand when you bang your funny bone) and many motor nerves all grouped together in a common bundle. There are many such nerves in the human body, and this type of grouping of motor and sensory neurons into bundles called nerves is common in vertebrate species.

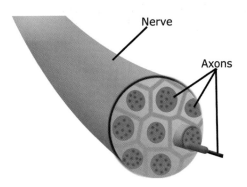

Nerve

Axons

Figure 30.3.3

Peripheral Nerve Anatomy
A "nerve" is made up of many individual neuron axons bound together. For example, your "funny bone" is really a nerve, called the ulnar nerve, which is close to the surface in the elbow area. It is easy to bump this nerve and get a little shock down the arm into the fourth and fifth digits. The ulnar nerve is a typical peripheral nerve made up of several hundred axons all wrapped together in a common covering. Peripheral nerves have many small groups of axons wound together in small bundles within the larger peripheral nerve.

30.4 NERVE PHYSIOLOGY: GENERAL

The way that a neuron works is actually quite fascinating. Motor, sensory, and interneurons all conduct the impulse the same way. When a neuron is at rest, it is **polarized**. This means the fluid outside the neuron has a different electrical charge than the fluid inside the neuron. Our nerves need appropriate ion concentrations to maintain the proper electrical charge across the neuron membrane. At rest, inside the neuron membrane potassium ions (K^+) are in high concentration while the outside of the neuron membrane sodium ions (Na^+) are in high concentration. This results in the inside of the cell being negatively charged as compared to the outside. As seen in the figure, this leads to a difference in electrical charge, called the **resting potential**. For most nerves, the resting potential is -70 mV (millivolts, a measure of electrical charge). Even though sodium and potassium are both positively charged ions, sodium has a stronger positive charge than potassium. There are many more sodium ions outside the cell membrane than there are inside the cell membrane. This means there are more positive charges outside the cell membrane than there are on the inside of the cell membrane. In fact, there is a relative charge difference of -70 mV of the inside of the cell as compared to the outside. The neuron is more negatively charged on the inside than it is on the outside. Also, there are many types of large and negatively charged ions inside the cell that help contribute to the negative charge of the interior of the neuron at rest.

Figure 30.4.1

Nerve at Rest

Our nerves communicate with each other and with our muscles using chemical electricity. At rest, there is a small charge across the membrane of every nerve in our body equal to about -70 millivolts (the negative means that the interior of the cell is negatively charged as compared to the exterior of the cell). The interior of the nerve is kept in a negative charge through the action of the sodium-potassium-ATP pump. Figure (a) shows the neuron membrane with a transmembrane protein pump called the sodium-potassium-ATP pump. Maintaining the resting negative charge of the neuron requires the cell to use ATP to pump sodium out of the cell and potassium into the cell. Even though potassium and sodium are both positively charged ions, sodium is more positive than potassium. Because of the constant out-pumping of sodium and in-pumping of potassium, sodium builds up on the outside of the cell membrane. Since more sodium is outside of the cell than inside of the cell, the outside of the cell has a higher positive charge than the inside. Another way of stating that is the inside of the cell has more negative charge than the outside of the cell. In addition, there are other negatively charged ions that build up on the inside of the cell; these contribute to the overall negative resting charge of the nerve cell membrane. Figure (b) shows a common way to portray the resting membrane potential of the nerve.

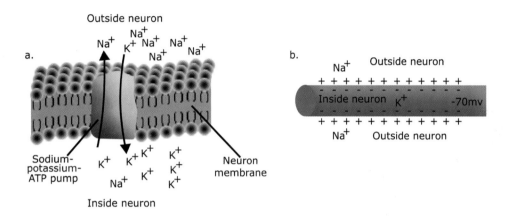

Since the cell must maintain the concentrations of sodium and potassium against the gradient, this process requires energy expenditure. The way the axon maintains the concentrations of sodium and potassium is through the actions of a transmembrane pump (an integral protein). This pump is called the **NA-K-ATP pump**, or sodium-potassium-ATP pump. It is called this because this membrane protein pumps sodium and potassium against their concentration gradients. Recall from earlier in the year that this requires energy. Energy is supplied in the form of ATP. The pump "pumps" sodium out of the nerve and potassium into the nerve.

30.5 NERVE PHYSIOLOGY: DEPOLARIZATION AND REPOLARIZATION

In order for the neuron to conduct an impulse, the electrical charge of the nerve changes. The charge of the nerve changes because the permeability of the nerve membrane changes. When a stimulus causes a nerve to conduct an impulse, the membrane quickly becomes permeable to sodium ions and relatively impermeable to potassium ions. Once the membrane becomes permeable to sodium, the positively-charged sodium ions are attracted to the negatively-charged interior of the cell and rapidly cross the cell membrane into the cell. As the sodium rushes into the cell, the polarity of that small segment of the neuron is changed so that the interior is now positively charged and the exterior is negatively charged. The membrane in that small area is now said to be **depolarized**. This process occurs in a wave down the entire length of the neuron and is called **depolarization**. The nerve membrane depolarizing as a wave is what generates the conductance of the neuron impulse. The movement of depolarization along the nerve membrane, or depolarization event, is called the **action potential**. Some define an action potential as a wave of depolarization down a neuron.

Once a given area of the membrane has depolarized, the sodium gates close and the membrane quickly becomes impermeable again to sodium. The Na-K-ATP pump actively pumps sodium out of the cell and potassium into the cell, which restores the resting membrane potential to the neuron. This process is called **repolarization**.

Like depolarization, repolarization occurs in a wave along the length of the neuron, closely following behind the wave of depolarization. The whole event of depolarization-repolarization takes less than five milliseconds (five one-thousandths of a second).

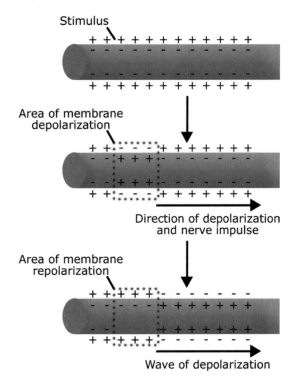

Stimulus

Area of membrane depolarization

Direction of depolarization and nerve impulse

Area of membrane repolarization

Wave of depolarization

Figure 30.5.1

Nerve Depolarization
The nerve at rest is shown on the top of the graphic. In order for a nerve to transmit an electrical impulse, the threshold must be reached. Once the threshold is reached, the nerve will conduct an impulse. For example, let's say the nerve shown below is a nerve that senses cold. As you move an ice cube closer to your hand, at first you do not feel the cold. This is because the threshold of the nerve has not been reached because the stimulus—the cold of the ice—is not strong enough. When the ice gets closer and the threshold has been reached, the nerve begins to fire an impulse. This means the ice has gotten close enough to your skin to cause the nerve to sense that it is a cold object, and it fires. Once the threshold has been reached, the nerve generates an impulse. The Na-K-ATP pump momentarily shuts off which allows sodium to flow into the cell and potassium out of the cell. The interior of the cell rapidly becomes positive as the sodium flows inward and the potassium outward. This change in the membrane charge is called depolarization. In a wave traveling down the neuron, the Na-K-ATP pumps all along the length of the nerve temporarily shut off, conducting an electrical impulse down the length of the nerve, as shown in the middle of the figure. As soon as any given area of the neuron depolarizes, the Na-K-ATP pump turns back on and pumps the sodium out of the cell and potassium into the cell to re-establish the normal resting state. Re-establishing the normal resting potential of -70 millivolts is called repolarization. It occurs in a wave down the length of the nerve just as depolarization does. As the wave of depolarization proceeds down the nerve, a wave of repolarization follows closely behind it.

A kind of neat thing is to think about this in practical terms. When you breathe, the impulse to do so originates in the brain. The impulse travels from the brain down the phrenic nerve to the diaphragm, telling the diaphragm muscle to contract. This makes you take a breath. Another way of looking at this is that every time you breathe, your phrenic nerve has to depolarize and repolarize to conduct the impulse to the diaphragm. If we figure that an average person, throughout their life, breathes twenty times per minute, then a person who lives to be eighty will have undergone 840,960,000 separate depolarization-repolarization events of the phrenic nerve, without fail.

30.6 NERVE PHYSIOLOGY: ALL OR NONE

A rather interesting feature about the depolarization of a neuron is that not all stimuli generate neuron depolarization and the formation of an action potential. Some stimuli are too weak to generate any response at all. For example, there are plenty of soft sounds that exist that you cannot hear. This is because they are not strong enough to cause the nerve for hearing (the acoustic nerve) to depolarize. In addition, there is some minimal strength stimulus that will generate a response. This is called the **threshold stimulus**. Threshold stimuli differ from person to person and nerve to nerve, but for any given nerve the threshold is the same. Once the threshold stimulus is reached, the nerve will depolarize and generate an action potential. No matter how strong, the nerve will depolarize and generate an action potential as long as it is above the threshold. This concept is referred to as the **all-or-none response**. Either a nerve "fires" or it does not. Either an impulse is sent or it is not.

If you were to be asked a question on a test like, "A person is touched lightly on the arm, but does not sense they have been touched. Why?" A reasonable answer is to say, "Because the threshold was not reached, therefore the nerve did not depolarize. Because the nerve did not depolarize, no message was sent to the brain that they were touched. This means the person could not sense they were touched because the proper sensory nerves did not fire (or conduct the impulse)".

30.7 NERVE PHYSIOLOGY: SALTATORY CONDUCTION

Myelinated axons (axons with myelin) are able to conduct electrical impulses much more quickly than unmyelinated axons. This is because myelin is such a good insulator that it does not allow sodium and potassium to move in and out of the cell where the myelin is wrapped around the neuron. Therefore, in order to conduct the impulse, electrical impulses "jump" from one node of Ranvier to another down the length of the neuron. This is called **saltatory conduction** (salutatory means to jump). Saltatory conduction results in much faster conduction speed because the nerve does not need to depolarize along its entire length, but only at the nodes. All motor neuron axons are myelinated, as are many sensory axons. This is the reason that our brain can communicate so quickly with the muscles.

30.8 NERVE PHYSIOLOGY: BRUSH

How exactly do nerves communicate with one another? As was shown in the figure of the structure of the neuron, the axon ends as a branched structure called the **brush**. The function of the brush is to transmit the impulses from the axon of one neuron to the dendrites of another neuron. This is not done directly, but through the use of **neurotransmitters**. Neurotransmitters are chemicals which nerves use to communicate signals to one another.

Figure 30.8.1

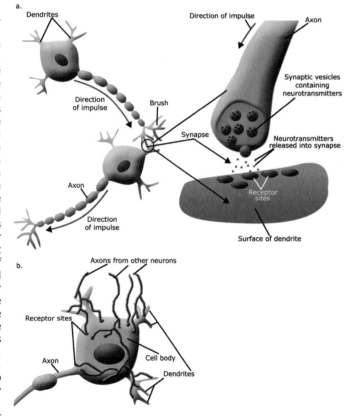

Neurotransmitters
The synapse is where the axon brush of one nerve comes into contact with dendrites of another nerve, another nerve cell body, or a muscle cell. However, the brush does not physically touch the dendrites, nerve cell bodies, or muscles. There is a small gap between them, and this gap is called the synapse. Nerves use neurotransmitters to communicate across the synapse. Neurotransmitters are chemicals released by neurons into a synapse. A typical synapse is seen in the top left of the graphic with the axon brush ending on some dendrites. However, as is seen in figure (b), there are a number of ways nerves can communicate with one another. Sometimes the axons end at dendrites and sometimes they end right on a cell body. Either way, a synapse forms wherever two nerves communicate with one another or with muscle cells. As can be seen in the right of figure (a), the axon contains small vesicles of neurotransmitters at the synapse. When an electrical impulse—or wave of depolarization—makes its way down the axon to the synapse, the electrical impulse causes the axon to dump neurotransmitter into the synapse. The neurotransmitter then causes the dendrites to do something. Some neurotransmitters cause the dendrites to increase their rate of firing. These are called excitatory neurotransmitters. Other neurotransmitters cause the dendrites to decrease or stop firing. These are called inhibitory neurotransmitters.

Two important structures are found in the tips of the axon brush. They are: **calcium ion gates** and **neurotransmitter vesicles**. As can be seen from the diagram, there is a small space between the tips of the brush and the dendrites of the neuron the brush communicates with. This space is called the **synaptic cleft**. When the impulse travels down the axon and nears the brush, the calcium gates open and allow the calcium ions, which are in much greater concentration outside of the cell than inside, to rush into the axon in the area of the brush. Once the calcium is inside the axon, it stimulates the vesicles containing the neurotransmitters to move toward the membrane. The vesicles fuse with the membrane, then the neurotransmitters inside are dumped into the synaptic cleft through the process of exocytosis. The neurotransmitters diffuse across the synaptic cleft and stimulate the dendrites.

30.9 NERVE PHYSIOLOGY: EXCITATORY AND INHIBITORY TRANSMITTERS

Some type of neurotransmitters cause the dendrite membrane to become more permeable to sodium, generating an action potential. These are called **excitatory neurotransmitters** because they increase the conductance of the neuron. This means it is easier for the nerve to conduct an impulse. Other neurotransmitters make the inside of the dendrite membrane more negative than it already is by letting more negatively-charged chloride ions into the cell, or more positively charged potassium ions out of the cell. This makes it more difficult to generate an action potential. These types of neurotransmitters are called **inhibitory neurotransmitters** because they decrease the conductance of the interneuron system. In other words, they make it harder for the nerve to conduct an impulse.

30.10 NERVOUS SYSTEM ANATOMY: PNS AND CNS

There are two components of the nervous system: the **peripheral nervous system** (PNS) and the **central nervous system** (CNS). The CNS consists of the brain and the spinal cord. The brain is the control center and the spinal cord is the pathway to communicate to/from the brain from/to the periphery. The peripheral nervous system consists of the peripheral nerves, also called spinal nerves. These are the sensory and motor nerves that carry impulses to and from the spinal cord.

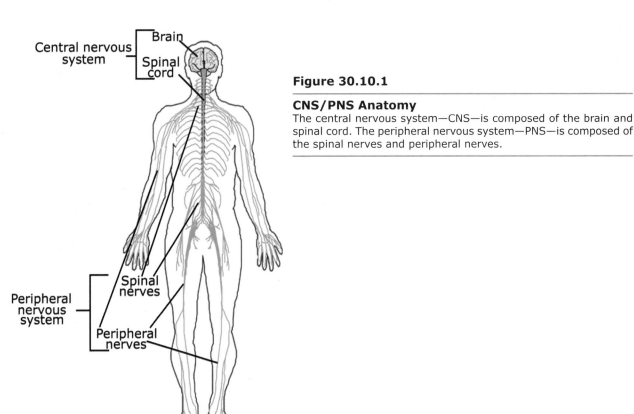

Figure 30.10.1

CNS/PNS Anatomy
The central nervous system—CNS—is composed of the brain and spinal cord. The peripheral nervous system—PNS—is composed of the spinal nerves and peripheral nerves.

30.11 NERVOUS SYSTEM ANATOMY: PROTECTIVE TISSUES

The human brain and spinal cord are highly developed and fragile. They are protected several ways. The brain is surrounded by the boney skull. The spinal cord is surrounded by the boney spinal column. In addition, both the brain and the spinal cord are surrounded by three protective tissues, called the **meninges**. The meningeal layer closest to the skull (i.e., farthest from the brain) is the **dura mater** ("tough mother," so named because it is thick and fibrous). The middle layer is the **arachnoid.** The layer in direct contact with the brain is the **pia mater** ("gentle mother," so named because it is a thin membrane).

30.12 NERVOUS SYSTEM ANATOMY: CNS

Grossly, the surface of the brain has ridges (or bumps) called **gyri** (singular **gyrus**) and crevices called **sulci** (singular **sulcus**). The foldings of the brain allow for far more space and volume to pack in the one billion neurons in the human brain. Between the pia mater and the arachnoid is fluid called **cerebral spinal fluid**, or **CSF.** CSF is made in the brain and freely flows around the spinal cord and back. CSF further protects the CNS by functioning as a shock absorber. Also, it fills the four small cavities, called **ventricles**, which exist in the hollow brain and spinal cord.

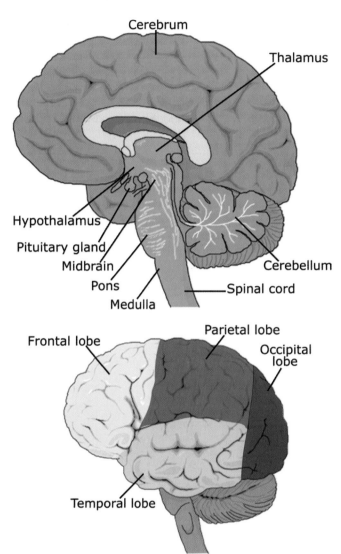

Figure 30.12.1

Brain Anatomy
The brain has well-described areas as shown in the top figure. There are two halves of the brain, a left and a right half. This figure is a view of one half of the brain with the other half removed. Each half of the brain contains the same structures. For example, there is a right cerebellum and a left cerebellum and there is a right cerebrum and a left. The brain-naming scheme is shown in the lower figure. The skull is formed when several different bones fuse to one another. Each bone of the skull has a name and the area of the brain is named after the bone overlying it. For example, the frontal lobe of the brain is covered by the frontal bone of the skull, and the temporal lobe of the brain is covered by the temporal bone of the skull. Realize, also, there are two of each lobe since there are two halves of the brain. For example, there is a right frontal lobe and a left frontal lobe.

The brain is divided into three sections, called the **forebrain**, **midbrain**, and **hindbrain**. The forebrain, or cerebrum, is the largest and is divided into hemispheres, or halves. Each hemisphere is further divided into four **lobes**, and the lobes are named after the bones of the skull that overlie them. They are: the **frontal lobe**, **parietal lobe**, **temporal lobe**, and **occipital lobe**. Also, the **thalamus and hypothalamus** are part of the forebrain, but not part of the cerebrum. The **midbrain** consists of some structures we will not cover here. The **hindbrain** consists of the **brain stem** and the cerebellum. The brain stem is made up of the **pons** and **medulla oblongata**. As can be seen from the Table, the areas of the brain have specific functions, but no area of the brain functions alone. They are all interconnected in such a complex way that we cannot begin to understand it. However, the left half of the brain controls the right half of the body, and the right half of the brain controls the left half of the body.

Figure 30.12.2

Topography and Function of the Human Brain

Area	Function
Forebrain	
olfactory bulb	receives sense of smell
frontal lobe	thinking; speech generation, motor control
parietal lobe	sensory perception—touch, taste, temperature, pain, hot, cold
temporal lobe	language processing; hearing
occipital lobe	vision
thalamus	switching center for sensory impulses
hypothalamus	maintains homeostasis; major organ of the endocrine system
Midbrain	receive, process, and transmit sensory information; pupil reflexes
Hindbrain	
pons medulla oblongata	switching station for all sensory and motor impulses; control heart rate, breathing, digestion
cerebellum	coordination; fine tunes muscle contractions

If the surface of the brain is cut into, there are two definite colors seen. The outer 4 mm of brain is colored grey, the so-called **grey matter**. The grey matter is where all of the cell bodies of the cerebrum are located. The other color that is noted is white, the so-called **white matter**. White matter appears white because it is composed of myelinated axons. Myelin appears white, and since the tissue of the white matter is largely made up of myelinated axons, the majority of the inside of the cerebrum appears white.

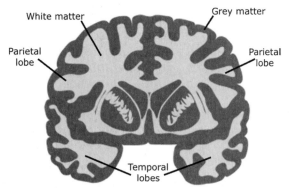

Figure 30.12.3

Grey and White Matter

This is a figure of what the brain looks like if you cut it in half. Note there is a small layer on the outer brain tissue which is grey. This tissue is called grey matter and is composed of neuron cell bodies. The white tissue is called white matter and is composed of axons covered with myelin. Myelin is kind of off-white colored substance and when there are many of them together, the tissue appears white.

As can be seen from the figures, the brain connects to the spinal cord through the midbrain, pons, and medulla. As the medulla continues down from the brain, it leaves the skull to form the spinal cord. The spinal cord is also topographically designed, meaning that, like the brain, certain areas of the spinal cord perform certain functions. You do not need to know which areas control which function; that is for medical school. However, it is interesting that the grey matter/white matter relationship in the spinal cord is the opposite of that in the brain. In the spinal cord, the white matter (myelinated axons) is located in the outer part of the spinal cord, while the grey matter (cell bodies) is located in the center of the cord.

30.13 NERVOUS SYSTEM ANATOMY: PNS

While the brain and the spinal cord represent the central nervous system, the **spinal nerves** represent the first level of the **PNS**. Spinal nerves carry motor axons out of the spinal cord and sensory axons into the spinal cord. Once the spinal nerve begins to travel away from the spinal cord into the extremities, it begins to branch into **peripheral nerves**. Recall that peripheral nerves are made up of hundreds, sometimes thousands, of individual motor and sensory neurons. Peripheral motor nerves then go on to contact (or **innervate**) the muscles and peripheral sensory nerves, then go on to innervate the skin. Recall that motor nerves innervate muscles and make you move. Sensory nerves innervate the skin and give you sensation.

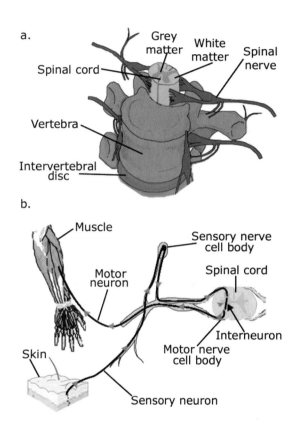

Figure 30.13.1

Spinal Cord Anatomy and Interneurons
Figure (a) shows the anatomy of the spinal cord. It is surrounded by mesodermally derived bones—vertebrae—which form the spinal column. The interior of the spinal cord is made up of grey matter and is surrounded by white matter. Spinal nerves—part of the peripheral nervous system—carry information to and from the spinal cord. Figure (b) shows an interneuron pathway. This particular pathway is a type of reflex arc. A reflex arc is a built-in protective pathway using interneurons to connect sensory nerves to motor nerves in the spinal cord. Interneurons are only found in the CNS (i.e., brain or spinal cord). They are responsible for transmitting information from one neuron to another. Interneurons play an important role in doing automatic things. For example, pulling your hand away from something that is hot or painful in some way. Let's say you cut your hand on a knife. The pain is sensed by the peripheral sensory nerves in the hand and transmitted to the spinal cord. In the spinal cord, there is a short cut pathway provided by interneurons to speed up the reaction time. Rather than send the information all the way up to the brain and back, the information to move the hand away from the sharp object is sent through interneurons in the spinal cord. This allows for a faster response.

30.14 NERVOUS SYSTEM ANATOMY: AUTONOMIC NERVOUS SYSTEM

There is a final "nervous system" in most vertebrates, including humans, called the **autonomic nervous system**. The autonomic system consists of "automatic" functions that we usually do not think about. The autonomic system controls sweating, blood vessel constriction, temperature, heartbeat, breathing, contraction of the intestines, and other automatic functions. It is composed of **sympathetic nerves** and **parasympathetic nerves**.

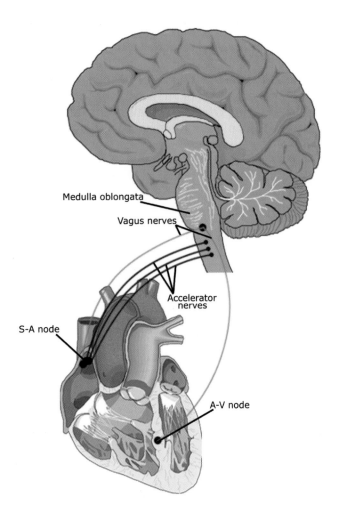

Medulla oblongata

Vagus nerves

Accelerator nerves

S-A node

A-V node

Figure 30.14.1

Autonomic System
There are two components of the autonomic nervous system. One of the components gets you excited, makes you sweat, and gets your heart rate and blood pressure up. This is the sympathetic nervous system. The sympathetic system is shown here as the "accelerator nerves." The other component of the autonomic system slows everything back down. This is the parasympathetic system. The parasympathetic system conducts information through the vagus nerve. The pathway for controlling heart rate is shown here. The SA and AV nodes are both areas of the heart that generate electrical impulses to tell the heart when to beat. The sympathetic accelerator nerves make the heart speed up and the parasympathetic nerves make it slow down.

The sympathetic system is often referred to as the "fight or flight" response. This is because the sympathetic system controls all of the following reactions in this next example. Let's say you are scared because a bully is messing with you. Your heart starts to beat fast and hard, your blood pressure rises because your blood vessels constrict, and you start to breathe faster. These responses are all caused by impulses from the sympathetic nervous system. It gets you ready to fight or run away. The sympathetic system does not have any one major nerve that it works through. It is more like a complex interwoven web of nerves.

The parasympathetic system performs just the opposite functions. The parasympathetic system quiets everything down. Let's say that while this bully was messing with you, your buff big brother comes and stands behind you and the bully leaves (with his sympathetic system working overtime). Once the bully leaves, the parasympathetic system starts to send out impulses because everything is okay. Your heart slows down and is no longer pounding, your breathing slows, and your blood pressure returns to normal because your blood vessels dilate (get bigger) again. One of the major nerves that affect parasympathetic control is called the **vagus nerve**. It has direct connections from the brain to the heart.

30.15 SPECIAL SENSES: VISION

Vision is considered a special sense because it is so complicated and is a well developed system. We will discuss the structures and their function in the order they are hit by light passing through the eye. The first structure light passes through is the **cornea**. It is part of the tough layer of connective tissue that forms the shape of the eye called the **sclera**. Most of the sclera is white (the "whites of the eyes"), but the cornea is completely transparent. Directly behind the cornea is the **aqueous humor**. This is a transparent fluid layer that helps to maintain the shape and pressure of the eye. The light then passes through a hole—called the **pupil**—the size of which is controlled by the **iris** (the colored part of the eye).

Next, light passes through the **lens**. This is a clear structure that has the ability to change shape in order to focus near and far images. After passing through the lens, light moves through a jelly-like material called the **vitreous**. The light then lands on the **retina**, where the cells that perceive light are located. The retina contains a lot of blood vessels to nourish it, some of them are located on "top" of the retina (called the **retinal arteries**) and some are located under the retina (called the **choroid**).

Figure 30.15.1

Eye Anatomy
Light passes through the cornea, pupil, lens, aqueous, and vitreous before it gets to the retina. In the retina, light is generally sensed by rods and color vision is sensed by cones. The iris is the muscle that controls the size of the pupil. In low light, the pupil is wide open to get as much light into the eye as possible. In bright light the opposite occurs.

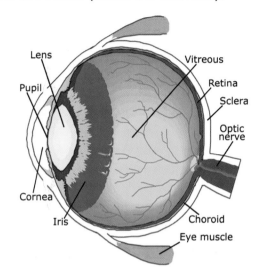

Once the light hits the retina, light sensitive cells are activated. The light sensitive cells are **rod cells** (**rods**) and **cone cells** (**cones**). **Rods** allow for vision in low levels of light, but are not able to process color. **Cones** are responsible for processing colors. Once light hits the rods and the cones, the pigment molecules contained in the cells undergo changes in their energy levels. This results in the transmission of impulses into the nerve cells of the **optic nerve**, which carries visual signals from the retina to the occipital lobes. Interestingly, when the image strikes the retina, it is upside down. However, processing in the occipital lobes inverts the image so it is right-side up.

30.16 SPECIAL SENSES: HEARING

We have already discussed the basics of hearing, but we will now cover it in more detail. The human ear consists of three parts: the **outer ear**, the **middle ear**, and the **inner ear**. The outer ear includes the actual ear (called the **pinna**) and the tube that carries the sound from the pinna to the middle ear (called the **auditory canal**). The division between the outer ear and the middle ear is the middle ear structure of the eardrum, tympanum, or tympanic membrane. When sound enters the auditory canal, it travels to the tympanum. When the sound waves hit the tympanum, they cause it to vibrate. The vibration is transmitted from the tympanum to the middle ear bones (or **ossicles**), the **malleus** (hammer), **incus** (anvil), and **stapes** (stirrup). The middle ear is composed of the tympanic membrane and the ossicles.

As the middle ear ossicles vibrate, they cause vibration of fluid in the inner ear structure called the **cochlea**. The cochlea is filled with fluid (called endolymph) and lined with millions of tiny hairs. When the fluid vibrates, it causes the hairs to move back and forth. The movement of the hairs is converted into electrical impulses that are carried to the brain by the acoustic (or auditory) nerve. The brain then processes and interprets the sounds. The inner ear is composed of two parts: the cochlea and the semicircular canals (also called vestibular canals). There are three semicircular canals in each ear. They are important for balance. Like the cochlea, they are also filled with endolymph. When the head moves, so does the endolymph in the semicircular canals and this triggers movement of the cilia on the surface of the semicircular canal cells. This information is processed by the brain to coordinate balance.

Figure 30.16.1

Ear Anatomy
The outer ear is composed of the pinna and the auditory canal. The middle ear is composed of the tympanic membrane and the ossicles. The inner ear is composed of the cochlea and the semicircular canals. Sound enters the auditory canal and hits the tympanic membrane (ear drum). As the sound vibrates the membrane, the three ear bones (ossicles) attached to the tympanic membrane also vibrate. This in turns causes the bones to move the oval window membrane which results in the movement of the endolymph in the inner canal. The movement of endolymph causes cilia on the hearing cells lining the inner ear to wave back and forth. The movement of the cilia causes nerve impulses to be sent to the brain for sound processing.

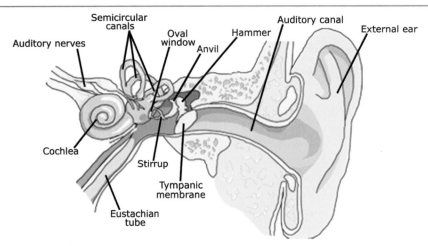

30.17 SPECIAL SENSES: TASTE AND SMELL

Taste and smell are included together because they are closely related. Much of what we "taste" is really what we "smell." You have probably experienced this relationship when you have a cold and your nose is stuffed up. Usually, it is hard to taste anything because you are not able to smell when your nose is plugged.

The sense of taste—called the **gustatory sense**—is transmitted through special cells on the tongue and the back of the throat called **taste buds**. It is traditionally taught that there are four basic taste sensations: **sweet, salty, sour and bitter**. However, there is probably a fifth taste called umami (oo-ma'-me), which is responsible for transmitting taste sensations from monosodium glutamate, but you should concentrate on the four tastes. Basically, taste buds respond best to one of the four different taste sensations. Taste buds are stimulated by certain shapes or charges of molecules.

When you eat something, the chemicals in the food stimulate taste buds to a different degree based on which sensation they are most sensitive to perceiving. Simply, if the chemical "fits into" the receptor on the taste bud, it is stimulated to fire an electrical impulse to the brain. The information is transmitted from the taste buds to the brain along one of three different nerves. The perceived taste of something is generated by complex interactions of all four taste sensations and the way the information is perceived in the brain.

Figure 30.17.1

Taste Zones of the Tongue

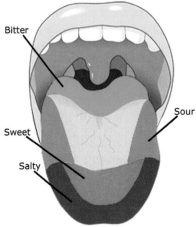

Smell works in much the same way, although instead of four different types of smell receptors, there are many more different types of smell receptors. As a result of the Human Genome Project, we know there are 347 separate functional genes that code for odor receptors. They are located in the upper portion of the nasal cavity and work like the taste buds do. When a particular chemical enters the nose, if it fits into a particular odor receptor, it will cause the odor receptor to fire. The electrical impulses are collected in the **olfactory bulb**, then transmitted to the brain for processing by the **olfactory nerve**.

Figure 30.17.2

Olfaction

Olfaction is similar to the sense of taste. Olfactory nerve fibers have receptors for specific chemicals to "fit into." If a chemical fits into the receptor, an electrical impulse is generated by the nerve and sent to the brain to process and interpret the smell.

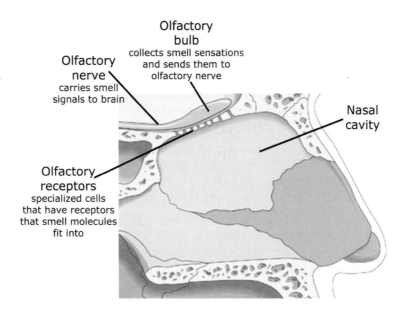

30.18 PEOPLE OF SCIENCE

Andreas Vesalius (1514–1564) was a Belgian anatomist. He was educated in France and Italy as a physician and became an excellent anatomist. Vesalius was responsible for properly describing human anatomy and was the preeminent anatomist for centuries following his death. In his day, the anatomy of the human body was inferred through the anatomy of animals, based on the quite inaccurate work by Galen, a Greek physician who described human anatomy based on animal's anatomy 1500 years earlier. Vesalius was not afraid to test the established dogma of his day. In so doing, he not only accurately described human anatomy, but also made many enemies. He advanced human anatomy by several hundred years by dissecting deceased humans himself and is considered the father of modern human anatomy. He died in a shipwreck following a pilgrimage to Jerusalem, where he had gone as a way to atone for supposedly dissecting a person who was not quite dead at the time.

30.19 KEY CHAPTER POINTS

- Humans are unique mainly because of our ability to think and reason.

- However, much of the anatomy and physiology of humans is similar to all other mammals.

- The nervous system components are the brain, spinal cord, peripheral nerves, eyes, ears, nose, and tongue.

- Nerve tissue is made up of nerve cells (called neurons) and support cells (called glial cells).

- The nervous system is divided into the central nervous system (CNS), the peripheral nervous system (PNS), and the autonomic nervous system (ANS).

- When a nerve is at rest, it is polarized. When it conducts an impulse, it depolarizes in an all-or-none fashion.

- Neurotransmitters are chemicals nerves use to communicate signals to one another.

- The parts of the nervous system have specific names and functions.

- The CNS includes the brain and the spinal cord.

- The PNS includes the motor and sensory nerves.

- The ANS includes the nerves that perform our automatic functions.

- The special senses are sight, hearing, taste, and smell.

30.20 DEFINITIONS

action potential
The movement of depolarization along the nerve membrane; depolarization event.

all-or-none response
The property of a nerve to either generate an action potential or not. As long as the threshold is reached, the nerve will depolarize, and an action potential will be generated.

aqueous humor
Transparent fluid layer directly behind the cornea that helps to maintain the shape and pressure of the eye.

arachnoid
The middle meningeal layer.

astrocytes
Supporting cells that hold the neurons and neural tissue together.

auditory canal
The tube that carries the sound from the pinna to the tympanic membrane.

autonomic nervous system
Nervous tissue that controls automatic functions.

axon
Largest projection of the neuron, responsible for carrying all impulses out and away from the nerve cell.

brain stem
The area of the brain that controls automatic functions.

brush
The branched network of ending nerve fibers that ends an axon.

calcium ion gates
Protein channels through which calcium flows.

cell body
Central portion of the neuron containing the nucleus.

central
Referring to the spinal cord and brain.

central nervous system
The brain and spinal cord.

cerebral spinal fluid (CSF)
Fluid that freely flows around the brain, around the spinal cord, and back to the brain, whose function is to protect the brain by acting as a shock absorber.

choroid
Blood vessels located under the retina.

cochlea
The inner ear structure filled with fluid and lined with millions of tiny hairs.

cone cells (cones)
Cells in the eye that are responsible for processing colors.

cornea
The first eye structure that light passes through.

dendrites
Projections of the neuron that carry impulses to the cell body.

depolarized
The state of a nerve when the Na-K-ATP channels are closed and the interior of the membrane is charged positively as compared to the outside.

depolarization
The process of the nerve membrane changing conductance so the potassium flows out of the nerve and sodium into the nerve, changing the membrane potential.

dura mater
The meningeal layer closest to the skull (farthest form the brain and spinal cord).

excitatory neurotransmitters
Neurotransmitters that cause the dendrite membrane to become more permeable to sodium, generating an action potential.

forebrain
The portion of the brain that is responsible for thinking.

frontal lobe
The lobe of the brain responsible for thinking and planning to move the body.

glial cells
Supporting cells that hold the neurons and neural tissue together.

grey matter
The outer 4 mm of brain and the interior of the spinal cord which appears grey. This is where all of the axon cell bodies are located.

gustatory sense
The sense of taste.

gyri (singular gyrus)
Ridges on the surface of the brain.

hindbrain
The "back" of the brain responsible for involuntary actions like heartbeat and breathing patterns.

hypothalamus
The direct connection between the brain and the endocrine system.

impulses
Messages sent and received by nervous tissue.

incus
One of the "ear bones"; commonly called the anvil.

inhibitory neurotransmitters
Neurotransmitters that make a nerve less likely to generate an action potential.

inner ear
The portion of the ear that processes sound and balance.

innervate
Nerve contacting an organ, skin, or muscle.

interneurons
Neurons that are responsible for transmitting information from one neuron to another.

iris
Colored part of the eye that changes the size of the pupil.

lens
Clear eye structure that has the ability to change shape in order to focus near and far images.

lobes
Divided parts of the brain; each lobe has a particular function.

malleus
One of the "ear bones"; commonly called the hammer.

medulla oblongata
A part of the hindbrain that helps to coordinate involuntary actions.

meninges
Layers of tissue surrounding the brain.

midbrain
The main connecting pathway between the hindbrain and the forebrain.

middle ear
The tympanic membrane and three ossicles.

motor neurons
Nerves that cause you to contract your muscles (or move).

myelin
An insulating layer of fat coating some neurons.

Na-K-ATP Pump (sodium-potassium-ATP pump)
Transmembrane pump which uses energy from ATP to actively pump sodium out of the cell and potassium into the cell.

neuron
An individual nerve cell.

neurotransmitter vesicles
Vesicle in the brush that contain neurotransmitters.

neurotransmitters
Chemicals used by nerves to communicate signals to one another.

nodes of Ranvier
Gaps from one unit of myelin to the next.

occipital lobe
That area of the brain responsible for processing vision.

olfactory bulb
Nasal structure that collects electrical impulses.

olfactory nerve
Transmits electrical impulses collected by the olfactory bulb to the brain.

optic nerve
Nerve which carries visual signals from the retina to the occipital lobes.

outer ear
The pinna and the auditory canal.

parasympathetic Nerves
Part of the autonomic nervous system which "slows things down" and returns the body to a resting state.

parietal lobe
That area of the brain responsible for processing sensory information.

peripheral nerves
Nerves in the arms and legs.

peripheral nervous system
The sensory and motor nerves in the body and extremities.

periphery
The body and the environment.

pia mater
The meningeal layer in direct contact with the brain.

pinna
The actual ear structure.

polarized
Refers to the fact that the resting nerve cell has a charge of -70 millivolts across the membrane.

pons
An area of the hindbrain.

pupil
Hole in the eye that light passes through.

repolarization
The process of the Na-K-ATP Pump actively pumping sodium out of the cell and potassium into the cell following depolarization, which restores the resting membrane potential of the neuron.

resting potential
A difference in electrical charge resulting from the inside of the cell being negatively charged as compared to the outside.

retina
Eye structure where the cells that perceive light are located.

retinal arteries
Blood vessels at the top of the retina.

rod cells (rods)
Light sensitive cells that allow for vision in low levels of light, but are not able to process color.

saltatory conduction
The property of myelinated nerves to conduct electricity from one node of Ranvier to another.

sclera
Tough layer of connective tissue that forms the shape of the eye.

sensory neurons
Nerves that make you feel, taste, see, smell, or hear.

sheath
 Refers to the tough connective tissue which holds axons into a bundle of a peripheral nerve.

spinal nerves
 The first level of the PNS. What the peripheral nerves are called immediately upon exiting the spinal cord.

stapes
 One of the "ear bones"; commonly called the stirrup.

stimulus
 An event that causes a sensory nerve to generate an impulse.

sulci (singular sulcus)
 Crevices on the surface of the brain.

sympathetic nerves
 Part of the autonomic nervous system that speeds things up and gets one ready for fight or flight.

synaptic cleft
 Small space between the tips of the brush and the dendrites of the neuron with which the brush communicates.

taste buds
 Cells on the tongue and the back of the throat that transmit taste.

temporal lobe
 The part of the brain responsible for hearing and processing speech.

thalamus
 Part of the midbrain that relays sensory information.

threshold stimulus
 The minimal strength stimulus that will generate an action potential.

vagus nerve
 The major nerve that effects parasympathetic control.

ventricles
 Four fluid-filled cavities of the brain.

vitreous
 Jelly-like material that light passes through in the eye.

white matter
 The area of the brain and spinal cord that appears white due to the high concentration of myelinated axons it contains.

STUDY QUESTIONS

1. What general functions does the nervous system perform?

2. What are the components of the nervous system?

3. What are the two basic types of cells of the nervous system and what are their functions?

4. Draw a typical neuron and label the parts.

5. _____nerves bring information into the brain from the environment and body. _____ nerves carry information from the brain to the muscles to make them move.

6. Start at the sensory nerve level. What is the pathway a nerve impulse would take to convey the message to the brain that something unpleasant is touching the skin of

the hand? What is the pathway the impulse would take from the brain to cause the person to move the hand?

7. What do you call the event that caused the sensory nerve to generate the impulse to the brain?

8. True or False? At rest, a neuron is depolarized.

9. Draw what happens during nerve depolarization and repolarization in regard to the membrane potential. What is the depolarization event called?

10. How does the nerve repolarize?

11. True or False? Nerves do not show an all-or-none response. This means that sometimes the nerve does not depolarize even though the threshold may have been reached.

12. True or False? The brush is an area where the axon of one nerve comes into direct contact with the dendrites of another nerve.

13. What is the Na-K-ATPase pump and why is it important to nerves?

14. The _____, _____ and _____ are protective tissue-coverings of the brain and spinal cord.

15. What are the components of the CNS? Of the PNS?

16. If a person suffered an injury to their frontal lobes of the brain, which functions would likely be impaired?

17. If a person suffered damage to the cerebellum, which functions would likely to be impaired?

18. True or False? A person who damages the occipital lobes of the brain could become blind.

19. True or False? The grey matter is the outer 4mm of brain tissue, while the white matter is on the interior of the brain.

20. What makes the white matter appear white?

21. What is contained in the grey matter of the brain and spinal cord?

22. What is the autonomic nervous system and what are its two components?

23. If you are a beam of light passing into someone's eye, describe the order you would pass through the following structures: vitreous, cornea, lens, pupil, and retina.

24. True or False? Rods are responsible for processing color and cones process black and white.

25. Describe the way that our hearing works.

26. What are the four accepted taste sensations and where are they located on the tongue?

27. Describe how taste and smell receptors are stimulated to generate an impulse.

Human Anatomy and Physiology II
Immunologic, Endocrine, and Excretory Systems

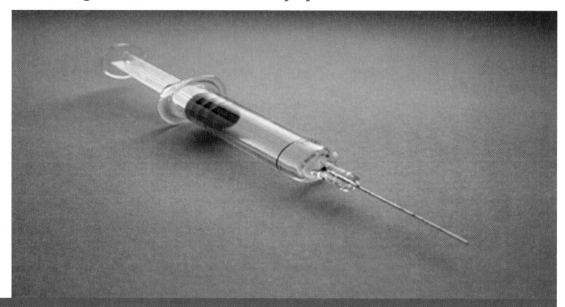

31

31.0 CHAPTER PREVIEW

In this chapter we will:

- Describe the components and function of the immune system.

- Discuss the specific and non-specific phases of the immune response.

- Define active and passive immunity.

- Discuss the condition of an autoimmune disease.

- Describe the anatomy of the endocrine system.

- Discuss the effects and control of the endocrine system.

- Investigate the anatomy and physiology of the excretory system.

31.1 OVERVIEW: IMMUNE SYSTEM

All organisms—even bacteria—have ways of protecting themselves against foreign invaders. Humans are no different. As you remember from our earlier discussion, there are a number of species that have the ability to infect humans. **Viruses**, **bacteria**, **yeasts**, **molds**, and **parasites** such as tapeworms and pinworms are some of the organisms that have the ability to infect humans as well as other organisms. These organisms also infect other animals such as reptiles, birds, amphibians, fish—and even one another. Infectious organisms enter the human body through the digestive tract (mouth, throat, stomach, and intestines), the respiratory tract (nose, sinuses, breathing tubes, and lungs), the eyes or ears, the blood and the skin. Once inside the body, they "set up shop" in the tissues and begin to grow there. If left unchecked, most of these infections would result in the organism's death. The **immune system** is a complex system, which protects us from infectious organisms. In medicine, organisms that can cause infection are called **pathogens**.

Figure 31.1.1

Pathogens

We have already covered the particles and organisms which can cause infections in humans and animals. Pathogens such as the pox virus family (seen filling up a host cell's nucleus; far left), gram-positive bacteria like *Staphylococcus* (middle left), diarrhea-causing spirochetes (*Campylobacter*; middle right), and parasitic flat worms (*Taenia*; far right) are successful at living for a short while in a host. Fortunately, they all provoke a strong immune reaction, which ultimately kills the organism and rids it from the system.

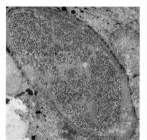 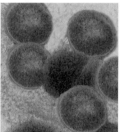 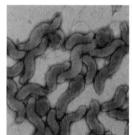 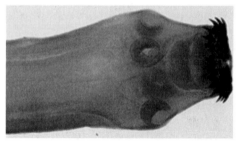

Figure 31.1.2

Immune System Components

The major immune system components are shown here. It all starts inside of bones. Almost all bones are hollow; this is where bone marrow is located. Bone marrow makes all of our blood cells. Red blood cells carry oxygen to the tissues, and white blood cells fight infection. There are a number of different types of white blood cells—lymphocytes, monocytes, and granulocytes. Granulocytes are white cells that eat pathogens, a process called phagocytosis. Therefore, this kind of cell is also called a phagocyte. Although they are all activated during infections, each type is specialized to fight certain pathogens. The lymph vessels, lymph nodes, and tonsils are specialized infection-fighting tissue which traps pathogens and holds them while white blood cells attack. Special types of white blood cells called T-cells (T stands for "thymus") are made in the bone marrow; they circulate to the thymus gland to mature. The spleen is an important organ for clearing bacteria with capsules from the blood.

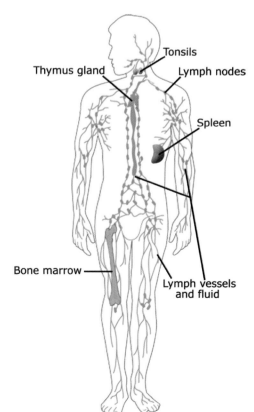

31.2 IMMUNE SYSTEM: BARRIERS

The immunologic system is made up of many components. There are general **physical** and **chemical barriers** to infection. These two barriers represent a non-specific system, so no matter what the foreign invader may be, these two systems are in place to try to keep it out. Physical barriers are the skin and the moist tissues of the mouth, nose, windpipe, and lungs called **mucous membranes**. In addition, the respiratory tract is lined with cilia, which sweep particle and pathogens out of the air we breathe. This prevents these particles from entering the lungs. These physical barriers serve to try to block the entry of pathogens into the system. Chemical barriers to infections are found mainly in the fluids of the eyes, mouth, and stomach. These chemicals are usually enzymes that break down the cell wall or membrane of the pathogen. They are present all the time, on stand-by, in case a pathogen gets past the physical barriers. In addition, the acidic environment of the stomach often kills pathogens.

Cilia

Figure 31.2.1

Physical Barriers
The cell here is taken from the respiratory tract. It is covered with cilia. The cilia beat back and forth to clear foreign particles and pathogens from the air we breathe. This is an effective way to keep our bodies clear of infectious organisms.

31.3 IMMUNE SYSTEM: NON-SPECIFIC RESPONSE

The next level of defense is termed the **non-specific response**. It is often effective at preventing entry of pathogens into the system, or removing them if they should enter the system. The non-specific response is similar to the physical/chemical barriers, it responds in a generic way to the presence of pathogens. If pathogens should get by the physical/chemical barriers, then the non-specific defense system is triggered.

The **non-specific response** consists of an **inflammatory reaction**, which occurs when there is an injury to the tissues. The inflammatory response occurs in reaction to an injury to tissues and is a way to further protect the body against infection. If you fall off your skateboard and scrape yourself on the ground, you have broken the physical barrier of the skin. There is now the potential for bacteria to enter the wound and infect it. However, almost immediately after the scrape occurs, there is a release of a chemical called **histamine**, which is what initiates the inflammatory response. Histamine causes the blood vessels around the wound to dilate, which increases the blood flow to the tissue in the area. This results in the swelling and redness that is typical following an injury.

As a result of the increased blood flow to the area, there are an increased number of cells called **phagocytes** in the area of the injury. Phagocytes engulf material by phagocytosis. There are two important types of phagocytes that respond to inflammation: **macrophages** and **neutrophils** (these are types of white blood cells). These two types of cells congregate where there is inflammation and look for things to engulf and remove, including dead cells, dead tissue, and pathogens. Phagocytes are effective at removing pathogens, but they do so in a non-specific way. This means that if there is any type of bacteria, virus, or other foreign body present, it will be engulfed by the phagocytes regardless of what it is.

Figure 31.3.1

Non-specific Response
The non-specific immune response, or inflammatory response, is initiated immediately after tissue is violated in some way. In figure (a), a nail has penetrated the skin. The chemical histamine is released by the surrounding skin cells. Histamine causes blood vessels to become larger in size, or dilate, and causes the area to retain extra water, or swell. Phagocytes move through the dilated capillary walls into the area to gobble up any pathogens and debris. In this way, the inflammatory response is not directed toward any particular pathogen. It is a first response system that tries to clear all potential infectious organisms before they have a chance to establish an infection. In (b), we see the end result of a successful inflammatory response. The capillaries have returned to normal size. The infectious particles have all been removed, and the inflammatory fluid, dead cells, and other debris have organized into pus underneath a scab. A type of phagocytic white blood cell called a macrophage is patrolling the area looking for any residual pathogens.

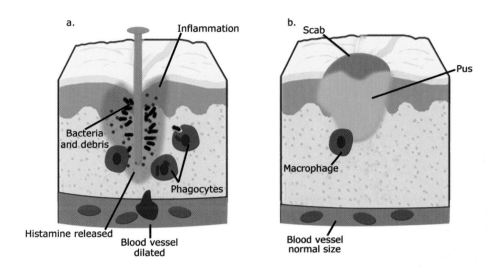

Often, a **fever** will occur in association with the inflammatory and infectious processes. A fever is an elevation in body temperature above the normal 98.6°F (37°C). Fevers of up to about 102°F (38.8°C) enhance the body's ability to fight off infections, but temperatures over the 103° or 104°F mark (39°- 40°C) can be unsafe. Fevers over 105°F (40.6°C) can be fatal.

31.4 IMMUNE SYSTEM: SPECIFIC RESPONSE; IMMUNE RESPONSE

Sometimes the localized inflammatory reaction and the phagocytic white blood cells engulfing the pathogens is not enough. When this happens, the pathogen can set up shop and start an infection in a tissue somewhere in the body. In that case, the immune system is stimulated to act. This is the specific immune response. The cells that make up the immune response are the **lymphocytes**. There are two types of lymphocytes called **B-lymphocytes** (or B-cells) and **T-lymphocytes** (called T-cells). There are two branches of the immune response that work together, the **humoral response** (also called the antibody response) and the **cell-mediated response**. B-cells make antibodies, so they make up the majority of cells of the humoral response. They are made and mature in the bone marrow. T-cells make up a majority of the cell-mediated response, although they both need the other to function optimally. They are made in the bone marrow, but once they are made, they circulate into the blood stream to the thymus gland. This is a gland in the upper part of the chest. T-cells mature in the *t*hymus gland (hence the "T" in T-cell).

Figure 31.4.1

White Blood Cells Types
On the left, a type of phagocytic white blood cell called a neutrophil is seen. Neutrophils have many nuclei in a single cell. The cell above it is a lymphocyte. There are two types of lymphocytes: 1) those that make antibodies, and 2) those that do not. The lymphocytes that make antibodies are called B-cells (called "B" because they mature in the bone marrow). The other population of lymphocytes either: 1) help the antibody cells make antibodies to specific pathogens (called helper T-cells); 2) kill pathogens coated with antibodies (called killer T-cells); 3) or turn the immune system off once the pathogens are all cleared (called suppressor T-cells). On the right, a type of phagocytic white blood cell called an eosinophil is responding to an infection called African sleeping sickness caused by *Trypanosoma gambiense*

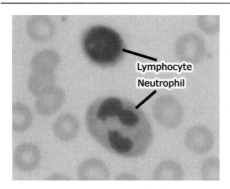
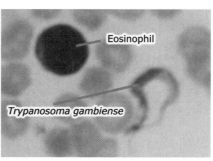

In order to understand how the immune system works, we need to understand that our bodies have a built-in method of recognizing itself so that our immune system does not attack our own bodies. This method is based upon proteins that are on the surface of all our cells. As long as a cell has the appropriate "self" proteins on the cell surface, it is recognized as part of the body and is not targeted for removal by the immune system. However, when a pathogen enters the body, it does not have the appropriate self proteins. Instead, pathogens have other proteins on their surfaces that stimulate the immune system to respond and target the pathogen for removal. These proteins are called **antigens**. An antigen is a protein that is not recognized as part of the body by the immune system. Therefore, it triggers the immune response.

Once an antigen has been recognized, the immune response is turned on. Macrophages engulf the pathogen and break them down, but they spare some of the antigen-containing parts of the cell. The macrophage then "presents" the antigen to a helper T-cell. The helper T-cell takes the antigen to two separate cells, the B-cell and the cytotoxic T-cells. This process occurs not only with one cell, but with thousands at the same time.

Helper T-cells present the pathogen's antigen to B-cells and cytotoxic T-cells. The B-cell takes the antigen, processes it, and begins to make antibodies directed specifically toward that one antigen. Antibodies are released by the B-cell into the blood stream. The antibody will only stick to the antigen on the pathogen. By sticking to the antigen, the antibody marks the pathogen and targets it for removal.

The cytotoxic T-cell takes the antigen from the helper T-cell, processes it, then makes proteins, called **receptors**, specific to that one antigen. The receptor on the cytotoxic T-cell will only stick to the antigen on the pathogen. Think of the antigen as an electrical plug, and the receptor as its socket. When the cytotoxic T-cell comes into contact with the pathogen, its receptor will stick to the antigen. After they stick together, the cytotoxic T-cell kills the pathogen. Many clones of the activated cytotoxic T-cell are made and function in this way.

After five days, or so, the B-cells are ready to release their antibodies into the blood and the cytotoxic T-cells are ready to kill the body cells infected by the pathogen. Cytotoxic T-cells do not directly kill the pathogen; they kill the body cells that are infected with the pathogen. B-cells that are making antibodies are called **plasma cells**. The antibodies from the plasma cells stick to the pathogen and either inactivate the pathogen, or make it easier for macrophages and neutrophils to ingest them. Body cells that have been infected with the pathogen have antigens sticking out from their cell surface. The cytotoxic T-cells stick to the infected body cells and kill them by poking holes in the cell membrane. This process continues until the infection is cleared. Once the infection clears, suppresser T-cells shut the immune response off.

a.

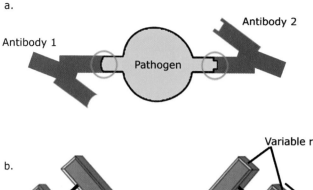

Figure 31.4.2

Antibody Specificity

Antibodies are proteins which are made to stick to specific antigens present on the surface of a pathogen (a). There are a limitless number of specific antibodies possible, because the part that sticks to the pathogen is in the variable area of the antibody molecule (b). The sequence of the amino acids in the variable area depends on which particular antigen the antibody is directed against. Our immune system is able to figure out the exact sequence of amino acids needed in the variable region so the antibody sticks only to the antigen. A pathogen that has antibodies stuck to it is targeted for destruction by neutrophils and macrophages.

b.

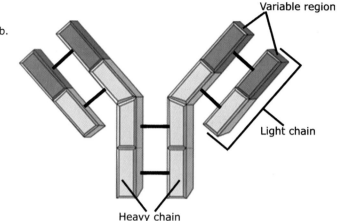

Following the resolution of the infection, the body maintains the ability to recognize that one particular pathogen and clears it quickly, without becoming infected if exposed to it again. This is referred to as **memory**. The body's ability to maintain memory of past infections to prevent future infections by the same pathogen is the reason that immunizations work. **Immunizations** safely expose the body to the antigens of a pathogen in order to stimulate the immune response and generate **memory cells**. Memory cells are the cells of the immune system that keep the body's ability for long-term protection against infections from a specific pathogen.

Figure 31.4.3

Components of the Immune Response

Component	Function
Physical Barriers	prevent entry of pathogens into body
skin	upper most layer of skin, composed of dead cells to make penetration into the skin difficult
mucus membranes	these line the digestive system, respiratory system, and excretory system; thick mucus traps pathogens, then phagocytic cells eat them
cilia	cilia line respiratory system and sweep pathogens out of the tract so that phagocytic cells can eat them
cooking food properly	kills bacteria and their spores in meat or other infected food
washing hands	removes pathogens
good sanitation systems	removes spillage of sewage (which contains significant amounts of illness-causing bacteria) into drinking water
Chemical Barriers	prevent entry of pathogens into body
enzymes	break down cell walls and cell membranes of pathogens
stomach acid	acid kills some pathogens
Non-Specific Response	prevents: pathogen from establishing infection once entry into body is obtained
histamine release	increases blood flow to infected area to increase numbers of infection-fighting cells in the area
phagocytic cells	macrophages and neutrophils engulf dead tissue and pathogens in non-specific manner to try to clear infection
fever	caused by release of chemicals at site of infection into blood stream; elevated body temperatures enhance ability to fight infection
Immune Response	once pathogens enter into body, this is a specific response aimed at the particular pathogen(s) causing infection
lymphocytes	B-cells make antibodies directed against a specific pathogen, natural killer cells kill virus infected cells, helper T-cells help to get the immune response revved up quickly and efficiently, cytotoxic (killer) T-cells specifically attack and kill infected body cells, suppresser T-cells shut the immune response down when the infection is cleared.

31.5 IMMUNE SYSTEM: ACTIVE AND PASSIVE IMMUNITY

Finally, there are two types of immunity. The type we have been discussing is called **active immunity**. Active immunity develops after becoming infected by a pathogen, then clearing it. Active immunity also develops following vaccines. **Passive immunity** is the type of immunity that develops as a result of transfer of antibodies from one individual to another. Infants who are breast-fed receive antibodies from the mother through the breast milk. Also, there are certain conditions where antibodies obtained from blood donors are injected into people who have been exposed to certain illnesses.

31.6 IMMUNE SYSTEM: AUTOIMMUNE RESPONSE

Sometimes, for some reason, the body does not properly recognize itself, and the immune system is stimulated to attack the body. This is called an **autoimmune disease**. There are many kinds of autoimmune diseases (see Figure 31.6.1) that affect humans. The general treatment goal when dealing with one of these diseases is to try to suppress the immune system with various drugs, so it will not attack the body too furiously. Usually, it is the cell-mediated component of the immune response that is targeted for suppression.

Figure 31.6.1

Autoimmune Diseases and the Organs/Sites They Attack

Disease	Site of Attack
rheumatoid arthritis	joints, lungs
multiple sclerosis	myelin of nerves
myasthenia gravis	thymus gland
juvenile diabetes mellitus (Type I diabetes)	pancreas
Grave's disease	thyroid
systemic lupus erythematosis (lupus)	connective tissue

Another condition that is becoming more common is the suppression of the immune system following organ transplantation. Since the transplanted organ is not "self," the recipient's body recognizes it as such. If nothing is done to suppress the immune system, then a vigorous immune response is mounted in the recipient, and the organ is quickly rejected. Again, cell-mediated immunity is targeted for suppression. The significant improvement in outcomes of organ transplantation is directly attributable to more and more successful suppression of the immune system.

31.7 ENDOCRINE SYSTEM: GENERAL

The endocrine system is a complex system using chemical messengers, called hormones, to allow one organ to communicate with another organ some distance away. Hormones are released into the blood stream by the organ that has synthesized it, referred to as a **gland**, then travels to the organ it is meant to communicate with, called the **target organ**. The target organ has specific proteins on the cell surface or in the cell cytoplasm that function as **receptors** for the hormone. When the hormone passes by the target cell that has a cell surface receptor, it sticks to the receptor. If the receptor is in the cytoplasm, the hormone first diffuses across the cell membrane, and then binds the receptor in the cytoplasm. Small amounts of hormones cause a big change in the way the target organ functions.

Figure 31.7.1

The Endocrine System
The major components of the endocrine system are shown here. The brain's hypothalamus is the master controller of the system. It senses when hormone levels are too high or too low by sampling the blood and detecting the levels of all of the hormones in the body. If a hormone level is too high or too low, the hypothalamus adjusts it accordingly. For many different hormone systems, the hypothalamus acts through the pituitary gland, signaling the pituitary when to send out hormones. The thyroid gland is a major target of the hypothalamus/pituitary. All tissues in our body are dependent upon thyroid hormones to remain healthy. The adrenal glands sit on top of the kidneys and make steroids. Steroids are important for a number of different tissues, such as muscle and bone, to stay healthy. The pancreas releases insulin into the blood in response to a sugary meal. Insulin stimulates our cells to take in glucose, which lowers the level of glucose in the blood. Diabetes is caused by an inability to make insulin, or an inability of the cells to respond to insulin.

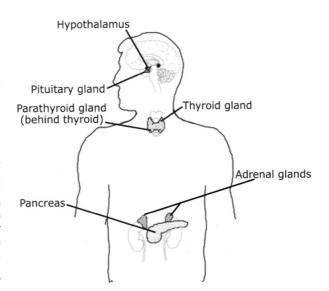

31.8 ENDOCRINE SYSTEM: HORMONES

Hormones are released by one organ in order to communicate with the target organ. There are two types of hormones: **amino acid—derived** hormones and **steroid** hormones. Amino acid hormones are basically proteins. Since they are not soluble in the lipid membrane, amino acid/protein hormones bind to a receptor on the cell surface. After the amino acid hormone binds the cell surface receptor, it initiates a cascade of events on the inside of the cell that alter the function of the cell.

Steroid hormones are made from a cholesterol base unit. They are lipid-soluble and can diffuse across the cell membrane. Therefore, steroid hormones often have intracellular receptors. Often, the steroid hormone-receptor complex will migrate into the nucleus and bind to the DNA at a specific location. This results in a change of the mRNA being made, which then alters the proteins that are being made by the cell. No matter where the receptor is located, once the hormone binds to it, the binding generally causes some enzyme to activate or de-activate. This results in the target organ changing its function.

31.9 ENDOCRINE SYSTEM: REGULATION

The overall "super controller" for the endocrine system is the **hypothalamus** of the brain. This is the direct connection between the brain and the endocrine system. The hypothalamus acts through the **pituitary gland**. The pituitary gland releases various types of hormones (that it either synthesizes or stores from the hypothalamus) upon commands from the hypothalamus. The most important functions of the hormones are summarized in Figure 31.9.3

Because small amounts of hormone result in huge changes in function of the target organ, the endocrine system is complexly tuned. One of the ways it regulates itself is through **feedback inhibition**. As an example, the thyroid gland makes several different thyroid hormones; we'll call them the "**thyroid hormones**." The thyroid does not release any of its hormones until it is told to do so by the hypothalamus. The hypothalamus is able to sense the body needs the thyroid hormones. It does this by being able to detect the level of thyroid hormones in the blood stream. If the level of thyroid hormones drops too low, the hypothalamus senses it and releases thyrotropin-releasing hormone (**TRH**). TRH causes the pituitary to release the thyroid-stimulating hormone (**TSH**) into the blood. TSH circulates in the blood and binds to the TSH receptors in the thyroid gland. Once these receptors are bound by TSH, the thyroid gland is stimulated to release its thyroid hormones into the blood.

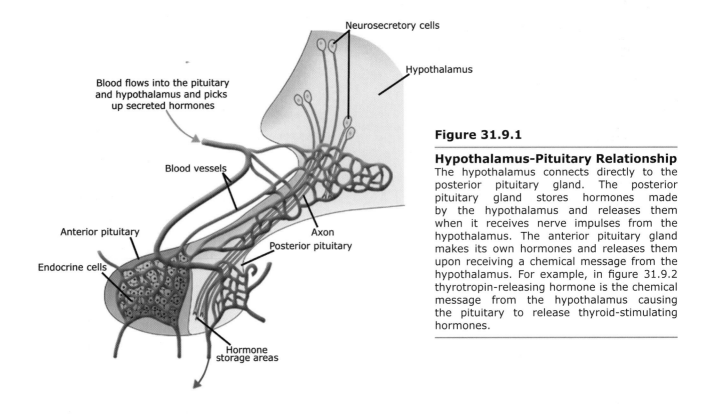

Figure 31.9.1

Hypothalamus-Pituitary Relationship
The hypothalamus connects directly to the posterior pituitary gland. The posterior pituitary gland stores hormones made by the hypothalamus and releases them when it receives nerve impulses from the hypothalamus. The anterior pituitary gland makes its own hormones and releases them upon receiving a chemical message from the hypothalamus. For example, in figure 31.9.2 thyrotropin-releasing hormone is the chemical message from the hypothalamus causing the pituitary to release thyroid-stimulating hormones.

Figure 31.9.2

Feedback Loop for Hormone Control
When looking at the feedback loop, keep the following hormone abbreviations and actions in mind. TRH = thyrotropin-releasing hormone, which causes the pituitary to release thyroid stimulating hormone (TSH). TSH causes the thyroid to release thyroid hormones.

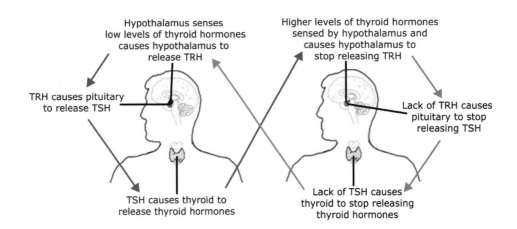

Eventually, the levels of the thyroid hormones reach a certain "normal" level in the body. This normal level gives feedback to the hypothalamus that there are enough thyroid hormones in the body. This causes the hypothalamus to stop releasing TRH into the blood which, in turn, causes the pituitary not to release TSH into the blood, telling the thyroid not to release any more thyroid hormones. When the level of thyroid hormones gets low enough again, the feedback to the hypothalamus will tell it the body needs more thyroid hormones, and the whole cycle starts over.

Figure 31.9.3

Important Hormones and their Effects on the Body

Hormone	Synthesizing Organ	Target	Function
Adrenocorticotropic hormone (ACTH)	anterior pituitary	adrenal cortex	stimulate release of cortisol and aldosterone
Cortisol	adrenal cortex	tissues	regulate metabolism of glucose
Aldosterone	adrenal cortex	kidneys	maintain proper water and salt balance
Follicular stimulating hormone (FSH)	anterior pituitary	testes (males) / ovaries (females)	stimulates sperm production in males and egg production in females
Prolactin	anterior pituitary	breast tissue	stimulates production of breast milk after birth
Growth hormone	anterior pituitary	muscle and bone	stimulates growth
Luteinizing hormone	anterior pituitary	testes (males) / ovaries (females)	stimulates production of testosterone (males) and estrogen (females)
Testosterone	testes	tissues	causes development of secondary sex characteristics
Estrogen	ovaries	tissues	causes development of secondary sex characteristics
Thyroid-stimulating hormone (TSH)	anterior pituitary	thyroid	regulates secretion of thyroid hormones
Thyroid hormones	thyroid	all tissues in body	regulates global body metabolism
Antidiuretic hormone	hypothalamus; stored and released from posterior pituitary	kidneys	stimulates reabsorption of water in kidneys
Oxytocin	hypothalamus; stored and released from posterior pituitary	uterine muscle	stimulates contraction of uterus during birth
Insulin	pancreas	all tissues	stimulates tissues to take up glucose from the blood stream
Glucagon	pancreas	liver	stimulates liver to break glycogen down into glucose and release into blood stream
Thymogen	thymus	T-cells	stimulates maturation of T-cells
Melatonin	pineal	brain	prepares brain for sleeping at night
Parathyroid hormone	parathyroid	bones	stimulates release of calcium from the bones to increase calcium level in blood
Gastrin	stomach	stomach	stimulates stomach cells to produce gastric acid and digestive enzymes after meal
Secretin	intestine	pancreas	stimulates pancreas to release digestive enzymes into small intestine

31.10 EXCRETORY SYSTEM

The excretory system is made up of the kidneys, ureters, urinary bladder, and urethra. The purpose of the excretory system is to filter the blood, removing wastes and spare water, ions, and nutrients. Your kidney is about the size of your fist. Usually people have two, but there are many people who are born with only one and never have any problems. The functional unit of the kidney is called the **nephron**. Each kidney contains about one million of these; they are the smallest unit at which blood filtration occurs. Each nephron is composed of a cup-shaped structure called **Bowman's capsule** surrounding a bed of capillaries called the **glomerulus**. This nephron is where the blood gets filtered and urine gets made. The glomerulus is the "blood side" of the nephron and Bowman's capsule is the "urine side" of the nephron.

Figure 31.10.1

Components of the Excretory System

Kidneys (2)	maintains proper water and ion balance; filters nitrogen wastes from blood and converts to urea and passes it to ureters; the product of this organ's function is collectively called urine
Ureters (2)	tube to transport the wastes made by the kidney to the bladder
Bladder (1)	muscular organ to store and eject urine
Urethra (1)	tube to transport urine from the bladder out of the body

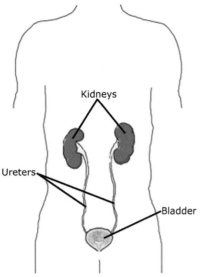

Kidneys

Ureters

Bladder

Figure 31.10.2

The Excretory System – Location
Anatomic position of the excretory system components.

Filtration occurs in the following way. Blood is carried to the kidney through an artery called the **renal artery**. Once inside the kidney, the renal artery branches many times into smaller and smaller arteries, eventually ending in the glomerulus. The cells of the glomerulus allow protein waste products (mainly **urea**), ions (like sodium, calcium, and potassium), water and nutrients to filter out of the blood and into Bowman's capsule. This filtered material is called **filtrate**. Blood cells and larger proteins cannot leave the glomerulus through the walls of the capillaries of the glomerulus. From Bowman's capsule, the filtrate moves into the **collecting duct** on its way to the ureters and the bladder. However, at this point, the filtrate is still in the kidney.

Figure 31.10.3

Excretory System—Detailed Anatomy
Figure (a) Most people have two kidneys, but 1 out of 750 people is born with one kidney. The kidney receives its blood supply from the renal arteries. The renal veins carry blood from the kidney to the heart. Ureters carry urine from the kidneys to the bladder. The bladder stores the urine until it is full, then you go to the bathroom. The urethra is the tube which carries the urine from the bladder out of the body.

Figure (b) The functional unit of the kidney is the nephron. Each kidney contains about a million nephrons. Each nephron is made up of a glomerulus and Bowman's capsule. A glomerulus is a capillary bed which removes wastes from the blood. The Bowman's capsule is a collecting system which collects the waste removed from each glomerulus. As the waste moves from Bowman's capsule to the collecting duct, ions and water are removed from the urine and reabsorbed back into the blood, leaving only urine to be collected and transported in the ureter to the bladder.

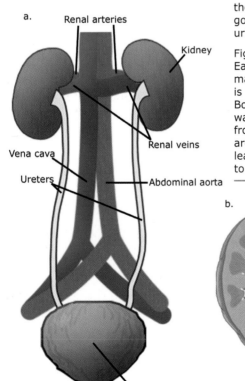

a.

Renal arteries

Kidney

Renal veins

Vena cava

Ureters

Abdominal aorta

Urethra   Urinary bladder

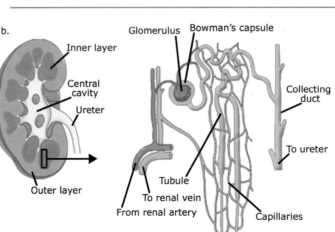

b.

Glomerulus   Bowman's capsule

Inner layer

Central cavity

Ureter

Outer layer

Collecting duct

To ureter

Tubule

To renal vein

From renal artery

Capillaries

You may be thinking that the glomerulus has allowed some useful substances—water, ions, and nutrients—to filter out into the "urine side" of the nephron. That is true, but there is a way the glomerulus recovers it. As the blood continues flowing through the glomerulus, it passes by the collecting duct and re-absorbs nutrients, water, and ions from the filtrate. In doing so, the substances the rest of the body needs are taken up into the blood again; nothing needed is lost. Urea and other waste products remain in the collecting duct and continue to pass from the urine-collecting duct system into the ureters and the bladder. The control of how much water and ions are reabsorbed is controlled ultimately by the hypothalamus. Once the nutrients, ions, and water are reabsorbed into the blood from the collecting tubule, the fluid remaining in the tubule is called **urine**. The urine moves into the bladder and is stored until the bladder becomes full. Once the bladder is full, you go the bathroom and empty the urine form the bladder.

Figure 31.10.4

Concentration of Various Substances in Blood and Urine
The relative concentrations of various substances are shown below in a normal, healthy person. The kidney is largely responsible for regulating the levels of these substances in the blood and urine.

Substance	Blood Concentration	Urine Concentration
water	high	low
urea	low	high
ions/salts	high	low
protein	high	low
amino acids	high	low
glucose	high	low
blood cells	present	absent

People who have **kidney failure** have kidneys that are unable to properly filter the blood. This can occur due to a number of different medical conditions such as uncontrolled high blood pressure, recurrent kidney infections, and diabetes. When kidney failure happens, unsafe levels of urea build up in the body, and proper water balance cannot be maintained. When this occurs, **dialysis** is started. Dialysis is an artificial way to filter the blood for patients with kidney failure. Generally, they receive dialysis three times per week for about four hour periods. This requires them to be hooked up to a machine to filter their blood. Some patients with kidney failure receive kidney transplants, in which a kidney from another person is surgically implanted in the patient and hooked up to the renal artery and ureter. This new kidney then can filter the blood and eliminate the need for dialysis.

31.11 PEOPLE OF SCIENCE

Charles Richard Drew (1904–1950) was born in Washington, D.C. He was an excellent athlete and the athletic director, football coach, and science teacher at Morgan State University before he enrolled in medical school. He was a gifted researcher and pioneered the discovery that blood could be separated into the components plasma (the liquid part of blood) and red blood cells. These two products could then be frozen and stored for longer periods than fresh blood. Dr. Drew found that plasma was a life-saving component of blood for those who have bled heavily, such as wounded soldiers. During World War II, Dr. Drew served as the head of the *Blood for Britain* project; following the war, he was named director of the Red Cross Blood Bank and the Assistant Director of the National Research Council. While holding this last position, Dr. Drew, a black man, was successful in getting the U.S. Armed Forces to drop their policy of separating blood on the basis of the color of the donor, a practice which had absolutely no merit. He was unfortunately killed in a car accident at the age of forty-six.

31.12 KEY CHAPTER POINTS

- All organisms have ways to fight off foreign invaders. In humans and other animals, it is called the immune system.

- There are many barriers—physical, chemical, non-specific, and specific—that are present to prevent entry of pathogens into the body.

- The specific response is the immune response.

- The immune response results in active immunity.

- The endocrine system is a complex system that uses chemical messengers to communicate with organs and tissues far from one another.

- The excretory system is the way the body eliminates waste materials.

31.13 DEFINITIONS

active immunity
Immunity to repeat exposure to the same pathogen that develops after becoming infected by a pathogen or receiving a vaccine.

antigens
A protein that is not recognized as part of the body by the immune system and triggers the immune response.

autoimmune disease
A disease that occurs when the body does not properly recognize self, and the immune system is stimulated to attack the body.

B-cells
Immune cells that make antibodies.

bacteria
A type of pathogen.

Bowman's capsule
A cup-shaped structure which collects urine in the nephron.

cell-mediated response
The immune response carried out by cells rather than antibodies.

chemical barriers
Enzymes that function to break down the cell wall or membrane of the pathogen.

collecting duct
Structure that holds kidney filtrate on its way to the ureters and the bladder.

dialysis
An artificial way to filter the blood for patients with kidney failure.

fever
An elevation in body temperature above the normal 98.6°F (37°C).

filtrate
Material filtered out of the blood in the kidneys.

gland
Organs that synthesize hormones.

glomerulus
A bed of capillaries in the kidney that is the blood side of the nephron.

histamine
A chemical that causes blood vessels to dilate and increase blood flow to the tissue in the area.

humoral response
The immune response carried out by antibodies.

immune system
A complex system that protects us from infectious organisms.

immunizations
Exposure of the body to the antigens of a pathogen in order to stimulate the immune response and generate memory cells.

inflammatory reaction
A non-specific response occuring in reaction to an injury to tissues as a way to further protect the body against infection.

kidney failure
A medical condition in which kidneys are not able to properly filter the blood, allowing protein waste materials to build up in the blood.

lymphocytes
Immune cells.

macrophages
A phagocyte that responds to inflammation.

memory
A property of the immune system in which it "remembers" the specific pathogens it has been exposed to in the past so that the pathogen can be cleared quickly if re-exposed.

memory cells
Cells of the immune system that maintain the body's ability for long-term protection against infections from a specific pathogen.

molds
Members of Fungi, which can be pathogenic.

mucous membranes
The moist tissues of the mouth, nose, windpipe, lungs, stomach, intestines, and excretory system.

nephron
The functional unit of the kidney.

neutrophils
A phagocyte that responds to inflammation.

non-specific response
The generalized inflammatory response which first occurs after tissue injury or exposure to a pathogen.

passive immunity
The type of immunity that develops as a result of transfer of antibodies from one individual to another.

pathogens
Infectious organisms.

phagocytes
Cells that respond to inflammation and engulf pathogens.

physical barriers
The skin and mucous membranes that try to block the entry of pathogens into the system.

pituitary gland
Gland that releases various types of hormones upon commands from the hypothalamus.

plasma cells
B-cells that are making antibodies.

hormone receptors
Proteins on the cell surface, or in the cell cytoplasm, of the target organ to which a hormone binds.

immune receptors
Proteins specific to a particular antigen.

renal artery
Artery that carries blood to the kidney.

steroid
A cholesterol-based hormone.

T-lymphocytes
A specific type of lymphocyte involved in the immune response.

target organ
The organ a hormone is meant to communicate with.

thyroid hormones
Hormones released by the thyroid gland.

Thyrotropin Releasing Hormone (TRH)
The hypothalamus hormone that stimulates the pituitary to release TSH.

Thyroid Stimulating Hormone (TSH)
The pituitary hormone which causes the release of thyroid hormones from the thyroid.

urea
Protein waste product.

urine
The waste products left in the urinary system after all the wastes are filtered out and the needed materials (water and ions) are reabsorbed.

yeasts
Members of Fungi which can be pathogenic.

STUDY QUESTIONS

1. What are organisms called which can infect people?

2. What is the body's defense system against infectious organisms called?

3. The components of the immune system include physical barriers, chemical barriers, the _____ _____, and the _____ _____.

4. What purpose do fevers serve?

5. The non-specific immune response includes _____ release, engulfing cells called _____, and _____ and fever.

6. Describe the two branches of the specific immune response. Briefly, what do they do?

7. What are the foreign proteins which stimulate an immune response called?

8. Describe the function of the helper T-cell, the killer T-cell and the suppressor T-cell.

9. What is "memory" as it relates to the immune system?

10. What is an autoimmune disease?

11. How do the components of the endocrine system communicate with one another?

12. What is the difference between hormones derived from amino acids and steroid hormones?

13. What is the main control organ (or gland) of the endocrine system?

14. Describe how an endocrine feedback loop works.

15. What is a hormone?

16. If you are a molecule of glucose and you are circulating in someone's blood, what will happen to you if the person releases insulin into their blood stream?

17. What does the thyroid gland do when the hypothalamus releases TRH?

18. List the components and function of the excretory system.

19. Draw a picture of a nephron and label the structures.

20. If you were testing someone's urine and found they had a high concentration of glucose, proteins, and ions in their urine, would you conclude the kidney was healthy or sick?

21. What is dialysis?

PLEASE TAKE TEST #13 IN TEST BOOKLET

Human Anatomy and Physiology III

Circulatory and Respiratory Systems

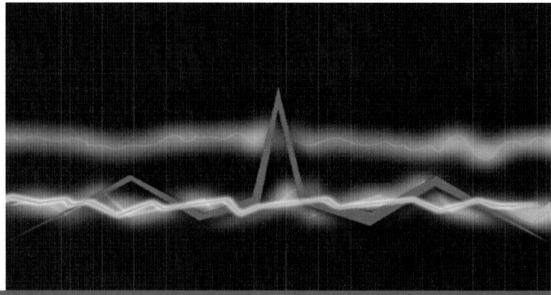

32

32.0 CHAPTER PREVIEW

In this chapter we will:

- Discuss the components of the circulatory system.

- Review the two-loop circulatory system.

- Examine the internal and external heart anatomy.

- Investigate the electrical activity of the heart and how it relates to EKG activity and the generation of blood pressure.

- Study the structure and function of blood.

- Discuss the anatomy of the respiratory system.

- Investigate how inhalation and exhalation occur.

32.1 CIRCULATORY SYSTEM: GENERAL

The purpose of the **circulatory system** is to move oxygen, hormones, and nutrients to tissues/organs; and carbon dioxide and wastes from tissues/organs. Up to this point, we have discussed the means many different species of organisms use to accomplish this goal. Vascular plants use the vascular tissues of xylem and phloem. Animal organisms can have "open" or "closed" circulatory systems. Humans and all vertebrates have a closed, two-loop circulatory system with a four-chambered heart.

The components of the circulatory system can be seen in Figure 32.1.1. Although blood is technically considered **connective tissue** (please remember this) we are going to discuss it with the circulatory system because it is such an integral part of the transport function.

Figure 32.1.1

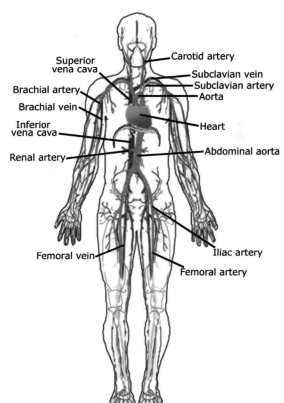

The Circulatory System
The major components of the circulatory system are shown here. The heart is the pump that propels the blood through the body. Arteries carry blood away from the heart and veins carry the blood back to the heart. The aorta is the main artery that exits the heart directly and serves as a distribution line. The rest of the arteries form as branches from the aorta. The carotid arteries carry blood to the head and brain, the renal arteries supply the kidneys, the subclavian arteries are the pathway for the blood to exit the chest to get to the arms, and the iliac arteries are the pathway for the blood to move from the pelvis into the legs. In the extremities, the brachial arteries carry the blood from the shoulder down into the forearms and hands. In the legs, it is the femoral arteries that carry blood through the thighs to the lower legs and feet.

The basic components of the system are listed in Figure 32.1.2. You will need to be familiar with the parts of the circulatory system and their functions to understand the remainder of this chapter.

Figure 32.1.2

Components and Functions of the Circulatory System.

Component	Function
Blood (technically part of the connective tissue system)	carries nutrients, hormones, and gasses to and from tissues
Heart	pumps blood through the system
Blood Vessels	carries blood to tissues from heart, and from tissues back to heart
arteries	carry blood **away** from heart
veins	carry blood **toward** heart
capillaries	small blood vessels that are the site of the exchange of nutrients, wastes, and gasses between blood and tissues; the diameter of the walls are so small that only one blood cell at a time can fit through; form in **beds** which are rich networks of capillaries

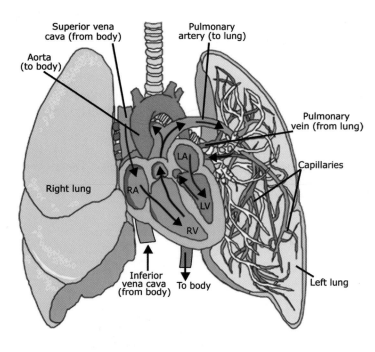

Superior vena cava (from body)

Pulmonary artery (to lung)

Aorta (to body)

Pulmonary vein (from lung)

Capillaries

Right lung

RA

LA

LV

RV

Inferior vena cava (from body)

To body

Left lung

Figure 32.1.3

Heart-lung Connection

Like all land animals, humans have a two loop circulatory system. In one loop the heart pumps blood to the lungs and back and the other loop goes to the tissues and back. The heart is made of four chambers. Bird hearts also have four chambers, as do crocodiles and alligators. The two chambers which receive blood coming into the heart are called atria (singular atrium) and the two chambers which pump the blood out of the heart are called ventricles. The left atrium (LA) receives oxygenated blood from the lungs through the pulmonary veins and passes it to the left ventricle (LV). The left ventricle contracts and the blood is pumped into the aorta and carried to the tissues. In the tissues it passes through the small vessels called capillaries, where gas exchange occurs. The blood then enters the veins. The head and upper extremity venous blood returns to the heart through the superior vena cava. The blood from the abdomen and legs returns through the inferior vena cava. The right atrium receives deoxygenated blood from these two large veins. The right atrium passes the blood to the right ventricle (RV). When the right ventricle contracts, the blood is pumped to the lungs through the pulmonary arteries. In the lungs, carbon dioxide is released from the blood, and oxygen is absorbed into the blood. The oxygenated blood then enters the pulmonary veins and returns to the left atrium.

32.2 CIRCULATORY SYSTEM: ANATOMY

Recall from earlier in the course that animals with lungs have a two-loop circulatory system. One loop of the system circulates the oxygenated blood—blood that has a high concentration of oxygen and a low concentration of carbon dioxide—from the heart to the tissues, then back to the heart. This is called the **peripheral loop** (or **systemic loop**). During circulation in the peripheral loop, oxygen is taken from the blood into the tissues and carbon dioxide is taken from the tissues into the blood. The second loop circulates the deoxygenated blood—blood that is low in oxygen content and high in carbon dioxide content—from the heart to the lung and back. This is called the **pulmonary loop**. During circulation in the pulmonary loop, carbon dioxide is taken from the blood and into the air in the lungs and oxygen is taken from the air in the lungs and into the blood. See Figure 32.2.1 for a graphic of the circulation of blood in the two loops and what happens during the transport of the blood from the heart and back again.

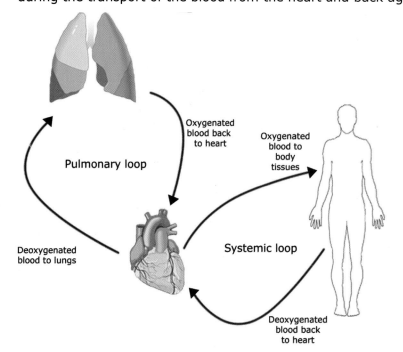

Oxygenated blood back to heart

Oxygenated blood to body tissues

Pulmonary loop

Deoxygenated blood to lungs

Systemic loop

Deoxygenated blood back to heart

Figure 32.2.1

The Two-Loop System

All land vertebrates and mammals have a two-loop circulatory system. One loop is the circuit to the lungs which allows the deoxygenated blood to release carbon dioxide and pick up oxygen. Then the newly oxygenated blood returns to the heart and the pulmonary loop is completed. The second circuit is the systemic loop which supplies the tissues with oxygen and removes carbon dioxide. The oxygenated blood is pumped out of the heart to the tissues where oxygen is absorbed from the blood and carbon dioxide is released into the blood. The blood is now deoxygenated and returns to the heart.

Your heart is about the size of your fist. It is all muscle. It has four chambers: **right atrium**, **left atrium**, **right ventricle**, and **left ventricle**. The atria and right ventricle are muscular, but not nearly as muscular as the left ventricle. The right atrium is a collecting chamber for the deoxygenated blood to collect as it returns from the tissues to the heart. The **superior vena cava** is the large vein that returns blood to the right atrium from the head, neck, and arms. The **inferior vena cava** returns blood to the right atrium from the legs and abdominal organs.

Figure 32.2.2

External Heart Anatomy
The anterior (front) and posterior (back) external heart anatomy of the heart is shown below. The aorta carries oxygenated blood from the heart to the body. The inferior and superior vena cava returns the deoxygenated blood from the tissues to the heart. The pulmonary arteries carry the deoxygenated blood from the heart to the lungs and the pulmonary veins bring it back to the heart full of oxygen.

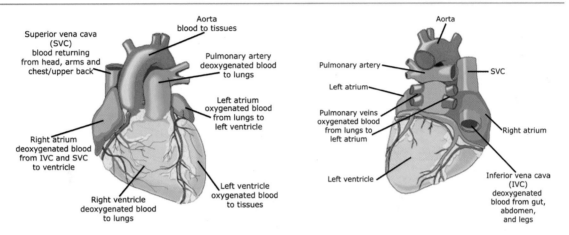

Once the right atrium is filled with blood, it contracts and the blood is pumped into the right ventricle. The right ventricle is somewhat muscular, but, again, not as muscular as the left ventricle. Separating the right atrium and ventricle is a tough, fibrous tissue called the **tricuspid valve**. This valve prevents the backflow of blood from the right ventricle into the right atrium when the right ventricle contracts. Once the right ventricle is filled with blood, it contracts and pumps blood into the lungs through the **pulmonary arteries**. The **pulmonic valve** prevents the backflow of blood from the pulmonary artery into the right ventricle.

Figure 32.2.3

Internal Heart Anatomy and Valves
Valves prevent the backflow of blood and the heart has four of them. Valves open to let blood flow one way and then close to prevent it from flowing in the opposite direction. The right atrium is separated from the right ventricle by the **tricuspid valve**. When the right atrium contracts, the tricuspid valve opens to let the blood flow into the ventricle. When the right ventricle is full and contracts to pump blood to the lungs, the tricuspid valve closes to prevent blood from flowing back into the right atrium. **The pulmonic** valve separates the right ventricle form the pulmonary artery. When the right ventricle contracts to pump blood into the lungs through the pulmonary artery, the pulmonic valve opens to let blood flow through. When the ventricle relaxes after pumping, the pulmonic valve closes to prevent blood from flowing from the pulmonary artery back into the right ventricle. The left atrium is separated from the left ventricle by the **mitral valve**. When the left atrium contracts, the mitral valve opens to let blood flow into the ventricle. When the left ventricle contracts to pump blood into the aorta, the mitral valve closes to prevent blood from flowing back into the left atrium. The final valve is the **aortic valve**. It separates the left ventricle form the aorta. When the left ventricle contracts, it opens to let the blood flow into the aorta. When the ventricle relaxes, the aortic valve closes to prevent blood from flowing back into the left ventricle.

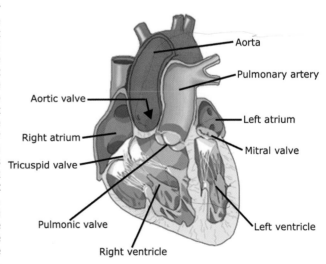

Once the blood enters into the vessels of the lungs, it rapidly moves through arteries which branch into smaller and smaller arteries, until the vessels become the width of one red blood cell. These small vessels are capillaries, and they form into extensive networks called **capillary beds**. In the capillary beds, the deoxygenated blood releases carbon dioxide into the air spaces in the lungs and picks up oxygen from the air spaces in the lungs. The blood is now oxygenated.

Figure 32.2.4

Gas and Nutrient Exchange
Capillaries are the tiny blood vessel connections between the arteries and veins. All gas and nutrient exchange occurs in the capillaries. This is possible because capillary walls are thin and allow a variety of substances to pass through. As the blood passes through the capillaries, it slows down to allow for the exchanges to take place. The blood flows slowly from the artery side of the capillary to the venous side of the capillary. As it does, oxygen diffuses from the blood into the tissues and the tissues release carbon dioxide into the blood. Also, cell waste products are released into the blood, while at the same time nutrients are absorbed. Our entire body is filled with millions of capillary beds where this occurs every second. Veins have structures in them called valves. These valves function like the heart valves. They prevent the back flow of blood in the veins. The pressure driving the blood to move in the veins is much lower than the pressure in the arteries. Also, usually the blood in veins is moving against gravity. Therefore, there are forces which do not favor the movement of blood in the proper direction in veins and valves counteract these forces.

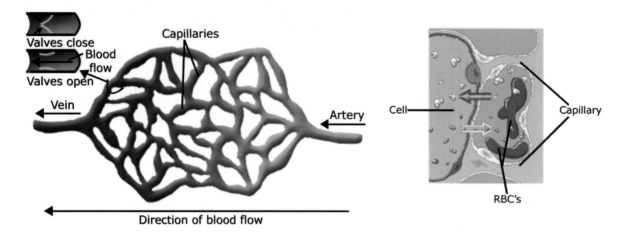

Direction of blood flow

The oxygenated blood then moves from the capillaries into the **pulmonary veins**. The pulmonary veins bring the blood into the left atrium of the heart. When the left atrium is filled, it contracts and pumps blood into the left ventricle. Once the muscular left ventricle is filled, it contracts and pumps blood into the **aorta** and the peripheral circulation. The **mitral valve** prevents the backflow of blood from the left ventricle into the left atrium when the left ventricle contracts. The **aortic valve** is between the left ventricle and aorta to prevent the backflow of blood from the aorta into the left ventricle after the ventricle contracts.

The aorta is the largest artery in the body and functions as the main highway to distribute blood to the peripheral circulation. As can be seen from the figures, the larger arteries branch into smaller and smaller arteries as they proceed to the tissues. Once the blood reaches the smallest branches of the blood vessel tree—the capillaries—gas and nutrient exchange occurs, and the blood moves into the veins and back to the heart. The blood pressure in veins is much less than that in the arteries. Because of this, larger veins have valves in them, as the heart does, to prevent the backflow of blood. The continuous flow of blood from the arteries into the capillaries, then into the veins, provides some of the needed pressure to "push" the blood through the veins. Also, each time a person breathes in, negative pressure—like a vacuum—develops in the chest cavity (where the heart is located). This negative pressure helps to "pull" the blood from the veins into the heart. Normally, even though the blood pressure in the veins is quite low, the "pushing" and "pulling" forces are more than enough to provide proper blood return from the tissues back to the heart.

SA = Pacemaker

Impulse (R) A

32.3 CIRCULATORY SYSTEM: PHYSIOLOGY OF A HEARTBEAT

The generation of the **heartbeat** is quite interesting. Although the heartbeat can be regulated somewhat by the brain through the neurological and endocrine systems, the source of the impulse for the heartbeat comes from the heart itself. Each impulse for the heart to beat is an electrical impulse that starts in the right atrium, in a bundle of tissue called the **sinoatrial node**, or **S-A node**. The S-A node is called the pacemaker of the heart. When the cells of the S-A node generate an electrical impulse, the impulse is carried in a wave across the right atrium to the left atrium. As the electrical impulse travels across the atria, it stimulates the muscles of the two atria to contract.

The electrical impulse then moves from the atria to the ventricles through a bundle of cells between the atria and the ventricles called **atrioventricular node**, or **A-V node**. The A-V node conducts the impulse from the atria into the ventricles after it delays the signal a bit. This allows the atria to contract before the ventricles. In doing so, the ventricles are able to fill completely with blood before they start to contract. Without the delay at the A-V node, the atria and ventricles would beat at almost the same time, which would make the heart inefficient at pumping the blood through the body. Once the electrical impulse travels from the A-V node into the ventricles, the ventricles contract and pump the blood into the pulmonary and systemic loops. Each time an impulse is generated in the S-A node, the heart beats.

Let's think of what the practical implications of the electrical impulse pathway of the heart are. When a human exercises, sometimes the heart rate can reach 180 beats per minute, or every one-third of a second. This means the impulse for the heart to beat must be generated from the S-A node, which is then transmitted through both atria, pauses briefly in the A-V node, and then is conducted into the ventricles all in three-tenths of a second or less. That is pretty amazing.

Figure 32.3.1

The Electrical Heart

The heart is a big ball of muscle tissue specialized to contract repeatedly and conduct electrical impulses. The impulse for the heartbeat starts at the top of the right atrium in the sinoatrial (SA) node. The SA node passes the electrical impulse to contract to the cells of the right atrium and almost instantaneously the impulse is transmitted from the right atrium to the left atrium. This results in an atrial contraction and can be seen on an ECG (electrocardiogram) tracing as the P wave. When the P wave is seen, the atria are contracting. Then the electrical impulse is gathered in tissue in the right ventricle called the atrioventricular (AV) node. There is a slight delay of transmission of the electrical impulse at the AV node allowing the ventricles to completely fill with blood. After a short pause in the AV node, the impulse is sent into the right, then left ventricles, and they contract. This corresponds to the QRS complex on the ECG. When the QRS complex occurs on the ECG the ventricles contract.

① generates impulse to beat
② transmitted thru BOTH Atria
④ conducted into Ventricles

Pacemaker
SA node

Pauses briefly here

③

AV node

Heart - spec muscle tissue - contracts repeatedly & conducts electrical impulses

P waves
SA → RA → LA → (R) Ventricles = AV node
(contracting)
slight delay - ventricles fill
QRS
Sent to RV then LV
contract

Atria contract

Ventricles contract

R

P

Q
S

T

QRS complex

A **heartbeat** (one contraction cycle of the heart) is divided into two phases. The first phase is called **systole** and corresponds to the contraction of the ventricles. During systole, the left ventricle contracts and pumps blood into the aorta. During this time, the aortic valve is open (if it was not open no blood could get into the aorta) and the pressure of the ventricle contracting closes the mitral valve. The closed mitral valve prevents backflow of blood from the left ventricle into the left atrium. Also during systole, the right ventricle contracts and pumps blood through an open pulmonic valve into the pulmonary arteries. The tricuspid valve is closed by the force of the contraction of the right ventricle. The closure of the tricuspid valve prevents backflow of blood from the right ventricle into the right atrium. Also note that during systole the atria are filling with blood.

The second phase is called **diastole**. Diastole corresponds to relaxation of the ventricles. During this time, the loss of pressure from the contracting ventricles causes the aortic and pulmonic valves to close, preventing backflow of blood into the ventricles. Since there is no longer any pressure in the ventricles to keep them closed, the mitral and tricuspid valves open, allowing blood to flow from the right atrium into the right ventricle and from left atrium into the left ventricle. Once the ventricles are filled, the whole cycle starts again. The number of times the heart beats per minute is called the **heart rate**.

32.4 CIRCULATORY SYSTEM: BLOOD PRESSURE

Blood pressure is the pressure that forms in the arteries as a result of the blood being pumped into them from the left ventricle. During systole, when the left ventricle contracts, the arteries fill with blood; their walls bulge out, and muscles within the arteries contract to keep the walls from bulging too much. After the artery bulges, it relaxes as the blood moves through it. This movement of the blood into the arteries and the muscular contraction of the artery walls create a pressure within the arteries that is called the blood pressure. The rhythmic bulge also creates the movement of the artery you can feel with your fingers, called the **pulse**. As the blood moves from larger to smaller arteries on its way to capillaries, the blood pressure begins to drop. Once the blood enters the capillaries, the blood pressure is low, which allows the blood to "stay" in the capillaries for a relatively long time (as compared to how long the blood remains in the artery). This allows for maximal nutrient and gas exchange to occur across the walls of the capillaries.

The "numbers" of the blood pressure correspond to two events during the heartbeat. The "first number" of a blood pressure reading is the **systolic blood pressure**. It corresponds to the pressure in the arteries during ventricle contraction. The "second number" of a blood pressure reading is the **diastolic blood pressure**. It corresponds to the pressure in the arteries during ventricle relaxation.

In order to measure blood pressure, a gauge is used that measures how much a column of mercury is displaced by the pressure in the arteries. The blood pressure cuff is wrapped around the arm and measures the pressure in the **brachial artery**. As the blood pressure cuff is inflated, it raises the pressure around the artery by progressively compressing the skin. Eventually, enough pressure is exerted on the artery to cause the artery to collapse, stopping the flow of blood through the artery. During the cuff inflation, the column of mercury on the gauge rises. When there is no longer any flow of blood through the artery, the air in the blood pressure cuff is slowly let out. Normally, the systolic pressure is higher than the diastolic blood pressure. At some point, the pressure the cuff is exerting on the artery is the same as the systolic pressure in the artery, and blood begins to shoot through the small opening in the artery. This is heard with the stethoscope placed over the brachial artery as a loud "swish." At that exact time, the level of displacement of the column of mercury is read by the person taking the blood pressure. The first sound that is heard corresponds to the systolic blood pressure. As the cuff is further deflated, the artery gradually assumes its more normal shape of being round. Until it does become completely round, though, there is turbulence in the artery as the blood flows through an irregularly shaped opening. This turbulence is able to be heard through the stethoscope. As soon as the pressure in the cuff equals the diastolic blood pressure the artery becomes completely round again, and there is no longer any turbulence in the artery. This means there is no more "swish" sound heard through the stethoscope. At that point, the pressure in the cuff corresponds to the diastolic blood pressure and the examiner notes the amount of displacement on the column of mercury.

Blood pressures are always written "systolic/diastolic." A blood pressure of 120/65 means that the pressure in the arteries during systole—when the left ventricle is actively pumping blood into the arteries—is enough to displace 120 mm of mercury. The diastolic blood pressure—when the left ventricle is at rest and not pumping blood into the arteries—is enough to displace 65 mm of mercury.

Based on testing many millions of people, we have been able to establish normal blood pressures and values for high blood pressure. High blood pressure is also called **hypertension**. A person with a systolic blood pressure more than 140 mm of mercury and/or a diastolic blood pressure more than 90 mm of mercury is said to be **hypertensive**. Because hypertension increases the risk of developing a number of medical problems, such as stroke and heart attacks, it is aggressively treated with lifestyle modifications, weight loss, and medications.

32.5 BLOOD

Blood is an inseparable part of the circulatory system, but it is considered a **connective tissue**. What is blood? See Figure 32.5.1 for the components of blood. Blood is a mixture of liquid—called **plasma**—in which blood cells are suspended. All blood cells are made in the bone marrow of the long bones, such as the leg bone (femur) and ribs; and the flat bones, such as the hip bone (ilium) and the breast bone (sternum).

Figure 32.5.1

Components of Blood

Component	Function	Source
white blood cells	fight infection	bone marrow
red blood cells	carry oxygen to and carbon dioxide from tissues	bone marrow
platelets	clot wounds to stop bleeding	fragments of cells (megakaryocytes) that are made in bone marrow and then break apart
plasma	liquid component of blood in which red and white blood cells and platelets are suspended; contains water (90%), proteins, nutrients, salts (ions), hormones, and cellular wastes	absorbed fluid from tissues and GI and excretory tracts

We have already discussed one of the cellular components of blood—white blood cells, also called **leukocytes**—and the way they fight infection. The other cellular component of blood is the **red blood cell**, also called **erythrocytes**. Red blood cells are the cells responsible for transporting oxygen from the lungs to the tissues and carbon dioxide from the tissues to the lungs.

Human red blood cells (**RBC's**) do not have a nucleus and are described as a **biconcave disc**. That means that RBC's are disc shaped, but each side of the cell is "pushed in," as can be seen from the diagram. They resemble two small saucers placed bottom to bottom. Each RBC carries the molecule **hemoglobin**. Hemoglobin is an iron-containing molecule; it easily binds to oxygen. Hemoglobin inside of red blood cells carries about 98% of the oxygen to the tissues. Hemoglobin carries some carbon dioxide from the tissues to the lungs, but most of the carbon dioxide is dissolved in the plasma.

In the capillaries of the lung, oxygen diffuses across the cell membranes of the capillaries and into the red blood cell, where it binds to hemoglobin. The oxygen-hemoglobin complex is called **oxyhemoglobin**. When the RBC containing the oxyhemoglobin circulates to the capillaries of the tissues, the oxygen is released from the hemoglobin and diffuses across the membrane of the capillary and into the tissues. Carbon dioxide released from the tissues diffuses across the capillary membrane into the blood. Some of the carbon dioxide binds to the hemoglobin in the RBC and some dissolves as ions in the plasma. When the blood returns to the lungs, the carbon dioxide is released from the hemoglobin and plasma and diffuses across the capillary membrane into the air in the lung.

Figure 32.5.2

Red Blood Cells
Red blood cells (RBC's) are known as biconcave discs. This means they are three-dimensional, flattened, and round structures (discs), with a depression in the middle ("biconcave"). They look like a donut and are filled with the complex molecule called hemoglobin. Hemoglobin is specialized to bind and carry oxygen.

32.6 RESPIRATORY SYSTEM: ANATOMY

We have already discussed some information regarding the respiratory system above. We will discuss the anatomy of the respiratory system in this section, as well as comment on the functions of the various parts. As we proceed through the discussion, you will be able to appreciate the complex inter-relatedness of all of the systems in the body.

The components of the respiratory system consist of the **upper respiratory tract** and the **lower respiratory tract**. The upper respiratory tract consists of the nose, mouth, sinuses, pharynx, larynx, and trachea. The lower respiratory tract consists of the bronchi (singular bronchus) and two lungs. When you inhale, the air first passes through the mouth and/or the nose. If the air enters through the nose, it then passes into the **nasal cavities**, or **sinuses**. The sinuses are air spaces in the skull that serve to warm the air. In addition, the sinuses are lined with mucosa, as is the entire respiratory system, which functions to trap particles and pathogens to prevent them from entering into the lower respiratory tract.

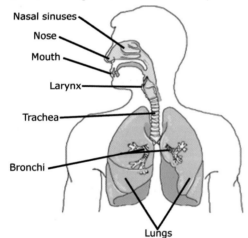

Figure 32.6.1

The Respiratory System
The respiratory system consists of many different specialized areas to get the air into and out of the lungs. The nose and mouth are the opening for the entire system. Nasal sinuses warm the air and trap pathogens and particles. The larynx (voice box) produces sound and speech. The trachea (wind pipe) is a tough tube protected by cartilage to conduct air into and out of the lungs. Bronchi are smaller branches of the respiratory tubes. Gas exchange takes place in the lungs.

After the air passes through the sinuses, it passes through the back of the throat, or **pharynx**. It continues to travel toward the lungs, passing by the **epiglottis**. The epiglottis is a rigid flap of tissue at the top of the entry into the lower respiratory tract that protects the lower respiratory tract from food or liquid entering into it. When we swallow, muscles in the throat pull the voice box, or **larynx**, upward. As it moves up, the opening to the lower respiratory tract is covered by the epiglottis, keeping anything we swallow from entering into the larynx.

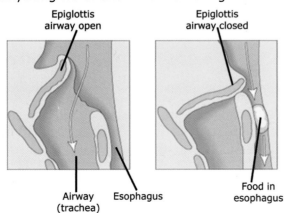

Figure 32.6.2

Epiglottis
The epiglottis protects the airway from anything entering it but air. When we swallow, muscles pull the throat and esophagus upward. This effectively closes the airway by pulling the opening into contact with the epiglottis. Food and liquid passes the airway without entering.

As noted, the larynx is also called the voice box. Within the larynx, on either side, are two folds of muscular tissue called the **vocal cords**. When we speak, the muscles of the vocal cords contract and move the cords together. This creates a restriction in the amount of air that can pass by them. This causes the vocal cords to vibrate, which is what generates the sound of our voices. The air passes the larynx and enters into the wind pipe, or trachea. The trachea carries air from the neck into the chest, or **thoracic cavity**. Inside the thoracic cavity, the trachea branches into two main pipes, called **bronchi**. One bronchus goes to the left lung and one bronchus goes to the right lung.

→ The larynx, trachea, and larger bronchi are all fairly large tubes and have a structure made from cartilage. The cartilage keeps these larger air tubes open when there is a large amount of air being inhaled quickly. Recall that the lining of the mucosa of the trachea and lower respiratory tract is lined with cilia, to further remove particles and pathogens from the air we breathe so nothing can reach the lower levels of the lung.

Each bronchus divides into smaller and smaller tubes as it enters the lung. As the air tubes get progressively smaller, they are called **bronchioles**. Bronchioles do not have a cartilage structure. Eventually, the bronchioles reach the lung tissue and end in an air sac called an **alveolus** (plural alveoli). The alveolus is where gas exchange occurs. There are about 300 million alveoli in human lungs. The lung itself is made of a spongy tissue. The presence of the alveoli significantly increases the surface area of the lungs, which makes gas exchange much more efficient. This property of folding tissue to increase effective surface area within the organ is a common structural component of many systems. We have already seen this with the nervous system (brain gyri and sulci), excretory system (kidney's glomeruli), and now the lungs. We will also see this in the digestive system.

Figure 32.6.3

Alveoli

Alveoli are the functional unit of the lung. An alveolus is basically a fluffy ball of tissue, often called an air sac. All alveoli are covered in capillaries (one alveolus is shown below without capillaries). When we inhale, air enters the alveolus interior. While it is in the alveolus, oxygen gas diffuses across the cell membrane of the alveolar cells and the capillaries and into the blood. At the same time, carbon dioxide diffuses out of the blood into the interior of the alveolus. When we exhale, the air from the interior of the alveolus, now filled with carbon dioxide, is expelled into the air around us.

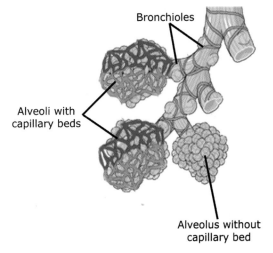

Bronchioles

Alveoli with capillary beds

Alveolus without capillary bed

32.7 RESPIRATORY SYSTEM: PHYSIOLOGY

The alveolus is the functional unit of the lung. Gas exchange occurs at the level of the alveolus. Gas exchange is called **respiration**. Each alveolus has a bed of capillaries surrounding it to allow for air exchange to take place. The transfer of carbon dioxide out of the blood into the air in the alveolus; the transfer of oxygen from the air in the alveolus into the blood, is accomplished through simple diffusion. The concentration of carbon dioxide is less in the air in the alveolus than the concentration of carbon dioxide in the blood of the capillary surrounding the alveolus. The carbon dioxide diffuses out of the blood and into the alveolus. Conversely, the concentration of oxygen is higher in the air of the alveolus than in the blood of the capillary surrounding the alveolus. The oxygen diffuses across its concentration gradient, from the air and into the blood. Diffusion is also responsible for the movement of gasses into and out of the tissues. The exchange of gasses from the blood to the air across the lungs is called **external respiration**, while the exchange of gasses from the blood across the tissues is referred to as **internal respiration**.

Inhalation, or breathing in, occurs through muscular contractions. Unlike the heart, which generates its own impulse for beating, the lungs receive their direction from the brain. Cells in the brainstem send impulses to the **diaphragm**. The diaphragm is a muscle separating the chest cavity from the abdominal cavity. When the brainstem sends the impulse to take a breath, the impulse travels from the brainstem, along the **phrenic nerve**, to the diaphragm. When the diaphragm receives the signal from the phrenic nerve, it contracts. As it contracts, it moves downward into the abdominal cavity. As it does so, it creates negative pressure in the chest cavity. This is the vacuum effect. Air then flows from regions of positive pressure (i.e., the area outside of the lungs) to areas of lower pressure (i.e. the lungs). This causes the lungs to expand, or inflate, as the air is drawn in through the mouth or nose and into the lungs.

Figure 32.7.1

Inhalation and Exhalation

In order to inhale, the diaphragm contracts, causing it to move downward in relation to the lungs. When the diaphragm moves downward, it creates negative pressure in the chest cavity, like a vacuum. Air moves from an area of higher pressure outside of the body, to the area of lower pressure inside the lungs. The pressure in the lungs is lower because of the vacuum effect caused by the contracting diaphragm. Exhalation is accomplished by the diaphragm relaxing. This allows the elastic recoil of the lungs to cause the lungs to deflate, releasing the air from the lungs into the atmosphere. Elastic recoil of the lungs is like the elastic recoil of a rubber band. When you pull a rubber band tight, it goes back to its normal resting state when you let it go. The diaphragm contracting and causing the lungs to fill with air pulls them tight. The diaphragm relaxing allows them to recoil back to their smaller state and release the air.

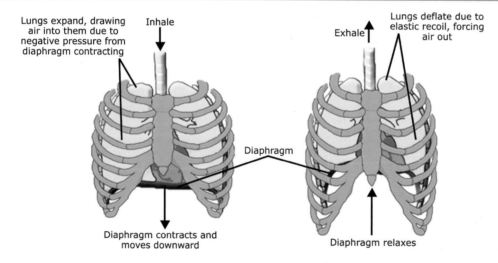

Exhalation, or breathing out, occurs because the lungs are **elastic**. Exhalation occurs due to the elastic recoil of the lungs. The lungs are made up of tissue that is like a rubber band. When the lungs are full of air, they are large, and the elastic connective tissue in the lungs is stretched tight. The pressure inside the lungs is greater than the pressure outside the lungs. When inhalation is completed, the elastic recoil of the lungs simply "pulls" them back into a smaller position. As the lungs are pulled into the smaller resting position, the air is forced out of them. The process of moving air into and out of the lungs (i.e., breathing) is called **ventilation** (as opposed to respiration which is the process of gas exchange).

How many times a person needs to breathe—called the **respiratory rate**, measures in breaths per minute—is controlled by the brain and brain stem. Sensors in the brain measure the amount of carbon dioxide in the blood. If the level of carbon dioxide begins to increase, the brain stem signals the diaphragm to contract more often—i.e., increase the respiratory rate. As the rate of breathing increases, more carbon dioxide is exchanged for oxygen in the lungs, and the level of CO_2 in the blood decreases. When the level of CO_2 decreases to the appropriate level, this is sensed by the cells in the brain and the respiratory rate is slowed down. The opposite effect occurs if the level of CO_2 decreases.

32.8 PEOPLE OF SCIENCE

William Harvey (1578–1657) was born in England and educated as a physician in Italy at the University of Padua. He was the personal physician to King James I and King Charles I. During the time that Harvey was practicing and researching, the teachings of Galen were still followed. In particular, the thinking at the time was that the venous and arterial systems were separate and had nothing to do with one another. Harvey's anatomic dissections showed, however, that the blood circulated from artery to vein and was pumped by the heart through a closed circulatory system. This revolutionary view was strongly resisted at first, but by the time of his death, Harvey's model of circulation was widely accepted.

32.9 KEY CHAPTER POINTS

- The purpose of the circulatory system is to move oxygen, hormones, and nutrients to tissues/organs and carbon dioxide as well as wastes from tissues/organs.

- The circulatory system of humans and all vertebrates is a closed, two-loop system. It is composed of a heart, arteries, veins, and capillaries.

- The heart has four chambers and four valves.

- The heart muscle is specialized to contract and to conduct electricity.

- Blood pressure is a measure of the pressure in the arteries during the period of time the ventricles beat (systole) and the period of time they do not beat (diastole).

- Blood is a connective tissue and is made up of red blood cells, white blood cells, platelets, and plasma.

- The purpose of the respiratory system is to exchange gasses.

- The respiratory system is composed of the upper and lower respiratory tract.

- Gas exchange in the tissues and lungs occurs through diffusion.

32.10 DEFINITIONS

alveolus (plural alveoli)
Air sac at the end of the bronchioles where gas exchange takes place.

aorta
The main artery, which carries blood directly out of the heart.

aortic valve
Valve between the aorta and the left ventricle that prevents the backflow of blood.

atrioventricular node (A-V node)
A bundle of cells between the atria and the ventricles that conducts the electrical impulse for contraction from the atria into the ventricles.

blood
A connective tissue made of a mixture of plasma, white blood cells, red blood cells, and molecules.

blood pressure
The pressure that forms in the arteries as a result of the blood being pumped into them from the left ventricle.

brachial artery
The artery that carries blood into the arms.

bronchi
The branches of the respiratory tract; they conduct air between the trachea and the bronchioles.

bronchioles
The smaller branches of the respiratory tract; they conduct air between the alveoli and the bronchi.

capillary beds
Extensive networks of capillaries where gas, nutrition, and waste exchange occurs in all tissues.

circulatory system
System to move oxygen and nutrients to tissues/organs; and carbon dioxide and wastes from tissues/organs.

connective tissue
A tissue connecting one part of the body to another.

diaphragm
The respiratory muscle separating the chest cavity from the abdominal cavity.

diastole
The second phase of the heartbeat; corresponds to relaxation and filling of the ventricles.

diastolic blood pressure
The blood pressure generated in the arteries during diastole.

elastic
The property of some types of tissue, such as lung tissue, to expand and recoil back to its resting position.

epiglottis
A rigid flap of tissue that keeps food and liquid from entering the trachea.

erythrocytes
Red blood cells.

external respiration
The exchange of gasses from the blood to the air across lung tissue.

heartbeat
One contraction cycle of the heart.

heart rate
The number of times the heart beats per minute.

hemoglobin
An iron-containing molecule; easily binds to oxygen and holds it in the red blood cell for transportation to the rest of the tissues.

hypertension
High blood pressure.

hypertensive
The condition of the systolic blood pressure being elevated to more than 140 mm of mercury and/or a diastolic blood pressure more than 90 mm of mercury.

inferior vena cava
The vein that returns blood to the right atrium from the legs and abdominal organs.

internal respiration
The exchange of gasses from the blood across the tissues.

larynx
The part of the respiratory tract where sound is generated. Also called the voice box.

left ventricle
The muscular chamber of the heart that pumps blood to the body.

leukocytes
White blood cells.

lower respiratory tract
That part of the respiratory tract consisting of the bronchi and two lungs.

mitral valve
Structure that prevents the backflow of blood from the left ventricle into the left atrium.

nasal cavities
That part of the respiratory tract where air initially enters the body.

oxyhemoglobin
The oxygen-hemoglobin complex; hemoglobin that is bound to oxygen.

peripheral loop
Blood moving from the heart to the tissues, then back to the heart.

phrenic nerve
Nerve that carries the impulse to take a breath from the brainstem to the diaphragm.

plasma
The liquid part of the blood in which blood cells are suspended.

pulmonary arteries
Arteries that carry deoxygenated blood into the lungs.

pulmonary loop
Blood moving from the heart to the lungs and back.

pulmonary veins
Veins that bring oxygenated blood into the left atrium of the heart.

pulmonic valve
Structure preventing the backflow of blood from the pulmonary artery into the right ventricle.

pulse
The rhythmic arterial bulge created by the heart beating; can be felt with the fingers.

red blood cells
Cells responsible for transporting oxygen from the lungs to the tissues and a small amount of the carbon dioxide from the tissues to the lungs.

respiratory rate
The number of times a person takes a breath every minute.

right ventricle
The chamber of the heart that pumps deoxygenated blood to the lungs.

sinoatrial node (S-A node)
The heart cells that generate the electrical impulse for the heart to beat; the pacemaker of the heart.

sinuses
Air spaces in the skull; they warm the air.

superior vena cava
The large vein returning blood to the right atrium from the head, neck, and arms.

systole
The first phase of the heartbeat, which corresponds to the contraction of the ventricles.

systolic blood pressure
The pressure generated in the arteries during systole.

thoracic cavity
That part of the body which holds the heart and lungs; the chest.

tricuspid valve
Structure preventing the backflow of blood from the right ventricle into the right atrium.

upper respiratory tract
The conductive system bringing air into and out of the lungs, consisting of the nose, mouth, sinuses, pharynx, larynx, and trachea.

ventilation
The process of moving air into and out of the lungs (i.e., breathing).

vocal cords
Muscular tissue that vibrates to generate sound.

STUDY QUESTIONS

1. True or False? Although the circulatory system cannot function without it, blood is considered to be part of the connective tissue system.

2. What is the function of the heart? Of veins? Of arteries? Of capillaries?

3. Is the human circulatory system a one or two-loop system?

4. Draw a two-loop circulatory system and label the parts.

5. If you are a red blood cell starting in the left atrium, list in order the following structures you will pass through on your way to the leg muscles and back to the heart: left atrium, aorta, inferior vena cava, femoral vein, lungs, left ventricle, iliac vein, iliac artery, pulmonary artery, mitral valve, pulmonic valve, right ventricle, pulmonary vein, tricuspid valve, femoral artery, systemic capillaries, pulmonary capillaries, aortic valve, and right atrium.

6. How many valves are there in the heart? What is their function?

7. Where does the electrical impulse for the heartbeat originate?

8. What does the A-V node do? What is a critical part of its function?

9. What are the two phases of the heartbeat called?

10. What is blood pressure?

11. What does "hypertension" mean?

12. What are the components of blood?

13. Describe the RBC's role in gas exchange. In which type of blood vessel does gas exchange occur?

14. What are the components of the upper respiratory tract? Of the lower respiratory tract?

15. Which structure is smaller in size (diameter), a bronchus or a bronchiole?

16. Describe how we are able to protect our airway when we swallow.

17. Describe the process of inhalation and exhalation.

Human Anatomy and Physiology IV

Digestive, Musculoskeletal/Connective Tissue, and Integumentary Systems

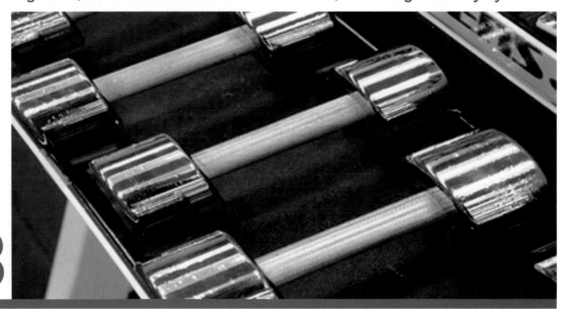

33

33.0 CHAPTER PREVIEW

In this chapter we will:

- Discuss the anatomy of the digestive system.

- Investigate the physiology of the digestive system with special attention to:
  - salivary glands and amylase
  - peristalsis
  - the mechanical actions of the stomach and the enzyme pepsinogen
  - the function of the duodenum, jejunum, ileum, gall bladder, liver, pancreas and colon
  - the absorptive capacity of villi and microvilli

- Discuss the structure and function of the three types of muscles—skeletal, cardiac, and smooth.

- Learn the structure and function of bone.

- Review the function of ligaments and tendons.

- Investigate joint types.

- Study the structure and function of the integumentary system (skin).

33.1 DIGESTIVE SYSTEM: GENERAL

The function of the digestive system is to break down and absorb the nutrients needed to sustain life. Humans need a variety of substances to live. These substances are called **nutrients**, and they are obtained by absorbing them from the food we eat and the liquids we drink. We need carbohydrates for energy production (to make molecules of ATP). Proteins are major structural components of cells and enzymes. **Fats** (**Lipids**) are necessary for the structure of the cell membranes and to obtain energy in certain conditions. **Vitamins** are complex organic molecules that serve as co-factors for enzymes to work properly. All vitamins must be absorbed from the food we eat except for **Vitamin D**. Although we can certainly absorb the vitamin D we need to survive, most of us convert cholesterol to Vitamin D through a process that uses enzymes in the intestine and the skin that are activated by sunlight. **Minerals** are inorganic substances required for normal functioning of the body. Finally, we all need **water** to be healthy. Water is more than 50% of our body weight and is required for about every metabolic reaction to work properly.

Figure 33.1.1

Vitamins: Sources and Functions

Vitamin	Sources	Function
A	fish, liver, kidney, yellow and green vegetables, butter, egg yolk	growth; eye health; proper function of the skin and mucus membranes
B1 (thiamine)	meat, soy, whole grains, green vegetables, yeast, eggs	growth; carbohydrate metabolism; proper functioning of the muscles, nerves, and heart
B2 (riboflavin)	meat, fowl, soy, green vegetables, milk, eggs	growth; healthy skin and mouth; carbohydrate metabolism; eye health; RBC formation
B3 (niacin)	meat, fowl, fish, peanut butter, potatoes, whole grains, tomatoes, leafy vegetables	growth; carbohydrate metabolism; proper functioning of the stomach, intestines, and nervous system
B6 (pyridoxine)	whole grains, liver, fish	coenzymes for metabolic functions
B12 (cyanocobalamin)	green vegetables, liver	prevent anemia, proper nerve functioning
C (ascorbic acid)	fruit, tomatoes, leafy vegetables	growth; strength of blood vessels; healthy teeth and gums
D	fish oil, liver, milk, eggs	growth; calcium and phosphorus metabolism; strong bones
E	leafy vegetables, milk, butter	normal reproduction
K	green vegetables, soy, tomatoes	proper blood clotting

Figure 33.1.2

Minerals: Sources and Functions

Mineral	Source	Function
calcium	milk, whole grains, vegetables, meat	healthy bones and teeth; proper function of heart, skeletal muscles, and nerves
iodine	seafood, water, iodized salt	proper thyroid gland function
iron	leafy vegetables, liver, meats, raisins, prunes	formation of RBC's
magnesium	vegetables	proper muscle and nerve function
phosphorus	milk, whole grains, vegetables, meat	healthy bones and teeth; formation of ATP
potassium	vegetables, citrus, banana, apricots	growth; maintaining acid-base balance; proper nerve function
sodium	table salt, vegetables	blood and other body tissues; proper nerve function

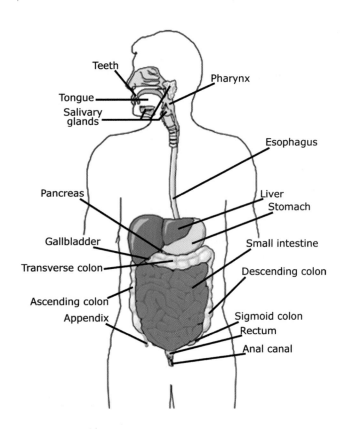

Teeth
Pharynx
Tongue
Salivary glands
Esophagus
Pancreas
Liver
Stomach
Gallbladder
Small intestine
Transverse colon
Descending colon
Ascending colon
Appendix
Sigmoid colon
Rectum
Anal canal

Figure 33.1.3

The GI Tract

The GI tract starts with the mouth, where food is readied for digestion and swallowing. Teeth mechanically begin to break food down, and enzymes released in the saliva chemically begin to break down carbohydrates. The food passes through the pharynx on its way to the esophagus. The stomach churns food and adds acid and enzymes to turn the food into a paste called chyme. Chyme is passed into the first part of the small intestine called the duodenum. More enzymes are added to the chyme and stomach acid is neutralized in the duodenum. The food passes into the second and third parts of the small intestine—the jejunum and ileum, respectively—where all nutrients are absorbed. The food is then prepared for expulsion in the colon.

The digestive system, also called the **GI tract** (GI stands for gastrointestinal), is used to break down food so we can extract and absorb the needed nutrients. The entire process of digestion is a two-armed process—physically breaking food into smaller pieces and chemically breaking the food down. The physical ways of breaking the food down are chewing and the muscular, churning contractions of the stomach. The chemical processes use specific enzymes and stomach acid, which serve to soften and degrade the ingested material. Look at Figures 33.1.3 and 33.1.4 for the components and functions of the digestive system.

Figure 33.1.4

Digestive System Components and Their Functions

Component	Function
teeth	bite and chew food; mechanically breaking food into smaller pieces
saliva	made in the salivary glands; contains fluid to lubricate food and an enzyme to begin breaking down starch
pharynx	receives food from mouth and starts it on its way to the stomach
esophagus	muscular tube which takes food from the mouth/pharynx to the stomach
stomach	muscular organ which squeezes food to mechanically break it up; secretes acids and enzymes to further break food down
small intestine	completes the breakdown of food and absorbs nutrients into blood stream
liver	manufactures bile, which is essential for breaking down and absorbing fats
gall bladder	stores bile and secretes into the small intestine during meal
pancreas	secretes amylase and lipase into small intestine to enzymatically break food down further
large intestine	absorbs water and propels waste out of body

33.2 DIGESTIVE SYSTEM: MOUTH

Digestion begins when we take a bite of food. In the **mouth**, the teeth mechanically break the food down into smaller pieces. Also, the **salivary glands**, specialized groupings of tissue around the jaw that empty into the mouth via ducts, produce saliva. Saliva contains mucus, which lubricates the food, and **amylase**. Amylase is an enzyme that begins breaking starch down into maltose. The mouth prepares to move the food mass, called a **bolus**, into the pharynx. Once in the pharynx, the bolus is propelled into the **esophagus**.

33.3 DIGESTIVE SYSTEM: ESOPHAGUS

The esophagus is a slender, muscular tube; it carries the bolus into the stomach. Recall that when we swallow, the airway is protected by the epiglottis. It squeezes the food down in waves of muscle contraction called **peristalsis**. Peristalsis is the term for a wave of muscular contractions that propel food through the entire GI tract. There is a muscular junction between the end of the esophagus and the opening of the stomach called the **esophageal sphincter**. The sphincter functions to prevent the contractions of the stomach from forcing the food back into the esophagus. Therefore, the esophageal sphincter is always closed unless a bolus of food is passing through it into the stomach.

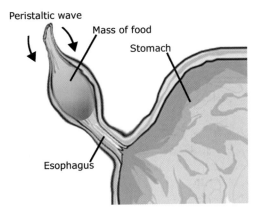

Figure 33.3.1

Peristalsis
Peristalsis describes waves of muscle contractions that propel food through the GI tract. Here, the bolus of food is seen passing from the lower esophagus into the stomach.

33.4 DIGESTIVE SYSTEM: STOMACH

Once in the **stomach**, the food begins to be broken down more. The stomach is muscular and churns the food up by contracting repeatedly. The stomach also has cells that secrete **hydrochloric acid** (pH of two) and the inactive enzyme **pepsinogen**. As soon as pepsinogen is exposed to the acidic environment in the stomach, it is converted into the active form of the enzyme, **pepsin**. The churning action serves to mechanically break the food down, and pepsin begins to enzymatically break down peptide bonds of proteins. Once the stomach has churned the food up to the consistency of an acidic paste, called **chyme**, it is slowly passed to the small intestine. Like the junction between the esophagus and the stomach, the opening between the stomach and the small intestine is surrounded by a sphincter called the **pyloric sphincter**. The pyloric sphincter opens to let material move from the stomach into the small intestine, then closes again.

Figure 33.4.1

Stomach Anatomy
The stomach receives food from the esophagus and mechanically and enzymatically breaks it down before passing it into the duodenum. The esophageal sphincter is a tight band of muscle to prevent food from moving backwards from the stomach into the esophagus. The pyloric sphincter is a band of muscle to prevent backwards movement of food from the duodenum into the stomach.

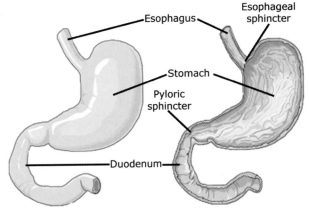

Stomach exterior   Stomach interior

33.5 DIGESTIVE SYSTEM: INTESTINES, PANCREAS, AND LIVER

The small intestine is about twenty-four feet long in a human adult. It is divided into three parts: the **duodenum**, the **jejunum**, and the **ileum**. The duodenum is the first part of the small intestine which receives the chyme from the stomach. Inside the duodenum, the food is completely broken down into an absorbable form. This is accomplished through the addition of multiple enzymes secreted into the duodenum by the **pancreas** to enzymatically break down fats, proteins, and carbohydrates. In addition, the pancreas releases sodium bicarbonate into the duodenum to neutralize the acid. The **gall bladder** releases **bile**, which is made in the **liver** and stored in the gall bladder, into the small intestine. Both the pancreas and gall bladder empty into the duodenum through the same opening. Bile contains several different substances, but the important ones for digestion are called **bile salts**. Bile salts coat the fats so they become soluble in water and can be enzymatically broken down by the enzymes secreted from the pancreas.

Figure 33.5.1

Other Digestive Organs

The liver is located on the right side of your abdomen just under the lower border of the rib cage. It produces bile, which is stored in the gall bladder. Bile is carried from the gall bladder to the duodenum through the bile duct, then released into the duodenum. It helps prepare fats for absorption. The pancreas sits behind the stomach and releases enzymes through the pancreatic duct into the duodenum, which help digest fats, carbohydrates, and proteins. Both the bile duct and the pancreatic duct join together to form the common bile duct for a short way before emptying into the duodenum. The pancreas also releases insulin into the blood when we eat.

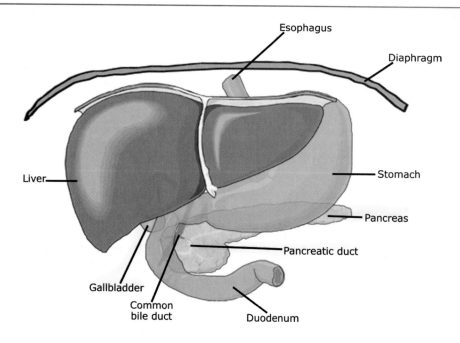

Once digestion is completed in the duodenum, the food material contains elemental (broken down) carbohydrates (glucose), amino acids, fats, and minerals that are available to be absorbed into the body. The material passes from the duodenum into the jejunum, then into the ileum. There are no sphincters between these junctions, but peristalsis does propel the material through the gut. The main function of the jejunum and ileum is absorption of the nutrients present in the digested food. As was the case in the lungs and the kidneys, the surface of the lining of the jejunum and the ileum are folded repeatedly in order to increase the surface area of the absorbing tissue. Due to the intricate folding patterns, the surface area of the jejunum and the ileum available for absorption is almost equal to the surface area of one tennis court.

On the interior of the small intestine are billions of microscopic, finger-like projections called **villi** (singular villus). The villi are the foldings of the intestinal membrane. On the surface of the villi are further foldings called **microvilli**. These foldings of the intestinal membranes greatly increase the surface area available for absorption of nutrients.

Inside the villi are capillary beds and **lacteals** that function to absorb the nutrients into the body. The lacteals specifically absorb fats and the capillaries absorb monosaccharides, dipeptides, amino acids, and minerals. The nutrients then move from the capillaries into the veins. Once they are in the bloodstream, everything is transported to the **liver**.

Figure 33.5.2

Intestinal Anatomy
When viewed with the naked eye, the inside of the small intestines looks like velvet. That is because it is covered with millions of villi and microvilli. The microvillus is the functional unit of intestinal absorption. Nutrients are absorbed through the walls of microvilli. There are rich capillary beds which absorb amino acids and carbohydrates from the digested food. Lacteals absorb the fat and carry it to the liver, where it is further processed before being released into the blood.

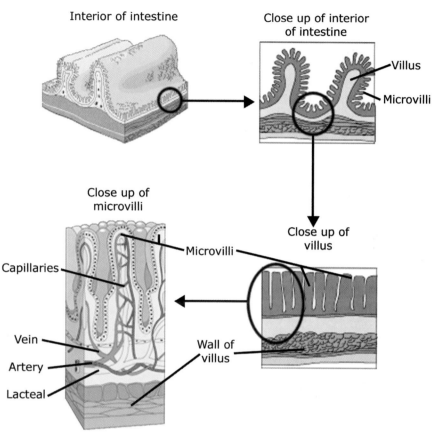

Inside the liver, some substances are processed further. For example, if the glucose level of the blood is getting too elevated after a meal, the hormone insulin from the pancreas instructs the liver to make glycogen from the absorbed glucose. This causes glucose from the absorbed meal to be removed from the bloodstream and stored in the liver as glycogen. Then, as more glucose is needed by the body, the hormone glucagon is released into the blood by the pancreas, which instructs the liver to break glycogen into glucose. In this way, the level of glucose in the bloodstream available for cells to use is tightly regulated, even while the meal is being absorbed. The liver also converts absorbed fatty acids into cholesterol and molecules of fat that are released into the blood stream. Once the absorbed molecules are released into the blood stream, they are available for use by the cells of the body.

After passing through the jejunum and ileum, most of the usable nutrients have been removed. Only undigestible solids and water are left. The material then passes into the large intestine, or **colon**. There is no sphincter between the ileum and the colon. There are two primary functions of the colon. One is to absorb water, and the other is to package leftover wastes for removal from the body. Once water has been removed from the material, it is called **feces**. Feces are transported to the end of the colon, called the **rectum**, where it is stored until it is eliminated through the **anus**. Also in the large intestine are many different types of bacteria that live as symbionts with humans. The material in the colon provides food for them to live, and they offer us protection from some diseases. Also, some bacteria make the vitamins B_{12} and K that are essential for humans.

33.6 MUSCULOSKELETAL/CONNECTIVE TISSUE SYSTEM: GENERAL

The function of the musculoskeletal system is to move and support the body. These systems are grouped together because they are closely linked, as many of the other systems are. Technically, the bones are part of the connective-tissue system, as are ligaments, tendons, and blood. Muscles are part of the muscular system. However, if we were to base groupings on how things function, we would put the muscles and the bones together. The musculoskeletal system includes the **muscles** (to move us) and the **skeleton** (to support us). Included in this system are the connective tissues of **ligaments**, which connect bones to bones; and **tendons**, which connect muscles to bones. Also included in the connective tissue category is the extracellular matrix, which we have previously discussed.

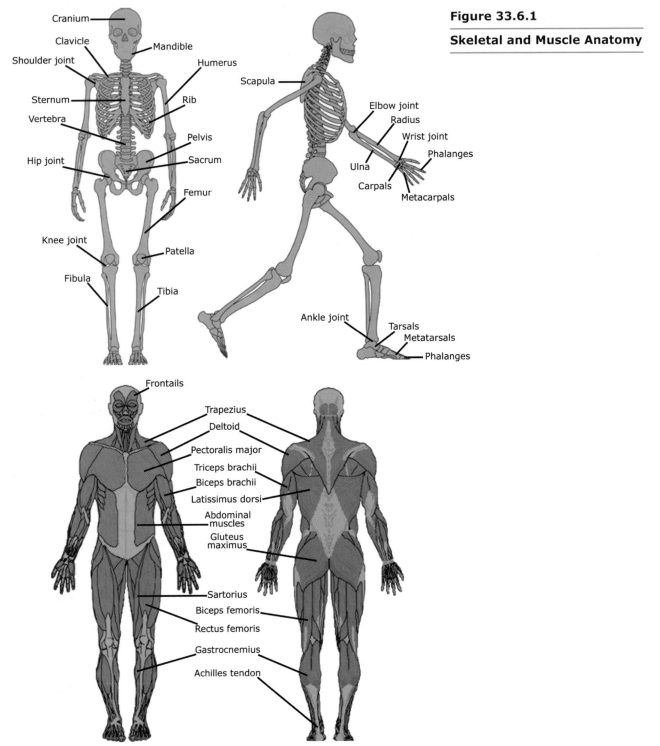

Figure 33.6.1

Skeletal and Muscle Anatomy

The skeleton provides the support our bodies need so that the muscles have something rigid to act upon. In this way, directed movement is possible. Also, some bones, such as the skull and vertebrae, function to protect important and fragile parts of our bodies, particularly the nervous system structures. Our skeleton is internal, called an endoskeleton, as are the skeletons of the fish, amphibians, reptiles and all other mammals. Many people have the wrong impression that bones are dry and dead structures. They are not. They are moist, living tissues that will bleed when broken and then repair themselves.

33.7 MUSCULOSKELETAL/CONNECTIVE TISSUE SYSTEM: BONES

The skeleton is divided into two parts: the **axial skeleton** and the **appendicular skeleton**. The axial skeleton consists of the vertebrae, the skull, the **ribs**, and the **sternum**. The appendicular skeleton includes all of the bones of the arms and legs, the clavicles (collar bones), scapulae (shoulder blades), and pelvis. Altogether, there are 206 bones in the human body.

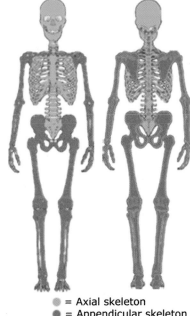

= Axial skeleton
= Appendicular skeleton

Figure 33.7.1

Two Skeletons
The appendicular skeleton is composed of the arm and leg bones, the shoulder blades, and the pelvis. The axial skeleton is composed of the skull, jaw, vertebrae, ribs, and sternum.

Even though bones come in different shapes and sizes, they have similar structures. The interior of bone is soft and porous. It is surrounded by a hard outer shell. The outer surface of bone is covered by a tough membrane called the **periosteum**. The periosteum contains a rich network of blood vessels to supply the bone with nutrients. It also contains many nerves. When a bone is broken, the nerves in the periosteum become stimulated and generate the painful impulse that accompanies a fracture.

Just under the periosteum is the hard shell of bone called **compact bone**. This thick, rigid layer allows the bone to withstand a lot of force. **Osteoblasts** are the cells that make bone. Osteoblasts secrete a matrix around them made up of a protein called **collagen**, and a calcium-based molecule. As the osteoblast secretes more of the matrix, the bone becomes hard, forming compact bone. Also, the osteoblast becomes trapped in its own mineral and collagen matrix. At that point, the osteoblast is referred to as a mature **osteocyte**. The osteocyte is the cell responsible for maintaining the health and structure of the bone.

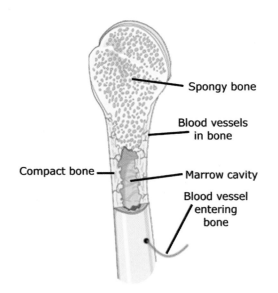

Figure 33.7.2

Bone Anatomy
The hard outer portion of bone is the compact bone. Inside is a more porous bone called spongy bone. Large blood vessels enter the bone through small holes, then break into smaller branches. Bone marrow fills the cavity on the inside of the bone. Recall bone marrow makes all of our blood cells.

As can be seen from figure 33.7.3, the structure of compact bone is that of many concentric cylinders. These cylinders are formed when the secreted matrix surrounds nerves and blood vessels of the bone, encircling them. In the center of the cylinder is a narrow channel called a **Haversian canal**. Blood vessels and nerves run through the interconnected Haversian canals to supply the bone with nutrition and oxygen.

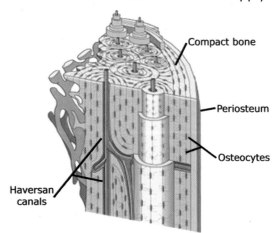

Figure 33.7.3

Haversian System
All bones are covered by a thin, but tough, layer of tissue called the periosteum. Periosteum has a rich nerve supply, which is the reason that broken bones hurt so much. Osteocytes are mature bone-making cells. They produce the hard bone substance called matrix. There are canals running through all of our bones called Haversian canals. Blood vessels and nerves run through Haversian canals.

Underneath the compact bone is a layer of **spongy bone**. Although the name makes it sound like it is soft, it is not. It is hard, but not as rigid as the compact bone. It forms a spiky-looking structure because the bone mineralizes in a strut fashion. It looks like a dried natural sponge. This serves to supply added strength to the compact bone.

In the interior of many bones (not all bones have bone marrow), especially the long bones like the femur, tibia, ilium, humerus, sternum, and ribs, is specialized tissue called **bone marrow**. **Red bone marrow** is responsible for making all the red and white blood cells and platelets found in the body. **Yellow bone marrow** is responsible for storing excess fat in the long bones. At some time, the yellow bone marrow is converted into red bone marrow to increase the blood cell producing capacity.

Most bones initially start out as **cartilage**, as the human develops as a fetus. It is tough and flexible. As fetal development continues, osteoblasts begin to replace the cartilage cells. As this happens, the osteoblasts begin to secrete the matrix and the bones begin to get hard. The process of osteoblasts replacing cartilage cells and forming bone is called **ossification**. Most human bones are partly ossified (or "boney") by the time they are born. Ossification continues until it is completed by the age of twenty or twenty-five.

One interesting exception to this process of creating bone from cartilage is the process by which the skull and facial bones are formed. The skull and facial bones are actually made up of many bones that fuse together. However, they do not form from cartilage; rather, osteoblasts develop within membranes and make bone directly. There is no "cartilage middleman."

As a person grows, the bones elongate from a region called the **epiphyseal plate** (or growth plate). The epiphyseal plates are located near the ends of the bones and are rich in cartilage-producing cells. The cartilage cells divide and form an ever-growing column of cells during the period of growth from birth until adolescence. The movement of the cartilage cells is toward the middle of the bone (away from the end of the bone). As the column grows, the cartilage cells die and are replaced by osteoblasts, then ossification occurs. When the cartilage cells stop growing, the epiphyseal plate becomes ossified and growth stops.

33.8 MUSCULOSKELETAL/CONNECTIVE TISSUE SYSTEM: LIGAMENTS AND JOINTS

Where bones meet, they form a **joint**. Two bones are held together by **ligament tissue**, or **ligaments**. Ligaments are tough and fibrous bands or sheets of collagen tissue that hold bones together. The surface of each bone is lined with cartilage where it comes into contact with the other bone of the joint. Cartilage supplies a soft surface so the bones can move smoothly past one another as the muscles move the joint. The joint is lined with a tissue called **synovium**, which secretes a slippery fluid, called **synovial fluid**, to lubricate the joint. Synovial fluid greatly reduces friction, and the cartilage cushions the joint.

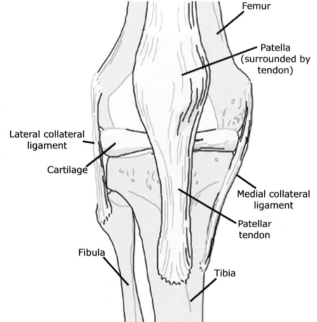

Figure 33.8.1

Ligaments of the Knee Joint
Ligaments hold one bone to another. They are found at every joint in our body. Cartilage is the connective tissue padding that acts as a shock absorber for our joints. Tendons connect muscles to bones.

There are several different types of joint in the human body: **fixed**, **semimovable**, and **movable**. Fixed joints do not move. This type of joint is found between the bones of the skull, where no movement is necessary. Semimovable joints are the type of joint formed by the vertebrae, and the joints where the ribs meet the sternum. They allow for some limited type of movement.

Movable joints are the ones we are more familiar with, though. They allow for much more motion than the fixed or semimovable joints. **Hinge joints** allow movement in one plane, like the hinge of a door. The elbow and knee joints are good examples of hinge joints. **Pivot joints** allow for rotational movement only. This is the type of joint that allows you to rotate your forearm so the palm of the hand faces up and down. It is the pivoting motion of one forearm bone around the other which allows this to occur. **Saddle joints** are found at the base of the thumbs and allow movements in several planes, but not all planes (try to bend your thumb certain ways and you will see what I mean). **Ball and socket joints** allow for a wider range of motion than any of the other joints. In fact, ball and socket joints allow motion in all planes. The joints between the humerus and the scapula (the "shoulder joint") and between the femur and the ilium (the "hip joint") are examples of ball and socket joints.

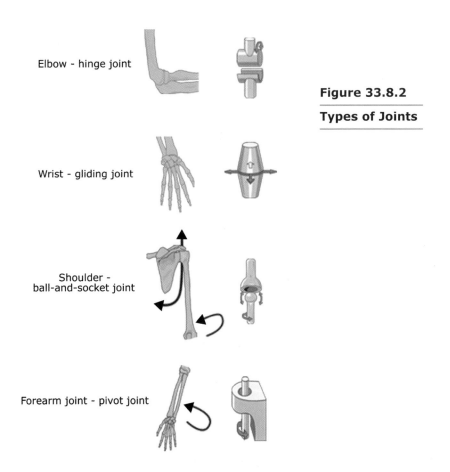

Figure 33.8.2

Types of Joints

33.9 MUSCULOSKELETAL/CONNECTIVE TISSUE SYSTEM: MUSCLES AND TENDONS

Joints would not be much good if we did not have muscles. We are all familiar with the concept that we have muscles in our bodies that make us move. This type of muscle is called **skeletal muscle**. Skeletal muscle is also called **voluntary muscle**, because we can voluntarily control their contractions. A "muscle" (like the biceps muscle) is made up of many individual muscle cells, called **muscle fibers**, grouped together in dense bundles called **fascicles**. Multiple fascicles are bound together by connective tissue to form a muscle. A muscle may be made up of a thousand or more muscle fibers. Under the microscope, we see that a muscle fiber is elongated and contains multiple nuclei. It is crossed by light and dark bands called **striations**, or stripes. For this reason, skeletal muscle is also called striated muscle.

Figure 33.9.1

Muscle Anatomy

Each "muscle" in our body is actually made up of thousands of individual muscle cells. These muscle cells are all oriented so that when the muscle contracts, all muscle cells pull in the same direction. In (a), the muscle called the biceps is shown. The biceps is composed of many individual muscle cells. Figure (b) indicates the organization of a muscle into many muscle fibers. Each striated muscle cell contains multiple nuclei. An individual muscle cell is also called a muscle fiber and bundles of fibers make up the biceps muscle. Also, the striped, or striated appearance of the muscle fiber is clearly seen. The area from one dark band to another is called a sarcomere. A sarcomere is the functional unit of the muscle cell. Figure (c) indicates that a muscle fiber is composed of units called fibrils, which are groups of proteins. In Figure (d), fibrils are broken into even smaller units, proteins called myofibrils. Figure (e) shows there are two types of myofibrils, the proteins actin and myosin. Actin and myosin are contractile proteins, which means they can move. Actin is also called a thin filament and myosin is called a thick filament. As can be seen, the actin and myosin overlap one another. The thin filaments are anchored to vertical bands called the Z line. The region from Z line to the next Z line represents a sarcomere. During a muscle contraction, each sarcomere contracts (gets shorter) which moves the Z lines closer together. The Z line gets shorter due to the interaction between actin and myosin. During a muscle contraction, then, the overall length of the muscle gets shorter due to the interaction of myosin and actin. As the muscle gets shorter, the joint it crosses bends. Muscle contractions require a lot of ATP!

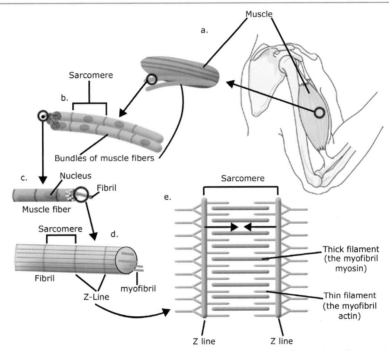

However, we also have muscles that we may not have thought about. We have muscles that form the muscular walls of arteries and squeeze the food through the digestive tract and the urine out of the urinary bladder, called **smooth muscle**. We also have muscle that makes up the structure of the heart, called **cardiac muscle**. Cardiac and smooth muscle are also called **involuntary muscle** because their contractions are not under active control.

Figure 33.9.2

Three Muscle Types

There are three types of muscle cells in our bodies: cardiac, smooth, and skeletal muscle cells. Skeletal muscle cells make up all the muscle tissue that we can voluntarily move. All muscles in the arms, legs, back, and face are composed of skeletal muscle cells. Skeletal muscle cells are long and contain multiple nuclei. They have a striated appearance because of the arrangement of sarcomeres. Skeletal muscle receives nerve supply from motor nerves and is specialized for short and powerful contractions. Smooth muscle cells are smaller and shorter than skeletal muscle cells and only have one nucleus per cell. It is not arranged in sarcomeres like skeletal muscle. Smooth muscle receives nerve supply from the autonomic nerves. It is specialized for rather continuous and rhythmical contractions. Cardiac muscle shares features with both smooth and skeletal muscle. Cardiac muscle cells tend to be long, but not as large as skeletal muscle. They contain one or two nuclei per cell. Cardiac muscle can generate strong contractions rhythmically. Cardiac actin and myosin are arranged similar to that of skeletal muscle which is the reason for the banding patterns seen on cardiac muscle.

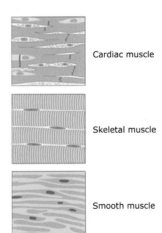

Smooth muscle cells are spindle shaped, do not have striations, and only contain one nucleus. Rather than form fascicles, they are woven together to form sheets. Cardiac muscle has characteristics of both smooth and skeletal muscle. It has striations and only one nucleus per cell.

Whether we are discussing smooth muscle, skeletal muscle, or cardiac muscle, there is a rich supply of nerves and blood vessels to the muscle. In addition, there is a dense network of connective tissue to hold the muscle together. In smooth and cardiac muscle, the connective tissue serves to keep the muscle the proper shape and to hold it together.

In skeletal muscle, **tendons** connect the muscle to the bone. Every muscle connects to a bone on each end of the muscle. This is called the **muscle attachment site**. All muscles cross the joint they move. Because of the way muscles work, when the muscle contracts and moves the joint, one end of the muscle does not move, while the other end of the muscle moves when the joint moves. This is another way of saying that when a joint is moved, a bone on one side of the joint moves, while a bone on the other end of the joint does not move. The site of attachment to the bone that does not move is called the **origin of the muscle**; the site of attachment to the bone that does move is called the **insertion of the muscle**.

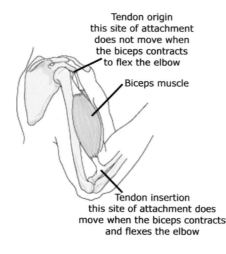

Tendon origin
this site of attachment
does not move when
the biceps contracts
to flex the elbow

Biceps muscle

Tendon insertion
this site of attachment does
move when the biceps contracts
and flexes the elbow

Figure 33.9.3

Tendons

Tendons attach muscles to bones. Every muscle has a tendon on each end. Usually, the end of the muscle that attaches closest to the body does so on a bone that does not move when the muscle contracts. This is the origin site of the tendon. The other tendon attaches to the bone that does move when the muscle contracts. This is called the insertion site of the tendon. All muscles cross at least one joint so that when they contract, the joint they cross moves.

Let's take a quick example to understand that concept better. We will look at the muscle called the brachialis. This is a muscle located in the upper arm. It is located underneath the biceps muscle. When you contract the right brachialis muscle, it causes the elbow to bend. One end of the brachialis muscle attaches to the humerus, and the other end crosses the elbow joint and attaches onto one of the bones in the forearm called the ulna. Which site is the origin and which is the insertion? To figure that out, bend and straighten your elbow a few times. When you do that, you are contracting the brachialis muscle. I am sure you see that as your elbow bends, your upper arm does not move, but your forearm does. Therefore, the origin of the brachialis is on the bone that does not move when the joint is moved, or the humerus. The insertion of the brachialis is on the bone that does move when the joint is moved, or the ulna.

Muscles are generally organized in opposing pairs and they work like a rope—they pull on the joint rather than push it (you can't push with a rope). If one muscle, or group of muscles, bends a joint—called **flexion**—there is another muscle, or group of muscles, to straighten- called **extension**—the joint. The muscles that act to flex a joint are called **flexors**, and those that extend the joint are called **extensors**. In the example above, the brachialis is one of three muscles that act as primary elbow flexors. The other two are the biceps brachii and the coracobrachialis. These three muscles are the elbow flexors. The corresponding extensor muscle of the elbow joint is the triceps muscle. Movement of any joint is a combination of fine, coordinated muscle contractions of the joint flexors and extensors.

Figure 33.9.4

Muscles Contract
Muscles contract because of actin and myosin interacting to shorten the sarcomeres. When sarcomeres get shorter, so does the muscle and this causes a muscle contraction. When a muscle contracts, the joint it crosses either bends (flexion) or straightens (extension).

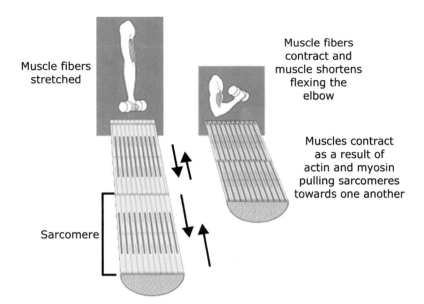

Muscle fibers stretched

Muscle fibers contract and muscle shortens flexing the elbow

Muscles contract as a result of actin and myosin pulling sarcomeres towards one another

Sarcomere

33.10 MUSCULOSKELETAL/CONNECTIVE TISSUE SYSTEM: MUSCLE PHYSIOLOGY

In order to understand how muscles contract, we need to dive deeper into the structure of the muscle and muscle fiber and its relationship to the nerve. All muscles receive significant nerve supply. The nerve supply includes axons from the spinal cord, which carry impulses to the muscle about when to start and stop the contraction and how hard to contract. Also, there are significant numbers of nerve signals carried from the muscle to the brain that include information about how hard the muscle is actually contracting, how short the muscles fibers are and how tired the muscle is (called **fatigue**). This is a highly and finely tuned system.

The impulse for the muscle to contract is carried from the brain, through the spinal cord, to the muscle. The area where the nerve and the muscle communicate with one another is called the **neuromuscular junction**, or **motor end plate**, or **synapse**. There is a small gap between the nerve and the muscle membrane at the neuromuscular junction. Once the impulse travels down the motor axon and reaches the nerve fibers at the neuromuscular junction, a neurotransmitter called **acetylcholine** is released from the nerve terminal. The acetylcholine diffuses across the gap of the neuromuscular junction and binds to receptors on the membrane of the muscle fiber. When the acetylcholine binds to the muscle membrane, it causes the muscle fiber to contract.

Muscle contractions are much like nerve impulses— they are an all-or-none response. However, this does not mean that the *entire* muscle is either contracting or not contracting. It means only the muscle fibers needed for a particular contraction are contracting. How, then, are we able to contract the muscles gently, as when holding an egg, and contract the same muscles strongly, as when holding a thirty pound dumbbell? In order to be able to accomplish this, muscle fibers are grouped into units called **motor units**. A motor unit consists of one motor axon and the muscle fibers it communicates with. An individual muscle may have hundreds of motor units. In order to be able to control how strongly the muscles contract, more or less motor units are recruited into the contraction of the muscle. If a gentle contraction is needed, then few motor units are given the impulse from the brain to contract. Only those motor units needed to do the job are contracting, but they are all contracting due to the all-or-none response. The other motor units in the muscle are quiet and are not firing, since they are not needed at the time. If slightly more strength is needed, then a few more motor units will be given the signal by the brain to contract. If great force is needed, then all of the motor units will be recruited.

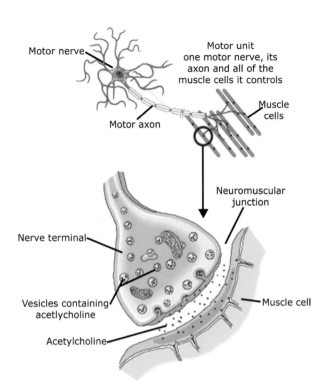

Motor nerve

Motor unit
one motor nerve, its
axon and all of the
muscle cells it controls

Muscle
cells

Motor axon

Neuromuscular
junction

Nerve terminal

Vesicles containing
acetlycholine

Muscle cell

Acetylcholine

Figure 33.10.1

Motor Unit
A motor unit is the functional unit of a motor nerve and muscle. A motor unit is a motor neuron, its axon, and all of the muscle fibers the motor nerve contacts and controls. When the impulse to contract is sent from the brain to the muscle, it travels down the motor axon to the muscle fibers of the motor unit. All fibers of the motor unit contract at the same time, allowing for coordinated and fine muscle contractions. Nerves communicate to muscles as they communicate to one another—through chemicals released into the synapse. Nerves do not directly contact muscles, though. There is a small gap between them called the synapse. This synapse is also called the neuromuscular junction. The nerve releases the chemical acetylcholine from vesicles stored in the nerve ending. The acetylcholine moves across the neuromuscular junction; when it contacts the muscle fiber, the muscle contracts.

As noted in the text of the figure above, muscle contraction requires a lot of energy and a lot of oxygen to funnel into the Kreb's cycle and make the ATP. However, it is fairly common that muscles are asked to perform rapid bursts of activity, during which they are not able to make enough ATP through respiration because not enough oxygen is delivered to the muscles. This is referred to as **oxygen debt**. The muscles are still able to function, however, by using anaerobic respiration to generate ATP. This is a much less efficient, but quicker, method to generate ATP. It allows muscles to continue to function for a short time while in oxygen debt. Besides ATP, a major end product of anaerobic metabolism is lactic acid. Lactic acid is the reason muscles ache when they are in oxygen debt. Following cessation of the activity, there are usually several minutes of rest to replace the oxygen.

33.11 INTEGUMENTARY SYSTEM

This is the final system we will cover. It consists of the **skin**, **nails**, and hair. Skin is actually an organ and is an important protective barrier against pathogens. It also participates in reducing loss of water and eliminating wastes through the process of sweating. The skin is rich in sensory nerve endings to allow us to sense changes in the external environment. The nerve endings in the skin also protect us from injury by transmitting pain and other potentially harmful impulses to the brain.

The skin is composed of two layers. The top layer of the skin is the **epidermis**. It is made up of cells called **epithelial cells**. These are flattened cells that are mainly dead on the upper layers of the epidermis. The cells of the epidermis are continually replaced since they are constantly scraped away. A primary component of epithelial cells is keratin. This is a protein that gives skin its toughness. Another component of skin is the pigment **melanin**. This is a brown pigment produced by the cells of the lower epidermis that gives our skin its color. People with darker skin have more melanin than those with lighter skin. Melanin also protects us from harmful ultra-violet rays of the sun. When we are exposed to the sun, more melanin is made by the epithelial cells, which is the reason we tan.

Figure 33.11.1

Skin Structure

Skin is a complicated organ. It is also the largest organ in the body. The epidermis is largely composed of dead cells and acts as a protective layer. Oil glands release small amounts of it onto the skin to keep it moist. The dermis is the thickest layer of skin. It contains specialized structures called hair follicles that grow hair. There are small muscles attached to hairs that raise the hair when we are cool and lay it down when we are warm; these also contract to cause goose bumps. There is a rich blood vessel supply in the skin, which all mammals use for temperature homeostasis. When we are cold, the skin vessels constrict and so the blood cannot flow through. This allows the blood to stay closer to the chest, abdomen, and brain to keep these vital organs warm. When we are hot, the skin vessels dilate, allowing a lot of blood to move through it under the skin. This has a radiator-like effect and keeps us cool by allowing heat to be released into the atmosphere.

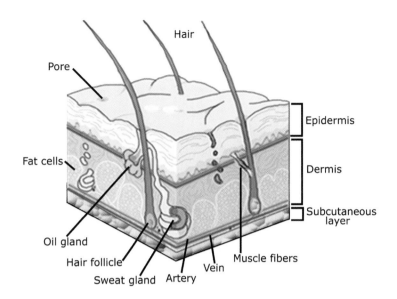

The bottom layer of the skin is called the **dermis**. All of the cells in the dermis are living. As can be seen from the figure, the dermis contains many structures including glands, hair follicles, blood vessels, and sensory nerves. There are two kinds of glands in the dermis—**sweat** and **oil glands**. Sweat glands produce sweat, which helps to cool the body by evaporating when it is warm. Oil glands secrete a fatty substance called **sebum**. Oil glands are in particularly high numbers in the face and scalp; when they become plugged, acne results. Hair follicles produce hair, which is composed of keratin and melanin. In humans, hair can provide some insulation against the cold, but in other mammalian species the function of hair to keep warm is a lot more obvious and important (polar bears, for example).

Blood vessels bring needed nutrition and oxygen to the dermis and epidermis, and carry wastes and carbon dioxide away. Blood vessels in the dermis are also important in temperature regulation. When we are too hot, these blood vessels dilate (get bigger) and fill with blood. Since the vessels are close to the surface, this has the effect of cooling our bodies. The opposite is true when we are cold. The blood vessels constrict and do not allow the blood to flow in great quantity to the skin. This causes less heat loss, and the body temperature increases. Finger and toe nails form from specialized skin cells in an area called the **nail root**. The cells in the nail root continually divide through mitosis. As they do, the nail grows.

33.12 PEOPLE OF SCIENCE

Wilhelm Roentgen (1845–1923) was born in Germany, but moved to the Netherlands when he was three. He received his early education in the Netherlands and received his PhD from the University of Zurich. During his research, while he was the Chairman of the Physics Department at the University of Wurzburg, he built a machine that emitted a new type of radiation wave, called the x-ray. The application of the x-ray to view broken bones and the insides of the body rapidly exploded all over the world. Despite the enormous amount of money he could have made, Roentgen refused to patent the machine, believing that making money on something so indispensable as medical care and the health of others was not moral. He received the first Nobel Prize in physics in 1901 for his discovery and donated the monetary award that comes with it to his university. The element Roentgenium, atomic number 111, is named after him.

33.13 KEY CHAPTER POINTS

- The function of the digestive system is to break down and absorb the nutrients needed to sustain life, and then to eliminate wastes that are left over.
- The GI system has many specialized parts which function to break down and absorb food.
- Food is prepared for absorption in the mouth, esophagus, stomach, and duodenum.
- Food is absorbed in the jejunum and ileum; water is absorbed in and waste expelled from the colon.
- The function of the musculoskeletal system is to support and move the body.
- Bones support; ligaments attach bones to bones; tendons attach muscles to bones; muscles move.
- Muscles contract through the actions of actin and myosin.
- The integumentary system in the covering of the body. Its purpose is protection. It includes hair, nails, and skin.

33.14 DEFINITIONS

acetylcholine
The neurotransmitter released from the nerve ending that causes muscles to contract.

amylase
An enzyme that begins to break starch down into maltose.

anus
Structure where feces is eliminated.

appendicular skeleton
Support structure consisting of all the bones of the arms, legs, clavicles, scapulae, and pelvis.

axial skeleton
Support structure consisting of the vertebrae, the skull, the ribs, and the sternum.

ball and socket joints
Joints that allow for a wider range of motion than any of the other joints.

bile
Substance that contains bile salts to aid in digestion.

bolus
The food mass propelled through the GI tract.

bone marrow
Tissue in the marrow cavity of bones that makes blood cells.

cardiac muscle
Muscle cells that makes up the structure of the heart.

cartilage
Tough and flexible structure that cushions joints or is the starting substance of bones.

chyme
Acidic paste formed from food as it is being digested in the stomach.

collagen
A type of connective tissue glycoprotein.

colon
The large intestine.

compact bone (cortical bone)
A type of bone characterized by small space which forms under the periosteum.

dermis
The bottom layer of skin.

duodenum
The first part of the small intestine, which receives chyme from the stomach.

epidermis
The top layer of the skin.

epiphyseal plate
The area of the bone where growth takes place; also called the growth plate.

epithelial cells
Cells that make up the epidermis.

esophageal sphincter
Muscular junction between the end of the esophagus and the opening of the stomach.

esophagus
A slender, muscular tube that carries the food from the mouth to the stomach.

extension
The movement of a joint that causes it to "straighten."

extensor
Muscle or group of muscles that straighten a joint.

fascicles
Muscle fibers grouped together in dense bundles.

fatigue
The property of a muscle to become tired after firing many times.

feces
Waste material.

flexion
Bending a joint.

flexor
Muscle or group of muscles that bends a joint.

gall bladder
Organ that stores bile made in the liver and releases it into the small intestine.

GI tract
The digestive system.

Haversian canal
Narrow channels which run through bones for the passage of blood vessels.

hinge joints
Joints allowing movement in one plane.

ileum
The last part of the small intestine.

insertion of the muscle
The site of muscle attachment to the bone that moves in a joint.

involuntary muscle
Muscles whose contractions are not under active control.

jejunum
The middle part of the small intestine.

joint
The place where two bones come together.

lacteals
Structures within the villi which absorb fats.

ligaments/ligament tissue
Tough and fibrous bands or sheets of collagen tissue connecting bones to bones.

liver
A large abdominal organ; makes bile and processes fats.

melanin
Pigment component of skin.

microvilli
Foldings on the surface of villi that absorb nutrients.

minerals
Inorganic substances required for normal functioning of the body.

motor end plate
The area where the nerve and the muscle communicate with one another.

motor units
Unit consisting of one motor nerve, its axon and the muscle fibers it communicates with.

muscle attachment site
A place on each end of a muscle that attaches to the bone.

muscle fibers
Individual muscle cells.

muscles
Tissue specialized for movement.

myofibrils
Protein components of muscle cells.

myosin
One of the myofibrils and a contractile muscle protein.

nail root
Structure containing the skin cells, which form finger and toe nails.

neuromuscular junction
The area where the nerve and the muscle communicate with one another.

nutrient
A substance needed to live.

oil glands
Glands that secrete a fatty substance called sebum.

origin of the muscle
The site of a muscle attachment to the bone that does not move.

ossification
The process of osteoblasts replacing cartilage cells and forming bone.

osteoblasts
The cells that make bone.

osteocyte
The cell responsible for maintaining the health and structure of the bone.

oxygen debt
The process of muscle running out of oxygen and fatiguing.

pancreas
Organ that secretes enzymes into the GI tract and insulin into the blood.

pepsin
An enzyme that breaks down proteins; the active form of pepsinogen.

pepsinogen
Inactive enzyme in the stomach.

periosteum
The tough membrane covering the outer surface of bone.

peristalsis
A muscle contraction; squeezes food through the GI tract in waves.

pivot joints
Joints that allow for rotational movement only.

pyloric sphincter
Opening between the stomach and the small intestine.

rectum
The end of the colon where feces is stored until it is eliminated.

red bone marrow
Tissue responsible for making all of the red and white blood cells, as well as platelets.

ribs
Bones that are part of the axial skeleton.

saddle joints
Joints that allow movement in several planes.

salivary glands
Groupings of tissue around the jaw that produce enzymes and mucus and empty into the mouth via ducts and produce saliva.

sarcomere
The functional unit of the muscle fiber.

sebum
Fatty substance secreted by oil glands.

skeletal muscle
The type of muscle that is composed of striated muscle and is under voluntary control.

skeleton
Support structure made of bone.

skin
The outer covering of the body.

smooth muscle
Type of muscle composed of smooth muscle cells; not under voluntary control.

spongy bone
A layer of bone that contains spaces and is found underneath the compact bone.

sternum
A part of the axial skeleton.

stomach
Part of the GI tract that churns food into chyme.

striations
  Light and dark banding pattern of skeletal muscle.

sweat glands
  Glands in the skin that produce sweat to help cool the body.

synapse
  The area where the nerve and the muscle communicate with one another.

synovial fluid
  slippery fluid secreted by the synovium which lubricates the joint.

synovium
  The tissue-lining joints.

tendons
  Structures connecting muscles to bones.

thick filament
  The myosin component of myofibrils.

thin filament
  The actin component of myofibrils.

villi (singular villus)
  Microscopic finger-like projections on the interior of the small intestine.

voluntary muscle
  Another name for skeletal muscle.

yellow bone marrow
  Tissue responsible for storing excess fat in the long bones.

Z line
  Vertical bands that anchor the thin filaments.

STUDY QUESTIONS

1. What are the functions of the digestive system?

2. You are a piece of food that is being chewed and then swallowed. List the structures you will pass through as you are digested from the following list: mouth, large intestine (colon), esophagus, pharynx, duodenum, stomach, jejunum, ileum, and rectum.

3. What is peristalsis?

4. What functions do sphincters serve? Name two GI sphincters.

5. How does pepsinogen work? Make sure to include all details.

6. What is food called after it has been mechanically digested by the stomach and enters the duodenum?

7. What is added to the food in the small intestine by the pancreas? By the gall bladder? Include the functions of each substance added.

8. What is the main function of the jejunum and ileum?

9. What is special about villi and microvilli as it relates to the absorptive function of the intestine?

10. What are lacteals?

11. What are the two main functions of the colon?

12. How are bones held to one another at the joints?

13. What attaches a muscle to bone?

14. What are osteoblasts and what function do they perform?

15. What is ossification and how does it occur for most bones?

16. Growth takes place at the _____ _____ of bones.

17. A _____ joint allows movement in only one plane, but _____ and _____ joints allow movements in all planes.

18. Do the "joints" of the skull represent fixed, moveable, or semimovable joints?

19. If I gave you three samples of muscles to look at under the microscope, how would you be able to tell the smooth muscle, skeletal muscle and cardiac muscle apart? Draw a picture of how you would expect them to appear.

20. When you bend your elbow, is that flexion or extension?

21. What is the neuromuscular junction?

22. Why is acetylcholine important in muscle-nerve relationships? How does it work?

23. True or False? The dermis is a deeper skin layer than the epidermis.

24. In which layer of skin are follicles found?

PLEASE TAKE TEST #14 IN TEST BOOKLET

Ecology

34

34.0 CHAPTER PREVIEW

In this chapter we will:

- Introduce basic concepts and terms of ecology.

- Investigate the dynamics of population studies.

- Discuss food chains, food webs, food pyramids and trophic levels.

- Define the differences between mimicry and camouflage and study examples of both.

- Investigate the hydrologic, carbon and oxygen cycles.

- Delve into the controversial topic of global warming.

- Discuss the seven land biomes as well as marine and fresh water biomes.

34.1 OVERVIEW

Plants, animals, and prokaryotic organisms interact with each other and their environments in many complex ways. **Ecology** is the study of the relationships living organisms have with one another and their physical environment. **Ecologists** are the scientists who study ecology. Like all other scientific disciplines, ecology will introduce a number of new definitions, which we will need to understand prior to diving in too deep.

34.2 BIOSPHERE

Ecologists divide the physical environments in which living organisms interact into different levels of complexity. The **biosphere** represents the greatest level of complexity in ecology. The biosphere represents the thin physical layer of the earth in which all living organisms are found. It is about thirteen miles thick and extends from the deepest ocean depths (about seven miles below the sea level) to mountainous regions (about six miles above sea level). In this narrow band around the earth, all life forms are found. If the earth were an apple, the biosphere would be about the thickness of the peel.

Figure 34.2.1

Biosphere
Ecologists define the biosphere as the global system in which all life processes occur. The biosphere physically encompasses a space of approximately thirteen miles of the earth's surface. All life on earth is found in an area from about six miles above sea level to about seven miles below sea level. The biosphere is further divided into smaller units called biomes. There are seven major biomes on earth. Biomes are further divided into ecosystems.

34.3 ECOSYSTEMS

Trying to study the complex interactions of all of the organisms on earth at the same time would be a rather difficult task. Therefore, ecologists further break down the biosphere into smaller and easier to study units called ecosystems. An **ecosystem** is defined as the association and interaction of all living organisms within their physical environment. Ecosystems can be as large as the Savannah in Africa, or as small as a backyard pond. Ecosystems sometimes have geographic boundaries (for example, an island in the middle of a lake is an ecosystem bounded by water on all sides), but more often, they meld into one another. The boundaries of an ecosystem are usually defined by each ecologist prior to starting the study.

Figure 34.3.1

Ecosystems
There is almost a limitless number of ecosystems in the world, mainly because an ecosystem is defined by the researcher who is studying it. An ecosystem can be lush, dry, wet, barren, on land, on ice, or underwater. Technically, an ecosystem is the association and interaction of all living things with their physical environment and one another.

34.4 BIOTIC AND ABIOTIC MASS

An important concept to understand is that the organisms of an ecosystem do not simply include the larger eukaryotic organisms that can be seen. They also include bacteria, protozoa, molds, fungi, and microscopic eukaryotes and algae. All of the living components of an ecosystem are referred to as the **biotic mass** (or "living" mass). Also, an ecosystem includes the non-living components, or **abiotic mass**, that is present such as water, rocks, sand, dirt, and chemicals.

Figure 34.4.1

Biotic and Abiotic Mass
All ecosystems have two basic components—those that are living (called biotic mass), and those that are not living (called abiotic mass). The mountain goat, grass, sea urchins, algae, coral, and bushes are all examples of biotic mass. Rocks, chains, and the dead tree are all examples of abiotic mass. Both are important to the stability of the ecosystem.

34.5 COMMUNITIES

Within the ecosystem, the biotic mass is further divided into **communities**. A community is all of the organisms present and interacting in the ecosystem. For example, if the ecosystem being studied is a backyard pond, then the members of the community would be all of the birds, fish, frogs, plants, algae, and microscopic eukaryotes and prokaryotes present within the borders of the pond—as defined by the ecologist studying the ecosystem.

Figure 34.5.1

Communities, Populations, and Individuals
Most ecosystems are made up of many different components. In the simple example to the left, the small ecosystem we are defining is the small area of the water hole seen in the picture. The community of this ecosystem is made up of a population of zebras and oryxes. The population of zebras contains three individuals, and the population of oryxes contains three individuals.

34.6 POPULATIONS

Further, within communities, there exist separate **populations** of organisms. A population is defined as all of the members of a certain species living at one place at one time. Normally, the community contains populations of all different types of animal and non-animal species. The smallest biotic unit of the ecosystem is the organism. An organism is simply one member of the population. The numbers of organisms within populations is generally counted, if possible, in order to obtain a **population size**. The population size is the number of organisms in a population.

34.7 POPULATION DENSITY

Sometimes it is not possible to accurately count the number of organisms that constitute a given population. For example, if a defined ecosystem was a forest that covered 100 square miles, it would be rather difficult to accurately count the number of maple trees in the entire 100 square mile area. Or, if you were trying to determine the population size of a certain protozoa in a pond, it would be impossible to count all of them. In those cases, estimates are made to determine the population size. For example, in the maple tree situation, the number of maple trees in one square mile in the ecosystem could be counted, then multiplied times 100 to get an estimate of the total population. For the protozoa, a water sample of one cubic millimeter could be obtained, and all of the protozoa contained in it counted. This number is multiplied by the total volume of the pond to obtain the population of organisms. **Population density** can also be obtained. Population density is the number of organisms per given area of land, or given area of an ecosystem. This number gives an idea of how **crowded** the population is.

Figure 34.7.1

Population Densities for the Year 2001
This table indicates that the most crowded country in the world is Monaco, in Africa. All three of the top countries have a relatively moderate absolute number of inhabitants. However, they are living in a small space, which makes the density very high. Note that China, the most populated country in the world with more than one billion people, has a low population density because the area of China is very large. When the large number of people is divided by a large land area, the density is lower.

Country	Population Density (individuals/km²)
Monaco	16,000
Bangladesh	926
Japan	336
United Kingdom	244
China	130
Mexico	52
United States	29
Russia	8.5
Canada	3.2
Greenland	0.03

Figure 34.7.2

Population Density
Population density maps are a helpful, graphical way to see how populated an area is. On the right is a population density map for the United States based on the 2000 census. To find the population density, the total number of people living in a certain area is divided by the area in which they are living. For example, to find the population density of New York, the total number of people living in New York is divided by the total area of New York. Note that population densities do NOT give direct information regarding the total number of individuals living in a given area. Rather, they give information regarding how crowded a given area is. For example, California has the most people living in it. It does not contain the densest population, though, because it is also a large state. When a large population is divided by a large area that houses the population, the population density is lower than if the same number of people were housed in a smaller area.

Population density
people per square mile
● = 1 - 103
● = 133 - 296
● = 401 - 703
● = 810 - 1134

34.8 POPULATION DISPERSION

Population dispersion is how spread out a population is. This is dependent on population density and other factors such as social relationships/abilities of the organisms. Populations disperse in three general ways: **clumped**, **random**, and **even**. Graphic representations of the three modes of dispersion are contained in 34.8.1.

Figure 34.8.1

Population Dispersion

Population dispersion provides information regarding how spread out the members of a population are. It differs from population density, though. Population density simply tells you how many individuals are in a given area. Population dispersion tells you where individuals live. Dispersion identifies how crowded areas of an ecosystem are based on exactly where the populations live. This is a way to breakdown the population density to understand what specific areas of an ecosystem are being inhabited. The graphic on the left depicts three distribution patterns: figure (a) represents a clumped dispersion pattern; figure (b) represents an even pattern; and figure (c) represents a random pattern. The figure on the right is a population density map, but it gives more information regarding the population dispersion. You can see that because the density information is listed for smaller areas of the ecosystem (Wisconsin), an idea regarding the distribution of the individuals in the state is obtained. For example, the population's density is higher in the southeast part of the state than it is in the northern part of the state. Therefore, the population is more crowded in the southeast part of the state than the north. Also, one can see that the population of Wisconsin follows a clumped distribution pattern. This is typical of human populations and other populations of animals that are social.

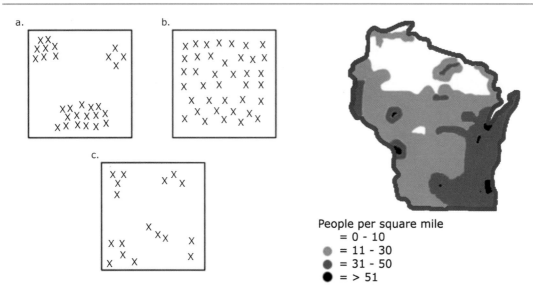

People per square mile
○ = 0 - 10
● = 11 - 30
● = 31 - 50
● = > 51

34.9 GROWTH RATE

Population sizes are not static entities; that is, they change over time. The change of the population size is called the **growth rate**. The growth rate is affected by movement of individuals into or out of the ecosystem, birth of new individuals, and death of existing organisms in the ecosystem. Some populations change due to migration of individuals. If there is more loss of individuals in a population than there is gain, the growth rate is negative. If there is more gain of individuals, the growth rate is positive.

Migration of individuals into an ecosystem is called **immigration**, and migration out of an ecosystem is called **emigration**. The number of individuals being born in a population is called the **birth rate** and is usually expressed as so many numbers of individuals born per 1,000 population for a specific period of time. For example, if the birth rate for one year of an ecosystem is 10 individuals per 1,000 organisms, and there are 50,000 organisms in the population, we know that for the year there were 500 births total in the population. (Fifty times 1,000 equals 50,000, or the total number of organisms in the population. Then multiply 50 times the number of births to obtain the total number of births.) The **death rate** is similar; it is the number of individuals which die in a given period of time. It is listed as the number of individuals that die in a given period of time per 1,000 population for a specified period of time.

Figure 34.9.1

Birth Rates for the Year 2001
The birth rate of 52.31 for Niger is the highest in the world. It means that for every 1,000 people living in Niger, there are about 52 people born per year. The population of Niger is estimated at about 116,000,000 people, or 116,000 times 1,000. By multiplying 116,000 times 52, we figure there were about 6,032,000 people born in Niger in 2001.

Country	Birth Rate (individuals born/1000 population)
Niger	52.31
Cambodia	41.05
Iraq	38.42
India	25.39
Mexico	24.99
World Average	22.00
United States	14.30
United Kingdom	11.90
Canada	11.86
Monaco	10.70
Japan	10.48
Russia	9.64

34.10 LIFE EXPECTANCY

A final important statistic in population studies is **life expectancy**. Life expectancy is the length of time an individual can be expected to live for the year they were born. Life expectancy for humans is dependent on many things, including the year and country in which you were born. For example, a person who was born in the United States in the year 1900 had a life expectancy of 49 years. That means, on average, all of the people born in 1900 lived until they were 49 years old. Of course there were people born in 1900 that lived until they were one hundred years old or more, just as there were many infants who died at or near birth. However, the average age for people who were born in 1900 was 49 years old. For those born in 1999, the life expectancy in the US was 73 years old for men and 80 years old for women. Life expectancies have continually risen over the past one hundred years due to improvements in sanitation and medical care.

The highest life expectancy is in the country of Andorra (sandwiched between France and Spain) and is 80 years old for men and 86 for women. The lowest life expectancy for those born in 1999 was 36 years old in the African country of Malawi. The reason for the reduced life expectancy is because Malawi is plagued with AIDS. AIDS is caused by the virus HIV (human immunodeficiency virus). AIDS causes the body's immune system to stop working; the person with AIDS usually dies from an infection they cannot fight.

Life expectancy is different than **life span**. Life span is the maximum amount of time that an organism or person can be expected to live. In essence, life span is the equal to the age of the oldest known organism which you are studying. In the case of humans, the life span is 122, years old because that is the oldest verifiable age to which a human has lived.

34.11 ENERGY TRANSFER

Recall an ecosystem is the association and interaction of all living organisms within their physical environment. A primary property of ecosystems is the **transfer of energy**. Hopefully, you recall our discussion of producers, consumers, and decomposers from the beginning of the year. We will review this as it is important in understanding the transfer of energy that occurs in ecosystems. One of the important aspects of ecosystems is the transfer of energy from one population to another and one organism to another.

34.12 THE FOOD CHAINS

The sun is the ultimate source of energy for almost all ecosystems, and the photoautotrophs convert the sun's energy into organic energy. (There are a small number of organisms that obtain their energy not from the sun, but from chemicals—the chemoautotrophs—but they produce only a small fraction of the total energy on earth.) Photoautotrophs are the producers in ecosystems. Recall organisms that eat the producers are called consumers. Therefore, the general transfer of energy is from the sun to the producers to the consumers. Recall there are three types of consumers in a food chain—herbivores, omnivores, and carnivores. This transfer of energy by one organism eating another is called the food chain. Another way of interpreting the food chain is that it represents a single pathway of feeding relationships in an ecosystem that result in transfer of energy from the organism being consumed to the organism doing the consuming.

Organisms can occupy different levels in the food chain. Anything that eats a producer is called a **primary consumer**. Cows, deer, a bear that eats berries, and baleen whales are all examples of primary consumers. Humans can also be primary consumers, as when we eat a salad or fruit. An organism that eats a primary consumer is called a **secondary consumer**, and an organism that eats a secondary consumer is called a **tertiary consumer**. Because organisms can occupy different levels on the food chain—for example, humans are primary consumers when we eat vegetables, secondary consumers when we eat steak, and tertiary consumers when we eat frog legs (the frog is itself a secondary consumer because it eats insects which are primary consumers). Because of this complexity in food chain relationships within ecosystems, energy transfer is viewed as a **food web** rather than a simple one-way chain.

Figure 34.12.1

Food Chain
This is a simple food chain, but it is effective at getting across "who eats who" in an ecosystem. The arrow pointing from the one organism to another indicates the organism the arrow is pointing to provides energy for the organism the arrow is pointing from. Essentially, it means that the organism the arrow is pointing to is eaten for energy by the organism the arrow is pointing from. In the case of the plant and sun, the plant derives energy from the sun to make glucose during photosynthesis. This linear relationship—owl eats snake, snake eats mouse, mouse eats plants—does somewhat explain the interactions of energy transfer between these organisms, but it is not that simple. Since the relationships are more complicated than this, ecologists have devised the food pyramid and food web relationships to further explain the producer-consumer relationships.

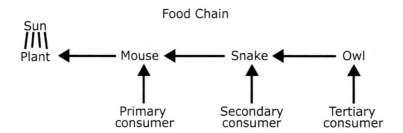

Figure 34.12.2

Food Web
The food web expands the food chain concept to take into account the true complexity of ecosystems. Inherent in this concept is the network of interactions present between consumers and producers of ecosystems. The feeding relationships are never as simple as a food chain, as can be seen below. The arrows indicate that the organism the arrow is pointing to uses the organism the arrow is coming from as a food source. In a food web, the top level consumers are usually placed at the top of the web and the producers at the bottom. Then the other organisms are placed in the web depending upon their relationship to other carnivores.

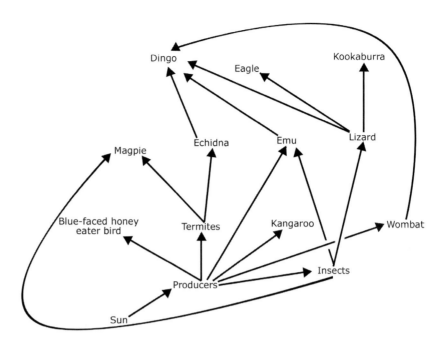

Note that in this scheme, decomposers have been left out. That is not because they are not important. Indeed, during the chapters on taxonomy, we learned that the decomposers are vital to return the molecules of dead organic matter back into useable forms. However, decomposers do not fit well into the food web scheme since the scheme focuses on the transfer of energy from living organisms to living organisms. It would be hard to put decomposers into the food web scheme, but they play a vital role in all ecosystems in breaking down and returning the elements back to an available source.

34.13 TROPHIC LEVELS AND FOOD PYRAMID

In order to help visualize what has been learned as a result of studying energy transfer in ecosystems, the relationships that producers have with consumers is often drawn as a **food pyramid**, or ecological pyramid. This is not the food pyramid that tells you how many servings of vegetables and fruit you should have in a day. It is the type of food pyramid that shows the relationship of energy transfer from producer to primary, secondary, and tertiary consumer. The position that an organisms occupies in the food web is called the **trophic level**.

Producers occupy the lowest trophic level, not because they are not important, but because they are the most plentiful organisms in all ecosystems. As a result, the producers have the highest amount of available energy to give to the ecosystem. Primary consumers occupy the second trophic level, secondary consumers the third trophic level, and so on. The first trophic level—that occupied by the producers—contains the largest amount of biomass and available energy in the ecosystem. The trophic level occupied by the highest organism on the food chain contains the lowest amount of biomass and available energy.

The concept of trophic levels is important because extensive study of ecosystems has shown that a significant amount of energy is lost during the transfer from one trophic level to the next. Approximately 90% of the available energy is lost when a primary consumer eats a producer, and when a secondary consumer eats a primary consumer, etc. This means that there needs to be a large supply of available energy from a lower trophic level to the one immediately above it.

Figure 34.13.1

The Food Pyramid

Ecologists have advanced the concept of the food pyramid to explain the transfer of energy within ecosystems. The total biotic mass of all organisms is broken into trophic levels. A trophic level, therefore, is the total amount of mass that a specific organism contributes to the ecosystem. The mass of an organism is directly related to the amount of energy that the organism can contribute to the other members of the ecosystem. The organisms with the most mass of every ecosystem are always the producers. This is because about 90% of all available energy in one trophic level is lost during the energy transfer. Producers are the base of the pyramid. The next trophic level is the primary consumer. The second level of a food pyramid is the secondary consumer, and so on. The reason there is such a large size difference between the trophic levels is because they are drawn to reflect the large difference in mass from one trophic level to another. Practically, this means that when a mouse eats a plant meal, it is only able to extract 10% of the energy available in the plant. The same happens when the snake eats the mouse or the owl eats the snake. The food pyramid is a graphic way of showing the energy transfer from producer to primary consumer, from primary consumer to secondary consumer, and so on.

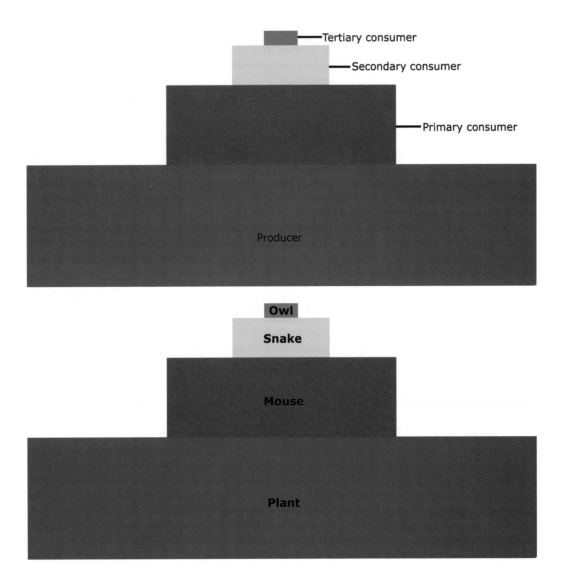

For example, let's consider a simple ecosystem in Africa for complete understanding. The biotic mass of the ecosystem consists of grasses, bushes, wildebeests, and lions. Wildebeests are herd animals—animals that stay together in large groups, which helps to protect them from predators. Wildebeests also migrate—or travel around the ecosystem—to find large supplies of grass and water to support their herds of hundreds to thousands. Wildebeests are **grazers** which means they kind of walk around slowly and eat as they walk. They eat pretty much all day long, and so you can imagine the enormous amount of grass that a herd of one thousand wildebeests could eat in a day. However, there is more than enough grass to support the wildebeests, as well as the other animals that eat grasses in Africa and share the same ecosystem with the wildebeest (gazelles, zebra, elephants, etc.). However, our example is only dealing with the ecosystem of the grass, wildebeest, and lion to keep things simple (realize things are much more complicated than this).

If you will look at the biological food pyramid in Figure 34.13.2 you will see that there is about nine times as much biomass of the grass the wildebeests eat as compared to the biomass of the wildebeest. This reflects the 90% loss of energy from one trophic level to the next. Every time the wildebeest eats grass, about 90% of the available energy in the grass is lost as heat or as undigested food that the animal defecates out. The lions, in turn, eat the wildebeest for their energy. Every time lions consume a wildebeest, about 90% of the available energy in the wildebeest is lost. Some is lost in the form of heat or incompletely digested food, and some is lost due to the inability to eat certain parts of the wildebeest (such as the bones). Again, note in the biological food pyramid that there is approximately nine times as much biomass of the wildebeest organisms as compared to the lion organisms due to the loss of energy from the primary consumer trophic level (wildebeests) to the secondary consumer level (lions). Each time that a move is made one trophic level upward in the food pyramid, about 90% of the available energy is lost.

Ecosystems depend on the stability of the trophic levels. This means the available energy in one trophic level needs to stay relatively the same from year to year for the ecosystem to thrive. If energy is lost from one of the trophic levels—let's say due to a huge fire that kills a lot of the grasses—there is less energy available to the trophic levels above it. In that case, many organisms from the higher trophic levels will not survive.

Thus far, we have been discussing **predator-prey** relationships in relation to the food web and trophic levels. The predator captures and kills the prey. Often, prey species are primary consumers, but not always. The predator-prey relationship determines where the animal is located in the food chain. Also, predator-prey relationships partially determine population control. If a predator population is severely reduced or eliminated altogether, it often allows the organisms in the lower trophic levels to reproduce and grow in large numbers—numbers so large the lower trophic levels cannot support them, and they begin to die of starvation. For example, in many states in the U.S., most or all of the natural predators of the white tailed deer were hunted and killed by humans. This allowed the white tailed deer population to explode, and now there are many areas where deer become pests by running into the roads all of the time or starve to death because there is not enough biomass in their ecosystem to support their numbers. Hunting helps to control the deer population, but sometimes even that is not enough.

Figure 34.13.3

Predator-prey Relationships

All primary consumers are potential prey species. That is because herbivores are not specialized to attack other organisms like carnivores are. However, primary consumers do have some defense mechanisms that allow them to escape a predator. Some herbivores have good defense mechanisms to protect them from being killed. Animals such as the impala and rabbit are fast and scare easily. Some herbivores, like elephants, hippos, and rhinos, are usually not attacked because they are so large. If they are attacked, they have the defense mechanism of large size and horns or tusks. The middle row depicts organisms that sometimes can be difficult to place as a prey or predator species. There are many such instances in nature. Spiders, frogs, and penguins are all predators in regard to obtaining their own food, but become prey if a larger predator is hungry. The bottom row depicts organisms that are almost never prey species (but can be in unusual instances). They, too, have special features that allow them to be good hunters. Sharks are large and have rows and rows of razor sharp teeth. They are also fast. Predatory birds like eagles and the Peregrine falcon have excellent eye sight that allow them to see their prey while they circle over head or perch. In addition, the Peregrine falcon is the fastest animal on earth, reaching speeds of over 180 miles per hour when diving. Cheetahs are the fastest land animals and can reach speeds of 70 miles per hour over short distances.

34.14 ADAPTATIONS FOR BETTER SURVIVAL

All animals have particular traits that allow them to live effectively in their ecosystem. These special traits are called adaptations. Predators have adaptations to make them better at capturing and killing their prey. They may have claws, long and sharp teeth, venom, a good sense of smell, or have good **camouflage** (colorings or markings that help them blend in with their environment, so they can sneak up better on their prey). Prey species also have adaptations which allow them to be better at escaping from the predators. They may be fast, or always on a high state of alert so that they startle easily. Some prey species also have camouflage, which helps them to blend into their environment and escape being eaten. Other prey species have the adaptation called **mimicry**. Mimicry can take two forms depending on the predator-prey relationship of the mimic. Prey express mimicry when they look like a dangerous or harmful species. This causes possible predators to avoid the harmless species because predators think it is a harmful one. Predators can also be mimics. In this situation, a predator looks like a harmless species to lure prey close to them.

Figure 34.14.1

Camouflage and Mimicry

Mimicry and camouflage are different concepts, but each one can be a benefit to predator or prey species. Mimicry is specifically related to one animal's appearance looking like another animal's for some reason, and camouflage specifically relates to an animal's ability to blend into its background. Mimicry exists when a harmless species looks like a harmful species, which causes predators to avoid it. Also, mimicry exists when a harmful species looks like a harmless one in order to be able to lure prey near to it and not frighten them away. The photo in the upper left is not a wasp, although it looks like one. It is a fly, called the yellow jacket hover fly. By looking like a nasty, stinging insect, many potential predators (and humans who would like to squish it) leave it alone. Camouflage is a pattern of coloring, body shape, or both, and allows an animal to blend into its environment. The walking stick in the middle of the top row is an excellent example of both. It looks like stick and is colored an off-brown or green color, which allows it to blend in perfectly with its environment. The cuttlefish in the top right photo is a type of mollusk similar to the octopus and squid. They are able to rapidly change their coloring to blend into their surroundings. The snowshoe hare in the bottom middle picture and the snowy owl in the bottom left both have the same adaptation but for different reasons. They are both colored white to blend into their snowy environments. The snowshoe hare's camouflage is to escape being eaten by the camouflaged snowy owl. Interestingly, the snowshoe changes its coloration to brown every spring and to white every winter in order to account for the changes in its environment. The object in the bottom right photo is not a leaf, it is an insect camouflaged to look like a leaf.

As we discussed in the taxonomy chapters, there are other relationships than predator-prey in ecosystems. We have already discussed symbiotic relationships and parasitic relationships. We will not discuss them further, but if you have any questions, you can look back to the taxonomy chapters.

34.15 ABIOTIC COMPONENTS OF ECOSYSTEMS

We have discussed the biotic components of ecosystems thus far, but as noted in the beginning of the chapter, abiotic components of the ecosystem are also important. Abiotic components include: temperature, water, chemicals, rocks, sand, soil, and air quality. Also, the boundary of the ecosystem is an important abiotic factor, but often exact boundaries are difficult to define. Usually, ecologists define the boundaries of the ecosystem they are studying, and other ecologists tend to agree with those, so when others study the ecosystem, accurate comparisons can be made. The more restricted the boundaries of an ecosystem are (i.e., the smaller it is), the easier it is to study. However, if the boundaries are restricted too much, the ability to completely understand interactions is limited.

Within ecosystems, and the biosphere as a whole, there are various cycles that exist. We have already discussed the cycle of the transfer of energy—from the sun to producer to consumer to decomposer and back to the producer. There are other well-studied, individual cycles that are important as well. The recycling of materials—water, nitrogen, oxygen, carbon, sulfur, etc.—occurs on a daily basis in all ecosystems. The recycling of materials in ecosystems in general is called the **biochemical cycle**. There are many specific biochemical cycles, and we will discuss the **water cycle**, the **oxygen cycle**, and the **carbon cycle** in some detail, but be aware the recycling occurs for all elements in nature.

34.16 THE WATER CYCLE

The water cycle, or **hydrologic cycle**, describes the pathway water takes to get to the earth's surface from the atmosphere, and then either return to the atmosphere or trickle into the earth to become **ground water**. Ground water is water stored below the surface of the earth in rock pores, soil, or **aquifers**. An aquifer is a large, underground deposit of water, the upper boundary of which is referred to as the **water table**. Basically, the hydrologic cycle describes how much water enters a given ecosystem, where the water comes from, and where it goes once it enters the ecosystem. Recall that water can exist in three different states in an ecosystem—liquid, solid (ice, sleet, hail, snow), or gas (referred to as **humidity** if the water is a gas in the atmosphere or **steam** if the water is super-heated from underground sources and emerges from the surface of the earth).

Figure 34.16.1

Summary of the Water Cycle Components

precipitation	water falling from the sky and entering into an ecosystem
evaporation	water turning from a liquid to a gas and re-entering the atmosphere
transpiration	loss of water from plants into the atmosphere
infiltration	water soaking into the ground and becoming ground water
run-off	water running over the surface of the earth directly into oceans or into a river that eventually empties into the ocean

In **terrestrial—**or "land"—ecosystems, water enters the ecosystem via **precipitation**. Precipitation is the process of water vapor condensing into clouds, then falling from the sky to the earth. The precipitation may be liquid (rain and fog) or may be solid (snow, sleet or hail). Once precipitation hits the earth, most of it is lost as **evaporation**, or water turning into the gas form and dissolving into the atmosphere of the ecosystem. In addition, some of the water is taken up by the autotrophs in the ecosystem and used for photosynthesis. Most of the water taken up by plants, however, is lost back to the atmosphere in a process called transpiration. Transpiration is essentially evaporation that occurs directly from plants. Depending on how porous the surface of the earth is in an ecosystem, more or less water will soak into the ground and become ground water. This process is called **infiltration**. The portion of water that is not involved in evaporation, transpiration, or infiltration is called **runoff**. Runoff water flows into streams, rivers, lakes, and oceans. The area of the land where the runoff collects is called a **watershed**.

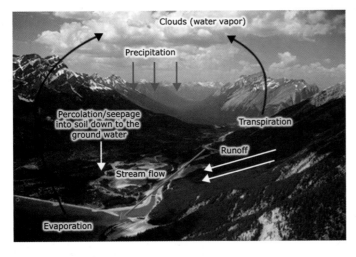

Figure 34.16.2

The Hydrologic Cycle
There is a constant flow of water between atmospheric form, ground form, and underground form. The typical pathway water can take is shown here, as would occur in a water shed. A water shed is an area where water collects for a large area of land. Typical water sheds are rivers and lakes. Water that falls from the sky is called precipitation. Once it hits the ground, it can soak into the ground (called percolation or seepage) to the water table, runoff into a stream or river, evaporate, or be taken up by plants. Plants take water up from the ground through their roots and then lose the water to the atmosphere during transpiration.

34.17 THE CARBON AND OXYGEN CYCLES

Most people are surprised to find out that the composition of the air we breathe is not all oxygen. It is not even mostly oxygen. Air is composed of 78% nitrogen, 21% oxygen, 0.935% argon, 0.033% carbon dioxide, and trace amounts of other chemicals. It is essential for the components of air to remain in the same relative concentrations, or else life will cease to exist. Because all of the components of air are consumed by life processes on earth, the biochemical cycle allows for the recycling of all elements back into the atmosphere. We will discuss the oxygen and carbon cycles to illustrate how nature accomplishes this.

Figure 34.17.1

The Carbon Cycle

The carbon cycle describes the pathway inorganic carbon takes to become organic carbon, and vice-versa. Recall that inorganic carbon is removed from the atmosphere by plants during photosynthesis. This is called carbon fixation and makes organic carbon available for all animal species. Dissolution occurs when carbon dioxide dissolves into water, which also removes some of the inorganic carbon from the atmosphere. Burning, cellular respiration and decomposition release organic carbon and return inorganic carbon to the atmosphere.

Because of the relationship autotrophic organisms and aerobic organisms have to carbon dioxide and oxygen, these two cycles are inextricably linked together. Through the process of photosynthesis, autotrophs incorporate the carbon from carbon dioxide into organic molecules. In the process, they release oxygen into the atmosphere. Recall that the majority of atmospheric oxygen is made not by plants, but by phytoplankton. The aerobic organisms—many bacteria, all fish, reptiles, amphibians, and mammals, for example—use the oxygen supplied by the autotrophs for the process of respiration. Recall that during respiration, a major byproduct is carbon dioxide, which is then released into the atmosphere. In addition, other important contributors to carbon dioxide in the atmosphere are volcanic eruptions and combustion—natural fires and man-made sources such as burning **fossil fuels** (oil, gas, coal, propane, etc.). Only 3% to 4% of the total amount of carbon dioxide released into the atmosphere is released by man-made sources. It is quite fascinating that the two largest sets of organisms on earth (autotrophs and aerobic organisms) rely on the byproducts of each other's metabolic activities in order to perform their own life-sustaining chemical reactions. Oxygen is restored through photosynthesis and carbon dioxide is restored through respiration.

Figure 34.17.2

The Oxygen Cycle

Oxygen is continually released into the atmosphere by plants and phytoplankton. Oxygen is continually used by burning fires, cellular respiration, and by being converted into ozone.

34.18 THE GREENHOUSE EFFECT

Even though carbon dioxide is a very small part of the atmospheric gasses—0.033%--it is one of the main gasses that contributes to the **greenhouse effect**. The greenhouse effect refers to process by which certain gasses in the atmosphere—carbon dioxide, methane, and water vapor (called the **greenhouse gasses**)—trap heat around the earth, just like the glass panes of a greenhouse trap heat. When rays of heat encounter the earth's atmosphere, many of them simply are reflected off by some of the atmospheric gasses. However, some of the rays pass through and strike the surface of the earth. Once they strike the earth, the earth gets warm and reflects some of the heat from its surface. This reflected heat then travels out toward space, but it does not leave the atmosphere. Instead, it is trapped and kept in the space around the earth, warming the air. This warming effect allows the planet to maintain temperatures 24 hours per day that are generally hospitable for life.

Figure 34.18.1

The Greenhouse Effect
The greenhouse effect refers to the process of atmospheric gasses trapping heat into the earth. This process is similar to the heat trapping that occurs in a greenhouse. The energy contained in sunlight passes through the glass panes of a greenhouse. Once in the greenhouse, the energy form the sunlight is expressed as heat. The glass panes keep the energy in the greenhouse and so the it stays warm, even in the winter. This is the model for the workings of the greenhouse gasses in the atmosphere. Without the greenhouse effect, life on earth would not exist, because it would be too cold. The "increasing" greenhouse effect has been implicated by some as causing the controversial global warming. It is thought that due to the increased concentration of one of the greenhouse gasses, carbon dioxide, more heat is trapped, and the overall temperature of the earth is increasing. There is considerable debate as to whether or not this actually is occurring.

The greenhouse effect is a poorly understood phenomenon. Many people have the mistaken impression the greenhouse effect is "bad". The greenhouse effect is not a new process nor is it "bad." If you believe in evolution, then the greenhouse effect has been occurring for at least 3 billion years. If you believe in the creationist view that the earth is about six thousand years old, then the greenhouse effect has been present since day two of creation, when land and water were created. Without the greenhouse effect, the warming effects of the air around the earth would not occur, our planet could not maintain a temperature that would allow life to flourish, and nothing would be here. There would be no life on earth without the greenhouse effect because it would be too cold. The main reason that life cannot exist on other planets is that they lack an atmosphere and, therefore, have no greenhouse effect. Without the greenhouse effect, it is too cold for life to exist on the other planets.

Isn't it fascinating that the atmosphere is composed of just the right mixture of molecules so that not too many heat rays enter the earth's atmosphere (resulting in a planet which is way too hot), and not too few enter the atmosphere (resulting in a planet which is too cold). Just enough heat rays are kept in—resulting in a planet that is just the right temperature.

34.19 GLOBAL WARMING (?)

The "increasing greenhouse effect" has been identified as a potential problem by some scientists. This increasing greenhouse effect results in the earth's temperature becoming warmer over time and leading to the **global warming effect**. Global warming is the theory that the overall combined average temperature of the earth is increasing, specifically because of burning fossil fuels by man over the past 150 years, or so. Fossil fuels are substances such as coal and gasoline. Prior to 150 years ago, there was very little fossil fuel burning. As the world became industrialized in the late 1800's and 1900's, fossil fuels played a critical part in that process.

However, global warming is not accepted as fact by many ecologists. There are those that think global warming is occurring and those that think it is not. It is commonly reported that global warming is fact, but like evolution, there is considerable debate as to whether it really is occurring, or not. What is an absolute fact, though, is that the concentration of carbon dioxide has increased in the atmosphere over the past one hundred years. However, whether this increase could lead to an increase in the average temperature of the earth is what is debated.

Those who believe global warming is occurring point to the fact that there has been an increase in the average temperatures of the earth as recorded from many points *on the ground* around the globe. These land-based readings indicate that temperature of the earth has increased an average of about $1°F$ ($0.5°C$) during the 1900s. Since carbon dioxide concentrations have increased in the past one hundred years and carbon dioxide is one of the main greenhouse gasses, the conclusion is two fold: global warming is happening and it is because of the higher carbon dioxide levels.

In addition, the scientists who believe in global warming have developed intricate computer programs to predict the earth's temperature into the future. However, the programs have been written based on the assumption that global warming actually is happening and is a fact and is directly related to the increase in atmospheric carbon dioxide. So, based on *their belief* that the planet is getting warmer, they have written programs that naturally predict the temperature of the planet will continue to rise.

One of the more dire consequences of global warming, if true, is that the polar ice caps would begin to melt. The polar ice caps are huge amounts of frozen water that are found in the north and south poles. They contain enough water, if completely melted, to cover the entire earth in water several miles deep.

Scientists who do not believe in global warming ask the question that the earth is warmer now *than when*? In order for there to be a consistent increase in the earth's temperature, there needs to be a common frame of reference consisting of accurate temperature recordings for thousands of years. We have only been maintaining accurate global temperatures for about sixty years. Since there are not accurate long-term temperature recordings we do not know that the earth is warmer now than it ever has been, just warmer than it was sixty years ago. Is this warming a definite trend to indicate global warming or is it simply a blip?

For example, there is good evidence that there was a warming period from 900 to 1300 AD, called the medieval warming period. This period lasted for 500 years, much longer than the sixty years we are seeing now. Many scientists believe it was probably a lot warmer then than the temperatures we are seeing now. If our temperatures now are warming because of burning fossil fuels, why did they increase a thousand years ago when no one was burning fossil fuels?

Also, we know there has been at least one ice age in the past. During an ice age, the average temperature of the earth decreases and more water is contained in the frozen form. Glaciers develop and covered a large portion of the northern hemisphere. Nothing man did in the past caused the temperature of the earth to decrease; it seems to be a natural event on earth. Why, then, can an increase in the planet's temperatures not also be a normal event (as it was during the medieval warming period)?

To complicate this issue further, burning fossil fuels not only releases the gasses responsible for keeping the earth's heat in, it also releases the gasses which reflect the heat from the sun. Perhaps the increase in the two types of gasses cancels one another out. The reflective gasses let less heat in, while the greenhouse gasses keep more heat in. That possibility has not been studied yet.

There is also great disagreement regarding the validity of using surface temperatures to accurately reflect the warmth of the atmosphere as a whole. Many believe that recording temperatures higher up in the air is a more reliable method of measuring the globe's temperatures. Those higher-up recordings do not show a significant trend in warming. The global warming issue really got hot in 1998, which was a warm year all over the planet. However, 1999 came along which was one of the coolest years in the last sixty years.

The temperatures of 1998 and 1999 are felt by the scientists who do not believe global warming to be true sum up the danger in making assumptions based on short time frames on a planet with a long history. Perhaps all we are seeing currently is either normal warming patterns following an ice age, or the normal waxing and waning of temperatures on a planet that normally has several thousand year cycles of temperature variation, but which we have only measured for sixty years. There needs to be more study into the issue of where the best place to monitor temperature is and the effect of not only increasing the levels of greenhouse gasses but also the gasses which reflect the sun's heat.

34.20 BIOMES

Whether global warming is an accurate assessment of the state of the earth's climates or not, the main large ecosystems of the earth, or **biomes**, remain as they have for the past many thousand years. A biome is a major regional group of distinctive plant and animal species in a common physical environment. There are seven terrestrial biomes, and each one contains many ecosystems within it (see Figures 34.20.1 and 34.20.4 for details). Biomes are defined by several characteristic traits, as can be seen in the table: average amount of precipitation per year, average temperature ranges, soil quality, and characteristic **flora** (plant species) and **fauna** (animal species).

Figure 34.20.1

Biomes
The biosphere is broken into seven major biomes, as shown below. A biome is defined by the characteristic plants and animals that inhabit the area.

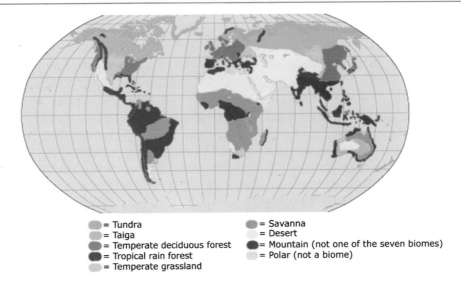

● = Tundra
● = Taiga
● = Temperate deciduous forest
● = Tropical rain forest
● = Temperate grassland
● = Savanna
● = Desert
● = Mountain (not one of the seven biomes)
● = Polar (not a biome)

The biome table in figure 34.20.3 brings up a few new terms that require explanation. The tundra soil is characterized by **permafrost**, which is a layer that is permanently frozen. In the tundra biomes, it does not matter how warm it gets, the ground is always frozen year-round at some depth. Many animals survive on the carpets of lichen growing in the tundra. Recall that "deciduous" means the trees lose their leaves every fall.

By looking at the biome map, you can probably tell that biomes, like ecosystems, do not have defined boundaries, but tend to flow into one another.

In addition to the terrestrial biomes, there is an eighth general type of biome that is based on ecosystems in bodies of water, called the **aquatic biome**. Aquatic biomes are further divided into **marine biomes** and **fresh water biomes**. Deep aquatic biomes are divided into **photic** and **aphotic zones**. The photic zone includes all the depths of water which light can penetrate. This is about six hundred feet, or so. Photosynthetic organisms are located within the photic zone. The aphotic zone is the zone where light cannot penetrate into. Do not be fooled into assuming there is no life below the photic zone. Indeed there is. The life that lives below the photic zone is usually based on a food pyramid that includes chemotrophs as the producer organism.

Figure 34.20.2

Aquatic Biomes

This shows the general areas of a near shore marine biome. The continental shelf is a gentle down-sloping of the underwater land that occurs as the continent ends and the ocean begins. There is an abrupt increase in water depth when the continental shelf ends. The photic zone is the depth of water that sunlight can penetrate and photosynthesis can occur. Most of the marine life lives in photic zones. However, there are also life forms clustered around thermal vents many miles below sea level. Thermal vents are locations where the heat from the earth's interior is released into the ocean. This warms the water and provides nutrients for producers to manufacture glucose and other carbohydrates. Since sunlight cannot penetrate the several miles below water that thermal vents are found, chemosynthetic bacteria are the producers.

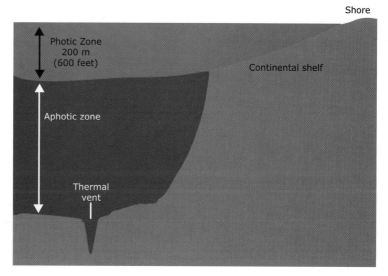

Figure 34.20.3

The Seven Major Terrestrial Biomes

The seven major terrestrial biomes with their typical features are listed below.

Biome	Ave. temp range	Ave. precipitation	Soil	Characteristic flora and fauna
Tundra	-26°C-12°C	<25cm	thin topsoil over layer of permafrost; poor nutrients	moss, lichens, largely treeless; one-fifth of world's land; caribou, snowy owl, arctic fox
Taiga	-10°C-14°C	35-75cm	acidic; poor nutrients	needled-evergreen trees; moose, bear, wolf, fox
Temperate deciduous forest	6°C-28°C	75-125cm	moist; moderate nutrients	broad-leaved trees and shrubs (oak, maple, birch); squirrel, white-tailed deer
Temperate grassland	0°C-25°C	25-75cm	deep topsoil; rich nutrients	grasses; called "prairie" in North America, "steppe in Asia, "pampas" in South America, "veldt" in Africa
Desert	7°C-38°C	<25cm	dry; often sand; poor nutrient	succulent plants adapted to store water; lizard, snake, small mammals
Savanna	16°C-34°C	75-150 cm with alternating wet and dry seasons	thin topsoil; low nutrient	tall grasses; scattered trees; large grazing animals, and carnivores
Tropical rain forest	20°C-34°C	200-400cm	thin topsoil; low nutrients	broad-leaved evergreen shrubs and trees; year-round growth; colorful birds; monkeys

Figure 34.20.4

Biome Examples
Top right, tundra. Middle row left, taiga. Middle row center, temperate deciduous. Middle row right temperate grassland. Bottom row left, desert. Bottom row center, savanna. Bottom row right, tropical rainforest.

Occasionally, ecosystems experience a catastrophe that significantly alters the stability of the ecosystem and sometimes destroys the ecosystem altogether. Examples of such events are volcanic eruptions, tidal waves, hurricanes, and widespread forest fires. When this occurs, the delicate balance of the ecosystem is disturbed and it takes time, sometimes as many as two hundred years, before the ecosystem re-establishes itself and becomes stable again.

In areas where the ecosystems have been greatly disturbed, or in areas in which there are no living creatures yet, life enters the area slowly and begins to populate it. The first organisms into an area are referred to as **pioneer species**. Pioneer species tend to be things that grow quickly and are not too picky about where they live. Weeds, grasses, lichens, and mosses are typical pioneer species. In addition to bringing the first life into a potential ecosystem, they also serve to break up the soil and, if they start to grow in and around rocks, split up the rocks. This allows for larger species to move into the area that would otherwise not be able to grow in an uninhabitable environment. Animal species that first inhabit new ecosystems vary depending on the location of the ecosystem, but animals inevitably also move in to populate an area.

Figure 34.20.5

Succession

After a previously established ecosystem has been destroyed, or a new ecosystem is being established in an area that previously did not have one, a predictable pattern of species populations occurs. In the example below, a previous ecosystem has been destroyed by a volcanic eruption (below). The first stage of colonization of an ecosystem is called primary succession (right). The first plant species into the area are called pioneer species. Pioneer species begin to grow on thin soil, barren rock or in lava. Their roots grow into rock cracks and split the rocks apart. Over time, this process makes soil. Common pioneer species are lichens, mosses, ferns, and various weeds. As the pioneer species begin to die, they decompose and, over time, pile up to form soil. Then the process of secondary succession occurs as new and less hardy plant species start to grow in the area (bottom left). Eventually, animals move into the area and many years later the ecosystem is stable and the climax community is reached, such as is seen in the bottom right photo. This is a volcano that has erupted and blown the entire top off. It has completed secondary succession and a climax community has been established.

The process of new species growing into an ecosystem that has been decimated by a catastrophe, or into a previously uninhabited area, is called **primary succession**. Over time, new species slowly begin to populate the area. **Secondary succession** is the sequential replacement of species over time following the emergence of pioneer species. The animal and plant life is slowly replaced during secondary succession until stability is reached, and no further significant changes occur in the ecosystem. When that occurs, the **climax community** is said to have been reached.

34.21 PEOPLE OF SCIENCE

Ernst Haeckel (1834–1919) was a German biologist who is best remembered for his purposefully inaccurate drawings of the developmental stages of embryos. He purposefully drew embryos of different species to look more similar during their development than they really are in an attempt to make evolution be perceived as true. However, he made important advances in other areas of biology that are not disputed. He was the first person to use the terms phylum and ecology. He combined the Greek words for household – "oikos" – and study – "logos" – to come up with the word that we now use to describe the study of the environment.

34.22 KEY CHAPTER POINTS

- Ecology is the study of the relationships of living things with one another and with their environment.

- Ecologists study ecosystems. An ecosystem is the association and interaction of all living organisms within a defined physical environment.

- Ecologists also study individuals, populations, and communities.

- One of the important concepts of ecology is understanding the transfer of energy within food webs that exist in ecosystems.

- Trophic levels on the food pyramid lose about 90% of the available energy when moving from a lower trophic level to the next higher one.

- Organisms have a variety of adaptations to make them better predators or better at eluding predators.

- Ecologists are also interested in the cycles that various critical molecules of life follow, such as water, carbon, and oxygen.

- The greenhouse effect is the trapping of heat around the earth caused by several different gasses. It is a necessary process for life on earth to exist because without it, earth would be too cold to support life.

- Carbon dioxide is a major component of the greenhouse gasses.

- The levels of carbon dioxide have been climbing in the past century and this is implicated by some scientists to be the cause of global warming.

- Global warming is not a scientific fact and further research needs to be conducted to ascertain whether it is really happening or not.

- The land on earth is divided into seven biomes.

- Water ecosystems are included in marine or freshwater biomes.

34.23 DEFINITIONS

abiotic Mass
All non-living components of an ecosystem.

aphotic zones
The depths of water where light cannot penetrate into.

aquatic Biome
Groups of ecosystems under water.

aquifer
A large underground deposit of water.

biochemical cycle
The recycling of elements and materials in ecosystems.

biological food pyramid
The relationship of energy transfer between producer and consumers in an ecosystem.

biomes
The main, large ecosystems of the earth.

biosphere
The thin physical layer of the earth in which all living organisms are found.

biotic mass
All of the living components of an ecosystem.

birth rate
The number of individuals being born per year in a population.

camouflage
Colorings or markings that help organisms blend in with their environment, allowing them to catch their prey more effectively or avoid being caught.

carbon cycle
The cyclic pathway carbon takes as it passes form organic to inorganic forms.

climax community
The point in an ecosystem where stability is reached and no further changes occur in the ecosystem.

communities
All of the organisms present and interacting in the ecosystem.

death rate
The number of individuals dying within a population in a given period of time.

ecologists
Scientists who study ecology.

ecology
The study of the relationships that living organisms have with one another and their physical environment.

emigration
Migration of individuals out of an ecosystem.

evaporation
Water turning into gas form and dissolving into the atmosphere.

fauna
Animal species.

flora
Plant species.

food web
The complex relationship that producers and consumers have with one another in an ecosystem.

fossil fuels
Fuels that are derived from carbon: such as oil, gas, coal, propane, etc.

fresh water biomes
Biomes that are found in bodies of fresh water.

global warming
The theory that the overall combined average temperature of the earth is increasing, mainly because of the burning of fossil fuels.

grazers
Organisms that walk around slowly and eat as they walk.

greenhouse effect
The process by which certain gasses in the atmosphere trap heat around the earth.

greenhouse gasses
The specific gasses that are responsible for creating the greenhouse effect: carbon dioxide, methane, and water vapor.

ground water
Water stored below the surface of the earth in rock pores, soil, or aquifers.

growth rate
The rate of change of a population size.

humidity
Water vapor in the atmosphere.

hydrologic cycle
The water cycle

immigration
Migration of individuals into an ecosystem.

infiltration
The process of water soaking into the ground and becoming ground water.

life expectancy
The length of time an individual can be expected to live.

marine biomes
Biomes located in bodies of salt water.

mimicry
A situation that exists when a prey species looks like a dangerous species to scare predators away, or the situation when a predator looks like a harmless species so as not to scare prey away.

oxygen cycle
The cyclic pathway oxygen takes as it passes form organic to inorganic forms.

permafrost
A layer of soil that is permanently frozen.

photic zones
All the depths of water which light can penetrate.

pioneer species
The first organisms into a previously unpopulated area.

population density
The number of organisms per a given area of land.

population size
The number of organisms in a population.

populations
All the members of a certain species living at one place at one time.

precipitation
The process of water vapor condensing into clouds, then falling from the sky to the earth.

predator-prey
A relationship between two organisms in which one is eaten by the other.

primary consumer
Anything that eats a producer.

primary succession
The process of new species moving into an ecosystem that has been decimated by a catastrophe or into a previously uninhabited area.

runoff

The portion of water that is not involved in evaporation, transpiration or infiltration.

secondary consumer

An organism that eats a primary consumer.

secondary succession

The sequential replacement of species over time following the emergence of pioneer species.

steam

Water that is super-heated from underground sources and emerges from the surface of the earth.

terrestrial

referring to land.

tertiary consumer

An organism that eats a secondary consumer.

transfer of energy

The relationship that exists between producers and consumers in all ecosystems and explains how one species obtains energy molecules/nutrition from another.

trophic level

The position that an organism occupies in the food pyramid.

water cycle

The pathway water takes to get to the earth's surface from the atmosphere, then either returning to the atmosphere or trickling into the earth to become ground water.

water table

The upper boundary of an aquifer.

watershed

The area of the land where runoff collects.

STUDY QUESTIONS

1. Define ecology.

2. What is the highest level of complexity in population studies? List the levels in order of decreasing complexity.

3. Let's say you were standing next to a river. You notice several trees, some birds, a few insects, and a squirrel. As you continue to observe, you notice some rocks and mud, a few small fish, some water lilies, water running through the river, a dead log on the bank, a snake, and a frog. Which of those things are biotic mass? Which are abiotic mass? Are there any members of the biotic mass that you cannot see but know they are there anyway? Would you say you are standing in an ecosystem?

4. True or False? Population density gives an idea of how crowded a population is?

5. True or False? If the population density goes up, it means the area is becoming less populated (i.e., less crowded).

6. All of the following can lead to an increase in population except (there may be more than one answer): immigration, emigration, rising birth rates, longer life expectancy, higher death rates.

7. Why do food webs usually explain the transfers of energy better than food chains?

8. How much energy is usually lost when moving from one trophic level to the next higher one?

9. We are studying an imaginary marine ecosystem which fortunately has few biotic components. The primary producer is algae. There does not seem to be any other producer in this ecosystem. There appears to be only one primary consumer, a small fish called the skuttle fish. These fish are numerous and found all over the ecosystem. It appears that all of the skuttle fish feed off of algae growing on the rocks. There is a population of fish larger than the skuttle fish called mockies. Mockies are definitely smaller in number than the skuttles, but there are still many of them. They seem to feed exclusively off of the skuttles. There are a small number of larger fish, called flawgs, in the area which eat the mockies and the skuttles. Every once in a while, there has been a shark patrolling the waters which target the larger flawgs and eats them. Please draw a trophic level diagram for this ecosystem, indicating the producers, primary, secondary, tertiary and quaternary consumers and the relative biotic mass of each based on what you know about energy transfer and ecosystems.

10. How is camouflage different than mimicry?

11. What is runoff? What is percolation? What do these terms refer to?

12. True or False? The greenhouse effect is bad. Why or Why not?

13. True or False? If global warming is true, it could have terrible consequences on the earth. Why did you answer the way you did?

14. _____ is the animal life in a biome and _____ is the plant life of a biome.

15. What is a pioneer species?

16. List the seven major biomes and typical animal and plant life one would see there.

PLEASE TAKE TEST #15 IN TEST BOOKLET

INDEX

Legend:

- Atomic number
- Symbol
- Element
- Atomic weight

1
H
Hydrogen
1.008

- Metal
- Metalloid
- Nonmetal gasses

1 H Hydrogen 1.008																	2 He Helium 4.003
3 Li Lithium 6.941	4 Be Beryllium 9.012											5 B Boron 10.81	6 C Carbon 12.01	7 N Nitrogen 14.01	8 O Oxygen 16.00	9 F Fluorine 19.00	10 Ne Neon 20.18
11 Na Sodium 22.99	12 Mg Magnesium 24.31											13 Al Aluminum 26.98	14 Si Silicone 28.09	15 P Phosphorus 32.97	16 S Sulfur 32.97	17 Cl Chlorine 35.45	18 Ar Argon 39.95
19 K Potassium 39.10	20 Ca Calcium 40.08	21 Sc Scandium 44.96	22 Ti Titanium 47.88	23 V Vanadium 50.94	24 Cr Chromium 52.00	25 Mn Manganese 54.94	26 Fe Iron 55.85	27 Co Cobalt 58.93	28 Ni Nickel 58.17	29 Cu Copper 63.55	30 Zn Zinc 65.38	31 Ga Gallium 69.72	32 Ge Germanium 72.59	33 As Arsenic 74.92	34 Se Selenium 78.96	35 Br Bromine 79.90	36 Kr Krypton 83.80
37 Rb Rubidium 85.47	38 Sr Strontium 87.62	39 Y Yttrium 88.91	40 Zr Zirconium 91.22	41 Nb Niobium 92.91	42 Mo Molybdenum 92.91	43 Tc Technetium 92.91	44 Ru Ruthenium 101.1	45 Rh Rhodium 102.9	46 Pd Palladium 106.4	47 Ag Silver 107.9	48 Cd Cadmium 112.4	49 In Indium 114.8	50 Sn Tin 118.7	51 Sb Antimony 121.8	52 Te Tellurium 127.6	53 I Iodine 126.9	54 Xe Xenon 131.3
55 Cs Cesium 132.9	56 Ba Barium 137.3	57 La* Lanthanum 138.9	72 Hf Hafnium 178.5	73 Ta Tantalum 180.9	74 W Wolfram (Tungsten) 183.9	75 Re Rhenium 186.2	76 Os Osmium 190.2	77 Ir Iridium 192.2	78 Pt Platinum 195.1	79 Au Gold 197.0	80 Hg Mercury 200.6	81 Tl Thallium 204.4	82 Pb Lead 207.2	83 Bi Bismuth 209.0	84 Po. Polonium (209)	85 At Astatine (210)	86 Rn Radon (222)
87 Fr Francium (223)	88 Ra Radium (226.0)	89 Ac** Actinium (227)	104 Rf Rutherfordium (261)	105 Db Dubnium (262)	106 Sg Seaborgium (263)	107 Bh Bohrium (262)	108 Hs Hassium (265)	109 Mt Meitnerium (266)	110 Uun Ununnilium (272)	111 Uuu Unununium (272)	112 Uub Ununbium (277)						

*Lanthanides

58 Ce Cerium 140.1	59 Pr Praseodynium 140.9	60 Nd Neodynium 144.2	61 Pm Promethium (145)	62 Sm Samarium 150.4	63 Eu Europium 152.0	64 Gd Gadolinium 157.3	65 Tb Terbium 158.9	66 Dy Dysprosium 162.9	67 Ho Holmium 164.9	68 Er Erbium 167.3	69 Tm Thulium 168.9	70 Yb Ytterbium 173.0	71 Lu Lutetium 175.0

**Actinides

90 Th Thorium 232.0	91 Pa Protactinium (231)	92 U Uranium 238.0	93 Np Neptunium (237)	94 Pu Plutonium (244)	95 Am Americium (243)	96 Cm Curium (247)	97 Bk Berkelium (247)	98 Cf Californium (251)	99 Es Einsteinium (252)	100 Fm Fermium (257)	101 Md Mendelevium (258)	102 No Nobelium (259)	103 Lr Lawrencium (260)

(handwritten annotations: "2 -3 bonding", "Full valence Shell", "outer most", "Full")